Complete Solutions
Manual for Stewart's

MULTIVARIABLE

CALCULUS
SECOND EDITION

CONCEPTS AND CONTEXTS

dan clegg
Palomar College

BROOKS/COLE
™
THOMSON LEARNING

Australia • Canada • Mexico • Singapore • Spain • United Kingdom • United States

Cover Design: *Vernon T. Boes*
Cover Photograph: *Erika Ede*

For more information about this or any other Brooks/Cole product, contact:
BROOKS/COLE
511 Forest Lodge Road
Pacific Grove, CA 93950 USA
www.brookscole.com
1-800-423-0563 (Thomson Learning Academic Resource Center)

For permission to use material from this work, contact us by
Web: www.thomsonrights.com
fax: 1-800-730-2215
phone: 1-800-730-2214

Printed in Canada

5   4   3   2   1

ISBN 0-534-37908-7

Preface

This *Complete Solutions Manual* contains detailed solutions to all exercises in the text *Multivariable Calculus: Concepts and Contexts, Second Edition* (Chapters 8–13 of *Calculus: Concepts and Contexts, Second Edition*) by James Stewart. A *Student Solutions Manual* is also available, which contains solutions to the odd-numbered exercises in each chapter section, review section, True-False Quiz, and Focus on Problem Solving section as well as all solutions to the Concept Check questions. (It does not, however, include solutions to any of the projects.)

While I have extended every effort to ensure the accuracy of the solutions presented, I would appreciate correspondence regarding any errors that may exist. Other suggestions or comments are also welcome, and can be sent to me at the email address or mailing address below.

I would like to thank James Stewart for entrusting me with the writing of this manual and offering suggestions, Kathi Townes and Stephanie Kuhns of TECH-arts for typesetting and producing this manual, and Brian Betsill of TECH-arts for creating the illustrations. Andy Bulman-Fleming prepared solutions for comparison of accuracy and style; his assistance and suggestions were very helpful and much appreciated. Finally, I would like to thank Gary W. Ostedt, Bob Pirtle, and Carol Ann Benedict of Brooks/Cole Publishing Company for their trust, assistance, and patience.

dan clegg
dclegg@palomar.edu
Palomar College
Department of Mathematics
1140 West Mission Road
San Marcos, CA 92069

Contents

13 VECTOR CALCULUS   417

APPENDIXES   473

8 ◆ Infinite Sequences and Series

 8.1 Sequences • • • • • • • • • • • • • • • •

1. (a) A sequence is an ordered list of numbers. It can also be defined as a function whose domain is the set of positive integers.

(b) The terms a_n approach 8 as n becomes large. In fact, we can make a_n as close to 8 as we like by taking n sufficiently large.

(c) The terms a_n become large as n becomes large.

2. (a) From Definition 1, a convergent sequence is a sequence for which $\lim\limits_{n \to \infty} a_n$ exists. Examples: $\{1/n\}$, $\{1/2^n\}$

(b) A divergent sequence is a sequence for which $\lim\limits_{n \to \infty} a_n$ *does not* exist. Examples: $\{n\}$, $\{\sin n\}$

3. The first six terms of $a_n = \dfrac{n}{2n+1}$ are: $\dfrac{1}{3}, \dfrac{2}{5}, \dfrac{3}{7}, \dfrac{4}{9}, \dfrac{5}{11}, \dfrac{6}{13}$. It appears that the sequence is approaching $\dfrac{1}{2}$.

$$\lim_{n \to \infty} \frac{n}{2n+1} = \lim_{n \to \infty} \frac{1}{2 + 1/n} = \frac{1}{2}$$

4. Let $n = 1$ to $n = 8$ in $\sin\left(n\frac{\pi}{2}\right)$.

$\left\{\sin\frac{\pi}{2}, \sin\pi, \sin\frac{3\pi}{2}, \sin 2\pi, \sin\frac{5\pi}{2}, \sin 3\pi, \sin\frac{7\pi}{2}, \sin 4\pi\right\} = \{1, 0, -1, 0, 1, 0, -1, 0\}$.

The sequence does not have a limit, since it repeats the pattern $1, 0, -1, 0$ over and over and therefore doesn't approach any fixed number.

5. $\left\{1, -\frac{2}{3}, \frac{4}{9}, -\frac{8}{27}, \dots\right\}$. Each term is $-\frac{2}{3}$ times the preceding one, so $a_n = \left(-\frac{2}{3}\right)^{n-1}$.

6. $\left\{-\frac{1}{4}, \frac{2}{9}, -\frac{3}{16}, \frac{4}{25}, \dots\right\}$. The numerator of the nth term is n and its denominator is $(n+1)^2$. Including the alternating signs, we get $a_n = (-1)^n \dfrac{n}{(n+1)^2}$.

7. $\{2, 7, 12, 17, \dots\}$. Each term is larger than the preceding one by 5, so
$a_n = a_1 + d(n-1) = 2 + 5(n-1) = 5n - 3$.

8. $\{0, 2, 0, 2, 0, 2, \dots\}$. The number 1 is halfway between 0 and 2, so we can think of alternately subtracting and adding 1 (from 1 and to 1) to obtain the given sequence: $a_n = 1 - (-1)^{n-1}$.

9. $a_n = n(n-1)$. $a_n \to \infty$ as $n \to \infty$, so the sequence diverges.

10. $a_n = \dfrac{n+1}{3n-1} = \dfrac{1 + 1/n}{3 - 1/n}$, so $a_n \to \dfrac{1+0}{3-0} = \dfrac{1}{3}$ as $n \to \infty$. Converges

11. $a_n = \dfrac{3 + 5n^2}{n + n^2} = \dfrac{(3 + 5n^2)/n^2}{(n + n^2)/n^2} = \dfrac{5 + 3/n^2}{1 + 1/n}$, so $a_n \to \dfrac{5+0}{1+0} = 5$ as $n \to \infty$. Converges

12. $a_n = \dfrac{\sqrt{n}}{1 + \sqrt{n}} = \dfrac{1}{1/\sqrt{n} + 1}$, so $a_n \to \dfrac{1}{0+1} = 1$ as $n \to \infty$. Converges

13. $a_n = \dfrac{2^n}{3^{n+1}} = \dfrac{1}{3}\left(\dfrac{2}{3}\right)^n$, so $\lim\limits_{n \to \infty} a_n = \dfrac{1}{3}\lim\limits_{n \to \infty}\left(\dfrac{2}{3}\right)^n = \dfrac{1}{3}\cdot 0 = 0$ by (6) with $r = \dfrac{2}{3}$. Converges

14. $a_n = \dfrac{n}{1 + \sqrt{n}} = \dfrac{\sqrt{n}}{1/\sqrt{n} + 1}$. The numerator approaches ∞ and the denominator approaches $0 + 1 = 1$ as

$n \to \infty$, so $a_n \to \infty$ as $n \to \infty$ and the sequence diverges.

15. $a_n = \dfrac{(-1)^{n-1} n}{n^2 + 1} = \dfrac{(-1)^{n-1}}{n + 1/n}$, so $0 \le |a_n| = \dfrac{1}{n + 1/n} \le \dfrac{1}{n} \to 0$ as $n \to \infty$, so $a_n \to 0$ by the Squeeze

Theorem and Theorem 4. Converges

16. $2n \to \infty$ as $n \to \infty$, so since $\lim\limits_{x \to \infty} \arctan x = \frac{\pi}{2}$, we have $\lim\limits_{n \to \infty} \arctan 2n = \frac{\pi}{2}$. Convergent

17. $a_n = 2 + \cos n\pi$, so

$\{a_n\} = \{2 + \cos \pi, 2 + \cos 2\pi, 2 + \cos 3\pi, 2 + \cos 4\pi, \dots\} = \{2 - 1, 2 + 1, 2 - 1, 2 + 1, \dots\}$

$= \{1, 3, 1, 3, \dots\}$

This sequence oscillates between 1 and 3, so it diverges.

18. $0 \le |a_n| = \dfrac{n |\cos n|}{n^2 + 1} \le \dfrac{n}{n^2 + 1} = \dfrac{1}{n + 1/n} \to 0$ as $n \to \infty$, so by the Squeeze Theorem and Theorem 4, $\{a_n\}$

converges to 0.

19. $\lim\limits_{x \to \infty} \dfrac{\ln(x^2)}{x} = \lim\limits_{x \to \infty} \dfrac{2 \ln x}{x} \overset{\text{H}}{=} \lim\limits_{x \to \infty} \dfrac{2/x}{1} = 0$, so by Theorem 2, $\left\{ \dfrac{\ln(n^2)}{n} \right\}$ converges to 0.

20. $\lim\limits_{n \to \infty} \sin\left(\dfrac{1}{n}\right) = \sin 0 = 0$ since $\dfrac{1}{n} \to 0$ as $n \to \infty$, so by Theorem 4, $\left\{ (-1)^n \sin\left(\dfrac{1}{n}\right) \right\}$ converges to 0.

21. $b_n = \sqrt{n+2} - \sqrt{n} = (\sqrt{n+2} - \sqrt{n}) \dfrac{\sqrt{n+2} + \sqrt{n}}{\sqrt{n+2} + \sqrt{n}} = \dfrac{2}{\sqrt{n+2} + \sqrt{n}} < \dfrac{2}{\sqrt{n} + \sqrt{n}} = \dfrac{2}{2\sqrt{n}} = \dfrac{1}{\sqrt{n}} \to 0$

as $n \to \infty$. So by the Squeeze Theorem with $a_n = 0$ and $c_n = 1/\sqrt{n}$, $\{ \sqrt{n+2} - \sqrt{n} \}$ converges to 0.

22. $\lim\limits_{x \to \infty} \dfrac{\ln(2 + e^x)}{3x} \overset{\text{H}}{=} \lim\limits_{x \to \infty} \dfrac{e^x/(2 + e^x)}{3} = \dfrac{1}{3} \lim\limits_{x \to \infty} \dfrac{e^x}{2 + e^x} \overset{\text{H}}{=} \dfrac{1}{3} \lim\limits_{x \to \infty} \dfrac{e^x}{e^x} = \dfrac{1}{3}(1) = \dfrac{1}{3}$, so by Theorem 2,

$\lim\limits_{n \to \infty} \dfrac{\ln(2 + e^n)}{3n} = \dfrac{1}{3}$. Convergent

23. $\lim\limits_{x \to \infty} \dfrac{x}{2^x} \overset{\text{H}}{=} \lim\limits_{x \to \infty} \dfrac{1}{(\ln 2)2^x} = 0$, so by Theorem 2, $\{n2^{-n}\}$ converges to 0.

24. $a_n = \ln(n + 1) - \ln n = \ln\left(\dfrac{n + 1}{n}\right) = \ln\left(1 + \dfrac{1}{n}\right) \to \ln(1) = 0$ as $n \to \infty$. Convergent

25. $0 \le \dfrac{\cos^2 n}{2^n} \le \dfrac{1}{2^n}$ [since $0 \le \cos^2 n \le 1$], so since $\lim\limits_{n \to \infty} \dfrac{1}{2^n} = 0$, $\left\{ \dfrac{\cos^2 n}{2^n} \right\}$ converges to 0 by the Squeeze

Theorem.

26. $0 < |a_n| = \dfrac{3^n}{n!} = \dfrac{3}{1} \cdot \dfrac{3}{2} \cdot \dfrac{3}{3} \cdot \cdots \cdot \dfrac{3}{(n-1)} \cdot \dfrac{3}{n} \le \dfrac{3}{1} \cdot \dfrac{3}{2} \cdot \dfrac{3}{n} = \dfrac{27}{2n} \to 0$ as $n \to \infty$, so by the Squeeze Theorem

and Theorem 4, $\{(-3)^n / n!\}$ converges to 0.

27.

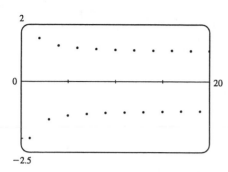

From the graph, we see that the sequence $\left\{(-1)^n \dfrac{n+1}{n}\right\}$ is divergent, since it oscillates between 1 and -1 (approximately).

28.

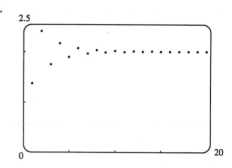

From the graph, it appears that the sequence converges to 2.

$\left\{\left(-\frac{2}{\pi}\right)^n\right\}$ converges to 0 by (6), and hence $\left\{2 + \left(-\frac{2}{\pi}\right)^n\right\}$ converges to $2 + 0 = 2$.

29.

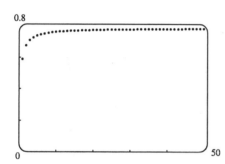

From the graph, it appears that the sequence converges to about 0.78.

$\lim\limits_{n\to\infty} \dfrac{2n}{2n+1} = \lim\limits_{n\to\infty} \dfrac{2}{2+1/n} = 1$, so

$\lim\limits_{n\to\infty} \arctan\left(\dfrac{2n}{2n+1}\right) = \arctan 1 = \dfrac{\pi}{4}$.

30.

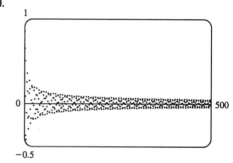

From the graph, it appears that the sequence converges (slowly) to 0.

$0 \le \dfrac{|\sin n|}{\sqrt{n}} \le \dfrac{1}{\sqrt{n}} \to 0$ as $n \to \infty$, so by the

Squeeze Theorem and Theorem 4, $\left\{\dfrac{\sin n}{\sqrt{n}}\right\}$

converges to 0.

31.

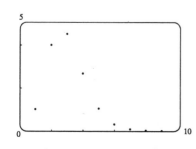

From the graph, it appears that the sequence converges to 0.

$0 < a_n = \dfrac{n^3}{n!} = \dfrac{n}{n} \cdot \dfrac{n}{(n-1)} \cdot \dfrac{n}{(n-2)} \cdot \dfrac{1}{(n-3)} \cdots \dfrac{1}{3} \cdot \dfrac{1}{2} \cdot \dfrac{1}{1}$

$\le \dfrac{n^2}{((n-1)(n-2)(n-3))}$ (for $n \ge 4$)

$= \dfrac{1/n}{(1 - 1/n)(1 - 2/n)(1 - 3/n)} \to 0$ as $n \to \infty$

So by the Squeeze Theorem, $\{n^3/n!\}$ converges to 0.

32.

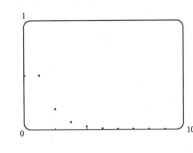

From the graph, it appears that the sequence approaches 0.

$$0 < a_n = \frac{1 \cdot 3 \cdot 5 \cdot \cdots \cdot (2n-1)}{(2n)^n} = \frac{1}{2n} \cdot \frac{3}{2n} \cdot \frac{5}{2n} \cdot \cdots \cdot \frac{2n-1}{2n}$$

$$\le \frac{1}{2n} \cdot (1) \cdot (1) \cdot \cdots \cdot (1) = \frac{1}{2n} \to 0 \text{ as } n \to \infty$$

So by the Squeeze Theorem, $\left\{ \dfrac{1 \cdot 3 \cdot 5 \cdot \cdots \cdot (2n-1)}{(2n)^n} \right\}$ converges

to 0.

33. (a) $a_n = 1000(1.06)^n \Rightarrow a_1 = 1060$, $a_2 = 1123.60$, $a_3 = 1191.02$, $a_4 = 1262.48$, and $a_5 = 1338.23$.

(b) $\lim\limits_{n \to \infty} a_n = 1000 \lim\limits_{n \to \infty} (1.06)^n$, so the sequence diverges by (6) with $r = 1.06 > 1$.

34. $a_{n+1} = \begin{cases} \frac{1}{2}a_n & \text{if } a_n \text{ is an even number} \\ 3a_n + 1 & \text{if } a_n \text{ is an odd number} \end{cases}$ When $a_1 = 11$, the first 40 terms are 11, 34, 17, 52, 26, 13, 40,

20, 10, 5, 16, 8, 4, 2, 1, 4, 2, 1, 4, 2, 1, 4, 2, 1, 4, 2, 1, 4, 2, 1, 4, 2, 1, 4, 2, 1, 4, 2, 1, 4. When $a_1 = 25$, the first

40 terms are 25, 76, 38, 19, 58, 29, 88, 44, 22, 11, 34, 17, 52, 26, 13, 40, 20, 10, 5, 16, 8, 4, 2, 1, 4, 2, 1, 4, 2, 1, 4,

2, 1, 4, 2, 1, 4, 2, 1, 4. The famous Collatz conjecture is that this sequence always reaches 1, regardless of the

starting point a_1.

35. (a) $a_1 = 1$, $a_2 = 4 - a_1 = 4 - 1 = 3$, $a_3 = 4 - a_2 = 4 - 3 = 1$, $a_4 = 4 - a_3 = 4 - 1 = 3$,

$a_5 = 4 - a_4 = 4 - 3 = 1$. Since the terms of the sequence alternate between 1 and 3, the sequence is

divergent.

(b) $a_1 = 2$, $a_2 = 4 - a_1 = 4 - 2 = 2$, $a_3 = 4 - a_2 = 4 - 2 = 2$. Since all of the terms are 2, $\lim\limits_{n \to \infty} a_n = 2$ and

hence, the sequence is convergent.

36. (a) Since $\lim\limits_{n \to \infty} a_n = L$, the terms a_n approach L as n becomes large. Because we can make a_n as close to L as we

wish, a_{n+1} will also be close, and so $\lim\limits_{n \to \infty} a_{n+1} = L$.

(b) $a_1 = 1$, $a_2 = \dfrac{1}{1 + a_1} = \dfrac{1}{1 + 1} = \dfrac{1}{2} = 0.5$, $a_3 = \dfrac{1}{1 + a_2} = \dfrac{1}{1 + \frac{1}{2}} = \dfrac{2}{3} \approx 0.66667$,

$a_4 = \dfrac{1}{1 + a_3} = \dfrac{1}{1 + \frac{2}{3}} = \dfrac{3}{5} = 0.6$, $a_5 = \dfrac{1}{1 + a_4} = \dfrac{1}{1 + \frac{3}{5}} = \dfrac{5}{8} = 0.625$,

$a_6 = \dfrac{1}{1 + a_5} = \dfrac{1}{1 + \frac{5}{8}} = \dfrac{8}{13} \approx 0.61538$, $a_7 = \dfrac{1}{1 + a_6} = \dfrac{1}{1 + \frac{8}{13}} = \dfrac{13}{21} \approx 0.61905$,

$a_8 = \dfrac{1}{1 + a_7} = \dfrac{1}{1 + \frac{13}{21}} = \dfrac{21}{34} \approx 0.61765$, $a_9 = \dfrac{1}{1 + a_8} = \dfrac{1}{1 + \frac{21}{34}} = \dfrac{34}{55} \approx 0.61818$,

$a_{10} = \dfrac{1}{1 + a_9} = \dfrac{1}{1 + \frac{34}{55}} = \dfrac{55}{89} \approx 0.61800$. It appears that $\lim\limits_{n \to \infty} a_n \approx 0.618$; hence, the sequence is

convergent.

(c) If $L = \lim\limits_{n \to \infty} a_n$ then $\lim\limits_{n \to \infty} a_{n+1} = L$ also, so L must satisfy

$L = 1/(1 + L) \Rightarrow L^2 + L - 1 = 0 \Rightarrow L = \frac{-1 + \sqrt{5}}{2} \approx 0.618$ (since L has to be non-negative if it

exists).

37. (a) Let a_n be the number of rabbit pairs in the nth month. Clearly $a_1 = 1 = a_2$. In the nth month, each pair that is

2 or more months old (that is, a_{n-2} pairs) will produce a new pair to add to the a_{n-1} pairs already present.

Thus, $a_n = a_{n-1} + a_{n-2}$, so that $\{a_n\} = \{f_n\}$, the Fibonacci sequence.

(b) $a_n = \dfrac{f_{n+1}}{f_n}$ $\Rightarrow$ $a_{n-1} = \dfrac{f_n}{f_{n-1}} = \dfrac{f_{n-1} + f_{n-2}}{f_{n-1}} = 1 + \dfrac{f_{n-2}}{f_{n-1}} = 1 + \dfrac{1}{f_{n-1}/f_{n-2}} = 1 + \dfrac{1}{a_{n-2}}$. If

$L = \lim\limits_{n \to \infty} a_n$, then $L = \lim\limits_{n \to \infty} a_{n-1}$ and $L = \lim\limits_{n \to \infty} a_{n-2}$, so L must satisfy $L = 1 + \dfrac{1}{L}$ $\Rightarrow$

$L^2 - L - 1 = 0$ $\Rightarrow$ $L = \frac{1 + \sqrt{5}}{2}$ (since L must be positive).

38. $a_1 = 2^{1/2}$, $a_2 = 2^{3/4}$, $a_3 = 2^{7/8}$, $\ldots$, so $a_n = 2^{(2^n - 1)/2^n} = 2^{1 - (1/2^n)}$. $\lim\limits_{n \to \infty} a_n = \lim\limits_{n \to \infty} 2^{1 - (1/2^n)} = 2^1 = 2$.

Alternate solution: Let $L = \lim\limits_{n \to \infty} a_n$. (We could show the limit exists by showing that $\{a_n\}$ is bounded and

increasing.) So L must satisfy $L = \sqrt{2 \cdot L}$ $\Rightarrow$ $L^2 = 2L$ $\Rightarrow$ $L(L - 2) = 0$ ($L \neq 0$ since the sequence

increases), so $L = 2$.

39. $a_n = \dfrac{1}{2n + 3}$ is decreasing since $a_{n+1} = \dfrac{1}{2(n+1) + 3} = \dfrac{1}{2n + 5} < \dfrac{1}{2n + 3} = a_n$ for each $n \geq 1$. The

sequence is bounded since $0 < a_n \leq \frac{1}{5}$ for all $n \geq 1$. Note that $a_1 = \frac{1}{5}$.

40. $a_n = \dfrac{2n - 3}{3n + 4}$ defines an increasing sequence since for $f(x) = \dfrac{2x - 3}{3x + 4}$,

$f'(x) = \dfrac{(3x + 4)(2) - (2x - 3)(3)}{(3x + 4)^2} = \dfrac{17}{(3x + 4)^2} > 0$. The sequence is bounded since $a_n \geq a_1 = -\frac{1}{7}$ for

$n \geq 1$, and $a_n < \dfrac{2n - 3}{3n} < \dfrac{2n}{3n} = \dfrac{2}{3}$ for $n \geq 1$.

41. $a_n = \cos(n\pi/2)$ is not monotonic. The first few terms are $0, -1, 0, 1, 0, -1, 0, 1, \ldots$. In fact, the sequence
consists of the terms $0, -1, 0, 1$ repeated over and over again in that order. The sequence is bounded since $|a_n| \leq 1$
for all $n \geq 1$.

42. $a_n = 3 + (-1)^n / n$ defines a sequence that is not monotonic. The first few terms are $2, 3.5, 2.\overline{6}, 3.25,$ and 2.8,
showing that the sequence is neither increasing nor decreasing. The sequence is bounded since $2 \leq a_n \leq 3.5$ for
all $n \geq 1$.

43. Since $\{a_n\}$ is a decreasing sequence, $a_n > a_{n+1}$ for all $n \geq 1$. Because all of its terms lie between 5 and 8, $\{a_n\}$ is
a bounded sequence. By the Monotonic Sequence Theorem, $\{a_n\}$ is convergent; that is, $\{a_n\}$ has a limit L. L must
be less than 8 since $\{a_n\}$ is decreasing, so $5 \leq L < 8$.

44. (a) Let P_n be the statement that $a_{n+1} \geq a_n$ and $a_n \leq 3$. P_1 is obviously true. We will assume that P_n is true and
then show that as a consequence P_{n+1} must also be true. $a_{n+2} \geq a_{n+1}$ $\Leftrightarrow$ $\sqrt{2 + a_{n+1}} \geq \sqrt{2 + a_n}$ $\Leftrightarrow$
$2 + a_{n+1} \geq 2 + a_n$ $\Leftrightarrow$ $a_{n+1} \geq a_n$, which is the induction hypothesis. $a_{n+1} \leq 3$ $\Leftrightarrow$ $\sqrt{2 + a_n} \leq 3$ $\Leftrightarrow$
$2 + a_n \leq 9$ $\Leftrightarrow$ $a_n \leq 7$, which is certainly true because we are assuming that $a_n \leq 3$. So P_n is true for all n,
and so $a_1 \leq a_n \leq 3$ (the sequence is bounded), and hence by the Monotonic Sequence Theorem, $\lim\limits_{n \to \infty} a_n$

exists.

(b) If $L = \lim\limits_{n \to \infty} a_n$, then $\lim\limits_{n \to \infty} a_{n+1} = L$ also, so $L = \sqrt{2 + L}$ $\Rightarrow$ $L^2 = 2 + L$ $\Leftrightarrow$ $L^2 - L - 2 = 0$ $\Leftrightarrow$
$(L + 1)(L - 2) = 0$ $\Leftrightarrow$ $L = 2$ (since L can't be negative).

45. We show by induction that $\{a_n\}$ is increasing and bounded above by 3.

Let P_n be the proposition that $a_{n+1} > a_n$ and $0 < a_n < 3$. Clearly P_1 is true. Assume that P_n is true. Then

$$a_{n+1} > a_n \quad \Rightarrow \quad \frac{1}{a_{n+1}} < \frac{1}{a_n} \quad \Rightarrow \quad -\frac{1}{a_{n+1}} > -\frac{1}{a_n}.$$

Now $a_{n+2} = 3 - \dfrac{1}{a_{n+1}} > 3 - \dfrac{1}{a_n} = a_{n+1} \quad \Leftrightarrow \quad P_{n+1}$. This proves that $\{a_n\}$ is increasing and bounded above

by 3, so $1 = a_1 < a_n < 3$, that is, $\{a_n\}$ is bounded, and hence convergent by the Monotonic Sequence Theorem. If

$L = \lim\limits_{n \to \infty} a_n$, then $\lim\limits_{n \to \infty} a_{n+1} = L$ also, so L must satisfy $L = 3 - 1/L \quad \Rightarrow \quad L^2 - 3L + 1 = 0 \quad \Rightarrow$

$L = \frac{3 \pm \sqrt{5}}{2}$. But $L > 1$, so $L = \frac{3 + \sqrt{5}}{2}$.

46. We use induction. Let P_n be the statement that $0 < a_{n+1} \leq a_n \leq 2$. Clearly P_1 is true, since $a_2 = 1/(3 - 2) = 1$.

Now assume that P_n is true. Then $a_{n+1} \leq a_n \quad \Rightarrow \quad -a_{n+1} \geq -a_n \quad \Rightarrow \quad 3 - a_{n+1} \geq 3 - a_n \quad \Rightarrow$

$a_{n+2} = \dfrac{1}{3 - a_{n+1}} \leq \dfrac{1}{3 - a_n} = a_{n+1}$. Also $a_{n+2} > 0$ (since $3 - a_{n+1}$ is positive) and $a_{n+1} \leq 2$ by the induction

hypothesis, so P_{n+1} is true.

To find the limit, we use the fact that $\lim\limits_{n \to \infty} a_n = \lim\limits_{n \to \infty} a_{n+1} \quad \Rightarrow \quad L = \frac{1}{3 - L} \quad \Rightarrow \quad L^2 - 3L + 1 = 0 \quad \Rightarrow$

$L = \frac{3 \pm \sqrt{5}}{2}$. But $L \leq 2$, so we must have $L = \frac{3 - \sqrt{5}}{2}$.

47. $(0.8)^n < 0.000001 \quad \Rightarrow \quad \ln(0.8)^n < \ln(0.000001) \quad \Rightarrow \quad n \ln(0.8) < \ln(0.000001) \quad \Rightarrow$

$n > \dfrac{\ln(0.000001)}{\ln(0.8)} \quad \Rightarrow \quad n > 61.9$, so n must be at least 62 to satisfy the given inequality.

48. (a) If f is continuous, then $f(L) = f\left(\lim\limits_{n \to \infty} a_n\right) = \lim\limits_{n \to \infty} f(a_n) = \lim\limits_{n \to \infty} a_{n+1} = L$ by Exercise 36(a).

(b) By repeatedly pressing the cosine key on the calculator (that is, taking cosine of the previous answer) until the displayed value stabilizes, we see that $L \approx 0.73909$.

49. (a) First we show that $a > a_1 > b_1 > b$.

$$a_1 - b_1 = \frac{a+b}{2} - \sqrt{ab} = \frac{1}{2}\left(a - 2\sqrt{ab} + b\right) = \frac{1}{2}\left(\sqrt{a} - \sqrt{b}\right)^2 > 0 \quad \text{(since } a > b) \quad \Rightarrow \quad a_1 > b_1. \text{ Also}$$

$a - a_1 = a - \frac{1}{2}(a + b) = \frac{1}{2}(a - b) > 0$ and $b - b_1 = b - \sqrt{ab} = \sqrt{b}\left(\sqrt{b} - \sqrt{a}\right) < 0$, so $a > a_1 > b_1 > b$.

In the same way we can show that $a_1 > a_2 > b_2 > b_1$ and so the given assertion is true for $n = 1$. Suppose it is true for $n = k$, that is, $a_k > a_{k+1} > b_{k+1} > b_k$. Then

$$a_{k+2} - b_{k+2} = \frac{1}{2}(a_{k+1} + b_{k+1}) - \sqrt{a_{k+1} b_{k+1}} = \frac{1}{2}\left(a_{k+1} - 2\sqrt{a_{k+1} b_{k+1}} + b_{k+1}\right)$$

$$= \frac{1}{2}\left(\sqrt{a_{k+1}} - \sqrt{b_{k+1}}\right)^2 > 0$$

$$a_{k+1} - a_{k+2} = a_{k+1} - \frac{1}{2}(a_{k+1} + b_{k+1}) = \frac{1}{2}(a_{k+1} - b_{k+1}) > 0$$

and $b_{k+1} - b_{k+2} = b_{k+1} - \sqrt{a_{k+1} b_{k+1}} = \sqrt{b_{k+1}}\left(\sqrt{b_{k+1}} - \sqrt{a_{k+1}}\right) < 0 \quad \Rightarrow$

$a_{k+1} > a_{k+2} > b_{k+2} > b_{k+1}$, so the assertion is true for $n = k + 1$. Thus, it is true for all n by mathematical induction.

(b) From part (a) we have $a > a_n > a_{n+1} > b_{n+1} > b_n > b$, which shows that both sequences, $\{a_n\}$ and $\{b_n\}$, are monotonic and bounded. So they are both convergent by the Monotonic Sequence Theorem.

(c) Let $\lim\limits_{n \to \infty} a_n = \alpha$ and $\lim\limits_{n \to \infty} b_n = \beta$. Then $\lim\limits_{n \to \infty} a_{n+1} = \lim\limits_{n \to \infty} \dfrac{a_n + b_n}{2} \quad \Rightarrow \quad \alpha = \dfrac{\alpha + \beta}{2} \quad \Rightarrow$

$2\alpha = \alpha + \beta \quad \Rightarrow \quad \alpha = \beta$.

50. $a_1 = 1$, $a_2 = 1 + \frac{1}{1+1} = \frac{3}{2} = 1.5$, $a_3 = 1 + \frac{1}{5/2} = \frac{7}{5} = 1.4$, $a_4 = 1 + \frac{1}{12/5} = \frac{17}{12} = 1.41\overline{6}$,

$a_5 = 1 + \frac{1}{29/12} = \frac{41}{29} \approx 1.413793$, $a_6 = 1 + \frac{1}{70/29} = \frac{99}{70} \approx 1.414286$, $a_7 = 1 + \frac{1}{169/70} = \frac{239}{169} \approx 1.414201$,

$a_8 = 1 + \frac{1}{408/169} = \frac{577}{408} \approx 1.414216$. Notice that $a_1 < a_3 < a_5 < a_7$ and $a_2 > a_4 > a_6 > a_8$. It appears that the

odd terms are increasing and the even terms are decreasing. Let's prove that $a_{2n-2} > a_{2n}$ and $a_{2n-1} < a_{2n+1}$ by

mathematical induction. Suppose that $a_{2k-2} > a_{2k}$. Then $1 + a_{2k-2} > 1 + a_{2k}$ $\Rightarrow$

$$\frac{1}{1+a_{2k-2}} < \frac{1}{1+a_{2k}} \quad \Rightarrow \quad 1 + \frac{1}{1+a_{2k-2}} < 1 + \frac{1}{1+a_{2k}} \quad \Rightarrow \quad a_{2k-1} < a_{2k+1} \quad \Rightarrow$$

$$1 + a_{2k-1} < 1 + a_{2k+1} \quad \Rightarrow \quad \frac{1}{1+a_{2k-1}} > \frac{1}{1+a_{2k+1}} \quad \Rightarrow \quad 1 + \frac{1}{1+a_{2k-1}} > 1 + \frac{1}{1+a_{2k+1}} \quad \Rightarrow$$

$a_{2k} > a_{2k+2}$. We have thus shown, by induction, that the odd terms are increasing and the even terms are

decreasing. Also all terms lie between 1 and 2, so both $\{a_n\}$ and $\{b_n\}$ are bounded monotonic sequences and

therefore convergent by the Monotonic Sequence Theorem. Let $\lim\limits_{n\to\infty} a_{2n} = L$. Then $\lim\limits_{n\to\infty} a_{2n+2} = L$ also. We

have $a_{n+2} = 1 + \dfrac{1}{1 + 1 + 1/(1+a_n)} = 1 + \dfrac{1}{(3+2a_n)/(1+a_n)} = \dfrac{4+3a_n}{3+2a_n}$, so $a_{2n+2} = \dfrac{4+3a_{2n}}{3+2a_{2n}}$. Taking

limits of both sides, we get $L = \dfrac{4+3L}{3+2L}$ $\Rightarrow$ $3L + 2L^2 = 4 + 3L$ $\Rightarrow$ $L^2 = 2$ $\Rightarrow$ $L = \sqrt{2}$ (since

$L > 0$). Thus, $\lim\limits_{n\to\infty} a_{2n} = \sqrt{2}$.

Similarly, we find that $\lim\limits_{n\to\infty} a_{2n+1} = \sqrt{2}$. Since the even terms approach $\sqrt{2}$ and the odd terms also approach

$\sqrt{2}$, it follows that the sequence as a whole approaches $\sqrt{2}$, that is, $\lim\limits_{n\to\infty} a_n = \sqrt{2}$.

Laboratory Project Logistic Sequences

1. To write such a program in Maple it is best to calculate all the points first and then graph them. One possible sequence of commands [taking $p_0 = \frac{1}{2}$ and $k = 1.5$ for the difference equation] is

```
p(0):=1/2;k:=1.5;
for j from 1 to 20  do p(j):=k*p(j-1)*(1-p(j-1)) od;
plot({[t,p(t)] $t=0..20},t=0..20,p=0..0.5,style=point);
```

In Mathematica, we can use the following program:

```
p[0]=1/2
k=1.5
p[j_]:=k*p[j-1]*(1-p[j-1])
P=Table[p[t],{t,20}]
ListPlot[P]
```

With $p_0 = \frac{1}{2}$ and $k = 1.5$:

n	p_n	n	p_n	n	p_n
0	0.5	7	0.3338465076	14	0.3333373303
1	0.375	8	0.3335895255	15	0.3333353318
2	0.3515625	9	0.3334613309	16	0.3333343326
3	0.3419494629	10	0.3333973076	17	0.3333338329
4	0.3375300416	11	0.3333653143	18	0.3333335831
5	0.3354052689	12	0.3333493223	19	0.3333334582
6	0.3343628617	13	0.3333413274	20	0.3333333958

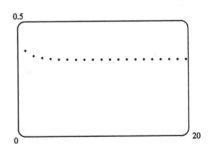

With $p_0 = \frac{1}{2}$ and $k = 2.5$:

n	p_n	n	p_n	n	p_n
0	0.5	7	0.6004164790	14	0.5999967417
1	0.625	8	0.5997913269	15	0.6000016291
2	0.5859375	9	0.6001042277	16	0.5999991854
3	0.6065368651	10	0.5999478590	17	0.6000004073
4	0.5966247409	11	0.6000260637	18	0.5999997964
5	0.6016591486	12	0.5999869664	19	0.6000001018
6	0.5991635437	13	0.6000065164	20	0.5999999491

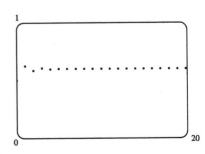

Both of these sequences seem to converge (the first to about $\frac{1}{3}$, the second to about 0.60).

With $p_0 = \frac{7}{8}$ and $k = 1.5$:

n	p_n	n	p_n	n	p_n
0	0.875	7	0.3239166554	14	0.3332554829
1	0.1640625	8	0.3284919837	15	0.3332943990
2	0.2057189941	9	0.3308775005	16	0.3333138639
3	0.2450980344	10	0.3320963702	17	0.3333235980
4	0.2775374819	11	0.3327125567	18	0.3333284655
5	0.3007656421	12	0.3330223670	19	0.3333308994
6	0.3154585059	13	0.3331777051	20	0.3333321164

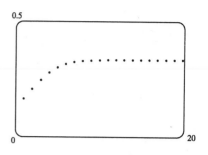

With $p_0 = \frac{7}{8}$ and $k = 2.5$:

n	p_n	n	p_n	n	p_n
0	0.875	7	0.6016572368	14	0.5999869815
1	0.2734375	8	0.5991645155	15	0.6000065088
2	0.4966735840	9	0.6004159972	16	0.5999967455
3	0.6249723374	10	0.5997915688	17	0.6000016272
4	0.5859547872	11	0.6001041070	18	0.5999991864
5	0.6065294364	12	0.5999479194	19	0.6000004068
6	0.5966286980	13	0.6000260335	20	0.5999997966

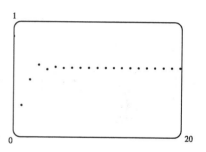

The limit of the sequence seems to depend on k, but not on p_0.

2. With $p_0 = \frac{7}{8}$ and $k = 3.2$:

n	p_n	n	p_n	n	p_n
0	0.875	7	0.5830728495	14	0.7990633827
1	0.35	8	0.7779164854	15	0.5137954979
2	0.728	9	0.5528397669	16	0.7993909896
3	0.6336512	10	0.7910654689	17	0.5131681132
4	0.7428395416	11	0.5288988570	18	0.7994451225
5	0.6112926626	12	0.7973275394	19	0.5130643795
6	0.7603646184	13	0.5171082698	20	0.7994538304

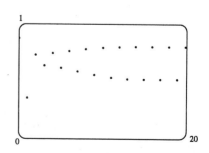

It seems that eventually the terms fluctuate between two values (about 0.5 and 0.8 in this case).

3. With $p_0 = \frac{7}{8}$ and $k = 3.42$:

n	p_n	n	p_n	n	p_n
0	0.875	7	0.4523028596	14	0.8442074951
1	0.3740625	8	0.8472194412	15	0.4498025048
2	0.8007579316	9	0.4426802161	16	0.8463823232
3	0.5456427596	10	0.8437633929	17	0.4446659586
4	0.8478752457	11	0.4508474156	18	0.8445284520
5	0.4411212220	12	0.8467373602	19	0.4490464985
6	0.8431438501	13	0.4438243545	20	0.8461207931

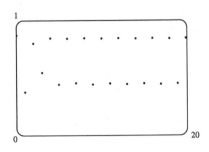

With $p_0 = \frac{7}{8}$ and $k = 3.45$:

n	p_n	n	p_n	n	p_n
0	0.875	7	0.4670259170	14	0.8403376122
1	0.37734375	8	0.8587488490	15	0.4628875685
2	0.8105962830	9	0.4184824586	16	0.8577482026
3	0.5296783241	10	0.8395743720	17	0.4209559716
4	0.8594612299	11	0.4646778983	18	0.8409445432
5	0.4167173034	12	0.8581956045	19	0.4614610237
6	0.8385707740	13	0.4198508858	20	0.8573758782

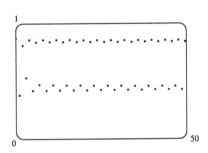

From the graphs above, it seems that for k between 3.4 and 3.5, the terms eventually fluctuate between four values. In the graph below, the pattern followed by the terms is $0.395, 0.832, 0.487, 0.869, 0.395, \ldots$. Note that even for $k = 3.42$ (as in the first graph), there are four distinct "branches; even after 1000 terms, the first and third terms in the pattern differ by about 2×10^{-9}, while the first and fifth terms differ by only 2×10^{-10}.

With $p_0 = \frac{7}{8}$ and $k = 3.48$:

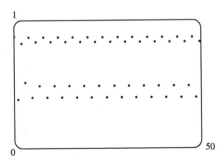

4.

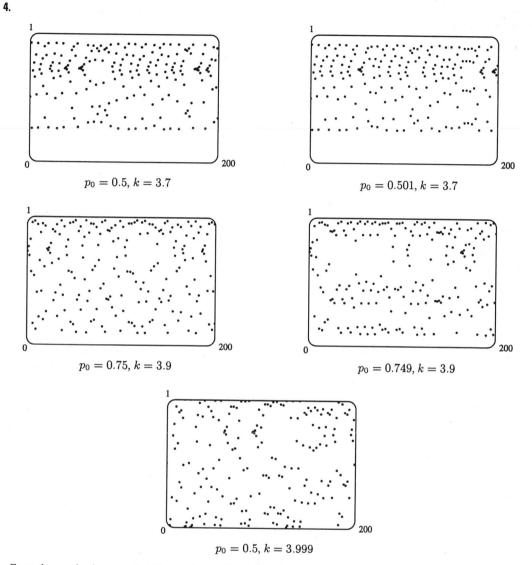

$p_0 = 0.5, k = 3.7$

$p_0 = 0.501, k = 3.7$

$p_0 = 0.75, k = 3.9$

$p_0 = 0.749, k = 3.9$

$p_0 = 0.5, k = 3.999$

From the graphs, it seems that if p_0 is changed by 0.001, the whole graph changes completely. (Note, however, that this might be partially due to accumulated round-off error in the CAS. These graphs were generated by Maple with 100-digit accuracy, and different degrees of accuracy give different graphs.) There seem to be some some fleeting patterns in these graphs, but on the whole they are certainly very chaotic. As k increases, the graph spreads out vertically, with more extreme values close to 0 or 1.

8.2 Series

1. (a) A sequence is an ordered list of numbers whereas a series is the *sum* of a list of numbers.

(b) A series is convergent if the sequence of partial sums is a convergent sequence. A series is divergent if it is not convergent.

2. $\sum_{n=1}^{\infty} a_n = 5$ means that by adding sufficiently many terms of the series we can get as close as we like to the number 5. In other words, it means that $\lim_{n\to\infty} s_n = 5$, where s_n is the nth partial sum, that is, $\sum_{i=1}^{n} a_i$.

3.

n	s_n
1	−2.40000
2	−1.92000
3	−2.01600
4	−1.99680
5	−2.00064
6	−1.99987
7	−2.00003
8	−1.99999
9	−2.00000
10	−2.00000

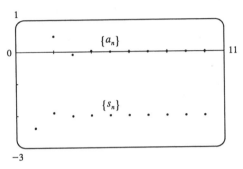

From the graph and the table, it seems that the series converges to -2. In fact, it is a geometric series with $a = -2.4$ and $r = -\frac{1}{5}$, so its sum is

$$\sum_{n=1}^{\infty} \frac{12}{(-5)^n} = \frac{-2.4}{1-\left(-\frac{1}{5}\right)} = \frac{-2.4}{1.2} = -2.$$ Note that the dot corresponding to $n = 1$ is part of both $\{a_n\}$ and $\{s_n\}$.

TI-86 Note: To graph $\{a_n\}$ and $\{s_n\}$, set your calculator to Param mode and DrawDot mode. (DrawDot is under GRAPH, MORE, FORMT (F3).) Now under E(t) = make the assignments: xt1=t, yt1=12/(-5)^t, xt2=t, yt2=sum seq(yt1,t,1,t,1). (sum and seq are under LIST, OPS (F5), MORE.) Under WIND use 1,10,1,0,10,1,−3,1,1 to obtain a graph similar to the one above. Then use TRACE (F4) to see the values.

4.

n	s_n
1	0.50000
2	1.90000
3	3.60000
4	5.42353
5	7.30814
6	9.22706
7	11.16706
8	13.12091
9	15.08432
10	17.05462

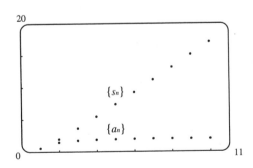

The series $\sum_{n=1}^{\infty} \frac{2n^2 - 1}{n^2 + 1}$ diverges, since its terms do not approach 0.

5.

n	s_n
1	1.55741
2	−0.62763
3	−0.77018
4	0.38764
5	−2.99287
6	−3.28388
7	−2.41243
8	−9.21214
9	−9.66446
10	−9.01610

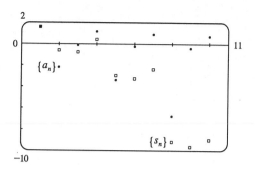

The series $\displaystyle\sum_{n=1}^{\infty} \tan n$ diverges, since its terms do not approach 0.

6.

n	s_n
1	1.00000
2	1.60000
3	1.96000
4	2.17600
5	2.30560
6	2.38336
7	2.43002
8	2.45801
9	2.47481
10	2.48488

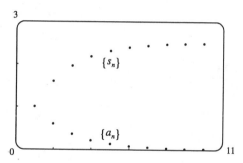

From the graph and the table, it seems that the series converges to 2.5. In fact, it is a geometric series with $a = 1$ and $r = 0.6$, so its sum is

$$\sum_{n=1}^{\infty}(0.6)^{n-1} = \frac{1}{1 - 0.6} = \frac{1}{2/5} = 2.5.$$

7.

n	s_n
1	0.64645
2	0.80755
3	0.87500
4	0.91056
5	0.93196
6	0.94601
7	0.95581
8	0.96296
9	0.96838
10	0.97259

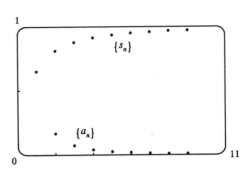

From the graph, it seems that the series converges to 1. To find the sum, we write

$$s_n = \sum_{i=1}^{n}\left(\frac{1}{i^{1.5}} - \frac{1}{(i+1)^{1.5}}\right) = \left(1 - \frac{1}{2^{1.5}}\right) + \left(\frac{1}{2^{1.5}} - \frac{1}{3^{1.5}}\right)$$

$$+ \left(\frac{1}{3^{1.5}} - \frac{1}{4^{1.5}}\right) + \cdots + \left(\frac{1}{n^{1.5}} - \frac{1}{(n+1)^{1.5}}\right) = 1 - \frac{1}{(n+1)^{1.5}}$$

So the sum is $\lim\limits_{n\to\infty} s_n = 1 - 0 = 1$.

8.

n	s_n
2	0.50000
3	0.66667
4	0.75000
5	0.80000
6	0.83333
7	0.85714
8	0.87500
9	0.88889
10	0.90000
11	0.90909
100	0.99000

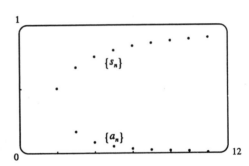

From the graph and the table, it seems that the series converges to 1. To find the sum, we write

$$s_n = \sum_{i=2}^{n}\frac{1}{i(i-1)} = \sum_{i=2}^{n}\left(\frac{1}{i-1} - \frac{1}{i}\right) \quad \text{[partial fractions]}$$

$$= \left(1 - \frac{1}{2}\right) + \left(\frac{1}{2} - \frac{1}{3}\right) + \left(\frac{1}{3} - \frac{1}{4}\right) + \cdots + \left(\frac{1}{n-1} - \frac{1}{n}\right) = 1 - \frac{1}{n},$$

and so the sum is $\lim\limits_{n\to\infty} s_n = 1 - 0 = 1$.

9. (a) $\lim\limits_{n\to\infty} a_n = \lim\limits_{n\to\infty} \dfrac{2n}{3n+1} = \dfrac{2}{3}$, so the *sequence* $\{a_n\}$ is convergent by (8.1.1).

(b) Since $\lim\limits_{n\to\infty} a_n = \frac{2}{3} \neq 0$, the *series* $\sum\limits_{n=1}^{\infty} a_n$ is divergent by the Test for Divergence (7).

10. (a) Both $\sum\limits_{i=1}^{n} a_i$ and $\sum\limits_{j=1}^{n} a_j$ represent the sum of the first n terms of the sequence $\{a_n\}$, that is, the nth partial sum.

(b) $\sum_{i=1}^{n} a_j = \underbrace{a_j + a_j + \cdots + a_j}_{n \text{ terms}} = na_j$, which, in general, is not the same as $\sum_{i=1}^{n} a_i = a_1 + a_2 + \cdots + a_n$.

11. $5 - \frac{10}{3} + \frac{20}{9} - \frac{40}{27} + \cdots$ is a geometric series with $a = 5$ and $r = -\frac{2}{3}$. Since $|r| = \frac{2}{3} < 1$, the series converges to $\frac{a}{1-r} = \frac{5}{1-(-2/3)} = \frac{5}{5/3} = 3$.

12. $1 + 0.4 + 0.16 + 0.064 + \cdots$ is a geometric series with ratio 0.4. The series converges to $\frac{a}{1-r} = \frac{1}{1-2/5} = \frac{5}{3}$ since $|r| = \frac{2}{5} < 1$.

13. $\sum_{n=1}^{\infty} 5\left(\frac{2}{3}\right)^{n-1}$ is a geometric series with $a = 5$ and $r = \frac{2}{3}$. Since $|r| = \frac{2}{3} < 1$, the series converges to

$\frac{a}{1-r} = \frac{5}{1-2/3} = \frac{5}{1/3} = 15$.

14. $\sum_{n=1}^{\infty} \frac{(-6)^{n-1}}{5^{n-1}}$ is a geometric series with $a = 1$ and $r = -\frac{6}{5}$. The series diverges since $|r| = \frac{6}{5} > 1$.

15. For $\sum_{n=1}^{\infty} 3^{-n}8^{n+1} = \sum_{n=1}^{\infty} \left(\frac{1}{3^n} \cdot \frac{8 \cdot 8^n}{1}\right) = \sum_{n=1}^{\infty} 8\left(\frac{8}{3}\right)^n$, $a = \frac{64}{3}$ and $|r| = \frac{8}{3} > 1$, so the series diverges.

16. $\sum_{n=1}^{\infty} \left(\frac{1}{e^2}\right)^n \quad \Rightarrow \quad a = \frac{1}{e^2} = |r| < 1$, so the series converges to $\frac{1/e^2}{1-1/e^2} = \frac{1}{e^2-1}$.

17. $\sum_{n=1}^{\infty} \frac{n}{n+5}$ diverges since $\lim_{n\to\infty} a_n = \lim_{n\to\infty} \frac{n}{n+5} = 1 \neq 0$. [Use (7), the Test for Divergence.]

18. $\sum_{n=1}^{\infty} \frac{3}{n} = 3\sum_{n=1}^{\infty} \frac{1}{n}$ diverges since each of its partial sums is 3 times the corresponding partial sum of the harmonic

series $\sum_{n=1}^{\infty} \frac{1}{n}$, which diverges. [If $\sum_{n=1}^{\infty} \frac{3}{n}$ were to converge, then $\sum_{n=1}^{\infty} \frac{1}{n}$ would also have to converge by

Theorem 8(i).] In general, constant multiples of divergent series are divergent.

19. Converges. $s_n = \sum_{i=1}^{n} \frac{1}{i(i+2)} = \sum_{i=1}^{n} \left(\frac{1/2}{i} - \frac{1/2}{i+2}\right)$ (using partial fractions) $= \frac{1}{2} \sum_{i=1}^{n} \left(\frac{1}{i} - \frac{1}{i+2}\right)$. The latter

sum is a telescoping series:

$\left(1 - \frac{1}{3}\right) + \left(\frac{1}{2} - \frac{1}{4}\right) + \left(\frac{1}{3} - \frac{1}{5}\right) + \cdots + \left(\frac{1}{n-1} - \frac{1}{n+1}\right) + \left(\frac{1}{n} - \frac{1}{n+2}\right) = 1 + \frac{1}{2} - \frac{1}{n+1} - \frac{1}{n+2}$

Thus, $\sum_{n=1}^{\infty} \frac{1}{n(n+2)} = \frac{1}{2} \lim_{n\to\infty} \left(1 + \frac{1}{2} - \frac{1}{n+1} - \frac{1}{n+2}\right) = \frac{1}{2}\left(1 + \frac{1}{2}\right) = \frac{3}{4}$.

20. $\sum_{n=1}^{\infty} \frac{(n+1)^2}{n(n+2)}$ diverges by (7), the Test for Divergence, since

$\lim_{n\to\infty} a_n = \lim_{n\to\infty} \frac{n^2 + 2n + 1}{n^2 + 2n} = \lim_{n\to\infty} \left(1 + \frac{1}{n^2 + 2n}\right) = 1 \neq 0$.

21. $\sum_{n=1}^{\infty} [2(0.1)^n + (0.2)^n] = 2\sum_{n=1}^{\infty} (0.1)^n + \sum_{n=1}^{\infty} (0.2)^n$. These are convergent geometric series and so by Theorem 8,

their sum is also convergent. $2\left(\frac{0.1}{1-0.1}\right) + \frac{0.2}{1-0.2} = \frac{2}{9} + \frac{1}{4} = \frac{17}{36}$

22. Converges. $s_n = \sum\limits_{i=1}^{n} \dfrac{2}{i^2 + 4i + 3} = \sum\limits_{i=1}^{n} \left(\dfrac{1}{i+1} - \dfrac{1}{i+3} \right)$ (using partial fractions). The latter sum is

$\left(\frac{1}{2} - \frac{1}{4} \right) + \left(\frac{1}{3} - \frac{1}{5} \right) + \left(\frac{1}{4} - \frac{1}{6} \right) + \left(\frac{1}{5} - \frac{1}{7} \right) + \cdots + \left(\frac{1}{n} - \frac{1}{n+2} \right) + \left(\frac{1}{n+1} - \frac{1}{n+3} \right) = \frac{1}{2} + \frac{1}{3} - \frac{1}{n+2} - \frac{1}{n+3}$

(telescoping series). Thus, $\sum\limits_{n=1}^{\infty} \dfrac{2}{n^2 + 4n + 3} = \lim\limits_{n\to\infty} \left(\dfrac{1}{2} + \dfrac{1}{3} - \dfrac{1}{n+2} - \dfrac{1}{n+3} \right) = \dfrac{1}{2} + \dfrac{1}{3} = \dfrac{5}{6}$.

23. Converges. $s_n = \left(\sin 1 - \sin \dfrac{1}{2} \right) + \left(\sin \dfrac{1}{2} - \sin \dfrac{1}{3} \right) + \cdots + \left(\sin \dfrac{1}{n} - \sin \dfrac{1}{n+1} \right) = \sin 1 - \sin \dfrac{1}{n+1}$, so

$\sum\limits_{n=1}^{\infty} \left(\sin \dfrac{1}{n} - \sin \dfrac{1}{n+1} \right) = \lim\limits_{n\to\infty} s_n = \sin 1 - \sin 0 = \sin 1$.

24. $\sum\limits_{n=1}^{\infty} \left(\dfrac{1}{2^{n-1}} + \dfrac{2}{3^{n-1}} \right) = \sum\limits_{n=1}^{\infty} \dfrac{1}{2^{n-1}} + 2 \sum\limits_{n=1}^{\infty} \dfrac{1}{3^{n-1}} = \dfrac{1}{1-1/2} + 2 \left(\dfrac{1}{1-1/3} \right) = 5$

25. Converges. $\sum\limits_{n=1}^{\infty} \dfrac{3^n + 2^n}{6^n} = \sum\limits_{n=1}^{\infty} \left(\dfrac{3^n}{6^n} + \dfrac{2^n}{6^n} \right) = \sum\limits_{n=1}^{\infty} \left[\left(\dfrac{1}{2} \right)^n + \left(\dfrac{1}{3} \right)^n \right] = \dfrac{1/2}{1-1/2} + \dfrac{1/3}{1-1/3} = 1 + \dfrac{1}{2} = \dfrac{3}{2}$

26. $\lim\limits_{n\to\infty} a_n = \lim\limits_{n\to\infty} \dfrac{1}{5 + 2^{-n}} = \dfrac{1}{5} \neq 0$, so the series diverges by the Test for Divergence.

27. $\lim\limits_{n\to\infty} a_n = \lim\limits_{n\to\infty} \arctan n = \dfrac{\pi}{2} \neq 0$, so the series diverges by the Test for Divergence.

28. $s_n = (\ln 1 - \ln 2) + (\ln 2 - \ln 3) + (\ln 3 - \ln 4) + \cdots + [\ln n - \ln(n+1)] = \ln 1 - \ln(n+1) = -\ln(n+1)$

(telescoping series). Thus, $\lim\limits_{n\to\infty} s_n = -\infty$, so the series is divergent.

29. $0.\overline{2} = \dfrac{2}{10} + \dfrac{2}{10^2} + \cdots$ is a geometric series with $a = \dfrac{2}{10}$ and $r = \dfrac{1}{10}$. It converges to $\dfrac{a}{1-r} = \dfrac{2/10}{1-1/10} = \dfrac{2}{9}$.

30. $0.\overline{73} = \dfrac{73}{10^2} + \dfrac{73}{10^4} + \cdots = \dfrac{73/10^2}{1-1/10^2} = \dfrac{73/100}{99/100} = \dfrac{73}{99}$

31. $3.\overline{417} = 3 + \dfrac{417}{10^3} + \dfrac{417}{10^6} + \cdots = 3 + \dfrac{417/10^3}{1-1/10^3} = 3 + \dfrac{417}{999} = \dfrac{3414}{999} = \dfrac{1138}{333}$

32. $6.2\overline{54} = 6.2 + \dfrac{54}{10^3} + \dfrac{54}{10^5} + \cdots = 6.2 + \dfrac{54/10^3}{1-1/10^2} = \dfrac{62}{10} + \dfrac{54}{990} = \dfrac{6192}{990} = \dfrac{344}{55}$

33. $\sum\limits_{n=1}^{\infty} \dfrac{x^n}{3^n} = \sum\limits_{n=1}^{\infty} \left(\dfrac{x}{3} \right)^n$ is a geometric series with $r = \dfrac{x}{3}$, so the series converges $\Leftrightarrow |r| < 1 \Leftrightarrow \dfrac{|x|}{3} < 1 \Leftrightarrow$

$|x| < 3$; that is, $-3 < x < 3$. In that case, the sum of the series is $\dfrac{a}{1-r} = \dfrac{x/3}{1-x/3} = \dfrac{x/3}{1-x/3} \cdot \dfrac{3}{3} = \dfrac{x}{3-x}$.

34. $\sum\limits_{n=0}^{\infty} 2^n (x+1)^n = \sum\limits_{n=0}^{\infty} [2(x+1)]^n = \sum\limits_{n=1}^{\infty} [2(x+1)]^{n-1}$ is a geometric series with $r = 2(x+1)$, so the series

converges $\Leftrightarrow |r| < 1 \Leftrightarrow |2(x+1)| < 1 \Leftrightarrow |x+1| < \dfrac{1}{2} \Leftrightarrow -\dfrac{1}{2} < x+1 < \dfrac{1}{2} \Leftrightarrow$

$-\dfrac{3}{2} < x < -\dfrac{1}{2}$. In that case, the sum of the series is $\dfrac{a}{1-r} = \dfrac{1}{1-2(x+1)} = \dfrac{1}{-1-2x}$ or $\dfrac{-1}{2x+1}$.

35. $\displaystyle\sum_{n=0}^{\infty}\left(\frac{1}{x}\right)^n = \sum_{n=1}^{\infty}\left(\frac{1}{x}\right)^{n-1}$ is geometric with $r = \dfrac{1}{x}$, so it converges whenever $\left|\dfrac{1}{x}\right| < 1 \;\Leftrightarrow$

$\dfrac{1}{|x|} < 1 \;\Leftrightarrow\; 1 < |x| \;\Leftrightarrow\; |x| > 1 \;\Leftrightarrow\; x > 1$ or $x < -1$, and the sum is

$$\frac{a}{1-r} = \frac{1}{1-1/x} = \frac{1}{1-1/x}\cdot\frac{x}{x} = \frac{x}{x-1}.$$

36. $\displaystyle\sum_{n=0}^{\infty}\tan^n x = \sum_{n=1}^{\infty}(\tan x)^{n-1}$ is geometric and converges when $|\tan x| < 1 \;\Leftrightarrow\; -1 < \tan x < 1 \;\Leftrightarrow$

$n\pi - \frac{\pi}{4} < x < n\pi + \frac{\pi}{4}$ (n any integer). On these intervals the sum is $\dfrac{1}{1-\tan x}$.

37. After defining f, We use `convert(f,parfrac);` in Maple, `Apart` in Mathematica, or `Expand Rational`

and `Simplify` in Derive to find that the general term is $\dfrac{1}{(4n+1)(4n-3)} = -\dfrac{1/4}{4n+1} + \dfrac{1/4}{4n-3}$. So the nth

partial sum is

$$s_n = \sum_{k=1}^{n}\left(-\frac{1/4}{4k+1} + \frac{1/4}{4k-3}\right) = \frac{1}{4}\sum_{k=1}^{n}\left(\frac{1}{4k-3} - \frac{1}{4k+1}\right)$$

$$= \frac{1}{4}\left[\left(1 - \frac{1}{5}\right) + \left(\frac{1}{5} - \frac{1}{9}\right) + \left(\frac{1}{9} - \frac{1}{13}\right) + \cdots + \left(\frac{1}{4n-3} - \frac{1}{4n+1}\right)\right] = \frac{1}{4}\left(1 - \frac{1}{4n+1}\right)$$

The series converges to $\displaystyle\lim_{n\to\infty} s_n = \frac{1}{4}$. This can be confirmed by directly computing the sum using

`sum(f,1..infinity);` (in Maple), `Sum[f,{n,1,Infinity}]` (in Mathematica), or `Calculus Sum`
(from 1 to ∞) and `Simplify` (in Derive).

38. See Exercise 37 for specific CAS commands. $\dfrac{n^2 + 3n + 1}{(n^2+n)^2} = \dfrac{1}{n^2} + \dfrac{1}{n} - \dfrac{1}{(n+1)^2} - \dfrac{1}{n+1}$. So the nth partial

sum is

$$s_n = \sum_{k=1}^{n}\left(\frac{1}{k^2} + \frac{1}{k} - \frac{1}{(k+1)^2} - \frac{1}{k+1}\right)$$

$$= \left(1 + 1 - \frac{1}{2^2} - \frac{1}{2}\right) + \left(\frac{1}{2^2} + \frac{1}{2} - \frac{1}{3^2} - \frac{1}{3}\right) + \cdots + \left(\frac{1}{n^2} + \frac{1}{n} - \frac{1}{(n+1)^2} - \frac{1}{n+1}\right)$$

$$= 1 + 1 - \frac{1}{(n+1)^2} - \frac{1}{n+1}$$

The series converges to $\displaystyle\lim_{n\to\infty} s_n = 2$.

39. For $n = 1$, $a_1 = 0$ since $s_1 = 0$. For $n > 1$,

$$a_n = s_n - s_{n-1} = \frac{n-1}{n+1} - \frac{(n-1)-1}{(n-1)+1} = \frac{(n-1)n - (n+1)(n-2)}{(n+1)n} = \frac{2}{n(n+1)}$$

Also, $\displaystyle\sum_{n=1}^{\infty} a_n = \lim_{n\to\infty} s_n = \lim_{n\to\infty}\frac{1 - 1/n}{1 + 1/n} = 1$.

40. $a_1 = s_1 = 3 - \frac{1}{2} = \frac{5}{2}$. For $n \neq 1$,

$$a_n = s_n - s_{n-1} = \left(3 - n2^{-n}\right) - \left[3 - (n-1)2^{-(n-1)}\right] = -\frac{n}{2^n} + \frac{n-1}{2^{n-1}}\cdot\frac{2}{2} = \frac{2(n-1)}{2^n} - \frac{n}{2^n} = \frac{n-2}{2^n}$$

Also, $\displaystyle\sum_{n=1}^{\infty} a_n = \lim_{n\to\infty} s_n = \lim_{n\to\infty}\left(3 - \frac{n}{2^n}\right) = 3$ because $\displaystyle\lim_{x\to\infty}\frac{x}{2^x} \overset{H}{=} \lim_{x\to\infty}\frac{1}{2^x \ln 2} = 0$.

41. (a) The first step in the chain occurs when the local government spends D dollars. The people who receive it spend a fraction c of those D dollars, that is, Dc dollars. Those who receive the Dc dollars spend a fraction c of it, that is, Dc^2 dollars. Continuing in this way, we see that the total spending after n transactions is

$$S_n = D + Dc + Dc^2 + \cdots + Dc^{n-1} = \frac{D(1-c^n)}{1-c} \text{ by (3)}.$$

(b) $\displaystyle\lim_{n\to\infty} S_n = \lim_{n\to\infty} \frac{D(1-c^n)}{1-c} = \frac{D}{1-c} \lim_{n\to\infty}(1-c^n) = \frac{D}{1-c}$ (since $0 < c < 1$ $\Rightarrow$ $\displaystyle\lim_{n\to\infty} c^n = 0$)

$= \dfrac{D}{s}$ (since $c + s = 1$) $= kD$ (since $k = 1/s$)

If $c = 0.8$, then $s = 1 - c = 0.2$ and the multiplier is $k = 1/s = 5$.

42. (a) Initially, the ball falls a distance H, then rebounds a distance rH, falls rH, rebounds r^2H, falls r^2H, etc. The total distance it travels is

$$H + 2rH + 2r^2H + 2r^3H + \cdots = H(1 + 2r + 2r^2 + 2r^3 + \cdots)$$

$$= H[1 + 2r(1 + r + r^2 + \cdots)] = H\left[1 + 2r\left(\frac{1}{1-r}\right)\right] = H\left(\frac{1+r}{1-r}\right) \text{ meters}$$

(b) From Example 3 in Section 2.1, we know that a ball falls $\frac{1}{2}gt^2$ meters in t seconds, where g is the gravitational acceleration. Thus, a ball falls h meters in $t = \sqrt{2h/g}$ seconds. The total travel time in seconds is

$$\sqrt{\frac{2H}{g}} + 2\sqrt{\frac{2H}{g}r} + 2\sqrt{\frac{2H}{g}r^2} + 2\sqrt{\frac{2H}{g}r^3} + \cdots = \sqrt{\frac{2H}{g}}\left[1 + 2\sqrt{r} + 2\sqrt{r^2} + 2\sqrt{r^3} + \cdots\right]$$

$$= \sqrt{\frac{2H}{g}}\left(1 + 2\sqrt{r}\left[1 + \sqrt{r} + \sqrt{r^2} + \cdots\right]\right) = \sqrt{\frac{2H}{g}}\left[1 + 2\sqrt{r}\left(\frac{1}{1-\sqrt{r}}\right)\right] = \sqrt{\frac{2H}{g}}\frac{1+\sqrt{r}}{1-\sqrt{r}}$$

(c) It will help to make a chart of the time for each descent and each rebound of the ball, together with the velocity just before and just after each bounce. Recall that the time in seconds needed to fall h meters is $\sqrt{2h/g}$. The ball hits the ground with velocity $-g\sqrt{2h/g} = -\sqrt{2hg}$ (taking the upward direction to be positive) and rebounds with velocity $kg\sqrt{2h/g} = k\sqrt{2hg}$, taking time $k\sqrt{2h/g}$ to reach the top of its bounce, where its velocity is 0. At that point, its height is k^2h. All these results follow from the formulas for vertical motion with gravitational acceleration $-g$: $\dfrac{d^2y}{dt^2} = -g$ $\Rightarrow$ $v = \dfrac{dy}{dt} = v_0 - gt$ $\Rightarrow$ $y = y_0 + v_0t - \frac{1}{2}gt^2$.

number of descent	time of descent	speed before bounce	speed after bounce	time of ascent	peak height
1	$\sqrt{2H/g}$	$\sqrt{2Hg}$	$k\sqrt{2Hg}$	$k\sqrt{2H/g}$	k^2H
2	$\sqrt{2k^2H/g}$	$\sqrt{2k^2Hg}$	$k\sqrt{2k^2Hg}$	$k\sqrt{2k^2H/g}$	k^4H
3	$\sqrt{2k^4H/g}$	$\sqrt{2k^4Hg}$	$k\sqrt{2k^4Hg}$	$k\sqrt{2k^4H/g}$	k^6H
...	...	...	...	...	...

The total travel time in seconds is

$$\sqrt{\frac{2H}{g}} + k\sqrt{\frac{2H}{g}} + k\sqrt{\frac{2H}{g}} + k^2\sqrt{\frac{2H}{g}} + k^2\sqrt{\frac{2H}{g}} + \cdots = \sqrt{\frac{2H}{g}}(1 + 2k + 2k^2 + 2k^3 + \cdots)$$

$$= \sqrt{\frac{2H}{g}}[1 + 2k(1 + k + k^2 + \cdots)] = \sqrt{\frac{2H}{g}}\left[1 + 2k\left(\frac{1}{1-k}\right)\right] = \sqrt{\frac{2H}{g}}\frac{1+k}{1-k}$$

Another method: We could use part (b). At the top of the bounce, the height is $k^2 h = rh$, so $\sqrt{r} = k$ and the result follows from part (b).

43. $\sum_{n=2}^{\infty}(1+c)^{-n}$ is a geometric series with $a = (1+c)^{-2}$ and $r = (1+c)^{-1}$, so the series converges when

$|(1+c)^{-1}| < 1 \iff |1+c| > 1 \iff 1+c > 1$ or $1+c < -1 \iff c > 0$ or $c < -2$. We calculate the sum

of the series and set it equal to 2: $\dfrac{(1+c)^{-2}}{1-(1+c)^{-1}} = 2 \iff \left(\dfrac{1}{1+c}\right)^2 = 2 - 2\left(\dfrac{1}{1+c}\right) \iff$

$1 = 2(1+c)^2 - 2(1+c) = 0 \iff 2c^2 + 2c - 1 = 0 \iff c = \dfrac{-2 \pm \sqrt{12}}{4} = \dfrac{\pm\sqrt{3}-1}{2}$. However, the negative

root is inadmissible because $-2 < \dfrac{-\sqrt{3}-1}{2} < 0$. So $c = \dfrac{\sqrt{3}-1}{2}$.

44. The area between $y = x^{n-1}$ and $y = x^n$ for $0 \le x \le 1$ is

$$\int_0^1 \left(x^{n-1} - x^n\right) dx = \left[\frac{x^n}{n} - \frac{x^{n+1}}{n+1}\right]_0^1 = \frac{1}{n} - \frac{1}{n+1}$$

$$= \frac{(n+1)-n}{n(n+1)} = \frac{1}{n(n+1)}$$

We can see from the diagram that as $n \to \infty$, the sum of the areas between the successive curves approaches the area of the unit

square, that is, 1. So $\displaystyle\sum_{n=1}^{\infty} \frac{1}{n(n+1)} = 1$.

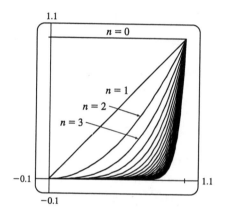

45. Let d_n be the diameter of C_n. We draw lines from the centers of the C_i to the center of D (or C), and using the Pythagorean

Theorem, we can write $1^2 + \left(1 - \tfrac{1}{2}d_1\right)^2 = \left(1 + \tfrac{1}{2}d_1\right)^2 \iff$

$1 = \left(1 + \tfrac{1}{2}d_1\right)^2 - \left(1 - \tfrac{1}{2}d_1\right)^2 = 2d_1$ (difference of squares)

$\Rightarrow d_1 = \tfrac{1}{2}$. Similarly,

$1 = \left(1 + \tfrac{1}{2}d_2\right)^2 - \left(1 - d_1 - \tfrac{1}{2}d_2\right)^2 = 2d_2 + 2d_1 - d_1^2 - d_1 d_2$

$= (2 - d_1)(d_1 + d_2) \iff$

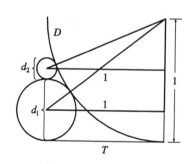

$d_2 = \dfrac{1}{2 - d_1} - d_1 = \dfrac{(1-d_1)^2}{2-d_1}$, $1 = \left(1 + \tfrac{1}{2}d_3\right)^2 - \left(1 - d_1 - d_2 - \tfrac{1}{2}d_3\right)^2 \iff d_3 = \dfrac{[1 - (d_1 + d_2)]^2}{2 - (d_1 + d_2)}$, and in

general, $d_{n+1} = \dfrac{\left(1 - \sum_{i=1}^{n} d_i\right)^2}{2 - \sum_{i=1}^{n} d_i}$. If we actually calculate d_2 and d_3 from the formulas above, we find that they

are $\dfrac{1}{6} = \dfrac{1}{2\cdot3}$ and $\dfrac{1}{12} = \dfrac{1}{3\cdot4}$ respectively, so we suspect that in general, $d_n = \dfrac{1}{n(n+1)}$. To prove this, we

use induction: assume that for all $k \le n$, $d_k = \dfrac{1}{k(k+1)} = \dfrac{1}{k} - \dfrac{1}{k+1}$. Then

$\displaystyle\sum_{i=1}^{n} d_i = 1 - \dfrac{1}{n+1} = \dfrac{n}{n+1}$ (telescoping sum). Substituting this into our formula for d_{n+1}, we get

$$d_{n+1} = \frac{\left[1 - \dfrac{n}{n+1}\right]^2}{2 - \left(\dfrac{n}{n+1}\right)} = \frac{\dfrac{1}{(n+1)^2}}{\dfrac{n+2}{n+1}} = \frac{1}{(n+1)(n+2)}, \text{ and the induction is complete.}$$

Now, we observe that the partial sums $\sum_{i=1}^{n} d_i$ of the diameters of the circles approach 1 as $n \to \infty$; that is,

$$\sum_{n=1}^{\infty} a_n = \sum_{n=1}^{\infty} \frac{1}{n(n+1)} = 1, \text{ which is what we wanted to prove.}$$

46. $|CD| = b \sin \theta$, $|DE| = |CD| \sin \theta = b \sin^2 \theta$, $|EF| = |DE| \sin \theta = b \sin^3 \theta$, ... Therefore,

$$|CD| + |DE| + |EF| + |FG| + \cdots = b \sum_{n=1}^{\infty} \sin^n \theta = b \left(\frac{\sin \theta}{1 - \sin \theta} \right) \text{ since this is a geometric series with}$$

$r = \sin \theta$ and $|\sin \theta| < 1$ (because $0 < \theta < \frac{\pi}{2}$).

47. The series $1 - 1 + 1 - 1 + 1 - 1 + \cdots$ diverges (geometric series with $r = -1$) so we cannot say that
$0 = 1 - 1 + 1 - 1 + 1 - 1 + \cdots$.

48. If $\sum_{n=1}^{\infty} a_n$ is convergent, then $\lim_{n \to \infty} a_n = 0$ by Theorem 6, so $\lim_{n \to \infty} \dfrac{1}{a_n} \neq 0$, and so $\sum_{n=1}^{\infty} \dfrac{1}{a_n}$ is divergent by the Test for Divergence.

49. Suppose on the contrary that $\sum(a_n + b_n)$ converges. Then $\sum(a_n + b_n)$ and $\sum a_n$ are convergent series. So by Theorem 8, $\sum [(a_n + b_n) - a_n]$ would also be convergent. But $\sum [(a_n + b_n) - a_n] = \sum b_n$, a contradiction, since $\sum b_n$ is given to be divergent.

50. No. For example, take $\sum a_n = \sum n$ and $\sum b_n = \sum(-n)$, which both diverge, yet $\sum(a_n + b_n) = \sum 0$, which converges with sum 0.

51. The partial sums $\{s_n\}$ form an increasing sequence, since $s_n - s_{n-1} = a_n > 0$ for all n. Also, the sequence $\{s_n\}$ is bounded since $s_n \leq 1000$ for all n. So by Theorem 8.1.7, the sequence of partial sums converges, that is, the series $\sum a_n$ is convergent.

52. (a) RHS $= \dfrac{1}{f_{n-1} f_n} - \dfrac{1}{f_n f_{n+1}} = \dfrac{f_n f_{n+1} - f_n f_{n-1}}{f_n^2 f_{n-1} f_{n+1}} = \dfrac{f_{n+1} - f_{n-1}}{f_n f_{n-1} f_{n+1}} = \dfrac{(f_{n-1} + f_n) - f_{n-1}}{f_n f_{n-1} f_{n+1}}$

$= \dfrac{1}{f_{n-1} f_{n+1}} = \text{LHS}$

(b) $\displaystyle\sum_{n=2}^{\infty} \frac{1}{f_{n-1} f_{n+1}} = \sum_{n=2}^{\infty} \left(\frac{1}{f_{n-1} f_n} - \frac{1}{f_n f_{n+1}} \right)$ [from part (a)]

$$= \lim_{n \to \infty} \left[\left(\frac{1}{f_1 f_2} - \frac{1}{f_2 f_3} \right) + \left(\frac{1}{f_2 f_3} - \frac{1}{f_3 f_4} \right) + \left(\frac{1}{f_3 f_4} - \frac{1}{f_4 f_5} \right) + \cdots \right.$$
$$\left. + \left(\frac{1}{f_{n-1} f_n} - \frac{1}{f_n f_{n+1}} \right) \right]$$

$$= \lim_{n \to \infty} \left(\frac{1}{f_1 f_2} - \frac{1}{f_n f_{n+1}} \right) = \frac{1}{f_1 f_2} - 0 = \frac{1}{1 \cdot 1} = 1 \text{ because } f_n \to \infty \text{ as } n \to \infty.$$

(c) $\displaystyle\sum_{n=2}^{\infty} \frac{f_n}{f_{n-1}f_{n+1}} = \sum_{n=2}^{\infty}\left(\frac{f_n}{f_{n-1}f_n} - \frac{f_n}{f_n f_{n+1}}\right)$ (as above)

$$= \sum_{n=2}^{\infty}\left(\frac{1}{f_{n-1}} - \frac{1}{f_{n+1}}\right)$$

$$= \lim_{n\to\infty}\left[\left(\frac{1}{f_1} - \frac{1}{f_3}\right) + \left(\frac{1}{f_2} - \frac{1}{f_4}\right) + \left(\frac{1}{f_3} - \frac{1}{f_5}\right) + \left(\frac{1}{f_4} - \frac{1}{f_6}\right) + \cdots \right.$$

$$\left. + \left(\frac{1}{f_{n-1}} - \frac{1}{f_{n+1}}\right)\right]$$

$$= \lim_{n\to\infty}\left(\frac{1}{f_1} + \frac{1}{f_2} - \frac{1}{f_n} - \frac{1}{f_{n+1}}\right) = 1 + 1 - 0 - 0 = 2 \text{ because } f_n \to \infty \text{ as } n \to \infty.$$

53. (a) At the first step, only the interval $\left(\frac{1}{3}, \frac{2}{3}\right)$ (length $\frac{1}{3}$) is removed. At the second step, we remove the intervals $\left(\frac{1}{9}, \frac{2}{9}\right)$ and $\left(\frac{7}{9}, \frac{8}{9}\right)$, which have a total length of $2 \cdot \left(\frac{1}{3}\right)^2$. At the third step, we remove 2^2 intervals, each of length $\left(\frac{1}{3}\right)^3$. In general, at the nth step we remove 2^{n-1} intervals, each of length $\left(\frac{1}{3}\right)^n$, for a length of $2^{n-1} \cdot \left(\frac{1}{3}\right)^n = \frac{1}{3}\left(\frac{2}{3}\right)^{n-1}$. Thus, the total length of all removed intervals is $\displaystyle\sum_{n=1}^{\infty} \frac{1}{3}\left(\frac{2}{3}\right)^{n-1} = \frac{1/3}{1-2/3} = 1$ (geometric series with $a = \frac{1}{3}$ and $r = \frac{2}{3}$). Notice that at the nth step, the leftmost interval that is removed is $\left(\left(\frac{1}{3}\right)^n, \left(\frac{2}{3}\right)^n\right)$, so we never remove 0, and 0 is in the Cantor set. Also, the rightmost interval removed is $\left(1 - \left(\frac{2}{3}\right)^n, 1 - \left(\frac{1}{3}\right)^n\right)$, so 1 is never removed. Some other numbers in the Cantor set are $\frac{1}{3}, \frac{2}{3}, \frac{1}{9}, \frac{2}{9}, \frac{7}{9},$ and $\frac{8}{9}$.

(b) The area removed at the first step is $\frac{1}{9}$; at the second step, $8 \cdot \left(\frac{1}{9}\right)^2$; at the third step, $(8)^2 \cdot \left(\frac{1}{9}\right)^3$. In general, the area removed at the nth step is $(8)^{n-1}\left(\frac{1}{9}\right)^n = \frac{1}{9}\left(\frac{8}{9}\right)^{n-1}$, so the total area of all removed squares is

$$\sum_{n=1}^{\infty} \frac{1}{9}\left(\frac{8}{9}\right)^{n-1} = \frac{1/9}{1-8/9} = 1.$$

54. (a)

a_1	1	2	4	1	1	1000
a_2	2	3	1	4	1000	1
a_3	1.5	2.5	2.5	2.5	500.5	500.5
a_4	1.75	2.75	1.75	3.25	750.25	250.75
a_5	1.625	2.625	2.125	2.875	625.375	375.625
a_6	1.6875	2.6875	1.9375	3.0625	687.813	313.188
a_7	1.65625	2.65625	2.03125	2.96875	656.594	344.406
a_8	1.67188	2.67188	1.98438	3.01563	672.203	328.797
a_9	1.66406	2.66406	2.00781	2.99219	664.398	336.602
a_{10}	1.66797	2.66797	1.99609	3.00391	668.301	332.699
a_{11}	1.66602	2.66602	2.00195	2.99805	666.350	334.650
a_{12}	1.66699	2.66699	1.99902	3.00098	667.325	333.675

The limits seem to be $\frac{5}{3}, \frac{8}{3}$, 2, 3, 667, and 334. Note that the limits appear to be "weighted" more toward a_2. In general, we guess that the limit is $\dfrac{a_1 + 2a_2}{3}$.

(b) $a_{n+1} - a_n = \frac{1}{2}(a_n + a_{n-1}) - a_n = -\frac{1}{2}(a_n - a_{n-1}) = -\frac{1}{2}\left[\frac{1}{2}(a_{n-1} + a_{n-2}) - a_{n-1}\right]$

$\qquad = -\frac{1}{2}\left[-\frac{1}{2}(a_{n-1} - a_{n-2})\right] = \cdots = \left(-\frac{1}{2}\right)^{n-1}(a_2 - a_1)$

Note that we have used the formula $a_k = \frac{1}{2}(a_{k-1} + a_{k-2})$ a total of $n-1$ times in this calculation, once for each k between 3 and $n+1$. Now we can write

$$a_n = a_1 + (a_2 - a_1) + (a_3 - a_2) + \cdots + (a_{n-1} - a_{n-2}) + (a_n - a_{n-1})$$

$$= a_1 + \sum_{k=1}^{n-1}(a_{k+1} - a_k) = a_1 + \sum_{k=1}^{n-1}\left(-\frac{1}{2}\right)^{k-1}(a_2 - a_1)$$

and so

$$\lim_{n\to\infty} a_n = a_1 + (a_2 - a_1)\sum_{k=1}^{\infty}\left(-\frac{1}{2}\right)^{k-1} = a_1 + (a_2 - a_1)\left[\frac{1}{1-(-1/2)}\right]$$

$$= a_1 + \frac{2}{3}(a_2 - a_1) = \frac{a_1 + 2a_2}{3}$$

55. (a) For $\sum_{n=1}^{\infty}\dfrac{n}{(n+1)!}$, $s_1 = \dfrac{1}{1\cdot 2} = \dfrac{1}{2}$, $s_2 = \dfrac{1}{2} + \dfrac{2}{1\cdot 2\cdot 3} = \dfrac{5}{6}$, $s_3 = \dfrac{5}{6} + \dfrac{3}{1\cdot 2\cdot 3\cdot 4} = \dfrac{23}{24}$,

$s_4 = \dfrac{23}{24} + \dfrac{4}{1\cdot 2\cdot 3\cdot 4\cdot 5} = \dfrac{119}{120}$. The denominators are $(n+1)!$, so a guess would be $s_n = \dfrac{(n+1)! - 1}{(n+1)!}$.

(b) For $n = 1$, $s_1 = \dfrac{1}{2} = \dfrac{2! - 1}{2!}$, so the formula holds for $n = 1$. Assume $s_k = \dfrac{(k+1)! - 1}{(k+1)!}$. Then

$$s_{k+1} = \dfrac{(k+1)! - 1}{(k+1)!} + \dfrac{k+1}{(k+2)!} = \dfrac{(k+1)! - 1}{(k+1)!} + \dfrac{k+1}{(k+1)!(k+2)}$$

$$= \dfrac{(k+2)! - (k+2) + k + 1}{(k+2)!} = \dfrac{(k+2)! - 1}{(k+2)!}$$

Thus, the formula is true for $n = k + 1$. So by induction, the guess is correct.

(c) $\lim_{n\to\infty} s_n = \lim_{n\to\infty} \dfrac{(n+1)! - 1}{(n+1)!} = \lim_{n\to\infty}\left[1 - \dfrac{1}{(n+1)!}\right] = 1$ and so $\sum_{n=1}^{\infty}\dfrac{n}{(n+1)!} = 1$.

56.

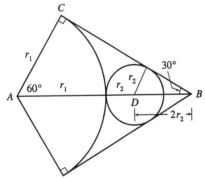

Let $r_1 = $ radius of the large circle, $r_2 = $ radius of next circle, and so on. From the figure we have $\angle BAC = 60°$ and $\cos 60° = r_1/|AB|$, so $|AB| = 2r_1$ and $|DB| = 2r_2$. Therefore, $2r_1 = r_1 + r_2 + 2r_2 = r_1 + 3r_2 \Rightarrow$ $r_1 = 3r_2$. In general, we have $r_{n+1} = \frac{1}{3}r_n$, so the total area is

$$A = \pi r_1^2 + 3\pi r_2^2 + 3\pi r_3^2 + \cdots$$

$$= \pi r_1^2 + 3\pi r_2^2\left(1 + \dfrac{1}{3^2} + \dfrac{1}{3^4} + \dfrac{1}{3^6} + \cdots\right)$$

$$= \pi r_1^2 + 3\pi r_2^2 \cdot \dfrac{1}{1 - 1/9} = \pi r_1^2 + \dfrac{27}{8}\pi r_2^2$$

Since the sides of the triangle have length 1, $|BC| = \frac{1}{2}$ and $\tan 30° = \dfrac{r_1}{1/2}$. Thus, $r_1 = \dfrac{\tan 30°}{2} = \dfrac{1}{2\sqrt{3}} \Rightarrow$

$r_2 = \dfrac{1}{6\sqrt{3}}$, so $A = \pi\left(\dfrac{1}{2\sqrt{3}}\right)^2 + \dfrac{27\pi}{8}\left(\dfrac{1}{6\sqrt{3}}\right)^2 = \dfrac{\pi}{12} + \dfrac{\pi}{32} = \dfrac{11\pi}{96}$. The area of the triangle is $\dfrac{\sqrt{3}}{4}$, so the circles occupy about 83.1% of the area of the triangle.

8.3 The Integral and Comparison Tests; Estimating Sums · · ·

1. The picture shows that $a_2 = \dfrac{1}{2^{1.3}} < \displaystyle\int_1^2 \dfrac{1}{x^{1.3}}\,dx$,

$a_3 = \dfrac{1}{3^{1.3}} < \displaystyle\int_2^3 \dfrac{1}{x^{1.3}}\,dx$, and so on, so $\displaystyle\sum_{n=2}^{\infty} \dfrac{1}{n^{1.3}} < \displaystyle\int_1^{\infty} \dfrac{1}{x^{1.3}}\,dx$. The

integral converges by (5.10.2) with $p = 1.3 > 1$, so the series converges.

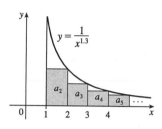

2. From the first figure, we see that

$\int_1^6 f(x)\,dx < \sum_{i=1}^{5} a_i$. From the second

figure, we see that

$\sum_{i=2}^{6} a_i < \int_1^6 f(x)\,dx$. Thus, we have

$\sum_{i=2}^{6} a_i < \int_1^6 f(x)\,dx < \sum_{i=1}^{5} a_i$.

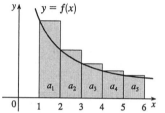 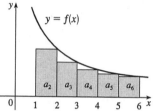

3. (a) We cannot say anything about $\sum a_n$. If $a_n > b_n$ for all n and $\sum b_n$ is convergent, then $\sum a_n$ could be convergent or divergent. (See the note on page 587.)

(b) If $a_n < b_n$ for all n, then $\sum a_n$ is convergent. [This is part (i) of the Comparison Test.]

4. (a) If $a_n > b_n$ for all n, then $\sum a_n$ is divergent. [This is part (ii) of the Comparison Test.]

(b) We cannot say anything about $\sum a_n$. If $a_n < b_n$ for all n and $\sum b_n$ is divergent, then $\sum a_n$ could be convergent or divergent.

5. $\displaystyle\sum_{n=1}^{\infty} n^b$ is a p-series with $p = -b$. $\displaystyle\sum_{n=1}^{\infty} b^n$ is a geometric series. By (1), the p-series is convergent if $p > 1$. In this

case, $\displaystyle\sum_{n=1}^{\infty} n^b = \displaystyle\sum_{n=1}^{\infty} (1/n^{-b})$, so $-b > 1 \iff b < -1$ are the values for which the series converge. A geometric

series $\displaystyle\sum_{n=1}^{\infty} ar^{n-1}$ converges if $|r| < 1$, so $\displaystyle\sum_{n=1}^{\infty} b^n$ converges if $|b| < 1 \iff -1 < b < 1$.

6. The function $f(x) = 1/\sqrt[4]{x} = x^{-1/4}$ is continuous, positive, and decreasing on $[1, \infty)$, so the Integral Test applies.
$\int_1^{\infty} x^{-1/4}\,dx = \lim_{t\to\infty} \int_1^t x^{-1/4}\,dx = \lim_{t\to\infty} \left[\frac{4}{3}x^{3/4}\right]_1^t = \lim_{t\to\infty}\left(\frac{4}{3}t^{3/4} - \frac{4}{3}\right) = \infty$, so $\sum_{n=1}^{\infty} 1/\sqrt[4]{n}$ diverges.

7. The function $f(x) = 1/x^4$ is continuous, positive, and decreasing on $[1, \infty)$, so the Integral Test applies.
$\displaystyle\int_1^{\infty} \frac{1}{x^4}\,dx = \lim_{t\to\infty} \int_1^t x^{-4}\,dx = \lim_{t\to\infty}\left[\frac{x^{-3}}{-3}\right]_1^t = \lim_{t\to\infty}\left(-\frac{1}{3t^3} + \frac{1}{3}\right) = \frac{1}{3}$. Since this improper integral is

convergent, the series $\displaystyle\sum_{n=1}^{\infty} \frac{1}{n^4}$ is also convergent by the Integral Test.

8. The function $f(x) = 1/(x^2 + 1)$ is continuous, positive, and decreasing on $[1, \infty)$, so the Integral Test applies.
$\displaystyle\int_1^{\infty} \frac{1}{x^2 + 1}\,dx = \lim_{t\to\infty} \int_1^t \frac{1}{x^2 + 1}\,dx = \lim_{t\to\infty}\left[\tan^{-1} x\right]_1^t = \lim_{t\to\infty}\left(\tan^{-1} t - \tan^{-1} 1\right) = \frac{\pi}{2} - \frac{\pi}{4} = \frac{\pi}{4}$, so

$\displaystyle\sum_{n=1}^{\infty} \frac{1}{n^2 + 1}$ converges.

9. $\dfrac{1}{n^2 + n + 1} < \dfrac{1}{n^2}$ for all $n \geq 1$, so $\displaystyle\sum_{n=1}^{\infty} \dfrac{1}{n^2 + n + 1}$ converges by comparison with $\displaystyle\sum_{n=1}^{\infty} \dfrac{1}{n^2}$, which converges because it is a p-series with $p = 2 > 1$.

10. $\dfrac{1}{2n-1} > \dfrac{1}{2n} = \dfrac{1}{2} \cdot \dfrac{1}{n}$ for all $n \geq 1$, so $\displaystyle\sum_{n=1}^{\infty} \dfrac{1}{2n-1}$ diverges by comparison with $\displaystyle\sum_{n=1}^{\infty} \dfrac{1}{2n} = \dfrac{1}{2} \sum_{n=1}^{\infty} \dfrac{1}{n}$, which diverges because it is a nonzero constant multiple of the divergent harmonic series.

11. $1 + \dfrac{1}{8} + \dfrac{1}{27} + \dfrac{1}{64} + \dfrac{1}{125} + \cdots = \displaystyle\sum_{n=1}^{\infty} \dfrac{1}{n^3}$. This is a p-series with $p = 3 > 1$, so it converges by (1).

12. $\displaystyle\sum_{n=1}^{\infty} \dfrac{1}{n^4}$ and $\displaystyle\sum_{n=1}^{\infty} \dfrac{1}{n^{3/2}}$ are convergent p-series with $p = 4 > 1$ and $p = \frac{3}{2} > 1$, respectively. Thus,

$\displaystyle\sum_{n=1}^{\infty} \left(\dfrac{5}{n^4} + \dfrac{4}{n\sqrt{n}} \right) = 5 \sum_{n=1}^{\infty} \dfrac{1}{n^4} + 4 \sum_{n=1}^{\infty} \dfrac{1}{n^{3/2}}$ is convergent by Theorems 8.2.8(i) and 8.2.8(ii).

13. $f(x) = xe^{-x^2}$ is continuous and positive on $[1, \infty)$, and since $f'(x) = e^{-x^2}\left(1 - 2x^2\right) < 0$ for $x > 1$, f is decreasing as well. Thus, we can use the Integral Test.

$\displaystyle\int_1^{\infty} xe^{-x^2}\, dx = \lim_{t \to \infty} \left[-\tfrac{1}{2} e^{-x^2} \right]_1^t = 0 - \left(-\tfrac{1}{2} e^{-1} \right) = 1/(2e)$. Since the integral converges, the series converges.

14. $f(x) = \dfrac{\ln x}{x^2}$ is continuous and positive for $x \geq 2$, and $f'(x) = \dfrac{1 - 2\ln x}{x^3} < 0$ for $x \geq 2$, so f is decreasing.

$\displaystyle\int_2^{\infty} \dfrac{\ln x}{x^2}\, dx = \lim_{t \to \infty} \left[-\dfrac{\ln x}{x} - \dfrac{1}{x} \right]_2^t$ [by parts] $\overset{H}{=} 1$. Thus, $\displaystyle\sum_{n=1}^{\infty} \dfrac{\ln n}{n^2} = \sum_{n=2}^{\infty} \dfrac{\ln n}{n^2}$ converges by the Integral Test.

15. $f(x) = \dfrac{1}{x \ln x}$ is continuous and positive on $[2, \infty)$, and also decreasing since $f'(x) = -\dfrac{1 + \ln x}{x^2 (\ln x)^2} < 0$ for $x > 2$,

so we can use the Integral Test. $\displaystyle\int_2^{\infty} \dfrac{1}{x \ln x}\, dx = \lim_{t \to \infty} \left[\ln(\ln x) \right]_2^t = \lim_{t \to \infty} \left[\ln(\ln t) - \ln(\ln 2) \right] = \infty$, so the series diverges.

16. $\dfrac{2}{n^3 + 4} < \dfrac{2}{n^3}$ for all $n \geq 1$, so $\displaystyle\sum_{n=1}^{\infty} \dfrac{2}{n^3 + 4}$ converges by comparison with $\displaystyle\sum_{n=1}^{\infty} \dfrac{2}{n^3} = 2 \sum_{n=1}^{\infty} \dfrac{1}{n^3}$, which converges because it is a constant multiple of a convergent p-series ($p = 3 > 1$).

17. $\dfrac{5}{2 + 3^n} < \dfrac{5}{3^n}$ for all $n \geq 1$, so $\displaystyle\sum_{n=1}^{\infty} \dfrac{5}{2 + 3^n}$ converges by comparison with $\displaystyle\sum_{n=1}^{\infty} \dfrac{5}{3^n} = 5 \sum_{n=1}^{\infty} \dfrac{1}{3^n}$, which converges because $\displaystyle\sum_{n=1}^{\infty} \dfrac{1}{3^n}$ is a convergent geometric series with $r = \frac{1}{3}$ ($|r| < 1$).

18. $\dfrac{\sin^2 n}{n\sqrt{n}} \leq \dfrac{1}{n\sqrt{n}} = \dfrac{1}{n^{3/2}}$ and $\displaystyle\sum_{n=1}^{\infty} \dfrac{1}{n^{3/2}}$ converges ($p = \frac{3}{2} > 1$), so $\displaystyle\sum_{n=1}^{\infty} \dfrac{\sin^2 n}{n\sqrt{n}}$ converges by the Comparison Test.

19. $\dfrac{n+1}{n^2} > \dfrac{n}{n^2} = \dfrac{1}{n}$ for all $n \geq 1$, so $\displaystyle\sum_{n=1}^{\infty} \dfrac{n+1}{n^2}$ diverges by comparison with the harmonic series $\displaystyle\sum_{n=1}^{\infty} \dfrac{1}{n}$.

20. $\dfrac{4 + 3^n}{2^n} > \dfrac{3^n}{2^n} = \left(\dfrac{3}{2} \right)^n$ for all $n \geq 1$, so $\displaystyle\sum_{n=1}^{\infty} \dfrac{4 + 3^n}{2^n}$ diverges by comparison with the divergent geometric series $\displaystyle\sum_{n=1}^{\infty} \left(\dfrac{3}{2} \right)^n$.

21. Let $a_n = \dfrac{n^2+1}{n^4+1}$ and $b_n = \dfrac{1}{n^2}$. Then $\sum a_n$ and $\sum b_n$ are series with positive terms and

$$\lim_{n\to\infty} \frac{a_n}{b_n} = \lim_{n\to\infty}\left(\frac{n^2+1}{n^4+1}\cdot\frac{n^2}{1}\right) = \lim_{n\to\infty}\frac{n^4+n^2}{n^4+1} = 1 > 0. \text{ Since } \sum_{n=1}^{\infty}\frac{1}{n^2} \text{ is a convergent } p\text{-series } (p = 2 > 1),$$

so is $\displaystyle\sum_{n=1}^{\infty}\frac{n^2+1}{n^4+1}$ by the Limit Comparison Test.

22. Let $a_n = \dfrac{1}{n^3-n}$ and $b_n = \dfrac{1}{n^3}$. Then $\displaystyle\sum_{n=2}^{\infty} a_n$ and $\displaystyle\sum_{n=2}^{\infty} b_n$ are series with positive terms and

$$\lim_{n\to\infty} \frac{a_n}{b_n} = \lim_{n\to\infty}\frac{n^3}{n^3-n} = 1 > 0. \text{ Since } \sum_{n=2}^{\infty}\frac{1}{n^3} \text{ is a convergent } p\text{-series without the } n = 1 \text{ term } (p = 3 > 1),$$

$$\sum_{n=2}^{\infty}\frac{1}{n^3-n} \text{ is convergent by the Limit Comparison Test.}$$

23. Use the Limit Comparison Test with $a_n = \sin\left(\dfrac{1}{n}\right)$ and $b_n = \dfrac{1}{n}$. Then $\sum a_n$ and $\sum b_n$ are series with positive

terms and $\displaystyle\lim_{n\to\infty} \frac{a_n}{b_n} = \lim_{n\to\infty}\frac{\sin(1/n)}{1/n} = \lim_{\theta\to 0}\frac{\sin\theta}{\theta} = 1 > 0. \text{ Since } \sum_{n=1}^{\infty} b_n \text{ is the divergent harmonic series,}$

$\sum_{n=1}^{\infty}\sin(1/n)$ also diverges. (Note that we could also use l'Hospital's Rule to evaluate the limit:

$$\lim_{x\to\infty}\frac{\sin(1/x)}{1/x} \overset{\text{H}}{=} \lim_{x\to\infty}\frac{\cos(1/x)\cdot(-1/x^2)}{-1/x^2} = \lim_{x\to\infty}\cos\frac{1}{x} = \cos 0 = 1.)$$

24. If $a_n = \dfrac{n+5}{\sqrt[3]{n^7+n^2}}$ and $b_n = \dfrac{n}{\sqrt[3]{n^7}} = \dfrac{n}{n^{7/3}} = \dfrac{1}{n^{4/3}}$, then

$$\lim_{n\to\infty} \frac{a_n}{b_n} = \lim_{n\to\infty}\frac{n^{7/3}+5n^{4/3}}{(n^7+n^2)^{1/3}}\cdot\frac{n^{-7/3}}{n^{-7/3}} = \lim_{n\to\infty}\frac{1+5/n}{[(n^7+n^2)/n^7]^{1/3}}$$

$$= \lim_{n\to\infty}\frac{1+5/n}{(1+1/n^5)^{1/3}} = \frac{1+0}{(1+0)^{1/3}} = 1 > 0,$$

so $\displaystyle\sum_{n=1}^{\infty}\frac{n+5}{\sqrt[3]{n^7+n^2}}$ converges by the Limit Comparison Test with the convergent p-series $\displaystyle\sum_{n=1}^{\infty}\frac{1}{n^{4/3}}$.

25. We have already shown (in Exercise 15) that when $p = 1$ the series $\displaystyle\sum_{n=2}^{\infty}\frac{1}{n(\ln n)^p}$ diverges, so assume that $p \neq 1$.

$f(x) = \dfrac{1}{x(\ln x)^p}$ is continuous and positive on $[2,\infty)$, and $f'(x) = -\dfrac{p+\ln x}{x^2(\ln x)^{p+1}} < 0 \text{ if } x > e^{-p}, \text{ so that } f \text{ is}$

eventually decreasing and we can use the Integral Test.

$$\int_{2}^{\infty}\frac{1}{x(\ln x)^p}\,dx = \lim_{t\to\infty}\left[\frac{(\ln x)^{1-p}}{1-p}\right]_{2}^{t} \quad (\text{for } p \neq 1) \;=\; \lim_{t\to\infty}\left[\frac{(\ln t)^{1-p}}{1-p}\right] - \frac{(\ln 2)^{1-p}}{1-p}$$

This limit exists whenever $1 - p < 0 \;\Leftrightarrow\; p > 1$, so the series converges for $p > 1$.

26. (a) $f(x) = 1/x^4$ is positive and continuous and $f'(x) = -4/x^5$ is negative for $x > 0$, and so the Integral

Test applies. $\displaystyle\sum_{n=1}^{\infty}\frac{1}{n^4} \approx s_{10} = \frac{1}{1^4}+\frac{1}{2^4}+\frac{1}{3^4}+\cdots+\frac{1}{10^4} \approx 1.082037.$

$$R_{10} \leq \int_{10}^{\infty}\frac{1}{x^4}\,dx = \lim_{t\to\infty}\left[\frac{1}{-3x^3}\right]_{10}^{t} = \lim_{t\to\infty}\left(-\frac{1}{3t^3}+\frac{1}{3(10)^3}\right) = \frac{1}{3000}, \text{ so the error is at most } 0.000\overline{3}.$$

(b) $s_{10} + \int_{11}^{\infty} \frac{1}{x^4}\,dx \leq s \leq s_{10} + \int_{10}^{\infty} \frac{1}{x^4}\,dx \quad \Rightarrow \quad s_{10} + \frac{1}{3(11)^3} \leq s \leq s_{10} + \frac{1}{3(10)^3} \quad \Rightarrow$

$1.082037 + 0.000250 = 1.082287 \leq s \leq 1.082037 + 0.000333 = 1.082370$, so we get $s \approx 1.08233$ with

error ≤ 0.00005.

(c) $R_n \leq \int_{n}^{\infty} \frac{1}{x^4}\,dx = \frac{1}{3n^3}$. So $R_n < 0.00001 \quad \Rightarrow \quad \frac{1}{3n^3} < \frac{1}{10^5} \quad \Rightarrow \quad 3n^3 > 10^5 \quad \Rightarrow$

$n > \sqrt[3]{(10)^5/3} \approx 32.2$, that is, for $n > 32$.

27. (a) $f(x) = \frac{1}{x^2}$ is positive and continuous and $f'(x) = -\frac{2}{x^3}$ is negative for $x > 0$, and so the Integral

Test applies. $\sum_{n=1}^{\infty} \frac{1}{n^2} \approx s_{10} = \frac{1}{1^2} + \frac{1}{2^2} + \frac{1}{3^2} + \cdots + \frac{1}{10^2} \approx 1.549768$.

$R_{10} \leq \int_{10}^{\infty} \frac{1}{x^2}\,dx = \lim_{t \to \infty} \left[\frac{-1}{x} \right]_{10}^{t} = \lim_{t \to \infty} \left(-\frac{1}{t} + \frac{1}{10} \right) = \frac{1}{10}$, so the error is at most 0.1.

(b) $s_{10} + \int_{11}^{\infty} \frac{1}{x^2}\,dx \leq s \leq s_{10} + \int_{10}^{\infty} \frac{1}{x^2}\,dx \quad \Rightarrow \quad s_{10} + \frac{1}{11} \leq s \leq s_{10} + \frac{1}{10} \quad \Rightarrow$

$1.549768 + 0.090909 = 1.640677 \leq s \leq 1.549768 + 0.1 = 1.649768$, so we get $s \approx 1.64522$ (the average of

1.640677 and 1.649768) with error ≤ 0.005 (the maximum of $1.649768 - 1.64522$ and $1.64522 - 1.640677$,

rounded up).

(c) $R_n \leq \int_{n}^{\infty} \frac{1}{x^2}\,dx = \frac{1}{n}$. So $R_n < 0.001$ if $\frac{1}{n} < \frac{1}{1000} \quad \Leftrightarrow \quad n > 1000$.

28. $f(x) = 1/x^5$ is positive and continuous and $f'(x) = -5/x^6$ is negative for $x > 0$, and so the Integral Test applies.

Using (3), $R_n \leq \int_{n}^{\infty} x^{-5}\,dx = \lim_{t \to \infty} \left[\frac{-1}{4x^4} \right]_{n}^{t} = \frac{1}{4n^4}$. If we take $n = 5$, then $s_5 \approx 1.036662$ and $R_5 \leq 0.0004$.

So $s \approx s_5 \approx 1.037$.

29. $f(x) = x^{-3/2}$ is positive and continuous and $f'(x) = -\frac{3}{2}x^{-5/2}$ is negative for $x > 0$, so the Integral Test applies.

From the end of Example 7, we see that the error is at most half the length of the interval. From (4), the interval is

$\left(s_n + \int_{n+1}^{\infty} f(x)\,dx, \; s_n + \int_{n}^{\infty} f(x)\,dx \right)$, so its length is $\int_{n}^{\infty} f(x)\,dx - \int_{n+1}^{\infty} f(x)\,dx$. Thus, we need n such that

$0.01 > \frac{1}{2} \left(\int_{n}^{\infty} x^{-3/2}\,dx - \int_{n+1}^{\infty} x^{-3/2}\,dx \right) = \frac{1}{2} \left(\lim_{t \to \infty} \left[\frac{-2}{\sqrt{x}} \right]_{n}^{t} - \lim_{t \to \infty} \left[\frac{-2}{\sqrt{x}} \right]_{n+1}^{t} \right) = \frac{1}{\sqrt{n}} - \frac{1}{\sqrt{n+1}}$

$\Leftrightarrow \quad n > 13.08$ (use a graphing calculator to solve $1/\sqrt{x} - 1/\sqrt{x+1} < 0.01$). Again from the end of Example 7,

we approximate s by the midpoint of this interval. In general, the midpoint is

$\frac{1}{2} \left[\left(s_n + \int_{n+1}^{\infty} f(x)\,dx \right) + \left(s_n + \int_{n}^{\infty} f(x)\,dx \right) \right] = s_n + \frac{1}{2} \left(\int_{n+1}^{\infty} f(x)\,dx + \int_{n}^{\infty} f(x)\,dx \right)$. So using $n = 14$,

we have $s \approx s_{14} + \frac{1}{2} \left(\int_{14}^{\infty} x^{-3/2}\,dx + \int_{15}^{\infty} x^{-3/2}\,dx \right) \approx 2.0872 + \frac{1}{\sqrt{14}} + \frac{1}{\sqrt{15}} \approx 2.6127 \approx 2.61$. Any larger

value of n will also work. For instance, $s \approx s_{30} + \frac{1}{\sqrt{30}} + \frac{1}{\sqrt{31}} \approx 2.6124$.

30. $f(x) = \frac{1}{x(\ln x)^2}$ is positive and continuous and $f'(x) = -\frac{\ln x + 2}{x^2(\ln x)^3}$ is negative for $x > 1$, so the Integral Test

applies. Using (3), we need $0.01 > \int_{n}^{\infty} \frac{dx}{x(\ln x)^2} = \lim_{t \to \infty} \left[\frac{-1}{\ln x} \right]_{n}^{t} = \frac{1}{\ln n}$. This is true for $n > e^{100}$, so we would

have to take this many terms, which would be problematic because $e^{100} \approx 2.7 \times 10^{43}$.

31. $\sum\limits_{n=1}^{10} \dfrac{1}{n^4 + n^2} = \dfrac{1}{2} + \dfrac{1}{20} + \dfrac{1}{90} + \cdots + \dfrac{1}{10,100} \approx 0.567975$. Now $\dfrac{1}{n^4 + n^2} < \dfrac{1}{n^4}$, so using the reasoning and

notation of Example 8, the error is $R_{10} \le T_{10} = \sum\limits_{n=11}^{\infty} \dfrac{1}{n^4} \le \int_{10}^{\infty} \dfrac{dx}{x^4} = \lim\limits_{t\to\infty} \left[-\dfrac{x^{-3}}{3} \right]_{10}^{t} = \dfrac{1}{3000} = 0.000\overline{3}$.

32. $\sum\limits_{n=1}^{10} \dfrac{n}{(n+1)3^n} = \dfrac{1}{6} + \dfrac{2}{27} + \dfrac{3}{108} + \cdots + \dfrac{10}{649,539} \approx 0.283597$. Now $\dfrac{n}{(n+1)3^n} < \dfrac{n}{n \cdot 3^n} = \dfrac{1}{3^n}$, so the error is

$R_{10} \le T_{10} = \sum\limits_{n=11}^{\infty} \dfrac{1}{3^n} = \dfrac{1/3^{11}}{1 - 1/3} \approx 0.0000085$.

33. (a) From the figure, $a_2 + a_3 + \cdots + a_n \le \int_1^n f(x)\,dx$, so with

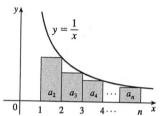

$f(x) = \dfrac{1}{x}, \dfrac{1}{2} + \dfrac{1}{3} + \dfrac{1}{4} + \cdots + \dfrac{1}{n} \le \int_1^n \dfrac{1}{x}\,dx = \ln n$. Thus,

$s_n = 1 + \dfrac{1}{2} + \dfrac{1}{3} + \dfrac{1}{4} + \cdots + \dfrac{1}{n} \le 1 + \ln n$.

(b) By part (a), $s_{10^6} \le 1 + \ln 10^6 \approx 14.82 < 15$ and $s_{10^9} \le 1 + \ln 10^9 \approx 21.72 < 22$.

34. $\sum\limits_{n=1}^{\infty} n^{-1.001} = \sum\limits_{n=1}^{\infty} \dfrac{1}{n^{1.001}}$ is a convergent p-series with $p = 1.001 > 1$. Using (3), we get

$R_n \le \int_n^{\infty} x^{-1.001}\,dx = \lim\limits_{t\to\infty} \left[\dfrac{x^{-0.001}}{-0.001} \right]_n^t = -1000 \lim\limits_{t\to\infty} \left[\dfrac{1}{x^{0.001}} \right]_n^t = -1000 \left(-\dfrac{1}{n^{0.001}} \right) = \dfrac{1000}{n^{0.001}}$. We want

$R_n < 0.000\,000\,005 \;\Leftrightarrow\; \dfrac{1000}{n^{0.001}} < 5 \times 10^{-9} \;\Leftrightarrow\; n^{0.001} > \dfrac{1000}{5 \times 10^{-9}} \;\Leftrightarrow\;$

$n > \left(2 \times 10^{11}\right)^{1000} = 2^{1000} \times 10^{11,000} \approx 1.07 \times 10^{301} \times 10^{11,000} = 1.07 \times 10^{11,301}$.

35. Since $\dfrac{d_n}{10^n} \le \dfrac{9}{10^n}$ for each n, and since $\sum\limits_{n=1}^{\infty} \dfrac{9}{10^n}$ is a convergent geometric series ($|r| = \frac{1}{10} < 1$),

$0.d_1 d_2 d_3 \ldots = \sum\limits_{n=1}^{\infty} \dfrac{d_n}{10^n}$ will always converge by the Comparison Test.

36. $b^{\ln n} = \left(e^{\ln b}\right)^{\ln n} = \left(e^{\ln n}\right)^{\ln b} = n^{\ln b} = \dfrac{1}{n^{-\ln b}}$. This is a p-series, which converges for all b such that $-\ln b > 1$

$\Leftrightarrow\; \ln b < -1 \;\Leftrightarrow\; b < e^{-1} \;\Leftrightarrow\; b < 1/e$ [with $b > 0$].

37. Yes. Since $\sum a_n$ is a convergent series with positive terms, $\lim\limits_{n\to\infty} a_n = 0$ by (8.2.6), and $\sum b_n = \sum \sin(a_n)$ is a

series with positive terms (for large enough n). The Limit Comparison Test gives us

$\lim\limits_{n\to\infty} \dfrac{b_n}{a_n} = \lim\limits_{n\to\infty} \dfrac{\sin(a_n)}{a_n} = 1 > 0$ by Theorem 3.4.2. Thus, $\sum b_n$ is also convergent.

38. First we observe that, by l'Hospital's Rule, $\lim\limits_{x\to\infty} \dfrac{\ln(1+x)}{x} = \lim\limits_{x\to\infty} \dfrac{1}{1+x} = 1$. Also, if $\sum a_n$ converges, then

$\lim\limits_{n\to\infty} a_n = 0$ by Theorem 8.2.6. Therefore, $\lim\limits_{n\to\infty} \dfrac{\ln(1+a_n)}{a_n} = 1 > 0$. We are given that $\sum a_n$ is convergent and

$a_n > 0$. Thus, $\sum \ln(1 + a_n)$ is convergent by the Limit Comparison Test.

8.4 **Other Convergence Tests** • • • • • • • • • • • •

1. (a) An alternating series is a series whose terms are alternately positive and negative.

(b) An alternating series $\sum_{n=1}^{\infty}(-1)^{n-1}b_n$ converges if $0 < b_{n+1} \le b_n$ for all n and $\lim_{n\to\infty} b_n = 0$. (This is the Alternating Series Test.)

(c) The error involved in using the partial sum s_n as an approximation to the total sum s is the remainder $R_n = s - s_n$ and the size of the error is smaller than b_{n+1}; that is, $|R_n| \le b_{n+1}$. (This is the Alternating Series Estimation Theorem.)

2. (a) Since $\lim_{n\to\infty}\left|\dfrac{a_{n+1}}{a_n}\right| = 8 > 1$, part (b) of the Ratio Test tells us that the series $\sum a_n$ is divergent.

(b) Since $\lim_{n\to\infty}\left|\dfrac{a_{n+1}}{a_n}\right| = 0.8 < 1$, part (a) of the Ratio Test tells us that the series $\sum a_n$ is absolutely convergent (and therefore convergent).

(c) Since $\lim_{n\to\infty}\left|\dfrac{a_{n+1}}{a_n}\right| = 1$, the Ratio Test fails and the series $\sum a_n$ might converge or it might diverge.

3. $\dfrac{4}{7} - \dfrac{4}{8} + \dfrac{4}{9} - \dfrac{4}{10} + \dfrac{4}{11} - \cdots = \sum_{n=1}^{\infty}(-1)^{n-1}\dfrac{4}{n+6}$. Now $b_n = \dfrac{4}{n+6} > 0$, $\{b_n\}$ is decreasing, and $\lim_{n\to\infty} b_n = 0$, so the series converges by the Alternating Series Test.

4. $-\dfrac{1}{3} + \dfrac{2}{4} - \dfrac{3}{5} + \dfrac{4}{6} - \dfrac{5}{7} + \cdots = \sum_{n=1}^{\infty}(-1)^n\dfrac{n}{n+2}$. Here $a_n = (-1)^n\dfrac{n}{n+2}$. Since $\lim_{n\to\infty} a_n \ne 0$ (in fact the limit does not exist), the series diverges by the Test for Divergence.

5. $b_n = \dfrac{1}{\sqrt{n}} > 0$, $\{b_n\}$ is decreasing, and $\lim_{n\to\infty} b_n = 0$, so the series $\sum_{n=1}^{\infty}\dfrac{(-1)^{n-1}}{\sqrt{n}}$ converges by the Alternating Series Test.

6. $\sum_{n=1}^{\infty} a_n = \sum_{n=1}^{\infty}(-1)^n\dfrac{\sqrt{n}}{1+2\sqrt{n}} = \sum_{n=1}^{\infty}(-1)^n b_n$. Now $\lim_{n\to\infty} b_n = \lim_{n\to\infty}\dfrac{1}{2+1/\sqrt{n}} = \dfrac{1}{2} \ne 0$. Since $\lim_{n\to\infty} a_n \ne 0$ (in fact the limit does not exist), the series diverges by the Test for Divergence.

7. $\sum_{n=1}^{\infty} a_n = \sum_{n=1}^{\infty}(-1)^n\dfrac{3n-1}{2n+1} = \sum_{n=1}^{\infty}(-1)^n b_n$. Now $\lim_{n\to\infty} b_n = \lim_{n\to\infty}\dfrac{3-1/n}{2+1/n} = \dfrac{3}{2} \ne 0$. Since $\lim_{n\to\infty} a_n \ne 0$ (in fact the limit does not exist), the series diverges by the Test for Divergence.

8. $\sum_{n=1}^{\infty}(-1)^{n-1}\left(\dfrac{\ln n}{n}\right) = 0 + \sum_{n=2}^{\infty}(-1)^{n-1}\left(\dfrac{\ln n}{n}\right)$. $b_n = \dfrac{\ln n}{n} > 0$ for $n \ge 2$, and if $f(x) = \dfrac{\ln x}{x}$, then $f'(x) = \dfrac{1-\ln x}{x^2} < 0$ for $x > e$, so $\{b_n\}$ is eventually decreasing. Also, $\lim_{n\to\infty} b_n = \lim_{n\to\infty}\dfrac{\ln n}{n} \overset{\text{H}}{=} \lim_{n\to\infty}\dfrac{1/n}{1} = 0$, so the series converges by the Alternating Series Test.

9. $\sum_{n=1}^{\infty}\dfrac{(-1)^{n-1}}{n} = 1 - \dfrac{1}{2} + \dfrac{1}{3} - \dfrac{1}{4} + \cdots + \dfrac{1}{49} - \dfrac{1}{50} + \dfrac{1}{51} - \dfrac{1}{52} + \cdots$. The 50th partial sum of this series is an underestimate, since $\sum_{n=1}^{\infty}\dfrac{(-1)^{n-1}}{n} = s_{50} + \left(\dfrac{1}{51} - \dfrac{1}{52}\right) + \left(\dfrac{1}{53} - \dfrac{1}{54}\right) + \cdots$, and the terms in parentheses are all positive. The result can be seen geometrically in Figure 1.

10.

n	a_n	s_n
1	1	1
2	-0.125	0.875
3	0.03704	0.91204
4	-0.01563	0.89641
5	0.008	0.90441
6	-0.00463	0.89978
7	0.00292	0.90270
8	-0.00195	0.90074
9	0.00137	0.90212
10	-0.001	0.90112

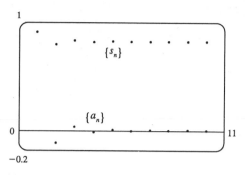

By the Alternating Series Estimation Theorem, the error in the

approximation $\displaystyle\sum_{n=1}^{\infty} \frac{(-1)^{n-1}}{n^3} \approx 0.90112$ is

$$|s - s_{10}| \le b_{11} = 1/11^3 \approx 0.0007513.$$

11. If $p > 0$, $\dfrac{1}{(n+1)^p} \le \dfrac{1}{n^p}$ ($\{1/n^p\}$ is decreasing) and $\displaystyle\lim_{n\to\infty} \frac{1}{n^p} = 0$, so the series converges by the Alternating

Series Test. If $p \le 0$, $\displaystyle\lim_{n\to\infty} \frac{(-1)^{n-1}}{n^p}$ does not exist, so the series diverges by the Test for Divergence. Thus,

$\displaystyle\sum_{n=1}^{\infty} \frac{(-1)^{n-1}}{n^p}$ converges $\Leftrightarrow$ $p > 0$.

12. The series $\displaystyle\sum_{n=1}^{\infty} (-1)^{n+1} \frac{1}{n^4}$ satisfies (a) of the Alternating Series Test because $\dfrac{1}{(n+1)^4} < \dfrac{1}{n^4}$ and

(b) $\displaystyle\lim_{n\to\infty} \frac{1}{n^4} = 0$, so the series is convergent. Now $b_5 = 1/5^4 = 0.0016 > 0.001$ and

$b_6 = 1/6^4 \approx 0.00077 < 0.001$, so by the Alternating Series Estimation Theorem, $n = 5$.

13. Using the Ratio Test with the series $\displaystyle\sum_{n=1}^{\infty} \frac{(-2)^n}{n!}$,

$$\lim_{n\to\infty} \left| \frac{a_{n+1}}{a_n} \right| = \lim_{n\to\infty} \left| a_{n+1} \cdot \frac{1}{a_n} \right| = \lim_{n\to\infty} \left| \frac{(-2)^{n+1}}{(n+1)!} \cdot \frac{n!}{(-2)^n} \right| = \lim_{n\to\infty} \left| \frac{-2}{n+1} \right|$$

$$= 2 \lim_{n\to\infty} \frac{1}{n+1} = 2(0) = 0 < 1,$$

so the series is absolutely convergent (and therefore convergent). Now $b_7 = 2^7/7! \approx 0.025 > 0.01$ and

$b_8 = 2^8/8! \approx 0.006 < 0.01$, so by the Alternating Series Estimation Theorem, $n = 7$. (That is, since the 8th term

is less than the desired error, we need to add the first 7 terms to get the sum to the desired accuracy.)

14. Using the Ratio Test with the series $\displaystyle\sum_{n=1}^{\infty} \frac{(-1)^n n}{4^n}$,

$$\lim_{n\to\infty} \left| \frac{a_{n+1}}{a_n} \right| = \lim_{n\to\infty} \left| \frac{(-1)^{n+1}(n+1)}{4^{n+1}} \cdot \frac{4^n}{(-1)^n n} \right| = \lim_{n\to\infty} \left| \frac{(-1)^1(n+1)}{4n} \right|$$

$$= \frac{1}{4} \lim_{n\to\infty} \frac{n+1}{n} = \frac{1}{4}(1) = \frac{1}{4} < 1,$$

so the series is absolutely convergent (and therefore convergent). Now $b_5 = 5/4^5 \approx 0.0049 > 0.002$ and

$b_6 = 6/4^6 \approx 0.0015 < 0.002$, so by the Alternating Series Estimation Theorem, $n = 5$.

15. The graph gives us an estimate for the sum of the series

$$\sum_{n=1}^{\infty} \frac{(-1)^{n-1}}{(2n-1)!} \text{ of } 0.84. \; b_5 = \frac{1}{(2 \cdot 5 - 1)!} = \frac{1}{362,880} \approx 0.000\,003,$$

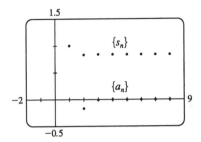

so $\displaystyle\sum_{n=1}^{\infty} \frac{(-1)^{n-1}}{(2n-1)!} \approx s_4 = \sum_{n=1}^{4} \frac{(-1)^{n-1}}{(2n-1)!} = 1 - \frac{1}{6} + \frac{1}{120} - \frac{1}{5040}$

$\approx 0.841468.$

Adding b_5 to s_4 does not change the fourth decimal place of s_4, so
the sum of the series, correct to four decimal places, is 0.8415.

16. The graph gives us an estimate for the sum of the series $\displaystyle\sum_{n=0}^{\infty} \frac{(-1)^n}{(2n)!}$

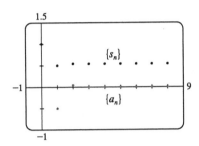

of 0.54. $b_4 = \dfrac{1}{(2 \cdot 4)!} = \dfrac{1}{40,320} \approx 0.000\,025$, so

$$\sum_{n=0}^{\infty} \frac{(-1)^n}{(2n)!} \approx s_3 = \sum_{n=0}^{3} \frac{(-1)^n}{(2n)!} = 1 - \frac{1}{2} + \frac{1}{24} - \frac{1}{720} \approx 0.540278.$$

Adding b_4 to s_3 does not change the fourth decimal place of s_3, so
the sum of the series, correct to four decimal places, is 0.5403.

17. $b_6 = \dfrac{1}{2^6 6!} = \dfrac{1}{46,080} \approx 0.000\,022$, so

$\displaystyle\sum_{n=0}^{\infty} \frac{(-1)^n}{2^n n!} \approx s_5 = \sum_{n=0}^{5} \frac{(-1)^n}{2^n n!} = 1 - \frac{1}{2} + \frac{1}{8} - \frac{1}{48} + \frac{1}{384} - \frac{1}{3840} \approx 0.606510.$ Adding b_6 to s_5 does not change

the fourth decimal place of s_5, so the sum of the series, correct to four decimal places, is 0.6065.

18. $b_8 = \dfrac{1}{8^6} = \dfrac{1}{262,144} \approx 0.000\,0038$, so

$\displaystyle\sum_{n=1}^{\infty} \frac{(-1)^{n-1}}{n^6} \approx s_7 = \sum_{n=1}^{7} \frac{(-1)^{n-1}}{n^6} = 1 - \frac{1}{64} + \frac{1}{729} - \frac{1}{4096} + \frac{1}{15,625} - \frac{1}{46,656} + \frac{1}{117,649} \approx 0.9855537.$

Subtracting b_8 from s_7 does not change the fifth decimal place of s_7, so the sum of the series, correct to five decimal
places, is 0.98555.

19. Consider the series whose terms are the absolute values of the terms of the given series.

$$\sum_{n=1}^{\infty} \left| \frac{(-1)^{n-1}}{\sqrt{n}} \right| = \sum_{n=1}^{\infty} \frac{1}{n^{1/2}}, \text{ which is a divergent } p\text{-series } (p = \tfrac{1}{2} \le 1). \text{ Thus, } \sum_{n=1}^{\infty} \frac{(-1)^{n-1}}{\sqrt{n}} \text{ is } not \text{ absolutely}$$

convergent.

20. The series $\displaystyle\sum_{n=1}^{\infty} \frac{n^2}{2^n}$ has positive terms and $\displaystyle\lim_{n \to \infty} \frac{a_{n+1}}{a_n} = \lim_{n \to \infty} \left[\frac{(n+1)^2}{2^{n+1}} \cdot \frac{2^n}{n^2} \right] = \lim_{n \to \infty} \left(1 + \frac{1}{n} \right)^2 \cdot \frac{1}{2} = \frac{1}{2} < 1,$

so the series is absolutely convergent by the Ratio Test.

21. Using the Ratio Test,

$$\lim_{n \to \infty} \left| \frac{a_{n+1}}{a_n} \right| = \lim_{n \to \infty} \left| \frac{(-3)^{n+1}/(n+1)^3}{(-3)^n/n^3} \right| = \lim_{n \to \infty} \left| \frac{(-3)n^3}{(n+1)^3} \right| = 3 \lim_{n \to \infty} \left(\frac{n}{n+1} \right)^3 = 3 > 1, \text{ so the series}$$

diverges.

22. Using the Ratio Test, $\displaystyle\lim_{n \to \infty} \left| \frac{a_{n+1}}{a_n} \right| = \lim_{n \to \infty} \left| \frac{(-3)^{n+1}/(n+1)!}{(-3)^n/n!} \right| = 3 \lim_{n \to \infty} \frac{1}{n+1} = 0 < 1$, so the series is

absolutely convergent

23. $\left| \dfrac{\sin 2n}{n^2} \right| \leq \dfrac{1}{n^2}$ and $\displaystyle\sum_{n=1}^{\infty} \dfrac{1}{n^2}$ converges (p-series, $p = 2 > 1$), so $\displaystyle\sum_{n=1}^{\infty} \dfrac{\sin 2n}{n^2}$ converges absolutely by the

Comparison Test.

24. $\displaystyle\sum_{n=1}^{\infty} \left| (-1)^n \dfrac{n}{n^2 + 1} \right| = \displaystyle\sum_{n=1}^{\infty} \dfrac{n}{n^2 + 1} = \displaystyle\sum_{n=1}^{\infty} a_n$. If $b_n = \dfrac{1}{n}$, then $\displaystyle\sum_{n=1}^{\infty} b_n$ is the divergent harmonic series. Applying

the Limit Comparison Test, $\displaystyle\lim_{n \to \infty} \dfrac{a_n}{b_n} = \lim_{n \to \infty} \dfrac{n/(n^2 + 1)}{1/n} = \lim_{n \to \infty} \dfrac{n^2}{n^2 + 1} = 1 > 0$, so both series diverge and

the given series is *not* absolutely convergent. (The Integral Test could also be used.)

25. $\displaystyle\lim_{n \to \infty} \left| \dfrac{a_{n+1}}{a_n} \right| = \lim_{n \to \infty} \left[\dfrac{10^{n+1}}{(n+2)4^{2(n+1)+1}} \cdot \dfrac{(n+1)4^{2n+1}}{10^n} \right] = \lim_{n \to \infty} \left[\dfrac{10^{n+1}}{(n+2)4^{2n+3}} \cdot \dfrac{(n+1)4^{2n+1}}{10^n} \right] =$

$\displaystyle\lim_{n \to \infty} \left(\dfrac{10}{4^2} \cdot \dfrac{n+1}{n+2} \right) = \dfrac{5}{8} < 1$, so the series is absolutely convergent by the Ratio Test. Since the terms of this

series are positive, absolute convergence is the same as convergence.

26. $\left| \cos \dfrac{n\pi}{6} \right| \leq 1$, so since $\displaystyle\sum_{n=1}^{\infty} \dfrac{1}{n\sqrt{n}}$ converges ($p = \dfrac{3}{2} > 1$), the given series converges absolutely by the

Comparison Test.

27. $\displaystyle\lim_{n \to \infty} \left| \dfrac{a_{n+1}}{a_n} \right| = \lim_{n \to \infty} \dfrac{(n+1)! / [1 \cdot 3 \cdot 5 \cdots (2n-1)(2n+1)]}{n! / [1 \cdot 3 \cdot 5 \cdots (2n-1)]} = \lim_{n \to \infty} \dfrac{n+1}{2n+1} = \dfrac{1}{2} < 1$, so the series

converges absolutely by the Ratio Test.

28. $\displaystyle\lim_{n \to \infty} \left| \dfrac{a_{n+1}}{a_n} \right| = \lim_{n \to \infty} \dfrac{5^n / [(n+2)^2 \, 4^{n+3}]}{5^{n-1} / [(n+1)^2 \, 4^{n+2}]} = \dfrac{5}{4} \lim_{n \to \infty} \left(\dfrac{n+1}{n+2} \right)^2 = \dfrac{5}{4} > 1$, so the series diverges by the

Ratio Test.

29. By the recursive definition, $\displaystyle\lim_{n \to \infty} \left| \dfrac{a_{n+1}}{a_n} \right| = \lim_{n \to \infty} \left| \dfrac{5n+1}{4n+3} \right| = \dfrac{5}{4} > 1$, so the series diverges by the Ratio Test.

30. By the recursive definition, $\displaystyle\lim_{n \to \infty} \left| \dfrac{a_{n+1}}{a_n} \right| = \lim_{n \to \infty} \left| \dfrac{2 + \cos n}{\sqrt{n}} \right| = 0 < 1$, so the series converges absolutely by the

Ratio Test.

31. (a) $\displaystyle\lim_{n \to \infty} \left| \dfrac{1/(n+1)^3}{1/n^3} \right| = \lim_{n \to \infty} \dfrac{n^3}{(n+1)^3} = \lim_{n \to \infty} \dfrac{1}{(1 + 1/n)^3} = 1$. Inconclusive.

(b) $\displaystyle\lim_{n \to \infty} \left| \dfrac{(n+1)}{2^{n+1}} \cdot \dfrac{2^n}{n} \right| = \lim_{n \to \infty} \dfrac{n+1}{2n} = \lim_{n \to \infty} \left(\dfrac{1}{2} + \dfrac{1}{2n} \right) = \dfrac{1}{2}$. Conclusive (convergent).

(c) $\displaystyle\lim_{n \to \infty} \left| \dfrac{(-3)^n}{\sqrt{n+1}} \cdot \dfrac{\sqrt{n}}{(-3)^{n-1}} \right| = 3 \lim_{n \to \infty} \sqrt{\dfrac{n}{n+1}} = 3 \lim_{n \to \infty} \sqrt{\dfrac{1}{1 + 1/n}} = 3$. Conclusive (divergent).

(d) $\displaystyle\lim_{n \to \infty} \left| \dfrac{\sqrt{n+1}}{1 + (n+1)^2} \cdot \dfrac{1 + n^2}{\sqrt{n}} \right| = \lim_{n \to \infty} \left[\sqrt{1 + \dfrac{1}{n}} \cdot \dfrac{1/n^2 + 1}{1/n^2 + (1 + 1/n)^2} \right] = 1$. Inconclusive.

32. We use the Ratio Test:

$$\lim_{n \to \infty} \left| \dfrac{a_{n+1}}{a_n} \right| = \lim_{n \to \infty} \left| \dfrac{[(n+1)!]^2 / [k(n+1)]!}{(n!)^2 / (kn)!} \right| = \lim_{n \to \infty} \left| \dfrac{(n+1)^2}{[k(n+1)] \, [k(n+1) - 1] \cdots [kn + 1]} \right|$$

(continued)

Now if $k = 1$, then this is equal to $\lim\limits_{n\to\infty} \left|\dfrac{(n+1)^2}{(n+1)}\right| = \infty$, so the series diverges; if $k = 2$, the limit is

$$\lim_{n\to\infty}\left|\dfrac{(n+1)^2}{(2n+2)(2n+1)}\right| = \dfrac{1}{4} < 1,$$ so the series converges, and if $k > 2$, then the highest power of n in the

denominator is larger than 2, and so the limit is 0, indicating convergence. So the series converges for $k \geq 2$.

33. (a) $\lim\limits_{n\to\infty}\left|\dfrac{a_{n+1}}{a_n}\right| = \lim\limits_{n\to\infty}\left|\dfrac{x^{n+1}}{(n+1)!}\cdot\dfrac{n!}{x^n}\right| = \lim\limits_{n\to\infty}\left|\dfrac{x}{n+1}\right| = |x|\lim\limits_{n\to\infty}\dfrac{1}{n+1} = |x|\cdot 0 = 0 < 1,$ so by the Ratio

Test the series $\sum\limits_{n=0}^{\infty}\dfrac{x^n}{n!}$ converges for all x.

(b) Since the series of part (a) always converges, we must have $\lim\limits_{n\to\infty}\dfrac{x^n}{n!} = 0$ by Theorem 8.2.6.

34. (a) $R_n = a_{n+1} + a_{n+2} + a_{n+3} + a_{n+4} + \cdots = a_{n+1}\left(1 + \dfrac{a_{n+2}}{a_{n+1}} + \dfrac{a_{n+3}}{a_{n+1}} + \dfrac{a_{n+4}}{a_{n+1}} + \cdots\right)$

$= a_{n+1}\left(1 + \dfrac{a_{n+2}}{a_{n+1}} + \dfrac{a_{n+3}\, a_{n+2}}{a_{n+2}\, a_{n+1}} + \dfrac{a_{n+4}\, a_{n+3}\, a_{n+2}}{a_{n+3}\, a_{n+2}\, a_{n+1}} + \cdots\right)$

$= a_{n+1}(1 + r_{n+1} + r_{n+2}r_{n+1} + r_{n+3}r_{n+2}r_{n+1} + \cdots)$ $(\star)$

$\leq a_{n+1}(1 + r_{n+1} + r_{n+1}^2 + r_{n+1}^3 + \cdots)$ [since $\{r_n\}$ is decreasing] $= \dfrac{a_{n+1}}{1 - r_{n+1}}$

(b) Note that since $\{r_n\}$ is increasing and $r_n \to L$ as $n \to \infty$, we have $r_n < L$ for all n. So, starting with equation $(\star)$,

$$R_n = a_{n+1}(1 + r_{n+1} + r_{n+2}r_{n+1} + r_{n+3}r_{n+2}r_{n+1} + \cdots) \leq a_{n+1}(1 + L + L^2 + L^3 + \cdots) = \dfrac{a_{n+1}}{1 - L}$$

35. (a) $s_5 = \sum\limits_{n=1}^{5}\dfrac{1}{n2^n} = \dfrac{1}{2} + \dfrac{1}{8} + \dfrac{1}{24} + \dfrac{1}{64} + \dfrac{1}{160} = \dfrac{661}{960} \approx 0.68854.$ Now the ratios

$r_n = \dfrac{a_{n+1}}{a_n} = \dfrac{n2^n}{(n+1)2^{n+1}} = \dfrac{n}{2(n+1)}$ form an increasing sequence, since

$r_{n+1} - r_n = \dfrac{n+1}{2(n+2)} - \dfrac{n}{2(n+1)} = \dfrac{(n+1)^2 - n(n+2)}{2(n+1)(n+2)} = \dfrac{1}{2(n+1)(n+2)} > 0.$ So by Exercise 34(b),

the error in using s_5 is $R_5 \leq \dfrac{a_6}{1 - \lim\limits_{n\to\infty} r_n} = \dfrac{1/(6\cdot 2^6)}{1 - 1/2} = \dfrac{1}{192} \approx 0.00521.$

(b) The error in using s_n as an approximation to the sum is $R_n = \dfrac{a_{n+1}}{1 - \frac{1}{2}} = \dfrac{2}{(n+1)2^{n+1}}.$ We want

$R_n < 0.00005 \iff \dfrac{1}{(n+1)2^n} < 0.00005 \iff (n+1)2^n > 20{,}000.$ To find such an n we can use trial

and error or a graph. We calculate $(11+1)2^{11} = 24{,}576,$ so $s_{11} = \sum\limits_{n=1}^{11}\dfrac{1}{n2^n} \approx 0.693109$ is within 0.00005 of

the actual sum.

36. $s_{10} = \sum\limits_{n=1}^{10}\dfrac{n}{2^n} = \dfrac{1}{2} + \dfrac{2}{4} + \dfrac{3}{8} + \cdots + \dfrac{10}{1024} \approx 1.988.$ The ratios

$r_n = \dfrac{a_{n+1}}{a_n} = \dfrac{n+1}{2^{n+1}}\cdot\dfrac{2^n}{n} = \dfrac{n+1}{2n} = \dfrac{1}{2}\left(1 + \dfrac{1}{n}\right)$ form a decreasing sequence, so $r_{11} = \dfrac{11+1}{2(11)} = \dfrac{12}{22} = \dfrac{6}{11},$

and by Exercise 34(a), the error in using s_{10} to approximate the sum of the series $\sum\limits_{n=1}^{\infty}\dfrac{n}{2^n}$ is

$R_{10} \leq \dfrac{a_{11}}{1 - r_{11}} = \dfrac{\frac{11}{2048}}{1 - \frac{6}{11}} = \dfrac{121}{10\,240} \approx 0.0118.$

8.5 Power Series • • • • • • • • • • • • • • • •

1. A power series is a series of the form $\sum_{n=0}^{\infty} c_n x^n = c_0 + c_1 x + c_2 x^2 + c_3 x^3 + \cdots$, where x is a variable and the c_n's are constants called the coefficients of the series.

More generally, a series of the form $\sum_{n=0}^{\infty} c_n (x-a)^n = c_0 + c_1(x-a) + c_2(x-a)^2 + \cdots$ is called a power series in $(x-a)$ or a power series centered at a or a power series about a, where a is a constant.

2. (a) Given the power series $\sum_{n=0}^{\infty} c_n (x-a)^n$, the radius of convergence is:

  (i) 0 if the series converges only when $x = a$

  (ii) ∞ if the series converges for all x, or

  (iii) a positive number R such that the series converges if $|x-a| < R$ and diverges if $|x-a| > R$.

  In most cases, R can be found by using the Ratio Test.

  (b) The interval of convergence of a power series is the interval that consists of all values of x for which the series converges. Corresponding to the cases in part (a), the interval of convergence is: (i) the single point $\{a\}$, (ii) all real numbers; that is, the real number line $(-\infty, \infty)$, or (iii) an interval with endpoints $a - R$ and $a + R$ which can contain neither, either, or both of the endpoints. In this case, we must test the series for convergence at each endpoint to determine the interval of convergence.

3. If $a_n = \dfrac{x^n}{\sqrt{n}}$, then $\lim\limits_{n \to \infty} \left| \dfrac{a_{n+1}}{a_n} \right| = \lim\limits_{n \to \infty} \left| \dfrac{x^{n+1}}{\sqrt{n+1}} \cdot \dfrac{\sqrt{n}}{x} \right| = \lim\limits_{n \to \infty} \left| \dfrac{x}{\sqrt{n+1}/\sqrt{n}} \right| = \lim\limits_{n \to \infty} \dfrac{|x|}{\sqrt{1+1/n}} = |x|.$

By the Ratio Test, the series $\sum\limits_{n=1}^{\infty} \dfrac{x^n}{\sqrt{n}}$ converges when $|x| < 1$, so the radius of convergence $R = 1$. When $x = 1$,

the series $\sum\limits_{n=1}^{\infty} \dfrac{1}{\sqrt{n}}$ diverges because it is a p-series with $p = \frac{1}{2} \leq 1$. When $x = -1$, the series $\sum\limits_{n=1}^{\infty} \dfrac{(-1)^n}{\sqrt{n}}$

converges by the Alternating Series Test. Thus, the interval of convergence is $I = [-1, 1)$.

4. If $a_n = \dfrac{(-1)^n x^n}{n+1}$, then $\lim\limits_{n \to \infty} \left| \dfrac{a_{n+1}}{a_n} \right| = \lim\limits_{n \to \infty} \left| \dfrac{x^{n+1}}{n+2} \cdot \dfrac{n+1}{x^n} \right| = \lim\limits_{n \to \infty} \dfrac{|x|}{1+1/(n+1)} = |x|.$ By the Ratio Test,

the series $\sum\limits_{n=0}^{\infty} \dfrac{(-1)^n x^n}{n+1}$ converges when $|x| < 1$, so $R = 1$. When $x = -1$, the series diverges because it is the

harmonic series; when $x = 1$, it is the alternating harmonic series, which converges by the Alternating Series Test. Thus, $I = (-1, 1]$.

5. If $a_n = n x^n$, then $\lim\limits_{n \to \infty} \left| \dfrac{a_{n+1}}{a_n} \right| = \lim\limits_{n \to \infty} \left| \dfrac{(n+1) x^{n+1}}{n x^n} \right| = \lim\limits_{n \to \infty} \left| \dfrac{x(n+1)}{n} \right| = |x| \lim\limits_{n \to \infty} \dfrac{n+1}{n} = |x| < 1$ for

convergence (by the Ratio Test), so $R = 1$. When $x = 1$ or -1, $\lim\limits_{n \to \infty} n x^n$ does not exist, so $\sum_{n=0}^{\infty} n x^n$ diverges

for $x = \pm 1$. Thus, $I = (-1, 1)$.

6. If $a_n = \dfrac{x^n}{n^2}$, then $\lim\limits_{n \to \infty} \left| \dfrac{a_{n+1}}{a_n} \right| = \lim\limits_{n \to \infty} \left| \dfrac{x^{n+1}}{(n+1)^2} \cdot \dfrac{n^2}{x^n} \right| = |x| \lim\limits_{n \to \infty} \left(\dfrac{n}{n+1} \right)^2 = |x| < 1$ for convergence

(by the Ratio Test), so $R = 1$. If $x = \pm 1$, $\sum\limits_{n=1}^{\infty} |a_n| = \sum\limits_{n=1}^{\infty} \dfrac{1}{n^2}$, which is a convergent p-series ($p = 2 > 1$).

Thus, $I = [-1, 1]$.

7. If $a_n = \dfrac{x^n}{n!}$, then $\lim\limits_{n \to \infty} \left| \dfrac{a_{n+1}}{a_n} \right| = \lim\limits_{n \to \infty} \left| \dfrac{x^{n+1}}{(n+1)!} \cdot \dfrac{n!}{x^n} \right| = \lim\limits_{n \to \infty} \left| \dfrac{x}{n+1} \right| = |x| \lim\limits_{n \to \infty} \dfrac{1}{n+1} = |x| \cdot 0 = 0 < 1$ for

all x. So, by the Ratio Test, $R = \infty$, and $I = (-\infty, \infty)$.

8. If $a_n = \dfrac{x^n}{n3^n}$, then $\displaystyle\lim_{n\to\infty}\left|\dfrac{a_{n+1}}{a_n}\right| = \lim_{n\to\infty}\left|\dfrac{x^{n+1}}{(n+1)3^{n+1}} \cdot \dfrac{n3^n}{x^n}\right| = \lim_{n\to\infty}\left|\dfrac{xn}{(n+1)3}\right| = \dfrac{|x|}{3}\lim_{n\to\infty}\dfrac{n}{n+1} = \dfrac{|x|}{3}$.

By the Ratio Test, the series converges when $\dfrac{|x|}{3} < 1 \iff |x| < 3$, so $R = 3$. When $x = -3$, the series is the alternating harmonic series, which converges by the Alternating Series Test. When $x = 3$, it is the harmonic series, which diverges. Thus, $I = [-3, 3)$.

9. If $a_n = \dfrac{3^n x^n}{(n+1)^2}$, then

$$\lim_{n\to\infty}\left|\dfrac{a_{n+1}}{a_n}\right| = \lim_{n\to\infty}\left|\dfrac{3^{n+1}x^{n+1}}{(n+2)^2} \cdot \dfrac{(n+1)^2}{3^n x^n}\right| = 3|x|\lim_{n\to\infty}\left(\dfrac{n+1}{n+2}\right)^2 = 3|x| \cdot 1 = 3|x|.$$ By the Ratio Test,

the series converges when $3|x| < 1 \iff |x| < \frac{1}{3}$, so $R = \frac{1}{3}$. When $x = \frac{1}{3}$,

$$\sum_{n=0}^{\infty}\dfrac{3^n x^n}{(n+1)^2} = \sum_{n=0}^{\infty}\dfrac{1}{(n+1)^2} = \sum_{n=1}^{\infty}\dfrac{1}{n^2},$$ which is a convergent p-series $(p = 2 > 1)$. When $x = -\frac{1}{3}$,

$$\sum_{n=0}^{\infty}\dfrac{3^n x^n}{(n+1)^2} = \sum_{n=0}^{\infty}\dfrac{(-1)^n}{(n+1)^2},$$ which converges by the Alternating Series Test. Thus, $I = \left[-\frac{1}{3}, \frac{1}{3}\right]$.

10. If $a_n = \dfrac{n^2 x^n}{10^n}$, then $\displaystyle\lim_{n\to\infty}\left|\dfrac{a_{n+1}}{a_n}\right| = \lim_{n\to\infty}\left|\dfrac{(n+1)^2 x^{n+1}}{10^{n+1}} \cdot \dfrac{10^n}{n^2 x^n}\right| = \dfrac{|x|}{10}\lim_{n\to\infty}\left(\dfrac{n+1}{n}\right)^2 = \dfrac{|x|}{10} < 1$ for

convergence (by the Ratio Test), so $R = 10$. If $x = \pm 10$, $|a_n| = n^2 \to \infty$ as $n \to \infty$, so $\sum_{n=0}^{\infty} a_n$ diverges (Test for Divergence) and $I = (-10, 10)$.

11. If $a_n = (-1)^n \dfrac{x^n}{4^n \ln n}$, then

$$\lim_{n\to\infty}\left|\dfrac{a_{n+1}}{a_n}\right| = \lim_{n\to\infty}\left|\dfrac{x^{n+1}}{4^{n+1}\ln(n+1)} \cdot \dfrac{4^n \ln n}{x^n}\right| = \dfrac{|x|}{4}\lim_{n\to\infty}\dfrac{\ln n}{\ln(n+1)} = \dfrac{|x|}{4} \cdot 1 \text{ (by l'Hospital's Rule)} = \dfrac{|x|}{4}.$$

By the Ratio Test, the series converges when $\dfrac{|x|}{4} < 1 \iff |x| < 4$, so $R = 4$. When $x = -4$,

$$\sum_{n=2}^{\infty}(-1)^n \dfrac{x^n}{4^n \ln n} = \sum_{n=2}^{\infty}\dfrac{(-1 \cdot -4)^n}{4^n \ln n} = \sum_{n=2}^{\infty}\dfrac{1}{\ln n}.$$ Since $\ln n < n$ for $n \geq 2$, $\dfrac{1}{\ln n} > \dfrac{1}{n}$ and $\sum_{n=2}^{\infty}\dfrac{1}{n}$ is the

divergent harmonic series (without the $n = 1$ term), $\displaystyle\sum_{n=2}^{\infty}\dfrac{1}{\ln n}$ is divergent by the Comparison Test. When $x = 4$,

$$\sum_{n=2}^{\infty}(-1)^n \dfrac{x^n}{4^n \ln n} = \sum_{n=2}^{\infty}(-1)^n \dfrac{1}{\ln n},$$ which converges by the Alternating Series Test. Thus, $I = (-4, 4]$.

12. If $a_n = n^3(x - 5)^n$, $\displaystyle\lim_{n\to\infty}\left|\dfrac{a_{n+1}}{a_n}\right| = \lim_{n\to\infty}\left|\dfrac{(n+1)^3(x-5)^{n+1}}{n^3(x-5)^n}\right| = \lim_{n\to\infty}\left(1 + \dfrac{1}{n}\right)^3 |x - 5| = |x - 5|.$ By the

Ratio Test, the series converges when $|x - 5| < 1 \iff -1 < x - 5 < 1 \iff 4 < x < 6$. When $x = 4$, the series becomes $\sum_{n=0}^{\infty}(-1)^n n^3$, which diverges by the Test for Divergence. When $x = 6$, the series becomes $\sum_{n=0}^{\infty} n^3$, which also diverges by the Test for Divergence. Thus, $R = 1$ and $I = (4, 6)$.

13. If $a_n = \sqrt{n}\,(x - 1)^n$, then $\displaystyle\lim_{n\to\infty}\left|\dfrac{a_{n+1}}{a_n}\right| = \lim_{n\to\infty}\left|\dfrac{\sqrt{n+1}\,|x - 1|^{n+1}}{\sqrt{n}\,|x - 1|^n}\right| = \lim_{n\to\infty}\sqrt{1 + \dfrac{1}{n}}\,|x - 1| = |x - 1|.$ By

the Ratio Test, the series converges when $|x - 1| < 1$ [so $R = 1$] $\iff -1 < x - 1 < 1 \iff 0 < x < 2$.

When $x = 0$, the series becomes $\sum_{n=0}^{\infty}(-1)^n \sqrt{n}$, which diverges by the Test for Divergence. When $x = 2$, the

series becomes $\sum_{n=0}^{\infty} \sqrt{n}$, which also diverges by the Test for Divergence. Thus, $I = (0, 2)$.

14. If $a_n = \dfrac{(-1)^n x^{2n-1}}{(2n-1)!}$, then $\lim\limits_{n\to\infty}\left|\dfrac{a_{n+1}}{a_n}\right| = \lim\limits_{n\to\infty}\left|\dfrac{x^{2n+1}}{(2n+1)!}\cdot\dfrac{(2n-1)!}{x^{2n-1}}\right| = \lim\limits_{n\to\infty}\dfrac{x^2}{(2n+1)(2n)} = 0 < 1$ for

all x. By the Ratio Test the series converges for all x, so $R = \infty$ and $I = (-\infty, \infty)$.

15. If $a_n = (-1)^n\dfrac{(x+2)^n}{n2^n}$, then

$\lim\limits_{n\to\infty}\left|\dfrac{a_{n+1}}{a_n}\right| = \lim\limits_{n\to\infty}\left[\dfrac{|x+2|^{n+1}}{(n+1)\,2^{n+1}}\cdot\dfrac{n2^n}{|x+2|^n}\right] = \lim\limits_{n\to\infty}\dfrac{n}{n+1}\cdot\dfrac{|x+2|}{2} = \dfrac{|x+2|}{2}$. By the Ratio Test, the

series converges when $\dfrac{|x+2|}{2} < 1 \ \Leftrightarrow\ |x+2| < 2$ [so $R = 2$] $\ \Leftrightarrow\ -2 < x+2 < 2 \ \Leftrightarrow\ -4 < x < 0$.

When $x = -4$, the series becomes $\sum\limits_{n=1}^{\infty}(-1)^n\dfrac{(-2)^n}{n2^n} = \sum\limits_{n=1}^{\infty}\dfrac{2^n}{n2^n} = \sum\limits_{n=1}^{\infty}\dfrac{1}{n}$, which is the divergent harmonic series.

When $x = 0$, the series is $\sum\limits_{n=1}^{\infty}\dfrac{(-1)^n}{n}$, the alternating harmonic series, which converges by the Alternating Series

Test. Thus, $I = (-4, 0]$.

16. If $a_n = \dfrac{(-2)^n}{\sqrt{n}}(x+3)^n$, then

$\lim\limits_{n\to\infty}\left|\dfrac{a_{n+1}}{a_n}\right| = \lim\limits_{n\to\infty}\left|\dfrac{(-2)^{n+1}(x+3)^{n+1}}{\sqrt{n+1}}\cdot\dfrac{\sqrt{n}}{(-2)^n(x+3)^n}\right| = \lim\limits_{n\to\infty}\dfrac{2|x+3|}{\sqrt{1+1/n}} = 2|x+3| < 1 \ \Leftrightarrow$

$|x+3| < \tfrac{1}{2}$ $\left[\text{so } R = \tfrac{1}{2}\right]$ $\ \Leftrightarrow\ -\tfrac{7}{2} < x < -\tfrac{5}{2}$. When $x = -\tfrac{7}{2}$, the series becomes $\sum\limits_{n=1}^{\infty}\dfrac{1}{\sqrt{n}}$, which diverges

because it is a p-series with $p = \tfrac{1}{2} \le 1$. When $x = -\tfrac{5}{2}$, the series becomes $\sum\limits_{n=1}^{\infty}\dfrac{(-1)^n}{\sqrt{n}}$, which converges by the

Alternating Series Test. Thus, $I = \left(-\tfrac{7}{2}, -\tfrac{5}{2}\right]$.

17. If $a_n = n!(2x-1)^n$, then $\lim\limits_{n\to\infty}\left|\dfrac{a_{n+1}}{a_n}\right| = \lim\limits_{n\to\infty}\left|\dfrac{(n+1)!(2x-1)^{n+1}}{n!(2x-1)^n}\right| = \lim\limits_{n\to\infty}(n+1)\,|2x-1| \to \infty$ as

$n \to \infty$ for all $x \ne \tfrac{1}{2}$. Since the series diverges for all $x \ne \tfrac{1}{2}$, $R = 0$ and $I = \left\{\tfrac{1}{2}\right\}$.

18. If $a_n = \dfrac{nx^n}{1\cdot3\cdot5\cdots(2n-1)}$, then

$\lim\limits_{n\to\infty}\left|\dfrac{a_{n+1}}{a_n}\right| = \lim\limits_{n\to\infty}\left|\dfrac{(n+1)x^{n+1}}{1\cdot3\cdot5\cdots(2n+1)}\cdot\dfrac{1\cdot3\cdot5\cdots(2n-1)}{nx^n}\right| = |x|\lim\limits_{n\to\infty}\dfrac{n+1}{n(2n+1)} = 0$ for all x.

By the Ratio Test, the series converges for all x, so $R = \infty$ and $I = (-\infty, \infty)$.

19. (a) We are given that the power series $\sum_{n=0}^{\infty}c_nx^n$ is convergent for $x = 4$. So by Theorem 3, it must converge for

at least $-4 < x \le 4$. In particular, it converges when $x = -2$; that is, $\sum_{n=0}^{\infty}c_n(-2)^n$ is convergent.

(b) It does not follow that $\sum_{n=0}^{\infty}c_n(-4)^n$ is necessarily convergent. [See the comments after Theorem 3 about

convergence at the endpoint of an interval. An example is $c_n = (-1)^n/(n4^n)$.]

20. We are given that the power series $\sum_{n=0}^{\infty}c_nx^n$ is convergent for $x = -4$ and divergent when $x = 6$. So by

Theorem 3 it converges for at least $-4 \le x < 4$ and diverges for at least $x \ge 6$ and $x < -6$. Therefore:

(a) It converges when $x = 1$; that is, $\sum c_n$ is convergent.

(b) It diverges when $x = 8$; that is, $\sum c_n8^n$ is divergent.

(c) It converges when $x = -3$; that is, $\sum c_n(-3)^n$ is convergent.

(d) It diverges when $x = -9$; that is, $\sum c_n(-9)^n = \sum(-1)^nc_n9^n$ is divergent.

21. If $a_n = \dfrac{(n!)^k}{(kn)!} x^n$, then

$$\lim_{n\to\infty} \left| \frac{a_{n+1}}{a_n} \right| = \lim_{n\to\infty} \frac{[(n+1)!]^k (kn)!}{(n!)^k [k(n+1)]!} |x| = \lim_{n\to\infty} \frac{(n+1)^k}{(kn+k)(kn+k-1)\cdots(kn+2)(kn+1)} |x|$$

$$= \lim_{n\to\infty} \left[\frac{(n+1)}{(kn+1)} \frac{(n+1)}{(kn+2)} \cdots \frac{(n+1)}{(kn+k)} \right] |x|$$

$$= \lim_{n\to\infty} \left[\frac{n+1}{kn+1} \right] \lim_{n\to\infty} \left[\frac{n+1}{kn+2} \right] \cdots \lim_{n\to\infty} \left[\frac{n+1}{kn+k} \right] |x| = \left(\frac{1}{k} \right)^k |x| < 1 \quad \Leftrightarrow$$

$|x| < k^k$ for convergence, and the radius of convergence is $R = k^k$.

22. The partial sums of the series $\sum_{n=0}^{\infty} x^n$ definitely do not converge to $f(x) = 1/(1-x)$ for $x \geq 1$, since f is undefined at $x = 1$ and negative on $(1, \infty)$, while all the partial sums are positive on this interval. The partial sums also fail to converge to f for $x \leq -1$, since $0 < f(x) < 1$ on this interval, while the partial sums are either larger than 1 or less than 0. The partial sums seem to converge to f on $(-1, 1)$. This graphical evidence is consistent with what we know about geometric series: convergence for $|x| < 1$, divergence for $|x| \geq 1$ (see Example 8.2.5).

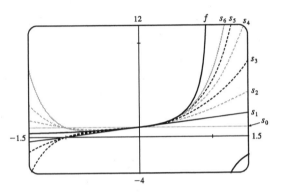

23. (a) If $a_n = \dfrac{(-1)^n x^{2n+1}}{n!(n+1)! 2^{2n+1}}$, then

$$\lim_{n\to\infty} \left| \frac{a_{n+1}}{a_n} \right| = \lim_{n\to\infty} \left| \frac{x^{2n+3}}{(n+1)!(n+2)! 2^{2n+3}} \cdot \frac{n!(n+1)! 2^{2n+1}}{x^{2n+1}} \right| = \left(\frac{x}{2} \right)^2 \lim_{n\to\infty} \frac{1}{(n+1)(n+2)} = 0 \text{ for}$$

all x. So $J_1(x)$ converges for all x and its domain is $(-\infty, \infty)$.

(b), (c) The initial terms of $J_1(x)$ up to $n = 5$ are $a_0 = \dfrac{x}{2}$,

$a_1 = -\dfrac{x^3}{16}$, $a_2 = \dfrac{x^5}{384}$, $a_3 = -\dfrac{x^7}{18{,}432}$,

$a_4 = \dfrac{x^9}{1{,}474{,}560}$, and $a_5 = -\dfrac{x^{11}}{176{,}947{,}200}$. The

partial sums seem to approximate $J_1(x)$ well near the origin, but as $|x|$ increases, we need to take a large number of terms to get a good approximation.

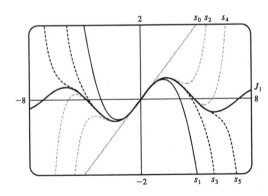

24. (a) $A(x) = 1 + \sum_{n=1}^{\infty} a_n$, where $a_n = \dfrac{x^{3n}}{2 \cdot 3 \cdot 5 \cdot 6 \cdots\cdots (3n-1)(3n)}$, so

$$\lim_{n\to\infty} \left| \frac{a_{n+1}}{a_n} \right| = |x|^3 \lim_{n\to\infty} \frac{1}{(3n+2)(3n+3)} = 0 \text{ for all } x, \text{ so the domain is } \mathbb{R}.$$

(b), (c)

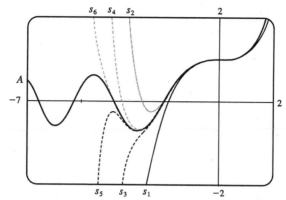

$s_0 = 1$ has been omitted from the graph. The partial sums seem to approximate $A(x)$ well near the origin, but as $|x|$ increases, we need to take a large number of terms to get a good approximation.

To plot A, we must first define $A(x)$ for the CAS. Note that for $n \geq 1$, the denominator of a_n is

$$2 \cdot 3 \cdot 5 \cdot 6 \cdots (3n - 1) \cdot 3n = \frac{(3n)!}{1 \cdot 4 \cdot 7 \cdots (3n - 2)} = \frac{(3n)!}{\prod_{k=1}^{n}(3k - 2)}, \text{ so } a_n = 1 + \frac{\prod_{k=1}^{n}(3k - 2)}{(3n)!} x^{3n}$$

and thus $A(x) = 1 + \sum_{n=1}^{\infty} \frac{\prod_{k=1}^{n}(3k - 2)}{(3n)!} x^{3n}$. Both Maple and Mathematica are able to plot A if we define it this way, and Derive is able to produce a similar graph using a suitable partial sum of $A(x)$.

Derive, Maple and Mathematica all have two initially known Airy functions, called AI_SERIES(z,m) and BI_SERIES(z,m) from BESSEL.MTH in Derive and AiryAi and AiryBi in Maple and Mathematica (just Ai and Bi in older versions of Maple). However, it is very difficult to solve for A in terms of the CAS's Airy functions, although in fact $A(x) = \dfrac{\sqrt{3}\,\text{AiryAi}(x) + \text{AiryBi}(x)}{\sqrt{3}\,\text{AiryAi}(0) + \text{AiryBi}(0)}$.

25. $s_{2n-1} = 1 + 2x + x^2 + 2x^3 + x^4 + 2x^5 + \cdots + x^{2n-2} + 2x^{2n-1}$

$= 1(1 + 2x) + x^2(1 + 2x) + x^4(1 + 2x) + \cdots + x^{2n-2}(1 + 2x)$

$= (1 + 2x)\left(1 + x^2 + x^4 + \cdots + x^{2n-2}\right)$

$= (1 + 2x)\dfrac{1 - x^{2n}}{1 - x^2}$ [by (8.2.3) with $r = x^2$] $\to \dfrac{1 + 2x}{1 - x^2}$ as $n \to \infty$ [by (8.2.4)],

when $|x| < 1$. Also $s_{2n} = s_{2n-1} + x^{2n} \to \dfrac{1 + 2x}{1 - x^2}$ since $x^{2n} \to 0$ for $|x| < 1$. Therefore, $s_n \to \dfrac{1 + 2x}{1 - x^2}$ since s_{2n} and s_{2n-1} both approach $\dfrac{1 + 2x}{1 - x^2}$ as $n \to \infty$. Thus, the interval of convergence is $(-1, 1)$ and $f(x) = \dfrac{1 + 2x}{1 - x^2}$.

26. $s_{4n-1} = c_0 + c_1 x + c_2 x^2 + c_3 x^3 + c_0 x^4 + c_1 x^5 + c_2 x^6 + c_3 x^7 + \cdots + c_3 x^{4n-1}$

$= \left(c_0 + c_1 x + c_2 x^2 + c_3 x^3\right)\left(1 + x^4 + x^8 + \cdots + x^{4n-4}\right) \to \dfrac{c_0 + c_1 x + c_2 x^2 + c_3 x^3}{1 - x^4}$ as $n \to \infty$

[by (8.2.4) with $r = x^4$] for $|x^4| < 1$ ⟺ $|x| < 1$. Also $s_{4n}, s_{4n+1}, s_{4n+2}$ have the same limits (for example, $s_{4n} = s_{4n-1} + c_0 x^{4n}$ and $x^{4n} \to 0$ for $|x| < 1$.) So if at least one of c_0, c_1, c_2, and c_3 is nonzero, then the interval of convergence is $(-1, 1)$ and $f(x) = \dfrac{c_0 + c_1 x + c_2 x^2 + c_3 x^3}{1 - x^4}$.

27. For $2 < x < 3$, $\sum c_n x^n$ diverges and $\sum d_n x^n$ converges. By Exercise 8.2.49, $\sum (c_n + d_n) x^n$ diverges. Since both series converge for $|x| < 2$, the radius of convergence of $\sum (c_n + d_n) x^n$ is 2.

28. Since $\sum c_n x^n$ converges whenever $|x| < R$, $\sum c_n x^{2n} = \sum c_n (x^2)^n$ converges whenever $|x^2| < R$ ⟺ $|x| < \sqrt{R}$, so the second series has radius of convergence $\sqrt{R}$.

 8.6 **Representations of Functions as Power Series** • • • • • •

1. If $f(x) = \sum_{n=0}^{\infty} c_n x^n$ has radius of convergence 10, then $f'(x) = \sum_{n=1}^{\infty} n c_n x^{n-1}$ also has radius of convergence 10 by Theorem 2.

2. If $f(x) = \sum_{n=0}^{\infty} b_n x^n$ converges on $(-2, 2)$, then $\int f(x) dx = C + \sum_{n=0}^{\infty} \frac{b_n}{n+1} x^{n+1}$ has the same radius of convergence (by Theorem 2), but may not have the same interval of convergence—it may happen that the integrated series converges at an endpoint (or both endpoints).

3. Our goal is to write the function in the form $\frac{1}{1-r}$, and then use Equation (1) to represent the function as a sum of a power series. $f(x) = \frac{1}{1+x} = \frac{1}{1-(-x)} = \sum_{n=0}^{\infty} (-x)^n = \sum_{n=0}^{\infty} (-1)^n x^n$ with $|-x| < 1$ ⟺ $|x| < 1$, so $R = 1$ and $I = (-1, 1)$.

4. $f(x) = \frac{x}{1-x} = x \left(\frac{1}{1-x} \right) = x \sum_{n=0}^{\infty} x^n = \sum_{n=0}^{\infty} x^{n+1} = \sum_{n=1}^{\infty} x^n$ with $R = 1$ and $I = (-1, 1)$.

5. Replacing x with x^3 in (1) gives $f(x) = \frac{1}{1-x^3} = \sum_{n=0}^{\infty} (x^3)^n = \sum_{n=0}^{\infty} x^{3n}$. The series converges when $|x^3| < 1$ ⟺ $|x|^3 < 1$ ⟺ $|x| < \sqrt[3]{1}$ ⟺ $|x| < 1$. Thus, $R = 1$ and $I = (-1, 1)$.

6. $f(x) = \frac{1}{1+9x^2} = \frac{1}{1-(-9x^2)} = \sum_{n=0}^{\infty} (-9x^2)^n = \sum_{n=0}^{\infty} (-1)^n 3^{2n} x^{2n}$. The series converges when $|-9x^2| < 1$; that is, when $|x| < \frac{1}{3}$, so $I = \left(-\frac{1}{3}, \frac{1}{3} \right)$.

7. If the constant term in the denominator is something other than 1, factor it out of the binomial to obtain a 1. $f(x) = \frac{1}{4+x^2} = \frac{1}{4} \left(\frac{1}{1+x^2/4} \right) = \frac{1}{4} \left(\frac{1}{1-(-x^2/4)} \right) = \frac{1}{4} \sum_{n=0}^{\infty} \left(-\frac{x^2}{4} \right)^n = \sum_{n=0}^{\infty} \frac{(-1)^n x^{2n}}{4^{n+1}}$. The series converges when $\left| -\frac{x^2}{4} \right| < 1$ ⟺ $x^2 < 4$ ⟺ $|x| < 2$, so $R = 2$ and $I = (-2, 2)$.

8. $f(x) = \frac{1+x^2}{1-x^2} = \frac{(1-x^2) + 2x^2}{1-x^2} = 1 + \frac{2x^2}{1-x^2} = 1 + 2x^2 \sum_{n=0}^{\infty} (x^2)^n = 1 + \sum_{n=0}^{\infty} 2x^{2n+2} = 1 + \sum_{n=1}^{\infty} 2x^{2n}$, with $|x^2| < 1$ ⟺ $|x| < 1$, so $R = 1$ and $I = (-1, 1)$.

9. $f(x) = \dfrac{1}{x-5} = -\dfrac{1}{5}\left(\dfrac{1}{1-x/5}\right) = -\dfrac{1}{5}\sum\limits_{n=0}^{\infty}\left(\dfrac{x}{5}\right)^n$ or equivalently, $-\sum\limits_{n=0}^{\infty}\dfrac{1}{5^{n+1}}x^n$. The series converges when

$\left|\dfrac{x}{5}\right| < 1$; that is, when $|x| < 5$, so $I = (-5, 5)$.

10. $f(x) = \dfrac{x}{4x+1} = x \cdot \dfrac{1}{1-(-4x)} = x\sum\limits_{n=0}^{\infty}(-4x)^n = \sum\limits_{n=0}^{\infty}(-1)^n 2^{2n}x^{n+1}$. The series converges when $|-4x| < 1$;

that is, when $|x| < \frac{1}{4}$, so $I = \left(-\frac{1}{4}, \frac{1}{4}\right)$.

11. (a) $f(x) = \dfrac{1}{(1+x)^2} = \dfrac{d}{dx}\left(\dfrac{-1}{1+x}\right) = -\dfrac{d}{dx}\left[\sum\limits_{n=0}^{\infty}(-1)^n x^n\right]$ [from Exercise 3]

$= \sum\limits_{n=1}^{\infty}(-1)^{n+1}nx^{n-1}$ [from Theorem 2(a)] $= \sum\limits_{n=0}^{\infty}(-1)^n(n+1)x^n$ with $R = 1$.

In the last step, note that we *decreased* the initial value of the summation variable n by 1, and then *increased*
each occurrence of n in the term by 1 [also note that $(-1)^{n+2} = (-1)^n$].

(b) $f(x) = \dfrac{1}{(1+x)^3} = -\dfrac{1}{2}\dfrac{d}{dx}\left[\dfrac{1}{(1+x)^2}\right] = -\dfrac{1}{2}\dfrac{d}{dx}\left[\sum\limits_{n=0}^{\infty}(-1)^n(n+1)x^n\right]$ [from part (a)]

$= -\dfrac{1}{2}\sum\limits_{n=1}^{\infty}(-1)^n(n+1)nx^{n-1} = \dfrac{1}{2}\sum\limits_{n=0}^{\infty}(-1)^n(n+2)(n+1)x^n$ with $R = 1$.

(c) $f(x) = \dfrac{x^2}{(1+x)^3} = x^2 \cdot \dfrac{1}{(1+x)^3} = x^2 \cdot \dfrac{1}{2}\sum\limits_{n=0}^{\infty}(-1)^n(n+2)(n+1)x^n$ [from part (b)]

$= \dfrac{1}{2}\sum\limits_{n=0}^{\infty}(-1)^n(n+2)(n+1)x^{n+2}$. To write the power series with x^n rather than x^{n+2},

we will *decrease* each occurrence of n in the term by 2 and *increase* the initial value of the summation variable

by 2. This gives us $\dfrac{1}{2}\sum\limits_{n=2}^{\infty}(-1)^n(n)(n-1)x^n$.

12. (a) $f(x) = \dfrac{1}{1+x} = \sum\limits_{n=0}^{\infty}(-1)^n x^n$ [geometric series with $R = 1$], so

$f(x) = \ln(1+x) = \displaystyle\int\dfrac{dx}{1+x} = \int\left[\sum\limits_{n=0}^{\infty}(-1)^n x^n\right]dx = C + \sum\limits_{n=0}^{\infty}(-1)^n\dfrac{x^{n+1}}{n+1}$

$= \sum\limits_{n=1}^{\infty}\dfrac{(-1)^{n-1}x^n}{n}$ [$C = 0$ since $f(0) = 0$], with $R = 1$

(b) $f(x) = x\ln(1+x) = x\left[\sum\limits_{n=1}^{\infty}\dfrac{(-1)^{n-1}x^n}{n}\right]$ [by part (a)] $= \sum\limits_{n=1}^{\infty}\dfrac{(-1)^{n-1}x^{n+1}}{n} = \sum\limits_{n=2}^{\infty}\dfrac{(-1)^n x^n}{n-1}$

with $R = 1$.

13. $f(x) = \ln(5-x) = -\displaystyle\int\dfrac{dx}{5-x} = -\dfrac{1}{5}\int\dfrac{dx}{1-x/5}$

$= -\dfrac{1}{5}\displaystyle\int\left[\sum\limits_{n=0}^{\infty}\left(\dfrac{x}{5}\right)^n\right]dx = C - \dfrac{1}{5}\sum\limits_{n=0}^{\infty}\dfrac{x^{n+1}}{5^n(n+1)} = C - \sum\limits_{n=1}^{\infty}\dfrac{x^n}{n5^n}$

Putting $x = 0$, we get $C = \ln 5$. The series converges for $|x/5| < 1$ $\Leftrightarrow$ $|x| < 5$, so $R = 5$.

14. We know that $\dfrac{1}{1-2x} = \sum\limits_{n=0}^{\infty} (2x)^n$. Differentiating, we get $\dfrac{2}{(1-2x)^2} = \sum\limits_{n=1}^{\infty} 2^n n x^{n-1} = \sum\limits_{n=0}^{\infty} 2^{n+1}(n+1)x^n$, so

$$f(x) = \dfrac{x^2}{(1-2x)^2} = \dfrac{x^2}{2} \cdot \dfrac{2}{(1-2x)^2} = \dfrac{x^2}{2} \sum\limits_{n=0}^{\infty} 2^{n+1}(n+1)x^n = \sum\limits_{n=0}^{\infty} 2^n(n+1)x^{n+2} \text{ or } \sum\limits_{n=2}^{\infty} 2^{n-2}(n-1)x^n,$$

with $R = \frac{1}{2}$.

15. $\dfrac{1}{2-x} = \dfrac{1}{2(1-x/2)} = \dfrac{1}{2}\sum\limits_{n=0}^{\infty}\left(\dfrac{x}{2}\right)^n = \sum\limits_{n=0}^{\infty} \dfrac{1}{2^{n+1}}x^n$ for $\left|\dfrac{x}{2}\right| < 1 \;\Leftrightarrow\; |x| < 2$. Now

$$\dfrac{1}{(x-2)^2} = \dfrac{d}{dx}\left(\dfrac{1}{2-x}\right) = \dfrac{d}{dx}\left(\sum\limits_{n=0}^{\infty}\dfrac{1}{2^{n+1}}x^n\right) = \sum\limits_{n=1}^{\infty}\dfrac{n}{2^{n+1}}x^{n-1} = \sum\limits_{n=0}^{\infty}\dfrac{n+1}{2^{n+2}}x^n. \text{ So}$$

$$f(x) = \dfrac{x^3}{(x-2)^2} = x^3\sum\limits_{n=0}^{\infty}\dfrac{n+1}{2^{n+2}}x^n = \sum\limits_{n=0}^{\infty}\dfrac{n+1}{2^{n+2}}x^{n+3} \text{ or } \sum\limits_{n=3}^{\infty}\dfrac{n-2}{2^{n-1}}x^n \text{ for } |x| < 2. \text{ Thus, } R = 2 \text{ and }$$

$I = (-2, 2)$.

16. From Example 7, $g(x) = \arctan x = \sum\limits_{n=0}^{\infty} (-1)^n \dfrac{x^{2n+1}}{2n+1}$. Thus,

$$f(x) = \arctan(x/3) = \sum\limits_{n=0}^{\infty} (-1)^n \dfrac{(x/3)^{2n+1}}{2n+1} = \sum\limits_{n=0}^{\infty} (-1)^n \dfrac{1}{3^{2n+1}(2n+1)}x^{2n+1} \text{ for } \left|\dfrac{x}{3}\right| < 1 \;\Leftrightarrow\; |x| < 3,$$

so $R = 3$.

17. $f(x) = \ln(3 + x) = \displaystyle\int \dfrac{dx}{3+x} = \dfrac{1}{3}\int\dfrac{dx}{1+x/3} = \dfrac{1}{3}\int\dfrac{dx}{1-(-x/3)} = \dfrac{1}{3}\int\sum\limits_{n=0}^{\infty}\left(-\dfrac{x}{3}\right)^n dx$

$= C + \dfrac{1}{3}\sum\limits_{n=0}^{\infty}\dfrac{(-1)^n}{(n+1)3^n}x^{n+1} = \ln 3 + \dfrac{1}{3}\sum\limits_{n=1}^{\infty}\dfrac{(-1)^{n-1}}{n3^{n-1}}x^n \quad [C = f(0) = \ln 3]$

$= \ln 3 + \sum\limits_{n=1}^{\infty}\dfrac{(-1)^{n-1}}{n3^n}x^n$. The series converges when $|-x/3| < 1 \;\Leftrightarrow\; |x| < 3$, so $R = 3$.

The terms of the series are $a_0 = \ln 3$, $a_1 = \dfrac{x}{3}$, $a_2 = -\dfrac{x^2}{18}$, $a_3 = \dfrac{x^3}{81}$, $a_4 = -\dfrac{x^4}{324}$, $a_5 = \dfrac{x^5}{1215}$, ...

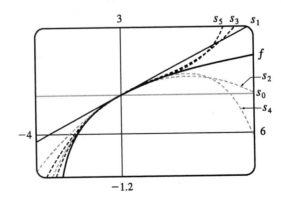

As n increases, $s_n(x)$ approximates f better on the interval of convergence, which is $(-3, 3)$.

18. $f(x) = \dfrac{1}{x^2 + 25} = \dfrac{1}{25}\left(\dfrac{1}{1 + x^2/25}\right) = \dfrac{1}{25}\left(\dfrac{1}{1 - (-x^2/25)}\right) = \dfrac{1}{25}\displaystyle\sum_{n=0}^{\infty}\left(-\dfrac{x^2}{25}\right)^n = \dfrac{1}{25}\displaystyle\sum_{n=0}^{\infty}(-1)^n\left(\dfrac{x}{5}\right)^{2n}.$

The series converges when $\left|-x^2/25\right| < 1 \iff x^2 < 25 \iff |x| < 5$, so $R = 5$. The terms of the series are

$a_0 = \dfrac{1}{25},\ a_1 = -\dfrac{x^2}{625},\ a_2 = \dfrac{x^4}{15{,}625},\ \dots$

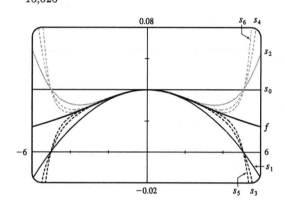

As n increases, $s_n(x)$ approximates f better on the interval of convergence, which is $(-5, 5)$.

19. $f(x) = \ln\left(\dfrac{1+x}{1-x}\right) = \ln(1+x) - \ln(1-x) = \displaystyle\int \dfrac{dx}{1+x} + \int \dfrac{dx}{1-x}$

$= \displaystyle\int \dfrac{dx}{1-(-x)} + \int \dfrac{dx}{1-x} = \int \left[\sum_{n=0}^{\infty}(-1)^n x^n + \sum_{n=0}^{\infty} x^n\right] dx$

$= \displaystyle\int \left[\left(1 - x + x^2 - x^3 + x^4 - \cdots\right) + \left(1 + x + x^2 + x^3 + x^4 + \cdots\right)\right] dx$

$= \displaystyle\int \left(2 + 2x^2 + 2x^4 + \cdots\right) dx = \int \sum_{n=0}^{\infty} 2x^{2n}\, dx = C + \sum_{n=0}^{\infty} \dfrac{2x^{2n+1}}{2n+1}$

But $f(0) = \ln\frac{1}{1} = 0$, so $C = 0$ and we have $f(x) = \displaystyle\sum_{n=0}^{\infty} \dfrac{2x^{2n+1}}{2n+1}$ with $R = 1$. If $x = \pm 1$, then

$f(x) = \pm 2 \displaystyle\sum_{n=0}^{\infty} \dfrac{1}{2n+1}$, which both diverge by the Limit Comparison Test with $b_n = \dfrac{1}{n}$.

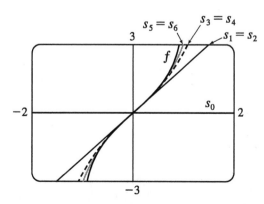

As n increases, $s_n(x)$ approximates f better on the interval of convergence, which is $(-1, 1)$.

20. $f(x) = \tan^{-1}(2x) = 2\int \dfrac{dx}{1 + 4x^2} = 2\int \sum\limits_{n=0}^{\infty} (-1)^n \left(4x^2\right)^n \, dx = 2\int \sum\limits_{n=0}^{\infty} (-1)^n 4^n x^{2n} \, dx$

$= C + 2\sum\limits_{n=0}^{\infty} \dfrac{(-1)^n 4^n x^{2n+1}}{2n+1} = \sum\limits_{n=0}^{\infty} \dfrac{(-1)^n 2^{2n+1} x^{2n+1}}{2n+1}$ $[f(0) = \tan^{-1} 0 = 0, \text{ so } C = 0].$

The series converges when $\left|4x^2\right| < 1 \iff |x| < \frac{1}{2},$ so $R = \frac{1}{2}.$ If $x = \pm\frac{1}{2},$ then $f(x) = \sum\limits_{n=0}^{\infty} (-1)^n \dfrac{1}{2n+1}$ and

$f(x) = \sum\limits_{n=0}^{\infty} (-1)^{n+1}\dfrac{1}{2n+1},$ respectively. Both series converge by the Alternating Series Test.

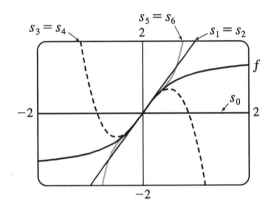

As n increases, $s_n(x)$ approximates f better on the interval of convergence, which is $\left[-\frac{1}{2}, \frac{1}{2}\right].$

21. $\int \dfrac{dx}{1 + x^4} = \int \dfrac{dx}{1 - (-x^4)} = \int \sum\limits_{n=0}^{\infty} \left(-x^4\right)^n dx = \int \sum\limits_{n=0}^{\infty} (-1)^n x^{4n} \, dx = C + \sum\limits_{n=0}^{\infty} \dfrac{(-1)^n x^{4n+1}}{4n+1}$ with $R = 1.$

22. $\dfrac{1}{1 + x^5} = \sum\limits_{n=0}^{\infty} (-1)^n x^{5n} \Rightarrow \dfrac{x}{1 + x^5} = \sum\limits_{n=0}^{\infty} (-1)^n x^{5n+1} \Rightarrow \int \dfrac{x}{1 + x^5} \, dx = C + \sum\limits_{n=0}^{\infty} \dfrac{(-1)^n x^{5n+2}}{5n+2}$
with $R = 1.$

23. By Example 7, $\arctan x = \sum\limits_{n=0}^{\infty} (-1)^n \dfrac{x^{2n+1}}{2n+1},$ so

$\int \dfrac{\arctan x}{x} \, dx = \int \sum\limits_{n=0}^{\infty} (-1)^n \dfrac{x^{2n}}{2n+1} \, dx = C + \sum\limits_{n=0}^{\infty} (-1)^n \dfrac{x^{2n+1}}{(2n+1)^2}$ with $R = 1.$

24. By Example 7, $\int \tan^{-1}\left(x^2\right) dx = \int \sum\limits_{n=0}^{\infty} (-1)^n \dfrac{\left(x^2\right)^{2n+1}}{2n+1} \, dx = C + \sum\limits_{n=0}^{\infty} (-1)^n \dfrac{x^{4n+3}}{(2n+1)(4n+3)}$ with $R = 1.$

25. $\dfrac{1}{1 + x^5} = \dfrac{1}{1 - (-x^5)} = \sum\limits_{n=0}^{\infty} \left(-x^5\right)^n = \sum\limits_{n=0}^{\infty} (-1)^n x^{5n} \Rightarrow$

$\int \dfrac{1}{1 + x^5} \, dx = \int \sum\limits_{n=0}^{\infty} (-1)^n x^{5n} \, dx = C + \sum\limits_{n=0}^{\infty} (-1)^n \dfrac{x^{5n+1}}{5n+1}.$ Thus,

$I = \displaystyle\int_0^{0.2} \dfrac{1}{1 + x^5} \, dx = \left[x - \dfrac{x^6}{6} + \dfrac{x^{11}}{11} - \cdots\right]_0^{0.2} = 0.2 - \dfrac{(0.2)^6}{6} + \dfrac{(0.2)^{11}}{11} - \cdots.$ The series is alternating, so

if we use the first two terms, the error is at most $(0.2)^{11}/11 \approx 1.9 \times 10^{-9}.$ So $I \approx 0.2 - (0.2)^6/6 \approx 0.199989$ to
six decimal places.

26. From Example 6 we know $\ln(1-x) = -\sum\limits_{n=1}^{\infty} \dfrac{x^n}{n}$, so

$$\ln\left(1+x^4\right) = \ln\left[1-\left(-x^4\right)\right] = -\sum_{n=1}^{\infty} \frac{\left(-x^4\right)^n}{n} = \sum_{n=1}^{\infty}(-1)^{n+1}\frac{x^{4n}}{n} \quad \Rightarrow$$

$$\int \ln\left(1+x^4\right) dx = \int \sum_{n=1}^{\infty}(-1)^{n+1}\frac{x^{4n}}{n}\, dx = C + \sum_{n=1}^{\infty}(-1)^{n+1}\frac{x^{4n+1}}{n(4n+1)}. \text{ Thus,}$$

$$I = \int_0^{0.4} \ln\left(1+x^4\right) dx = \left[\frac{x^5}{5} - \frac{x^9}{18} + \frac{x^{13}}{39} - \frac{x^{17}}{68} + \cdots\right]_0^{0.4} = \frac{(0.4)^5}{5} - \frac{(0.4)^9}{18} + \frac{(0.4)^{13}}{39} - \frac{(0.4)^{17}}{68} + \cdots.$$

The series is alternating, so if we use the first three terms, the error is at most $(0.4)^{17}/68 \approx 2.5 \times 10^{-9}$. So $I \approx (0.4)^5/5 - (0.4)^9/18 + (0.9)^{13}/39 \approx 0.002034$ to six decimal places.

27. We substitute x^4 for x in Example 7, and find that

$$\int x^2 \tan^{-1}\left(x^4\right) dx = \int x^2 \sum_{n=0}^{\infty}(-1)^n \frac{\left(x^4\right)^{2n+1}}{2n+1}\, dx$$

$$= \int \sum_{n=0}^{\infty}(-1)^n \frac{x^{8n+6}}{2n+1}\, dx = C + \sum_{n=0}^{\infty}(-1)^n \frac{x^{8n+7}}{(2n+1)(8n+7)}$$

So $\int_0^{1/3} x^2 \tan^{-1}\left(x^4\right) dx = \left[\dfrac{x^7}{7} - \dfrac{x^{15}}{45} + \cdots\right]_0^{1/3} = \dfrac{1}{7\cdot3^7} - \dfrac{1}{45\cdot3^{15}} + \cdots.$ The series is alternating, so if we use only one term, the error is at most $1/\left(45\cdot3^{15}\right) \approx 1.5 \times 10^{-9}$. So $\int_0^{1/3} x^2 \tan^{-1}\left(x^4\right) dx \approx 1/\left(7\cdot3^7\right) \approx 0.000065$ to six decimal places.

28. $\displaystyle\int_0^{0.5} \frac{dx}{1+x^6} = \int_0^{0.5} \sum_{n=0}^{\infty}(-1)^n x^{6n}\, dx = \sum_{n=0}^{\infty}\left[\frac{(-1)^n x^{6n+1}}{6n+1}\right]_0^{1/2} = \sum_{n=0}^{\infty} \frac{(-1)^n}{(6n+1)2^{6n+1}}$

$$= \frac{1}{2} - \frac{1}{7\cdot2^7} + \frac{1}{13\cdot2^{13}} - \frac{1}{19\cdot2^{19}} + \cdots$$

The series is alternating, so if we use only three terms, the error is at most $\dfrac{1}{19\cdot2^{19}} \approx 1.0 \times 10^{-7}$. So, to six

decimal places, $\displaystyle\int_0^{0.5} \frac{dx}{1+x^6} \approx \frac{1}{2} - \frac{1}{7\cdot2^7} + \frac{1}{13\cdot2^{13}} \approx 0.498893.$

29. Using the result of Example 6, $\ln(1-x) = -\sum\limits_{n=1}^{\infty} \dfrac{x^n}{n}$, with $x = -0.1$, we have

$$\ln 1.1 = \ln[1-(-0.1)] = 0.1 - \frac{0.01}{2} + \frac{0.001}{3} - \frac{0.0001}{4} + \frac{0.00001}{5} - \cdots. \text{ The series is alternating, so if}$$

we use only the first four terms, the error is at most $\dfrac{0.00001}{5} = 0.000002.$ So

$$\ln 1.1 \approx 0.1 - \frac{0.01}{2} + \frac{0.001}{3} - \frac{0.0001}{4} \approx 0.09531.$$

30. $f(x) = \sum\limits_{n=0}^{\infty} \dfrac{(-1)^n x^{2n}}{(2n)!} \quad \Rightarrow \quad f'(x) = \sum\limits_{n=1}^{\infty} \dfrac{(-1)^n 2n x^{2n-1}}{(2n)!}$ (the first term disappears), so

$$f''(x) = \sum_{n=1}^{\infty} \frac{(-1)^n (2n)(2n-1)x^{2n-2}}{(2n)!} = \sum_{n=1}^{\infty} \frac{(-1)^n x^{2(n-1)}}{[2(n-1)]!} = \sum_{n=0}^{\infty} \frac{(-1)^{n+1} x^{2n}}{(2n)!} \quad \text{(substituting } n+1 \text{ for } n\text{)}$$

$$= -\sum_{n=0}^{\infty} \frac{(-1)^n x^{2n}}{(2n)!} = -f(x) \quad \Rightarrow \quad f''(x) + f(x) = 0.$$

31. (a) $J_0(x) = \sum_{n=0}^{\infty} \frac{(-1)^n x^{2n}}{2^{2n}(n!)^2}$, $J_0'(x) = \sum_{n=1}^{\infty} \frac{(-1)^n 2nx^{2n-1}}{2^{2n}(n!)^2}$, and $J_0''(x) = \sum_{n=1}^{\infty} \frac{(-1)^n 2n(2n-1)x^{2n-2}}{2^{2n}(n!)^2}$, so

$$x^2 J_0''(x) + x J_0'(x) + x^2 J_0(x) = \sum_{n=1}^{\infty} \frac{(-1)^n 2n(2n-1)x^{2n}}{2^{2n}(n!)^2} + \sum_{n=1}^{\infty} \frac{(-1)^n 2nx^{2n}}{2^{2n}(n!)^2} + \sum_{n=0}^{\infty} \frac{(-1)^n x^{2n+2}}{2^{2n}(n!)^2}$$

$$= \sum_{n=1}^{\infty} \frac{(-1)^n 2n(2n-1)x^{2n}}{2^{2n}(n!)^2} + \sum_{n=1}^{\infty} \frac{(-1)^n 2nx^{2n}}{2^{2n}(n!)^2} + \sum_{n=1}^{\infty} \frac{(-1)^{n-1} x^{2n}}{2^{2n-2}[(n-1)!]^2}$$

$$= \sum_{n=1}^{\infty} \frac{(-1)^n 2n(2n-1)x^{2n}}{2^{2n}(n!)^2} + \sum_{n=1}^{\infty} \frac{(-1)^n 2nx^{2n}}{2^{2n}(n!)^2} + \sum_{n=1}^{\infty} \frac{(-1)^n(-1)^{-1}2^2 n^2 x^{2n}}{2^{2n}(n!)^2}$$

$$= \sum_{n=1}^{\infty} (-1)^n \left[\frac{2n(2n-1) + 2n - 2^2 n^2}{2^{2n}(n!)^2} \right] x^{2n} = \sum_{n=1}^{\infty} (-1)^n \left[\frac{4n^2 - 2n + 2n - 4n^2}{2^{2n}(n!)^2} \right] x^{2n} = 0$$

(b) $\int_0^1 J_0(x)\, dx = \int_0^1 \left[\sum_{n=0}^{\infty} \frac{(-1)^n x^{2n}}{2^{2n}(n!)^2} \right] dx = \int_0^1 \left(1 - \frac{x^2}{4} + \frac{x^4}{64} - \frac{x^6}{2304} + \cdots \right) dx$

$$= \left[x - \frac{x^3}{3 \cdot 4} + \frac{x^5}{5 \cdot 64} - \frac{x^7}{7 \cdot 2304} + \cdots \right]_0^1 = 1 - \frac{1}{12} + \frac{1}{320} - \frac{1}{16{,}128} + \cdots$$

Since $\frac{1}{16{,}128} \approx 0.000062$, it follows from The Alternating Series Estimation Theorem that, correct to three decimal places, $\int_0^1 J_0(x)\, dx \approx 1 - \frac{1}{12} + \frac{1}{320} \approx 0.920$.

32. (a) $J_1(x) = \sum_{n=0}^{\infty} \frac{(-1)^n x^{2n+1}}{n!(n+1)! 2^{2n+1}}$, $J_1'(x) = \sum_{n=0}^{\infty} \frac{(-1)^n (2n+1) x^{2n}}{n!(n+1)! 2^{2n+1}}$, and

$J_1''(x) = \sum_{n=1}^{\infty} \frac{(-1)^n (2n+1)(2n) x^{2n-1}}{n!(n+1)! 2^{2n+1}}$.

$x^2 J_1''(x) + x J_1'(x) + (x^2 - 1) J_1(x)$

$$= \sum_{n=1}^{\infty} \frac{(-1)^n (2n+1)(2n)x^{2n+1}}{n!(n+1)! 2^{2n+1}} + \sum_{n=0}^{\infty} \frac{(-1)^n (2n+1)x^{2n+1}}{n!(n+1)! 2^{2n+1}}$$

$$+ \sum_{n=0}^{\infty} \frac{(-1)^n x^{2n+3}}{n!(n+1)! 2^{2n+1}} - \sum_{n=0}^{\infty} \frac{(-1)^n x^{2n+1}}{n!(n+1)! 2^{2n+1}}$$

$$= \sum_{n=1}^{\infty} \frac{(-1)^n (2n+1)(2n)x^{2n+1}}{n!(n+1)! 2^{2n+1}} + \sum_{n=0}^{\infty} \frac{(-1)^n (2n+1)x^{2n+1}}{n!(n+1)! 2^{2n+1}}$$

$$- \sum_{n=1}^{\infty} \frac{(-1)^n x^{2n+1}}{(n-1)! n! 2^{2n-1}} - \sum_{n=0}^{\infty} \frac{(-1)^n x^{2n+1}}{n!(n+1)! 2^{2n+1}} \qquad \begin{pmatrix} \text{Replace } n \text{ with } n-1 \\ \text{in the third term} \end{pmatrix}$$

$$= \frac{x}{2} - \frac{x}{2} + \sum_{n=1}^{\infty} (-1)^n \left[\frac{(2n+1)(2n) + (2n+1) - (n)((n+1)2^2 - 1)}{n!(n+1)! 2^{2n+1}} \right] x^{2n+1} = 0$$

(b) $J_0(x) = \sum\limits_{n=0}^{\infty} \dfrac{(-1)^n x^{2n}}{2^{2n}(n!)^2}$ $\Rightarrow$

$J_0'(x) = \sum\limits_{n=1}^{\infty} \dfrac{(-1)^n (2n)x^{2n-1}}{2^{2n}(n!)^2} = \sum\limits_{n=0}^{\infty} \dfrac{(-1)^{n+1} 2(n+1)x^{2n+1}}{2^{2n+2}[(n+1)!]^2}$ (Replace n with $n+1$)

$\quad = -\sum\limits_{n=0}^{\infty} \dfrac{(-1)^n x^{2n+1}}{2^{2n+1}(n+1)!\,n!}$ (cancel 2 and $n+1$; take -1 outside sum) $= -J_1(x)$

33. (a) $f(x) = \sum\limits_{n=0}^{\infty} \dfrac{x^n}{n!}$ $\Rightarrow$ $f'(x) = \sum\limits_{n=1}^{\infty} \dfrac{nx^{n-1}}{n!} = \sum\limits_{n=1}^{\infty} \dfrac{x^{n-1}}{(n-1)!} = \sum\limits_{n=0}^{\infty} \dfrac{x^n}{n!} = f(x)$

(b) By Theorem 7.4.2, the only solution to the differential equation $df(x)/dx = f(x)$ is $f(x) = Ke^x$, but $f(0) = 1$, so $K = 1$ and $f(x) = e^x$.

Or: We could solve the equation $df(x)/dx = f(x)$ as a separable differential equation.

34. $\dfrac{|\sin nx|}{n^2} \le \dfrac{1}{n^2}$, so $\sum\limits_{n=1}^{\infty} \dfrac{\sin nx}{n^2}$ converges by the Comparison Test. $\dfrac{d}{dx}\left(\dfrac{\sin nx}{n^2}\right) = \dfrac{\cos nx}{n}$, so when $x = 2k\pi$

(k an integer), $\sum\limits_{n=1}^{\infty} f_n'(x) = \sum\limits_{n=1}^{\infty} \dfrac{\cos(2kn\pi)}{n} = \sum\limits_{n=1}^{\infty} \dfrac{1}{n}$, which diverges (harmonic series). $f_n''(x) = -\sin nx$, so

$\sum\limits_{n=1}^{\infty} f_n''(x) = -\sum\limits_{n=1}^{\infty} \sin nx$, which converges only if $\sin nx = 0$, or $x = k\pi$ (k an integer).

35. If $a_n = \dfrac{x^n}{n^2}$, then by the Ratio Test, $\lim\limits_{n\to\infty}\left|\dfrac{a_{n+1}}{a_n}\right| = \lim\limits_{n\to\infty}\left|\dfrac{x^{n+1}}{(n+1)^2} \cdot \dfrac{n^2}{x^n}\right| = |x| \lim\limits_{n\to\infty}\left(\dfrac{n}{n+1}\right)^2 = |x| < 1$ for

convergence, so $R = 1$. When $x = \pm 1$, $\sum\limits_{n=1}^{\infty}\left|\dfrac{x^n}{n^2}\right| = \sum\limits_{n=1}^{\infty} \dfrac{1}{n^2}$ which is a convergent p-series ($p = 2 > 1$), so the

interval of convergence for f is $[-1, 1]$. By Theorem 2, the radii of convergence of f' and f'' are both 1, so we need

only check the endpoints. $f(x) = \sum\limits_{n=1}^{\infty} \dfrac{x^n}{n^2}$ $\Rightarrow$ $f'(x) = \sum\limits_{n=1}^{\infty} \dfrac{nx^{n-1}}{n^2} = \sum\limits_{n=0}^{\infty} \dfrac{x^n}{n+1}$, and this series diverges for

$x = 1$ (harmonic series) and converges for $x = -1$ (Alternating Series Test), so the interval of convergence

is $[-1, 1)$. $f''(x) = \sum\limits_{n=1}^{\infty} \dfrac{nx^{n-1}}{n+1}$ diverges at both 1 and -1 (Test for Divergence) since $\lim\limits_{n\to\infty} \dfrac{n}{n+1} = 1 \ne 0$, so its

interval of convergence is $(-1, 1)$.

36. (a) $\sum\limits_{n=1}^{\infty} nx^{n-1} = \sum\limits_{n=0}^{\infty} \dfrac{d}{dx} x^n = \dfrac{d}{dx}\left[\sum\limits_{n=0}^{\infty} x_n\right] = \dfrac{d}{dx}\left[\dfrac{1}{1-x}\right] = -\dfrac{1}{(1-x)^2}(-1) = \dfrac{1}{(1-x)^2}$, $|x| < 1$.

(b) (i) $\sum\limits_{n=1}^{\infty} nx^n = x\sum\limits_{n=1}^{\infty} nx^{n-1} = x\left[\dfrac{1}{(1-x)^2}\right]$ [from part (a)] $= \dfrac{x}{(1-x)^2}$ for $|x| < 1$.

(ii) Put $x = \frac{1}{2}$ in (i): $\sum\limits_{n=1}^{\infty} \dfrac{n}{2^n} = \sum\limits_{n=1}^{\infty} n\left(\tfrac{1}{2}\right)^n = \dfrac{1/2}{(1-1/2)^2} = 2$.

(c) (i) $\sum\limits_{n=2}^{\infty} n(n-1)x^n = x^2\sum\limits_{n=2}^{\infty} n(n-1)x^{n-2} = x^2 \dfrac{d}{dx}\left[\sum\limits_{n=1}^{\infty} nx^{n-1}\right] = x^2 \dfrac{d}{dx}\dfrac{1}{(1-x)^2}$

$\quad = x^2\dfrac{2}{(1-x)^3} = \dfrac{2x^2}{(1-x)^3}$ for $|x| < 1$.

(ii) Put $x = \frac{1}{2}$ in (i): $\sum\limits_{n=2}^{\infty} \dfrac{n^2-n}{2^n} = \sum\limits_{n=2}^{\infty} n(n-1)\left(\tfrac{1}{2}\right)^n = \dfrac{2(1/2)^2}{(1-1/2)^3} = 4$.

(iii) From (b)(ii) and (c)(ii), we have $\sum\limits_{n=1}^{\infty} \dfrac{n^2}{2^n} = \sum\limits_{n=1}^{\infty} \dfrac{n^2-n}{2^n} + \sum\limits_{n=1}^{\infty} \dfrac{n}{2^n} = 4 + 2 = 6$.

8.7 Taylor and Maclaurin Series • • • • • • • • • • •

1. Using Theorem 5 with $\sum\limits_{n=0}^{\infty} b_n (x - 5)^n$, $b_n = \dfrac{f^{(n)}(a)}{n!}$, so $b_8 = \dfrac{f^{(8)}(5)}{8!}$.

2. (a) Using Formula 6, a power series expansion of f at 1 must have the form $f(1) + f'(1)(x - 1) + \cdots$. Comparing to the given series, $1.6 - 0.8(x - 1) + \cdots$, we must have $f'(1) = -0.8$. But from the graph, $f'(1)$ is positive. Hence, the given series is *not* the Taylor series of f centered at 1.

(b) A power series expansion of f at 2 must have the form $f(2) + f'(2)(x - 2) + \frac{1}{2} f''(2)(x - 2)^2 + \cdots$. Comparing to the given series, $2.8 + 0.5(x - 2) + 1.5(x - 2)^2 - 0.1(x - 2)^3 + \cdots$, we must have $\frac{1}{2} f''(2) = 1.5$; that is, $f''(2)$ is positive. But from the graph, f is concave downward near $x = 2$, so $f''(2)$ must be negative. Hence, the given series is *not* the Taylor series of f centered at 2.

3.

n	$f^{(n)}(x)$	$f^{(n)}(0)$
0	$\cos x$	1
1	$-\sin x$	0
2	$-\cos x$	-1
3	$\sin x$	0
4	$\cos x$	1
⋮	⋮	⋮

We use Equation 7 with $f(x) = \cos x$.

$$\cos x = f(0) + f'(0)x + \frac{f''(0)}{2!}x^2 + \frac{f^{(3)}(0)}{3!}x^3 + \frac{f^{(4)}(0)}{4!}x^4 + \cdots$$

$$= 1 - \frac{x^2}{2!} + \frac{x^4}{4!} - \cdots = \sum_{n=0}^{\infty} \frac{(-1)^n x^{2n}}{(2n)!}$$

If $a_n = \dfrac{(-1)^n x^{2n}}{(2n)!}$, then

$$\lim_{n\to\infty} \left| \frac{a_{n+1}}{a_n} \right| = \lim_{n\to\infty} \left| \frac{x^{2n+2}}{(2n+2)!} \cdot \frac{(2n)!}{x^{2n}} \right| = x^2 \lim_{n\to\infty} \frac{1}{(2n+2)(2n+1)} = 0 < 1 \text{ for all } x.$$

So $R = \infty$ (Ratio Test).

4.

n	$f^{(n)}(x)$	$f^{(n)}(0)$
0	$\sin 2x$	0
1	$2\cos 2x$	2
2	$-2^2 \sin 2x$	0
3	$-2^3 \cos 2x$	-2^3
4	$2^4 \sin 2x$	0
⋮	⋮	⋮

$f^{(n)}(0) = 0$ if n is even and $f^{(2n+1)}(0) = (-1)^n 2^{2n+1}$, so

$$\sin 2x = \sum_{n=0}^{\infty} \frac{f^{(n)}(0)}{n!} x^n = \sum_{n=0}^{\infty} \frac{f^{(2n+1)}(0)}{(2n+1)!} x^{2n+1}$$

$$= \sum_{n=0}^{\infty} \frac{(-1)^n 2^{2n+1} x^{2n+1}}{(2n+1)!}$$

$$\lim_{n\to\infty} \left| \frac{a_{n+1}}{a_n} \right| = \lim_{n\to\infty} \frac{2^2 |x|^2}{(2n+3)(2n+2)} = 0 < 1 \text{ for all } x,$$

so $R = \infty$ (Ratio Test).

5.

n	$f^{(n)}(x)$	$f^{(n)}(0)$
0	$(1+x)^{-3}$	1
1	$-3(1+x)^{-4}$	-3
2	$12(1+x)^{-5}$	12
3	$-60(1+x)^{-6}$	-60
4	$360(1+x)^{-7}$	360
⋮	⋮	⋮

$$(1+x)^{-3} = f(0) + f'(0)x + \frac{f''(0)}{2!}x^2 + \frac{f'''(0)}{3!}x^3 + \frac{f^{(4)}(0)}{4!}x^4 + \cdots$$

$$= 1 - 3x + \frac{4 \cdot 3}{2!}x^2 - \frac{5 \cdot 4 \cdot 3}{3!}x^3 + \frac{6 \cdot 5 \cdot 4 \cdot 3}{4!}x^4 - \cdots$$

$$= 1 - 3x + \frac{4 \cdot 3 \cdot 2}{2 \cdot 2!}x^2 - \frac{5 \cdot 4 \cdot 3 \cdot 2}{2 \cdot 3!}x^3 + \frac{6 \cdot 5 \cdot 4 \cdot 3 \cdot 2}{2 \cdot 4!}x^4 - \cdots$$

$$= \sum_{n=0}^{\infty} \frac{(-1)^n (n+2)! \, x^n}{2(n!)} = \sum_{n=0}^{\infty} \frac{(-1)^n (n+2)(n+1)x^n}{2}$$

$$\lim_{n \to \infty} \left| \frac{a_{n+1}}{a_n} \right| = \lim_{n \to \infty} \left| \frac{(n+3)(n+2)x^{n+1}}{2} \cdot \frac{2}{(n+2)(n+1)x^n} \right| = |x| \lim_{n \to \infty} \frac{n+3}{n+1} = |x| < 1 \text{ for convergence,}$$

so $R = 1$ (Ratio Test).

6.

n	$f^{(n)}(x)$	$f^{(n)}(0)$
0	$\ln(1+x)$	0
1	$(1+x)^{-1}$	1
2	$-(1+x)^{-2}$	-1
3	$2(1+x)^{-3}$	2
4	$-6(1+x)^{-4}$	-6
5	$24(1+x)^{-5}$	24
⋮	⋮	⋮

$$\ln(1+x) = f(0) + f'(0)x + \frac{f''(0)}{2!}x^2 + \frac{f'''(0)}{3!}x^3$$

$$+ \frac{f^{(4)}(0)}{4!}x^4 + \frac{f^{(5)}(0)}{5!}x^5 + \cdots$$

$$= x - \tfrac{1}{2}x^2 + \tfrac{2}{6}x^3 - \tfrac{6}{24}x^4 + \tfrac{24}{120}x^5 - \cdots$$

$$= x - \frac{x^2}{2} + \frac{x^3}{3} - \frac{x^4}{4} + \frac{x^5}{5} - \cdots = \sum_{n=1}^{\infty} \frac{(-1)^{n-1}}{n}x^n$$

$$\lim_{n \to \infty} \left| \frac{a_{n+1}}{a_n} \right| = \lim_{n \to \infty} \left| \frac{x^{n+1}}{n+1} \cdot \frac{n}{x^n} \right| = \lim_{n \to \infty} \frac{|x|}{1 + 1/n} = |x| < 1 \text{ for}$$

convergence, so $R = 1$.

7.

n	$f^{(n)}(x)$	$f^{(n)}(2)$
0	$1 + x + x^2$	7
1	$1 + 2x$	5
2	2	2
3	0	0
4	0	0
⋮	⋮	⋮

$$f(x) = 7 + 5(x-2) + \frac{2}{2!}(x-2)^2 + \sum_{n=3}^{\infty} \frac{0}{n!}(x-2)^n$$

$$= 7 + 5(x-2) + (x-2)^2$$

Since $a_n = 0$ for large n, $R = \infty$.

8.

n	$f^{(n)}(x)$	$f^{(n)}(-1)$
0	x^3	-1
1	$3x^2$	3
2	$6x$	-6
3	6	6
4	0	0
5	0	0
$\vdots$	$\vdots$	$\vdots$

$$f(x) = -1 + 3(x+1) - \frac{6}{2!}(x+1)^2 + \frac{6}{3!}(x+1)^3$$
$$= -1 + 3(x+1) - 3(x+1)^2 + (x+1)^3$$

Since $a_n = 0$ for large n, $R = \infty$.

9. Clearly, $f^{(n)}(x) = e^x$, so $f^{(n)}(3) = e^3$ and $e^x = \sum\limits_{n=0}^{\infty} \frac{e^3}{n!}(x-3)^n$. If $a_n = \frac{e^3}{n!}(x-3)^n$, then

$$\lim_{n\to\infty}\left|\frac{a_{n+1}}{a_n}\right| = \lim_{n\to\infty}\left|\frac{e^3(x-3)^{n+1}}{(n+1)!}\cdot\frac{n!}{e^3(x-3)^n}\right| = \lim_{n\to\infty}\frac{|x-3|}{n+1} = 0 < 1 \text{ for all } x, \text{ so } R = \infty.$$

10.

n	$f^{(n)}(x)$	$f^{(n)}(2)$
0	$\ln x$	$\ln 2$
1	x^{-1}	$\frac{1}{2}$
2	$-x^{-2}$	$-\frac{1}{4}$
3	$2x^{-3}$	$\frac{2}{8}$
4	$-3\cdot 2x^{-4}$	$-\frac{3\cdot 2}{16}$
$\vdots$	$\vdots$	$\vdots$

$$f^{(n)}(2) = \frac{(-1)^{n-1}(n-1)!}{2^n} \text{ for } n \geq 1, \text{ so } \ln x = \ln 2 + \sum_{n=1}^{\infty}\frac{(-1)^{n-1}(x-2)^n}{n\cdot 2^n}.$$

$$\lim_{n\to\infty}\left|\frac{a_{n+1}}{a_n}\right| = \frac{|x-2|}{2}\lim_{n\to\infty}\frac{n}{n+1} = \frac{|x-2|}{2} < 1 \text{ for convergence, so } |x-2| < 2 \implies R = 2.$$

11.

n	$f^{(n)}(x)$	$f^{(n)}(1)$
0	x^{-1}	1
1	$-x^{-2}$	-1
2	$2x^{-3}$	2
3	$-3\cdot 2x^{-4}$	$-3\cdot 2$
4	$4\cdot 3\cdot 2x^{-5}$	$4\cdot 3\cdot 2$
$\vdots$	$\vdots$	$\vdots$

So $f^{(n)}(1) = (-1)^n n!$, and $\frac{1}{x} = \sum\limits_{n=0}^{\infty}\frac{(-1)^n n!}{n!}(x-1)^n = \sum\limits_{n=0}^{\infty}(-1)^n(x-1)^n$. If $a_n = (-1)^n(x-1)^n$ then

$$\lim_{n\to\infty}\left|\frac{a_{n+1}}{a_n}\right| = |x-1| < 1 \text{ for convergence, so } R = 1.$$

12.

n	$f^{(n)}(x)$	$f^{(n)}(4)$
0	$x^{1/2}$	2
1	$\frac{1}{2}x^{-1/2}$	2^{-2}
2	$-\frac{1}{4}x^{-3/2}$	-2^{-5}
3	$\frac{3}{8}x^{-5/2}$	$3 \cdot 2^{-8}$
4	$-\frac{15}{16}x^{-7/2}$	$-15 \cdot 2^{-11}$
$\vdots$	$\vdots$	$\vdots$

$$f^{(n)}(4) = \frac{(-1)^{n-1}1 \cdot 3 \cdot 5 \cdots (2n-3)}{2^{3n-1}} \text{ for } n \geq 2, \text{ so}$$

$$\sqrt{x} = 2 + \frac{x-4}{4} + \sum_{n=2}^{\infty} \frac{(-1)^{n-1}1 \cdot 3 \cdot 5 \cdots (2n-3)}{2^{3n-1}n!}(x-4)^n.$$

$$\lim_{n \to \infty}\left|\frac{a_{n+1}}{a_n}\right| = \lim_{n \to \infty}\left|\frac{1 \cdot 3 \cdot 5 \cdots (2n-3)(2n-1)(x-4)^{n+1}}{2^{3n+2}(n+1)!} \cdot \frac{2^{3n-1}n!}{1 \cdot 3 \cdot 5 \cdots (2n-3)(x-4)^n}\right|$$

$$= \frac{|x-4|}{8}\lim_{n \to \infty}\left(\frac{2n-1}{n+1}\right) = \frac{|x-4|}{8} \cdot 2 = \frac{|x-4|}{4} < 1 \text{ for convergence,}$$

so $|x-4| < 4 \;\Rightarrow\; R = 4$.

13.

n	$f^{(n)}(x)$	$f^{(n)}\left(\frac{\pi}{4}\right)$
0	$\sin x$	$\sqrt{2}/2$
1	$\cos x$	$\sqrt{2}/2$
2	$-\sin x$	$-\sqrt{2}/2$
3	$-\cos x$	$-\sqrt{2}/2$
4	$\sin x$	$\sqrt{2}/2$
$\vdots$	$\vdots$	$\vdots$

$$\sin x = f\left(\tfrac{\pi}{4}\right) + f'\left(\tfrac{\pi}{4}\right)\left(x-\tfrac{\pi}{4}\right) + \frac{f''\left(\tfrac{\pi}{4}\right)}{2!}\left(x-\tfrac{\pi}{4}\right)^2 + \frac{f^{(3)}\left(\tfrac{\pi}{4}\right)}{3!}\left(x-\tfrac{\pi}{4}\right)^3 + \frac{f^{(4)}\left(\tfrac{\pi}{4}\right)}{4!}\left(x-\tfrac{\pi}{4}\right)^4 + \cdots$$

$$= \frac{\sqrt{2}}{2}\left[1 + \left(x-\tfrac{\pi}{4}\right) - \tfrac{1}{2!}\left(x-\tfrac{\pi}{4}\right)^2 - \tfrac{1}{3!}\left(x-\tfrac{\pi}{4}\right)^3 + \tfrac{1}{4!}\left(x-\tfrac{\pi}{4}\right)^4 + \cdots\right]$$

$$= \frac{\sqrt{2}}{2}\left[1 - \tfrac{1}{2!}\left(x-\tfrac{\pi}{4}\right)^2 + \tfrac{1}{4!}\left(x-\tfrac{\pi}{4}\right)^4 - \cdots\right] + \frac{\sqrt{2}}{2}\left[\left(x-\tfrac{\pi}{4}\right) - \tfrac{1}{3!}\left(x-\tfrac{\pi}{4}\right)^3 + \cdots\right]$$

$$= \frac{\sqrt{2}}{2}\sum_{n=0}^{\infty}(-1)^n\left[\tfrac{1}{(2n)!}\left(x-\tfrac{\pi}{4}\right)^{2n} + \tfrac{1}{(2n+1)!}\left(x-\tfrac{\pi}{4}\right)^{2n+1}\right]$$

The series can also be written in the more elegant form $\sin x = \dfrac{\sqrt{2}}{2}\displaystyle\sum_{n=0}^{\infty}\dfrac{(-1)^{n(n-1)/2}\left(x-\frac{\pi}{4}\right)^n}{n!}$. If

$$a_n = \frac{(-1)^{n(n-1)/2}\left(x-\frac{\pi}{4}\right)^n}{n!}, \text{ then } \lim_{n \to \infty}\left|\frac{a_{n+1}}{a_n}\right| = \lim_{n \to \infty}\frac{\left|x-\frac{\pi}{4}\right|}{n+1} = 0 < 1 \text{ for all } x, \text{ so } R = \infty.$$

14.

n	$f^{(n)}(x)$	$f^{(n)}\left(-\frac{\pi}{4}\right)$
0	$\cos x$	$\sqrt{2}/2$
1	$-\sin x$	$\sqrt{2}/2$
2	$-\cos x$	$-\sqrt{2}/2$
3	$\sin x$	$-\sqrt{2}/2$
4	$\cos x$	$\sqrt{2}/2$
⋮	⋮	⋮

$$\cos x = f\left(-\tfrac{\pi}{4}\right) + f'\left(-\tfrac{\pi}{4}\right)\left(x + \tfrac{\pi}{4}\right) + \frac{f''\left(-\tfrac{\pi}{4}\right)}{2!}\left(x + \tfrac{\pi}{4}\right)^2$$

$$+ \frac{f^{(3)}\left(-\tfrac{\pi}{4}\right)}{3!}\left(x + \tfrac{\pi}{4}\right)^3 + \frac{f^{(4)}\left(-\tfrac{\pi}{4}\right)}{4!}\left(x + \tfrac{\pi}{4}\right)^4 + \cdots$$

$$= \tfrac{\sqrt{2}}{2}\left[1 + \left(x + \tfrac{\pi}{4}\right) - \tfrac{1}{2!}\left(x + \tfrac{\pi}{4}\right)^2 \right.$$

$$\left. - \tfrac{1}{3!}\left(x + \tfrac{\pi}{4}\right)^3 + \tfrac{1}{4!}\left(x + \tfrac{\pi}{4}\right)^4 + \cdots\right]$$

$$= \tfrac{\sqrt{2}}{2}\left[1 - \tfrac{1}{2!}\left(x + \tfrac{\pi}{4}\right)^2 + \tfrac{1}{4!}\left(x + \tfrac{\pi}{4}\right)^4 - \cdots\right]$$

$$+ \tfrac{\sqrt{2}}{2}\left[\left(x + \tfrac{\pi}{4}\right) - \tfrac{1}{3!}\left(x + \tfrac{\pi}{4}\right)^3 + \cdots\right]$$

$$= \tfrac{\sqrt{2}}{2}\sum_{n=0}^{\infty}(-1)^n\left[\tfrac{1}{(2n)!}\left(x + \tfrac{\pi}{4}\right)^{2n} + \tfrac{1}{(2n+1)!}\left(x + \tfrac{\pi}{4}\right)^{2n+1}\right]$$

The series can also be written in the more elegant form $\dfrac{\sqrt{2}}{2}\displaystyle\sum_{n=0}^{\infty}\dfrac{(-1)^{n(n-1)/2}\left(x + \tfrac{\pi}{4}\right)^n}{n!}$ with $R = \infty$ by the Ratio Test (as in Exercise 13).

15. If $f(x) = \cos x$, then by Formula 9 with $a = 0$, $|R_n(x)| \le \dfrac{\left|f^{(n+1)}(x)\right|}{(n+1)!}|x|^{n+1}$. But $f^{(n+1)}(x) = \pm\sin x$ or $\pm\cos x$. In each case, $\left|f^{(n+1)}(x)\right| \le 1$, so $|R_n(x)| \le \dfrac{1}{(n+1)!}|x|^{n+1} \to 0$ as $n \to \infty$ by Equation 10. So $\lim\limits_{n\to\infty} R_n(x) = 0$ and, by Theorem 8, the series in Exercise 3 represents $\cos x$ for all x.

16. If $f(x) = \sin x$, then by Formula 9 with $a = \tfrac{\pi}{4}$, $|R_n(x)| \le \dfrac{\left|f^{(n+1)}(x)\right|}{(n+1)!}\left|x - \tfrac{\pi}{4}\right|^{n+1}$. But $f^{(n+1)}(x) = \pm\sin x$ or $\pm\cos x$. In each case, $\left|f^{(n+1)}(x)\right| \le 1$, so $|R_n(x)| \le \dfrac{1}{(n+1)!}\left|x - \tfrac{\pi}{4}\right|^{n+1} \to 0$ as $n \to \infty$ by Equation 10. So $\lim\limits_{n\to\infty} R_n(x) = 0$ and, by Theorem 8, the series in Exercise 13 represents $\sin x$ for all x.

17. $\cos x = \displaystyle\sum_{n=0}^{\infty}(-1)^n\dfrac{x^{2n}}{(2n)!} \quad\Rightarrow\quad f(x) = \cos(\pi x) = \displaystyle\sum_{n=0}^{\infty}\dfrac{(-1)^n(\pi x)^{2n}}{(2n)!} = \displaystyle\sum_{n=0}^{\infty}\dfrac{(-1)^n\pi^{2n}x^{2n}}{(2n)!}, R = \infty$

18. $e^x = \displaystyle\sum_{n=0}^{\infty}\dfrac{x^n}{n!} \quad\Rightarrow\quad f(x) = e^{-x/2} = \displaystyle\sum_{n=0}^{\infty}\dfrac{(-x/2)^n}{n!} = \displaystyle\sum_{n=0}^{\infty}\dfrac{(-1)^n}{2^n\,n!}x^n, R = \infty$

19. $\tan^{-1}x = \displaystyle\sum_{n=0}^{\infty}(-1)^n\dfrac{x^{2n+1}}{2n+1} \quad\Rightarrow\quad f(x) = x\tan^{-1}x = x\displaystyle\sum_{n=0}^{\infty}(-1)^n\dfrac{x^{2n+1}}{2n+1} = \displaystyle\sum_{n=0}^{\infty}(-1)^n\dfrac{x^{2n+2}}{2n+1}, R = 1$

20. $\sin x = \displaystyle\sum_{n=0}^{\infty}(-1)^n\dfrac{x^{2n+1}}{(2n+1)!} \quad\Rightarrow\quad f(x) = \sin(x^4) = \displaystyle\sum_{n=0}^{\infty}(-1)^n\dfrac{(x^4)^{2n+1}}{(2n+1)!} = \displaystyle\sum_{n=0}^{\infty}\dfrac{(-1)^n}{(2n+1)!}x^{8n+4}, R = \infty$

21. $e^x = \displaystyle\sum_{n=0}^{\infty}\dfrac{x^n}{n!} \quad\Rightarrow\quad f(x) = x^2e^{-x} = x^2\displaystyle\sum_{n=0}^{\infty}\dfrac{(-x)^n}{n!} = \displaystyle\sum_{n=0}^{\infty}\dfrac{(-1)^n\,x^{n+2}}{n!}, R = \infty$

22. $\cos x = \sum\limits_{n=0}^{\infty} (-1)^n \dfrac{x^{2n}}{(2n)!}$ $\Rightarrow$ $\cos 2x = \sum\limits_{n=0}^{\infty} (-1)^n \dfrac{(2x)^{2n}}{(2n)!} = \sum\limits_{n=0}^{\infty} \dfrac{(-1)^n \, 2^{2n}}{(2n)!} x^{2n}$ $\Rightarrow$

$f(x) = x\cos 2x = \sum\limits_{n=0}^{\infty} \dfrac{(-1)^n \, 2^{2n}}{(2n)!} x^{2n+1}, \ R = \infty$

23. $\sin^2 x = \tfrac{1}{2}[1 - \cos 2x] = \dfrac{1}{2}\left[1 - \sum\limits_{n=0}^{\infty} \dfrac{(-1)^n (2x)^{2n}}{(2n)!}\right] = 2^{-1}\left[1 - 1 - \sum\limits_{n=1}^{\infty} \dfrac{(-1)^n (2x)^{2n}}{(2n)!}\right]$

$= \sum\limits_{n=1}^{\infty} \dfrac{(-1)^{n+1} 2^{2n-1} x^{2n}}{(2n)!}, \ R = \infty$

24. $\dfrac{\sin x}{x} = \dfrac{1}{x} \sum\limits_{n=0}^{\infty} \dfrac{(-1)^n x^{2n+1}}{(2n+1)!} = \sum\limits_{n=0}^{\infty} \dfrac{(-1)^n x^{2n}}{(2n+1)!}$ and this series also gives the required value at $x = 0$ (namely 1),

so $R = \infty$.

25.

n	$f^{(n)}(x)$	$f^{(n)}(0)$
0	$(1+x)^{1/2}$	1
1	$\tfrac{1}{2}(1+x)^{-1/2}$	$\tfrac{1}{2}$
2	$-\tfrac{1}{4}(1+x)^{-3/2}$	$-\tfrac{1}{4}$
3	$\tfrac{3}{8}(1+x)^{-5/2}$	$\tfrac{3}{8}$
4	$-\tfrac{15}{16}(1+x)^{-7/2}$	$-\tfrac{15}{16}$
$\vdots$	$\vdots$	$\vdots$

So $f^{(n)}(0) = \dfrac{(-1)^{n-1} 1 \cdot 3 \cdot 5 \cdot \,\cdots\, \cdot (2n-3)}{2^n}$ for $n \geq 2$, and

$\sqrt{1+x} = 1 + \dfrac{x}{2} + \sum\limits_{n=2}^{\infty} \dfrac{(-1)^{n-1} 1 \cdot 3 \cdot 5 \cdot \,\cdots\, \cdot (2n-3)}{2^n n!} x^n$. If $a_n = \dfrac{(-1)^{n-1} 1 \cdot 3 \cdot 5 \cdot \,\cdots\, \cdot (2n-3)}{2^n n!} x^n$,

then $\lim\limits_{n \to \infty} \left| \dfrac{a_{n+1}}{a_n} \right| = \lim\limits_{n \to \infty} \left| \dfrac{1 \cdot 3 \cdot 5 \cdot \,\cdots\, \cdot (2n-3)(2n-1)x^{n+1}}{2^{n+1}(n+1)!} \cdot \dfrac{2^n n!}{1 \cdot 3 \cdot 5 \cdot \,\cdots\, \cdot (2n-3)x^n} \right|$

$= \dfrac{|x|}{2} \lim\limits_{n \to \infty} \dfrac{2n-1}{n+1} = \dfrac{|x|}{2} \cdot 2 = |x| < 1$ for convergence, so $R = 1$.

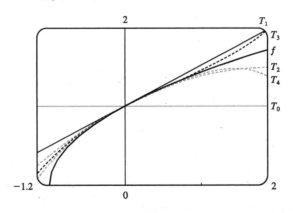

Notice that, as n increases, $T_n(x)$ becomes a better approximation to $f(x)$ for $-1 < x < 1$.

26.

n	$f^{(n)}(x)$	$f^{(n)}(0)$
0	$(1+2x)^{-1/2}$	1
1	$-\frac{1}{2}(1+2x)^{-3/2}(2)$	-1
2	$\frac{3}{2}(1+2x)^{-5/2}(2)$	3
3	$-3 \cdot \frac{5}{2}(1+2x)^{-7/2}(2)$	$-3 \cdot 5$
⋮	⋮	⋮

$f^{(n)}(0) = (-1)^n \, 1 \cdot 3 \cdot 5 \cdot 7 \cdots (2n-1)$, so

$$(1+2x)^{-1/2} = \sum_{n=0}^{\infty} \frac{f^{(n)}(0)}{n!} x^n$$

$$= \sum_{n=0}^{\infty} \frac{(-1)^n \, 1 \cdot 3 \cdot 5 \cdots (2n-1)}{n!} x^n$$

$\displaystyle\lim_{n\to\infty} \left| \frac{a_{n+1}}{a_n} \right| = \lim_{n\to\infty} \frac{2n+1}{n+1} |x| = 2|x| < 1$ for

convergence, so $R = \frac{1}{2}$.

Another method: Use Exercise 25 and differentiate.

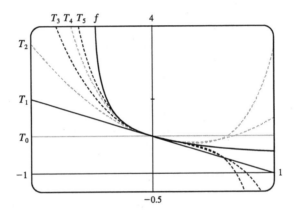

Notice that, as n increases, $T_n(x)$ becomes a better approximation to $f(x)$ for $-0.5 < x < 0.5$.

27. $\cos x = \displaystyle\sum_{n=0}^{\infty} (-1)^n \frac{x^{2n}}{(2n)!} \quad \Rightarrow \quad f(x) = \cos(x^2) = \sum_{n=0}^{\infty} \frac{(-1)^n \left(x^2\right)^{2n}}{(2n)!} = \sum_{n=0}^{\infty} \frac{(-1)^n x^{4n}}{(2n)!}, \; R = \infty$

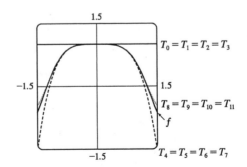

Notice that, as n increases, $T_n(x)$ becomes a better approximation to $f(x)$.

28. $2^x = \left(e^{\ln 2}\right)^x$

$\qquad = e^{x \ln 2}$

$\qquad = \displaystyle\sum_{n=0}^{\infty} \frac{(x \ln 2)^n}{n!}$

$\qquad = \displaystyle\sum_{n=0}^{\infty} \frac{(\ln 2)^n x^n}{n!}, \ R = \infty.$

Notice that, as n increases, $T_n(x)$ becomes
a better approximation to $f(x)$.

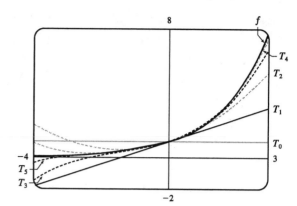

29. $e^x = \displaystyle\sum_{n=0}^{\infty} \frac{x^n}{n!}$, so

$e^{-0.2} = \displaystyle\sum_{n=0}^{\infty} \frac{(-0.2)^n}{n!} = 1 - 0.2 + \frac{1}{2!}(0.2)^2 - \frac{1}{3!}(0.2)^3 + \frac{1}{4!}(0.2)^4 - \frac{1}{5!}(0.2)^5 + \frac{1}{6!}(0.2)^6 - \cdots.$ But

$\dfrac{1}{6!}(0.2)^6 = 8.\overline{8} \times 10^{-8}$, so by the Alternating Series Estimation Theorem, $e^{-0.2} \approx \displaystyle\sum_{n=0}^{5} \frac{(-0.2)^n}{n!} \approx 0.81873,$

correct to five decimal places.

30. $3° = \frac{\pi}{60}$ radians and $\sin x = \displaystyle\sum_{n=0}^{\infty} \frac{(-1)^n x^{2n+1}}{(2n+1)!}$, so

$\sin \frac{\pi}{60} = \frac{\pi}{60} - \frac{\left(\frac{\pi}{60}\right)^3}{3!} + \frac{\left(\frac{\pi}{60}\right)^5}{5!} - \cdots = \frac{\pi}{60} - \frac{\pi^3}{1{,}296{,}000} + \frac{\pi^5}{93{,}312{,}000{,}000} - \cdots.$

But $\dfrac{\pi^5}{93{,}312{,}000{,}000} < 10^{-8}$, so by the Alternating Series Estimation Theorem,

$\sin \frac{\pi}{60} \approx \frac{\pi}{60} - \frac{\pi^3}{1{,}296{,}000} \approx 0.05234.$

31. $\displaystyle\int \sin(x^2)\, dx = \int \sum_{n=0}^{\infty} (-1)^n \frac{(x^2)^{2n+1}}{(2n+1)!}\, dx = \int \sum_{n=0}^{\infty} \frac{(-1)^n x^{4n+2}}{(2n+1)!}\, dx = C + \sum_{n=0}^{\infty} \frac{(-1)^n x^{4n+3}}{(4n+3)(2n+1)!}$

32. $\dfrac{\sin x}{x} = \dfrac{1}{x} \displaystyle\sum_{n=0}^{\infty} \frac{(-1)^n x^{2n+1}}{(2n+1)!} = \sum_{n=0}^{\infty} \frac{(-1)^n x^{2n}}{(2n+1)!}$, so

$\displaystyle\int \frac{\sin x}{x}\, dx = \int \sum_{n=0}^{\infty} \frac{(-1)^n x^{2n}}{(2n+1)!}\, dx = C + \sum_{n=0}^{\infty} \frac{(-1)^n x^{2n+1}}{(2n+1)(2n+1)!}$

33. Using the series from Exercise 25 and substituting x^3 for x, we get

$$\int \sqrt{x^3 + 1}\, dx = \int \left[1 + \frac{x^3}{2} + \sum_{n=2}^{\infty} \frac{(-1)^{n-1} 1 \cdot 3 \cdot 5 \cdots (2n-3)}{2^n n!} x^{3n}\right] dx$$

$$= C + x + \frac{x^4}{8} + \sum_{n=2}^{\infty} \frac{(-1)^{n-1} 1 \cdot 3 \cdot 5 \cdots (2n-3)}{2^n n!(3n+1)} x^{3n+1}$$

34. $\displaystyle\int e^{x^3}\, dx = \int \sum_{n=0}^{\infty} \frac{(x^3)^n}{n!}\, dx = C + \sum_{n=0}^{\infty} \frac{x^{3n+1}}{(3n+1)n!}$

35. Using our series from Exercise 31, we get

$$\int_0^1 \sin(x^2)\, dx = \sum_{n=0}^\infty \left[\frac{(-1)^n\, x^{4n+3}}{(4n+3)(2n+1)!}\right]_0^1 = \sum_{n=0}^\infty \frac{(-1)^n}{(4n+3)(2n+1)!} \text{ and}$$

$$|c_3| = \frac{1}{75{,}600} < 0.000014,\text{ so by the Alternating Series Estimation Theorem, we have}$$

$$\int_0^1 \sin(x^2)\, dx \approx \sum_{n=0}^2 \frac{(-1)^n}{(4n+3)(2n+1)!} = \frac{1}{3} - \frac{1}{42} + \frac{1}{1320} \approx 0.310 \text{ (correct to three decimal places)}.$$

36. $\cos(x^2) = \sum_{n=0}^\infty \dfrac{(-1)^n\, (x^2)^{2n}}{(2n)!}$, so

$$\int_0^{0.5} \cos(x^2)\, dx = \int_0^{0.5} \sum_{n=0}^\infty \frac{(-1)^n\, x^{4n}}{(2n)!}\, dx = \sum_{n=0}^\infty \left[\frac{(-1)^n\, x^{4n+1}}{(4n+1)(2n)!}\right]_0^{0.5} = 0.5 - \frac{(0.5)^5}{5\cdot 2!} + \frac{(0.5)^9}{9\cdot 4!} - \cdots, \text{ but}$$

$$\frac{(0.5)^9}{9\cdot 4!} \approx 0.000009,\text{ so by the Alternating Series Estimation Theorem, } \int_0^{0.5} \cos(x^2)\, dx \approx 0.5 - \frac{(0.5)^5}{5\cdot 2!} \approx 0.497$$

(correct to three decimal places).

37. We first find a series representation for $f(x) = (1+x)^{-1/2}$, and then substitute.

n	$f^{(n)}(x)$	$f^{(n)}(0)$
0	$(1+x)^{-1/2}$	1
1	$-\frac{1}{2}(1+x)^{-3/2}$	$-\frac{1}{2}$
2	$\frac{3}{4}(1+x)^{-5/2}$	$\frac{3}{4}$
3	$-\frac{15}{8}(1+x)^{-7/2}$	$-\frac{15}{8}$
$\vdots$	$\vdots$	$\vdots$

$$\frac{1}{\sqrt{1+x}} = 1 - \frac{x}{2} + \frac{3}{4}\left(\frac{x^2}{2!}\right) - \frac{15}{8}\left(\frac{x^3}{3!}\right) + \cdots \quad \Rightarrow \quad \frac{1}{\sqrt{1+x^3}} = 1 - \frac{1}{2}x^3 + \frac{3}{8}x^6 - \frac{5}{16}x^9 + \cdots \quad \Rightarrow$$

$$\int_0^{0.1} \frac{dx}{\sqrt{1+x^3}} = \left[x - \frac{1}{8}x^4 + \frac{3}{56}x^7 - \frac{1}{32}x^{10} + \cdots\right]_0^{0.1} \approx (0.1) - \frac{1}{8}(0.1)^4,\text{ by the Alternating Series}$$

Estimation Theorem, since $\frac{3}{56}(0.1)^7 \approx 0.0000000054 < 10^{-8}$, which is the maximum desired error. Therefore,

$$\int_0^{0.1} \frac{dx}{\sqrt{1+x^3}} \approx 0.09998750.$$

38. $\int_0^{0.5} x^2 e^{-x^2}\, dx = \int_0^{0.5} \sum_{n=0}^\infty \frac{(-1)^n\, x^{2n+2}}{n!}\, dx = \sum_{n=0}^\infty \left[\frac{(-1)^n\, x^{2n+3}}{n!(2n+3)}\right]_0^{1/2} = \sum_{n=0}^\infty \frac{(-1)^n}{n!(2n+3)2^{2n+3}}$ and since

$$c_2 = \frac{1}{1792} < 0.001 \text{ we use } \sum_{n=0}^1 \frac{(-1)^n}{n!(2n+3)2^{2n+3}} = \frac{1}{24} - \frac{1}{160} \approx 0.0354.$$

39. $\displaystyle\lim_{x\to 0} \frac{x - \tan^{-1}x}{x^3} = \lim_{x\to 0} \frac{x - \left(x - \frac{1}{3}x^3 + \frac{1}{5}x^5 - \frac{1}{7}x^7 + \cdots\right)}{x^3} = \lim_{x\to 0} \frac{\frac{1}{3}x^3 - \frac{1}{5}x^5 + \frac{1}{7}x^7 - \cdots}{x^3}$

$$= \lim_{x\to 0}\left(\tfrac{1}{3} - \tfrac{1}{5}x^2 + \tfrac{1}{7}x^4 - \cdots\right) = \tfrac{1}{3}$$

since power series are continuous functions.

40. $\displaystyle\lim_{x\to0}\frac{1-\cos x}{1+x-e^x}=\lim_{x\to0}\frac{1-\left(1-\frac{1}{2!}x^2+\frac{1}{4!}x^4-\frac{1}{6!}x^6+\cdots\right)}{1+x-\left(1+x+\frac{1}{2!}x^2+\frac{1}{3!}x^3+\frac{1}{4!}x^4+\frac{1}{5!}x^5+\frac{1}{6!}x^6+\cdots\right)}$

$\displaystyle=\lim_{x\to0}\frac{\frac{1}{2!}x^2-\frac{1}{4!}x^4+\frac{1}{6!}x^6-\cdots}{-\frac{1}{2!}x^2-\frac{1}{3!}x^3-\frac{1}{4!}x^4-\frac{1}{5!}x^5-\frac{1}{6!}x^6-\cdots}$

$\displaystyle=\lim_{x\to0}\frac{\frac{1}{2!}-\frac{1}{4!}x^2+\frac{1}{6!}x^4-\cdots}{-\frac{1}{2!}-\frac{1}{3!}x-\frac{1}{4!}x^2-\frac{1}{5!}x^3-\frac{1}{6!}x^4-\cdots}=\frac{\frac{1}{2}-0}{-\frac{1}{2}-0}=-1$

since power series are continuous functions.

41. $\displaystyle\lim_{x\to0}\frac{\sin x-x+\frac{1}{6}x^3}{x^5}=\lim_{x\to0}\frac{\left(x-\frac{1}{3!}x^3+\frac{1}{5!}x^5-\frac{1}{7!}x^7+\cdots\right)-x+\frac{1}{6}x^3}{x^5}$

$\displaystyle=\lim_{x\to0}\frac{\frac{1}{5!}x^5-\frac{1}{7!}x^7+\cdots}{x^5}=\lim_{x\to0}\left(\frac{1}{5!}-\frac{x^2}{7!}+\frac{x^4}{9!}-\cdots\right)=\frac{1}{5!}=\frac{1}{120}$

since power series are continuous functions.

42. $\displaystyle\lim_{x\to0}\frac{\tan x-x}{x^3}=\lim_{x\to0}\frac{\left(x+\frac{1}{3}x^3+\frac{2}{15}x^5+\cdots\right)-x}{x^3}=\lim_{x\to0}\frac{\frac{1}{3}x^3+\frac{2}{15}x^5+\cdots}{x^3}=\lim_{x\to0}\left(\frac{1}{3}+\frac{2}{15}x^2+\cdots\right)=\frac{1}{3}$

since power series are continuous functions.

43. As in Example 8(a), we have $e^{-x^2}=1-\dfrac{x^2}{1!}+\dfrac{x^4}{2!}-\dfrac{x^6}{3!}+\cdots$ and we know that $\cos x=1-\dfrac{x^2}{2!}+\dfrac{x^4}{4!}-\cdots$

from Equation 16. Therefore, $e^{-x^2}\cos x=\left(1-x^2+\frac{1}{2}x^4-\cdots\right)\left(1-\frac{1}{2}x^2+\frac{1}{24}x^4-\cdots\right)$. Writing only the

terms with degree ≤4, we get $e^{-x^2}\cos x=1-\frac{1}{2}x^2+\frac{1}{24}x^4-x^2+\frac{1}{2}x^4+\frac{1}{2}x^4+\cdots=1-\frac{3}{2}x^2+\frac{25}{24}x^4+\cdots$.

44.

$$
\begin{array}{r}
1+\frac{1}{2}x^2+\frac{5}{24}x^4+\cdots \\
1-\frac{1}{2}x^2+\frac{1}{24}x^4-\cdots\overline{\smash{\big)}\,1} \\
\underline{1-\frac{1}{2}x^2+\frac{1}{24}x^4-\cdots} \\
\frac{1}{2}x^2-\frac{1}{24}x^4+\cdots \\
\underline{\frac{1}{2}x^2-\frac{1}{4}x^4+\cdots} \\
\frac{5}{24}x^4+\cdots \\
\underline{\frac{5}{24}x^4+\cdots} \\
\cdots
\end{array}
$$

$\sec x=\dfrac{1}{\cos x}=\dfrac{1}{1-\frac{1}{2}x^2+\frac{1}{24}x^4-\cdots}$.

From the long division above,

$\sec x=1+\frac{1}{2}x^2+\frac{5}{24}x^4+\cdots$.

45.

$$
\begin{array}{r}
-x+\frac{1}{2}x^2-\frac{1}{3}x^3+\cdots \\
1+x+\frac{1}{2}x^2+\frac{1}{6}x^3+\cdots\overline{\smash{\big)}\,-x-\frac{1}{2}x^2-\frac{1}{3}x^3-\cdots} \\
\underline{-x-x^2-\frac{1}{2}x^3-\cdots} \\
\frac{1}{2}x^2+\frac{1}{6}x^3-\cdots \\
\underline{\frac{1}{2}x^2+\frac{1}{2}x^3+\cdots} \\
-\frac{1}{3}x^3+\cdots \\
\underline{-\frac{1}{3}x^3+\cdots} \\
\cdots
\end{array}
$$

From Example 6 in Section 8.6, we have

$\ln(1-x)=-x-\frac{1}{2}x^2-\frac{1}{3}x^3-\cdots,\ |x|<1$.

Therefore,

$y=\dfrac{\ln(1-x)}{e^x}=\dfrac{-x-\frac{1}{2}x^2-\frac{1}{3}x^3-\cdots}{1+x+\frac{1}{2}x^2+\frac{1}{6}x^3+\cdots}$.

So by the long division above,

$\dfrac{\ln(1-x)}{e^x}=-x+\dfrac{x^2}{2}-\dfrac{x^3}{3}+\cdots,\ |x|<1$.

46. From Example 6 in Section 8.6, we have $\ln(1-x) = -x - \frac{1}{2}x^2 - \frac{1}{3}x^3 - \cdots$, $|x| < 1$. Therefore,

$$e^x \ln(1-x) = \left(1 + x + \frac{1}{2}x^2 + \cdots\right)\left(-x - \frac{1}{2}x^2 - \frac{1}{3}x^3 - \cdots\right)$$

$$= -x - \frac{1}{2}x^2 - \frac{1}{3}x^3 - x^2 - \frac{1}{2}x^3 - \frac{1}{2}x^3 - \cdots$$

$$= -x - \frac{3}{2}x^2 - \frac{4}{3}x^3 - \cdots, \quad |x| < 1$$

47. $\displaystyle\sum_{n=0}^{\infty}(-1)^n\frac{x^{4n}}{n!} = \sum_{n=0}^{\infty}\frac{\left(-x^4\right)^n}{n!} = e^{-x^4}$, by (11).

48. $\displaystyle\sum_{n=0}^{\infty}\frac{(-1)^n\,\pi^{2n}}{6^{2n}(2n)!} = \sum_{n=0}^{\infty}(-1)^n\frac{\left(\frac{\pi}{6}\right)^{2n}}{(2n)!} = \cos\frac{\pi}{6} = \frac{\sqrt{3}}{2}$, by (16).

49. $\displaystyle\sum_{n=0}^{\infty}\frac{(-1)^n\,\pi^{2n+1}}{4^{2n+1}(2n+1)!} = \sum_{n=0}^{\infty}\frac{(-1)^n\left(\frac{\pi}{4}\right)^{2n+1}}{(2n+1)!} = \sin\frac{\pi}{4} = \frac{1}{\sqrt{2}}$, by (15).

50. $\displaystyle\sum_{n=0}^{\infty}\frac{3^n}{5^n\,n!} = \sum_{n=0}^{\infty}\frac{(3/5)^n}{n!} = e^{3/5}$, by (11).

51. $3 + \dfrac{9}{2!} + \dfrac{27}{3!} + \dfrac{81}{4!} + \cdots = \dfrac{3^1}{1!} + \dfrac{3^2}{2!} + \dfrac{3^3}{3!} + \dfrac{3^4}{4!} + \cdots = \displaystyle\sum_{n=1}^{\infty}\dfrac{3^n}{n!} = \sum_{n=0}^{\infty}\dfrac{3^n}{n!} - 1 = e^3 - 1$, by (11).

52. $1 - \ln 2 + \dfrac{(\ln 2)^2}{2!} - \dfrac{(\ln 2)^3}{3!} + \cdots = \displaystyle\sum_{n=0}^{\infty}\dfrac{(-\ln 2)^n}{n!} = e^{-\ln 2} = \left(e^{\ln 2}\right)^{-1} = 2^{-1} = \frac{1}{2}$, by (11).

53. Assume that $|f'''(x)| \le M$, so $f'''(x) \le M$ for $a \le x \le a+d$. Now $\int_a^x f'''(t)\,dt \le \int_a^x M\,dt \;\Rightarrow$

$f''(x) - f''(a) \le M(x-a) \;\Rightarrow\; f''(x) \le f''(a) + M(x-a)$. Thus, $\int_a^x f''(t)\,dt \le \int_a^x [f''(a) + M(t-a)]\,dt$

$\Rightarrow\; f'(x) - f'(a) \le f''(a)(x-a) + \frac{1}{2}M(x-a)^2 \;\Rightarrow\; f'(x) \le f'(a) + f''(a)(x-a) + \frac{1}{2}M(x-a)^2 \;\Rightarrow$

$\int_a^x f'(t)\,dt \le \int_a^x \left[f'(a) + f''(a)(t-a) + \frac{1}{2}M(t-a)^2\right]dt \;\Rightarrow$

$f(x) - f(a) \le f'(a)(x-a) + \frac{1}{2}f''(a)(x-a)^2 + \frac{1}{6}M(x-a)^3$. So

$f(x) - f(a) - f'(a)(x-a) - \frac{1}{2}f''(a)(x-a)^2 \le \frac{1}{6}M(x-a)^3$. But

$R_2(x) = f(x) - T_2(x) = f(x) - f(a) - f'(a)(x-a) - \frac{1}{2}f''(a)(x-a)^2$, so $R_2(x) \le \frac{1}{6}M(x-a)^3$. A similar

argument using $f'''(x) \ge -M$ shows that $R_2(x) \ge -\frac{1}{6}M(x-a)^3$. So $|R_2(x_2)| \le \frac{1}{6}M\,|x-a|^3$.

Although we have assumed that $x > a$, a similar calculation shows that this inequality is also true if $x < a$.

54. (a) $f(x) = \begin{cases} e^{-1/x^2} & \text{if } x \ne 0 \\ 0 & \text{if } x = 0 \end{cases}$ so

$f'(0) = \displaystyle\lim_{x \to 0}\frac{f(x) - f(0)}{x - 0} = \lim_{x \to 0}\frac{e^{-1/x^2}}{x} = \lim_{x \to 0}\frac{1/x}{e^{1/x^2}} = \lim_{x \to 0}\frac{x}{2e^{1/x^2}} = 0$ (using l'Hospital's Rule and

simplifying in the penultimate step). Similarly, we can use the definition of the derivative and l'Hospital's Rule

to show that $f''(0) = 0$, $f^{(3)}(0) = 0, \ldots, f^{(n)}(0) = 0$, so that the Maclaurin series for f consists entirely of

zero terms. But since $f(x) \ne 0$ except for $x = 0$, we see that f cannot equal its Maclaurin series except

at $x = 0$.

(b)

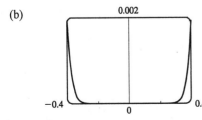

From the graph, it seems that the function is extremely flat at the origin. In fact, it could be said to be "infinitely flat" at $x = 0$, since all of its derivatives are 0 there.

8.8 **The Binomial Series** · · · · · · · · · · · · · · ·

1. The general binomial series in (2) is

$$(1+x)^k = \sum_{n=0}^{\infty} \binom{k}{n} x^n = 1 + kx + \frac{k(k-1)}{2!}x^2 + \frac{k(k-1)(k-2)}{3!}x^3 + \cdots.$$

$$(1+x)^{1/2} = \sum_{n=0}^{\infty} \binom{\frac{1}{2}}{n} x^n = 1 + \left(\tfrac{1}{2}\right)x + \frac{\left(\frac{1}{2}\right)\left(-\frac{1}{2}\right)}{2!}x^2 + \frac{\left(\frac{1}{2}\right)\left(-\frac{1}{2}\right)\left(-\frac{3}{2}\right)}{3!}x^3 + \cdots$$

$$= 1 + \frac{x}{2} - \frac{x^2}{2^2 \cdot 2!} + \frac{1 \cdot 3 \cdot x^3}{2^3 \cdot 3!} - \frac{1 \cdot 3 \cdot 5 \cdot x^4}{2^4 \cdot 4!} + \cdots$$

$$= 1 + \frac{x}{2} + \sum_{n=2}^{\infty} \frac{(-1)^{n-1} 1 \cdot 3 \cdot 5 \cdots \cdots (2n-3)x^n}{2^n \cdot n!} \quad \text{for } |x| < 1, \text{ so } R = 1$$

2. $\dfrac{1}{(1+x)^4} = (1+x)^{-4} = \sum\limits_{n=0}^{\infty} \dbinom{-4}{n} x^n$. The binomial coefficient is

$$\binom{-4}{n} = \frac{(-4)(-5)(-6)\cdots\cdots(-4-n+1)}{n!} = \frac{(-4)(-5)(-6)\cdots\cdots[-(n+3)]}{n!}$$

$$= \frac{(-1)^n \cdot 2 \cdot 3 \cdot 4 \cdot 5 \cdot 6 \cdots\cdots(n+1)(n+2)(n+3)}{2 \cdot 3 \cdot n!} = \frac{(-1)^n(n+1)(n+2)(n+3)}{6}$$

Thus, $\dfrac{1}{(1+x)^4} = \sum\limits_{n=0}^{\infty} \dfrac{(-1)^n(n+1)(n+2)(n+3)}{6} x^n$ for $|x| < 1$, so $R = 1$.

3. $\dfrac{1}{(2+x)^3} = \dfrac{1}{[2(1+x/2)]^3} = \dfrac{1}{8}\left(1+\dfrac{x}{2}\right)^{-3} = \dfrac{1}{8}\sum\limits_{n=0}^{\infty}\dbinom{-3}{n}\left(\dfrac{x}{2}\right)^n$. The binomial coefficient is

$$\binom{-3}{n} = \frac{(-3)(-4)(-5)\cdots\cdots(-3-n+1)}{n!} = \frac{(-3)(-4)(-5)\cdots\cdots[-(n+2)]}{n!}$$

$$= \frac{(-1)^n \cdot 2 \cdot 3 \cdot 4 \cdot 5 \cdots\cdots(n+1)(n+2)}{2 \cdot n!} = \frac{(-1)^n(n+1)(n+2)}{2}$$

Thus, $\dfrac{1}{(2+x)^3} = \dfrac{1}{8}\sum\limits_{n=0}^{\infty}\dfrac{(-1)^n(n+1)(n+2)}{2}\dfrac{x^n}{2^n} = \sum\limits_{n=0}^{\infty}\dfrac{(-1)^n(n+1)(n+2)x^n}{2^{n+4}}$ for $\left|\dfrac{x}{2}\right| < 1 \iff$

$|x| < 2$, so $R = 2$.

4. $(1+x^2)^{1/3} = \sum\limits_{n=0}^{\infty}\dbinom{\frac{1}{3}}{n}x^{2n} = 1 + \dfrac{x^2}{3} + \dfrac{\left(\frac{1}{3}\right)\left(-\frac{2}{3}\right)}{2!}x^4 + \dfrac{\left(\frac{1}{3}\right)\left(-\frac{2}{3}\right)\left(-\frac{5}{3}\right)}{3!}x^6 + \cdots$

$$= 1 + \frac{x^2}{3} + \sum_{n=2}^{\infty} \frac{(-1)^{n-1} \cdot 2 \cdot 5 \cdot 8 \cdots\cdots(3n-4)x^{2n}}{3^n n!}, \text{ with } R = 1.$$

5. We must write the binomial in the form (1+ expression), so we'll factor out a 4.

$$\frac{x}{\sqrt{4+x^2}} = \frac{x}{\sqrt{4(1+x^2/4)}} = \frac{x}{2\sqrt{1+x^2/4}} = \frac{x}{2}\left(1+\frac{x^2}{4}\right)^{-1/2} = \frac{x}{2}\sum_{n=0}^{\infty}\binom{-\frac{1}{2}}{n}\left(\frac{x^2}{4}\right)^n$$

$$= \frac{x}{2}\left[1+\left(-\tfrac{1}{2}\right)\frac{x^2}{4} + \frac{\left(-\frac{1}{2}\right)\left(-\frac{3}{2}\right)}{2!}\left(\frac{x^2}{4}\right)^2 + \frac{\left(-\frac{1}{2}\right)\left(-\frac{3}{2}\right)\left(-\frac{5}{2}\right)}{3!}\left(\frac{x^2}{4}\right)^3 + \cdots\right]$$

$$= \frac{x}{2} + \frac{x}{2}\sum_{n=1}^{\infty}(-1)^n\frac{1\cdot3\cdot5\cdot\cdots\cdot(2n-1)}{2^n\cdot4^n\cdot n!}x^{2n}$$

$$= \frac{x}{2} + \sum_{n=1}^{\infty}(-1)^n\frac{1\cdot3\cdot5\cdot\cdots\cdot(2n-1)}{n!\,2^{3n+1}}x^{2n+1} \text{ and } \frac{x^2}{4} < 1 \Leftrightarrow \frac{|x|}{2} < 1 \Leftrightarrow$$

$|x| < 2$, so $R = 2$.

6.
$$\frac{x^2}{\sqrt{2+x}} = \frac{x^2}{\sqrt{2(1+x/2)}} = \frac{x^2}{\sqrt{2}}\left(1+\frac{x}{2}\right)^{-1/2} = \frac{x^2}{\sqrt{2}}\sum_{n=0}^{\infty}\binom{-\frac{1}{2}}{n}\left(\frac{x}{2}\right)^n$$

$$= \frac{x^2}{\sqrt{2}}\left[1+\left(-\tfrac{1}{2}\right)\left(\frac{x}{2}\right) + \frac{\left(-\frac{1}{2}\right)\left(-\frac{3}{2}\right)}{2!}\left(\frac{x}{2}\right)^2 + \frac{\left(-\frac{1}{2}\right)\left(-\frac{3}{2}\right)\left(-\frac{5}{2}\right)}{3!}\left(\frac{x}{2}\right)^3 + \cdots\right]$$

$$= \frac{x^2}{\sqrt{2}} + \frac{x^2}{\sqrt{2}}\sum_{n=1}^{\infty}(-1)^n\frac{1\cdot3\cdot5\cdot\cdots\cdot(2n-1)}{n!\,2^{2n}}x^n$$

$$= \frac{x^2}{\sqrt{2}} + \sum_{n=1}^{\infty}(-1)^n\frac{1\cdot3\cdot5\cdot\cdots\cdot(2n-1)}{n!\,2^{2n+1/2}}x^{n+2} \text{ and } \left|\frac{x}{2}\right| < 1 \Leftrightarrow |x| < 2, \text{ so } R = 2.$$

7.
$$\frac{1}{\sqrt[3]{8+x}} = \frac{1}{\sqrt[3]{8(1+x/8)}} = \frac{1}{\sqrt[3]{8}\sqrt[3]{1+x/8}} = \frac{1}{2}\left(1+\frac{x}{8}\right)^{-1/3}$$

$$= \frac{1}{2}\left[1+\left(-\frac{1}{3}\right)\left(\frac{x}{8}\right) + \frac{\left(-\frac{1}{3}\right)\left(-\frac{4}{3}\right)}{2!}\left(\frac{x}{8}\right)^2 + \frac{\left(-\frac{1}{3}\right)\left(-\frac{4}{3}\right)\left(-\frac{7}{3}\right)}{3!}\left(\frac{x}{8}\right)^3 + \cdots\right]$$

$$= \frac{1}{2}\left[1+\sum_{n=1}^{\infty}\frac{(-1)^n 1\cdot4\cdot7\cdot\cdots\cdot(3n-2)}{3^n\cdot n!\,8^n}x^n\right]$$

$$= \frac{1}{2} + \frac{1}{2}\sum_{n=1}^{\infty}\frac{(-1)^n 1\cdot4\cdot7\cdot\cdots\cdot(3n-2)}{24^n\,n!}x^n \text{ and } \left|\frac{x}{8}\right| < 1 \Leftrightarrow |x| < 8, \text{ so } R = 8.$$

The three Taylor polynomials are $T_1(x) = \frac{1}{2} - \frac{1}{48}x$, $T_2(x) = \frac{1}{2} - \frac{1}{48}x + \frac{1}{576}x^2$, and

$T_3(x) = \frac{1}{2} - \frac{1}{48}x + \frac{1}{576}x^2 - \frac{7}{41,472}x^3$.

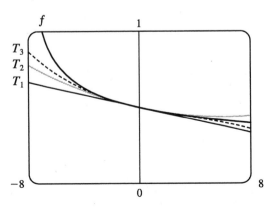

8. $(4+x)^{3/2} = \left[4\left(1+\frac{x}{4}\right)\right]^{3/2} = 4^{3/2}\left(1+\frac{x}{4}\right)^{3/2} = 8\left(1+\frac{x}{4}\right)^{3/2} = 8\sum_{n=0}^{\infty}\binom{\frac{3}{2}}{n}\left(\frac{x}{4}\right)^n$

$= 8\left[1+\frac{3}{2}\left(\frac{x}{4}\right)+\frac{\left(\frac{3}{2}\right)\left(\frac{1}{2}\right)}{2!}\left(\frac{x}{4}\right)^2+\frac{\left(\frac{3}{2}\right)\left(\frac{1}{2}\right)\left(-\frac{1}{2}\right)}{3!}\left(\frac{x}{4}\right)^3+\cdots\right]$

$= 8+3x+\sum_{n=2}^{\infty}\frac{(3)(1)(-1)\cdots\cdots(5-2n)x^n}{8^{n-1}\cdot n!}$ and $\left|\frac{x}{4}\right|<1 \iff |x|<4$, so $R=4$.

The three Taylor polynomials are $T_1(x) = 8+3x$, $T_2(x) = 8+3x+\frac{3}{16}x^2$, and
$T_3(x) = 8+3x+\frac{3}{16}x^2-\frac{1}{128}x^3$.

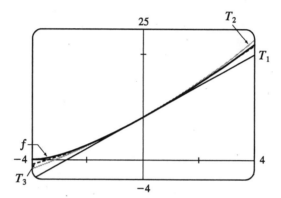

9. (a) $1/\sqrt{1-x^2} = \left[1+\left(-x^2\right)\right]^{-1/2}$

$= 1+\left(-\frac{1}{2}\right)\left(-x^2\right)+\frac{\left(-\frac{1}{2}\right)\left(-\frac{3}{2}\right)}{2!}\left(-x^2\right)^2+\frac{\left(-\frac{1}{2}\right)\left(-\frac{3}{2}\right)\left(-\frac{5}{2}\right)}{3!}\left(-x^2\right)^3+\cdots$

$= 1+\sum_{n=1}^{\infty}\frac{1\cdot3\cdot5\cdots\cdots(2n-1)}{2^n\cdot n!}x^{2n}$

(b) $\sin^{-1}x = \int\frac{1}{\sqrt{1-x^2}}\,dx = C+x+\sum_{n=1}^{\infty}\frac{1\cdot3\cdot5\cdots\cdots(2n-1)}{(2n+1)2^n\cdot n!}x^{2n+1}$

$= x+\sum_{n=1}^{\infty}\frac{1\cdot3\cdot5\cdots\cdots(2n-1)}{(2n+1)2^n\cdot n!}x^{2n+1}$ since $0 = \sin^{-1}0 = C$.

10. (a) $\sqrt[3]{8+x} = \sqrt[3]{8(1+x/8)} = \sqrt[3]{8}\sqrt[3]{1+x/8} = 2\left(1+\frac{x}{8}\right)^{1/3} = 2\sum_{n=0}^{\infty}\binom{\frac{1}{3}}{n}\left(\frac{x}{8}\right)^n$

$= 2\left[1+\frac{1}{3}\left(\frac{x}{8}\right)+\frac{\left(\frac{1}{3}\right)\left(-\frac{2}{3}\right)}{2!}\left(\frac{x}{8}\right)^2+\frac{\left(\frac{1}{3}\right)\left(-\frac{2}{3}\right)\left(-\frac{5}{3}\right)}{3!}\left(\frac{x}{8}\right)^3+\cdots\right]$

$= 2\left[1+\frac{x}{24}+\sum_{n=2}^{\infty}\frac{(-1)^{n-1}\cdot2\cdot5\cdots\cdots(3n-4)x^n}{24^n\cdot n!}\right]$

(b) $(8+0.2)^{1/3} = 2\left[1+\frac{0.2}{24}-\frac{(0.2)^2}{24^2}+\frac{2\cdot5(0.2)^3}{24^3\cdot3!}-\cdots\right]\approx 2\left[1+\frac{0.2}{24}-\frac{(0.2)^2}{24^2}\right]$

since $2\cdot\frac{2\cdot5(0.2)^3}{24^3\cdot3!}\approx 0.000002$, so $\sqrt[3]{8.2}\approx 2.0165$.

11. (a) $[1 + (-x)]^{-2} = 1 + (-2)(-x) + \dfrac{(-2)(-3)}{2!}(-x)^2 + \dfrac{(-2)(-3)(-4)}{3!}(-x)^3 + \cdots$

$$= 1 + 2x + 3x^2 + 4x^3 + \cdots = \sum_{n=0}^{\infty}(n+1)x^n,$$

so $\dfrac{x}{(1-x)^2} = x\sum_{n=0}^{\infty}(n+1)x^n = \sum_{n=0}^{\infty}(n+1)x^{n+1} = \sum_{n=1}^{\infty}nx^n.$

(b) With $x = \frac{1}{2}$ in part (a), we have $\sum_{n=1}^{\infty}n\left(\frac{1}{2}\right)^n = \sum_{n=1}^{\infty}\dfrac{n}{2^n} = \dfrac{\frac{1}{2}}{\left(1-\frac{1}{2}\right)^2} = \dfrac{\frac{1}{2}}{\frac{1}{4}} = 2.$

12. (a) $[1 + (-x)]^{-3} = \sum_{n=0}^{\infty}\binom{-3}{n}(-x)^n$

$$= 1 + (-3)(-x) + \dfrac{(-3)(-4)}{2!}(-x)^2 + \dfrac{(-3)(-4)(-5)}{3!}(-x)^3 + \cdots$$

$$= 1 + \sum_{n=1}^{\infty}\dfrac{3\cdot4\cdot5\cdots\cdots(n+2)}{n!}x^n = \sum_{n=0}^{\infty}\dfrac{2\cdot3\cdot4\cdot5\cdots\cdots(n+2)}{2\cdot n!}x^n$$

$$= \sum_{n=0}^{\infty}\dfrac{(n+1)(n+2)}{2}x^n \quad\Rightarrow$$

$(x + x^2)[1 + (-x)]^{-3} = x[1 + (-x)]^{-3} + x^2[1 + (-x)]^{-3}$

$$= \sum_{n=0}^{\infty}\dfrac{(n+1)(n+2)}{2}x^{n+1} + \sum_{n=0}^{\infty}\dfrac{(n+1)(n+2)}{2}x^{n+2}$$

$$= \sum_{n=1}^{\infty}\dfrac{n(n+1)}{2}x^n + \sum_{n=1}^{\infty}\dfrac{n(n+1)}{2}x^{n+1}$$

$$= x + \sum_{n=2}^{\infty}\dfrac{n(n+1)}{2}x^n + \sum_{n=2}^{\infty}\dfrac{(n-1)n}{2}x^n = x + \sum_{n=2}^{\infty}\left[\dfrac{n(n+1)}{2} + \dfrac{(n-1)n}{2}\right]x^n$$

$$= x + \sum_{n=2}^{\infty}n^2x^n = \sum_{n=1}^{\infty}n^2x^n, \; -1 < x < 1$$

(b) Setting $x = \frac{1}{2}$ in the last series above gives the required series, so $\sum_{n=1}^{\infty}\dfrac{n^2}{2^n} = \dfrac{\frac{1}{2}+\left(\frac{1}{2}\right)^2}{\left(1-\frac{1}{2}\right)^3} = \dfrac{\frac{3}{4}}{\frac{1}{8}} = 6.$

13. (a) $(1 + x^2)^{1/2} = 1 + \left(\frac{1}{2}\right)x^2 + \dfrac{\left(\frac{1}{2}\right)\left(-\frac{1}{2}\right)}{2!}(x^2)^2 + \dfrac{\left(\frac{1}{2}\right)\left(-\frac{1}{2}\right)\left(-\frac{3}{2}\right)}{3!}(x^2)^3 + \cdots$

$$= 1 + \dfrac{x^2}{2} + \sum_{n=2}^{\infty}\dfrac{(-1)^{n-1}1\cdot3\cdot5\cdots\cdots(2n-3)}{2^n\cdot n!}x^{2n}$$

(b) The coefficient of x^{10} (corresponding to $n = 5$) in the above Maclaurin series is $\dfrac{f^{(10)}(0)}{10!}$, so

$$\dfrac{f^{(10)}(0)}{10!} = \dfrac{(-1)^4\cdot1\cdot3\cdot5\cdot7}{2^5\cdot5!} \quad\Rightarrow\quad f^{(10)}(0) = 10!\left(\dfrac{1\cdot3\cdot5\cdot7}{2^5\cdot5!}\right) = 99{,}225.$$

14. (a) $(1 + x^3)^{-1/2} = \sum_{n=0}^{\infty}\binom{-\frac{1}{2}}{n}(x^3)^n$

$$= 1 + \left(-\frac{1}{2}\right)(x^3) + \dfrac{\left(-\frac{1}{2}\right)\left(-\frac{3}{2}\right)}{2!}(x^3)^2 + \dfrac{\left(-\frac{1}{2}\right)\left(-\frac{3}{2}\right)\left(-\frac{5}{2}\right)}{3!}(x^3)^3 + \cdots$$

$$= 1 + \sum_{n=1}^{\infty}\dfrac{(-1)^n1\cdot3\cdot5\cdots\cdots(2n-1)\,x^{3n}}{2^n\cdot n!}$$

(b) The coefficient of x^9 (corresponding to $n = 3$) in the preceding series is

$$\frac{f^{(9)}(0)}{9!}, \text{ so } \frac{f^{(9)}(0)}{9!} = \frac{(-1)^3 \, 1 \cdot 3 \cdot 5}{2^3 \cdot 3!} \quad \Rightarrow \quad f^{(9)}(0) = -\frac{9! \cdot 5}{8 \cdot 2} = -113{,}400.$$

15. (a) $g(x) = \sum\limits_{n=0}^{\infty} \binom{k}{n} x^n \quad \Rightarrow \quad g'(x) = \sum\limits_{n=1}^{\infty} \binom{k}{n} n x^{n-1}$, so

$$(1+x)g'(x) = (1+x) \sum_{n=1}^{\infty} \binom{k}{n} n x^{n-1} = \sum_{n=1}^{\infty} \binom{k}{n} n x^{n-1} + \sum_{n=1}^{\infty} \binom{k}{n} n x^n$$

$$= \sum_{n=0}^{\infty} \binom{k}{n+1} (n+1) x^n + \sum_{n=0}^{\infty} \binom{k}{n} n x^n \quad \begin{bmatrix} \text{Replace } n \text{ with } n+1 \\ \text{in the first series} \end{bmatrix}$$

$$= \sum_{n=0}^{\infty} (n+1) \frac{k(k-1)(k-2)\cdots(k-n+1)(k-n)}{(n+1)!} x^n$$

$$+ \sum_{n=0}^{\infty} \left[(n) \frac{k(k-1)(k-2)\cdots(k-n+1)}{n!} \right] x^n$$

$$= \sum_{n=0}^{\infty} \frac{(n+1)k(k-1)(k-2)\cdots(k-n+1)}{(n+1)!} [(k-n)+n] \, x^n$$

$$= k \sum_{n=0}^{\infty} \frac{k(k-1)(k-2)\cdots(k-n+1)}{n!} x^n = k \sum_{n=0}^{\infty} \binom{k}{n} x^n = kg(x)$$

Thus, $g'(x) = \dfrac{kg(x)}{1+x}$.

(b) $h(x) = (1+x)^{-k} g(x) \quad \Rightarrow$

$$h'(x) = -k(1+x)^{-k-1} g(x) + (1+x)^{-k} g'(x) \quad \text{[Product Rule]}$$

$$= -k(1+x)^{-k-1} g(x) + (1+x)^{-k} \frac{kg(x)}{1+x} \quad \text{[from part (a)]}$$

$$= -k(1+x)^{-k-1} g(x) + k(1+x)^{-k-1} g(x) = 0$$

(c) From part (b) we see that $h(x)$ must be constant for $x \in (-1, 1)$, so $h(x) = h(0) = 1$ for $x \in (-1, 1)$.

Thus, $h(x) = 1 = (1+x)^{-k} g(x) \quad \Leftrightarrow \quad g(x) = (1+x)^k$ for $x \in (-1, 1)$.

16. (a) $4\sqrt{\dfrac{L}{g}} \displaystyle\int_0^{\pi/2} \dfrac{dx}{\sqrt{1 - k^2 \sin^2 x}} = 4\sqrt{\dfrac{L}{g}} \displaystyle\int_0^{\pi/2} \left[1 + (-k^2 \sin^2 x)\right]^{-1/2} dx$

$$= 4\sqrt{\frac{L}{g}} \int_0^{\pi/2} \left[1 - \frac{1}{2}(-k^2 \sin^2 x) + \frac{\frac{1}{2} \cdot \frac{3}{2}}{2!}(-k^2 \sin^2 x)^2 - \frac{\frac{1}{2} \cdot \frac{3}{2} \cdot \frac{5}{2}}{3!}(-k^2 \sin^2 x)^3 + \cdots \right] dx$$

$$= 4\sqrt{\frac{L}{g}} \int_0^{\pi/2} \left[1 + \left(\frac{1}{2}\right) k^2 \sin^2 x + \left(\frac{1 \cdot 3}{2 \cdot 4}\right) k^4 \sin^4 x + \left(\frac{1 \cdot 3 \cdot 5}{2 \cdot 4 \cdot 6}\right) k^6 \sin^6 x + \cdots \right] dx$$

[split up the integral and use the result from Exercise 5.6.36]

$$= 4\sqrt{\frac{L}{g}} \left[\frac{\pi}{2} + \left(\frac{1}{2}\right)\left(\frac{1}{2} \cdot \frac{\pi}{2}\right) k^2 + \left(\frac{1 \cdot 3}{2 \cdot 4}\right)\left(\frac{1 \cdot 3}{2 \cdot 4} \cdot \frac{\pi}{2}\right) k^4 \right.$$

$$\left. + \left(\frac{1 \cdot 3 \cdot 5}{2 \cdot 4 \cdot 6}\right)\left(\frac{1 \cdot 3 \cdot 5}{2 \cdot 4 \cdot 6} \cdot \frac{\pi}{2}\right) k^6 + \cdots \right]$$

$$= 2\pi \sqrt{\frac{L}{g}} \left[1 + \frac{1^2}{2^2} k^2 + \frac{1^2 \cdot 3^2}{2^2 \cdot 4^2} k^4 + \frac{1^2 \cdot 3^2 \cdot 5^2}{2^2 \cdot 4^2 \cdot 6^2} k^6 + \cdots \right]$$

(b) The first of the two inequalities is true because all of the terms in the series are positive. For the second,

$$T = 2\pi \sqrt{\frac{L}{g}} \left[1 + \frac{1^2}{2^2}k^2 + \frac{1^2 \cdot 3^2}{2^2 \cdot 4^2}k^4 + \frac{1^2 \cdot 3^2 \cdot 5^2}{2^2 \cdot 4^2 \cdot 6^2}k^6 + \frac{1^2 \cdot 3^2 \cdot 5^2 \cdot 7^2}{2^2 \cdot 4^2 \cdot 6^2 \cdot 8^2}k^8 + \cdots \right]$$

$$\leq 2\pi \sqrt{\frac{L}{g}} \left[1 + \frac{1}{4}k^2 + \frac{1}{4}k^4 + \frac{1}{4}k^6 + \frac{1}{4}k^8 + \cdots \right]$$

The terms in brackets (after the first) form a geometric series with $a = \frac{1}{4}k^2$ and $r = k^2 = \sin^2\left(\frac{1}{2}\theta_0\right) < 1$.

So $T \leq 2\pi \sqrt{\frac{L}{g}} \left[1 + \frac{k^2/4}{1 - k^2} \right] = 2\pi \sqrt{\frac{L}{g} \frac{4 - 3k^2}{4 - 4k^2}}$.

(c) We substitute $L = 1$, $g = 9.8$, and $k = \sin(10°/2) \approx 0.08716$, and the inequality from part (b) becomes
$2.01090 \leq T \leq 2.01093$, so $T \approx 2.0109$. The estimate $T \approx 2\pi\sqrt{L/g} \approx 2.0071$ differs by about 0.2%.
If $\theta_0 = 42°$, then $k \approx 0.35837$ and the inequality becomes $2.07153 \leq T \leq 2.08103$, so $T \approx 2.0763$. The
one-term estimate is the same, and the discrepancy between the two estimates increases to about 3.4%.

◆8.9◆ Applications of Taylor Polynomials • • • • • • • • •

1. (a)

n	$f^{(n)}(x)$	$f^{(n)}(0)$	$T_n(x)$
0	$\cos x$	1	1
1	$-\sin x$	0	1
2	$-\cos x$	-1	$1 - \frac{1}{2}x^2$
3	$\sin x$	0	$1 - \frac{1}{2}x^2$
4	$\cos x$	1	$1 - \frac{1}{2}x^2 + \frac{1}{24}x^4$
5	$-\sin x$	0	$1 - \frac{1}{2}x^2 + \frac{1}{24}x^4$
6	$-\cos x$	-1	$1 - \frac{1}{2}x^2 + \frac{1}{24}x^4 - \frac{1}{720}x^6$

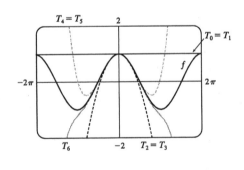

(b)

x	f	$T_0 = T_1$	$T_2 = T_3$	$T_4 = T_5$	T_6
$\frac{\pi}{4}$	0.7071	1	0.6916	0.7074	0.7071
$\frac{\pi}{2}$	0	1	-0.2337	0.0200	-0.0009
π	-1	1	-3.9348	0.1239	-1.2114

(c) As n increases, $T_n(x)$ is a good approximation to $f(x)$ on a larger and larger interval.

2. (a)

n	$f^{(n)}(x)$	$f^{(n)}(1)$	$T_n(x)$
0	x^{-1}	1	1
1	$-x^{-2}$	-1	$1 - (x-1) = 2 - x$
2	$2x^{-3}$	2	$1 - (x-1) + (x-1)^2 = x^2 - 3x + 3$
3	$-6x^{-4}$	-6	$1 - (x-1) + (x-1)^2 - (x-1)^3 = -x^3 + 4x^2 - 6x + 4$

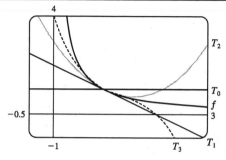

(b)

x	f	T_0	T_1	T_2	T_3
0.9	$1.\overline{1}$	1	1.1	1.11	1.111
1.3	0.7692	1	0.7	0.79	0.763

(c) As n increases, $T_n(x)$ is a good approximation to $f(x)$ on a larger and larger interval.

3.

n	$f^{(n)}(x)$	$f^{(n)}(1)$
0	$\ln x$	0
1	$1/x$	1
2	$-1/x^2$	-1
3	$2/x^3$	2
4	$-6/x^4$	-6

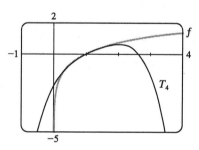

$$T_4(x) = \sum_{n=0}^{4} \frac{f^{(n)}(1)}{n!}(x-1)^n = 0 + (x-1) - \tfrac{1}{2}(x-1)^2 + \tfrac{1}{3}(x-1)^3 - \tfrac{1}{4}(x-1)^4$$

4.

n	$f^{(n)}(x)$	$f^{(n)}(2)$
0	e^x	e^2
1	e^x	e^2
2	e^x	e^2
3	e^x	e^2

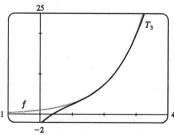

$$T_3(x) = \sum_{n=0}^{3} \frac{f^{(n)}(2)}{n!}(x-2)^n = e^2 + e^2(x-2) + \frac{e^2}{2}(x-2)^2 + \frac{e^2}{6}(x-2)^3$$

5.

n	$f^{(n)}(x)$	$f^{(n)}\left(\frac{\pi}{6}\right)$
0	$\sin x$	$\frac{1}{2}$
1	$\cos x$	$\frac{\sqrt{3}}{2}$
2	$-\sin x$	$-\frac{1}{2}$
3	$-\cos x$	$-\frac{\sqrt{3}}{2}$

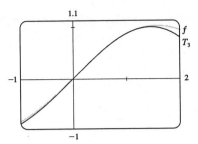

$$T_3(x) = \sum_{n=0}^{3} \frac{f^{(n)}\left(\frac{\pi}{6}\right)}{n!}\left(x - \tfrac{\pi}{6}\right)^n = \tfrac{1}{2} + \tfrac{\sqrt{3}}{2}\left(x - \tfrac{\pi}{6}\right) - \tfrac{1}{4}\left(x - \tfrac{\pi}{6}\right)^2 - \tfrac{\sqrt{3}}{12}\left(x - \tfrac{\pi}{6}\right)^3$$

6.

n	$f^{(n)}(x)$	$f^{(n)}\left(\frac{2\pi}{3}\right)$
0	$\cos x$	$-\frac{1}{2}$
1	$-\sin x$	$-\frac{\sqrt{3}}{2}$
2	$-\cos x$	$\frac{1}{2}$
3	$\sin x$	$\frac{\sqrt{3}}{2}$
4	$\cos x$	$-\frac{1}{2}$

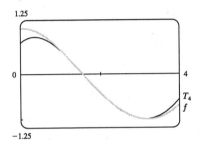

$$T_4(x) = \sum_{n=0}^{4} \frac{f^{(n)}\left(\frac{2\pi}{3}\right)}{n!}\left(x - \tfrac{2\pi}{3}\right)^n = -\tfrac{1}{2} - \tfrac{\sqrt{3}}{2}\left(x - \tfrac{2\pi}{3}\right) + \tfrac{1}{4}\left(x - \tfrac{2\pi}{3}\right)^2 + \tfrac{\sqrt{3}}{12}\left(x - \tfrac{2\pi}{3}\right)^3 - \tfrac{1}{48}\left(x - \tfrac{2\pi}{3}\right)^4$$

7.

n	$f^{(n)}(x)$	$f^{(n)}(0)$
0	$e^x \sin x$	0
1	$e^x(\sin x + \cos x)$	1
2	$2e^x \cos x$	2
3	$2e^x(\cos x - \sin x)$	2

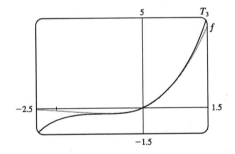

$$T_3(x) = \sum_{n=0}^{3} \frac{f^{(n)}(0)}{n!}x^n = x + x^2 + \tfrac{1}{3}x^3$$

8.

n	$f^{(n)}(x)$	$f^{(n)}(1)$
0	$(3 + x^2)^{1/2}$	2
1	$x(3 + x^2)^{-1/2}$	$\frac{1}{2}$
2	$3(3 + x^2)^{-3/2}$	$\frac{3}{8}$

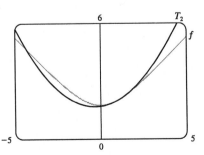

$$T_2(x) = \sum_{n=0}^{2} \frac{f^{(n)}(1)}{n!}(x - 1)^n = 2 + \tfrac{1}{2}(x - 1) + \tfrac{3/8}{2}(x - 1)^2 = 2 + \tfrac{1}{2}(x - 1) + \tfrac{3}{16}(x - 1)^2$$

9. In Maple, we can find the Taylor polynomials by the following method: first define `f:=sec(x);` and then set
`T2:=convert(taylor(f,x=0,3),polynom);`, `T4:=convert(taylor(f,x=0,5),polynom);`,
etc. (The third argument in the `taylor` function is one more than the degree of the desired polynomial). We must
convert to the type `polynom` because the output of the
`taylor` function contains an error term which we do not
want. In Mathematica, we use
`Tn:=Normal[Series[f,{x,0,n}]]`, with n=2, 4,
etc. Note that in Mathematica, the "degree" argument is the
same as the degree of the desired polynomial. In Derive,
author sec x, then enter `Calculus,Taylor,8,0`; and
then simplify the expression. The eighth Taylor polynomial is
$T_8(x) = 1 + \frac{1}{2}x^2 + \frac{5}{24}x^4 + \frac{61}{720}x^6 + \frac{277}{8064}x^8$.

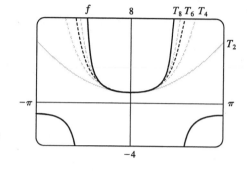

10. See Exercise 9 for the CAS commands used to generate the
Taylor polynomials. The ninth Taylor polynomial for $\tan x$ is
$T_9(x) = x + \frac{1}{3}x^3 + \frac{2}{15}x^5 + \frac{17}{315}x^7 + \frac{62}{2835}x^9$.

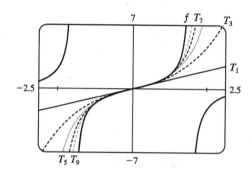

11.

$$f(x) = \sqrt{x} \qquad f(4) = 2$$
$$f'(x) = \frac{1}{2}x^{-1/2} \qquad f'(4) = \frac{1}{4}$$
$$f''(x) = -\frac{1}{4}x^{-3/2} \qquad f''(4) = -\frac{1}{32}$$
$$f'''(x) = \frac{3}{8}x^{-5/2}$$

(a) $f(x) = \sqrt{x} \approx T_2(x) = 2 + \frac{1}{4}(x-4) - \frac{1/32}{2!}(x-4)^2 = 2 + \frac{1}{4}(x-4) - \frac{1}{64}(x-4)^2$

(b) $|R_2(x)| \leq \frac{M}{3!}|x-4|^3$, where $|f'''(x)| \leq M$. Now $4 \leq x \leq 4.2 \;\Rightarrow\; |x-4| \leq 0.2 \;\Rightarrow\;$
$|x-4|^3 \leq 0.008$. Since $f'''(x)$ is decreasing on $[4, 4.2]$, we can take $M = |f'''(4)| = \frac{3}{8}4^{-5/2} = \frac{3}{256}$, so
$|R_2(x)| \leq \frac{3/256}{6}(0.008) = \frac{0.008}{512} = 0.000015625$.

(c) From the graph of $|R_2(x)| = |\sqrt{x} - T_2(x)|$, it seems that the error is
less than 1.52×10^{-5} on $[4, 4.2]$.

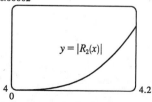

12.
$$f(x) = x^{-2} \qquad f(1) = 1$$
$$f'(x) = -2x^{-3} \qquad f'(1) = -2$$
$$f''(x) = 6x^{-4} \qquad f''(4) = 6$$
$$f'''(x) = -24x^{-5}$$

(a) $f(x) = x^{-2} \approx T_2(x)$
$$= 1 - 2(x - 1) + \tfrac{6}{2!}(x - 1)^2$$
$$= 1 - 2(x - 1) + 3(x - 1)^2$$

(b) $|R_2(x)| \leq \dfrac{M}{3!} |x - 1|^3$, where $|f'''(x)| \leq M$. Now

$0.9 \leq x \leq 1.1 \;\Rightarrow\; |x - 1| \leq 0.1 \;\Rightarrow$

$|x - 1|^3 \leq 0.001$. Since $f'''(x)$ is decreasing on

$[0.9, 1.1]$, we can take $M = |f'''(0.9)| = \frac{24}{(0.9)^5}$, so

$|R_2(x)| \leq \dfrac{24/(0.9)^5}{6}(0.001) = \dfrac{0.004}{0.59049}$
$$\approx 0.00677404$$

(c)

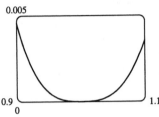

From the graph of $|R_2(x)| = |x^{-2} - T_2(x)|$,
it seems that the error is less than 0.0046
on $[0.9, 1.1]$.

13.
$$f(x) = e^{x^2} \qquad f(0) = 1 \qquad f'''(x) = e^{x^2}(12x + 8x^3) \qquad f'''(0) = 0$$
$$f'(x) = e^{x^2}(2x) \qquad f'(0) = 0 \qquad f^{(4)}(x) = e^{x^2}(12 + 48x^2 + 16x^4)$$
$$f''(x) = e^{x^2}(2 + 4x^2) \qquad f''(0) = 2$$

(a) $f(x) = e^{x^2} \approx T_3(x) = 1 + \tfrac{2}{2!}x^2 = 1 + x^2$

(b) $|R_3(x)| \leq \dfrac{M}{4!} |x|^4$, where $\left|f^{(4)}(x)\right| \leq M$.

Now $0 \leq x \leq 0.1 \;\Rightarrow\; x^4 \leq (0.1)^4$, and

letting $x = 0.1$ gives

$|R_3(x)| \leq \dfrac{e^{0.01}(12 + 0.48 + 0.0016)}{24}(0.1)^4 \approx$

0.00006.

(c)   0.00008

From the graph of

$|R_3(x)| = \left|e^{x^2} - (1 + x^2)\right|$, it appears that

the error is less than 0.000051 on $[0, 0.1]$.

14.
$$f(x) = \cos x \qquad f\!\left(\tfrac{\pi}{3}\right) = \tfrac{1}{2} \qquad f'''(x) = \sin x \qquad f'''\!\left(\tfrac{\pi}{3}\right) = \tfrac{\sqrt{3}}{2}$$
$$f'(x) = -\sin x \qquad f'\!\left(\tfrac{\pi}{3}\right) = -\tfrac{\sqrt{3}}{2} \qquad f^{(4)}(x) = \cos x \qquad f^{(4)}\!\left(\tfrac{\pi}{3}\right) = \tfrac{1}{2}$$
$$f''(x) = -\cos x \qquad f''\!\left(\tfrac{\pi}{3}\right) = -\tfrac{1}{2} \qquad f^{(5)}(x) = -\sin x$$

(a) $f(x) = \cos x \approx T_4(x)$
$$= \tfrac{1}{2} - \tfrac{\sqrt{3}}{2}\left(x - \tfrac{\pi}{3}\right) - \tfrac{1}{4}\left(x - \tfrac{\pi}{3}\right)^2 + \tfrac{\sqrt{3}}{12}\left(x - \tfrac{\pi}{3}\right)^3 + \tfrac{1}{48}\left(x - \tfrac{\pi}{3}\right)^4$$

(b) $|R_4(x)| \leq \dfrac{M}{5!} \left|x - \tfrac{\pi}{3}\right|^5$, where $\left|f^{(5)}(x)\right| \leq M$. Now $0 \leq x \leq \tfrac{2\pi}{3} \;\Rightarrow\; \left(x - \tfrac{\pi}{3}\right)^5 \leq \left(\tfrac{\pi}{3}\right)^5$, and letting

$x = \tfrac{\pi}{2}$ gives $M = 1$, so $|R_4(x)| \leq \tfrac{1}{5!}\left(\tfrac{\pi}{3}\right)^5 \approx 0.0105$.

(c)

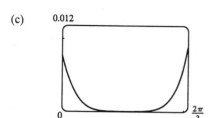

0.012

0      $\frac{2\pi}{3}$

From the graph of $|R_4(x)| = |\cos x - T_4(x)|$, it seems that the error is less than 0.01 on $\left[0, \frac{2\pi}{3}\right]$.

15.

$$f(x) = \tan x \qquad\qquad f(0) = 0 \qquad\qquad f'''(x) = 4\sec^2 x \tan^2 x + 2\sec^4 x \qquad\qquad f'''(0) = 2$$

$$f'(x) = \sec^2 x \qquad\qquad f'(0) = 1 \qquad\qquad f^{(4)}(x) = 8\sec^2 x \tan^3 x + 16\sec^4 x \tan x$$

$$f''(x) = 2\sec^2 x \tan x \qquad f''(0) = 0$$

(a) $f(x) = \tan x \approx T_3(x) = x + \frac{1}{3}x^3$

(b) $|R_3(x)| \leq \dfrac{M}{4!}|x|^4$, where $\left|f^{(4)}(x)\right| \leq M$. Now

$0 \leq x \leq \frac{\pi}{6} \ \Rightarrow\ x^4 \leq \left(\frac{\pi}{6}\right)^4$, and letting $x = \frac{\pi}{6}$

gives

$$|R_3(x)| \leq \frac{8\left(\frac{2}{\sqrt{3}}\right)^2\left(\frac{1}{\sqrt{3}}\right)^3 + 16\left(\frac{2}{\sqrt{3}}\right)^4\left(\frac{1}{\sqrt{3}}\right)}{4!}\left(\frac{\pi}{6}\right)^4$$

$$= \tfrac{4\sqrt{3}}{9}\left(\tfrac{\pi}{6}\right)^4 \approx 0.057859$$

(c)

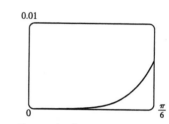

0.01

0      $\frac{\pi}{6}$

From the graph of
$|R_3(x)| = |\tan x - T_3(3)|$, it seems that
the error is less than 0.006 on $[0, \pi/6]$.

16.

$$f(x) = \ln(1 + 2x) \qquad\qquad f(1) = \ln 3$$

$$f'(x) = 2/(1 + 2x) \qquad\qquad f'(1) = \tfrac{2}{3}$$

$$f''(x) = -4/(1 + 2x)^2 \qquad\qquad f''(1) = -\tfrac{4}{9} \qquad\qquad f''(1)/2! = -\tfrac{2}{9}$$

$$f'''(x) = 16/(1 + 2x)^3 \qquad\qquad f'''(1) = \tfrac{16}{27} \qquad\qquad f'''(1)/3! = \tfrac{8}{81}$$

$$f^{(4)}(x) = -96/(1 + 2x)^4$$

(a) $f(x) = \ln(1 + 2x) \approx T_3(x)$

$$= \ln 3 + \tfrac{2}{3}(x - 1) - \tfrac{2}{9}(x - 1)^2 + \tfrac{8}{81}(x - 1)^3$$

(b) $|R_3(x)| \leq \dfrac{M}{4!}|x - 1|^4$, where $\left|f^{(4)}(x)\right| \leq M$.

Now $0.5 \leq x \leq 1.5 \ \Rightarrow\ -0.5 \leq x - 1 \leq 0.5$

$\Rightarrow\ |x - 1| \leq 0.5 \ \Rightarrow\ |x - 1|^4 \leq \frac{1}{16}$, and

letting $x = 0.5$ gives $M = 6$, so

$$|R_3(x)| \leq \frac{6}{4!}\cdot\frac{1}{16} = \frac{1}{64} = 0.015625.$$

(c)

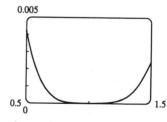

0.005

0.5   1.5

From the graph of
$|R_3(x)| = |\ln(1 + 2x) - T_3(x)|$, it seems
that the error is less than 0.005 on $[0.5, 1.5]$.

17. From Exercise 5, $\sin x = \frac{1}{2} + \frac{\sqrt{3}}{2}\left(x - \frac{\pi}{6}\right) - \frac{1}{4}\left(x - \frac{\pi}{6}\right)^2 - \frac{\sqrt{3}}{12}\left(x - \frac{\pi}{6}\right)^3 + R_3(x)$, where $|R_3(x)| \leq \dfrac{M}{4!}\left|x - \frac{\pi}{6}\right|^4$

with $\left|f^{(4)}(x)\right| = |\sin x| \leq M = 1$. Now $x = 35° = (30° + 5°) = \left(\frac{\pi}{6} + \frac{\pi}{36}\right)$ radians, so the error is

$$\left|R_3\left(\tfrac{\pi}{36}\right)\right| \leq \frac{\left(\frac{\pi}{36}\right)^4}{4!} < 0.000003. \text{ Therefore, to five decimal places,}$$

$$\sin 35° \approx \tfrac{1}{2} + \tfrac{\sqrt{3}}{2}\left(\tfrac{\pi}{36}\right) - \tfrac{1}{4}\left(\tfrac{\pi}{36}\right)^2 - \tfrac{\sqrt{3}}{12}\left(\tfrac{\pi}{36}\right)^3 \approx 0.57358.$$

18. From Exercise 14, $\cos x = \frac{1}{2} - \frac{\sqrt{3}}{2}\left(x - \frac{\pi}{3}\right) - \frac{1}{4}\left(x - \frac{\pi}{3}\right)^2 + \frac{\sqrt{3}}{12}\left(x - \frac{\pi}{3}\right)^3 + \frac{1}{48}\left(x - \frac{\pi}{3}\right)^4 + R_4(x)$. Now since

$x = 69° = (60° + 9°) = \left(\frac{\pi}{3} + \frac{\pi}{20}\right)$ radians, the error is $|R_4(x)| \le \dfrac{\left(\frac{\pi}{20}\right)^5}{5!} < 8 \times 10^{-7}$. Therefore, to five

decimal places, $\cos 69° \approx \frac{1}{2} - \frac{\sqrt{3}}{2}\left(\frac{\pi}{20}\right) - \frac{1}{4}\left(\frac{\pi}{20}\right)^2 + \frac{\sqrt{3}}{12}\left(\frac{\pi}{20}\right)^3 + \frac{1}{48}\left(\frac{\pi}{20}\right)^4 \approx 0.35837$.

19. All derivatives of e^x are e^x, so $|R_n(x)| \le \dfrac{e^x}{(n+1)!}|x|^{n+1}$, where $0 < x < 0.1$. Letting $x = 0.1$,

$R_n(0.1) \le \dfrac{e^{0.1}}{(n+1)!}(0.1)^{n+1} < 0.00001$, and by trial and error we find that $n = 3$ satisfies this inequality since

$R_3(0.1) < 0.0000046$. Thus, by adding the four terms of the Maclaurin series for e^x corresponding to $n = 0, 1, 2,$

and 3, we can estimate $e^{0.1}$ to within 0.00001. (In fact, this sum is $1.10516\overline{6}$ and $e^{0.1} \approx 1.10517$.)

20. Example 6 in Section 8.6 gives the Maclaurin series for $\ln(1 + x)$ as $\displaystyle\sum_{n=1}^{\infty} \frac{x^n}{n}$ for $|x| < 1$. Thus,

$\ln 1.4 = \ln[1 - (-0.4)] = -\displaystyle\sum_{n=1}^{\infty} \frac{(-0.4)^n}{n} = \sum_{n=1}^{\infty} (-1)^{n+1} \frac{(0.4)^n}{n}$. Since this is an alternating series, the error is

less than the first neglected term by the Alternating Series Estimation Theorem, and we find that

$|a_6| = (0.4)^6/6 \approx 0.0007 < 0.001$. So we need the first five (non-zero) terms of the Maclaurin series for the

desired accuracy. (In fact, this sum is approximately 0.33698 and $\ln 1.4 \approx 0.33647$.)

21. $\sin x = x - \frac{1}{3!}x^3 + \frac{1}{5!}x^5 - \cdots$. By the Alternating

Series Estimation Theorem, the error in the

approximation $\sin x = x - \frac{1}{3!}x^3$ is less than

$\left|\frac{1}{5!}x^5\right| < 0.01 \iff |x^5| < 120(0.01) \iff$

$|x| < (1.2)^{1/5} \approx 1.037$. The curves intersect at

$x \approx 1.043$, so the graph confirms our estimate. Since

both the sine function and the given approximation are

odd functions, we need to check the estimate only for

$x > 0$. Thus, the desired range of values for x is

$-1.037 < x < 1.037$.

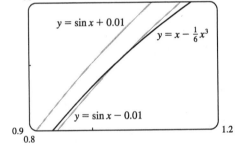

22. $\cos x = 1 - \frac{1}{2!}x^2 + \frac{1}{4!}x^4 - \frac{1}{6!}x^6 + \cdots$. By the

Alternating Series Estimation Theorem, the error is less

than $\left|-\frac{1}{6!}x^6\right| < 0.005 \iff x^6 < 720(0.005) \iff$

$|x| < (3.6)^{1/6} \approx 1.238$. The curves intersect at

$x \approx 1.244$, so the graph confirms our estimate. Since

both the cosine function and the given approximation

are even functions, we need to check the estimate only

for $x > 0$. Thus, the desired range of values for x is

$-1.238 < x < 1.238$.

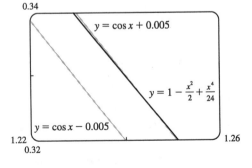

23. Let $s(t)$ be the position function of the car, and for convenience set $s(0) = 0$. The velocity of the car is $v(t) = s'(t)$ and the acceleration is $a(t) = s''(t)$, so the second degree Taylor polynomial is

$$T_2(t) = s(0) + v(0)t + \frac{a(0)}{2}t^2 = 20t + t^2.$$ We estimate the distance travelled during the next second to be

$s(1) \approx T_2(1) = 20 + 1 = 21$ m. The function $T_2(t)$ would not be accurate over a full minute, since the car could not possibly maintain an acceleration of 2 m/s² for that long (if it did, its final speed would be 140 m/s $\approx$ 313 mi/h!)

24. (a) $\dfrac{n_1}{\ell_o} + \dfrac{n_2}{\ell_i} = \dfrac{1}{R}\left(\dfrac{n_2 s_i}{\ell_i} - \dfrac{n_1 s_o}{\ell_o}\right)$ (Equation 1) where

$$\ell_o = \sqrt{R^2 + (s_o + R)^2 - 2R(s_o + R)\cos\phi} \quad \text{and} \quad \ell_i = \sqrt{R^2 + (s_i - R)^2 + 2R(s_i - R)\cos\phi} \quad (2)$$

Using $\cos\phi \approx 1$ gives

$$\ell_o = \sqrt{R^2 + (s_o + R)^2 - 2R(s_o + R)} = \sqrt{R^2 + s_o^2 + 2Rs_o + R^2 - 2Rs_o - 2R^2} = \sqrt{s_o^2} = s_o$$

and similarly, $\ell_i = s_i$. Thus, Equation 1 becomes

$$\frac{n_1}{s_o} + \frac{n_2}{s_i} = \frac{1}{R}\left(\frac{n_2 s_i}{s_i} - \frac{n_1 s_o}{s_o}\right) \quad \Rightarrow \quad \frac{n_1}{s_o} + \frac{n_2}{s_i} = \frac{n_2 - n_1}{R}$$

(b) Using $\cos\phi \approx 1 - \frac{1}{2}\phi^2$ in (2) gives us

$$\ell_o = \sqrt{R^2 + (s_o + R)^2 - 2R(s_o + R)\left(1 - \frac{1}{2}\phi^2\right)}$$

$$= \sqrt{R^2 + s_o^2 + 2Rs_o + R^2 - 2Rs_o + Rs_o\phi^2 - 2R^2 + R^2\phi^2} = \sqrt{s_o^2 + Rs_o\phi^2 + R^2\phi^2}$$

Anticipating that we will use the binomial series expansion $(1 + x)^k \approx 1 + kx$, we can write the last expression for ℓ_o as $s_o\sqrt{1 + \phi^2\left(\dfrac{R}{s_o} + \dfrac{R^2}{s_o^2}\right)}$ and similarly, $\ell_i = s_i\sqrt{1 - \phi^2\left(\dfrac{R}{s_i} - \dfrac{R^2}{s_i^2}\right)}$. Thus, from Equation 1,

$$\frac{n_1}{\ell_o} + \frac{n_2}{\ell_i} = \frac{1}{R}\left(\frac{n_2 s_i}{\ell_i} - \frac{n_1 s_o}{\ell_o}\right) \quad \Leftrightarrow \quad n_1\ell_o^{-1} + n_2\ell_i^{-1} = \frac{n_2}{R}\cdot\frac{s_i}{\ell_i} - \frac{n_1}{R}\cdot\frac{s_o}{\ell_o} \quad \Leftrightarrow$$

$$\frac{n_1}{s_o}\left[1 + \phi^2\left(\frac{R}{s_o} + \frac{R^2}{s_o^2}\right)\right]^{-1/2} + \frac{n_2}{s_i}\left[1 - \phi^2\left(\frac{R}{s_i} - \frac{R^2}{s_i^2}\right)\right]^{-1/2}$$

$$= \frac{n_2}{R}\left[1 - \phi^2\left(\frac{R}{s_i} - \frac{R^2}{s_i^2}\right)\right]^{-1/2} - \frac{n_1}{R}\left[1 + \phi^2\left(\frac{R}{s_o} + \frac{R^2}{s_o^2}\right)\right]^{-1/2}$$

Approximating the expressions for ℓ_o^{-1} and ℓ_i^{-1} by the first two terms in their binomial series, we get

$$\frac{n_1}{s_o}\left[1 - \frac{1}{2}\phi^2\left(\frac{R}{s_o} + \frac{R^2}{s_o^2}\right)\right] + \frac{n_2}{s_i}\left[1 + \frac{1}{2}\phi^2\left(\frac{R}{s_i} - \frac{R^2}{s_i^2}\right)\right]$$

$$= \frac{n_2}{R}\left[1 + \frac{1}{2}\phi^2\left(\frac{R}{s_i} - \frac{R^2}{s_i^2}\right)\right] - \frac{n_1}{R}\left[1 - \frac{1}{2}\phi^2\left(\frac{R}{s_o} + \frac{R^2}{s_o^2}\right)\right] \quad \Leftrightarrow$$

$$\frac{n_1}{s_o} - \frac{n_1\phi^2}{2s_o}\left(\frac{R}{s_o} + \frac{R^2}{s_o^2}\right) + \frac{n_2}{s_i} + \frac{n_2\phi^2}{2s_i}\left(\frac{R}{s_i} - \frac{R^2}{s_i^2}\right)$$

$$= \frac{n_2}{R} + \frac{n_2\phi^2}{2R}\left(\frac{R}{s_i} - \frac{R^2}{s_i^2}\right) - \frac{n_1}{R} + \frac{n_1\phi^2}{2R}\left(\frac{R}{s_o} + \frac{R^2}{s_o^2}\right) \quad \Leftrightarrow$$

$$\frac{n_1}{s_o} + \frac{n_2}{s_i} = \frac{n_2}{R} - \frac{n_1}{R} + \frac{n_1\phi^2}{2s_o}\left(\frac{R}{s_o} + \frac{R^2}{s_o^2}\right) + \frac{n_1\phi^2}{2R}\left(\frac{R}{s_o} + \frac{R^2}{s_o^2}\right) + \frac{n_2\phi^2}{2R}\left(\frac{R}{s_i} - \frac{R^2}{s_i^2}\right) - \frac{n_2\phi^2}{2s_i}\left(\frac{R}{s_i} - \frac{R^2}{s_i^2}\right)$$

$$= \frac{n_2 - n_1}{R} + \frac{n_1\phi^2}{2}\left(\frac{R}{s_o} + \frac{R^2}{s_o^2}\right)\left(\frac{1}{s_o} + \frac{1}{R}\right) + \frac{n_2\phi^2}{2}\left(\frac{R}{s_i} - \frac{R^2}{s_i^2}\right)\left(\frac{1}{R} - \frac{1}{s_i}\right)$$

$$= \frac{n_2 - n_1}{R} + \frac{n_1\phi^2 R^2}{2s_o}\left(\frac{1}{R} + \frac{1}{s_o}\right)\left(\frac{1}{R} + \frac{1}{s_o}\right) + \frac{n_2\phi^2 R^2}{2s_i}\left(\frac{1}{R} - \frac{1}{s_i}\right)\left(\frac{1}{R} - \frac{1}{s_i}\right)$$

$$= \frac{n_2 - n_1}{R} + \phi^2 R^2\left[\frac{n_1}{2s_o}\left(\frac{1}{R} + \frac{1}{s_o}\right)^2 + \frac{n_2}{2s_i}\left(\frac{1}{R} - \frac{1}{s_i}\right)^2\right]$$

From Figure 8, we see that $\sin\phi = h/R$. So if we approximate $\sin\phi$ with ϕ, we get $h = R\phi$ and $h^2 = \phi^2 R^2$ and hence, Equation 4, as desired.

25. $E = \dfrac{q}{D^2} - \dfrac{q}{(D+d)^2} = \dfrac{q}{D^2} - \dfrac{q}{D^2(1+d/D)^2} = \dfrac{q}{D^2}\left[1 - \left(1 + \dfrac{d}{D}\right)^{-2}\right].$

We use the Binomial Series to expand $(1 + d/D)^{-2}$:

$$E = \frac{q}{D^2}\left[1 - \left(1 - 2\left(\frac{d}{D}\right) + \frac{2\cdot 3}{2!}\left(\frac{d}{D}\right)^2 - \frac{2\cdot 3\cdot 4}{3!}\left(\frac{d}{D}\right)^3 + \cdots\right)\right]$$

$$= \frac{q}{D^2}\left[2\left(\frac{d}{D}\right) - 3\left(\frac{d}{D}\right)^2 + 4\left(\frac{d}{D}\right)^3 - \cdots\right] \approx \frac{q}{D^2}\cdot 2\left(\frac{d}{D}\right) = 2qd\cdot\frac{1}{D^3}$$

when D is much larger than d; that is, when P is far away from the dipole.

26. (a)

$$\rho(t) = \rho_{20}e^{\alpha(t-20)} \qquad\qquad \rho(20) = \rho_{20}$$

$$\rho'(t) = \alpha\rho_{20}e^{\alpha(t-20)} \qquad\qquad \rho'(20) = \alpha\rho_{20}$$

$$\rho''(t) = \alpha^2\rho_{20}e^{\alpha(t-20)} \qquad\qquad \rho''(20) = \alpha^2\rho_{20}$$

The linear approximation is $T_1(t) = \rho(20) + \rho'(20)(t - 20) = \rho_{20}\left[1 + \alpha(t - 20)\right]$. The quadratic approximation is

$$T_2(t) = \rho(20) + \rho'(20)(t - 20) + \frac{\rho''(20)}{2}(t - 20)^2 = \rho_{20}\left[1 + \alpha(t - 20) + \tfrac{1}{2}\alpha^2(t - 20)^2\right]$$

(b)

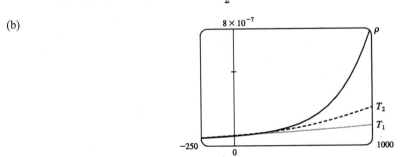

(c)

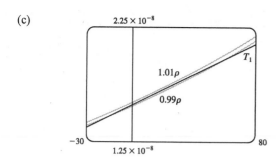

From the graph, it seems that $T_1(t)$ is within 1% of $\rho(t)$, that is, $0.99\rho(t) \leq T_1(t) \leq 1.01\rho(t)$, for $-14\,°C \leq t \leq 58\,°C$.

27. Using $f(x) = T_n(x) + R_n(x)$ with $n = 1$ and $x = r$, we have $f(r) = T_1(r) + R_1(r)$, where T_1 is the first-degree Taylor polynomial of f at a. Because $a = x_n$, $f(r) = f(x_n) + f'(x_n)(r - x_n) + R_1(r)$. But r is a root of f, so $f(r) = 0$ and we have $0 = f(x_n) + f'(x_n)(r - x_n) + R_1(r)$. Taking the first two terms to the left side and dividing by $f'(x_n)$, we have $f'(x_n)(x_n - r) - f(x_n) = R_1(r) \Rightarrow x_n - r - \dfrac{f(x_n)}{f'(x_n)} = \dfrac{R_1(r)}{f'(x_n)}$. By the formula for Newton's method, the left side of the preceding equation is $x_{n+1} - r$, so $|x_{n+1} - r| = \left| \dfrac{R_1(r)}{f'(x_n)} \right|$.

Taylor's Inequality gives us $|R_1(r)| \leq \dfrac{|f''(r)|}{2!} |r - x_n|^2$. Combining this inequality with the facts $|f''(x)| \leq M$ and $|f'(x)| \geq K$ gives us $|x_{n+1} - r| \leq \dfrac{M}{2K} |x_n - r|^2$.

Applied Project

Radiation from the Stars

1. If we write $f(\lambda) = \dfrac{8\pi hc\lambda^{-5}}{e^{hc/(\lambda kT)} - 1} = \dfrac{a\lambda^{-5}}{e^{b/(\lambda T)} - 1}$, then as $\lambda \to 0^+$, it is of the form ∞/∞, and as $\lambda \to \infty$ it is of the form $0/0$, so in either case we can use l'Hospital's Rule. First of all,

$$\lim_{\lambda \to \infty} f(\lambda) \overset{\text{H}}{=} \lim_{\lambda \to \infty} \frac{a\left(-5\lambda^{-6}\right)}{-\dfrac{bT}{(\lambda T)^2}e^{b/(\lambda T)}} = 5\frac{aT}{b} \lim_{\lambda \to \infty} \frac{\lambda^2 \lambda^{-6}}{e^{b/(\lambda T)}} = 5\frac{aT}{b} \lim_{\lambda \to \infty} \frac{\lambda^{-4}}{e^{b/(\lambda T)}} = 0$$

Also,

$$\lim_{\lambda \to 0^+} f(\lambda) \overset{\text{H}}{=} 5\frac{aT}{b} \lim_{\lambda \to 0^+} \frac{\lambda^{-4}}{e^{b/(\lambda T)}} \overset{\text{H}}{=} 5\frac{aT}{b} \lim_{\lambda \to 0^+} \frac{-4\lambda^{-5}}{-\dfrac{bT}{(\lambda T)^2}e^{b/(\lambda T)}} = 20\frac{aT^2}{b^2} \lim_{\lambda \to 0^+} \frac{\lambda^{-3}}{e^{b/(\lambda T)}} .$$

This is still indeterminate, but note that each time we use l'Hospital's Rule, we gain a factor of λ in the numerator, as well as a constant factor, and the denominator is unchanged. So if we use l'Hospital's Rule three more times, the exponent of λ in the numerator will become 0. That is, for some $\{k_i\}$, all constant,

$$\lim_{\lambda \to 0^+} f(\lambda) \overset{\text{H}}{=} k_1 \lim_{\lambda \to 0^+} \frac{\lambda^{-3}}{e^{b/(\lambda T)}} \overset{\text{H}}{=} k_2 \lim_{\lambda \to 0^+} \frac{\lambda^{-2}}{e^{b/(\lambda T)}} \overset{\text{H}}{=} k_3 \lim_{\lambda \to 0^+} \frac{\lambda^{-1}}{e^{b/(\lambda T)}} \overset{\text{H}}{=} k_4 \lim_{\lambda \to 0^+} \frac{1}{e^{b/(\lambda T)}} = 0$$

2. We expand the denominator of Planck's Law using the Taylor series $e^x = 1 + x + \dfrac{x^2}{2!} + \dfrac{x^3}{3!} + \cdots$ with $x = \dfrac{hc}{\lambda kT}$,

and use the fact that if λ is large, then all subsequent terms in the Taylor expansion are very small compared to the first one, so we can approximate using the Taylor polynomial T_1:

$$f(\lambda) = \frac{8\pi hc\lambda^{-5}}{e^{hc/(\lambda kT)} - 1}$$

$$= \frac{8\pi hc\lambda^{-5}}{\left[1 + \dfrac{hc}{\lambda kT} + \dfrac{1}{2!}\left(\dfrac{hc}{\lambda kT} \right)^2 + \dfrac{1}{3!}\left(\dfrac{hc}{\lambda kT} \right)^3 + \cdots \right] - 1}$$

$$\approx \frac{8\pi hc\lambda^{-5}}{\left(1 + \dfrac{hc}{\lambda kT} \right) - 1} = \frac{8\pi kT}{\lambda^4}$$

which is the Rayleigh-Jeans Law.

3. To convert to μm, we substitute $\lambda/10^6$ for λ in both laws. The first figure shows that the two laws are similar for large λ. The second figure shows that the two laws are very different for short wavelengths (Planck's Law gives a maximum at $\lambda \approx 0.51\ \mu$m; the Rayleigh-Jeans Law gives no minimum or maximum.).

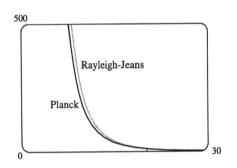

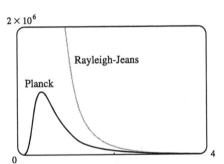

4. From the graph in Problem 3, $f(\lambda)$ has a maximum under Planck's Law at $\lambda \approx 0.51\ \mu$m.

5.

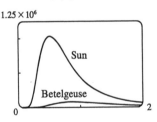

As T gets larger, the total area under the curve increases, as we would expect: the hotter the star, the more energy it emits. Also, as T increases, the λ-value of the maximum decreases, so the higher the temperature, the shorter the peak wavelength (and consequently the average wavelength) of light emitted. This is why Sirius is a blue star and Betelgeuse is a red star: most of Sirius's light is of a fairly short wavelength; that is, a higher frequency, toward the blue end of the spectrum, whereas most of Betelgeuse's light is of a lower frequency, toward the red end of the spectrum.

8.10 **Using Series to Solve Differential Equations** • • • • •

1. Let $y(x) = \sum\limits_{n=0}^{\infty} c_n x^n$. Then $y'(x) = \sum\limits_{n=1}^{\infty} n c_n x^{n-1}$ and the given equation, $y' - y = 0$, becomes

$\sum\limits_{n=1}^{\infty} n c_n x^{n-1} - \sum\limits_{n=0}^{\infty} c_n x^n = 0$. Replacing n by $n+1$ in the first sum gives $\sum\limits_{n=0}^{\infty} (n+1) c_{n+1} x^n - \sum\limits_{n=0}^{\infty} c_n x^n = 0$,

so $\sum\limits_{n=0}^{\infty} [(n+1)c_{n+1} - c_n] x^n = 0$. Equating coefficients gives $(n+1)c_{n+1} - c_n = 0$, so the recursion relation is

$c_{n+1} = \dfrac{c_n}{n+1}$, $n = 0, 1, 2, \ldots$. Then $c_1 = c_0$, $c_2 = \dfrac{1}{2} c_1 = \dfrac{c_0}{2}$, $c_3 = \dfrac{1}{3} c_2 = \dfrac{1}{3} \cdot \dfrac{1}{2} c_0 = \dfrac{c_0}{3!}$, $c_4 = \dfrac{1}{4} c_3 = \dfrac{c_0}{4!}$, and

in general, $c_n = \dfrac{c_0}{n!}$. Thus, the solution is

$$y(x) = \sum_{n=0}^{\infty} c_n x^n = \sum_{n=0}^{\infty} \frac{c_0}{n!} x^n = c_0 \sum_{n=0}^{\infty} \frac{x^n}{n!} = c_0 e^x$$

2. Let $y(x) = \sum\limits_{n=0}^{\infty} c_n x^n$. Then $y' = xy$ $\Rightarrow$ $y' - xy = 0$ $\Rightarrow$ $\sum\limits_{n=1}^{\infty} n c_n x^{n-1} - x \sum\limits_{n=0}^{\infty} c_n x^n = 0$ or

$\sum\limits_{n=1}^{\infty} n c_n x^{n-1} - \sum\limits_{n=0}^{\infty} c_n x^{n+1} = 0$. Replacing n with $n+1$ in the first sum and n with $n-1$ in the second gives

$\sum\limits_{n=0}^{\infty} (n+1) c_{n+1} x^n - \sum\limits_{n=1}^{\infty} c_{n-1} x^n = 0$ or $c_1 + \sum\limits_{n=1}^{\infty} (n+1) c_{n+1} x^n - \sum\limits_{n=1}^{\infty} c_{n-1} x^n = 0$. Thus,

$c_1 + \sum\limits_{n=1}^{\infty} [(n+1)c_{n+1} - c_{n-1}] x^n = 0$. Equating coefficients gives $c_1 = 0$ and $(n+1) c_{n+1} - c_{n-1} = 0$. Thus,

the recursion relation is $c_{n+1} = \dfrac{c_{n-1}}{n+1}$, $n = 1, 2, \ldots$. But $c_1 = 0$, so $c_3 = 0$ and $c_5 = 0$ and in general $c_{2n+1} = 0$.

Also, $c_2 = \dfrac{c_0}{2}$, $c_4 = \dfrac{c_2}{4} = \dfrac{c_0}{4 \cdot 2} = \dfrac{c_0}{2^2 \cdot 2!}$, $c_6 = \dfrac{c_4}{6} = \dfrac{c_0}{6 \cdot 4 \cdot 2} = \dfrac{c_0}{2^3 \cdot 3!}$ and in general $c_{2n} = \dfrac{c_0}{2^n \cdot n!}$. Thus, the

solution is

$$y(x) = \sum_{n=0}^{\infty} c_n x^n = \sum_{n=0}^{\infty} c_{2n} x^{2n} = \sum_{n=0}^{\infty} \frac{c_0}{2^n \cdot n!} x^{2n} = c_0 \sum_{n=0}^{\infty} \frac{\left(x^2/2\right)^n}{n!} = c_0 e^{x^2/2}$$

3. Assuming $y(x) = \sum\limits_{n=0}^{\infty} c_n x^n$, we have $y'(x) = \sum\limits_{n=1}^{\infty} n c_n x^{n-1} = \sum\limits_{n=0}^{\infty} (n+1) c_{n+1} x^n$ and

$-x^2 y = - \sum\limits_{n=0}^{\infty} c_n x^{n+2} = - \sum\limits_{n=2}^{\infty} c_{n-2} x^n$. Hence, the equation $y' = x^2 y$ becomes

$\sum\limits_{n=0}^{\infty} (n+1) c_{n+1} x^n - \sum\limits_{n=2}^{\infty} c_{n-2} x^n = 0$ or $c_1 + 2c_2 x + \sum\limits_{n=2}^{\infty} [(n+1)c_{n+1} - c_{n-2}] x^n = 0$. Equating coefficients

gives $c_1 = c_2 = 0$ and $c_{n+1} = \dfrac{c_{n-2}}{n+1}$ for $n = 2, 3, \ldots$. But $c_1 = 0$, so $c_4 = 0$ and $c_7 = 0$ and in general

$c_{3n+1} = 0$. Similarly $c_2 = 0$ so $c_{3n+2} = 0$. Finally $c_3 = \dfrac{c_0}{3}$, $c_6 = \dfrac{c_3}{6} = \dfrac{c_0}{6 \cdot 3} = \dfrac{c_0}{3^2 \cdot 2!}$,

$c_9 = \dfrac{c_6}{9} = \dfrac{c_0}{9 \cdot 6 \cdot 3} = \dfrac{c_0}{3^3 \cdot 3!}, \ldots$, and $c_{3n} = \dfrac{c_0}{3^n \cdot n!}$. Thus, the solution is

$$y(x) = \sum_{n=0}^{\infty} c_n x^n = \sum_{n=0}^{\infty} c_{3n} x^{3n} = \sum_{n=0}^{\infty} \frac{c_0}{3^n \cdot n!} x^{3n} = c_0 \sum_{n=0}^{\infty} \frac{x^{3n}}{3^n n!} = c_0 \sum_{n=0}^{\infty} \frac{\left(x^3/3\right)^n}{n!} = c_0 e^{x^3/3}$$

4. Let $y(x) = \sum\limits_{n=0}^{\infty} c_n x^n$. Then $y''(x) = \sum\limits_{n=2}^{\infty} n(n-1)c_n x^{n-2} = \sum\limits_{n=0}^{\infty} (n+2)(n+1)c_{n+2} x^n$. Hence, the equation

$y'' = y$ becomes $\sum\limits_{n=0}^{\infty} (n+2)(n+1)c_{n+2} x^n - \sum\limits_{n=0}^{\infty} c_n x^n = 0$ or $\sum\limits_{n=0}^{\infty} [(n+2)(n+1)c_{n+2} - c_n]x^n = 0$. So the

recursion relation is $c_{n+2} = \dfrac{c_n}{(n+2)(n+1)}$, $n = 0, 1, \ldots$. Given c_0 and c_1, $c_2 = \dfrac{c_0}{2 \cdot 1}$, $c_4 = \dfrac{c_2}{4 \cdot 3} = \dfrac{c_0}{4!}$,

$c_6 = \dfrac{c_4}{6 \cdot 5} = \dfrac{c_0}{6!}, \ldots, c_{2n} = \dfrac{c_0}{(2n)!}$ and $c_3 = \dfrac{c_1}{3 \cdot 2}$, $c_5 = \dfrac{c_3}{5 \cdot 4} = \dfrac{c_1}{5 \cdot 4 \cdot 3 \cdot 2} = \dfrac{c_1}{5!}$, $c_7 = \dfrac{c_5}{7 \cdot 6} = \dfrac{c_1}{7!}, \ldots,$

$c_{2n+1} = \dfrac{c_1}{(2n+1)!}$. Thus, the solution is

$$y(x) = \sum_{n=0}^{\infty} c_n x^n = \sum_{n=0}^{\infty} c_{2n} x^{2n} + \sum_{n=0}^{\infty} c_{2n+1} x^{2n+1} = c_0 \sum_{n=0}^{\infty} \frac{x^{2n}}{(2n)!} + c_1 \sum_{n=0}^{\infty} \frac{x^{2n+1}}{(2n+1)!}$$

The solution can be written as $y(x) = c_0 \cosh x + c_1 \sinh x$

$$\left[\text{or } y(x) = c_0 \frac{e^x + e^{-x}}{2} + c_1 \frac{e^x - e^{-x}}{2} = \frac{c_0 + c_1}{2} e^x + \frac{c_0 - c_1}{2} e^{-x} \right].$$

5. Let $y(x) = \sum\limits_{n=0}^{\infty} c_n x^n$. Then $3xy'(x) = 3x \sum\limits_{n=1}^{\infty} nc_n x^{n-1} = \sum\limits_{n=0}^{\infty} 3nc_n x^n$,

$y''(x) = \sum\limits_{n=2}^{\infty} n(n-1)c_n x^{n-2} = \sum\limits_{n=0}^{\infty} (n+2)(n+1)c_{n+2} x^n$, and the equation

$y'' + 3xy' + 3y = 0$ becomes $\sum\limits_{n=0}^{\infty} (n+2)(n+1)c_{n+2} x^n + \sum\limits_{n=0}^{\infty} 3nc_n x^n + \sum\limits_{n=0}^{\infty} 3c_n x^n = 0 \quad \Leftrightarrow$

$\sum\limits_{n=0}^{\infty} [(n+2)(n+1)c_{n+2} + 3nc_n + 3c_n]x^n = 0$. Thus, the recursion relation is

$c_{n+2} = \dfrac{-3nc_n - 3c_n}{(n+2)(n+1)} = \dfrac{-3c_n(n+1)}{(n+2)(n+1)} = -\dfrac{3c_n}{n+2}$ for $n = 0, 1, 2, \ldots$. Given c_0 and c_1, $c_2 = -\dfrac{3c_0}{2}$,

$c_4 = -\dfrac{3c_2}{4} = (-1)^2 \dfrac{3^2 c_0}{2^2 \cdot 2!}$, $c_6 = -\dfrac{3c_4}{6} = (-1)^3 \dfrac{3^3 c_0}{2^3 \cdot 3!}, \ldots, c_{2n} = (-1)^n \dfrac{3^n c_0}{2^n n!}$ or, equivalently,

$c_0 \left(-\dfrac{3}{2}\right)^n \dfrac{1}{n!}$. Also, $c_3 = -\dfrac{3c_1}{3}$, $c_5 = -\dfrac{3c_3}{5} = (-1)^2 \dfrac{3^2 c_1}{5 \cdot 3}$, $c_7 = -\dfrac{3c_5}{7} = (-1)^3 \dfrac{3^3 c_1}{7 \cdot 5 \cdot 3}, \ldots,$

$c_{2n+1} = (-1)^n \dfrac{3^n c_1}{(2n+1)(2n-1) \cdots \cdots 5 \cdot 3}$. Since $(2n+1)(2n-1) \cdots \cdots 5 \cdot 3$ can be written as

$$\frac{(2n+1) \ (2n) \ (2n-1) \ (2n-2) \ \cdots \cdots 5 \cdot \ 4 \ \cdot \ 3 \ \cdot 2}{(2 \cdot n) \quad \cdot \quad [2(n-1)] \quad \cdot \quad (2 \cdot 2) \ \cdot \ (2 \cdot 1)} = \frac{(2n+1)!}{2^n \cdot n!},$$

c_{2n+1} can be written as $(-1)^n \dfrac{3^n c_1 2^n n!}{(2n+1)!} = c_1 \dfrac{(-6)^n n!}{(2n+1)!}$. Thus, the solution is

$$y(x) = \sum_{n=0}^{\infty} c_{2n} x^{2n} + \sum_{n=0}^{\infty} c_{2n+1} x^{2n+1} = c_0 \sum_{n=0}^{\infty} \left(-\frac{3}{2}\right)^n \frac{1}{n!} x^{2n} + c_1 \sum_{n=0}^{\infty} \frac{(-6)^n n!}{(2n+1)!} x^{2n+1}$$

Note that the c_0-term can be written as $c_0 \sum\limits_{n=0}^{\infty} \left(-\dfrac{3x^2}{2}\right)^n \dfrac{1}{n!} = c_0 e^{-3x^2/2}$.

6. Assuming $y(x) = \sum\limits_{n=0}^{\infty} c_n x^n$, $y''(x) = \sum\limits_{n=2}^{\infty} n(n-1)c_n x^{n-2} = \sum\limits_{n=0}^{\infty} (n+2)(n+1)c_{n+2} x^n$ and

$-xy(x) = -\sum\limits_{n=0}^{\infty} c_n x^{n+1} = -\sum\limits_{n=1}^{\infty} c_{n-1} x^n$. The equation $y'' = xy$ becomes

$\sum\limits_{n=0}^{\infty} (n+2)(n+1)c_{n+2} x^n - \sum\limits_{n=1}^{\infty} c_{n-1} x^n = 0$ or $2c_2 + \sum\limits_{n=1}^{\infty} [(n+2)(n+1)c_{n+2} - c_{n-1}] x^n = 0$. Equating

coefficients gives $c_2 = 0$ and $c_{n+2} = \dfrac{c_{n-1}}{(n+2)(n+1)}$ for $n = 1, 2, \ldots$. Since $c_2 = 0$,

$c_{3n+2} = 0$ for $n = 0, 1, 2, \ldots$. Given c_0, $c_3 = \dfrac{c_0}{3 \cdot 2}$, $c_6 = \dfrac{c_3}{6 \cdot 5} = \dfrac{c_0}{6 \cdot 5 \cdot 3 \cdot 2}, \ldots$,

$c_{3n} = \dfrac{c_0}{3n(3n-1)(3n-3)(3n-4) \cdot \ldots \cdot 6 \cdot 5 \cdot 3 \cdot 2}$. Given c_1, $c_4 = \dfrac{c_1}{4 \cdot 3}$, $c_7 = \dfrac{c_4}{7 \cdot 6} = \dfrac{c_1}{7 \cdot 6 \cdot 4 \cdot 3}, \ldots$,

$c_{3n+1} = \dfrac{c_1}{(3n+1)3n(3n-2)(3n-3)\ldots 7 \cdot 6 \cdot 4 \cdot 3}$. The solution can be written as

$$y(x) = c_0 \sum_{n=0}^{\infty} \frac{(3n-2)(3n-5) \cdot \ldots \cdot 7 \cdot 4 \cdot 1}{(3n)!} x^{3n} + c_1 \sum_{n=0}^{\infty} \frac{(3n-1)(3n-4) \cdot \ldots \cdot 8 \cdot 5 \cdot 2}{(3n+1)!} x^{3n+1}$$

7. Let $y(x) = \sum\limits_{n=0}^{\infty} c_n x^n$. Then $-xy'(x) = -x \sum\limits_{n=1}^{\infty} n c_n x^{n-1} = -\sum\limits_{n=1}^{\infty} n c_n x^n = -\sum\limits_{n=0}^{\infty} n c_n x^n$,

$y''(x) = \sum\limits_{n=0}^{\infty} (n+2)(n+1)c_{n+2} x^n$, and the equation $y'' - xy' - y = 0$ becomes

$\sum\limits_{n=0}^{\infty} [(n+2)(n+1)c_{n+2} - n c_n - c_n] x^n = 0$. Thus, the recursion relation is

$c_{n+2} = \dfrac{n c_n + c_n}{(n+2)(n+1)} = \dfrac{c_n(n+1)}{(n+2)(n+1)} = \dfrac{c_n}{n+2}$ for $n = 0, 1, 2, \ldots$. One of the given conditions is

$y(0) = 1$. But $y(0) = \sum\limits_{n=0}^{\infty} c_n(0)^n = c_0 + 0 + 0 + \cdots = c_0$, so $c_0 = 1$. Hence, $c_2 = \dfrac{c_0}{2} = \dfrac{1}{2}$, $c_4 = \dfrac{c_2}{4} = \dfrac{1}{2 \cdot 4}$,

$c_6 = \dfrac{c_4}{6} = \dfrac{1}{2 \cdot 4 \cdot 6}, \ldots, c_{2n} = \dfrac{1}{2^n n!}$. The other given condition is $y'(0) = 0$. But

$y'(0) = \sum\limits_{n=1}^{\infty} n c_n(0)^{n-1} = c_1 + 0 + 0 + \cdots = c_1$, so $c_1 = 0$. By the recursion relation, $c_3 = \dfrac{c_1}{3} = 0$, $c_5 = 0, \ldots$,

$c_{2n+1} = 0$ for $n = 0, 1, 2, \ldots$. Thus, the solution to the initial-value problem is

$$y(x) = \sum_{n=0}^{\infty} c_n x^n = \sum_{n=0}^{\infty} c_{2n} x^{2n} = \sum_{n=0}^{\infty} \frac{x^{2n}}{2^n n!} = \sum_{n=0}^{\infty} \frac{(x^2/2)^n}{n!} = e^{x^2/2}$$

8. Assuming that $y(x) = \sum\limits_{n=0}^{\infty} c_n x^n$, we have $x^2 y = \sum\limits_{n=0}^{\infty} c_n x^{n+2}$ and

$$y''(x) = \sum_{n=2}^{\infty} n(n-1)c_n x^{n-2} = \sum_{n=-2}^{\infty} (n+4)(n+3)c_{n+4} x^{n+2}$$

$$= 2c_2 + 6c_3 x + \sum_{n=0}^{\infty} (n+4)(n+3)c_{n+4} x^{n+2}$$

Thus, the equation $y'' + x^2 y = 0$ becomes $2c_2 + 6c_3 x + \sum\limits_{n=0}^{\infty} [(n+4)(n+3)c_{n+4} + c_n] x^{n+2} = 0$. So

$c_2 = c_3 = 0$ and the recursion relation is $c_{n+4} = -\dfrac{c_n}{(n+4)(n+3)}$, $n = 0, 1, 2, \ldots$.

But $c_1 = y'(0) = 0 = c_2 = c_3$ and by the recursion relation, $c_{4n+1} = c_{4n+2} = c_{4n+3} = 0$ for $n = 0, 1, 2, \ldots$.
Also, $c_0 = y(0) = 1$, so

$$c_4 = -\frac{c_0}{4 \cdot 3} = -\frac{1}{4 \cdot 3}, \quad c_8 = -\frac{c_4}{8 \cdot 7} = \frac{(-1)^2}{8 \cdot 7 \cdot 4 \cdot 3}, \ldots, c_{4n} = \frac{(-1)^n}{4n(4n-1)(4n-4)(4n-5) \cdots \cdot 4 \cdot 3}.$$

Thus, the solution to the initial-value problem is

$$y(x) = \sum_{n=0}^{\infty} c_n x^n = c_0 + \sum_{n=0}^{\infty} c_{4n} x^{4n} = 1 + \sum_{n=1}^{\infty} (-1)^n \frac{x^{4n}}{4n(4n-1)(4n-4)(4n-5) \cdots \cdot 4 \cdot 3}$$

9. Assuming that $y(x) = \sum\limits_{n=0}^{\infty} c_n x^n$, we have $xy = x \sum\limits_{n=0}^{\infty} c_n x^n = \sum\limits_{n=0}^{\infty} c_n x^{n+1}$,

$$x^2 y' = x^2 \sum_{n=1}^{\infty} n c_n x^{n-1} = \sum_{n=0}^{\infty} n c_n x^{n+1},$$

$$y''(x) = \sum_{n=2}^{\infty} n(n-1) c_n x^{n-2} = \sum_{n=-1}^{\infty} (n+3)(n+2) c_{n+3} x^{n+1} \quad \text{[replace n with $n+3$]}$$

$$= 2c_2 + \sum_{n=0}^{\infty} (n+3)(n+2) c_{n+3} x^{n+1},$$

and the equation $y'' + x^2 y' + xy = 0$ becomes $2c_2 + \sum\limits_{n=0}^{\infty} [(n+3)(n+2) c_{n+3} + n c_n + c_n] x^{n+1} = 0$.

So $c_2 = 0$ and the recursion relation is $c_{n+3} = \dfrac{-n c_n - c_n}{(n+3)(n+2)} = -\dfrac{(n+1) c_n}{(n+3)(n+2)}$, $n = 0, 1, 2, \ldots$.

But $c_0 = y(0) = 0 = c_2$ and by the recursion relation, $c_{3n} = c_{3n+2} = 0$ for $n = 0, 1, 2, \ldots$.
Also, $c_1 = y'(0) = 1$, so

$$c_4 = -\frac{2c_1}{4 \cdot 3} = -\frac{2}{4 \cdot 3}, \quad c_7 = -\frac{5c_4}{7 \cdot 6} = (-1)^2 \frac{2 \cdot 5}{7 \cdot 6 \cdot 4 \cdot 3} = (-1)^2 \frac{2^2 5^2}{7!}, \ldots,$$

$c_{3n+1} = (-1)^n \dfrac{2^2 5^2 \cdots (3n-1)^2}{(3n+1)!}$. Thus, the solution is

$$y(x) = \sum_{n=0}^{\infty} c_n x^n = x + \sum_{n=1}^{\infty} \left[(-1)^n \frac{2^2 5^2 \cdots (3n-1)^2 x^{3n+1}}{(3n+1)!} \right]$$

10. (a) Let $y(x) = \sum\limits_{n=0}^{\infty} c_n x^n$. Then $x^2 y''(x) = \sum\limits_{n=2}^{\infty} n(n-1) c_n x^n = \sum\limits_{n=0}^{\infty} (n+2)(n+1) c_{n+2} x^{n+2}$,

$xy'(x) = \sum\limits_{n=1}^{\infty} n c_n x^n = \sum\limits_{n=-1}^{\infty} (n+2) c_{n+2} x^{n+2} = c_1 x + \sum\limits_{n=0}^{\infty} (n+2) c_{n+2} x^{n+2}$, and the equation

$x^2 y'' + xy' + x^2 y = 0$ becomes $c_1 x + \sum\limits_{n=0}^{\infty} \{[(n+2)(n+1) + (n+2)] c_{n+2} + c_n\} x^{n+2} = 0$. So $c_1 = 0$

and the recursion relation is $c_{n+2} = -\dfrac{c_n}{(n+2)^2}$, $n = 0, 1, 2, \ldots$. But $c_1 = y'(0) = 0$ so $c_{2n+1} = 0$ for

$n = 0, 1, 2, \ldots$. Also, $c_0 = y(0) = 1$, so $c_2 = -\dfrac{1}{2^2}$, $c_4 = -\dfrac{c_2}{4^2} = (-1)^2 \dfrac{1}{4^2 2^2} = (-1)^2 \dfrac{1}{2^4 (2!)^2}$,

$c_6 = -\dfrac{c_4}{6^2} = (-1)^3 \dfrac{1}{2^6 (3!)^2}, \ldots, c_{2n} = (-1)^n \dfrac{1}{2^{2n} (n!)^2}$. The solution is

$$y(x) = \sum_{n=0}^{\infty} c_n x^n = \sum_{n=0}^{\infty} (-1)^n \frac{x^{2n}}{2^{2n} (n!)^2}$$

(b) The Taylor polynomials T_0 to T_{12} are shown in the graph. Because T_{10} and T_{12} are close together throughout the interval $[-5, 5]$, it is reasonable to assume that T_{12} is a good approximation to the Bessel function on that interval.

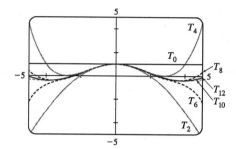

 Review

─── • **CONCEPT CHECK** • ───

1. (a) See Definition 8.1.1.

(b) See Definition 8.2.2.

(c) The terms of the sequence $\{a_n\}$ approach 3 as n becomes large.

(d) By adding sufficiently many terms of the series, we can make the partial sums as close to 3 as we like.

2. (a) See the definition on page 569.

(b) A sequence is monotonic if it is either increasing or decreasing.

(c) By Theorem 8.1.7, every bounded, monotonic sequence is convergent.

3. (a) See (4) in Section 8.2.

(b) See (1) in Section 8.3.

4. If $\sum a_n = 3$, then $\lim\limits_{n \to \infty} a_n = 0$ and $\lim\limits_{n \to \infty} s_n = 3$.

5. (a) See the Test for Divergence on page 578.

(b) See the Integral Test on page 584.

(c) See the Comparison Test on page 586.

(d) See the Limit Comparison Test on page 588.

(e) See the Alternating Series Test on page 593.

(f) See the Ratio Test on page 597.

6. (a) See the definition on page 595.

(b) By (8.4.1), it is convergent.

7. (a) Use (4) in Section 8.3.

(b) See Example 8 in Section 8.4.

(c) By adding terms until you reach the desired accuracy given by the Alternating Series Estimation Theorem on page 594.

8. (a) $\sum_{n=0}^{\infty} c_n(x-a)^n$

(b) Given the power series $\sum_{n=0}^{\infty} c_n(x-a)^n$, the radius of convergence is:

   (i) 0 if the series converges only when $x = a$

   (ii) ∞ if the series converges for all x, or

   (iii) a positive number R such that the series converges if $|x-a| < R$ and diverges if $|x-a| > R$.

(c) The interval of convergence of a power series is the interval that consists of all values of x for which the series converges. Corresponding to the cases in part (b), the interval of convergence is: (i) the single point $\{a\}$, (ii) all real numbers, that is, the real number line $(-\infty, \infty)$, or (iii) an interval with endpoints $a - R$ and $a + R$ which can contain neither, either, or both of the endpoints. In this case, we must test the series for convergence at each endpoint to determine the interval of convergence.

9. (a), (b) See Theorem 8.6.2.

10. (a) $T_n(x) = \sum_{i=0}^{n} \dfrac{f^{(i)}(a)}{i!}(x-a)^i$

(b) $\sum_{n=0}^{\infty} \dfrac{f^{(n)}(a)}{n!}(x-a)^n$

(c) $\sum_{n=0}^{\infty} \dfrac{f^{(n)}(0)}{n!}x^n$ [$a = 0$ in part (b)]

(d) See Theorem 8.7.8.

(e) See Taylor's Inequality (8.7.9).

11. (a) – (e) See the table on page 618.

12. See the Binomial Series (8.8.2) for the expansion. The radius of convergence for the binomial series is 1.

▲ **TRUE–FALSE QUIZ** ▲

---

1. False. See Note 2 after Theorem 8.2.6.

2. True by Theorem 8.5.3.

   Or: Use the Comparison Test to show that $\sum c_n(-2)^n$ converges absolutely.

3. False. For example, take $c_n = (-1)^n / (n6^n)$.

4. True by Theorem 8.5.3.

5. False, since $\lim\limits_{n\to\infty} \left| \dfrac{a_{n+1}}{a_n} \right| = \lim\limits_{n\to\infty} \left| \dfrac{n^3}{(n+1)^3} \right| = \lim\limits_{n\to\infty} \dfrac{1}{(1+1/n)^3} = 1$.

6. True, since $\lim\limits_{n\to\infty} \left| \dfrac{a_{n+1}}{a_n} \right| = \lim\limits_{n\to\infty} \left| \dfrac{n!}{(n+1)!} \right| = \lim\limits_{n\to\infty} \dfrac{1}{n+1} = 0 < 1$.

7. False. See the note after Example 4 in Section 8.3.

8. True, since $\dfrac{1}{e} = e^{-1}$ and $e^x = \sum\limits_{n=0}^{\infty} \dfrac{x^n}{n!}$, so $e^{-1} = \sum\limits_{n=0}^{\infty} \dfrac{(-1)^n}{n!}$.

9. True. See (6) in Section 8.1.

10. True, because if $\sum |a_n|$ is convergent, then so is $\sum a_n$ by Theorem 8.4.1.

11. True. By Theorem 8.7.5 the coefficient of x^3 is $\dfrac{f'''(0)}{3!} = \dfrac{1}{3} \Rightarrow f'''(0) = 2$.

   Or: Use Theorem 8.6.2 to differentiate f three times.

12. False. Let $a_n = n$ and $b_n = -n$. Then $\{a_n\}$ and $\{b_n\}$ are divergent, but $a_n + b_n = 0$, so $\{a_n + b_n\}$ is convergent.

13. False. For example, let $a_n = b_n = (-1)^n$. Then $\{a_n\}$ and $\{b_n\}$ are divergent, but $a_n b_n = 1$, so $\{a_n b_n\}$ is convergent.

14. True by Theorem 8.1.7 (the Monotonic Sequence Theorem), since $\{a_n\}$ is decreasing and $0 < a_n \le a_1$ for all n
$\Rightarrow \{a_n\}$ is bounded.

15. True by Theorem 8.4.1. $\left[\sum (-1)^n \, a_n \text{ is absolutely convergent and hence convergent.} \right]$

16. True. $\lim\limits_{n\to\infty} \dfrac{a_{n+1}}{a_n} < 1 \;\Rightarrow\; \sum a_n$ converges (Ratio Test) $\;\Rightarrow\; \lim\limits_{n\to\infty} a_n = 0$ [Theorem 8.2.6].

17. False. The Integral Test tells us that the series $\sum_{n=1}^{\infty} a_n$ also converges, but its value is not equal to the value of $\int_1^{\infty} f(x)\,dx$. In fact, a picture like Figure 2 on page 584 shows that the sum of the series is larger than the value of the integral.

◆ **EXERCISES** ◆

---

1. $\left\{ \dfrac{2 + n^3}{1 + 2n^3} \right\}$ converges since $\lim\limits_{n\to\infty} \dfrac{2 + n^3}{1 + 2n^3} = \lim\limits_{n\to\infty} \dfrac{2/n^3 + 1}{1/n^3 + 2} = \dfrac{1}{2}$.

2. $a_n = \dfrac{9^{n+1}}{10^n} = 9 \cdot \left(\dfrac{9}{10}\right)^n$, so $\lim\limits_{n\to\infty} a_n = 9 \lim\limits_{n\to\infty} \left(\dfrac{9}{10}\right)^n = 9 \cdot 0 = 0$ by (8.1.6).

3. $\lim\limits_{n\to\infty} a_n = \lim\limits_{n\to\infty} \dfrac{n^3}{1 + n^2} = \lim\limits_{n\to\infty} \dfrac{n}{1/n^2 + 1} = \infty$, so the sequence diverges.

4. $\left\{ \dfrac{n}{\ln n} \right\}$ diverges, since $\lim\limits_{x\to\infty} \dfrac{x}{\ln x} \overset{\text{H}}{=} \lim\limits_{x\to\infty} \dfrac{1}{1/x} = \lim\limits_{x\to\infty} x = \infty$.

5. $\{\sin n\}$ is divergent since $\lim\limits_{n\to\infty} \sin n$ does not exist.

6. $\left\{ \dfrac{\sin n}{n} \right\}$ converges, since $-\dfrac{1}{n} \le \dfrac{\sin n}{n} \le \dfrac{1}{n}$ and $\pm\dfrac{1}{n} \to 0$ as $n \to \infty$, so $\lim\limits_{n\to\infty} \dfrac{\sin n}{n} = 0$ by the Squeeze Theorem.

7. $\left\{ \left(1 + \dfrac{3}{n}\right)^{4n} \right\}$ is convergent. Let $y = \left(1 + \dfrac{3}{x}\right)^{4x}$. Then

$$\lim\limits_{x\to\infty} \ln y = \lim\limits_{x\to\infty} 4x \ln(1 + 3/x) = \lim\limits_{x\to\infty} \dfrac{\ln(1 + 3/x)}{1/(4x)} \overset{\text{H}}{=} \lim\limits_{x\to\infty} \dfrac{\dfrac{1}{1 + 3/x}\left(-\dfrac{3}{x^2}\right)}{-1/(4x^2)} = \lim\limits_{x\to\infty} \dfrac{12}{1 + 3/x} = 12$$

so $\lim\limits_{x\to\infty} y = \lim\limits_{n\to\infty} \left(1 + \dfrac{3}{n}\right)^{4n} = e^{12}$.

8. We use induction, hypothesizing that $a_{n-1} < a_n < 2$. Note first that $a_1 = 1 < a_2 = \frac{1}{3}(1 + 5) = \frac{5}{3} < 2$, so the hypothesis holds for $n = 2$. Now assume that $a_{k-1} < a_k < 2$. Then
$a_k = \frac{1}{3}(a_{k-1} + 4) < \frac{1}{3}(a_k + 4) < \frac{1}{3}(2 + 4) = 2$. So $a_k < a_{k+1} < 2$, and the induction is complete. To find the limit of the sequence, we note that $L = \lim\limits_{n\to\infty} a_n = \lim\limits_{n\to\infty} a_{n+1} \;\Rightarrow\; L = \frac{1}{3}(L + 4) \;\Rightarrow$
$3L = L + 4 \;\Rightarrow\; 2L = 4 \;\Rightarrow\; L = 2$.

9. $\dfrac{n}{n^3 + 1} < \dfrac{n}{n^3} = \dfrac{1}{n^2}$, so $\sum\limits_{n=1}^{\infty} \dfrac{n}{n^3 + 1}$ converges by the Comparison Test with the convergent p-series $\sum\limits_{n=1}^{\infty} \dfrac{1}{n^2}$ $(p = 2 > 1)$.

10. Let $a_n = \dfrac{n^2 + 1}{n^3 + 1}$ and $b_n = \dfrac{1}{n}$, so $\lim\limits_{n\to\infty} \dfrac{a_n}{b_n} = \lim\limits_{n\to\infty} \dfrac{n^3 + n}{n^3 + 1} = \lim\limits_{n\to\infty} \dfrac{1 + 1/n^2}{1 + 1/n^3} = 1 > 0$. Since $\sum_{n=1}^{\infty} b_n$ is the

divergent harmonic series, $\sum_{n=1}^{\infty} a_n$ also diverges by the Limit Comparison Test.

11. $\lim\limits_{n\to\infty} \left| \dfrac{a_{n+1}}{a_n} \right| = \lim\limits_{n\to\infty} \left[\dfrac{(n+1)^3}{5^{n+1}} \cdot \dfrac{5^n}{n^3} \right] = \lim\limits_{n\to\infty} \left(1 + \dfrac{1}{n} \right)^3 \cdot \dfrac{1}{5} = \dfrac{1}{5} < 1$, so $\sum\limits_{n=1}^{\infty} \dfrac{n^3}{5^n}$ converges by the Ratio Test.

12. Let $b_n = \dfrac{1}{\sqrt{n+1}}$. Then b_n is positive for $n \geq 1$, the sequence $\{b_n\}$ is decreasing, and $\lim\limits_{n\to\infty} b_n = 0$, so

$\sum\limits_{n=1}^{\infty} \dfrac{(-1)^n}{\sqrt{n+1}}$ converges by the Alternating Series Test.

13. $\left| \dfrac{\sin n}{1 + n^2} \right| \leq \dfrac{1}{1 + n^2} < \dfrac{1}{n^2}$ and since $\sum\limits_{n=1}^{\infty} \dfrac{1}{n^2}$ converges (p-series with $p = 2 > 1$), so does $\sum\limits_{n=1}^{\infty} \left| \dfrac{\sin n}{1 + n^2} \right|$ by the

Comparison Test, and so does $\sum\limits_{n=1}^{\infty} \dfrac{\sin n}{1 + n^2}$ by Theorem 8.4.1.

14. $\lim\limits_{n\to\infty} \dfrac{n}{3n + 1} = \dfrac{1}{3}$, so $\lim\limits_{n\to\infty} \ln\left(\dfrac{n}{3n + 1} \right) = \ln \dfrac{1}{3} \neq 0$. Thus, $\sum\limits_{n=1}^{\infty} \ln\left(\dfrac{n}{3n + 1} \right)$ diverges by the Test for

Divergence.

15. Let $b_n = \dfrac{\sqrt{n}}{n + 1} > 0$. Then $0 \leq \lim\limits_{n\to\infty} b_n = \lim\limits_{n\to\infty} \dfrac{\sqrt{n}}{n + 1} \leq \lim\limits_{n\to\infty} \dfrac{\sqrt{n}}{n} = \lim\limits_{n\to\infty} \dfrac{1}{\sqrt{n}} = 0$, so $\lim\limits_{n\to\infty} b_n = 0$. If

$f(x) = \dfrac{\sqrt{x}}{x + 1}$ for $x > 0$, then $f'(x) = \dfrac{(x + 1) \cdot \frac{1}{2\sqrt{x}} - \sqrt{x} \cdot 1}{(x + 1)^2} = \dfrac{(x + 1) - 2x}{2\sqrt{x}\,(x + 1)^2} = \dfrac{1 - x}{2\sqrt{x}\,(x + 1)^2}$, so

$f'(x) < 0$ for $x > 1$. It follows that $f(1) > f(2) > f(3) > \cdots$; that is, $b_n > b_{n+1}$ for all n. Thus,

$\sum\limits_{n=1}^{\infty} (-1)^{n-1} \dfrac{\sqrt{n}}{n + 1}$ converges by the Alternating Series Test.

16. $f(x) = \dfrac{1}{x\,(\ln x)^2}$ is continuous, positive, and decreasing on $(2, \infty)$, so we can use the Integral Test.

$\int_2^{\infty} \dfrac{dx}{x\,(\ln x)^2} = \lim\limits_{t\to\infty} \left[\dfrac{-1}{\ln x} \right]_2^t = \dfrac{1}{\ln 2}$, so the series $\sum\limits_{n=2}^{\infty} \dfrac{1}{n\,(\ln n)^2}$ also converges.

17. $\lim\limits_{n\to\infty} \left| \dfrac{a_{n+1}}{a_n} \right| = \lim\limits_{n\to\infty} \dfrac{1 \cdot 3 \cdot 5 \cdot \cdots \cdot (2n - 1)(2n + 1)}{5^{n+1}(n + 1)!} \cdot \dfrac{5^n n!}{1 \cdot 3 \cdot 5 \cdot \cdots \cdot (2n - 1)} = \lim\limits_{n\to\infty} \dfrac{2n + 1}{5(n + 1)} = \dfrac{2}{5} < 1$, so

the series converges by the Ratio Test.

18. $\sum\limits_{n=1}^{\infty} \dfrac{(-5)^{2n}}{n^2 9^n} = \sum\limits_{n=1}^{\infty} \dfrac{1}{n^2} \left(\dfrac{25}{9} \right)^n$. Now $\lim\limits_{n\to\infty} \left| \dfrac{a_{n+1}}{a_n} \right| = \lim\limits_{n\to\infty} \dfrac{n^2}{(n + 1)^2} \left(\dfrac{25}{9} \right)^{n+1} \left(\dfrac{9}{25} \right)^n = \dfrac{25}{9} > 1$, so the series

diverges by the Ratio Test.

19. This is a convergent geometric series with $r = \dfrac{4}{5}$.

$\sum\limits_{n=1}^{\infty} \dfrac{2^{2n+1}}{5^n} = \sum\limits_{n=1}^{\infty} \dfrac{(2^2)^n \cdot 2^1}{5^n} = 2 \sum\limits_{n=1}^{\infty} \dfrac{4^n}{5^n} = 2 \sum\limits_{n=1}^{\infty} \left(\dfrac{4}{5} \right)^n = 2 \left(\dfrac{\frac{4}{5}}{1 - \frac{4}{5}} \right) = 2(4) = 8.$

20. $\sum\limits_{n=1}^{\infty} \dfrac{1}{n(n + 3)} = \sum\limits_{n=1}^{\infty} \left[\dfrac{1}{3n} - \dfrac{1}{3(n + 3)} \right]$ (partial fractions).

$s_n = \sum\limits_{i=1}^{n} \left[\dfrac{1}{3i} - \dfrac{1}{3(i + 3)} \right] = \dfrac{1}{3} + \dfrac{1}{6} + \dfrac{1}{9} - \dfrac{1}{3(n + 1)} - \dfrac{1}{3(n + 2)} - \dfrac{1}{3(n + 3)}$ (telescoping sum), so

$\sum\limits_{n=1}^{\infty} \dfrac{1}{n(n + 3)} = \lim\limits_{n\to\infty} s_n = \dfrac{1}{3} + \dfrac{1}{6} + \dfrac{1}{9} = \dfrac{11}{18}.$

21. $\sum_{n=1}^{\infty} \left[\tan^{-1}(n+1) - \tan^{-1} n \right] = \lim_{n \to \infty} \left[(\tan^{-1} 2 - \tan^{-1} 1) + (\tan^{-1} 3 - \tan^{-1} 2) + \cdots \right.$

$$+ \left. (\tan^{-1}(n+1) - \tan^{-1} n) \right]$$

$$= \lim_{n \to \infty} \left[\tan^{-1}(n+1) - \tan^{-1} 1 \right] = \frac{\pi}{2} - \frac{\pi}{4} = \frac{\pi}{4}$$

22. $\displaystyle\sum_{n=0}^{\infty} \frac{(-1)^n x^n}{2^{2n} n!} = \sum_{n=0}^{\infty} \frac{(-1)^n x^n}{4^n n!} = \sum_{n=0}^{\infty} \frac{(-x/4)^n}{n!} = e^{-x/4}$

23. $1.2345345345\ldots = 1.2 + 0.0\overline{345} = \dfrac{12}{10} + \dfrac{345/10,000}{1 - 1/1000} = \dfrac{12}{10} + \dfrac{345}{9990} = \dfrac{4111}{3330}$

24. This is a geometric series which converges whenever $|\ln x| < 1 \ \Rightarrow \ -1 < \ln x < 1 \ \Rightarrow \ e^{-1} < x < e$.

25. $b_8 = \dfrac{1}{8^5} = \dfrac{1}{32{,}768} \approx 0.000\,031$, so

$$\sum_{n=1}^{\infty} \frac{(-1)^{n+1}}{n^5} \approx s_7 = \sum_{n=1}^{7} \frac{(-1)^{n+1}}{n^5} = 1 - \frac{1}{32} + \frac{1}{243} - \frac{1}{1024} + \frac{1}{3125} - \frac{1}{7776} + \frac{1}{16{,}807} \approx 0.972140.$$

Subtracting b_8 from s_7 does not change the fourth decimal place of s_7, so the sum of the series, correct to four decimal places, is 0.9721.

26. (a) $s_5 = \displaystyle\sum_{n=1}^{5} \frac{1}{n^6} = 1 + \frac{1}{2^6} + \frac{1}{3^6} + \frac{1}{4^6} + \frac{1}{5^6} \approx 1.017305$. The series $\displaystyle\sum_{n=1}^{\infty} \frac{1}{n^6}$ converges by the Integral Test, so

we estimate the remainder R_5 with (8.3.3): $R_5 \leq \displaystyle\int_5^{\infty} \frac{dx}{x^6} = \left[-\frac{x^{-5}}{5} \right]_5^{\infty} = \frac{5^{-5}}{5} = 0.000064$. So the error is

at most 0.000064.

(b) In general, $R_n \leq \displaystyle\int_n^{\infty} \frac{dx}{x^6} = \frac{1}{5n^5}$. If we take $n = 9$, then $s_9 \approx 1.01734$ and $R_9 \leq \dfrac{1}{5 \cdot 9^5} \approx 3.4 \times 10^{-6}$. So to

five decimal places, $\displaystyle\sum_{n=1}^{\infty} \frac{1}{n^5} \approx \sum_{n=1}^{9} \frac{1}{n^5} \approx 1.01734$.

Another method: Use (8.3.4) instead of (8.3.3).

27. $\displaystyle\sum_{n=1}^{\infty} \frac{1}{2 + 5^n} \approx \sum_{n=1}^{8} \frac{1}{2 + 5^n} \approx 0.18976224$. To estimate the error, note that $\dfrac{1}{2 + 5^n} < \dfrac{1}{5^n}$, so the remainder term is

$R_8 = \displaystyle\sum_{n=9}^{\infty} \frac{1}{2 + 5^n} < \sum_{n=9}^{\infty} \frac{1}{5^n} = \frac{1/5^9}{1 - 1/5} = 6.4 \times 10^{-7}$ (geometric series with $a = \frac{1}{5^9}$ and $r = \frac{1}{5}$).

28. (a) $\displaystyle\lim_{n \to \infty} \left| \frac{a_{n+1}}{a_n} \right| = \lim_{n \to \infty} \frac{(n+1)^{n+1}(2n)!}{(2n+2)! \, n^n} = \lim_{n \to \infty} \frac{(n+1)^n (n+1)^1}{(2n+2)(2n+1) n^n}$

$$= \lim_{n \to \infty} \left(1 + \frac{1}{n} \right)^n \frac{1}{2(2n+1)} = e \cdot 0 = 0 < 1$$

so the series converges by the Ratio Test.

(b) The series in part (a) is convergent, so $\displaystyle\lim_{n \to \infty} a_n = 0$ by Theorem 8.2.6.

29. Use the Limit Comparison Test. $\displaystyle\lim_{n \to \infty} \left| \frac{\left(\frac{n+1}{n} \right) a_n}{a_n} \right| = \lim_{n \to \infty} \frac{n+1}{n} = \lim_{n \to \infty} \left(1 + \frac{1}{n} \right) = 1 > 0$. Since $\sum |a_n|$ is

convergent, so is $\displaystyle\sum \left| \left(\frac{n+1}{n} \right) a_n \right|$, by the Limit Comparison Test.

30. $\lim\limits_{n\to\infty}\left|\dfrac{a_{n+1}}{a_n}\right|=\lim\limits_{n\to\infty}\left|\dfrac{x^{n+1}}{(n+1)^2\,5^{n+1}}\cdot\dfrac{n^2 5^n}{x^n}\right|=\lim\limits_{n\to\infty}\dfrac{1}{(1+1/n)^2}\dfrac{|x|}{5}=\dfrac{|x|}{5}$, so by the Ratio Test,

$\sum\limits_{n=1}^{\infty}(-1)^n\dfrac{x^n}{n^2 5^n}$ converges when $|x|<5$. $R=5$. When $x=-5$, the series becomes the convergent p-series

$\sum\limits_{n=1}^{\infty}\dfrac{1}{n^2}$ with $p=2>1$. When $x=5$, the series becomes $\sum\limits_{n=1}^{\infty}\dfrac{(-1)^n}{n^2}$, which converges by the Alternating Series

Test. Thus, $I=[-5,5]$.

31. $\lim\limits_{n\to\infty}\left|\dfrac{a_{n+1}}{a_n}\right|=\lim\limits_{n\to\infty}\left[\dfrac{|x+2|^{n+1}}{(n+1)\,4^{n+1}}\cdot\dfrac{n4^n}{|x+2|^n}\right]=\lim\limits_{n\to\infty}\left[\dfrac{n}{n+1}\dfrac{|x+2|}{4}\right]=\dfrac{|x+2|}{4}<1\ \Leftrightarrow\ |x+2|<4,$

so $R=4$. $|x+2|<4\ \Leftrightarrow\ -4<x+2<4\ \Leftrightarrow\ -6<x<2$. If $x=-6$, then the series becomes

$\sum\limits_{n=1}^{\infty}\dfrac{(-4)^n}{n4^n}=\sum\limits_{n=1}^{\infty}\dfrac{(-1)^n}{n}$, the alternating harmonic series, which converges by the Alternating Series Test. When

$x=2$, the series becomes the harmonic series $\sum\limits_{n=1}^{\infty}\dfrac{1}{n}$, which diverges. Thus, $I=[-6,2)$.

32. $\lim\limits_{n\to\infty}\left|\dfrac{a_{n+1}}{a_n}\right|=\lim\limits_{n\to\infty}\left|\dfrac{2^{n+1}(x-2)^{n+1}}{(n+3)!}\cdot\dfrac{(n+2)!}{2^n(x-2)^n}\right|=\lim\limits_{n\to\infty}\dfrac{2}{n+3}\,|x-2|=0<1$, so the series

$\sum\limits_{n=1}^{\infty}\dfrac{2^n(x-2)^n}{(n+2)!}$ converges for all x. $R=\infty$ and $I=\mathbb{R}$.

33. $\lim\limits_{n\to\infty}\left|\dfrac{a_{n+1}}{a_n}\right|=\lim\limits_{n\to\infty}\left|\dfrac{2^{n+1}(x-3)^{n+1}}{\sqrt{n+4}}\cdot\dfrac{\sqrt{n+3}}{2^n(x-3)^n}\right|=2\,|x-3|\lim\limits_{n\to\infty}\sqrt{\dfrac{n+3}{n+4}}=2\,|x-3|<1\ \Leftrightarrow$

$|x-3|<\tfrac{1}{2}\ \left[\text{so }R=\tfrac{1}{2}\right]\ \Leftrightarrow\ -\tfrac{1}{2}<x-3<\tfrac{1}{2}\ \Leftrightarrow\ \tfrac{5}{2}<x<\tfrac{7}{2}$. When $x=\tfrac{5}{2}$, the series becomes

$\sum\limits_{n=0}^{\infty}\dfrac{(-1)^n}{\sqrt{n+3}}$, which is a convergent alternating series. When $x=\tfrac{7}{2}$, the series becomes $\sum\limits_{n=0}^{\infty}\dfrac{1}{\sqrt{n+3}}=\sum\limits_{n=3}^{\infty}\dfrac{1}{n^{1/2}}$,

which diverges $(p=\tfrac{1}{2}\le 1)$. Thus, $I=\left[\tfrac{5}{2},\tfrac{7}{2}\right)$.

34. If $a_n=\dfrac{(2n)!\,x^n}{(n)!^2}$, then

$\lim\limits_{n\to\infty}\left|\dfrac{a_{n+1}}{a_n}\right|=\lim\limits_{n\to\infty}\left|\dfrac{(2n+2)!\,x^{n+1}}{[(n+1)!]^2}\cdot\dfrac{(n!)^2}{(2n)!\,x^n}\right|=\lim\limits_{n\to\infty}\dfrac{(2n+2)(2n+1)}{(n+1)(n+1)}\,|x|=4\,|x|<1$ to converge,

so $R=\tfrac{1}{4}$.

35.

$f(x)=\sin x$	$f\!\left(\tfrac{\pi}{6}\right)=\tfrac{1}{2}$	$f'''(x)=-\cos x$	$f'''\!\left(\tfrac{\pi}{6}\right)=-\tfrac{\sqrt{3}}{2}$
$f'(x)=\cos x$	$f'\!\left(\tfrac{\pi}{6}\right)=\tfrac{\sqrt{3}}{2}$	$f^{(4)}(x)=\sin x$	$f^{(4)}\!\left(\tfrac{\pi}{6}\right)=\tfrac{1}{2}$
$f''(x)=-\sin x$	$f''\!\left(\tfrac{\pi}{6}\right)=-\tfrac{1}{2}$	$\vdots$	$\vdots$

Note that $f^{(2n)}\!\left(\tfrac{\pi}{6}\right)=(-1)^n\cdot\tfrac{1}{2}$ and $f^{(2n+1)}\!\left(\tfrac{\pi}{6}\right)=(-1)^n\cdot\tfrac{\sqrt{3}}{2}$.

$$\sin x=\sum\limits_{n=0}^{\infty}\dfrac{f^{(n)}\!\left(\tfrac{\pi}{6}\right)}{n!}\left(x-\tfrac{\pi}{6}\right)^n=\sum\limits_{n=0}^{\infty}\dfrac{(-1)^n}{2(2n)!}\left(x-\tfrac{\pi}{6}\right)^{2n}+\sum\limits_{n=0}^{\infty}\dfrac{(-1)^n\sqrt{3}}{2(2n+1)!}\left(x-\tfrac{\pi}{6}\right)^{2n+1}$$

$$=\dfrac{1}{2}\sum\limits_{n=0}^{\infty}(-1)^n\left[\dfrac{1}{(2n)!}\left(x-\tfrac{\pi}{6}\right)^{2n}+\dfrac{\sqrt{3}}{(2n+1)!}\left(x-\tfrac{\pi}{6}\right)^{2n+1}\right]$$

36.

$$f(x) = \cos x \qquad f\left(\tfrac{\pi}{3}\right) = \tfrac{1}{2} \qquad\qquad f'''(x) = \sin x \qquad f'''\left(\tfrac{\pi}{3}\right) = \tfrac{\sqrt{3}}{2}$$

$$f'(x) = -\sin x \qquad f'\left(\tfrac{\pi}{3}\right) = -\tfrac{\sqrt{3}}{2} \qquad f^{(4)}(x) = \cos x \qquad f^{(4)}\left(\tfrac{\pi}{3}\right) = \tfrac{1}{2}$$

$$f''(x) = -\cos x \qquad f''\left(\tfrac{\pi}{3}\right) = -\tfrac{1}{2}$$

$$\vdots \qquad\qquad\qquad \vdots$$

Note that $f^{(2n)}\left(\tfrac{\pi}{3}\right) = (-1)^n \cdot \tfrac{1}{2}$ and $f^{(2n+1)}\left(\tfrac{\pi}{3}\right) = (-1)^{n+1} \cdot \tfrac{\sqrt{3}}{2}$.

$$\cos x = \sum_{n=0}^{\infty} \frac{f^{(n)}\left(\tfrac{\pi}{3}\right)}{n!}\left(x - \tfrac{\pi}{3}\right)^n = \sum_{n=0}^{\infty} \frac{(-1)^n}{2(2n)!}\left(x - \tfrac{\pi}{3}\right)^{2n} + \sum_{n=0}^{\infty} \frac{(-1)^{n+1}\sqrt{3}}{2(2n+1)!}\left(x - \tfrac{\pi}{3}\right)^{2n+1}$$

$$= \frac{1}{2}\sum_{n=0}^{\infty}(-1)^n\left[\frac{1}{(2n)!}\left(x - \tfrac{\pi}{3}\right)^{2n} - \frac{\sqrt{3}}{(2n+1)!}\left(x - \tfrac{\pi}{3}\right)^{2n+1}\right]$$

37. $\dfrac{1}{1+x} = \dfrac{1}{1-(-x)} = \displaystyle\sum_{n=0}^{\infty}(-x)^n = \sum_{n=0}^{\infty}(-1)^n x^n$ for $|x| < 1 \;\Rightarrow\; \dfrac{x^2}{1+x} = \displaystyle\sum_{n=0}^{\infty}(-1)^n x^{n+2}$ with $R = 1$.

38. $\tan^{-1}x = \displaystyle\sum_{n=0}^{\infty}(-1)^n \frac{x^{2n+1}}{2n+1}$ with interval of convergence $[-1, 1]$, so

$$\tan^{-1}(x^2) = \sum_{n=0}^{\infty}(-1)^n \frac{\left(x^2\right)^{2n+1}}{2n+1} = \sum_{n=0}^{\infty}(-1)^n \frac{x^{4n+2}}{2n+1}, \text{ which converges when } x^2 \in [-1, 1] \;\Leftrightarrow\; x \in [-1, 1].$$

Therefore, $R = 1$.

39. $\dfrac{1}{1-x} = \displaystyle\sum_{n=0}^{\infty} x^n$ for $|x| < 1 \;\Rightarrow\; \ln(1-x) = -\displaystyle\int \frac{dx}{1-x} = -\int \sum_{n=0}^{\infty} x^n\, dx = C - \sum_{n=0}^{\infty} \frac{x^{n+1}}{n+1}$.

$\ln(1-0) = C - 0 \;\Rightarrow\; C = 0 \;\Rightarrow\; \ln(1-x) = -\displaystyle\sum_{n=0}^{\infty}\frac{x^{n+1}}{n+1} = -\sum_{n=1}^{\infty}\frac{x^n}{n}$ with $R = 1$.

40. $e^x = \displaystyle\sum_{n=0}^{\infty}\frac{x^n}{n!} \;\Rightarrow\; xe^{2x} = x\sum_{n=0}^{\infty}\frac{(2x)^n}{n!} = \sum_{n=0}^{\infty}\frac{2^n x^{n+1}}{n!}, \; R = \infty$

41. $\sin x = \displaystyle\sum_{n=0}^{\infty}\frac{(-1)^n x^{2n+1}}{(2n+1)!} \;\Rightarrow\; \sin(x^4) = \sum_{n=0}^{\infty}\frac{(-1)^n\left(x^4\right)^{2n+1}}{(2n+1)!} = \sum_{n=0}^{\infty}\frac{(-1)^n x^{8n+4}}{(2n+1)!}$ for all x, so the radius of convergence is ∞.

42. $10^x = \left(e^{\ln 10}\right)^x = e^{x\ln 10} = \displaystyle\sum_{n=0}^{\infty}\frac{(x\ln 10)^n}{n!} = \sum_{n=0}^{\infty}\frac{(\ln 10)^n x^n}{n!}, \; R = \infty$

43. $f(x) = \dfrac{1}{\sqrt[4]{16-x}} = \dfrac{1}{\sqrt[4]{16(1-x/16)}} = \dfrac{1}{\sqrt[4]{16}\left(1-\tfrac{1}{16}x\right)^{1/4}} = \tfrac{1}{2}\left(1 - \tfrac{1}{16}x\right)^{-1/4}$

$$= \frac{1}{2}\left[1 + \left(-\tfrac{1}{4}\right)\left(-\tfrac{x}{16}\right) + \frac{\left(-\tfrac{1}{4}\right)\left(-\tfrac{5}{4}\right)}{2!}\left(-\tfrac{x}{16}\right)^2 + \frac{\left(-\tfrac{1}{4}\right)\left(-\tfrac{5}{4}\right)\left(-\tfrac{9}{4}\right)}{3!}\left(-\tfrac{x}{16}\right)^3 + \cdots\right]$$

$$= \frac{1}{2} + \sum_{n=1}^{\infty}\frac{1\cdot 5\cdot 9\cdot\cdots\cdot(4n-3)}{2\cdot 4^n\cdot n!\cdot 16^n}\,x^n = \frac{1}{2} + \sum_{n=1}^{\infty}\frac{1\cdot 5\cdot 9\cdot\cdots\cdot(4n-3)}{2^1\cdot 2^{2n}\cdot n!\cdot 2^{4n}}\,x^n$$

$$= \frac{1}{2} + \sum_{n=1}^{\infty}\frac{1\cdot 5\cdot 9\cdot\cdots\cdot(4n-3)}{2^{6n+1}\cdot n!}\,x^n$$

for $\left|-\dfrac{x}{16}\right| < 1 \;\Rightarrow\; |x| < 16 \;\Rightarrow\; R = 16$.

44. $(1-3x)^{-5} = \sum\limits_{n=0}^{\infty} \binom{-5}{n}(-3x)^n = 1 + (-5)(-3x) + \dfrac{(-5)(-6)}{2!}(-3x)^2 + \dfrac{(-5)(-6)(-7)}{3!}(-3x)^3 + \cdots$

$$= 1 + \sum\limits_{n=1}^{\infty} \dfrac{5 \cdot 6 \cdots \cdots (n+4) \cdot 3^n x^n}{n!}, \; |-3x| < 1 \text{ so } R = \tfrac{1}{3}.$$

45. $e^x = \sum\limits_{n=0}^{\infty} \dfrac{x^n}{n!}$, so $\dfrac{e^x}{x} = \dfrac{1}{x}\sum\limits_{n=0}^{\infty}\dfrac{x^n}{n!} = \sum\limits_{n=0}^{\infty}\dfrac{x^{n-1}}{n!} = x^{-1} + \sum\limits_{n=1}^{\infty}\dfrac{x^{n-1}}{n!} = \dfrac{1}{x} + \sum\limits_{n=1}^{\infty}\dfrac{x^{n-1}}{n!}$ and

$$\int \dfrac{e^x}{x}\,dx = C + \ln|x| + \sum\limits_{n=1}^{\infty}\dfrac{x^n}{n \cdot n!}.$$

46. $(1+x^4)^{1/2} = \sum\limits_{n=0}^{\infty}\binom{\frac{1}{2}}{n}(x^4)^n = 1 + \left(\tfrac{1}{2}\right)x^4 + \dfrac{\left(\frac{1}{2}\right)\left(-\frac{1}{2}\right)}{2!}(x^4)^2 + \dfrac{\left(\frac{1}{2}\right)\left(-\frac{1}{2}\right)\left(-\frac{3}{2}\right)}{3!}(x^4)^3 + \cdots$

$$= 1 + \tfrac{1}{2}x^4 - \tfrac{1}{8}x^8 + \tfrac{1}{16}x^{12} - \cdots$$

so $\int_0^1(1+x^4)^{1/2}\,dx = \left[x + \tfrac{1}{10}x^5 - \tfrac{1}{72}x^9 + \tfrac{1}{208}x^{13} - \cdots\right]_0^1 = 1 + \tfrac{1}{10} - \tfrac{1}{72} + \tfrac{1}{208} - \cdots$. This is an alternating

series, so by the Alternating Series Test, the error in the approximation $\int_0^1(1+x^4)^{1/2}\,dx \approx 1 + \tfrac{1}{10} - \tfrac{1}{72} \approx 1.086$

is less than $\tfrac{1}{208} \approx 0.0048$, sufficient for the desired accuracy. Thus, correct to two decimal places,

$\int_0^1(1+x^4)^{1/2}\,dx \approx 1.09$.

47. (a)

$$f(x) = x^{1/2} \qquad f(1) = 1 \qquad f'''(x) = \tfrac{3}{8}x^{-5/2} \qquad f'''(1) = \tfrac{3}{8}$$

$$f'(x) = \tfrac{1}{2}x^{-1/2} \qquad f'(1) = \tfrac{1}{2} \qquad f^{(4)}(x) = -\tfrac{15}{16}x^{-7/2}$$

$$f''(x) = -\tfrac{1}{4}x^{-3/2} \qquad f''(1) = -\tfrac{1}{4}$$

$$\sqrt{x} \approx T_3(x) = 1 + \dfrac{1/2}{1!}(x-1) - \dfrac{1/4}{2!}(x-1)^2 + \dfrac{3/8}{3!}(x-1)^3$$

$$= 1 + \tfrac{1}{2}(x-1) - \tfrac{1}{8}(x-1)^2 + \tfrac{1}{16}(x-1)^3$$

(b)

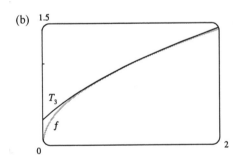

(c) $|R_3(x)| \le \dfrac{M}{4!}|x-1|^4$, where $\left|f^{(4)}(x)\right| \le M$ with

$f^{(4)}(x) = -\tfrac{15}{16}x^{-7/2}$. Now $0.9 \le x \le 1.1 \;\Rightarrow$

$-0.1 \le x - 1 \le 0.1 \;\Rightarrow\; |x-1| \le 0.1 \;\Rightarrow$

$(x-1)^4 \le (0.1)^4$, and letting $x = 0.9$ gives

$M = \dfrac{15}{16(0.9)^{7/2}}$, so

$|R_3(x)| \le \dfrac{15}{16(0.9)^{7/2}4!}(0.1)^4 \approx 0.000005648$

$\approx 0.000006 = 6 \times 10^{-6}$.

(d)

From the graph of $|R_3(x)| = |\sqrt{x} - T_3(x)|$, it appears that the error

is less than 4.7×10^{-6} on $[0.9, 1.1]$.

48. (a)

$$f(x) = \sec x$$
$$f'(x) = \sec x \tan x$$
$$f''(x) = \sec x \tan^2 x + \sec^3 x$$
$$f'''(x) = \sec x \tan^3 x + 5 \sec^3 x \tan x$$

$$f(0) = 1 \qquad \sec x \approx T_2(x) = 1 + \tfrac{1}{2}x^2$$
$$f'(0) = 0$$
$$f''(0) = 1$$

(b)

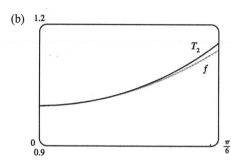

(c) $|R_2(x)| \leq \dfrac{M}{3!}|x|^3$, where $\left|f^{(3)}(x)\right| \leq M$ with

$f^{(3)}(x) = \sec x \tan^3 x + 5 \sec^3 x \tan x$. Now

$0 \leq x \leq \frac{\pi}{6} \;\Rightarrow\; x^3 \leq \left(\frac{\pi}{6}\right)^3$, and letting $x = \frac{\pi}{6}$

gives $M = \frac{14}{3}$, so

$$|R_2(x)| \leq \tfrac{14}{3 \cdot 6}\left(\tfrac{\pi}{6}\right)^3 \approx 0.111648.$$

(d)

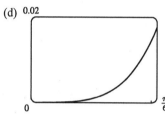

From the graph of $|R_2(x)| = |\sec x - T_2(x)|$, it appears that the error is less than 0.02 on $\left[0, \frac{\pi}{6}\right]$.

49. $\sin x = \displaystyle\sum_{n=0}^{\infty} (-1)^n \frac{x^{2n+1}}{(2n+1)!} = x - \frac{x^3}{3!} + \frac{x^5}{5!} - \frac{x^7}{7!} + \cdots$, so $\sin x - x = -\dfrac{x^3}{3!} + \dfrac{x^5}{5!} - \dfrac{x^7}{7!} + \cdots$ and

$\dfrac{\sin x - x}{x^3} = -\dfrac{1}{3!} + \dfrac{x^2}{5!} - \dfrac{x^4}{7!} + \cdots$ and $\displaystyle\lim_{x \to 0} \dfrac{\sin x - x}{x^3} = \lim_{x \to 0}\left(-\dfrac{1}{6} + \dfrac{x^2}{120} - \dfrac{x^4}{5040} + \cdots\right) = -\dfrac{1}{6}$.

50. (a) $F = \dfrac{mgR^2}{(R+h)^2} = \dfrac{mgR^2/R^2}{(R+h)^2/R^2} = \dfrac{mg}{(1+h/R)^2} = mg\left(1 + \dfrac{h}{R}\right)^{-2} = mg \displaystyle\sum_{n=0}^{\infty} \binom{-2}{n}\left(\dfrac{h}{R}\right)^n$

(Binomial Series)

(b) We expand $F = mg\left[1 - 2(h/R) + 3(h/R)^2 - \cdots\right]$. This is an alternating series, so by the Alternating Series Estimation Theorem, the error in the approximation $F = mg$ is less than $2mgh/R$, so for accuracy

within 1% we want $\left|\dfrac{2mgh/R}{mgR^2/(R+h)^2}\right| < 0.01 \;\Leftrightarrow\; \dfrac{2h(R+h)^2}{R^3} < 0.01$. This inequality would be difficult

to solve for h, so we substitute $R = 6{,}400$ km and plot both sides of the inequality. It appears that the approximation is accurate to within 1% for $h < 31$ km.

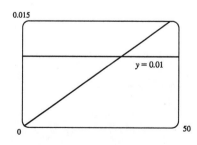

51. Let $y(x) = \sum_{n=0}^{\infty} c_n x^n$. Then $xy' = x \sum_{n=1}^{\infty} nc_n x^{n-1} = \sum_{n=0}^{\infty} nc_n x^n$,

$y''(x) = \sum_{n=2}^{\infty} n(n-1)c_n x^{n-2} = \sum_{n=0}^{\infty} (n+2)(n+1)c_{n+2} x^n$, and the equation $y'' + xy' + y = 0$ becomes

$\sum_{n=0}^{\infty} [(n+2)(n+1)c_{n+2} + nc_n + c_n]x^n = 0$. Thus, the recursion relation is

$c_{n+2} = \dfrac{-nc_n - c_n}{(n+2)(n+1)} = \dfrac{-c_n(n+1)}{(n+2)(n+1)} = -\dfrac{c_n}{n+2}$ for $n = 0, 1, 2, \ldots$. But $c_0 = y(0) = 0$, so $c_{2n} = 0$

for $n = 0, 1, 2, \ldots$. Also, $c_1 = y'(0) = 1$, so $c_3 = -\dfrac{c_1}{3} = -\dfrac{1}{3}$, $c_5 = \dfrac{(-1)^2}{3 \cdot 5} = \dfrac{(-1)^2 2^2 2!}{5!}$,

$c_7 = \dfrac{(-1)^3}{3 \cdot 5 \cdot 7} = \dfrac{(-1)^3 2^3 3!}{7!}, \ldots, c_{2n+1} = \dfrac{(-1)^n 2^n n!}{(2n+1)!} = \dfrac{(-2)^n n!}{(2n+1)!}$ for $n = 0, 1, 2, \ldots$. Note that

$2^n n! = (2 \cdot 1) \cdot (2 \cdot 2) \cdot (2 \cdot 3) \cdot \cdots \cdot (2 \cdot n)$. Thus, the solution to the initial-value problem is

$$y(x) = \sum_{n=0}^{\infty} c_n x^n = \sum_{n=0}^{\infty} \dfrac{(-2)^n n!}{(2n+1)!} x^{2n+1}$$

52. Let $y(x) = \sum_{n=0}^{\infty} c_n x^n$. Then $xy' = x \sum_{n=1}^{\infty} nc_n x^{n-1} = \sum_{n=0}^{\infty} nc_n x^n$,

$y''(x) = \sum_{n=2}^{\infty} n(n-1)c_n x^{n-2} = \sum_{n=0}^{\infty} (n+2)(n+1) c_{n+2} x^n$, and the equation $y'' - xy' - 2y = 0$ becomes

$\sum_{n=0}^{\infty} [(n+2)(n+1)c_{n+2} - nc_n - 2c_n]x^n = 0$. Thus, the recursion relation is

$c_{n+2} = \dfrac{nc_n + 2c_n}{(n+2)(n+1)} = \dfrac{c_n(n+2)}{(n+2)(n+1)} = \dfrac{c_n}{n+1}$ for $n = 0, 1, 2, \ldots$.

Given c_0, we have $c_2 = \dfrac{c_0}{1}$, $c_4 = \dfrac{c_2}{3} = \dfrac{c_0}{1 \cdot 3}$,

$c_6 = \dfrac{c_4}{5} = \dfrac{c_0}{1 \cdot 3 \cdot 5}, \ldots, c_{2n} = \dfrac{c_0}{1 \cdot 3 \cdot 5 \cdot \cdots \cdot (2n-1)} = c_0 \dfrac{2 \cdot 4 \cdot 6 \cdot \cdots \cdot (2n-2)}{1 \cdot 2 \cdot 3 \cdot 4 \cdot 5 \cdot \cdots \cdot (2n-1)} = c_0 \dfrac{2^{n-1}(n-1)!}{(2n-1)!}$.

Given c_1, $c_3 = \dfrac{c_1}{2}$, $c_5 = \dfrac{c_3}{4} = \dfrac{c_1}{2 \cdot 4}$, $c_7 = \dfrac{c_5}{6} = \dfrac{c_1}{2 \cdot 4 \cdot 6}, \ldots, c_{2n+1} = \dfrac{c_1}{2 \cdot 4 \cdot 6 \cdot \cdots \cdot 2n} = \dfrac{c_1}{2^n n!}$.

Thus, the general solution is

$$y(x) = \sum_{n=0}^{\infty} c_n x^n = c_0 + c_0 \sum_{n=1}^{\infty} \dfrac{2^{n-1}(n-1)! x^{2n}}{(2n-1)!} + c_1 \sum_{n=0}^{\infty} \dfrac{x^{2n+1}}{2^n n!}$$

But $\sum_{n=0}^{\infty} \dfrac{x^{2n+1}}{2^n n!} = x \sum_{n=0}^{\infty} \dfrac{(x^2/2)^n}{n!} = xe^{x^2/2}$, so

$$y(x) = c_1 xe^{x^2/2} + c_0 + c_0 \sum_{n=1}^{\infty} \dfrac{2^{n-1}(n-1)! x^{2n}}{(2n-1)!}$$

53. (a) From Formula 14a in Appendix C, with $x = y = \theta$, we get $\tan 2\theta = \dfrac{2 \tan \theta}{1 - \tan^2 \theta}$, so $\cot 2\theta = \dfrac{1 - \tan^2 \theta}{2 \tan \theta} \Rightarrow$

$2 \cot 2\theta = \dfrac{1 - \tan^2 \theta}{\tan \theta} = \cot \theta - \tan \theta$. Replacing θ by $\frac{1}{2}x$, we get $2 \cot x = \cot \frac{1}{2}x - \tan \frac{1}{2}x$,

or $\tan \frac{1}{2}x = \cot \frac{1}{2}x - 2 \cot x$.

(b) From part (a), $\tan\dfrac{x}{2^n} = \cot\dfrac{x}{2^n} - 2\cot\dfrac{x}{2^{n-1}}$, so the nth partial sum of $\displaystyle\sum_{n=1}^{\infty}\dfrac{1}{2^n}\tan\dfrac{x}{2^n}$ is

$$s_n = \frac{\tan(x/2)}{2} + \frac{\tan(x/4)}{4} + \frac{\tan(x/8)}{8} + \cdots + \frac{\tan(x/2^n)}{2^n}$$

$$= \left[\frac{\cot(x/2)}{2} - \cot x\right] + \left[\frac{\cot(x/4)}{4} - \frac{\cot(x/2)}{2}\right] + \left[\frac{\cot(x/8)}{8} - \frac{\cot(x/4)}{4}\right] + \cdots$$

$$+ \left[\frac{\cot(x/2^n)}{2^n} - \frac{\cot\left(x/2^{n-1}\right)}{2^{n-1}}\right] = -\cot x + \frac{\cot(x/2^n)}{2^n} \quad \text{[telescoping sum]}$$

Now $\dfrac{\cot(x/2^n)}{2^n} = \dfrac{\cos(x/2^n)}{2^n\sin(x/2^n)} = \dfrac{\cos(x/2^n)}{x}\cdot\dfrac{x/2^n}{\sin(x/2^n)} \to \dfrac{1}{x}\cdot 1 = \dfrac{1}{x}$ as $n \to \infty$ since $x/2^n \to 0$

for $x \neq 0$. Therefore, if $x \neq 0$ and $x \neq n\pi$, then

$$\sum_{n=1}^{\infty}\frac{1}{2^n}\tan\frac{x}{2^n} = \lim_{n\to\infty}\left(-\cot x + \frac{1}{2^n}\cot\frac{x}{2^n}\right) = -\cot x + \frac{1}{x}.$$

If $x = 0$, then all terms in the series are 0, so the sum is 0.

54. We use the problem-solving strategy of taking cases:

Case (i): If $|x| < 1$, then $0 \leq x^2 < 1$, so $\displaystyle\lim_{n\to\infty}x^{2n} = 0$ (see Example 8 in Section 8.1)

and $f(x) = \displaystyle\lim_{n\to\infty}\frac{x^{2n}-1}{x^{2n}+1} = \frac{0-1}{0+1} = -1$.

Case (ii): If $|x| = 1$, that is, $x = \pm 1$, then $x^2 = 1$, so $f(x) = \displaystyle\lim_{n\to\infty}\frac{1-1}{1+1} = 0$.

Case (iii): If $|x| > 1$, then $x^2 > 1$, so $\displaystyle\lim_{n\to\infty}x^{2n} = \infty$ and

$$f(x) = \lim_{n\to\infty}\frac{x^{2n}-1}{x^{2n}+1} = \lim_{n\to\infty}\frac{1-\left(1/x^{2n}\right)}{1+\left(1/x^{2n}\right)} = \frac{1-0}{1+0} = 1.$$

Thus, $f(x) = \begin{cases} 1 & \text{if } x < -1 \\ 0 & \text{if } x = -1 \\ -1 & \text{if } -1 < x < 1 \\ 0 & \text{if } x = 1 \\ 1 & \text{if } x > 1 \end{cases}$

The graph shows that f is continuous everywhere except at $x = \pm 1$.

Focus on Problem Solving

1. It would be far too much work to compute 15 derivatives of f. The key idea is to remember that $f^{(n)}(0)$ occurs in the coefficient of x^n in the Maclaurin series of f. We start with the Maclaurin series for sin:

$$\sin x = x - \frac{x^3}{3!} + \frac{x^5}{5!} - \cdots . \text{ Then } \sin(x^3) = x^3 - \frac{x^9}{3!} + \frac{x^{15}}{5!} - \cdots \text{ and so the coefficient of } x^{15} \text{ is}$$

$$\frac{f^{(15)}(0)}{15!} = \frac{1}{5!}. \text{ Therefore, } f^{(15)}(0) = \frac{15!}{5!} = 6 \cdot 7 \cdot 8 \cdot 9 \cdot 10 \cdot 11 \cdot 12 \cdot 13 \cdot 14 \cdot 15 = 10,897,286,400.$$

2. $|AP_2|^2 = 2, \; |AP_3|^2 = 2 + 2^2, \; |AP_4|^2 = 2 + 2^2 + \left(2^2\right)^2, \; |AP_5|^2 = 2 + 2^2 + \left(2^2\right)^2 + \left(2^3\right)^2, \ldots,$

$$|AP_n|^2 = 2 + 2^2 + \left(2^2\right)^2 + \cdots + \left(2^{n-2}\right)^2 \text{ (for } n \geq 3\text{)} = 2 + \left(4 + 4^2 + 4^3 + \cdots + 4^{n-2}\right)$$

$$= 2 + \frac{4\left(4^{n-2} - 1\right)}{4 - 1} \text{ (finite geometric sum with } a = 4, r = 4\text{)} = \frac{6}{3} + \frac{4^{n-1} - 4}{3} = \frac{2}{3} + \frac{4^{n-1}}{3}$$

So $\tan \angle P_n A P_{n+1} = \dfrac{|P_n P_{n+1}|}{|AP_n|} = \dfrac{2^{n-1}}{\sqrt{\dfrac{2}{3} + \dfrac{4^{n-1}}{3}}} = \dfrac{\sqrt{4^{n-1}}}{\sqrt{\dfrac{2}{3} + \dfrac{4^{n-1}}{3}}} = \dfrac{1}{\sqrt{\dfrac{2}{3 \cdot 4^{n-1}} + \dfrac{1}{3}}} \rightarrow \sqrt{3}$ as $n \rightarrow \infty$, so

$\angle P_n A P_{n+1} \rightarrow \frac{\pi}{3}$ as $n \rightarrow \infty$.

3. (a) Let $a = \arctan x$ and $b = \arctan y$. Then, from Formula 14b in Appendix C,

$$\tan(a - b) = \frac{\tan a - \tan b}{1 + \tan a \tan b} = \frac{\tan(\arctan x) - \tan(\arctan y)}{1 + \tan(\arctan x) \tan(\arctan y)} = \frac{x - y}{1 + xy} \quad \Rightarrow$$

$$\arctan x - \arctan y = a - b = \arctan \frac{x - y}{1 + xy} \quad \text{since } -\frac{\pi}{2} < \arctan x - \arctan y < \frac{\pi}{2}$$

(b) From part (a) we have

$$\arctan \tfrac{120}{119} - \arctan \tfrac{1}{239} = \arctan \frac{\frac{120}{119} - \frac{1}{239}}{1 + \frac{120}{119} \cdot \frac{1}{239}} = \arctan \frac{\frac{28,561}{28,441}}{\frac{28,561}{28,441}} = \arctan 1 = \tfrac{\pi}{4}$$

(c) Replacing y by $-y$ in the formula of part (a), we get $\arctan x + \arctan y = \arctan \dfrac{x + y}{1 - xy}$. So

$$4 \arctan \tfrac{1}{5} = 2\left(\arctan \tfrac{1}{5} + \arctan \tfrac{1}{5}\right) = 2 \arctan \frac{\frac{1}{5} + \frac{1}{5}}{1 - \frac{1}{5} \cdot \frac{1}{5}} = 2 \arctan \tfrac{5}{12} = \arctan \tfrac{5}{12} + \arctan \tfrac{5}{12}$$

$$= \arctan \frac{\frac{5}{12} + \frac{5}{12}}{1 - \frac{5}{12} \cdot \frac{5}{12}} = \arctan \tfrac{120}{119}$$

Thus, from part (b), we have $4 \arctan \tfrac{1}{5} - \arctan \tfrac{1}{239} = \arctan \tfrac{120}{119} - \arctan \tfrac{1}{239} = \tfrac{\pi}{4}$.

(d) From Example 7 in Section 8.6 we have $\arctan x = x - \dfrac{x^3}{3} + \dfrac{x^5}{5} - \dfrac{x^7}{7} + \dfrac{x^9}{9} - \dfrac{x^{11}}{11} + \cdots$, so

$$\arctan \frac{1}{5} = \frac{1}{5} - \frac{1}{3 \cdot 5^3} + \frac{1}{5 \cdot 5^5} - \frac{1}{7 \cdot 5^7} + \frac{1}{9 \cdot 5^9} - \frac{1}{11 \cdot 5^{11}} + \cdots$$

This is an alternating series and the size of the terms decreases to 0, so by the Alternating Series Estimation Theorem, the sum lies between s_5 and s_6, that is, $0.197395560 < \arctan \frac{1}{5} < 0.197395562$.

(e) From the series in part (d) we get $\arctan \dfrac{1}{239} = \dfrac{1}{239} - \dfrac{1}{3 \cdot 239^3} + \dfrac{1}{5 \cdot 239^5} - \cdots$. The third term is less than 2.6×10^{-13}, so by the Alternating Series Estimation Theorem we have, to nine decimal places, $\arctan \frac{1}{239} \approx s_2 \approx 0.004184076$. Thus, $0.004184075 < \arctan \frac{1}{239} < 0.004184077$.

(f) From part (c) we have $\pi = 16 \arctan \frac{1}{5} - 4 \arctan \frac{1}{239}$, so from parts (d) and (e) we have
$16(0.197395560) - 4(0.004184077) < \pi < 16(0.197395562) - 4(0.004184075) \;\Rightarrow$
$3.141592652 < \pi < 3.141592692$. So, to 7 decimal places, $\pi \approx 3.1415927$.

4. Let's first try the case $k = 1$: $a_0 + a_1 = 0 \;\Rightarrow\; a_1 = -a_0 \;\Rightarrow$

$$\lim_{n \to \infty} \left(a_0 \sqrt{n} + a_1 \sqrt{n+1} \right) = \lim_{n \to \infty} \left(a_0 \sqrt{n} - a_0 \sqrt{n+1} \right) = a_0 \lim_{n \to \infty} \left(\sqrt{n} - \sqrt{n+1} \right) \frac{\sqrt{n} + \sqrt{n+1}}{\sqrt{n} + \sqrt{n+1}}$$

$$= a_0 \lim_{n \to \infty} \frac{-1}{\sqrt{n} + \sqrt{n+1}} = 0$$

In general we have $a_0 + a_1 + \cdots + a_k = 0 \;\Rightarrow\; a_k = -a_0 - a_1 - \cdots - a_{k-1} \;\Rightarrow$

$$\lim_{n \to \infty} \left(a_0 \sqrt{n} + a_1 \sqrt{n+1} + a_2 \sqrt{n+2} + \cdots + a_k \sqrt{n+k} \right)$$

$$= \lim_{n \to \infty} \left(a_0 \sqrt{n} + a_1 \sqrt{n+1} + \cdots + a_{k-1} \sqrt{n+k-1} - a_0 \sqrt{n+k} - a_1 \sqrt{n+k} - \cdots - a_{k-1} \sqrt{n+k} \right)$$

$$= a_0 \lim_{n \to \infty} \left(\sqrt{n} - \sqrt{n+k} \right) + a_1 \lim_{n \to \infty} \left(\sqrt{n+1} - \sqrt{n+k} \right) + \cdots + a_{k-1} \lim_{n \to \infty} \left(\sqrt{n+k-1} - \sqrt{n+k} \right)$$

Each of these limits is 0 by the same type of simplification as in the case $k = 1$. So we have

$$\lim_{n \to \infty} \left(a_0 \sqrt{n} + a_1 \sqrt{n+1} + a_2 \sqrt{n+2} + \cdots + a_k \sqrt{n+k} \right) = a_0(0) + a_1(0) + \cdots + a_{k-1}(0) = 0$$

5. (a) At each stage, each side is replaced by four shorter sides, each of length $\frac{1}{3}$ of the side length at the preceding stage. Writing s_0 and ℓ_0 for the number of sides and the length of the side of the initial triangle, we generate the table at right. In general, we have $s_n = 3 \cdot 4^n$ and $\ell_n = \left(\frac{1}{3} \right)^n$, so the length of the perimeter at the nth stage of construction is $p_n = s_n \ell_n = 3 \cdot 4^n \cdot \left(\frac{1}{3} \right)^n = 3 \cdot \left(\frac{4}{3} \right)^n$.

$s_0 = 3$	$\ell_0 = 1$
$s_1 = 3 \cdot 4$	$\ell_1 = 1/3$
$s_2 = 3 \cdot 4^2$	$\ell_2 = 1/3^2$
$s_3 = 3 \cdot 4^3$	$\ell_3 = 1/3^3$
$\vdots$	$\vdots$

(b) $p_n = \dfrac{4^n}{3^{n-1}} = 4 \left(\dfrac{4}{3} \right)^{n-1}$. Since $\frac{4}{3} > 1$, $p_n \to \infty$ as $n \to \infty$.

(c) The area of each of the small triangles added at a given stage is one-ninth of the area of the triangle added at the preceding stage. Let a be the area of the original triangle. Then the area a_n of each of the small triangles added at stage n is $a_n = a \cdot \dfrac{1}{9^n} = \dfrac{a}{9^n}$. Since a small triangle is added to each side at every stage, it follows that the total area A_n added to the figure at the nth stage is $A_n = s_{n-1} \cdot a_n = 3 \cdot 4^{n-1} \cdot \dfrac{a}{9^n} = a \cdot \dfrac{4^{n-1}}{3^{2n-1}}$.

Then the total area enclosed by the snowflake curve is

$A = a + A_1 + A_2 + A_3 + \cdots = a + a \cdot \dfrac{1}{3} + a \cdot \dfrac{4}{3^3} + a \cdot \dfrac{4^2}{3^5} + a \cdot \dfrac{4^3}{3^7} + \cdots$. After the first term, this is a

geometric series with common ratio $\frac{4}{9}$, so $A = a + \dfrac{a/3}{1 - \frac{4}{9}} = a + \dfrac{a}{3} \cdot \dfrac{9}{5} = \dfrac{8a}{5}$. But the area of the original

equilateral triangle with side 1 is $a = \frac{1}{2} \cdot 1 \cdot \sin \frac{\pi}{3} = \frac{\sqrt{3}}{4}$. So the area enclosed by the snowflake curve is

$\frac{8}{5} \cdot \frac{\sqrt{3}}{4} = \frac{2\sqrt{3}}{5}$.

6. Let the series be S. Then every term in S is of the form $\dfrac{1}{2^m 3^n}$, $m, n \geq 0$, and furthermore each term occurs only

once. So we can write

$$S = \sum_{m=0}^{\infty} \sum_{n=0}^{\infty} \frac{1}{2^m 3^n} = \sum_{m=0}^{\infty} \sum_{n=0}^{\infty} \frac{1}{2^m} \frac{1}{3^n} = \sum_{m=0}^{\infty} \frac{1}{2^m} \sum_{n=0}^{\infty} \frac{1}{3^n} = \frac{1}{1 - \frac{1}{2}} \cdot \frac{1}{1 - \frac{1}{3}} = 2 \cdot \frac{3}{2} = 3$$

7. We start with the geometric series $\sum_{n=0}^{\infty} x^n = \dfrac{1}{1-x}$, $|x| < 1$, and differentiate:

$\sum_{n=1}^{\infty} n x^{n-1} = \dfrac{d}{dx}\left(\sum_{n=0}^{\infty} x^n\right) = \dfrac{d}{dx}\left(\dfrac{1}{1-x}\right) = \dfrac{1}{(1-x)^2}$ for $|x| < 1 \Rightarrow$

$\sum_{n=1}^{\infty} n x^n = x \sum_{n=1}^{\infty} n x^{n-1} = \dfrac{x}{(1-x)^2}$ for $|x| < 1$. Differentiate again:

$\sum_{n=1}^{\infty} n^2 x^{n-1} = \dfrac{d}{dx} \dfrac{x}{(1-x)^2} = \dfrac{(1-x)^2 - x \cdot 2(1-x)(-1)}{(1-x)^4} = \dfrac{x+1}{(1-x)^3} \Rightarrow \sum_{n=1}^{\infty} n^2 x^n = \dfrac{x^2 + x}{(1-x)^3} \Rightarrow$

$\sum_{n=1}^{\infty} n^3 x^{n-1} = \dfrac{d}{dx} \dfrac{x^2 + x}{(1-x)^3} = \dfrac{(1-x)^3(2x+1) - (x^2+x)3(1-x)^2(-1)}{(1-x)^6} = \dfrac{x^2 + 4x + 1}{(1-x)^4} \Rightarrow$

$\sum_{n=1}^{\infty} n^3 x^n = \dfrac{x^3 + 4x^2 + x}{(1-x)^4}$, $|x| < 1$. The radius of convergence is 1 because that is the radius of convergence for

the geometric series we started with. If $x = \pm 1$, the series is $\sum n^3(\pm 1)^n$, which diverges by the Test For

Divergence, so the interval of convergence is $(-1, 1)$.

8. Place the y-axis as shown and let the length of each book be L. We want to
show that the center of mass of the system of n books lies above the table,
that is, $\bar{x} < L$. The x-coordinates of the centers of mass of the books are

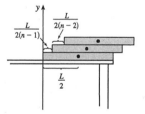

$x_1 = \dfrac{L}{2}, x_2 = \dfrac{L}{2(n-1)} + \dfrac{L}{2}, x_3 = \dfrac{L}{2(n-1)} + \dfrac{L}{2(n-2)} + \dfrac{L}{2}$, and

so on. Each book has the same mass m, so if there are n books, then

$$\bar{x} = \frac{mx_1 + mx_2 + \cdots + mx_n}{mn} = \frac{x_1 + x_2 + \cdots + x_n}{n}$$

$$= \frac{1}{n}\left[\frac{L}{2} + \left(\frac{L}{2(n-1)} + \frac{L}{2}\right) + \left(\frac{L}{2(n-1)} + \frac{L}{2(n-2)} + \frac{L}{2}\right) + \cdots \right.$$

$$\left. + \left(\frac{L}{2(n-1)} + \frac{L}{2(n-2)} + \cdots + \frac{L}{4} + \frac{L}{2} + \frac{L}{2}\right)\right]$$

$$= \frac{L}{n}\left[\frac{n-1}{2(n-1)} + \frac{n-2}{2(n-2)} + \cdots + \frac{2}{4} + \frac{1}{2} + \frac{n}{2}\right] = \frac{L}{n}\left[(n-1)\frac{1}{2} + \frac{n}{2}\right] = \frac{2n-1}{2n}L < L$$

This shows that, no matter how many books are added according to the given scheme, the center of mass lies above the table. It remains to observe that the series $\frac{1}{2} + \frac{1}{4} + \frac{1}{6} + \frac{1}{8} + \cdots = \frac{1}{2}\sum(1/n)$ is divergent (harmonic series), so we can make the top book extend as far as we like beyond the edge of the table if we add enough books.

9. $u = 1 + \dfrac{x^3}{3!} + \dfrac{x^6}{6!} + \dfrac{x^9}{9!} + \cdots,\ v = x + \dfrac{x^4}{4!} + \dfrac{x^7}{7!} + \dfrac{x^{10}}{10!} + \cdots,\ w = \dfrac{x^2}{2!} + \dfrac{x^5}{5!} + \dfrac{x^8}{8!} + \cdots.$ The key idea is to

differentiate: $\dfrac{du}{dx} = \dfrac{3x^2}{3!} + \dfrac{6x^5}{6!} + \dfrac{9x^8}{9!} + \cdots = \dfrac{x^2}{2!} + \dfrac{x^5}{5!} + \dfrac{x^8}{8!} + \cdots = w.$ Similarly,

$\dfrac{dv}{dx} = 1 + \dfrac{x^3}{3!} + \dfrac{x^6}{6!} + \dfrac{x^9}{9!} + \cdots = u$, and $\dfrac{dw}{dx} = x + \dfrac{x^4}{4!} + \dfrac{x^7}{7!} + \dfrac{x^{10}}{10!} + \cdots = v.$ So $u' = w$, $v' = u$, and $w' = v$.

Now differentiate the left hand side of the desired equation:

$$\frac{d}{dx}\left(u^3 + v^3 + w^3 - 3uvw\right) = 3u^2 u' + 3v^2 v' + 3w^2 w' - 3\left(u'vw + uv'w + uvw'\right)$$

$$= 3u^2 w + 3v^2 u + 3w^2 v - 3\left(vw^2 + u^2 w + uv^2\right) = 0 \quad \Rightarrow$$

$u^3 + v^3 + w^3 - 3uvw = C.$ To find the value of the constant C, we put $x = 0$ in the last equation and get $1^3 + 0^3 + 0^3 - 3(1 \cdot 0 \cdot 0) = C \Rightarrow C = 1$, so $u^3 + v^3 + w^3 - 3uvw = 1.$

10. First notice that both series are absolutely convergent (p-series with $p > 1$.) Let the given expression be called x. Then

$$x = \frac{1 + \dfrac{1}{2^p} + \dfrac{1}{3^p} + \dfrac{1}{4^p} + \cdots}{1 - \dfrac{1}{2^p} + \dfrac{1}{3^p} - \dfrac{1}{4^p} + \cdots} = \frac{1 + \left(2 \cdot \dfrac{1}{2^p} - \dfrac{1}{2^p}\right) + \dfrac{1}{3^p} + \left(2 \cdot \dfrac{1}{4^p} - \dfrac{1}{4^p}\right) + \cdots}{1 - \dfrac{1}{2^p} + \dfrac{1}{3^p} - \dfrac{1}{4^p} + \cdots}$$

$$= \frac{\left(1 - \dfrac{1}{2^p} + \dfrac{1}{3^p} - \dfrac{1}{4^p} + \cdots\right) + \left(2 \cdot \dfrac{1}{2^p} + 2 \cdot \dfrac{1}{4^p} + 2 \cdot \dfrac{1}{6^p} + \cdots\right)}{1 - \dfrac{1}{2^p} + \dfrac{1}{3^p} - \dfrac{1}{4^p} + \cdots}$$

$$= 1 + \frac{2\left(\dfrac{1}{2^p} + \dfrac{1}{4^p} + \dfrac{1}{6^p} + \dfrac{1}{8^p} + \cdots\right)}{1 - \dfrac{1}{2^p} + \dfrac{1}{3^p} - \dfrac{1}{4^p} + \cdots} = 1 + \frac{\dfrac{1}{2^{p-1}}\left(1 + \dfrac{1}{2^p} + \dfrac{1}{3^p} + \dfrac{1}{4^p} + \cdots\right)}{1 - \dfrac{1}{2^p} + \dfrac{1}{3^p} - \dfrac{1}{4^p} + \cdots} = 1 + 2^{1-p}x$$

Therefore, $x = 1 + 2^{1-p}x \iff x - 2^{1-p}x = 1 \iff x\left(1 - 2^{1-p}\right) = 1 \iff x = \dfrac{1}{1 - 2^{1-p}}.$

11. If L is the length of a side of the equilateral triangle, then the area is $A = \frac{1}{2}L \cdot \frac{\sqrt{3}}{2}L = \frac{\sqrt{3}}{4}L^2$ and so $L^2 = \frac{4}{\sqrt{3}}A$. Let r be the radius of one of the circles. When there are n rows of circles, the figure shows that

$$L = \sqrt{3}\,r + r + (n-2)(2r) + r + \sqrt{3}\,r = r\left(2n - 2 + 2\sqrt{3}\right), \text{ so } r = \frac{L}{2\left(n + \sqrt{3} - 1\right)}. \text{ The number of circles is}$$

$$1 + 2 + \cdots + n = \frac{n(n+1)}{2} \text{ and so the total area of the circles is}$$

$$A_n = \frac{n(n+1)}{2}\pi r^2 = \frac{n(n+1)}{2}\pi \frac{L^2}{4\left(n + \sqrt{3} - 1\right)^2} = \frac{n(n+1)}{2}\pi \frac{4A/\sqrt{3}}{4\left(n + \sqrt{3} - 1\right)^2}$$

$$= \frac{n(n+1)}{\left(n + \sqrt{3} - 1\right)^2}\frac{\pi A}{2\sqrt{3}} \quad \Rightarrow$$

$$\frac{A_n}{A} = \frac{n(n+1)}{\left(n + \sqrt{3} - 1\right)^2}\frac{\pi}{2\sqrt{3}}$$

$$= \frac{1 + 1/n}{\left[1 + \left(\sqrt{3} - 1\right)/n\right]^2}\frac{\pi}{2\sqrt{3}} \to \frac{\pi}{2\sqrt{3}} \text{ as } n \to \infty$$

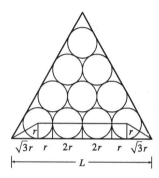

$$\sqrt{3}r \quad r \quad 2r \quad 2r \quad r \quad \sqrt{3}r$$
$$\longmapsto\!\!\longmapsto L \longmapsto\!\!\longmapsto$$

12. Given $a_0 = a_1 = 1$ and $a_n = \dfrac{(n-1)(n-2)a_{n-1} - (n-3)a_{n-2}}{n(n-1)}$, we calculate the next few terms of the

sequence: $a_2 = \dfrac{1 \cdot 0 \cdot a_1 - (-1)a_0}{2 \cdot 1} = \dfrac{1}{2}$, $a_3 = \dfrac{2 \cdot 1 \cdot a_2 - 0a_1}{3 \cdot 2} = \dfrac{1}{6}$, $a_4 = \dfrac{3 \cdot 2 \cdot a_3 - 1a_2}{4 \cdot 3} = \dfrac{1}{24}$. It seems that

$a_n = \dfrac{1}{n!}$, so we try to prove this by induction. The first step is done, so assume $a_k = \dfrac{1}{k!}$ and $a_{k-1} = \dfrac{1}{(k-1)!}$.

Then

$$a_{k+1} = \frac{k(k-1)a_k - (k-2)a_{k-1}}{(k+1)k} = \frac{\dfrac{k(k-1)}{k!} - \dfrac{k-2}{(k-1)!}}{(k+1)k} = \frac{(k-1) - (k-2)}{[(k+1)(k)](k-1)!} = \frac{1}{(k+1)!}$$

and the induction is complete. Therefore, $\sum_{n=0}^{\infty} a_n = \sum_{n=0}^{\infty} 1/n! = e$.

13. Call the series S. We group the terms according to the number of digits in their denominators:

$$S = \underbrace{\left(1 + \tfrac{1}{2} + \cdots + \tfrac{1}{8} + \tfrac{1}{9}\right)}_{g_1} + \underbrace{\left(\tfrac{1}{11} + \cdots + \tfrac{1}{99}\right)}_{g_2} + \underbrace{\left(\tfrac{1}{111} + \cdots + \tfrac{1}{999}\right)}_{g_3} + \cdots$$

Now in the group g_n, there are 9^n terms, since we have 9 choices for each of the n digits in the denominator. Furthermore, each term in g_n is less than $\frac{1}{10^{n-1}}$. So $g_n < 9^n \cdot \frac{1}{10^{n-1}} = 9\left(\frac{9}{10}\right)^{n-1}$. Now $\sum_{n=1}^{\infty} 9\left(\frac{9}{10}\right)^{n-1}$ is a geometric series with $a = 9$ and $r = \frac{9}{10} < 1$. Therefore, by the Comparison Test,

$$S = \sum_{n=1}^{\infty} g_n < \sum_{n=1}^{\infty} 9\left(\frac{9}{10}\right)^{n-1} = \frac{9}{1 - 9/10} = 90.$$

14. (a) Since P_n is defined as the midpoint of $P_{n-4}P_{n-3}$, $x_n = \frac{1}{2}(x_{n-4} + x_{n-3})$ for $n \geq 5$. So we prove by induction that $\frac{1}{2}x_n + x_{n+1} + x_{n+2} + x_{n+3} = 2$. The case $n = 1$ is immediate, since $\frac{1}{2}0 + 1 + 1 + 0 = 2$. Assume that the result holds for $n = k - 1$, that is, $\frac{1}{2}x_{k-1} + x_k + x_{k+1} + x_{k+2} = 2$. Then for $n = k$,

$$\frac{1}{2}x_k + x_{k+1} + x_{k+2} + x_{k+3} = \frac{1}{2}x_k + x_{k+1} + x_{k+2} + \frac{1}{2}(x_{k+3-4} + x_{k+3-3}) \quad \text{(by above)}$$

$$= \frac{1}{2}x_{k-1} + x_k + x_{k+1} + x_{k+2} = 2 \quad \text{(by the induction hypothesis)}$$

Similarly, for $n \geq 5$, $y_n = \frac{1}{2}(y_{n-4} + y_{n-3})$, so the same argument as above holds for y, with 2 replaced by $\frac{1}{2}y_1 + y_2 + y_3 + y_4 = \frac{1}{2}1 + 1 + 0 + 0 = \frac{3}{2}$. So $\frac{1}{2}y_n + y_{n+1} + y_{n+2} + y_{n+3} = \frac{3}{2}$ for all n.

(b) $\displaystyle\lim_{n\to\infty} \left(\frac{1}{2}x_n + x_{n+1} + x_{n+2} + x_{n+3}\right) = \frac{1}{2}\lim_{n\to\infty} x_n + \lim_{n\to\infty} x_{n+1} + \lim_{n\to\infty} x_{n+2} + \lim_{n\to\infty} x_{n+3} = 2$. Since all the limits on the left hand side are the same, we get $\frac{7}{2}\displaystyle\lim_{n\to\infty} x_n = 2 \Rightarrow \displaystyle\lim_{n\to\infty} x_n = \frac{4}{7}$. In the same way, $\displaystyle\lim_{n\to\infty} y_n = \frac{3}{7}$, so $P = \left(\frac{4}{7}, \frac{3}{7}\right)$.

15. Let $f(x) = \sum_{m=0}^{\infty} c_m x^m$ and $g(x) = e^{f(x)} = \sum_{n=0}^{\infty} d_n x^n$. Then $g'(x) = \sum_{n=0}^{\infty} n d_n x^{n-1}$, so $n d_n$ occurs as the coefficient of x^{n-1}. But also

$$g'(x) = e^{f(x)} f'(x) = \left(\sum_{n=0}^{\infty} d_n x^n\right)\left(\sum_{m=1}^{\infty} m c_m x^{m-1}\right)$$

$$= \left(d_0 + d_1 x + d_2 x^2 + \cdots + d_{n-1} x^{n-1} + \cdots\right)\left(c_1 + 2c_2 x + 3c_3 x^2 + \cdots + n c_n x^{n-1} + \cdots\right)$$

so the coefficient of x^{n-1} is $c_1 d_{n-1} + 2c_2 d_{n-2} + 3c_3 d_{n-3} + \cdots + n c_n d_0 = \sum_{i=1}^{n} i c_i d_{n-i}$. Therefore, $n d_n = \sum_{i=1}^{n} i c_i d_{n-i}$.

16. (a) Let $f(x) = \dfrac{x}{1 - x - x^2} = \sum_{n=0}^{\infty} c_n x^n = c_0 + c_1 x + c_2 x^2 + c_3 x^3 + \cdots$. Then

$$x = \left(1 - x - x^2\right)\left(c_0 + c_1 x + c_2 x^2 + c_3 x^3 + \cdots\right)$$

$$x = c_0 + c_1 x + c_2 x^2 + c_3 x^3 + c_4 x^4 + c_5 x^5 + \cdots$$
$$- c_0 x - c_1 x^2 - c_2 x^3 - c_3 x^4 - c_4 x^5 - \cdots$$
$$- c_0 x^2 - c_1 x^3 - c_2 x^4 - c_3 x^5 - \cdots$$

$$x = c_0 + (c_1 - c_0)x + (c_2 - c_1 - c_0)x^2 + (c_3 - c_2 - c_1)x^3 + \cdots$$

Comparing coefficients of powers of x gives us $c_0 = 0$ and

$$c_1 - c_0 = 1 \qquad \Rightarrow \quad c_1 = c_0 + 1 = 1$$
$$c_2 - c_1 - c_0 = 0 \quad \Rightarrow \quad c_2 = c_1 + c_0 = 1 + 0 = 1$$
$$c_3 - c_2 - c_1 = 0 \quad \Rightarrow \quad c_3 = c_2 + c_1 = 1 + 1 = 2$$

In general, we have $c_n = c_{n-1} + c_{n-2}$ for $n \geq 3$. Each c_n is equal to the nth Fibonacci number; that is,

$$\sum_{n=0}^{\infty} c_n x^n = \sum_{n=1}^{\infty} c_n x^n = \sum_{n=1}^{\infty} f_n x^n$$

(b) Completing the square on $x^2 + x - 1$ gives us

$$\left(x^2 + x + \frac{1}{4}\right) - 1 - \frac{1}{4} = \left(x + \frac{1}{2}\right)^2 - \frac{5}{4} = \left(x + \frac{1}{2}\right)^2 - \left(\frac{\sqrt{5}}{2}\right)^2$$

$$= \left(x + \frac{1}{2} + \frac{\sqrt{5}}{2}\right)\left(x + \frac{1}{2} - \frac{\sqrt{5}}{2}\right) = \left(x + \frac{1 + \sqrt{5}}{2}\right)\left(x + \frac{1 - \sqrt{5}}{2}\right)$$

So $\dfrac{x}{1 - x - x^2} = \dfrac{-x}{x^2 + x - 1} = \dfrac{-x}{\left(x + \frac{1+\sqrt{5}}{2}\right)\left(x + \frac{1-\sqrt{5}}{2}\right)}$. The factors in the denominator are linear, so the partial fraction decomposition is

$$\frac{-x}{\left(x + \frac{1+\sqrt{5}}{2}\right)\left(x + \frac{1-\sqrt{5}}{2}\right)} = \frac{A}{x + \frac{1+\sqrt{5}}{2}} + \frac{B}{x + \frac{1-\sqrt{5}}{2}}$$

$$-x = A\left(x + \frac{1-\sqrt{5}}{2}\right) + B\left(x + \frac{1+\sqrt{5}}{2}\right)$$

If $x = \frac{-1+\sqrt{5}}{2}$, then $-\frac{-1+\sqrt{5}}{2} = B\sqrt{5} \;\Rightarrow\; B = \frac{1-\sqrt{5}}{2\sqrt{5}}$.

If $x = \frac{-1-\sqrt{5}}{2}$, then $-\frac{-1-\sqrt{5}}{2} = A(-\sqrt{5}) \;\Rightarrow\; A = \frac{1+\sqrt{5}}{-2\sqrt{5}}$. Thus,

$$\frac{x}{1 - x - x^2} = \frac{\frac{1+\sqrt{5}}{-2\sqrt{5}}}{x + \frac{1+\sqrt{5}}{2}} + \frac{\frac{1-\sqrt{5}}{2\sqrt{5}}}{x + \frac{1-\sqrt{5}}{2}}$$

$$= \frac{\frac{1+\sqrt{5}}{-2\sqrt{5}} \cdot \frac{2}{1+\sqrt{5}}}{x + \frac{1+\sqrt{5}}{2} \cdot \frac{2}{1+\sqrt{5}}} + \frac{\frac{1-\sqrt{5}}{2\sqrt{5}} \cdot \frac{2}{1-\sqrt{5}}}{x + \frac{1-\sqrt{5}}{2} \cdot \frac{2}{1-\sqrt{5}}}$$

$$= \frac{-1/\sqrt{5}}{1 + \frac{2}{1+\sqrt{5}}x} + \frac{1/\sqrt{5}}{1 + \frac{2}{1-\sqrt{5}}x}$$

$$= -\frac{1}{\sqrt{5}}\sum_{n=0}^{\infty}\left(-\frac{2}{1+\sqrt{5}}x\right)^n + \frac{1}{\sqrt{5}}\sum_{n=0}^{\infty}\left(-\frac{2}{1-\sqrt{5}}x\right)^n$$

$$= \frac{1}{\sqrt{5}}\sum_{n=0}^{\infty}\left[\left(\frac{-2}{1-\sqrt{5}}\right)^n - \left(\frac{-2}{1+\sqrt{5}}\right)^n\right]x^n$$

$$= \frac{1}{\sqrt{5}}\sum_{n=1}^{\infty}\left[\frac{(-2)^n(1+\sqrt{5})^n - (-2)^n(1-\sqrt{5})^n}{(1-\sqrt{5})^n(1+\sqrt{5})^n}\right]x^n \quad \text{[the } n = 0 \text{ term is 0]}$$

$$= \frac{1}{\sqrt{5}}\sum_{n=1}^{\infty}\left[\frac{(-2)^n\left((1+\sqrt{5})^n - (1-\sqrt{5})^n\right)}{(1-5)^n}\right]x^n$$

$$= \frac{1}{\sqrt{5}}\sum_{n=1}^{\infty}\left[\frac{(1+\sqrt{5})^n - (1-\sqrt{5})^n}{2^n}\right]x^n \quad\quad [(-4)^n = (-2)^n \cdot 2^n]$$

From part (a), this series must equal $\displaystyle\sum_{n=1}^{\infty} f_n x^n$, so $f_n = \dfrac{(1+\sqrt{5})^n - (1-\sqrt{5})^n}{2^n\sqrt{5}}$, which is an explicit formula for the nth Fibonacci number.

9 Vectors and the Geometry of Space

9.1 Three-Dimensional Coordinate Systems · · · · · · · ·

1. We start at the origin, which has coordinates $(0, 0, 0)$. First we move 4 units along the positive x-axis, affecting only the x-coordinate, bringing us to the point $(4, 0, 0)$. We then move 3 units straight downward, in the negative z-direction. Thus only the z-coordinate is affected, and we arrive at $(4, 0, -3)$.

2.

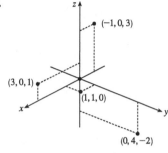

3. The distance from a point to the xz-plane is the absolute value of the y-coordinate of the point. $Q(-5, -1, 4)$ has the y-coordinate with the smallest absolute value, so Q is the point closest to the xz-plane. $R(0, 3, 8)$ must lie in the yz-plane since the distance from R to the yz-plane, given by the x-coordinate of R, is 0.

4. The projection of $(2, 3, 5)$ on the xy-plane is $(2, 3, 0)$; on the yz-plane, $(0, 3, 5)$; on the xz-plane, $(2, 0, 5)$.

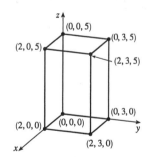

The length of the diagonal of the box is the distance between the origin and $(2, 3, 5)$, given by

$$\sqrt{(2 - 0)^2 + (3 - 0)^2 + (5 - 0)^2} = \sqrt{38} \approx 6.16.$$

5. The equation $x + y = 2$ represents the set of all points in $\mathbb{R}^3$ whose x- and y-coordinates have a sum of 2, or equivalently where $y = 2 - x$. This is the set $\{(x, 2 - x, z) \mid x \in \mathbb{R}, z \in \mathbb{R}\}$ which is a vertical plane that intersects the xy-plane in the line $y = 2 - x$, $z = 0$.

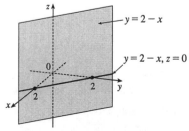

6. (a) In $\mathbb{R}^2$, the equation $x = 4$ represents a line parallel to the y-axis. In $\mathbb{R}^3$, the equation $x = 4$ represents the set $\{(x, y, z) \mid x = 4\}$, the set of all points whose x-coordinate is 4. This is the vertical plane that is parallel to the yz-plane and 4 units in front of it.

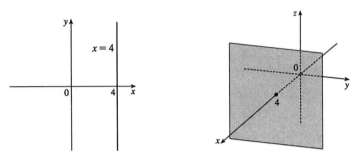

(b) In $\mathbb{R}^3$, the equation $y = 3$ represents a vertical plane that is parallel to the xz-plane and 3 units to the right of it. The equation $z = 5$ represents a horizontal plane parallel to the xy-plane and 5 units above it. The pair of equations $y = 3$, $z = 5$ represents the set of points that are simultaneously on both planes, or in other words, the line of intersection of the planes $y = 3$, $z = 5$. This line can also be described as the set $\{(x, 3, 5) \mid x \in \mathbb{R}\}$, which is the set of all points in $\mathbb{R}^3$ whose x-coordinate may vary but whose y- and z-coordinates are fixed at 3 and 5, respectively. Thus the line is parallel to the x-axis and intersects the yz-plane in the point $(0, 3, 5)$.

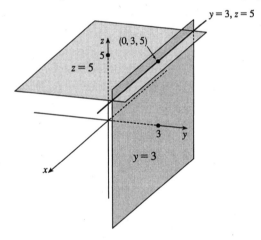

7. We can find the lengths of the sides of the triangle by using the distance formula between pairs of vertices:

$$|AB| = \sqrt{(5 - 3)^2 + [-3 - (-4)]^2 + (0 - 1)^2} = \sqrt{4 + 1 + 1} = \sqrt{6}$$

$$|BC| = \sqrt{(6 - 5)^2 + [-7 - (-3)]^2 + (4 - 0)^2} = \sqrt{1 + 16 + 16} = \sqrt{33}$$

$$|CA| = \sqrt{(3 - 6)^2 + [-4 - (-7)]^2 + (1 - 4)^2} = \sqrt{9 + 9 + 9} = \sqrt{27} = 3\sqrt{3}$$

Since the Pythagorean Theorem is satisfied by $|AB|^2 + |CA|^2 = |BC|^2$, ABC is a right triangle. ABC is not isosceles, as no two sides have the same length.

8. (a) The distance from a point to the xy-plane is the absolute value of the z-coordinate of the point. Thus, the distance is $|-5| = 5$.

(b) Similarly, the distance is the absolute value of the x-coordinate of the point: $|3| = 3$.

(c) The distance is the absolute value of the y-coordinate of the point: $|7| = 7$.

(d) The point on the x-axis closest to $(3, 7, -5)$ is the point $(3, 0, 0)$. (Approach the x-axis perpendicularly.) The distance from $(3, 7, -5)$ to the x-axis is the distance between these two points:

$$\sqrt{(3-3)^2 + (7-0)^2 + (-5-0)^2} = \sqrt{74} \approx 8.60.$$

(e) The point on the y-axis closest to $(3, 7, -5)$ is $(0, 7, 0)$. The distance between these points is

$$\sqrt{(3-0)^2 + (7-7)^2 + (-5-0)^2} = \sqrt{34} \approx 5.83.$$

(f) The point on the z-axis closest to $(3, 7, -5)$ is $(0, 0, -5)$. The distance between these points is

$$\sqrt{(3-0)^2 + (7-0)^2 + [-5-(-5)]^2} = \sqrt{58} \approx 7.62.$$

9. (a) First we find the distances between points:

$$|AB| = \sqrt{(7-5)^2 + (9-1)^2 + (-1-3)^2} = \sqrt{84} = 2\sqrt{21}$$

$$|BC| = \sqrt{(1-7)^2 + (-15-9)^2 + [11-(-1)]^2} = \sqrt{756} = 6\sqrt{21}$$

$$|AC| = \sqrt{(1-5)^2 + (-15-1)^2 + (11-3)^2} = \sqrt{336} = 4\sqrt{21}$$

In order for the points to lie on a straight line, the sum of the two shortest distances must be equal to the longest distance. Since $|AB| + |AC| = |BC|$, the three points lie on a straight line.

(b) The distances between points are

$$|KL| = \sqrt{(1-0)^2 + (2-3)^2 + [-2-(-4)]^2} = \sqrt{6}$$

$$|LM| = \sqrt{(3-1)^2 + (0-2)^2 + [1-(-2)]^2} = \sqrt{17}$$

$$|KM| = \sqrt{(3-0)^2 + (0-3)^2 + [1-(-4)]^2} = \sqrt{43}$$

Since $\sqrt{6} + \sqrt{17} \neq \sqrt{43}$, the three points do not lie on a straight line.

10. An equation of the sphere with center $(6, 5, -2)$ and radius $\sqrt{7}$ is $(x - 6)^2 + (y - 5)^2 + [z - (-2)]^2 = \left(\sqrt{7}\right)^2$ or $(x - 6)^2 + (y - 5) + (z + 2)^2 = 7$. The intersection of this sphere with the xy-plane is the set of points on the sphere whose z-coordinate is 0. Putting $z = 0$ into the equation, we have $(x - 6)^2 + (y - 5)^2 = 3, z = 0$ which represents a circle in the xy-plane with center $(6, 5, 0)$ and radius $\sqrt{3}$. To find the intersection with the xz-plane, we set $y = 0$: $(x - 6)^2 + (z + 2)^2 = -18$. Since no points satisfy this equation, the sphere does not intersect the xz-plane. (Also note that the distance from the center of the sphere to the xz-plane is greater than the radius of the sphere.) Similarly, the sphere does not intersect the yz-plane since substituting $x = 0$ into the equation gives $(y - 5)^2 + (z + 2)^2 = -29$.

11. The radius of the sphere is the distance between $(4, 3, -1)$ and $(3, 8, 1)$:

$$r = \sqrt{(3-4)^2 + (8-3)^2 + [1-(-1)]^2} = \sqrt{30}.$$ Thus, an equation of the sphere is

$(x - 3)^2 + (y - 8)^2 + (z - 1)^2 = 30$.

12. If the sphere passes through the origin, the radius of the sphere must be the distance from the origin to the

point $(1, 2, 3)$: $r = \sqrt{(1-0)^2 + (2-0)^2 + (3-0)^2} = \sqrt{14}$. Then an equation of the sphere is

$(x - 1)^2 + (y - 2)^2 + (z - 3)^2 = 14$.

13. Completing squares in the equation gives $\left(x^2 - x + \frac{1}{4}\right) + \left(y^2 - y + \frac{1}{4}\right) + \left(z^2 - z + \frac{1}{4}\right) = \frac{1}{4} + \frac{1}{4} + \frac{1}{4}$ $\Rightarrow$

$\left(x - \frac{1}{2}\right)^2 + \left(y - \frac{1}{2}\right)^2 + \left(z - \frac{1}{2}\right)^2 = \frac{3}{4}$ which we recognize as an equation of a sphere with center $\left(\frac{1}{2}, \frac{1}{2}, \frac{1}{2}\right)$ and

radius $\sqrt{\frac{3}{4}} = \frac{\sqrt{3}}{2}$.

14. Completing squares in the equation gives $4\left(x^2 - 2x + 1\right) + 4\left(y^2 + 4y + 4\right) + 4z^2 = 1 + 4 + 16$ $\Rightarrow$

$4(x - 1)^2 + 4(y + 2)^2 + 4z^2 = 21$ $\Rightarrow$ $(x - 1)^2 + (y + 2)^2 + z^2 = \frac{21}{4}$, which we recognize as an equation of

a sphere with center $(1, -2, 0)$ and radius $\sqrt{\frac{21}{4}} = \frac{\sqrt{21}}{2}$.

15. (a) If the midpoint of the line segment from $P_1(x_1, y_1, z_1)$ to $P_2(x_2, y_2, z_2)$ is

$Q = \left(\frac{x_1 + x_2}{2}, \frac{y_1 + y_2}{2}, \frac{z_1 + z_2}{2}\right)$, then the distances $|P_1Q|$ and $|QP_2|$ are equal, and each is half of $|P_1P_2|$.

We verify that this is the case:

$$|P_1P_2| = \sqrt{(x_2 - x_1)^2 + (y_2 - y_1)^2 + (z_2 - z_1)^2}$$

$$|P_1Q| = \sqrt{\left[\tfrac{1}{2}(x_1 + x_2) - x_1\right]^2 + \left[\tfrac{1}{2}(y_1 + y_2) - y_1\right]^2 + \left[\tfrac{1}{2}(z_1 + z_2) - z_1\right]^2}$$

$$= \sqrt{\left(\tfrac{1}{2}x_2 - \tfrac{1}{2}x_1\right)^2 + \left(\tfrac{1}{2}y_2 - \tfrac{1}{2}y_1\right)^2 + \left(\tfrac{1}{2}z_2 - \tfrac{1}{2}z_1\right)^2}$$

$$= \sqrt{\left(\tfrac{1}{2}\right)^2 \left[(x_2 - x_1)^2 + (y_2 - y_1)^2 + (z_2 - z_1)^2\right]}$$

$$= \tfrac{1}{2}\sqrt{(x_2 - x_1)^2 + (y_2 - y_1)^2 + (z_2 - z_1)^2}$$

$$= \tfrac{1}{2}|P_1P_2|$$

$$|QP_2| = \sqrt{\left[x_2 - \tfrac{1}{2}(x_1 + x_2)\right]^2 + \left[y_2 - \tfrac{1}{2}(y_1 + y_2)\right]^2 + \left[z_2 - \tfrac{1}{2}(z_1 + z_2)\right]^2}$$

$$= \sqrt{\left(\tfrac{1}{2}x_2 - \tfrac{1}{2}x_1\right)^2 + \left(\tfrac{1}{2}y_2 - \tfrac{1}{2}y_1\right)^2 + \left(\tfrac{1}{2}z_2 - \tfrac{1}{2}z_1\right)^2}$$

$$= \sqrt{\left(\tfrac{1}{2}\right)^2 \left[(x_2 - x_1)^2 + (y_2 - y_1)^2 + (z_2 - z_1)^2\right]}$$

$$= \tfrac{1}{2}\sqrt{(x_2 - x_1)^2 + (y_2 - y_1)^2 + (z_2 - z_1)^2}$$

$$= \tfrac{1}{2}|P_1P_2|$$

So Q is indeed the midpoint of P_1P_2.

(b) By part (a), the midpoints of sides AB, BC and CA are $P_1\left(-\frac{1}{2}, 1, 4\right)$, $P_2\left(1, \frac{1}{2}, 5\right)$ and $P_3\left(\frac{5}{2}, \frac{3}{2}, 4\right)$. (Recall that a median of a triangle is a line segment from a vertex to the midpoint of the opposite side.) Then the lengths of the medians are:

$$|AP_2| = \sqrt{0^2 + \left(\tfrac{1}{2} - 2\right)^2 + (5 - 3)^2} = \sqrt{\tfrac{9}{4} + 4} = \sqrt{\tfrac{25}{4}} = \tfrac{5}{2}$$

$$|BP_3| = \sqrt{\left(\tfrac{5}{2} + 2\right)^2 + \left(\tfrac{3}{2}\right)^2 + (4 - 5)^2} = \sqrt{\tfrac{81}{4} + \tfrac{9}{4} + 1} = \sqrt{\tfrac{94}{4}} = \tfrac{1}{2}\sqrt{94}$$

$$|CP_1| = \sqrt{\left(-\tfrac{1}{2} - 4\right)^2 + (1 - 1)^2 + (4 - 5)^2} = \sqrt{\tfrac{81}{4} + 1} = \tfrac{1}{2}\sqrt{85}$$

16. By Exercise 15(a), the midpoint of the diameter (and thus the center of the sphere) is $C(3, 2, 7)$. The radius is half

the diameter, so $r = \frac{1}{2}\sqrt{(4-2)^2 + (3-1)^2 + (10-4)^2} = \frac{1}{2}\sqrt{44} = \sqrt{11}$. Therefore an equation of the sphere

is $(x-3)^2 + (y-2)^2 + (z-7)^2 = 11$.

17. (a) Since the sphere touches the xy-plane, its radius is the distance from its center, $(2, -3, 6)$, to the xy-plane,

namely 6. Therefore $r = 6$ and an equation of the sphere is $(x-2)^2 + (y+3)^2 + (z-6)^2 = 6^2 = 36$.

(b) The radius of this sphere is the distance from its center $(2, -3, 6)$ to the yz-plane, which is 2. Therefore, an

equation is $(x-2)^2 + (y+3)^2 + (z-6)^2 = 4$.

(c) Here the radius is the distance from the center $(2, -3, 6)$ to the xz-plane, which is 3. Therefore, an equation is

$(x-2)^2 + (y+3)^2 + (z-6)^2 = 9$.

18. The largest sphere contained in the first octant must have a radius equal to the minimum distance from the center

$(5, 4, 9)$ to any of the three coordinate planes. The shortest such distance is to the xz-plane, a distance of 4. Thus an

equation of the sphere is $(x-5)^2 + (y-4)^2 + (z-9)^2 = 16$.

19. The equation $y = -4$ represents a plane parallel to the xz-plane and 4 units to the left of it.

20. The equation $x = 10$ represents a plane parallel to the yz-plane and 10 units in front of it.

21. The inequality $x > 3$ represents a half-space consisting of all points in front of the plane $x = 3$.

22. The inequality $y \geq 0$ represents a half-space consisting of all points on or to the right of the xz-plane.

23. The inequality $0 \leq z \leq 6$ represents all points on or between the horizontal planes $z = 0$ (the xy-plane) and $z = 6$.

24. The equation $y = z$ represents a plane perpendicular to the yz-plane and intersecting the yz-plane in the line $y = z$,

$x = 0$.

25. The inequality $x^2 + y^2 + z^2 > 1$ is equivalent to $\sqrt{x^2 + y^2 + z^2} > 1$, so the region consists of those points whose

distance from the origin is greater than 1. This is the set of all points outside the sphere with radius 1 and

center $(0, 0, 0)$.

26. The inequality $1 \leq x^2 + y^2 + z^2 \leq 25$ is equivalent to $1 \leq \sqrt{x^2 + y^2 + z^2} \leq 5$, so the region consists of those

points whose distance from the origin is at least 1 and at most 5. This is the set of all points on or between the

concentric spheres with radii 1 and 5 and center $(0, 0, 0)$.

27. Here $x^2 + z^2 \leq 9$ or equivalently $\sqrt{x^2 + z^2} \leq 3$ which describes the set of all points in $\mathbb{R}^3$ whose distance from

the y-axis is at most 3. Thus, the inequality represents the region consisting of all points on or inside a circular

cylinder of radius 3 with axis the y-axis.

28. The equation $xyz = 0$ is satisfied when any of x, y, or z is 0. Thus, the equation represents the region consisting of

all points on the three coordinate planes $x = 0$, $y = 0$, and $z = 0$.

29. This describes all points with negative y-coordinates, that is, $y < 0$.

30. Because the box lies in the first quadrant, each point must comprise only non-negative coordinates. So inequalities

describing the region are $0 \leq x \leq 1$, $0 \leq y \leq 2$, $0 \leq z \leq 3$.

31. This describes a region all of whose points have a distance to the origin which is greater than r, but smaller than R.

So inequalities describing the region are $r < \sqrt{x^2 + y^2 + z^2} < R$, or $r^2 < x^2 + y^2 + z^2 < R^2$.

32. The solid sphere itself is represented by $\sqrt{x^2 + y^2 + z^2} \leq 2$. Since we want only the upper hemisphere, we restrict

the z-coordinate to non-negative values. Then inequalities describing the region are $\sqrt{x^2 + y^2 + z^2} \leq 2$, $z \geq 0$, or

$x^2 + y^2 + z^2 \leq 4$, $z \geq 0$.

33. (a) To find the x- and y-coordinates of the point P, we project it onto L_2 and project the resulting point Q onto the x- and y-axes. To find the z-coordinate, we project P onto either the xz-plane or the yz-plane (using our knowledge of its x- or y-coordinate) and then project the resulting point onto the z-axis. (Or, we could draw a line parallel to QO from P to the z-axis.) The coordinates of P are $(2, 1, 4)$.

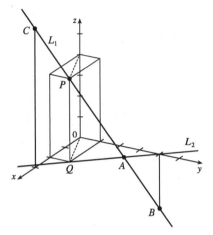

(b) A is the intersection of L_1 and L_2, B is directly below the y-intercept of L_2, and C is directly above the x-intercept of L_2.

34. Let $P = (x, y, z)$. Then $2|PB| = |PA| \Leftrightarrow 4|PB|^2 = |PA|^2 \Leftrightarrow$
$4\left((x-6)^2 + (y-2)^2 + (z+2)^2\right) = (x+1)^2 + (y-5)^2 + (z-3)^2 \Leftrightarrow$
$4\left(x^2 - 12x + 36\right) - x^2 - 2x + 4\left(y^2 - 4y + 4\right) - y^2 + 10y + 4\left(z^2 + 4z + 4\right) - z^2 + 6z = 35 \Leftrightarrow$
$3x^2 - 50x + 3y^2 - 6y + 3z^2 + 22z = 35 - 144 - 16 - 16 \Leftrightarrow x^2 - \frac{50}{3}x + y^2 - 2y + z^2 + \frac{22}{3}z = -\frac{141}{3}$. By completing the square three times we get $\left(x - \frac{25}{3}\right)^2 + (y-1)^2 + \left(z + \frac{11}{3}\right)^2 = \frac{332}{9}$, which is an equation of a sphere with center $\left(\frac{25}{3}, 1, -\frac{11}{3}\right)$ and radius $\frac{\sqrt{332}}{3}$.

35. We need to find a set of points $\{P(x, y, z) \,|\, |AP| = |BP|\}$.
$\sqrt{(x+1)^2 + (y-5)^2 + (z-3)^2} = \sqrt{(x-6)^2 + (y-2)^2 + (z+2)^2} \Rightarrow$
$(x+1)^2 + (y-5) + (z-3)^2 = (x-6)^2 + (y-2)^2 + (z+2)^2 \Rightarrow$
$x^2 + 2x + 1 + y^2 - 10y + 25 + z^2 - 6z + 9 = x^2 - 12x + 36 + y^2 - 4y + 4 + z^2 + 4z + 4 \Rightarrow$
$14x - 6y - 10z = 9$. Thus the set of points is a plane perpendicular to the line segment joining A and B (since this plane must contain the perpendicular bisector of the line segment AB).

36. Completing the square three times in the first equation gives $(x+2)^2 + (y-1)^2 + (z+2)^2 = 2^2$, a sphere with center $(-2, 1, 2)$ and radius 2. The second equation is that of a sphere with center $(0, 0, 0)$ and radius 2. The distance between the centers of the spheres is $\sqrt{(-2-0)^2 + (1-0)^2 + (-2-0)^2} = \sqrt{4 + 1 + 4} = 3$.

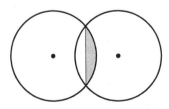

Since the spheres have the same radius, the volume inside both spheres is symmetrical about the plane containing the circle of intersection of the spheres. The distance from this plane to the center of the circles is $\frac{3}{2}$. So the region inside both spheres consists of two caps of spheres of height $h = 2 - \frac{3}{2} = \frac{1}{2}$. From Exercise 6.2.19, the volume of a cap of a sphere is $V = \frac{1}{3}\pi h^2(3r - h) = \frac{1}{3}\pi\left(\frac{1}{2}\right)^2\left(3 \cdot 2 - \frac{1}{2}\right) = \frac{11\pi}{24}$. So the total volume is $2 \cdot \frac{11\pi}{24} = \frac{11\pi}{12}$.

9.2 Vectors · · · · · · · · · · · · · · · · ·

1. (a) The cost of a theater ticket is a scalar, because it has only magnitude.

(b) The current in a river is a vector, because it has both magnitude (the speed of the current) and direction at any given location.

(c) If we assume that the initial path is linear, the initial flight path from Houston to Dallas is a vector, because it has both magnitude (distance) and direction.

(d) The population of the world is a scalar, because it has only magnitude.

2. If the initial point of the vector $\langle 4, 7 \rangle$ is placed at the

origin, then $\langle 4, 7 \rangle$ is the position vector of the point $(4, 7)$.

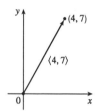

3. Vectors are equal when they share the same length and direction (but not necessarily location). Using the symmetry of the parallelogram as a guide, we see that $\overrightarrow{AB} = \overrightarrow{DC}, \overrightarrow{DA} = \overrightarrow{CB}, \overrightarrow{DE} = \overrightarrow{EB}$, and $\overrightarrow{EA} = \overrightarrow{CE}$.

4. (a) The initial point of $\overrightarrow{QR}$ is positioned at the terminal point of $\overrightarrow{PQ}$, so by the Triangle Law the sum $\overrightarrow{PQ} + \overrightarrow{QR}$ is the vector with initial point P and terminal point R, namely $\overrightarrow{PR}$.

(b) By the Triangle Law, $\overrightarrow{RP} + \overrightarrow{PS}$ is the vector with initial point R and terminal point S, namely $\overrightarrow{RS}$.

(c) First we consider $\overrightarrow{QS} - \overrightarrow{PS}$ as $\overrightarrow{QS} + \left(-\overrightarrow{PS}\right)$. Then since $-\overrightarrow{PS}$ has the same length as $\overrightarrow{PS}$ but points in the opposite direction, we have $-\overrightarrow{PS} = \overrightarrow{SP}$ and so $\overrightarrow{QS} - \overrightarrow{PS} = \overrightarrow{QS} + \overrightarrow{SP} = \overrightarrow{QP}$.

(d) We use the Triangle Law twice: $\overrightarrow{RS} + \overrightarrow{SP} + \overrightarrow{PQ} = \left(\overrightarrow{RS} + \overrightarrow{SP}\right) + \overrightarrow{PQ} = \overrightarrow{RP} + \overrightarrow{PQ} = \overrightarrow{RQ}$

5. (a)

(b)

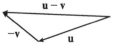

(c)

(d)

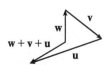

6. (a)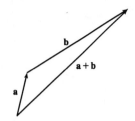

(b)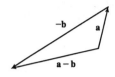

(c)

(d)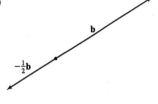

(e)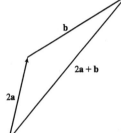

(f)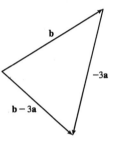

7. $\mathbf{a} = \langle -3 - (-1), 4 - (-1) \rangle = \langle -2, 5 \rangle$

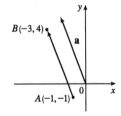

8. $\mathbf{a} = \langle 3 - (-2), 0 - 2 \rangle = \langle 5, -2 \rangle$

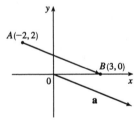

9. $\mathbf{a} = \langle 2 - 0, 3 - 3, -1 - 1 \rangle = \langle 2, 0, -2 \rangle$

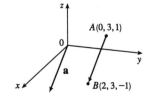

10. $\mathbf{a} = \langle 1 - 1, -2 + 2, 3 - 0 \rangle = \langle 0, 0, 3 \rangle$

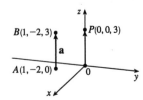

11. $\langle 3, -1 \rangle + \langle -2, 4 \rangle = \langle 3 + (-2), -1 + 4 \rangle = \langle 1, 3 \rangle$

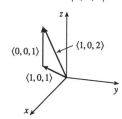

12. $\langle -1, 2 \rangle + \langle 5, 3 \rangle = \langle -1 + 5, 2 + 3 \rangle = \langle 4, 5 \rangle$

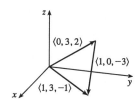

13. $\langle 1, 0, 1 \rangle + \langle 0, 0, 1 \rangle = \langle 1 + 0, 0 + 0, 1 + 1 \rangle$
$$= \langle 1, 0, 2 \rangle$$

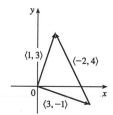

14. $\langle 0, 3, 2 \rangle + \langle 1, 0, -3 \rangle = \langle 1, 3, -1 \rangle$

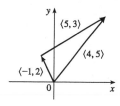

15. $|\mathbf{a}| = \sqrt{(-4)^2 + 3^2} = \sqrt{25} = 5$
$\mathbf{a} + \mathbf{b} = \langle -4 + 6, 3 + 2 \rangle = \langle 2, 5 \rangle$
$\mathbf{a} - \mathbf{b} = \langle -4 - 6, 3 - 2 \rangle = \langle -10, 1 \rangle$
$2\mathbf{a} = \langle 2(-4), 2(3) \rangle = \langle -8, 6 \rangle$
$3\mathbf{a} + 4\mathbf{b} = \langle -12, 9 \rangle + \langle 24, 8 \rangle = \langle 12, 17 \rangle$

16. $|\mathbf{a}| = \sqrt{2^2 + (-3)^2} = \sqrt{13}$
$\mathbf{a} + \mathbf{b} = (2\mathbf{i} - 3\mathbf{j}) + (\mathbf{i} + 5\mathbf{j}) = 3\mathbf{i} + 2\mathbf{j}$
$\mathbf{a} - \mathbf{b} = (2\mathbf{i} - 3\mathbf{j}) - (\mathbf{i} + 5\mathbf{j}) = \mathbf{i} - 8\mathbf{j}$
$2\mathbf{a} = 2(2\mathbf{i} - 3\mathbf{j}) = 4\mathbf{i} - 6\mathbf{j}$
$3\mathbf{a} + 4\mathbf{b} = 3(2\mathbf{i} - 3\mathbf{j}) + 4(\mathbf{i} + 5\mathbf{j})$
$\qquad = 6\mathbf{i} - 9\mathbf{j} + 4\mathbf{i} + 20\mathbf{j} = 10\mathbf{i} + 11\mathbf{j}$

17. $|\mathbf{a}| = \sqrt{1^2 + (-2)^2 + 1^2} = \sqrt{6}$
$\mathbf{a} + \mathbf{b} = (\mathbf{i} - 2\mathbf{j} + \mathbf{k}) + (\mathbf{j} + 2\mathbf{k}) = \mathbf{i} - \mathbf{j} + 3\mathbf{k}$
$\mathbf{a} - \mathbf{b} = (\mathbf{i} - 2\mathbf{j} + \mathbf{k}) - (\mathbf{j} + 2\mathbf{k}) = \mathbf{i} - 3\mathbf{j} - \mathbf{k}$
$2\mathbf{a} = 2(\mathbf{i} - 2\mathbf{j} + \mathbf{k}) = 2\mathbf{i} - 4\mathbf{j} + 2\mathbf{k}$
$3\mathbf{a} + 4\mathbf{b} = 3(\mathbf{i} - 2\mathbf{j} + \mathbf{k}) + 4(\mathbf{j} + 2\mathbf{k})$
$\qquad = 3\mathbf{i} - 6\mathbf{j} + 3\mathbf{k} + 4\mathbf{j} + 8\mathbf{k}$
$\qquad = 3\mathbf{i} - 2\mathbf{j} + 11\mathbf{k}$

18. $|\mathbf{a}| = \sqrt{3^2 + 0^2 + (-2)^2} = \sqrt{13}$
$\mathbf{a} + \mathbf{b} = (3\mathbf{i} - 2\mathbf{k}) + (\mathbf{i} - \mathbf{j} + \mathbf{k}) = 4\mathbf{i} - \mathbf{j} - \mathbf{k}$
$\mathbf{a} - \mathbf{b} = (3\mathbf{i} - 2\mathbf{k}) - (\mathbf{i} - \mathbf{j} + \mathbf{k}) = 2\mathbf{i} + \mathbf{j} - 3\mathbf{k}$
$2\mathbf{a} = 2(3\mathbf{i} - 2\mathbf{k}) = 6\mathbf{i} - 4\mathbf{k}$
$3\mathbf{a} + 4\mathbf{b} = 3(3\mathbf{i} - 2\mathbf{k}) + 4(\mathbf{i} - \mathbf{j} + \mathbf{k})$
$\qquad = 9\mathbf{i} - 6\mathbf{k} + 4\mathbf{i} - 4\mathbf{j} + 4\mathbf{k}$
$\qquad = 13\mathbf{i} - 4\mathbf{j} - 2\mathbf{k}$

19. The vector $8\mathbf{i} - \mathbf{j} + 4\mathbf{k}$ has length $|8\mathbf{i} - \mathbf{j} + 4\mathbf{k}| = \sqrt{8^2 + (-1)^2 + 4^2} = \sqrt{81} = 9$, so by Equation 4 the unit vector with the same direction is $\frac{1}{9}(8\mathbf{i} - \mathbf{j} + 4\mathbf{k}) = \frac{8}{9}\mathbf{i} - \frac{1}{9}\mathbf{j} + \frac{4}{9}\mathbf{k}$.

20. $|\langle -2, 4, 2 \rangle| = \sqrt{(-2)^2 + 4^2 + 2^2} = \sqrt{24} = 2\sqrt{6}$, so a unit vector in the direction of $\langle -2, 4, 2 \rangle$ is $\mathbf{u} = \dfrac{1}{2\sqrt{6}} \langle -2, 4, 2 \rangle$. A vector in the same direction but with length 6 is
$$6\mathbf{u} = 6 \cdot \frac{1}{2\sqrt{6}} \langle -2, 4, 2 \rangle = \left\langle -\frac{6}{\sqrt{6}}, \frac{12}{\sqrt{6}}, \frac{6}{\sqrt{6}} \right\rangle \text{ or } \langle -\sqrt{6}, 2\sqrt{6}, \sqrt{6} \rangle.$$

21. From the figure, we see that the x-component of $\mathbf{v}$ is

$v_1 = |\mathbf{v}| \cos(\pi/3) = 4 \cdot \frac{1}{2} = 2$ and the y-component is

$v_2 = |\mathbf{v}| \sin(\pi/3) = 4 \cdot \frac{\sqrt{3}}{2} = 2\sqrt{3}$. Thus

$\mathbf{v} = \langle v_1, v_2 \rangle = \langle 2, 2\sqrt{3} \rangle$.

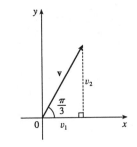

22. From the figure, we see that the horizontal component of the

force $\mathbf{F}$ is $|\mathbf{F}| \cos 38° = 50 \cos 38° \approx 39.4$ N, and the

vertical component is $|\mathbf{F}| \sin 38° = 50 \sin 38° \approx 30.8$ N.

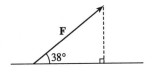

23. $|\mathbf{F}_1| = 10$ lb and $|\mathbf{F}_2| = 12$ lb.

$\mathbf{F}_1 = -|\mathbf{F}_1| \cos 45° \, \mathbf{i} + |\mathbf{F}_1| \sin 45° \, \mathbf{j} = -10 \cos 45° \, \mathbf{i} + 10 \sin 45° \, \mathbf{j}$

$\quad = -5\sqrt{2}\,\mathbf{i} + 5\sqrt{2}\,\mathbf{j}$

$\mathbf{F}_2 = |\mathbf{F}_2| \cos 30° \, \mathbf{i} + |\mathbf{F}_2| \sin 30° \, \mathbf{j} = 12 \cos 30° \, \mathbf{i} + 12 \sin 30° \, \mathbf{j} = 6\sqrt{3}\,\mathbf{i} + 6\,\mathbf{j}$

$\mathbf{F} = \mathbf{F}_1 + \mathbf{F}_2 = \left(6\sqrt{3} - 5\sqrt{2}\right)\mathbf{i} + \left(6 + 5\sqrt{2}\right)\mathbf{j} \approx 3.32\,\mathbf{i} + 13.07\,\mathbf{j}$

$|\mathbf{F}| \approx \sqrt{(3.32)^2 + (13.07)^2} \approx 13.5$ lb. $\tan\theta = \dfrac{6 + 5\sqrt{2}}{6\sqrt{3} - 5\sqrt{2}}$ $\Rightarrow$ $\theta = \tan^{-1} \dfrac{6 + 5\sqrt{2}}{6\sqrt{3} - 5\sqrt{2}} \approx 76°$.

24. Set up the coordinate axes so that north is the positive y-direction, and east is the positive x-direction. The wind is
blowing at 50 km/h from the direction N 45° W, so that its velocity vector is 50 km/h S 45° E, which can be
written as $\mathbf{v}_{\text{wind}} = 50(\cos 45° \, \mathbf{i} - \sin 45° \, \mathbf{j})$. With respect to the still air, the velocity vector of the plane is
250 km/h N 60° E, or equivalently $\mathbf{v}_{\text{plane}} = 250(\cos 30° \, \mathbf{i} + \sin 30° \, \mathbf{j})$. The velocity of the plane relative to the
ground is

$$\mathbf{v} = \mathbf{v}_{\text{wind}} + \mathbf{v}_{\text{plane}} = (50 \cos 45° + 250 \cos 30°)\,\mathbf{i} + (-50 \sin 45° + 250 \sin 30°)\,\mathbf{j}$$

$$= \left(25\sqrt{2} + 125\sqrt{3}\right)\mathbf{i} + \left(125 - 25\sqrt{2}\right)\mathbf{j} \approx 251.9\,\mathbf{i} + 89.6\,\mathbf{j}$$

The ground speed is $|\mathbf{v}| \approx \sqrt{(251.9)^2 + (89.6)^2} \approx 267$ km/h. The angle the velocity vector makes with the x-axis
is $\theta \approx \tan^{-1} \frac{89.6}{251.9} \approx 20°$. Therefore, the true course of the plane is about N $(90 - 20)° \, \text{E} = \text{N}\,70°\,\text{E}$.

25. With respect to the water's surface, the woman's velocity is the vector sum of the velocity of the ship with respect to
the water, and the woman's velocity with respect to the ship. If we let north be the positive y-direction, then
$\mathbf{v} = \langle 0, 22 \rangle + \langle -3, 0 \rangle = \langle -3, 22 \rangle$. The woman's speed is $|\mathbf{v}| = \sqrt{9 + 484} \approx 22.2$ mi/h. The vector $\mathbf{v}$ makes an
angle θ with the east, where $\theta = \tan^{-1} \frac{22}{-3} \approx 98°$. Therefore, the woman's direction is about
N $(98 - 90)° \, \text{W} = \text{N}\,8°\,\text{W}$.

26. Call the two tensile forces $\mathbf{T}_3$ and $\mathbf{T}_5$, corresponding to the ropes of length 3 m and 5 m. In terms of vertical and horizontal components, $\mathbf{T}_3 = -|\mathbf{T}_3|\cos 52° \,\mathbf{i} + |\mathbf{T}_3|\sin 52° \,\mathbf{j}$ (1) and $\mathbf{T}_5 = |\mathbf{T}_5|\cos 40° \,\mathbf{i} + |\mathbf{T}_5|\sin 40° \,\mathbf{j}$ (2). The resultant of these forces, $\mathbf{T}_3 + \mathbf{T}_5$, counterbalances the force of gravity acting on the decoration [which is $-5g\,\mathbf{j} \approx -5\,(9.8)\,\mathbf{j} = -49\,\mathbf{j}$]. So $\mathbf{T}_3 + \mathbf{T}_5 = 49\,\mathbf{j}$. Hence $\mathbf{T}_3 + \mathbf{T}_5 = (-|\mathbf{T}_3|\cos 52° + |\mathbf{T}_5|\cos 40°)\,\mathbf{i} + (|\mathbf{T}_3|\sin 52° + |\mathbf{T}_5|\sin 40°)\,\mathbf{j} = 49\,\mathbf{j}$. Thus $-|\mathbf{T}_3|\cos 52° + |\mathbf{T}_5|\cos 40° = 0$ and $|\mathbf{T}_3|\sin 52° + |\mathbf{T}_5|\sin 40° = 49$.

From the first of these two equations $|\mathbf{T}_3| = |\mathbf{T}_5|\dfrac{\cos 40°}{\cos 52°}$. Substituting this into the second equation gives

$|\mathbf{T}_5| = \dfrac{49}{\cos 40° \tan 52° + \sin 40°} \approx 30$ N. Therefore, $|\mathbf{T}_3| = |\mathbf{T}_5|\dfrac{\cos 40°}{\cos 52°} \approx 38$ N. Finally, from (1) and (2),

$\mathbf{T}_3 \approx -23\,\mathbf{i} + 30\,\mathbf{j}$, and $\mathbf{T}_5 \approx 23\,\mathbf{i} + 19\,\mathbf{j}$.

27. Let $\mathbf{T}_1$ and $\mathbf{T}_2$ represent the tension vectors in each side of the clothesline as shown in the figure. $\mathbf{T}_1$ and $\mathbf{T}_2$ have equal vertical components and opposite horizontal components, so we can write $\mathbf{T}_1 = -a\,\mathbf{i} + b\,\mathbf{j}$ and $\mathbf{T}_2 = a\,\mathbf{i} + b\,\mathbf{j}$ $(a, b > 0)$.

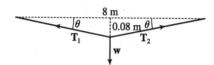

By similar triangles, $\dfrac{b}{a} = \dfrac{0.08}{4} \;\Rightarrow\; a = 50b$. The force due to gravity acting on the shirt has magnitude $0.8g \approx (0.8)\,(9.8) = 7.84$ N, hence we have $\mathbf{w} = -7.84\,\mathbf{j}$. The resultant $\mathbf{T}_1 + \mathbf{T}_2$ of the tensile forces counterbalances $\mathbf{w}$, so $\mathbf{T}_1 + \mathbf{T}_2 = -\mathbf{w} \;\Rightarrow\; (-a\,\mathbf{i} + b\,\mathbf{j}) + (a\,\mathbf{i} + b\,\mathbf{j}) = 7.84\,\mathbf{j} \;\Rightarrow\; (-50b\,\mathbf{i} + b\,\mathbf{j}) + (50b\,\mathbf{i} + b\,\mathbf{j}) = 2b\,\mathbf{j} = 7.84\,\mathbf{j} \;\Rightarrow\; b = \frac{7.84}{2} = 3.92$ and $a = 50b = 196$. Thus the tensions are $\mathbf{T}_1 = -a\,\mathbf{i} + b\,\mathbf{j} = -196\,\mathbf{i} + 3.92\,\mathbf{j}$ and $\mathbf{T}_2 = a\,\mathbf{i} + b\,\mathbf{j} = 196\,\mathbf{i} + 3.92\,\mathbf{j}$.

Alternatively, we can find the value of θ and proceed as in Example 7.

28. We can consider the weight of the chain to be concentrated at its midpoint. The forces acting on the chain then are the tension vectors $\mathbf{T}_1$, $\mathbf{T}_2$ in each end of the chain and the weight $\mathbf{w}$, as shown in the figure. We know $|\mathbf{T}_1| = |\mathbf{T}_2| = 25$ N so, in terms of vertical and horizontal components, we have

$$\mathbf{T}_1 = -25\cos 37° \,\mathbf{i} + 25\sin 37° \,\mathbf{j}$$

$$\mathbf{T}_2 = 25\cos 37° \,\mathbf{i} + 25\sin 37° \,\mathbf{j}$$

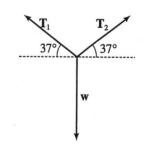

The resultant vector $\mathbf{T}_1 + \mathbf{T}_2$ of the tensions counterbalances the weight $\mathbf{w}$, giving $\mathbf{T}_1 + \mathbf{T}_2 = -\mathbf{w}$. Since $\mathbf{w} = -|\mathbf{w}|\,\mathbf{j}$, we have $(-25\cos 37° \,\mathbf{i} + 25\sin 37° \,\mathbf{j}) + (25\cos 37° \,\mathbf{i} + 25\sin 37° \,\mathbf{j}) = |\mathbf{w}|\,\mathbf{j} \;\Rightarrow\; 50\sin 37° \,\mathbf{j} = |\mathbf{w}|\,\mathbf{j} \;\Rightarrow\; |\mathbf{w}| = 50\sin 37° \approx 30.1$. So the weight is 30.1 N, and since $w = mg$, the mass is $\frac{30.1}{9.8} \approx 3.07$ kg.

29. (a), (b)

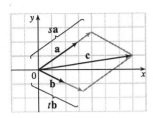

(c) From the sketch, we estimate that $s \approx 1.3$ and $t \approx 1.6$.

(d) $\mathbf{c} = s\,\mathbf{a} + t\,\mathbf{b}$ $\Leftrightarrow$ $7 = 3s + 2t$ and $1 = 2s - t$.

Solving these equations gives $s = \frac{9}{7}$ and $t = \frac{11}{7}$.

30. Draw $\mathbf{a}$, $\mathbf{b}$, and $\mathbf{c}$ emanating from the origin. Extend $\mathbf{a}$ and $\mathbf{b}$ to form lines A and B, and draw lines A' and B' parallel to these two lines through the terminal point of c.

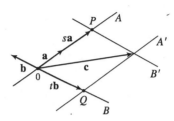

Since $\mathbf{a}$ and $\mathbf{b}$ are not parallel, A and B' must meet (at P), and A' and B must also meet (at Q). Now we see that

$\overrightarrow{OP} + \overrightarrow{OQ} = \mathbf{c}$, so if $s = \dfrac{\left|\overrightarrow{OP}\right|}{|\mathbf{a}|}$ $\left(\text{or its negative, if } \mathbf{a} \text{ points in the direction opposite } \overrightarrow{OP}\right)$ and $t = \dfrac{\left|\overrightarrow{OQ}\right|}{|\mathbf{b}|}$ (or its

negative, as in the diagram), then $\mathbf{c} = s\mathbf{a} + t\mathbf{b}$, as required.

Argument using components: Since $\mathbf{a}$, $\mathbf{b}$, and $\mathbf{c}$ all lie in the same plane, we can consider them to be vectors in two

dimensions. Let $\mathbf{a} = \langle a_1, a_2 \rangle$, $\mathbf{b} = \langle b_1, b_2 \rangle$, and $\mathbf{c} = \langle c_1, c_2 \rangle$. We need $sa_1 + tb_1 = c_1$ and $sa_2 + tb_2 = c_2$.

Multiplying the first equation by a_2 and the second by a_1 and subtracting, we get $t = \dfrac{c_2 a_1 - c_1 a_2}{b_2 a_1 - b_1 a_2}$. Similarly

$s = \dfrac{b_2 c_1 - b_1 c_2}{b_2 a_1 - b_1 a_2}$. Since $\mathbf{a} \neq \mathbf{0}$ and $\mathbf{b} \neq \mathbf{0}$ and $\mathbf{a}$ is not a scalar multiple of $\mathbf{b}$, the denominator is not zero.

31.

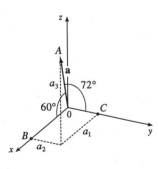

Let $\mathbf{a} = \langle a_1, a_2, a_3 \rangle$, as shown in the figure. Since $|\mathbf{a}| = 1$ and triangle ABO is

a right triangle, we have $\cos 60° = \dfrac{a_1}{1}$ $\Rightarrow$ $a_1 = \cos 60°$. Similarly, triangle

ACO is a right triangle, so $a_2 = \cos 72°$. Finally, since $|\mathbf{a}| = 1$ we have

$$\sqrt{(\cos 60°)^2 + (\cos 72°)^2 + a_3^2} = 1 \Rightarrow$$

$$a_3^2 = 1 - (\cos 60°)^2 - (\cos 72°)^2 \Rightarrow$$

$$a_3 = \sqrt{1 - (\cos 60°)^2 - (\cos 72°)^2}.\ \text{Thus}$$

$$\mathbf{a} = \left\langle \cos 60°, \cos 72°, \sqrt{1 - (\cos 60°)^2 - (\cos 72°)^2} \right\rangle$$

$$\approx \langle 0.50, 0.31, 0.81 \rangle$$

32. Let $\mathbf{a} = \langle a_1, a_2, a_3 \rangle$. As in Exercise 31, we can use right triangles to determine that $a_1 = |\mathbf{a}| \cos \alpha$ and
$a_2 = |\mathbf{a}| \cos \beta$. Similarly, by considering the right triangle with vertices the origin, the terminal point of $\mathbf{a}$, and the
point $(0, 0, a_3)$ we have $a_3 = |\mathbf{a}| \cos \gamma$. By writing $\cos \alpha = \dfrac{a_1}{|\mathbf{a}|}$, $\cos \beta = \dfrac{a_2}{|\mathbf{a}|}$, and $\cos \gamma = \dfrac{a_3}{|\mathbf{a}|}$, we have

$$\cos^2 \alpha + \cos^2 \beta + \cos^2 \gamma = \left(\frac{a_1}{|\mathbf{a}|}\right)^2 + \left(\frac{a_2}{|\mathbf{a}|}\right)^2 + \left(\frac{a_3}{|\mathbf{a}|}\right)^2 = \frac{1}{|\mathbf{a}|^2} \left(a_1^2 + a_2^2 + a_3^2\right)$$

$$= \frac{1}{|\mathbf{a}|^2} \left(|\mathbf{a}|^2\right) = 1 \text{ as desired.}$$

33. $|\mathbf{r} - \mathbf{r}_0|$ is the distance between the points (x, y, z) and (x_0, y_0, z_0), so the set of points is a sphere with radius 1
and center (x_0, y_0, z_0).

Alternate Method: $|\mathbf{r} - \mathbf{r}_0| = 1 \iff \sqrt{(x - x_0)^2 + (y - y_0)^2 + (z - z_0)^2} = 1 \iff$
$(x - x_0)^2 + (y - y_0)^2 + (z - z_0)^2 = 1$, which is the equation of a sphere with radius 1 and center (x_0, y_0, z_0).

34. Let P_1 and P_2 be the points with position vectors $\mathbf{r}_1$ and $\mathbf{r}_2$ respectively. Then $|\mathbf{r} - \mathbf{r}_1| + |\mathbf{r} - \mathbf{r}_2|$ is the sum of the
distances from (x, y) to P_1 and P_2. Since this sum is constant, the set of points (x, y) represents an ellipse with foci
P_1 and P_2. The condition $k > |\mathbf{r}_1 - \mathbf{r}_2|$ assures us that the ellipse is not degenerate.

35. $\mathbf{a} + (\mathbf{b} + \mathbf{c}) = \langle a_1, a_2 \rangle + (\langle b_1, b_2 \rangle + \langle c_1, c_2 \rangle) = \langle a_1, a_2 \rangle + \langle b_1 + c_1, b_2 + c_2 \rangle$

$\qquad = \langle a_1 + b_1 + c_1, a_2 + b_2 + c_2 \rangle = \langle (a_1 + b_1) + c_1, (a_2 + b_2) + c_2 \rangle$

$\qquad = \langle a_1 + b_1, a_2 + b_2 \rangle + \langle c_1, c_2 \rangle = (\langle a_1, a_2 \rangle + \langle b_1, b_2 \rangle) + \langle c_1, c_2 \rangle$

$\qquad = (\mathbf{a} + \mathbf{b}) + \mathbf{c}$

36. *Algebraically:*

$$c(\mathbf{a} + \mathbf{b}) = c(\langle a_1, a_2, a_3 \rangle + \langle b_1, b_2, b_3 \rangle) = c\langle a_1 + b_1, a_2 + b_2, a_3 + b_3 \rangle$$

$$= \langle c(a_1 + b_1), c(a_2 + b_2), c(a_3 + b_3) \rangle = \langle ca_1 + cb_1, ca_2 + cb_2, ca_3 + cb_3 \rangle$$

$$= \langle ca_1, ca_2, ca_3 \rangle + \langle cb_1, cb_2, cb_3 \rangle = c\mathbf{a} + c\mathbf{b}$$

Geometrically:

According to the Triangle Law, if $\mathbf{a} = \overrightarrow{PQ}$ and $\mathbf{b} = \overrightarrow{QR}$, then
$\mathbf{a} + \mathbf{b} = \overrightarrow{PR}$. Construct triangle PST as shown so that $\overrightarrow{PS} = c\mathbf{a}$
and $\overrightarrow{ST} = c\mathbf{b}$. (We have drawn the case where $c > 1$.) By the
Triangle Law, $\overrightarrow{PT} = c\mathbf{a} + c\mathbf{b}$. But triangle PQR and
triangle PST are similar triangles because $c\mathbf{b}$ is parallel to $\mathbf{b}$.
Therefore, $\overrightarrow{PR}$ and $\overrightarrow{PT}$ are parallel and, in fact, $\overrightarrow{PT} = c\overrightarrow{PR}$.
Thus, $c\mathbf{a} + c\mathbf{b} = c(\mathbf{a} + \mathbf{b})$.

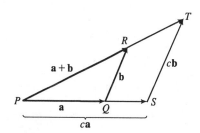

37. Consider triangle ABC, where D and E are the midpoints of AB and BC. We know that $\overrightarrow{AB} + \overrightarrow{BC} = \overrightarrow{AC}$ (1) and $\overrightarrow{DB} + \overrightarrow{BE} = \overrightarrow{DE}$ (2). However, $\overrightarrow{DB} = \frac{1}{2}\overrightarrow{AB}$, and $\overrightarrow{BE} = \frac{1}{2}\overrightarrow{BC}$. Substituting these expressions for $\overrightarrow{DB}$ and $\overrightarrow{BE}$ into (2) gives $\frac{1}{2}\overrightarrow{AB} + \frac{1}{2}\overrightarrow{BC} = \overrightarrow{DE}$. Comparing this with (1) gives $\overrightarrow{DE} = \frac{1}{2}\overrightarrow{AC}$. Therefore $\overrightarrow{AC}$ and $\overrightarrow{DE}$ are parallel and $\left|\overrightarrow{DE}\right| = \frac{1}{2}\left|\overrightarrow{AC}\right|$.

38.

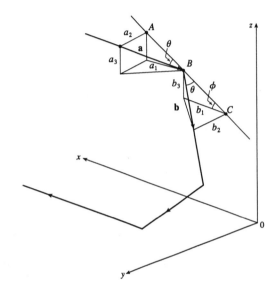

The question states that the light ray strikes all three mirrors, so it is not parallel to any of them and $a_1 \neq 0$, $a_2 \neq 0$ and $a_3 \neq 0$. Let $\mathbf{b} = \langle b_1, b_2, b_3 \rangle$, as in the diagram. We can let $|\mathbf{b}| = |\mathbf{a}|$, since only its direction is important. Then $\dfrac{|b_2|}{|\mathbf{b}|} = \sin\theta = \dfrac{|a_2|}{|\mathbf{a}|} \Rightarrow |b_2| = |a_2|$.

From the diagram $b_2\,\mathbf{j}$ and $a_2\,\mathbf{j}$ point in opposite directions, so $b_2 = -a_2$. $|AB| = |BC|$, so $|b_3| = \sin\phi\,|BC| = \sin\phi\,|AB| = |a_3|$, and $|b_1| = \cos\phi\,|BC| = \cos\phi\,|AB| = |a_1|$. $b_3\,\mathbf{k}$ and $a_3\,\mathbf{k}$ have the same direction, as do $b_1\,\mathbf{i}$ and $a_1\,\mathbf{i}$, so $\mathbf{b} = \langle a_1, -a_2, a_3 \rangle$. When the ray hits the other mirrors, similar arguments show that these reflections will reverse the signs of the other two coordinates, so the final reflected ray will be $\langle -a_1, -a_2, -a_3 \rangle = -\mathbf{a}$, which is parallel to $\mathbf{a}$.

◆9.3◆ The Dot Product • • • • • • • • • • • • • • • • •

1. (a) $\mathbf{a} \cdot \mathbf{b}$ is a scalar, and the dot product is defined only for vectors, so $(\mathbf{a} \cdot \mathbf{b}) \cdot \mathbf{c}$ has no meaning.

(b) $(\mathbf{a} \cdot \mathbf{b})\,\mathbf{c}$ is a scalar multiple of a vector, so it does have meaning.

(c) Both $|\mathbf{a}|$ and $\mathbf{b} \cdot \mathbf{c}$ are scalars, so $|\mathbf{a}|\,(\mathbf{b} \cdot \mathbf{c})$ is an ordinary product of real numbers, and has meaning.

(d) Both $\mathbf{a}$ and $\mathbf{b} + \mathbf{c}$ are vectors, so the dot product $\mathbf{a} \cdot (\mathbf{b} + \mathbf{c})$ has meaning.

(e) $\mathbf{a} \cdot \mathbf{b}$ is a scalar, but $\mathbf{c}$ is a vector, and so the two quantities cannot be added and this expression has no meaning.

(f) $|\mathbf{a}|$ is a scalar, and the dot product is defined only for vectors, so $|\mathbf{a}| \cdot (\mathbf{b} + \mathbf{c})$ has no meaning.

2. Let the vectors be $\mathbf{a}$ and $\mathbf{b}$. Then by definition of the dot product,
$$\mathbf{a} \cdot \mathbf{b} = |\mathbf{a}|\,|\mathbf{b}|\cos\theta = (6)\left(\tfrac{1}{3}\right)\cos\tfrac{\pi}{4} = \tfrac{6}{3\sqrt{2}} = \sqrt{2}.$$

3. $\mathbf{a} \cdot \mathbf{b} = |\mathbf{a}|\,|\mathbf{b}|\cos\theta = (12)(15)\cos\tfrac{\pi}{6} = 180 \cdot \tfrac{\sqrt{3}}{2} = 90\sqrt{3} \approx 155.9$

4. $\mathbf{a} \cdot \mathbf{b} = \langle \tfrac{1}{2}, 4 \rangle \cdot \langle -8, -3 \rangle = \left(\tfrac{1}{2}\right)(-8) + (4)(-3) = -16$

5. $\mathbf{a} \cdot \mathbf{b} = \langle 5, 0, -2 \rangle \cdot \langle 3, -1, 10 \rangle = (5)(3) + (0)(-1) + (-2)(10) = -5$

6. $\mathbf{a} \cdot \mathbf{b} = \langle s, 2s, 3s \rangle \cdot \langle t, -t, 5t \rangle = (s)(t) + (2s)(-t) + (3s)(5t) = st - 2st + 15st = 14st$

7. $\mathbf{a} \cdot \mathbf{b} = (\mathbf{i} - 2\mathbf{j} + 3\mathbf{k}) \cdot (5\mathbf{i} + 9\mathbf{k}) = (1)(5) + (-2)(0) + (3)(9) = 32$

8. $\mathbf{a} \cdot \mathbf{b} = (4\mathbf{j} - 3\mathbf{k}) \cdot (2\mathbf{i} + 4\mathbf{j} + 6\mathbf{k}) = (0)(2) + (4)(4) + (-3)(6) = -2$

9. $\mathbf{u}$, $\mathbf{v}$, and $\mathbf{w}$ are all unit vectors, so the triangle is an equilateral triangle. Thus the angle between $\mathbf{u}$ and $\mathbf{v}$ is $60\,°$ and $\mathbf{u} \cdot \mathbf{v} = |\mathbf{u}|\,|\mathbf{v}|\cos 60\,° = (1)(1)\left(\frac{1}{2}\right) = \frac{1}{2}$. If $\mathbf{w}$ is moved so it has the same initial point as $\mathbf{u}$, we can see that the angle between them is $120\,°$ and we have $\mathbf{u} \cdot \mathbf{w} = |\mathbf{u}|\,|\mathbf{w}|\cos 120\,° = (1)(1)\left(-\frac{1}{2}\right) = -\frac{1}{2}$.

10. $\mathbf{u}$ is a unit vector, so $\mathbf{w}$ is also a unit vector, and $|\mathbf{v}|$ can be determined by examining the right triangle formed by $\mathbf{u}$ and $\mathbf{v}$. Since the angle between $\mathbf{u}$ and $\mathbf{v}$ is $45\,°$, we have $|\mathbf{v}| = |\mathbf{u}|\cos 45\,° = \frac{\sqrt{2}}{2}$. Then $\mathbf{u} \cdot \mathbf{v} = |\mathbf{u}|\,|\mathbf{v}|\cos 45\,° = (1)\left(\frac{\sqrt{2}}{2}\right)\frac{\sqrt{2}}{2} = \frac{1}{2}$. Since $\mathbf{u}$ and $\mathbf{w}$ are orthogonal, $\mathbf{u} \cdot \mathbf{w} = 0$.

11. (a) $\mathbf{i} \cdot \mathbf{j} = \langle 1, 0, 0\rangle \cdot \langle 0, 1, 0\rangle = (1)(0) + (0)(1) + (0)(0) = 0$. Similarly $\mathbf{j} \cdot \mathbf{k} = (0)(0) + (1)(0) + (0)(1) = 0$ and $\mathbf{k} \cdot \mathbf{i} = (0)(1) + (0)(0) + (1)(0) = 0$.

Another Method: Because $\mathbf{i}$, $\mathbf{j}$, and $\mathbf{k}$ are mutually perpendicular, the cosine factor in each dot product is $\cos\frac{\pi}{2} = 0$.

(b) By Property 1 of the dot product, $\mathbf{i} \cdot \mathbf{i} = |\mathbf{i}|^2 = 1^2 = 1$ since $\mathbf{i}$ is a unit vector. Similarly, $\mathbf{j} \cdot \mathbf{j} = |\mathbf{j}|^2 = 1$ and $\mathbf{k} \cdot \mathbf{k} = |\mathbf{k}|^2 = 1$.

12. The dot product $\mathbf{A} \cdot \mathbf{P}$ is

$$\langle a, b, c\rangle \cdot \langle 2, 1.5, 1\rangle = a(2) + b(1.5) + c(1)$$

$$= (\text{number of hamburgers sold})(\text{price per hamburger})$$

$$+ (\text{number of hot dogs sold})(\text{price per hot dog})$$

$$+ (\text{number of soft drinks sold})(\text{price per soft drink})$$

so it is equal to the vendor's total revenue for that day.

13. $|\mathbf{a}| = \sqrt{3^2 + 4^2} = 5$, $|\mathbf{b}| = \sqrt{5^2 + 12^2} = 13$, and $\mathbf{a} \cdot \mathbf{b} = (3)(5) + (4)(12) = 63$. From the definition of the dot product, we have $\cos\theta = \dfrac{\mathbf{a} \cdot \mathbf{b}}{|\mathbf{a}|\,|\mathbf{b}|} = \dfrac{63}{5 \cdot 13} = \dfrac{63}{65}$. So the angle between $\mathbf{a}$ and $\mathbf{b}$ is $\theta = \cos^{-1}\left(\frac{63}{65}\right) \approx 14\,°$.

14. $|\mathbf{a}| = \sqrt{6^2 + (-3)^2 + 2^2} = 7$, $|\mathbf{b}| = \sqrt{2^2 + 1^2 + (-2)^2} = 3$, and $\mathbf{a} \cdot \mathbf{b} = (6)(2) + (-3)(1) + (2)(-2) = 5$. Then $\cos\theta = \dfrac{\mathbf{a} \cdot \mathbf{b}}{|\mathbf{a}|\,|\mathbf{b}|} = \dfrac{5}{7 \cdot 3} = \dfrac{5}{21}$ and $\theta = \cos^{-1}\left(\frac{5}{21}\right) \approx 76\,°$.

15. $|\mathbf{a}| = \sqrt{0^2 + 1^2 + 1^2} = \sqrt{2}$, $|\mathbf{b}| = \sqrt{1^2 + 2^2 + (-3)^2} = \sqrt{14}$, and $\mathbf{a} \cdot \mathbf{b} = (0)(1) + (1)(2) + (1)(-3) = -1$. Then $\cos\theta = \dfrac{\mathbf{a} \cdot \mathbf{b}}{|\mathbf{a}|\,|\mathbf{b}|} = \dfrac{-1}{\sqrt{2} \cdot \sqrt{14}} = \dfrac{-1}{2\sqrt{7}}$ and $\theta = \cos^{-1}\left(-\dfrac{1}{2\sqrt{7}}\right) \approx 101\,°$.

16. Let p, q and r be the angles at vertices P, Q and R. Then p is the angle between vectors $\overrightarrow{PQ}$ and $\overrightarrow{PR}$, q is the angle between vectors $\overrightarrow{QP}$ and $\overrightarrow{QR}$, and r is the angle between vectors $\overrightarrow{RP}$ and $\overrightarrow{RQ}$. Thus

$$\cos p = \frac{\overrightarrow{PQ} \cdot \overrightarrow{PR}}{|\overrightarrow{PQ}|\,|\overrightarrow{PR}|} = \frac{\langle 2, 2, -9\rangle \cdot \langle 5, 5, -4\rangle}{\sqrt{89}\,\sqrt{66}} = \frac{56}{\sqrt{5874}}, \text{ so } p = \cos^{-1}\frac{56}{\sqrt{5874}} \approx 43\,°;$$

$$\cos q = \frac{\overrightarrow{QP} \cdot \overrightarrow{QR}}{|\overrightarrow{QP}||\overrightarrow{QR}|} = \frac{\langle -2, -2, 9 \rangle \cdot \langle 3, 3, 5 \rangle}{\sqrt{89}\,\sqrt{43}} = \frac{33}{\sqrt{3827}}, \text{ so } q = \cos^{-1}\frac{33}{\sqrt{3827}} \approx 58\,°; \text{ and}$$

$r \approx 180\,° - (43\,° + 58\,°) = 79\,°.$

Alternate Solution: Apply the Law of Cosines three times as follows:

$$\cos p = \frac{\left|\overrightarrow{QR}\right|^2 - \left|\overrightarrow{PQ}\right|^2 - \left|\overrightarrow{PR}\right|^2}{2\left|\overrightarrow{PQ}\right|\left|\overrightarrow{PR}\right|}, \quad \cos q = \frac{\left|\overrightarrow{PR}\right|^2 - \left|\overrightarrow{PQ}\right|^2 - \left|\overrightarrow{QR}\right|^2}{2\left|\overrightarrow{PQ}\right|\left|\overrightarrow{QR}\right|}, \quad \cos r = \frac{\left|\overrightarrow{PQ}\right|^2 - \left|\overrightarrow{PR}\right|^2 - \left|\overrightarrow{QR}\right|^2}{2\left|\overrightarrow{PR}\right|\left|\overrightarrow{QR}\right|}.$$

17. (a) $\mathbf{a} \cdot \mathbf{b} = (-5)(6) + (3)(-8) + (7)(2) = -40 \neq 0$, so $\mathbf{a}$ and $\mathbf{b}$ are not orthogonal. Also, since $\mathbf{a}$ is not a scalar

multiple of $\mathbf{b}$, $\mathbf{a}$ and $\mathbf{b}$ are not parallel.

(b) $\mathbf{a} \cdot \mathbf{b} = (4)(-3) + (6)(2) = 0$, so $\mathbf{a}$ and $\mathbf{b}$ are orthogonal (and not parallel).

(c) $\mathbf{a} \cdot \mathbf{b} = (-1)(3) + (2)(4) + (5)(-1) = 0$, so $\mathbf{a}$ and $\mathbf{b}$ are orthogonal (and not parallel).

(d) Because $\mathbf{a} = -\frac{2}{3}\mathbf{b}$, $\mathbf{a}$ and $\mathbf{b}$ are parallel.

18. $\langle -6, b, 2 \rangle$ and $\langle b, b^2, b \rangle$ are orthogonal when $\langle -6, b, 2 \rangle \cdot \langle b, b^2, b \rangle = 0 \quad \Leftrightarrow \quad (-6)(b) + (b)(b^2) + (2)(b) = 0$

$\Leftrightarrow \quad b^3 - 4b = 0 \quad \Leftrightarrow \quad b(b+2)(b-2) = 0 \quad \Leftrightarrow \quad b = 0 \text{ or } b = \pm 2.$

19. Let $\mathbf{a} = a_1\mathbf{i} + a_2\mathbf{j} + a_3\mathbf{k}$ be a vector orthogonal to both $\mathbf{i}+\mathbf{j}$ and $\mathbf{i}+\mathbf{k}$. Then $\mathbf{a} \cdot (\mathbf{i}+\mathbf{j}) = 0 \quad \Leftrightarrow \quad a_1 + a_2 = 0$

and $\mathbf{a} \cdot (\mathbf{i}+\mathbf{k}) = 0 \quad \Leftrightarrow \quad a_1 + a_3 = 0$, so $a_1 = -a_2 = -a_3$. Furthermore $\mathbf{a}$ is to be a unit vector, so

$1 = a_1^2 + a_2^2 + a_3^2 = 3a_1^2$ implies $a_1 = \pm\frac{1}{\sqrt{3}}$. Thus $\mathbf{a} = \frac{1}{\sqrt{3}}\mathbf{i} - \frac{1}{\sqrt{3}}\mathbf{j} - \frac{1}{\sqrt{3}}\mathbf{k}$ and $\mathbf{a} = -\frac{1}{\sqrt{3}}\mathbf{i} + \frac{1}{\sqrt{3}}\mathbf{j} + \frac{1}{\sqrt{3}}\mathbf{k}$ are

two such unit vectors.

20. According to the definition of the dot product, we need

$\langle 1, 2, 1 \rangle \cdot \langle 1, 0, c \rangle = |\langle 1, 2, 1 \rangle||\langle 1, 0, c \rangle| \cos 60° \quad \Leftrightarrow \quad 1 + c = \sqrt{6}\sqrt{1+c^2} \cdot \frac{1}{2} \quad \Leftrightarrow \quad 2(1+c) = \sqrt{6}\sqrt{1+c^2}.$

Squaring both sides gives $6(1+c^2) = 4(1 + 2c + c^2)$. Thus $6 + 6c^2 = 4 + 8c + 4c^2$ or $2c^2 - 8c + 2 = 0$ and

$c = \frac{4 \pm \sqrt{16-4}}{2} = 2 \pm \sqrt{3}$. Each of these values for c can be checked to show it gives a solution.

21. $|\mathbf{a}| = \sqrt{4+9} = \sqrt{13}$. The scalar projection of $\mathbf{b}$ onto $\mathbf{a}$ is $\text{comp}_\mathbf{a}\,\mathbf{b} = \dfrac{\mathbf{a} \cdot \mathbf{b}}{|\mathbf{a}|} = \dfrac{2 \cdot 4 + 3 \cdot 1}{\sqrt{13}} = \dfrac{11}{\sqrt{13}}.$

The vector projection of $\mathbf{b}$ onto $\mathbf{a}$ is $\text{proj}_\mathbf{a}\,\mathbf{b} = \dfrac{11}{\sqrt{13}}\dfrac{\mathbf{a}}{|\mathbf{a}|} = \dfrac{11}{\sqrt{13}} \cdot \dfrac{1}{\sqrt{13}}\langle 2, 3 \rangle = \dfrac{11}{13}\langle 2, 3 \rangle = \left\langle \dfrac{22}{13}, \dfrac{33}{13} \right\rangle.$

22. $|\mathbf{a}| = \sqrt{9+1} = \sqrt{10}$. The scalar projection of $\mathbf{b}$ onto $\mathbf{a}$ is $\text{comp}_\mathbf{a}\,\mathbf{b} = \dfrac{\mathbf{a} \cdot \mathbf{b}}{|\mathbf{a}|} = \dfrac{3 \cdot 2 - 1 \cdot 3}{\sqrt{10}} = \dfrac{3}{\sqrt{10}}.$

The vector projection of $\mathbf{b}$ onto $\mathbf{a}$ is $\text{proj}_\mathbf{a}\,\mathbf{b} = \dfrac{3}{\sqrt{10}}\dfrac{\mathbf{a}}{|\mathbf{a}|} = \dfrac{3}{\sqrt{10}} \cdot \dfrac{1}{\sqrt{10}}\langle 3, -1 \rangle = \dfrac{3}{10}\langle 3, -1 \rangle = \left\langle \dfrac{9}{10}, -\dfrac{3}{10} \right\rangle.$

23. $|\mathbf{a}| = \sqrt{16+4+0} = 2\sqrt{5}$ so the scalar projection of $\mathbf{b}$ onto $\mathbf{a}$ is $\text{comp}_\mathbf{a}\mathbf{b} = \dfrac{\mathbf{a} \cdot \mathbf{b}}{|\mathbf{a}|} = \dfrac{1}{2\sqrt{5}}(4 + 2 + 0) = \dfrac{3}{\sqrt{5}}.$

The vector projection of $\mathbf{b}$ onto $\mathbf{a}$ is $\text{proj}_\mathbf{a}\mathbf{b} = \dfrac{3}{\sqrt{5}}\dfrac{\mathbf{a}}{|\mathbf{a}|} = \dfrac{3}{\sqrt{5}} \cdot \dfrac{1}{2\sqrt{5}}\langle 4, 2, 0 \rangle = \dfrac{1}{5}\langle 6, 3, 0 \rangle = \left\langle \dfrac{6}{5}, \dfrac{3}{5}, 0 \right\rangle.$

24. $|\mathbf{a}| = \sqrt{4+9+1} = \sqrt{14}$, so the scalar projection of $\mathbf{b}$ onto $\mathbf{a}$ is

$\text{comp}_\mathbf{a}\,\mathbf{b} = \dfrac{\mathbf{a} \cdot \mathbf{b}}{|\mathbf{a}|} = \dfrac{2 - 18 - 2}{\sqrt{14}} = -\dfrac{18}{\sqrt{14}}$ while the vector projection of $\mathbf{b}$ onto $\mathbf{a}$ is

$\text{proj}_\mathbf{a}\,\mathbf{b} = -\dfrac{18}{\sqrt{14}}\dfrac{\mathbf{a}}{|\mathbf{a}|} = -\dfrac{18}{\sqrt{14}} \cdot \dfrac{2\mathbf{i} - 3\mathbf{j} + \mathbf{k}}{\sqrt{14}} = -\dfrac{9}{7}(2\mathbf{i} - 3\mathbf{j} + \mathbf{k}).$

25. $(\text{orth}_a\, b) \cdot a = (b - \text{proj}_a\, b) \cdot a = b \cdot a - (\text{proj}_a\, b) \cdot a = b \cdot a - \dfrac{a \cdot b}{|a|^2}\, a \cdot a$

$$= b \cdot a - \dfrac{a \cdot b}{|a|^2}\, |a|^2 = b \cdot a - a \cdot b = 0$$

So they are orthogonal by (2).

26. Using the result of Exercise 22, we have

$$\text{orth}_a\, b = b - \text{proj}_a\, b$$

$$= \langle 2, 3 \rangle - \langle \tfrac{9}{10}, -\tfrac{3}{10} \rangle$$

$$= \langle 1.1, 3.3 \rangle$$

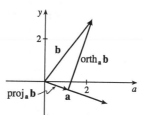

27. $\text{comp}_a\, b = \dfrac{a \cdot b}{|a|} = 2 \iff a \cdot b = 2\,|a| = 2\sqrt{10}$. If $b = \langle b_1, b_2, b_3 \rangle$, then we need $3b_1 + 0b_2 - 1b_3 = 2\sqrt{10}$.

One possible solution is obtained by taking $b_1 = 0$, $b_2 = 0$, $b_3 = -2\sqrt{10}$.

In general, $b = \langle s, t, 3s - 2\sqrt{10} \rangle$, $s, t \in \mathbb{R}$.

28. (a) $\text{comp}_a\, b = \text{comp}_b\, a \iff \dfrac{a \cdot b}{|a|} = \dfrac{b \cdot a}{|b|} \iff \dfrac{1}{|a|} = \dfrac{1}{|b|}$ or $a \cdot b = 0 \iff |b| = |a|$ or $a \cdot b = 0$. That

is, if a and b are orthogonal or if they have the same length.

(b) $\text{proj}_a\, b = \text{proj}_b\, a \iff \dfrac{a \cdot b}{|a|^2}\, a = \dfrac{b \cdot a}{|b|^2}\, b \iff a \cdot b = 0$ or $\dfrac{a}{|a|^2} = \dfrac{b}{|b|^2}$. But $\dfrac{a}{|a|^2} = \dfrac{b}{|b|^2} \Rightarrow$

$\dfrac{|a|}{|a|^2} = \dfrac{|b|}{|b|^2} \Rightarrow |a| = |b|$. Substituting this into the previous equation gives $a = b$. So $\text{proj}_a\, b = \text{proj}_b\, a$

$\iff$ a and b are orthogonal, or they are equal.

29. Here $D = (4-2)\,i + (9-3)\,j + (15-0)\,k = 2\,i + 6\,j + 15\,k$ so $W = F \cdot D = 20 + 108 - 90 = 38$ joules.

30. $W = |F|\,|D|\cos\theta = (20)(4)\cos 40°$

≈ 61 ft-lb

31. $W = |F|\,|D|\cos\theta = (25)(10)\cos 20°$

≈ 235 ft-lb

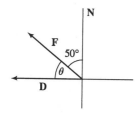

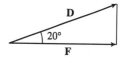

32. Here $|D| = 100$ m, $|F| = 50$ N, and $\theta = 30°$. Thus $W = |F|\,|D|\cos\theta = (50)(100)\left(\tfrac{\sqrt{3}}{2}\right) = 2500\sqrt{3}$ joules.

33. First note that $n = \langle a, b \rangle$ is perpendicular to the line, because if $Q_1 = (a_1, b_1)$ and $Q_2 = (a_2, b_2)$ lie on the line,

then $n \cdot \overrightarrow{Q_1 Q_2} = aa_2 - aa_1 + bb_2 - bb_1 = 0$, since $aa_2 + bb_2 = -c = aa_1 + bb_1$ from the equation of the line.

Let $P_2 = (x_2, y_2)$ lie on the line. Then the distance from P_1 to the line is the absolute value of the scalar projection of $\overrightarrow{P_1P_2}$ onto **n**. $\text{comp}_{\mathbf{n}}\left(\overrightarrow{P_1P_2}\right) = \dfrac{|\mathbf{n}\cdot\langle x_2 - x_1, y_2 - y_1\rangle|}{|\mathbf{n}|} = \dfrac{|ax_2 - ax_1 + by_2 - by_1|}{\sqrt{a^2 + b^2}} = \dfrac{|ax_1 + by_1 + c|}{\sqrt{a^2 + b^2}}$

since $ax_2 + by_2 = -c$. The required distance is $\dfrac{|3\cdot -2 + -4\cdot 3 + 5|}{\sqrt{3^2 + 4^2}} = \dfrac{13}{5}$.

34. $(\mathbf{r} - \mathbf{a})\cdot(\mathbf{r} - \mathbf{b}) = 0$ implies that the vectors $\mathbf{r} - \mathbf{a}$ and $\mathbf{r} - \mathbf{b}$ are orthogonal. From the diagram (in which A, B and R are the terminal points of the vectors), we see that this implies that R lies on a sphere whose diameter is the line from A to B. The center of this circle is the midpoint of AB, that is,

$\frac{1}{2}(\mathbf{a} + \mathbf{b}) = \langle \frac{1}{2}(a_1 + b_1), \frac{1}{2}(a_2 + b_2), \frac{1}{2}(a_3 + b_3)\rangle$, and its radius is

$\frac{1}{2}|\mathbf{a} - \mathbf{b}| = \frac{1}{2}\sqrt{(a_1 - b_1)^2 + (a_2 - b_2)^2 + (a_3 - b_3)^2}$.

Or: Expand the given equation, substitute $\mathbf{r}\cdot\mathbf{r} = x^2 + y^2 + z^2$ and complete the squares.

35. For convenience, consider the unit cube positioned so that its back left corner is at the origin, and its edges lie along the coordinate axes. The diagonal of the cube that begins at the origin and ends at $(1, 1, 1)$ has vector representation $\langle 1, 1, 1\rangle$. The angle θ between this vector and the vector of the edge which also begins at the origin and runs along the x-axis [that is, $\langle 1, 0, 0\rangle$] is given by $\cos\theta = \dfrac{\langle 1, 1, 1\rangle \cdot \langle 1, 0, 0\rangle}{|\langle 1, 1, 1\rangle||\langle 1, 0, 0\rangle|} = \dfrac{1}{\sqrt{3}} \;\Rightarrow\; \theta = \cos^{-1}\left(\frac{1}{\sqrt{3}}\right) \approx 55°$.

36. Consider a cube with sides of unit length, wholly within the first octant and with edges along each of the three coordinate axes. $\mathbf{i} + \mathbf{j} + \mathbf{k}$ and $\mathbf{i} + \mathbf{j}$ are vector representations of a diagonal of the cube and a diagonal of one of its faces. If θ is the angle between these diagonals, then $\cos\theta = \dfrac{(\mathbf{i} + \mathbf{j} + \mathbf{k})\cdot(\mathbf{i} + \mathbf{j})}{|\mathbf{i} + \mathbf{j} + \mathbf{k}|\,|\mathbf{i} + \mathbf{j}|} = \dfrac{1 + 1}{\sqrt{3}\sqrt{2}} = \sqrt{\dfrac{2}{3}} \;\Rightarrow$

$\theta = \cos^{-1}\sqrt{\frac{2}{3}} \approx 35°$.

37. Consider the H-C-H combination consisting of the sole carbon atom and the two hydrogen atoms that are at $(1, 0, 0)$ and $(0, 1, 0)$ (or any H-C-H combination, for that matter). Vector representations of the line segments emanating from the carbon atom and extending to these two hydrogen atoms are $\langle 1 - \frac{1}{2}, 0 - \frac{1}{2}, 0 - \frac{1}{2}\rangle = \langle \frac{1}{2}, -\frac{1}{2}, -\frac{1}{2}\rangle$ and $\langle 0 - \frac{1}{2}, 1 - \frac{1}{2}, 0 - \frac{1}{2}\rangle = \langle -\frac{1}{2}, \frac{1}{2}, -\frac{1}{2}\rangle$. The bond angle, θ, is therefore given by

$\cos\theta = \dfrac{\langle \frac{1}{2}, -\frac{1}{2}, -\frac{1}{2}\rangle \cdot \langle -\frac{1}{2}, \frac{1}{2}, -\frac{1}{2}\rangle}{|\langle \frac{1}{2}, -\frac{1}{2}, -\frac{1}{2}\rangle||\langle -\frac{1}{2}, \frac{1}{2}, -\frac{1}{2}\rangle|} = \dfrac{-\frac{1}{4} - \frac{1}{4} + \frac{1}{4}}{\sqrt{\frac{3}{4}}\sqrt{\frac{3}{4}}} = -\dfrac{1}{3} \;\Rightarrow\; \theta = \cos^{-1}\left(-\frac{1}{3}\right) \approx 109.5°$.

38. Let α be the angle between $\mathbf{a}$ and $\mathbf{c}$ and β be the angle between $\mathbf{c}$ and $\mathbf{b}$. We need to show that $\alpha = \beta$. Now

$\cos\alpha = \dfrac{\mathbf{a}\cdot\mathbf{c}}{|\mathbf{a}||\mathbf{c}|} = \dfrac{\mathbf{a}\cdot|\mathbf{a}|\mathbf{b} + \mathbf{a}\cdot|\mathbf{b}|\mathbf{a}}{|\mathbf{a}||\mathbf{c}|} = \dfrac{|\mathbf{a}|\mathbf{a}\cdot\mathbf{b} + |\mathbf{a}|^2|\mathbf{b}|}{|\mathbf{a}||\mathbf{c}|} = \dfrac{\mathbf{a}\cdot\mathbf{b} + |\mathbf{a}||\mathbf{b}|}{|\mathbf{c}|}$. Similarly,

$\cos\beta = \dfrac{\mathbf{b}\cdot\mathbf{c}}{|\mathbf{b}||\mathbf{c}|} = \dfrac{|\mathbf{a}||\mathbf{b}| + \mathbf{b}\cdot\mathbf{a}}{|\mathbf{c}|}$. Thus $\cos\alpha = \cos\beta$. However $0° \le \alpha \le 180°$ and $0° \le \beta \le 180°$, so $\alpha = \beta$ and $\mathbf{c}$ bisects the angle between $\mathbf{a}$ and $\mathbf{b}$.

39. If $c = 0$ then $c\mathbf{a} = \mathbf{0}$, so $(c\mathbf{a}) \cdot \mathbf{b} = \mathbf{0} \cdot \mathbf{b} = 0$ by Property 5. Similarly, $\mathbf{a} \cdot (c\mathbf{b}) = \mathbf{a} \cdot \mathbf{0} = 0$, and $c(\mathbf{a} \cdot \mathbf{b}) = 0(|\mathbf{a}|\,|\mathbf{b}|\cos\theta) = 0$, thus $(c\mathbf{a}) \cdot \mathbf{b} = c(\mathbf{a} \cdot \mathbf{b}) = \mathbf{a} \cdot (c\mathbf{b})$. If $c > 0$, the angle θ between $\mathbf{a}$ and $\mathbf{b}$ coincides with the angle between $c\mathbf{a}$ and $\mathbf{b}$, so by definition of the dot product, $(c\mathbf{a}) \cdot \mathbf{b} = |c\mathbf{a}|\,|\mathbf{b}|\cos\theta = |c|\,|\mathbf{a}|\,|\mathbf{b}|\cos\theta = c\,|\mathbf{a}|\,|\mathbf{b}|\cos\theta$. Similarly, $\mathbf{a} \cdot (c\mathbf{b}) = |\mathbf{a}|\,|c\mathbf{b}|\cos\theta = |\mathbf{a}|\,|c|\,|\mathbf{b}|\cos\theta = c\,|\mathbf{a}|\,|\mathbf{b}|\cos\theta$, and $c(\mathbf{a} \cdot \mathbf{b}) = c\,|\mathbf{a}|\,|\mathbf{b}|\cos\theta$. Thus, $(c\mathbf{a}) \cdot \mathbf{b} = c(\mathbf{a} \cdot \mathbf{b}) = \mathbf{a} \cdot (c\mathbf{b})$. The case for $c < 0$ is similar.

Using components, let $\mathbf{a} = \langle a_1, a_2, a_3 \rangle$ and $\mathbf{b} = \langle b_1, b_2, b_3 \rangle$. Then

$$(c\mathbf{a}) \cdot \mathbf{b} = \langle ca_1, ca_2, ca_3 \rangle \cdot \langle b_1, b_2, b_3 \rangle = (ca_1)b_1 + (ca_2)b_2 + (ca_3)b_3$$

$$= c(a_1b_1 + a_2b_2 + a_3b_3) = c(\mathbf{a} \cdot \mathbf{b})$$

$$= a_1(cb_1) + a_2(cb_2) + a_3(cb_3) = \langle a_1, a_2, a_3 \rangle \cdot \langle cb_1, cb_2, cb_3 \rangle = \mathbf{a} \cdot (c\mathbf{b})$$

40. Let the figure be called quadrilateral $ABCD$. The diagonals can be represented by $\overrightarrow{AC}$ and $\overrightarrow{BD}$. $\overrightarrow{AC} = \overrightarrow{AB} + \overrightarrow{BC}$ and $\overrightarrow{BD} = \overrightarrow{BC} + \overrightarrow{CD} = \overrightarrow{BC} - \overrightarrow{DC} = \overrightarrow{BC} - \overrightarrow{AB}$ (Since opposite sides of the object are of the same length and parallel, $\overrightarrow{AB} = \overrightarrow{DC}$.) Thus

$$\overrightarrow{AC} \cdot \overrightarrow{BD} = \left(\overrightarrow{AB} + \overrightarrow{BC}\right) \cdot \left(\overrightarrow{BC} - \overrightarrow{AB}\right) = \overrightarrow{AB} \cdot \left(\overrightarrow{BC} - \overrightarrow{AB}\right) + \overrightarrow{BC} \cdot \left(\overrightarrow{BC} - \overrightarrow{AB}\right)$$

$$= \overrightarrow{AB} \cdot \overrightarrow{BC} - \left|\overrightarrow{AB}\right|^2 + \left|\overrightarrow{BC}\right|^2 - \overrightarrow{AB} \cdot \overrightarrow{BC} = \left|\overrightarrow{BC}\right|^2 - \left|\overrightarrow{AB}\right|^2$$

But $\left|\overrightarrow{AB}\right|^2 = \left|\overrightarrow{BC}\right|^2$ because all sides of the quadrilateral are equal in length. Therefore $\overrightarrow{AC} \cdot \overrightarrow{BD} = 0$, and since both of these vectors are nonzero this tells us that the diagonals of the quadrilateral are perpendicular.

41. $|\mathbf{a} \cdot \mathbf{b}| = |\,|\mathbf{a}|\,|\mathbf{b}|\cos\theta\,| = |\mathbf{a}|\,|\mathbf{b}|\,|\cos\theta|$. Since $|\cos\theta| \le 1$, $|\mathbf{a} \cdot \mathbf{b}| = |\mathbf{a}|\,|\mathbf{b}|\,|\cos\theta| \le |\mathbf{a}|\,|\mathbf{b}|$.

Note: We have equality in the case of $\cos\theta = \pm 1$, so $\theta = 0$ or $\theta = \pi$, thus equality when $\mathbf{a}$ and $\mathbf{b}$ are parallel.

42. (a)

The Triangle Inequality states that the length of the longest side of a triangle is less than or equal to the sum of the lengths of the two shortest sides.

(b) $|\mathbf{a} + \mathbf{b}|^2 = (\mathbf{a} + \mathbf{b}) \cdot (\mathbf{a} + \mathbf{b}) = (\mathbf{a} \cdot \mathbf{a}) + 2(\mathbf{a} \cdot \mathbf{b}) + (\mathbf{b} \cdot \mathbf{b}) = |\mathbf{a}|^2 + 2(\mathbf{a} \cdot \mathbf{b}) + |\mathbf{b}|^2$

$$\le |\mathbf{a}|^2 + 2\,|\mathbf{a}|\,|\mathbf{b}| + |\mathbf{b}|^2 \quad \text{(by the Cauchy-Schwartz Inequality)}$$

$$= (|\mathbf{a}| + |\mathbf{b}|)^2$$

Thus, taking the square root of both sides, $|\mathbf{a} + \mathbf{b}| \le |\mathbf{a}| + |\mathbf{b}|$.

43. (a)

The Parallelogram Law states that the sum of the squares of the lengths of the diagonals of a parallelogram equals the sum of the squares of its (four) sides.

(b) $|\mathbf{a} + \mathbf{b}|^2 = (\mathbf{a} + \mathbf{b}) \cdot (\mathbf{a} + \mathbf{b}) = |\mathbf{a}|^2 + 2(\mathbf{a} \cdot \mathbf{b}) + |\mathbf{b}|^2$ and

$|\mathbf{a} - \mathbf{b}|^2 = (\mathbf{a} - \mathbf{b}) \cdot (\mathbf{a} - \mathbf{b}) = |\mathbf{a}|^2 - 2(\mathbf{a} \cdot \mathbf{b}) + |\mathbf{b}|^2$. Adding these two equations gives

$|\mathbf{a} + \mathbf{b}|^2 + |\mathbf{a} - \mathbf{b}|^2 = 2\,|\mathbf{a}|^2 + 2\,|\mathbf{b}|^2$.

9.4 **The Cross Product** • • • • • • • • • • • •

1. (a) Since $\mathbf{b} \times \mathbf{c}$ is a vector, the dot product $\mathbf{a} \cdot (\mathbf{b} \times \mathbf{c})$ is meaningful and is a scalar.

(b) $\mathbf{b} \cdot \mathbf{c}$ is a scalar, so $\mathbf{a} \times (\mathbf{b} \cdot \mathbf{c})$ is meaningless, as the cross product is defined only for two *vectors*.

(c) Since $\mathbf{b} \times \mathbf{c}$ is a vector, the cross product $\mathbf{a} \times (\mathbf{b} \times \mathbf{c})$ is meaningful and results in another vector.

(d) $\mathbf{a} \cdot \mathbf{b}$ is a scalar, so the cross product $(\mathbf{a} \cdot \mathbf{b}) \times \mathbf{c}$ is meaningless.

(e) Since $(\mathbf{a} \cdot \mathbf{b})$ and $(\mathbf{c} \cdot \mathbf{d})$ are both scalars, the cross product $(\mathbf{a} \cdot \mathbf{b}) \times (\mathbf{c} \cdot \mathbf{d})$ is meaningless.

(f) $\mathbf{a} \times \mathbf{b}$ and $\mathbf{c} \times \mathbf{d}$ are both vectors, so the dot product $(\mathbf{a} \times \mathbf{b}) \cdot (\mathbf{c} \times \mathbf{d})$ is meaningful and is a scalar.

2. $|\mathbf{u} \times \mathbf{v}| = |\mathbf{u}|\,|\mathbf{v}| \sin\theta = (5)(10) \sin 60^\circ = 25\sqrt{3}$. By the right-hand rule, $\mathbf{u} \times \mathbf{v}$ is directed into the page.

3. If we sketch $\mathbf{u}$ and $\mathbf{v}$ starting from the same initial point, we see that
the angle between them is 30°, so
$|\mathbf{u} \times \mathbf{v}| = |\mathbf{u}|\,|\mathbf{v}| \sin 30^\circ = (6)(8)\left(\frac{1}{2}\right) = 24$. By the right-hand
rule, $\mathbf{u} \times \mathbf{v}$ is directed into the page.

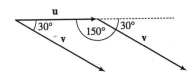

4. (a) $|\mathbf{a} \times \mathbf{b}| = |\mathbf{a}|\,|\mathbf{b}| \sin\theta = 3 \cdot 2 \cdot \sin\frac{\pi}{2} = 6$

(b) $\mathbf{a} \times \mathbf{b}$ is orthogonal to $\mathbf{k}$, so it lies in the xy-plane, and its
z-coordinate is 0. By the right-hand rule, its y-component is
negative and its x-component is positive.

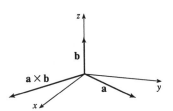

5. The magnitude of the torque is
$$|\boldsymbol{\tau}| = |\mathbf{r} \times \mathbf{F}| = |\mathbf{r}|\,|\mathbf{F}| \sin\theta = (0.18\text{ m})(60\text{ N}) \sin(70 + 10)^\circ = 10.8 \sin 80^\circ \approx 10.6 \text{ J.}$$

6. $|\mathbf{r}| = \sqrt{4^2 + 4^2} = 4\sqrt{2}$ ft. A line drawn from the point P to the point of application of the force
makes an angle of $180^\circ - (45 + 30)^\circ = 105^\circ$ with the force vector. Therefore,
$$|\boldsymbol{\tau}| = |\mathbf{r} \times \mathbf{F}| = |\mathbf{r}|\,|\mathbf{F}| \sin\theta = \left(4\sqrt{2}\right)(36) \sin 105^\circ \approx 197 \text{ ft-lb.}$$

7. $\mathbf{a} \times \mathbf{b} = \begin{vmatrix} \mathbf{i} & \mathbf{j} & \mathbf{k} \\ 1 & -1 & 0 \\ 3 & 2 & 1 \end{vmatrix} = \begin{vmatrix} -1 & 0 \\ 2 & 1 \end{vmatrix}\mathbf{i} - \begin{vmatrix} 1 & 0 \\ 3 & 1 \end{vmatrix}\mathbf{j} + \begin{vmatrix} 1 & -1 \\ 3 & 2 \end{vmatrix}\mathbf{k} = (-1 - 0)\mathbf{i} - (1 - 0)\mathbf{j} + [2 - (-3)]\mathbf{k} = -\mathbf{i} - \mathbf{j} + 5\mathbf{k}$

Since $(\mathbf{a} \times \mathbf{b}) \cdot \mathbf{a} = \langle -1, -1, 5 \rangle \cdot \langle 1, -1, 0 \rangle = -1 + 1 + 0 = 0$, $\mathbf{a} \times \mathbf{b}$ is orthogonal to $\mathbf{a}$.
Since $(\mathbf{a} \times \mathbf{b}) \cdot \mathbf{b} = \langle -1, -1, 5 \rangle \cdot \langle 3, 2, 1 \rangle = -3 - 2 + 5 = 0$, $\mathbf{a} \times \mathbf{b}$ is orthogonal to $\mathbf{b}$.

8. $\mathbf{a} \times \mathbf{b} = \begin{vmatrix} \mathbf{i} & \mathbf{j} & \mathbf{k} \\ -3 & 2 & 2 \\ 6 & 3 & 1 \end{vmatrix} = \begin{vmatrix} 2 & 2 \\ 3 & 1 \end{vmatrix}\mathbf{i} - \begin{vmatrix} -3 & 2 \\ 6 & 1 \end{vmatrix}\mathbf{j} + \begin{vmatrix} -3 & 2 \\ 6 & 3 \end{vmatrix}\mathbf{k}$

$= (2 - 6)\mathbf{i} - (-3 - 12)\mathbf{j} + (-9 - 12)\mathbf{k} = -4\mathbf{i} + 15\mathbf{j} - 21\mathbf{k}$

Since $(\mathbf{a} \times \mathbf{b}) \cdot \mathbf{a} = \langle -4, 15, -21 \rangle \cdot \langle -3, 2, 2 \rangle = 12 + 30 - 42 = 0$, $\mathbf{a} \times \mathbf{b}$ is orthogonal to $\mathbf{a}$.
Since $(\mathbf{a} \times \mathbf{b}) \cdot \mathbf{b} = \langle -4, 15, -21 \rangle \cdot \langle 6, 3, 1 \rangle = -24 + 45 - 21 = 0$, $\mathbf{a} \times \mathbf{b}$ is orthogonal to $\mathbf{b}$.

9. $\mathbf{a} \times \mathbf{b} = \begin{vmatrix} \mathbf{i} & \mathbf{j} & \mathbf{k} \\ t & t^2 & t^3 \\ 1 & 2t & 3t^2 \end{vmatrix} = \begin{vmatrix} t^2 & t^3 \\ 2t & 3t^2 \end{vmatrix} \mathbf{i} - \begin{vmatrix} t & t^3 \\ 1 & 3t^2 \end{vmatrix} \mathbf{j} + \begin{vmatrix} t & t^2 \\ 1 & 2t \end{vmatrix} \mathbf{k}$

$= (3t^4 - 2t^4)\mathbf{i} - (3t^3 - t^3)\mathbf{j} + (2t^2 - t^2)\mathbf{k} = t^4\mathbf{i} - 2t^3\mathbf{j} + t^2\mathbf{k}$

Since $(\mathbf{a} \times \mathbf{b}) \cdot \mathbf{a} = \langle t^4, -2t^3, t^2 \rangle \cdot \langle t, t^2, t^3 \rangle = t^5 - 2t^5 + t^5 = 0$, $\mathbf{a} \times \mathbf{b}$ is orthogonal to $\mathbf{a}$.

Since $(\mathbf{a} \times \mathbf{b}) \cdot \mathbf{b} = \langle t^4, -2t^3, t^2 \rangle \cdot \langle 1, 2t, 3t^2 \rangle = t^4 - 4t^4 + 3t^4 = 0$, $\mathbf{a} \times \mathbf{b}$ is orthogonal to $\mathbf{b}$.

10. $\mathbf{a} \times \mathbf{b} = \begin{vmatrix} \mathbf{i} & \mathbf{j} & \mathbf{k} \\ 1 & e^t & e^{-t} \\ 2 & e^t & -e^{-t} \end{vmatrix} = \begin{vmatrix} e^t & e^{-t} \\ e^t & -e^{-t} \end{vmatrix} \mathbf{i} - \begin{vmatrix} 1 & e^{-t} \\ 2 & -e^{-t} \end{vmatrix} \mathbf{j} + \begin{vmatrix} 1 & e^t \\ 2 & e^t \end{vmatrix} \mathbf{k}$

$= (-1 - 1)\mathbf{i} - (-e^{-t} - 2e^{-t})\mathbf{j} + (e^t - 2e^t)\mathbf{k} = -2\mathbf{i} + 3e^{-t}\mathbf{j} - e^t\mathbf{k}$

Since $(\mathbf{a} \times \mathbf{b}) \cdot \mathbf{a} = (-2\mathbf{i} + 3e^{-t}\mathbf{j} - e^t\mathbf{k}) \cdot (\mathbf{i} + e^t\mathbf{j} + e^{-t}\mathbf{k}) = -2 + 3 - 1 = 0$, $\mathbf{a} \times \mathbf{b}$ is orthogonal to $\mathbf{a}$.

Since $(\mathbf{a} \times \mathbf{b}) \cdot \mathbf{b} = (-2\mathbf{i} + 3e^{-t}\mathbf{j} - e^t\mathbf{k}) \cdot (2\mathbf{i} + e^t\mathbf{j} - e^{-t}\mathbf{k}) = -4 + 3 + 1 = 0$, $\mathbf{a} \times \mathbf{b}$ is orthogonal to $\mathbf{b}$.

11. $\mathbf{a} \times \mathbf{b} = \begin{vmatrix} \mathbf{i} & \mathbf{j} & \mathbf{k} \\ 3 & 2 & 4 \\ 1 & -2 & -3 \end{vmatrix} = \begin{vmatrix} 2 & 4 \\ -2 & -3 \end{vmatrix} \mathbf{i} - \begin{vmatrix} 3 & 4 \\ 1 & -3 \end{vmatrix} \mathbf{j} + \begin{vmatrix} 3 & 2 \\ 1 & -2 \end{vmatrix} \mathbf{k}$

$\mathbf{a} \times \mathbf{b} = [-6 - (-8)]\mathbf{i} - (-9 - 4)\mathbf{j} + (-6 - 2)\mathbf{k} = 2\mathbf{i} + 13\mathbf{j} - 8\mathbf{k}$

Since $(\mathbf{a} \times \mathbf{b}) \cdot \mathbf{a} = (2\mathbf{i} + 13\mathbf{j} - 8\mathbf{k}) \cdot (3\mathbf{i} + 2\mathbf{j} + 4\mathbf{k}) = 6 + 26 - 32 = 0$, $\mathbf{a} \times \mathbf{b}$ is orthogonal to $\mathbf{a}$.

Since $(\mathbf{a} \times \mathbf{b}) \cdot \mathbf{b} = (2\mathbf{i} + 13\mathbf{j} - 8\mathbf{k}) \cdot (\mathbf{i} - 2\mathbf{j} - 3\mathbf{k}) = 2 - 26 + 24 = 0$, $\mathbf{a} \times \mathbf{b}$ is orthogonal to $\mathbf{b}$.

12. $\mathbf{a} \times \mathbf{b} = \begin{vmatrix} \mathbf{i} & \mathbf{j} & \mathbf{k} \\ 1 & 0 & -2 \\ 0 & 1 & 1 \end{vmatrix} = \begin{vmatrix} 0 & -2 \\ 1 & 1 \end{vmatrix} \mathbf{i} - \begin{vmatrix} 1 & -2 \\ 0 & 1 \end{vmatrix} \mathbf{j} + \begin{vmatrix} 1 & 0 \\ 0 & 1 \end{vmatrix} \mathbf{k}$

$= 2\mathbf{i} - \mathbf{j} + \mathbf{k}$

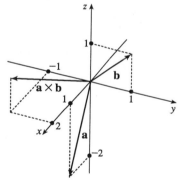

13. We know that the cross product of two vectors is orthogonal to both. So we calculate

$\langle 1, -1, 1 \rangle \times \langle 0, 4, 4 \rangle = \begin{vmatrix} \mathbf{i} & \mathbf{j} & \mathbf{k} \\ 1 & -1 & 1 \\ 0 & 4 & 4 \end{vmatrix} = \begin{vmatrix} -1 & 1 \\ 4 & 4 \end{vmatrix} \mathbf{i} - \begin{vmatrix} 1 & 1 \\ 0 & 4 \end{vmatrix} \mathbf{j} + \begin{vmatrix} 1 & -1 \\ 0 & 4 \end{vmatrix} \mathbf{k} = -8\mathbf{i} - 4\mathbf{j} + 4\mathbf{k}$. So two unit vectors

orthogonal to both are $\pm \dfrac{\langle -8, -4, 4 \rangle}{\sqrt{64 + 16 + 16}} = \pm \dfrac{\langle -8, -4, 4 \rangle}{4\sqrt{6}}$, that is, $\left\langle -\dfrac{2}{\sqrt{6}}, -\dfrac{1}{\sqrt{6}}, \dfrac{1}{\sqrt{6}} \right\rangle$ and $\left\langle \dfrac{2}{\sqrt{6}}, \dfrac{1}{\sqrt{6}}, -\dfrac{1}{\sqrt{6}} \right\rangle$.

14. We know that the cross product of two vectors is orthogonal to both. So we calculate

$\begin{vmatrix} \mathbf{i} & \mathbf{j} & \mathbf{k} \\ 1 & 1 & 0 \\ 1 & -1 & 1 \end{vmatrix} = \begin{vmatrix} 1 & 0 \\ -1 & 1 \end{vmatrix} \mathbf{i} - \begin{vmatrix} 1 & 0 \\ 1 & 1 \end{vmatrix} \mathbf{j} + \begin{vmatrix} 1 & 1 \\ 1 & -1 \end{vmatrix} \mathbf{k} = \mathbf{i} - \mathbf{j} - 2\mathbf{k}$. Thus, two unit vectors orthogonal to both are

$\pm \dfrac{1}{\sqrt{6}} \langle 1, -1, -2 \rangle$, that is, $\left\langle \dfrac{1}{\sqrt{6}}, -\dfrac{1}{\sqrt{6}}, -\dfrac{2}{\sqrt{6}} \right\rangle$ and $\left\langle -\dfrac{1}{\sqrt{6}}, \dfrac{1}{\sqrt{6}}, \dfrac{2}{\sqrt{6}} \right\rangle$.

15. By plotting the vertices, we can see that the parallelogram is determined by

the vectors $\overrightarrow{AB} = \langle 2, 3 \rangle$ and $\overrightarrow{AD} = \langle 4, -2 \rangle$. We know that the area of the

parallelogram determined by two vectors is equal to the length of the cross

product of these vectors. In order to compute the cross product, we consider

the vector $\overrightarrow{AB}$ as the three-dimensional vector $\langle 2, 3, 0 \rangle$ (and similarly for

$\overrightarrow{AD}$), and then the area of parallelogram $ABCD$ is

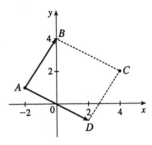

$$\left| \overrightarrow{AB} \times \overrightarrow{AD} \right| = \begin{vmatrix} \mathbf{i} & \mathbf{j} & \mathbf{k} \\ 2 & 3 & 0 \\ 4 & -2 & 0 \end{vmatrix} = |(0)\mathbf{i} - (0)\mathbf{j} + (-4 - 12)\,\mathbf{k}| = |-16\,\mathbf{k}| = 16.$$

16. The parallelogram is determined by the vectors $\overrightarrow{KL} = \langle 0, 1, 3 \rangle$

and $\overrightarrow{KN} = \langle 2, 5, 0 \rangle$, so the area of parallelogram $KLMN$ is

$$\left| \overrightarrow{KL} \times \overrightarrow{KN} \right| = \begin{vmatrix} \mathbf{i} & \mathbf{j} & \mathbf{k} \\ 0 & 1 & 3 \\ 2 & 5 & 0 \end{vmatrix} = |(-15)\,\mathbf{i} - (-6)\mathbf{j} + (-2)\mathbf{k}| = |-15\,\mathbf{i} + 6\,\mathbf{j} - 2\,\mathbf{k}| = \sqrt{265} \approx 16.28.$$

17. (a) Because the plane through P, Q, and R contains the vectors $\overrightarrow{PQ}$ and $\overrightarrow{PR}$, a vector orthogonal to both of these

vectors (such as their cross product) is also orthogonal to the plane. Here $\overrightarrow{PQ} = \langle -1, 2, 0 \rangle$ and

$\overrightarrow{PR} = \langle -1, 0, 3 \rangle$, so

$$\overrightarrow{PQ} \times \overrightarrow{PR} = \langle (2)(3) - (0)(0), (0)(-1) - (-1)(3), (-1)(0) - (2)(-1) \rangle = \langle 6, 3, 2 \rangle$$

Therefore, $\langle 6, 3, 2 \rangle$ (or any scalar multiple thereof) is orthogonal to the plane through P, Q, and R.

(b) Note that the area of the triangle determined by P, Q, and R is equal to half of the area of the parallelogram

determined by the three points. From part (a), the area of the parallelogram is

$\left| \overrightarrow{PQ} \times \overrightarrow{PR} \right| = |\langle 6, 3, 2 \rangle| = \sqrt{36 + 9 + 4} = 7$, so the area of the triangle is $\frac{1}{2}(7) = \frac{7}{2}$.

18. (a) $\overrightarrow{PQ} = \langle 1, 1, 3 \rangle$ and $\overrightarrow{PR} = \langle 3, 2, 5 \rangle$, so a vector orthogonal to the plane through P, Q, and R is

$\overrightarrow{PQ} \times \overrightarrow{PR} = \langle (1)(5) - (3)(2), (3)(3) - (1)(5), (1)(2) - (1)(3) \rangle = \langle -1, 4, -1 \rangle$ (or any scalar multiple

thereof).

(b) The area of the parallelogram determined by $\overrightarrow{PQ}$ and $\overrightarrow{PR}$ is

$\left| \overrightarrow{PQ} \times \overrightarrow{PR} \right| = |\langle -1, 4, -1 \rangle| = \sqrt{1 + 16 + 1} = \sqrt{18} = 3\sqrt{2}$, so the area of triangle PQR is

$\frac{1}{2} \cdot 3\sqrt{2} = \frac{3}{2}\sqrt{2}$.

19. Using the notation of (1), $\mathbf{r} = \langle 0, 0.3, 0 \rangle$ and $\mathbf{F}$ has direction $\langle 0, 3, -4 \rangle$. The angle θ between them can be

determined by $\cos\theta = \dfrac{\langle 0, 0.3, 0 \rangle \cdot \langle 0, 3, -4 \rangle}{|\langle 0, 0.3, 0 \rangle| \, |\langle 0, 3, -4 \rangle|} \;\Rightarrow\; \cos\theta = \dfrac{0.9}{(0.3)(5)} \;\Rightarrow\; \cos\theta = 0.6 \;\Rightarrow\; \theta \approx 53.1°$.

Then $|\tau| = |\mathbf{r}|\,|\mathbf{F}|\sin\theta \;\Rightarrow\; 100 = 0.3\,|\mathbf{F}|\sin 53.1° \;\Rightarrow\; |\mathbf{F}| \approx 417$ N.

20. Since $|\mathbf{u} \times \mathbf{v}| = |\mathbf{u}|\,|\mathbf{v}| \sin\theta$, $0 \le \theta \le \pi$, $|\mathbf{u} \times \mathbf{v}|$ achieves its maximum value for $\sin\theta = 1 \Rightarrow \theta = \frac{\pi}{2}$, in which case $|\mathbf{u} \times \mathbf{v}| = |\mathbf{u}|\,|\mathbf{v}| = 15$. The minimum value is zero, which occurs when $\sin\theta = 0 \Rightarrow \theta = 0$ or π, so when $\mathbf{u}$, $\mathbf{v}$ are parallel. Thus, when $\mathbf{u}$ points in the same direction as $\mathbf{v}$, so $\mathbf{u} = 3\mathbf{j}$, $|\mathbf{u} \times \mathbf{v}| = 0$. As $\mathbf{u}$ rotates counterclockwise, $\mathbf{u} \times \mathbf{v}$ is directed in the negative z-direction (by the right-hand rule) and the length increases until $\theta = \frac{\pi}{2}$, in which case $\mathbf{u} = -3\mathbf{i}$ and $|\mathbf{u} \times \mathbf{v}| = 15$. As $\mathbf{u}$ rotates to the negative y-axis, $\mathbf{u} \times \mathbf{v}$ remains pointed in the negative z-direction and the length of $\mathbf{u} \times \mathbf{v}$ decreases to 0, after which the direction of $\mathbf{u} \times \mathbf{v}$ reverses to point in the positive z-direction and $|\mathbf{u} \times \mathbf{v}|$ increases. When $\mathbf{u} = 3\mathbf{i}$ (so $\theta = \frac{\pi}{2}$), $|\mathbf{u} \times \mathbf{v}|$ again reaches its maximum of 15, after which $|\mathbf{u} \times \mathbf{v}|$ decreases to 0 as $\mathbf{u}$ rotates to the positive y-axis.

21. We know that the volume of the parallelepiped determined by $\mathbf{a}$, $\mathbf{b}$, and $\mathbf{c}$ is the magnitude of their scalar triple product, which is

$$\mathbf{a} \cdot (\mathbf{b} \times \mathbf{c}) = \begin{vmatrix} 6 & 3 & -1 \\ 0 & 1 & 2 \\ 4 & -2 & 5 \end{vmatrix} = 6 \begin{vmatrix} 1 & 2 \\ -2 & 5 \end{vmatrix} - 3 \begin{vmatrix} 0 & 2 \\ 4 & 5 \end{vmatrix} + (-1) \begin{vmatrix} 0 & 1 \\ 4 & -2 \end{vmatrix}$$

$$= 6(5+4) - 3(0-8) - (0-4) = 82$$

Thus the volume of the parallelepiped is 82 cubic units.

22. $\mathbf{a} \cdot (\mathbf{b} \times \mathbf{c}) = \begin{vmatrix} 2 & 3 & -2 \\ 1 & -1 & 0 \\ 2 & 0 & 3 \end{vmatrix} = 2 \begin{vmatrix} -1 & 0 \\ 0 & 3 \end{vmatrix} - 3 \begin{vmatrix} 1 & 0 \\ 2 & 3 \end{vmatrix} + (-2) \begin{vmatrix} 1 & -1 \\ 2 & 0 \end{vmatrix} = -6 - 9 - 4 = -19$. So the volume of

the parallelepiped determined by $\mathbf{a}$, $\mathbf{b}$ and $\mathbf{c}$ is $|-19| = 19$ cubic units.

23. $\mathbf{a} = \overrightarrow{PQ} = \langle 1, -1, 2 \rangle$, $\mathbf{b} = \overrightarrow{PR} = \langle 3, 0, 6 \rangle$ and $\mathbf{c} = \overrightarrow{PS} = \langle 2, -2, -3 \rangle$.

$$\mathbf{a} \cdot (\mathbf{b} \times \mathbf{c}) = \begin{vmatrix} 1 & -1 & 2 \\ 3 & 0 & 6 \\ 2 & -2 & -3 \end{vmatrix} = 1 \begin{vmatrix} 0 & 6 \\ -2 & -3 \end{vmatrix} - (-1) \begin{vmatrix} 3 & 6 \\ 2 & -3 \end{vmatrix} + 2 \begin{vmatrix} 3 & 0 \\ 2 & -2 \end{vmatrix} = 12 - 21 - 12 = -21$, so the volume

of the parallelepiped is 21 cubic units.

24. $\mathbf{a} = \overrightarrow{PQ} = \langle 2, 3, 3 \rangle$, $\mathbf{b} = \overrightarrow{PR} = \langle -1, -1, -1 \rangle$ and $\mathbf{c} = \overrightarrow{PS} = \langle 6, -2, 2 \rangle$.

$$\mathbf{a} \cdot (\mathbf{b} \times \mathbf{c}) = \begin{vmatrix} 2 & 3 & 3 \\ -1 & -1 & -1 \\ 6 & -2 & 2 \end{vmatrix} = 2 \begin{vmatrix} -1 & -1 \\ -2 & 2 \end{vmatrix} - 3 \begin{vmatrix} -1 & -1 \\ 6 & 2 \end{vmatrix} + 3 \begin{vmatrix} -1 & -1 \\ 6 & -2 \end{vmatrix} = -8 - 12 + 24 = 4$, so the volume of

the parallelepiped is 4 cubic units.

25. $\mathbf{a} \cdot (\mathbf{b} \times \mathbf{c}) = \begin{vmatrix} 2 & 3 & 1 \\ 1 & -1 & 0 \\ 7 & 3 & 2 \end{vmatrix} = 2 \begin{vmatrix} -1 & 0 \\ 3 & 2 \end{vmatrix} - 3 \begin{vmatrix} 1 & 0 \\ 7 & 2 \end{vmatrix} + 1 \begin{vmatrix} 1 & -1 \\ 7 & 3 \end{vmatrix} = -4 - 6 + 10 = 0$, which says that the volume

of the parallelepiped determined by $\mathbf{a}$, $\mathbf{b}$ and $\mathbf{c}$ is 0, and thus these three vectors are coplanar.

26. $\mathbf{a} = \overrightarrow{PQ} = \langle 1, 4, 5 \rangle$, $\mathbf{b} = \overrightarrow{PR} = \langle 2, -1, 1 \rangle$ and $\mathbf{c} = \overrightarrow{PS} = \langle 5, 2, 7 \rangle$.

$$\mathbf{a} \cdot (\mathbf{b} \times \mathbf{c}) = \begin{vmatrix} 1 & 4 & 5 \\ 2 & -1 & 1 \\ 5 & 2 & 7 \end{vmatrix} = 1 \begin{vmatrix} -1 & 1 \\ 2 & 7 \end{vmatrix} - 4 \begin{vmatrix} 2 & 1 \\ 5 & 7 \end{vmatrix} + 5 \begin{vmatrix} 2 & -1 \\ 5 & 2 \end{vmatrix} = -9 - 36 + 45 = 0$, so the volume of the

parallelepiped determined by $\mathbf{a}$, $\mathbf{b}$ and $\mathbf{c}$ is 0, which says these vectors lie in the same plane. Therefore, their initial and terminal points P, Q, R and S also lie in the same plane.

27. (a)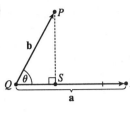

The distance between a point and a line is the length of the perpendicular from the point to the line, here $\left|\overrightarrow{PS}\right| = d$. But referring to triangle PQS, $d = \left|\overrightarrow{PS}\right| = \left|\overrightarrow{QP}\right| \sin\theta = |\mathbf{b}| \sin\theta$. But θ is the angle between $\overrightarrow{QP} = \mathbf{b}$ and $\overrightarrow{QR} = \mathbf{a}$. Thus by definition of the cross product, $\sin\theta = \dfrac{|\mathbf{a} \times \mathbf{b}|}{|\mathbf{a}|\,|\mathbf{b}|}$ and so $d = |\mathbf{b}| \sin\theta = \dfrac{|\mathbf{b}|\,|\mathbf{a} \times \mathbf{b}|}{|\mathbf{a}|\,|\mathbf{b}|} = \dfrac{|\mathbf{a} \times \mathbf{b}|}{|\mathbf{a}|}$.

(b) $\mathbf{a} = \overrightarrow{QR} = \langle -1, -2, -1 \rangle$ and $\mathbf{b} = \overrightarrow{QP} = \langle 1, -5, -7 \rangle$. Then

$\mathbf{a} \times \mathbf{b} = \langle (-2)(-7) - (-1)(-5), (-1)(1) - (-1)(-7), (-1)(-5) - (-2)(1) \rangle = \langle 9, -8, 7 \rangle$. Thus the

distance is $d = \dfrac{|\mathbf{a} \times \mathbf{b}|}{|\mathbf{a}|} = \dfrac{1}{\sqrt{6}}\sqrt{81 + 64 + 49} = \sqrt{\dfrac{194}{6}} = \sqrt{\dfrac{97}{3}}$.

28. (a)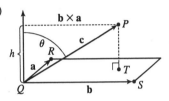

The distance between a point and a plane is the length of the perpendicular from the point to the plane, here $\left|\overrightarrow{TP}\right| = d$. But $\overrightarrow{TP}$ is parallel to $\mathbf{b} \times \mathbf{a}$ (because $\mathbf{b} \times \mathbf{a}$ is perpendicular to $\mathbf{b}$ and $\mathbf{a}$) and $d = \left|\overrightarrow{TP}\right| = $ the absolute value of the scalar projection of $\mathbf{c}$ along $\mathbf{b} \times \mathbf{a}$, which is $|\mathbf{c}|\,|\cos\theta|$. (Notice that this is the same setup as the development of the volume of a parallelepiped with $h = |\mathbf{c}|\,|\cos\theta|$.) Thus $d = |\mathbf{c}|\,|\cos\theta| = h = V/A$ where $A = |\mathbf{a} \times \mathbf{b}|$, the area of the base. So finally $d = \dfrac{V}{A} = \dfrac{|\mathbf{a} \cdot (\mathbf{b} \times \mathbf{c})|}{|\mathbf{a} \times \mathbf{b}|}$.

(b) $\mathbf{a} = \overrightarrow{QR} = \langle -1, 2, 0 \rangle$, $\mathbf{b} = \overrightarrow{QS} = \langle -1, 0, 3 \rangle$ and $\mathbf{c} = \overrightarrow{QP} = \langle 1, 1, 4 \rangle$. Then

$$\mathbf{a} \cdot (\mathbf{b} \times \mathbf{c}) = \begin{vmatrix} -1 & 2 & 0 \\ -1 & 0 & 3 \\ 1 & 1 & 4 \end{vmatrix} = (-1)\begin{vmatrix} 0 & 3 \\ 1 & 4 \end{vmatrix} - 2\begin{vmatrix} -1 & 3 \\ 1 & 4 \end{vmatrix} + 0 = 17$$

and

$$\mathbf{a} \times \mathbf{b} = \begin{vmatrix} \mathbf{i} & \mathbf{j} & \mathbf{k} \\ -1 & 2 & 0 \\ -1 & 0 & 3 \end{vmatrix} = \begin{vmatrix} 2 & 0 \\ 0 & 3 \end{vmatrix}\mathbf{i} - \begin{vmatrix} -1 & 0 \\ -1 & 3 \end{vmatrix}\mathbf{j} + \begin{vmatrix} -1 & 2 \\ -1 & 0 \end{vmatrix}\mathbf{k} = 6\mathbf{i} + 3\mathbf{j} + 2\mathbf{k}$$

Thus $d = \dfrac{|\mathbf{a} \cdot (\mathbf{b} \times \mathbf{c})|}{|\mathbf{a} \times \mathbf{b}|} = \dfrac{17}{\sqrt{36 + 9 + 4}} = \dfrac{17}{7}$.

29. $(\mathbf{a} - \mathbf{b}) \times (\mathbf{a} + \mathbf{b}) = (\mathbf{a} - \mathbf{b}) \times \mathbf{a} + (\mathbf{a} - \mathbf{b}) \times \mathbf{b}$ by Property 3 of the cross product

$\qquad\qquad\qquad = \mathbf{a} \times \mathbf{a} + (-\mathbf{b}) \times \mathbf{a} + \mathbf{a} \times \mathbf{b} + (-\mathbf{b}) \times \mathbf{b}$ by Property 4

$\qquad\qquad\qquad = (\mathbf{a} \times \mathbf{a}) - (\mathbf{b} \times \mathbf{a}) + (\mathbf{a} \times \mathbf{b}) - (\mathbf{b} \times \mathbf{b})$ by Property 2 (with $c = -1$)

$\qquad\qquad\qquad = \mathbf{0} - (\mathbf{b} \times \mathbf{a}) + (\mathbf{a} \times \mathbf{b}) - \mathbf{0}$ by the margin note on page 668

$\qquad\qquad\qquad = (\mathbf{a} \times \mathbf{b}) + (\mathbf{a} \times \mathbf{b})$ by Property 1

$\qquad\qquad\qquad = 2(\mathbf{a} \times \mathbf{b})$

30. Let $\mathbf{a} = \langle a_1, a_2, a_3 \rangle$, $\mathbf{b} = \langle b_1, b_2, b_3 \rangle$ and $\mathbf{c} = \langle c_1, c_2, c_3 \rangle$, so $\mathbf{b} \times \mathbf{c} = \langle b_2 c_3 - b_3 c_2, b_3 c_1 - b_1 c_3, b_1 c_2 - b_2 c_1 \rangle$ and

$$\mathbf{a} \times (\mathbf{b} \times \mathbf{c}) = \langle a_2(b_1 c_2 - b_2 c_1) - a_3(b_3 c_1 - b_1 c_3), a_3(b_2 c_3 - b_3 c_2) - a_1(b_1 c_2 - b_2 c_1),$$
$$a_1(b_3 c_1 - b_1 c_3) - a_2(b_2 c_3 - b_3 c_2) \rangle$$

$$= \langle a_2 b_1 c_2 - a_2 b_2 c_1 - a_3 b_3 c_1 + a_3 b_1 c_3, a_3 b_2 c_3 - a_3 b_3 c_2 - a_1 b_1 c_2 + a_1 b_2 c_1,$$
$$a_1 b_3 c_1 - a_1 b_1 c_3 - a_2 b_2 c_3 + a_2 b_3 c_2 \rangle$$

$$= \langle (a_2 c_2 + a_3 c_3) b_1 - (a_2 b_2 + a_3 b_3) c_1, (a_1 c_1 + a_3 c_3) b_2 - (a_1 b_1 + a_3 b_3) c_2,$$
$$(a_1 c_1 + a_2 c_2) b_3 - (a_1 b_1 + a_2 b_2) c_3 \rangle$$

$(\star) \quad = \langle (a_2 c_2 + a_3 c_3) b_1 - (a_2 b_2 + a_3 b_3) c_1 + a_1 b_1 c_1 - a_1 b_1 c_1,$
$$(a_1 c_1 + a_3 c_3) b_2 - (a_1 b_1 + a_3 b_3) c_2 + a_2 b_2 c_2 - a_2 b_2 c_2,$$
$$(a_1 c_1 + a_2 c_2) b_3 - (a_1 b_1 + a_2 b_2) c_3 + a_3 b_3 c_3 - a_3 b_3 c_3 \rangle$$

$$= \langle (a_1 c_1 + a_2 c_2 + a_3 c_3) b_1 - (a_1 b_1 + a_2 b_2 + a_3 b_3) c_1,$$
$$(a_1 c_1 + a_2 c_2 + a_3 c_3) b_2 - (a_1 b_1 + a_2 b_2 + a_3 b_3) c_2,$$
$$(a_1 c_1 + a_2 c_2 + a_3 c_3) b_3 - (a_1 b_1 + a_2 b_2 + a_3 b_3) c_3 \rangle$$

$$= (a_1 c_1 + a_2 c_2 + a_3 c_3) \langle b_1, b_2, b_3 \rangle - (a_1 b_1 + a_2 b_2 + a_3 b_3) \langle c_1, c_2, c_3 \rangle$$

$$= (\mathbf{a} \cdot \mathbf{c}) \mathbf{b} - (\mathbf{a} \cdot \mathbf{b}) \mathbf{c}$$

$(\star)$ Here we look ahead to see what terms are still needed to arrive at the desired equation. By adding and subtracting the same terms, we don't change the value of the component.

31. $\mathbf{a} \times (\mathbf{b} \times \mathbf{c}) + \mathbf{b} \times (\mathbf{c} \times \mathbf{a}) + \mathbf{c} \times (\mathbf{a} \times \mathbf{b})$

$$= [(\mathbf{a} \cdot \mathbf{c}) \mathbf{b} - (\mathbf{a} \cdot \mathbf{b}) \mathbf{c}] + [(\mathbf{b} \cdot \mathbf{a}) \mathbf{c} - (\mathbf{b} \cdot \mathbf{c}) \mathbf{a}] + [(\mathbf{c} \cdot \mathbf{b}) \mathbf{a} - (\mathbf{c} \cdot \mathbf{a}) \mathbf{b}] \qquad \text{by Exercise 30}$$

$$= (\mathbf{a} \cdot \mathbf{c}) \mathbf{b} - (\mathbf{a} \cdot \mathbf{b}) \mathbf{c} + (\mathbf{a} \cdot \mathbf{b}) \mathbf{c} - (\mathbf{b} \cdot \mathbf{c}) \mathbf{a} + (\mathbf{b} \cdot \mathbf{c}) \mathbf{a} - (\mathbf{a} \cdot \mathbf{c}) \mathbf{b} = \mathbf{0}$$

32. Let $\mathbf{c} \times \mathbf{d} = \mathbf{v}$. Then

$$(\mathbf{a} \times \mathbf{b}) \cdot (\mathbf{c} \times \mathbf{d}) = (\mathbf{a} \times \mathbf{b}) \cdot \mathbf{v} = \mathbf{a} \cdot (\mathbf{b} \times \mathbf{v}) \qquad \text{by (6)}$$

$$= \mathbf{a} \cdot [\mathbf{b} \times (\mathbf{c} \times \mathbf{d})]$$

$$= \mathbf{a} \cdot [(\mathbf{b} \cdot \mathbf{d}) \mathbf{c} - (\mathbf{b} \cdot \mathbf{c}) \mathbf{d}] \qquad \text{by Exercise 30}$$

$$= (\mathbf{b} \cdot \mathbf{d})(\mathbf{a} \cdot \mathbf{c}) - (\mathbf{b} \cdot \mathbf{c})(\mathbf{a} \cdot \mathbf{d}) \qquad \text{by Properties 3 and 4 of the dot product}$$

$$= \begin{vmatrix} \mathbf{a} \cdot \mathbf{c} & \mathbf{b} \cdot \mathbf{c} \\ \mathbf{a} \cdot \mathbf{d} & \mathbf{b} \cdot \mathbf{d} \end{vmatrix}$$

33. (a) No. If $\mathbf{a} \cdot \mathbf{b} = \mathbf{a} \cdot \mathbf{c}$, then $\mathbf{a} \cdot (\mathbf{b} - \mathbf{c}) = 0$, so $\mathbf{a}$ is perpendicular to $\mathbf{b} - \mathbf{c}$, which can happen if $\mathbf{b} \neq \mathbf{c}$. For example, let $\mathbf{a} = \langle 1, 1, 1 \rangle$, $\mathbf{b} = \langle 1, 0, 0 \rangle$ and $\mathbf{c} = \langle 0, 1, 0 \rangle$.

(b) No. If $\mathbf{a} \times \mathbf{b} = \mathbf{a} \times \mathbf{c}$ then $\mathbf{a} \times (\mathbf{b} - \mathbf{c}) = \mathbf{0}$, which implies that $\mathbf{a}$ is parallel to $\mathbf{b} - \mathbf{c}$, which of course can happen if $\mathbf{b} \neq \mathbf{c}$.

(c) Yes. Since $\mathbf{a} \cdot \mathbf{c} = \mathbf{a} \cdot \mathbf{b}$, $\mathbf{a}$ is perpendicular to $\mathbf{b} - \mathbf{c}$, by part (a). From part (b), $\mathbf{a}$ is also parallel to $\mathbf{b} - \mathbf{c}$. Thus since $\mathbf{a} \neq \mathbf{0}$ but is both parallel and perpendicular to $\mathbf{b} - \mathbf{c}$, we have $\mathbf{b} - \mathbf{c} = \mathbf{0}$, so $\mathbf{b} = \mathbf{c}$.

34. (a) $\mathbf{k}_i$ is perpendicular to $\mathbf{v}_i$ if $i \neq j$ by the definition of $\mathbf{k}_i$ and the fact that the cross product of two vectors is perpendicular to both.

(b) $\mathbf{k}_1 \cdot \mathbf{v}_1 = \dfrac{\mathbf{v}_2 \times \mathbf{v}_3}{\mathbf{v}_1 \cdot (\mathbf{v}_2 \times \mathbf{v}_3)} \cdot \mathbf{v}_1 = \dfrac{\mathbf{v}_1 \cdot (\mathbf{v}_2 \times \mathbf{v}_3)}{\mathbf{v}_1 \cdot (\mathbf{v}_2 \times \mathbf{v}_3)} = 1$

$\mathbf{k}_2 \cdot \mathbf{v}_2 = \dfrac{\mathbf{v}_3 \times \mathbf{v}_1}{\mathbf{v}_1 \cdot (\mathbf{v}_2 \times \mathbf{v}_3)} \cdot \mathbf{v}_2 = \dfrac{\mathbf{v}_2 \cdot (\mathbf{v}_3 \times \mathbf{v}_1)}{\mathbf{v}_1 \cdot (\mathbf{v}_2 \times \mathbf{v}_3)} = \dfrac{(\mathbf{v}_2 \times \mathbf{v}_3) \cdot \mathbf{v}_1}{\mathbf{v}_1 \cdot (\mathbf{v}_2 \times \mathbf{v}_3)} = 1 \text{ by (6)}$

$\mathbf{k}_3 \cdot \mathbf{v}_3 = \dfrac{(\mathbf{v}_1 \times \mathbf{v}_2) \cdot \mathbf{v}_3}{\mathbf{v}_1 \cdot (\mathbf{v}_2 \times \mathbf{v}_3)} = \dfrac{\mathbf{v}_1 \cdot (\mathbf{v}_2 \times \mathbf{v}_3)}{\mathbf{v}_1 \cdot (\mathbf{v}_2 \times \mathbf{v}_3)} = 1 \text{ by (6)}$

(c) $\mathbf{k}_1 \cdot (\mathbf{k}_2 \times \mathbf{k}_3) = \mathbf{k}_1 \cdot \left(\dfrac{\mathbf{v}_3 \times \mathbf{v}_1}{\mathbf{v}_1 \cdot (\mathbf{v}_2 \times \mathbf{v}_3)} \times \dfrac{\mathbf{v}_1 \times \mathbf{v}_2}{\mathbf{v}_1 \cdot (\mathbf{v}_2 \times \mathbf{v}_3)} \right) = \dfrac{\mathbf{k}_1}{[\mathbf{v}_1 \cdot (\mathbf{v}_2 \times \mathbf{v}_3)]^2} \cdot [(\mathbf{v}_3 \times \mathbf{v}_1) \times (\mathbf{v}_1 \times \mathbf{v}_2)]$

$= \dfrac{\mathbf{k}_1}{[\mathbf{v}_1 \cdot (\mathbf{v}_2 \times \mathbf{v}_3)]^2} \cdot ([(\mathbf{v}_3 \times \mathbf{v}_1) \cdot \mathbf{v}_2] \mathbf{v}_1 - [(\mathbf{v}_3 \times \mathbf{v}_1) \cdot \mathbf{v}_1] \mathbf{v}_2) \text{ by Exercise 30.}$

But $(\mathbf{v}_3 \times \mathbf{v}_1) \cdot \mathbf{v}_1 = 0$ since $\mathbf{v}_3 \times \mathbf{v}_1$ is orthogonal to $\mathbf{v}_1$, and
$(\mathbf{v}_3 \times \mathbf{v}_1) \cdot \mathbf{v}_2 = \mathbf{v}_2 \cdot (\mathbf{v}_3 \times \mathbf{v}_1) = (\mathbf{v}_2 \times \mathbf{v}_3) \cdot \mathbf{v}_1 = \mathbf{v}_1 \cdot (\mathbf{v}_2 \times \mathbf{v}_3)$. Thus

$$\mathbf{k}_1 \cdot (\mathbf{k}_2 \times \mathbf{k}_3) = \dfrac{\mathbf{k}_1}{[\mathbf{v}_1 \cdot (\mathbf{v}_2 \times \mathbf{v}_3)]^2} \cdot [\mathbf{v}_1 \cdot (\mathbf{v}_2 \times \mathbf{v}_3)] \mathbf{v}_1 = \dfrac{\mathbf{k}_1 \cdot \mathbf{v}_1}{\mathbf{v}_1 \cdot (\mathbf{v}_2 \times \mathbf{v}_3)}$$

$$= \dfrac{1}{\mathbf{v}_1 \cdot (\mathbf{v}_2 \times \mathbf{v}_3)} \text{ by part (b).}$$

Discovery Project	**The Geometry of a Tetrahedron**

1. Set up a coordinate system so that vertex S is at the origin, $R = (0, y_1, 0)$, $Q = (x_2, y_2, 0)$, $P = (x_3, y_3, z_3)$. Then $\overrightarrow{SR} = \langle 0, y_1, 0 \rangle$, $\overrightarrow{SQ} = \langle x_2, y_2, 0 \rangle$, $\overrightarrow{SP} = \langle x_3, y_3, z_3 \rangle$, $\overrightarrow{QR} = \langle -x_2, y_1 - y_2, 0 \rangle$, and $\overrightarrow{QP} = \langle x_3 - x_2, y_3 - y_2, z_3 \rangle$.

Let

$$\mathbf{v}_S = \overrightarrow{QR} \times \overrightarrow{QP}$$
$$= (y_1 z_3 - y_2 z_3)\, \mathbf{i} + x_2 z_3\, \mathbf{j} + (-x_2 y_3 - x_3 y_1 + x_3 y_2 + x_2 y_1)\, \mathbf{k}$$

Then $\mathbf{v}_S$ is an outward normal to the face opposite vertex S. Similarly,

$\mathbf{v}_R = \overrightarrow{SQ} \times \overrightarrow{SP} = y_2 z_3\, \mathbf{i} - x_2 z_3\, \mathbf{j} + (x_2 y_3 - x_3 y_2)\, \mathbf{k}$, $\mathbf{v}_Q = \overrightarrow{SP} \times \overrightarrow{SR} = -y_1 z_3\, \mathbf{i} + x_3 y_1\, \mathbf{k}$, and $\mathbf{v}_P = \overrightarrow{SR} \times \overrightarrow{SQ} = -x_2 y_1\, \mathbf{k} \;\Rightarrow\; \mathbf{v}_S + \mathbf{v}_R + \mathbf{v}_Q + \mathbf{v}_P = \mathbf{0}$. Now

$$|\mathbf{v}_S| = \text{area of the parallelogram determined by } \overrightarrow{QR} \text{ and } \overrightarrow{QP}$$
$$= 2\,(\text{area of triangle } RQP)$$
$$= 2|\mathbf{v}_1|$$

So $\mathbf{v}_S = 2\mathbf{v}_1$, and similarly $\mathbf{v}_R = 2\mathbf{v}_2$, $\mathbf{v}_Q = 2\mathbf{v}_3$, $\mathbf{v}_P = 2\mathbf{v}_4$. Thus $\mathbf{v}_1 + \mathbf{v}_2 + \mathbf{v}_3 + \mathbf{v}_4 = \mathbf{0}$.

2. (a) Let $S = (x_0, y_0, z_0)$, $R = (x_1, y_1, z_1)$, $Q = (x_2, y_2, z_2)$, $P = (x_3, y_3, z_3)$ be the four vertices. Then

$$\text{Volume} = \tfrac{1}{3}\,(\text{distance from } S \text{ to plane } RQP) \times (\text{area of triangle } RQP)$$
$$= \frac{1}{3}\frac{\left|\mathbf{N} \cdot \overrightarrow{SR}\right|}{|\mathbf{N}|} \cdot \frac{1}{2}\left|\overrightarrow{RQ} \times \overrightarrow{RP}\right|$$

where $\mathbf{N}$ is a vector which is normal to the face RQP. Thus $\mathbf{N} = \overrightarrow{RQ} \times \overrightarrow{RP}$. Therefore

$$V = \left|\tfrac{1}{6}\left(\overrightarrow{RQ} \times \overrightarrow{RP}\right) \cdot \overrightarrow{SR}\right| = \frac{1}{6}\begin{vmatrix} x_0 - x & y_0 - y_1 & z_0 - z_1 \\ x_2 - x_1 & y_2 - y_1 & z_2 - z_1 \\ x_3 - x_1 & y_3 - y_1 & z_3 - z_1 \end{vmatrix}.$$

(b) Using the formula from part (a), $V = \dfrac{1}{6}\begin{vmatrix} 1-1 & 1-2 & 1-3 \\ 1-1 & 1-2 & 2-3 \\ 3-1 & -1-2 & 2-3 \end{vmatrix} = \dfrac{1}{6}\,|2(1-2)| = \dfrac{1}{3}.$

3. We define a vector $\mathbf{v}_1$ to have length equal to the area of the face opposite vertex P, so we can say $|\mathbf{v}_1| = A$, and direction perpendicular to the face and pointing outward, as in Problem 1. Similarly, we define $\mathbf{v}_2$, $\mathbf{v}_3$, and $\mathbf{v}_4$ so that $|\mathbf{v}_2| = B$, $|\mathbf{v}_3| = C$, and $|\mathbf{v}_4| = D$ and with the analogous directions. From Problem 1, we know $\mathbf{v}_1 + \mathbf{v}_2 + \mathbf{v}_3 + \mathbf{v}_4 = \mathbf{0} \;\Rightarrow\; \mathbf{v}_4 = -(\mathbf{v}_1 + \mathbf{v}_2 + \mathbf{v}_3) \;\Rightarrow\; |\mathbf{v}_4| = |-(\mathbf{v}_1 + \mathbf{v}_2 + \mathbf{v}_3)| = |\mathbf{v}_1 + \mathbf{v}_2 + \mathbf{v}_3|$
$\Rightarrow\; |\mathbf{v}_4|^2 = |\mathbf{v}_1 + \mathbf{v}_2 + \mathbf{v}_3|^2 \;\Rightarrow$

$$\mathbf{v}_4 \cdot \mathbf{v}_4 = (\mathbf{v}_1 + \mathbf{v}_2 + \mathbf{v}_3) \cdot (\mathbf{v}_1 + \mathbf{v}_2 + \mathbf{v}_3)$$
$$= \mathbf{v}_1 \cdot \mathbf{v}_1 + \mathbf{v}_1 \cdot \mathbf{v}_2 + \mathbf{v}_1 \cdot \mathbf{v}_3 + \mathbf{v}_2 \cdot \mathbf{v}_1 + \mathbf{v}_2 \cdot \mathbf{v}_2 + \mathbf{v}_2 \cdot \mathbf{v}_3 + \mathbf{v}_3 \cdot \mathbf{v}_1 + \mathbf{v}_3 \cdot \mathbf{v}_2 + \mathbf{v}_3 \cdot \mathbf{v}_3$$

Since the vertex S is trirectangular, we know the three faces meeting at S are mutually perpendicular, so the vectors $\mathbf{v}_1$, $\mathbf{v}_2$, $\mathbf{v}_3$ are also mutually perpendicular. Therefore, $\mathbf{v}_i \cdot \mathbf{v}_j = 0$ for $i \neq j$ and $i, j \in \{1, 2, 3\}$. Thus we have

$$\mathbf{v}_4 \cdot \mathbf{v}_4 = \mathbf{v}_1 \cdot \mathbf{v}_1 + \mathbf{v}_2 \cdot \mathbf{v}_2 + \mathbf{v}_3 \cdot \mathbf{v}_3 \quad \Rightarrow \quad |\mathbf{v}_4|^2 = |\mathbf{v}_1|^2 + |\mathbf{v}_2|^2 + |\mathbf{v}_3|^2 \quad \Rightarrow \quad D^2 = A^2 + B^2 + C^2.$$

Another Method: We introduce a coordinate system, as shown. Recall that the area of the parallelogram spanned by two vectors is equal to the length of their cross product, so since

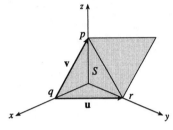

$$\mathbf{u} \times \mathbf{v} = \langle -q, r, 0 \rangle \times \langle -q, 0, p \rangle = \langle pr, pq, qr \rangle, \text{ we have}$$

$$|\mathbf{u} \times \mathbf{v}| = \sqrt{(pr)^2 + (pq)^2 + (qr)^2}, \text{ and therefore}$$

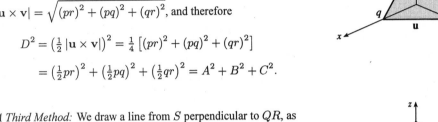

$$D^2 = \left(\tfrac{1}{2} |\mathbf{u} \times \mathbf{v}| \right)^2 = \tfrac{1}{4} \left[(pr)^2 + (pq)^2 + (qr)^2 \right]$$

$$= \left(\tfrac{1}{2} pr \right)^2 + \left(\tfrac{1}{2} pq \right)^2 + \left(\tfrac{1}{2} qr \right)^2 = A^2 + B^2 + C^2.$$

A Third Method: We draw a line from S perpendicular to QR, as shown. Now $D = \tfrac{1}{2} ch$, so $D^2 = \tfrac{1}{4} c^2 h^2$. Substituting $h^2 = p^2 + k^2$, we get $D^2 = \tfrac{1}{4} c^2 \left(p^2 + k^2 \right) = \tfrac{1}{4} c^2 p^2 + \tfrac{1}{4} c^2 k^2$. But $C = \tfrac{1}{2} ck$, so $D^2 = \tfrac{1}{4} c^2 p^2 + C^2$. Now substituting $c^2 = q^2 + r^2$ gives

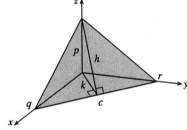

$$D^2 = \tfrac{1}{4} p^2 q^2 + \tfrac{1}{4} q^2 r^2 + C^2 = A^2 + B^2 + C^2.$$

9.5 **Equations of Lines and Planes** • • • • • • • • • • •

1. (a) True; each of the first two lines has a direction vector parallel to the direction vector of the third line, so these vectors are each scalar multiples of the third direction vector. Then the first two direction vectors are also scalar multiples of each other, so these vectors, and hence the two lines, are parallel.

(b) False; for example, the x- and y-axes are both perpendicular to the z-axis, yet the x- and y-axes are not parallel.

(c) True; each of the first two planes has a normal vector parallel to the normal vector of the third plane, so these two normal vectors are parallel to each other and the planes are parallel.

(d) False; for example, the xy- and yz-planes are not parallel, yet they are both perpendicular to the xz-plane.

(e) False; the x- and y-axes are not parallel, yet they are both parallel to the plane $z = 1$.

(f) True; if each line is perpendicular to a plane, then the lines' direction vectors are both parallel to a normal vector for the plane. Thus, the direction vectors are parallel to each other and the lines are parallel.

(g) False; the planes $y = 1$ and $z = 1$ are not parallel, yet they are both parallel to the x-axis.

(h) True; if each plane is perpendicular to a line, then any normal vector for each plane is parallel to a direction vector for the line. Thus, the normal vectors are parallel to each other and the planes are parallel.

(i) True; see Figure 9 and the accompanying discussion.

(j) False; they can be skew, as in Example 3.

(k) True. Consider any normal vector for the plane and any direction vector for the line. If the normal vector is perpendicular to the direction vector, the line and plane are parallel. Otherwise, the vectors meet at an angle θ, $0° \le \theta < 90°$, and the line will intersect the plane at an angle $90° - \theta$.

2. For this line, we have $\mathbf{r}_0 = \mathbf{i} - 3\,\mathbf{k}$ and $\mathbf{v} = 2\,\mathbf{i} - 4\,\mathbf{j} + 5\,\mathbf{k}$, so a vector equation is
$\mathbf{r} = \mathbf{r}_0 + t\,\mathbf{v} = (\mathbf{i} - 3\,\mathbf{k}) + t\,(2\,\mathbf{i} - 4\,\mathbf{j} + 5\,\mathbf{k}) = (1 + 2t)\,\mathbf{i} - 4t\,\mathbf{j} + (-3 + 5t)\,\mathbf{k}$ and parametric equations are
$x = 1 + 2t,\, y = -4t,\, z = -3 + 5t$.

3. For this line, we have $\mathbf{r}_0 = -2\,\mathbf{i} + 4\,\mathbf{j} + 10\,\mathbf{k}$ and $\mathbf{v} = 3\,\mathbf{i} + \mathbf{j} - 8\,\mathbf{k}$, so a vector equation is
$\mathbf{r} = \mathbf{r}_0 + t\,\mathbf{v} = (-2\,\mathbf{i} + 4\,\mathbf{j} + 10\,\mathbf{k}) + t(3\,\mathbf{i} + \mathbf{j} - 8\,\mathbf{k}) = (-2 + 3t)\,\mathbf{i} + (4 + t)\,\mathbf{j} + (10 - 8t)\,\mathbf{k}$ and parametric
equations are $x = -2 + 3t,\, y = 4 + t,\, z = 10 - 8t$.

4. This line has the same direction as the given line, $\mathbf{v} = 2\,\mathbf{i} - \mathbf{j} + 3\,\mathbf{k}$. Here $\mathbf{r}_0 = 0\,\mathbf{i} + 0\,\mathbf{j} + 0\,\mathbf{k}$, so a vector equation
is $\mathbf{r} = (0\,\mathbf{i} + 0\,\mathbf{j} + 0\,\mathbf{k}) + t\,(2\,\mathbf{i} - \mathbf{j} + 3\,\mathbf{k}) = 2t\,\mathbf{i} - t\,\mathbf{j} + 3t\,\mathbf{k}$ and parametric equations are
$x = 2t,\, y = -t,\, z = 3t$.

5. A line perpendicular to the given plane has the same direction as a normal vector to the plane, such as $\mathbf{n} = \langle 1, 3, 1 \rangle$.
So $\mathbf{r}_0 = \mathbf{i} + 6\,\mathbf{k}$, and we can take $\mathbf{v} = \mathbf{i} + 3\,\mathbf{j} + \mathbf{k}$. Then a vector equation is
$\mathbf{r} = (\mathbf{i} + 6\,\mathbf{k}) + t(\mathbf{i} + 3\,\mathbf{j} + \mathbf{k}) = (1 + t)\,\mathbf{i} + 3t\,\mathbf{j} + (6 + t)\,\mathbf{k}$, and parametric equations are
$x = 1 + t,\, y = 3t,\, z = 6 + t$.

6. The vector $\mathbf{v} = \langle 1 - 0, 2 - 0, 3 - 0 \rangle = \langle 1, 2, 3 \rangle$ is parallel to the line. Letting $P_0 = (0, 0, 0)$, parametric equations
are $x = 0 + 1 \cdot t = t,\, y = 0 + 2 \cdot t = 2t,\, z = 0 + 3 \cdot t = 3t$, while symmetric equations are $x = \dfrac{y}{2} = \dfrac{z}{3}$.

7. $\mathbf{v} = \langle 3 - 3, 2 - 1, -6 - (-1) \rangle = \langle 0, 1, -5 \rangle$, and letting $P_0 = (3, 1, -1)$, parametric equations are $x = 3$,
$y = 1 + t,\, z = -1 - 5t$, while symmetric equations are $x = 3,\, y - 1 = (z + 1)/(-5)$. Notice here that the
direction number $a = 0$, so rather than writing $(x - 3)/0$ in the symmetric equation we must write the equation
$x = 3$ separately.

8. $\mathbf{v} = \langle 4 - (-1), -3 - 0, 3 - 5 \rangle = \langle 5, -3, -2 \rangle$, and letting $P_0 = (-1, 0, 5)$, parametric equations are

$x = -1 + 5t$, $y = -3t$, $z = 5 - 2t$, while symmetric equations are $\dfrac{x + 1}{5} = \dfrac{y}{-3} = \dfrac{z - 5}{-2}$.

9. $\mathbf{v} = \langle 2 - 0, 1 - \frac{1}{2}, -3 - 1 \rangle = \langle 2, \frac{1}{2}, -4 \rangle$, and letting $P_0 = (2, 1, -3)$, parametric equations are $x = 2 + 2t$,

$y = 1 + \frac{1}{2}t$, $z = -3 - 4t$, while symmetric equations are $\dfrac{x - 2}{2} = \dfrac{y - 1}{1/2} = \dfrac{z + 3}{-4}$ or $\dfrac{x - 2}{2} = 2y - 2 = \dfrac{z + 3}{-4}$.

10. Setting $x = 0$, we see that $(0, 1, 0)$ satisfies the equations of both planes, so they do in fact have a line of intersection. $\mathbf{v} = \mathbf{n}_1 \times \mathbf{n}_2 = \langle 1, 1, 1 \rangle \times \langle 1, 0, 1 \rangle = \langle 1, 0, -1 \rangle$ is the direction of this line. Taking the point $(0, 1, 0)$ as P_0, parametric equations are $x = t$, $y = 1$, $z = -t$, and symmetric equations are $x = -z$, $y = 1$.

11. Direction vectors of the lines are $\mathbf{v}_1 = \langle 6, 9, 12 \rangle$ and $\mathbf{v}_2 = \langle 4, 6, 8 \rangle$, and since $\mathbf{v}_1 = \frac{3}{2}\mathbf{v}_2$, the direction vectors and thus the lines are parallel.

12. Direction vectors of the lines are $\mathbf{v}_1 = \langle 1, -2, 5 \rangle$ and $\mathbf{v}_2 = \langle 3, 4, 1 \rangle$. Since $\mathbf{v}_1 \cdot \mathbf{v}_2 = 3 - 8 + 5 = 0$, the direction vectors and thus the lines are perpendicular.

13. (a) A direction vector of the line with parametric equations $x = 1 + 2t$, $y = 3t$, $z = 5 - 7t$ is $\mathbf{v} = \langle 2, 3, -7 \rangle$ and the desired parallel line must also have $\mathbf{v}$ as a direction vector. Here $P_0 = (0, 2, -1)$, so symmetric equations for the line are $\dfrac{x}{2} = \dfrac{y - 2}{3} = \dfrac{z + 1}{-7}$.

(b) The line intersects the xy-plane when $z = 0$, so we need $\dfrac{x}{2} = \dfrac{y - 2}{3} = \dfrac{1}{-7}$ or $x = -\frac{2}{7}$, $y = \frac{11}{7}$. Thus the point of intersection with the xy-plane is $\left(-\frac{2}{7}, \frac{11}{7}, 0\right)$. Similarly for the yz-plane, we need $x = 0$ ⟺

$0 = \dfrac{y - 2}{3} = \dfrac{z + 1}{-7}$ ⟺ $y = 2$, $z = -1$. Thus the line intersects the yz-plane at $(0, 2, -1)$. For the

xz-plane, we need $y = 0$ ⟺ $\dfrac{x}{2} = -\dfrac{2}{3} = \dfrac{z + 1}{-7}$ ⟺ $x = -\frac{4}{3}$, $z = \frac{11}{3}$. So the line intersects the xz-plane

at $\left(-\frac{4}{3}, 0, \frac{11}{3}\right)$.

14. (a) A vector normal to the plane $2x - y + z = 1$ is $\mathbf{n} = \langle 2, -1, 1 \rangle$, and since the line is to be perpendicular to the plane, $\mathbf{n}$ is also a direction vector for the line. Thus parametric equations of the line are $x = 5 + 2t$, $y = 1 - t$, $z = t$.

(b) On the xy-plane, $z = 0$. So $z = t = 0$ in the parametric equations of the line, and therefore $x = 5$ and $y = 1$, giving the point of intersection $(5, 1, 0)$. For the yz-plane, $x = 0$ which implies $t = -\frac{5}{2}$, so $y = \frac{7}{2}$ and $z = -\frac{5}{2}$ and the point is $\left(0, \frac{7}{2}, -\frac{5}{2}\right)$. For the xz-plane, $y = 0$ which implies $t = 1$, so $x = 7$ and $z = 1$ and the point of intersection is $(7, 0, 1)$.

15. The lines aren't parallel since the direction vectors $\langle 2, 4, -3 \rangle$ and $\langle 1, 3, 2 \rangle$ aren't parallel, so we check to see if the lines intersect. The parametric equations of the lines are L_1: $x = 4 + 2t$, $y = -5 + 4t$, $z = 1 - 3t$ and L_2: $x = 2 + s$, $y = -1 + 3s$, $z = 2s$. For the lines to intersect we must be able to find one value of t and one value of s satisfying the following three equations: $4 + 2t = 2 + s$, $-5 + 4t = -1 + 3s$, $1 - 3t = 2s$. Solving the first two equations we get $t = -5$, $s = -8$ and checking, we see that these values don't satisfy the third equation. Thus L_1 and L_2 aren't parallel and don't intersect, so they must be skew lines.

16. Since the direction vectors $\langle 2, 1, 4 \rangle$ and $\langle 1, 2, 3 \rangle$ aren't parallel, the lines aren't parallel. Here the parametric equations are L_1: $x = 1 + 2t$, $y = t$, $z = 1 + 4t$; L_2: $x = s$, $y = -2 + 2s$, $z = -2 + 3s$. Thus, for the lines to intersect, the three equations $1 + 2t = s$, $t = -2 + 2s$ and $1 + 4t = -2 + 3s$ must be satisfied simultaneously. Solving the first two equations gives $t = 0$, $s = 1$ and, checking, we see these values do satisfy the third equation, so the lines intersect when $t = 0$ and $s = 1$, that is, at the point $(1, 0, 1)$.

17. Since the direction vectors are $\mathbf{v}_1 = \langle -6, 9, -3 \rangle$ and $\mathbf{v}_2 = \langle 2, -3, 1 \rangle$, we have $\mathbf{v}_1 = -3\mathbf{v}_2$ so the lines are parallel.

18. Since the direction vectors are $\langle 1, -1, 3 \rangle$ and $\langle -1, 2, 1 \rangle$, the lines aren't parallel. For the lines to intersect, the three equations $1 + t = 2 - s$, $2 - t = 1 + 2s$, $3t = 4 + s$ must be satisfied simultaneously. Solving the first two equations gives $t = 1$, $s = 0$ and, checking, we see these values don't satisfy the third equation. Thus L_1 and L_2 aren't parallel and don't intersect, so they must be skew lines.

19. Since the plane is perpendicular to the vector $\langle -2, 1, 5 \rangle$, we can take $\langle -2, 1, 5 \rangle$ as a normal vector to the plane. $(6, 3, 2)$ is a point on the plane, so setting $a = -2$, $b = 1$, $c = 5$ and $x_0 = 6$, $y_0 = 3$, $z_0 = 2$ in Equation 6 gives $-2(x - 6) + 1(y - 3) + 5(z - 2) = 0$ or $-2x + y + 5z = 1$ to be an equation of the plane.

20. $\mathbf{j} + 2\mathbf{k} = \langle 0, 1, 2 \rangle$ is a normal vector to the plane and $(4, 0, -3)$ is a point on the plane, so setting $a = 0$, $b = 1$, $c = 2$, $x_0 = 4$, $y_0 = 0$, $z_0 = -3$ in Equation 6 gives $0(x - 4) + 1(y - 0) + 2[z - (-3)] = 0$ or $y + 2z = -6$ to be an equation of the plane.

21. Since the two planes are parallel, they will have the same normal vectors. So we can take $\mathbf{n} = \langle 2, -1, 3 \rangle$, and an equation of the plane is $2(x - 0) - 1(y - 0) + 3(z - 0) = 0$ or $2x - y + 3z = 0$.

22. First, a normal vector for the plane $2x + 4y + 8z = 17$ is $\mathbf{n} = \langle 2, 4, 8 \rangle$. A direction vector for the line is $\mathbf{v} = \langle 2, 1, -1 \rangle$, and since $\mathbf{n} \cdot \mathbf{v} = 0$ we know the line is perpendicular to $\mathbf{n}$ and hence parallel to the plane. Thus, there is a parallel plane which contains the line. By putting $t = 0$, we know the point $(3, 0, 8)$ is on the line and hence the new plane. We can use the same normal vector $\mathbf{n} = \langle 2, 4, 8 \rangle$, so an equation of the plane is $2(x - 3) + 4(y - 0) + 8(z - 8) = 0$ or $x + 2y + 4z = 35$.

23. Here the vectors $\mathbf{a} = \langle 1 - 0, 0 - 1, 1 - 1 \rangle = \langle 1, -1, 0 \rangle$ and $\mathbf{b} = \langle 1 - 0, 1 - 1, 0 - 1 \rangle = \langle 1, 0, -1 \rangle$ lie in the plane, so $\mathbf{a} \times \mathbf{b}$ is a normal vector to the plane. Thus, we can take $\mathbf{n} = \mathbf{a} \times \mathbf{b} = \langle 1 - 0, 0 + 1, 0 + 1 \rangle = \langle 1, 1, 1 \rangle$. If P_0 is the point $(0, 1, 1)$, an equation of the plane is $1(x - 0) + 1(y - 1) + 1(z - 1) = 0$ or $x + y + z = 2$.

24. Here the vectors $\mathbf{a} = \langle 2, -4, 6 \rangle$ and $\mathbf{b} = \langle 5, 1, 3 \rangle$ lie in the plane, so $\mathbf{n} = \mathbf{a} \times \mathbf{b} = \langle -12 - 6, 30 - 6, 2 + 20 \rangle = \langle -18, 24, 22 \rangle$ is a normal vector to the plane and an equation of the plane is $-18(x - 0) + 24(y - 0) + 22(z - 0) = 0$ or $-18x + 24y + 22z = 0$.

25. If we first find two nonparallel vectors in the plane, their cross product will be a normal vector to the plane. Since the given line lies in the plane, its direction vector $\mathbf{a} = \langle -2, 5, 4 \rangle$ is one vector in the plane. We can verify that the given point $(6, 0, -2)$ does not lie on this line, so to find another nonparallel vector $\mathbf{b}$ which lies in the plane, we can pick any point on the line and find a vector connecting the points. If we put $t = 0$, we see that $(4, 3, 7)$ is on the line, so $\mathbf{b} = \langle 6 - 4, 0 - 3, -2 - 7 \rangle = \langle 2, -3, -9 \rangle$ and $\mathbf{n} = \mathbf{a} \times \mathbf{b} = \langle -45 + 12, 8 - 18, 6 - 10 \rangle = \langle -33, -10, -4 \rangle$. Thus, an equation of the plane is $-33(x - 6) - 10(y - 0) - 4[z - (-2)] = 0$ or $33x + 10y + 4z = 190$.

26. Since the line $x = 2y = 3z$, or $x = \dfrac{y}{1/2} = \dfrac{z}{1/3}$, lies in the plane, its direction vector $\mathbf{a} = \langle 1, \frac{1}{2}, \frac{1}{3} \rangle$ is parallel to the plane. The point $(0, 0, 0)$ is on the line (put $t = 0$), and we can verify that the given point $(1, -1, 1)$ in the plane is not on the line. The vector connecting these two points, $\mathbf{b} = \langle 1, -1, 1 \rangle$, is therefore parallel to the plane, but not parallel to $\langle 1, 2, 3 \rangle$. Then $\mathbf{a} \times \mathbf{b} = \langle \frac{1}{2} + \frac{1}{3}, \frac{1}{3} - 1, -1 - \frac{1}{2} \rangle = \langle \frac{5}{6}, -\frac{2}{3}, -\frac{3}{2} \rangle$ is a normal vector to the plane, and an equation of the plane is $\frac{5}{6}(x - 0) - \frac{2}{3}(y - 0) - \frac{3}{2}(z - 0) = 0$ or $5x - 4y - 9z = 0$.

27. A direction vector for the line of intersection is $\mathbf{a} = \mathbf{n}_1 \times \mathbf{n}_2 = \langle 1, 1, -1 \rangle \times \langle 2, -1, 3 \rangle = \langle 2, -5, -3 \rangle$, and $\mathbf{a}$ is parallel to the desired plane. Another vector parallel to the plane is the vector connecting any point on the line of intersection to the given point $(-1, 2, 1)$ in the plane. Setting $x = 0$, the equations of the planes reduce to $y - z = 2$ and $-y + 3z = 1$ with simultaneous solution $y = \frac{7}{2}$ and $z = \frac{3}{2}$. So a point on the line is $\left(0, \frac{7}{2}, \frac{3}{2}\right)$ and another vector parallel to the plane is $\left\langle -1, -\frac{3}{2}, -\frac{1}{2} \right\rangle$. Then a normal vector to the plane is
$\mathbf{n} = \langle 2, -5, -3 \rangle \times \left\langle -1, -\frac{3}{2}, -\frac{1}{2} \right\rangle = \langle -2, 4, -8 \rangle$ and an equation of the plane is
$-2(x + 1) + 4(y - 2) - 8(z - 1) = 0$ or $x - 2y + 4z = -1$.

28. $\mathbf{n}_1 = \langle 1, 0, -1 \rangle$ and $\mathbf{n}_2 = \langle 0, 1, 2 \rangle$. Setting $z = 0$, it is easy to see that $(1, 3, 0)$ is a point on the line of intersection of $x - z = 1$ and $y + 2z = 3$. The direction of this line is $\mathbf{v}_1 = \mathbf{n}_1 \times \mathbf{n}_2 = \langle -1, 2, 1 \rangle$. A second vector parallel to the desired plane is $\mathbf{v}_2 = \langle 1, 1, -2 \rangle$, since it is perpendicular to $x + y - 2z = 1$. Therefore, the normal of the plane in question is $\mathbf{n} = \mathbf{v}_1 \times \mathbf{v}_2 = \langle 4 - 1, 1 + 2, 1 + 2 \rangle = 3\langle 1, 1, 1 \rangle$. Taking $(x_0, y_0, z_0) = (1, 3, 0)$, the equation we are looking for is $(x - 1) + (y - 3) + z = 0 \iff x + y + z = 4$.

29. Substituting the parametric equations of the line into the equation of the plane gives
$2x + y - z + 5 = 2(1 + 2t) + (-1) - t + 5 = 0 \Rightarrow 3t + 6 = 0 \Rightarrow t = -2$. Therefore, the point of intersection is given by $x = 1 + 2(-2) = -3$, $y = -1$ and $z = -2$, that is, the point $(-3, -1, -2)$.

30. Substitution into the equation of the plane of the parametric expressions for x, y and z gives
$z = 1 - 2x + y \Rightarrow (1 + t) = 1 - 2(1 - t) + t \Rightarrow -2 + 2t = 0 \Rightarrow t = 1$. Thus, $x = 1 - 1$, $y = 1$ and $z = 1 + 1$ and the point of intersection is $(0, 1, 2)$.

31. The normal vectors to the planes are $\mathbf{n}_1 = \langle 1, 0, 1 \rangle$ and $\mathbf{n}_2 = \langle 0, 1, 1 \rangle$. Thus the normal vectors (and consequently the planes) aren't parallel. Furthermore, $\mathbf{n}_1 \cdot \mathbf{n}_2 = 1 \neq 0$ so the planes aren't perpendicular. Letting θ be the angle between the two planes, we have $\cos \theta = \dfrac{\mathbf{n}_1 \cdot \mathbf{n}_2}{|\mathbf{n}_1| \, |\mathbf{n}_2|} = \dfrac{1}{\sqrt{2}\sqrt{2}} = \dfrac{1}{2}$ and $\theta = \cos^{-1}\left(\frac{1}{2}\right) = 60°$.

32. Here the normals are $\mathbf{n}_1 = \langle -8, -6, 2 \rangle$ and $\mathbf{n}_2 = \langle 4, 3, -1 \rangle$. Since $\mathbf{n}_1 = -2\mathbf{n}_2$, the normals (and thus the planes) are parallel.

33. The normals are $\mathbf{n}_1 = \langle 1, 4, -3 \rangle$ and $\mathbf{n}_2 = \langle -3, 6, 7 \rangle$, so the normals (and thus the planes) aren't parallel. But $\mathbf{n}_1 \cdot \mathbf{n}_2 = -3 + 24 - 21 = 0$, so the normals (and thus the planes) are perpendicular.

34. The normals are $\mathbf{n}_1 = \langle 2, 2, -1 \rangle$ and $\mathbf{n}_2 = \langle 6, -3, 2 \rangle$ so the planes aren't parallel. Furthermore, $\mathbf{n}_1 \cdot \mathbf{n}_2 = 12 - 6 - 2 = 4 \neq 0$, so the planes aren't perpendicular. Then $\cos \theta = \dfrac{4}{\sqrt{9}\sqrt{49}} = \dfrac{4}{21}$ and $\theta = \cos^{-1}\left(\frac{4}{21}\right) \approx 79°$.

35. (a) To find a point on the line of intersection, set one of the variables equal to a constant, say $z = 0$. (This will only work if the line of intersection crosses the xy-plane; otherwise, try setting x or y equal to 0.) Then the equations of the planes reduce to $x + y = 2$ and $3x - 4y = 6$. Solving these two equations gives $x = 2$, $y = 0$. So a point on the line of intersection is $(2, 0, 0)$. The direction of the line is
$\mathbf{v} = \mathbf{n}_1 \times \mathbf{n}_2 = \langle 5 - 4, -3 - 5, -4 - 3 \rangle = \langle 1, -8, -7 \rangle$, and symmetric equations for the line are
$x - 2 = \dfrac{y}{-8} = \dfrac{z}{-7}$.

(b) The angle between the planes satisfies $\cos \theta = \dfrac{\mathbf{n}_1 \cdot \mathbf{n}_2}{|\mathbf{n}_1| \, |\mathbf{n}_2|} = \dfrac{3 - 4 - 5}{\sqrt{3}\sqrt{50}} = -\dfrac{\sqrt{6}}{5}$. Therefore
$\theta = \cos^{-1}\left(-\frac{\sqrt{6}}{5}\right) \approx 119°$ (or $61°$).

36. The plane will contain all perpendicular bisectors of the line segment joining the two points. Thus, a point in the plane is $P_0 = (-1, -1, 2)$, the midpoint of the line segment joining the two given points, and a normal to the plane is $\mathbf{n} = \langle 6, -6, 2 \rangle$, the vector connecting the two points. So an equation of the plane is $6(x + 1) - 6(y + 1) + 2(z - 2) = 0$ or $3x - 3y + z = 2$.

37. The plane contains the points $(a, 0, 0)$, $(0, b, 0)$ and $(0, 0, c)$. Thus the vectors $\mathbf{a} = \langle -a, b, 0 \rangle$ and $\mathbf{b} = \langle -a, 0, c \rangle$ lie in the plane, and $\mathbf{n} = \mathbf{a} \times \mathbf{b} = \langle bc - 0, 0 + ac, 0 + ab \rangle = \langle bc, ac, ab \rangle$ is a normal vector to the plane. The equation of the plane is therefore $bcx + acy + abz = abc + 0 + 0$ or $bcx + acy + abz = abc$. Notice that if $a \neq 0$, $b \neq 0$ and $c \neq 0$ then we can rewrite the equation as $\dfrac{x}{a} + \dfrac{y}{b} + \dfrac{z}{c} = 1$. This is a good equation to remember!

38. (a) For the lines to intersect, we must be able to find one value of t and one value of s satisfying the three equations $1 + t = 2 - s$, $1 - t = s$ and $2t = 2$. From the third we get $t = 1$, and putting this in the second gives $s = 0$. These values of s and t do satisfy the first equation, so the lines intersect at the point $P_0 = (1 + 1, 1 - 1, 2(1)) = (2, 0, 2)$.

(b) The direction vectors of the lines are $\langle 1, -1, 2 \rangle$ and $\langle -1, 1, 0 \rangle$, so a normal vector for the plane is $\langle -1, 1, 0 \rangle \times \langle 1, -1, 2 \rangle = \langle 2, 2, 0 \rangle$ and it contains the point $(2, 0, 2)$. Then the equation of the plane is $2(x - 2) + 2(y - 0) + 0(z - 2) = 0 \iff x + y = 2$.

39. Two vectors which are perpendicular to the required line are the normal of the given plane, $\langle 1, 1, 1 \rangle$, and a direction vector for the given line, $\langle 1, -1, 2 \rangle$. So a direction vector for the required line is $\langle 1, 1, 1 \rangle \times \langle 1, -1, 2 \rangle = \langle 3, -1, -2 \rangle$. Thus L is given by $\langle x, y, z \rangle = \langle 0, 1, 2 \rangle + t \langle 3, -1, -2 \rangle$, or in parametric form, $x = 3t$, $y = 1 - t$, $z = 2 - 2t$.

40. Let L be the given line. Then $(1, 1, 0)$ is the point on L corresponding to $t = 0$. L is in the direction of $\mathbf{a} = \langle 1, -1, 2 \rangle$ and $\mathbf{b} = \langle -1, 0, 2 \rangle$ is the vector joining $(1, 1, 0)$ and $(0, 1, 2)$. Then

$$\mathbf{b} - \text{proj}_{\mathbf{a}}\,\mathbf{b} = \langle -1, 0, 2 \rangle - \frac{\langle 1, -1, 2 \rangle \cdot \langle -1, 0, 2 \rangle}{1^2 + (-1)^2 + 2^2} \langle 1, -1, 2 \rangle = \langle -1, 0, 2 \rangle - \tfrac{1}{2}\langle 1, -1, 2 \rangle = \left\langle -\tfrac{3}{2}, \tfrac{1}{2}, 1 \right\rangle \text{ is a}$$

direction vector for the required line. Thus $2\left\langle -\tfrac{3}{2}, \tfrac{1}{2}, 1 \right\rangle = \langle -3, 1, 2 \rangle$ is also a direction vector, and the line has parametric equations $x = -3t$, $y = 1 + t$, $z = 2 + 2t$. (Notice that this is the same line as in Exercise 39.)

41. Let P_i have normal vector $\mathbf{n}_i$. Then $\mathbf{n}_1 = \langle 4, -2, 6 \rangle$, $\mathbf{n}_2 = \langle 4, -2, -2 \rangle$, $\mathbf{n}_3 = \langle -6, 3, -9 \rangle$, $\mathbf{n}_4 = \langle 2, -1, -1 \rangle$. Now $\mathbf{n}_1 = -\tfrac{2}{3}\mathbf{n}_3$, so $\mathbf{n}_1$ and $\mathbf{n}_3$ are parallel, and hence P_1 and P_3 are parallel; similarly P_2 and P_4 are parallel because $\mathbf{n}_2 = 2\mathbf{n}_4$. However, $\mathbf{n}_1$ and $\mathbf{n}_2$ are not parallel. $\left(0, 0, \tfrac{1}{2}\right)$ lies on P_1, but not on P_3, so they are not the same plane, but both P_2 and P_4 contain the point $(0, 0, -3)$, so these two planes are identical.

42. Let L_i have direction vector $\mathbf{v}_i$. Then $\mathbf{v}_1 = \langle 1, 1, -5 \rangle$, $\mathbf{v}_2 = \langle 1, 1, -1 \rangle$, $\mathbf{v}_3 = \langle 1, 1, -1 \rangle$, $\mathbf{v}_4 = \langle 2, 2, -10 \rangle$. $\mathbf{v}_2$ and $\mathbf{v}_3$ are equal so they're parallel. $\mathbf{v}_4 = 2\mathbf{v}_1$, so L_4 and L_1 are parallel. L_3 contains the point $(1, 4, 1)$, but this point does not lie on L_2, so they're not equal. $(2, 1, -3)$ lies on L_4, and on L_1, with $t = 1$. So L_1 and L_4 are identical.

43. Let $Q = (2, 2, 0)$ and $R = (3, -1, 5)$, points on the line corresponding to $t = 0$ and $t = 1$. Let $P = (1, 2, 3)$. Then $\mathbf{a} = \overrightarrow{QR} = \langle 1, -3, 5 \rangle$, $\mathbf{b} = \overrightarrow{QP} = \langle -1, 0, 3 \rangle$. The distance is

$$d = \frac{|\mathbf{a} \times \mathbf{b}|}{|\mathbf{a}|} = \frac{|\langle 1, -3, 5 \rangle \times \langle -1, 0, 3 \rangle|}{|\langle 1, -3, 5 \rangle|} = \frac{|\langle -9, -8, -3 \rangle|}{|\langle 1, -3, 5 \rangle|} = \frac{\sqrt{9^2 + 8^2 + 3^2}}{\sqrt{1^2 + 3^2 + 5^2}} = \frac{\sqrt{154}}{\sqrt{35}} = \sqrt{\frac{22}{5}}.$$

44. Let $Q = (5, 0, 1)$ and $R = (4, 3, 3)$, points on the line corresponding to $t = 0$ and $t = 1$. Let $P = (1, 0, -1)$. Then $\mathbf{a} = \overrightarrow{QR} = \langle -1, 3, 2 \rangle$ and $\mathbf{b} = \overrightarrow{QP} = \langle -4, 0, -2 \rangle$. The distance is

$$d = \frac{|\mathbf{a} \times \mathbf{b}|}{|\mathbf{a}|} = \frac{|\langle -1, 3, 2 \rangle \times \langle -4, 0, -2 \rangle|}{|\langle -1, 3, 2 \rangle|} = \frac{|\langle -6, -10, 12 \rangle|}{|\langle -1, 3, 2 \rangle|} = \frac{2\sqrt{3^2 + 5^2 + 6^2}}{\sqrt{1^2 + 3^2 + 2^2}} = \frac{2\sqrt{70}}{\sqrt{14}} = 2\sqrt{5}.$$

45. By Equation 8, the distance is $D = \dfrac{1}{\sqrt{1+4+4}}\,[(1)(2) + (-2)(8) + (-2)(5) - 1] = \dfrac{25}{3}$.

46. By Equation 8, the distance is $D = \dfrac{1}{\sqrt{16 + 36 + 1}}\,[4(3) + (-6)(-2) + 1(7) - 5] = \dfrac{26}{\sqrt{53}}$.

47. Put $y = z = 0$ in the equation of the first plane, to get the point $(-1, 0, 0)$ on the plane. Because the planes are parallel, the distance D between them is the distance from $(-1, 0, 0)$ to the second plane. By Equation 8,

$$D = \frac{|3(-1) + 6(0) - 3(0) - 4|}{\sqrt{3^2 + 6^2 + (-3)^2}} = \frac{7}{3\sqrt{6}} \text{ or } \frac{7\sqrt{6}}{18}.$$

48. Put $y = z = 0$ in the equation of the first plane to get the point $\left(\frac{4}{3}, 0, 0\right)$ on the plane. Because the planes are parallel the distance D between them is the distance from $\left(\frac{4}{3}, 0, 0\right)$ to the second plane. By Equation 8,

$$D = \frac{\left|1\left(\frac{4}{3}\right) + 2(0) - 3(0) - 1\right|}{\sqrt{1^2 + 2^2 + (-3)^2}} = \frac{1}{3\sqrt{14}}.$$

49. The distance between two parallel planes is the same as the distance between a point on one of the planes and the other plane. Let $P_0 = (x_0, y_0, z_0)$ be a point on the plane given by $ax + by + cz + d_1 = 0$. Then $ax_0 + by_0 + cz_0 + d_1 = 0$ and the distance between P_0 and the plane given by $ax + by + cz + d_2 = 0$ is, from

Equation 8, $D = \dfrac{|ax_0 + by_0 + cz_0 + d_2|}{\sqrt{a^2 + b^2 + c^2}} = \dfrac{|-d_1 + d_2|}{\sqrt{a^2 + b^2 + c^2}} = \dfrac{|d_1 - d_2|}{\sqrt{a^2 + b^2 + c^2}}$.

50. The planes must have parallel normal vectors, so if $ax + by + cz + d = 0$ is such a plane, then for some $t \neq 0$, $\langle a, b, c\rangle = t\langle 1, 2, -2\rangle = \langle t, 2t, -2t\rangle$. So this plane is given by the equation $x + 2y - 2z + e = 0$, where $e = d/t$.

By Exercise 49, the distance between the planes is $2 = \dfrac{|1 - e|}{\sqrt{1^2 + 2^2 + (-2)^2}} \iff 6 = |1 - e| \iff e = 7 \text{ or } -5$.

So the desired planes have equations $x + 2y - 2z = 7$ and $x + 2y - 2z = -5$.

51. $L_1: x = y = z \implies x = y$ (1). $L_2: x + 1 = y/2 = z/3 \implies x + 1 = y/2$ (2). The solution of (1) and (2) is $x = y = -2$. However, when $x = -2$, $x = z \implies z = -2$, but $x + 1 = z/3 \implies z = -3$, a contradiction. Hence the lines do not intersect. For L_1, $\mathbf{v}_1 = \langle 1, 1, 1\rangle$, and for L_2, $\mathbf{v}_2 = \langle 1, 2, 3\rangle$, so the lines are not parallel. Thus the lines are skew lines. If two lines are skew, they can be viewed as lying in two parallel planes and so the distance between the skew lines would be the same as the distance between these parallel planes. The common normal vector to the planes must be perpendicular to both $\langle 1, 1, 1\rangle$ and $\langle 1, 2, 3\rangle$, the direction vectors of the two lines. So set $\mathbf{n} = \langle 1, 1, 1\rangle \times \langle 1, 2, 3\rangle = \langle 3 - 2, -3 + 1, 2 - 1\rangle = \langle 1, -2, 1\rangle$. From above, we know that $(-2, -2, -2)$ and $(-2, -2, -3)$ are points of L_1 and L_2 respectively. So in the notation of Equation 7, $1(-2) - 2(-2) + 1(-2) + d_1 = 0 \implies d_1 = 0$ and $1(-2) - 2(-2) + 1(-3) + d_2 = 0 \implies d_2 = 1$.

By Exercise 49, the distance between these two skew lines is $D = \dfrac{|0 - 1|}{\sqrt{1 + 4 + 1}} = \dfrac{1}{\sqrt{6}}$.

Alternate solution (without reference to planes): A vector which is perpendicular to both of the lines is $\mathbf{n} = \langle 1, 1, 1\rangle \times \langle 1, 2, 3\rangle = \langle 1, -2, 1\rangle$. Pick any point on each of the lines, say $(-2, -2, -2)$ and $(-2, -2, -3)$, and form the vector $\mathbf{b} = \langle 0, 0, 1\rangle$ connecting the two points. The distance between the two skew lines is the absolute value of the scalar projection of $\mathbf{b}$ along $\mathbf{n}$, that is, $D = \dfrac{|\mathbf{n} \cdot \mathbf{b}|}{|\mathbf{n}|} = \dfrac{|1 \cdot 0 - 2 \cdot 0 + 1 \cdot 1|}{\sqrt{1 + 4 + 1}} = \dfrac{1}{\sqrt{6}}$.

52. First notice that if two lines are skew, they can be viewed as lying in two parallel planes and so the distance between the skew lines would be the same as the distance between these parallel planes. The common normal vector to the planes must be perpendicular to both $\mathbf{v}_1 = \langle 1, 6, 2 \rangle$ and $\mathbf{v}_2 = \langle 2, 15, 6 \rangle$, the direction vectors of the two lines respectively. Thus set $\mathbf{n} = \mathbf{v}_1 \times \mathbf{v}_2 = \langle 36 - 30, 4 - 6, 15 - 12 \rangle = \langle 6, -2, 3 \rangle$. Setting $t = 0$ and $s = 0$ gives the points $(1, 1, 0)$ and $(1, 5, -2)$. So in the notation of Equation 7, $6 - 2 + 0 + d_1 = 0 \Rightarrow d_1 = -4$ and $6 - 10 - 6 + d_2 = 0 \Rightarrow d_2 = 10$. Then by Exercise 49, the distance between the two skew lines is given by
$$D = \frac{|-4 - 10|}{\sqrt{36 + 4 + 9}} = \frac{14}{7} = 2.$$
Alternate solution (without reference to planes): We already know that the direction vectors of the two lines are $\mathbf{v}_1 = \langle 1, 6, 2 \rangle$ and $\mathbf{v}_2 = \langle 2, 15, 6 \rangle$. Then $\mathbf{n} = \mathbf{v}_1 \times \mathbf{v}_2 = \langle 6, -2, 3 \rangle$ is perpendicular to both lines. Pick any point on each of the lines, say $(1, 1, 0)$ and $(1, 5, -2)$, and form the vector $\mathbf{b} = \langle 0, 4, -2 \rangle$ connecting the two points. Then the distance between the two skew lines is the absolute value of the scalar projection of $\mathbf{b}$ along $\mathbf{n}$, that is,
$$D = \frac{|\mathbf{n} \cdot \mathbf{b}|}{|\mathbf{n}|} = \frac{1}{\sqrt{36 + 4 + 9}} |0 - 8 - 6| = \frac{14}{7} = 2.$$

53. If $a \neq 0$, then $ax + by + cz + d = 0 \Rightarrow a(x + d/a) + b(y - 0) + c(z - 0) = 0$ which by (6) is the scalar equation of the plane through the point $(-d/a, 0, 0)$ with normal vector $\langle a, b, c \rangle$. Similarly, if $b \neq 0$ (or if $c \neq 0$) the equation of the plane can be rewritten as $a(x - 0) + b(y + d/b) + c(z - 0) = 0$ [or as $a(x - 0) + b(y - 0) + c(z + d/c) = 0$] which by (6) is the scalar equation of a plane through the point $(0, -d/b, 0)$ [or the point $(0, 0, -d/c)$] with normal vector $\langle a, b, c \rangle$.

54. (a) The planes $x + y + z = c$ have normal vector $\langle 1, 1, 1 \rangle$, so they are all parallel. Their x-, y-, and z-intercepts are all c. When $c > 0$ their intersection with the first octant is an equilateral triangle and when $c < 0$ their intersection with the octant diagonally opposite the first is an equilateral triangle.

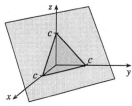

(b) The planes $x + y + cz = 1$ have x-intercept 1, y-intercept 1, and z-intercept $1/c$. The plane with $c = 0$ is parallel to the z-axis. As c gets larger, the planes get closer to the xy-plane.

(c) The planes $y \cos \theta + z \cos \theta = 1$ have normal vectors $\langle 0, \cos \theta, \sin \theta \rangle$, which are perpendicular to the x-axis, and so the planes are parallel to the x-axis. We look at their intersection with the yz-plane. These are lines that are perpendicular to $\langle \cos \theta, \sin \theta \rangle$ and pass through $(\cos \theta, \sin \theta)$, since $\cos^2 \theta + \sin^2 \theta = 1$. So these are the tangent lines to the unit circle. Thus the family consists of all planes tangent to the circular cylinder with radius 1 and axis the x-axis.

9.6 Functions and Surfaces · · · · · · · · · · · · · ·

1. (a) According to Table 1, $f(40, 15) = 25$, which means that if a 40-knot wind has been blowing in the open sea for 15 hours, it will create waves with estimated heights of 25 feet.

   (b) $h = f(30, t)$ means we fix v at 30 and allow t to vary, resulting in a function of one variable. Thus here, $h = f(30, t)$ gives the wave heights produced by 30-knot winds blowing for t hours. From the table (look at the row corresponding to $v = 30$), the function increases but at a declining rate as t increases. In fact, the function values appear to be approaching a limiting value of approximately 19, which suggests that 30-knot winds cannot produce waves higher than about 19 feet.

   (c) $h = f(v, 30)$ means we fix t at 30, again giving a function of one variable. So, $h = f(v, 30)$ gives the wave heights produced by winds of speed v blowing for 30 hours. From the table (look at the column corresponding to $t = 30$), the function appears to increase at an increasing rate, with no apparent limiting value. This suggests that faster winds (lasting 30 hours) always create higher waves.

2. Graph III has these traces. One indication is found by noting that the higher z-values occur for negative values of y in the traces in $x = 1$ and $x = 2$, and for positive values of x in the traces in $y = -1$ and $y = -2$. Thus the graph should have a "hill" over the fourth quadrant of the xy-plane. Similarly, we should expect a "valley" corresponding to the second quadrant of the xy-plane.

3. (a) $f(2, 0) = 2^2 e^{3(2)(0)} = 4(1) = 4$

   (b) Since both x^2 and the exponential function are defined everywhere, $x^2 e^{3xy}$ is defined for all choices of values for x and y. Thus, the domain of f is $\mathbb{R}^2$.

   (c) Because the range of $g(x, y) = 3xy$ is $\mathbb{R}$, and the range of e^x is $(0, \infty)$, the range of $e^{g(x,y)} = e^{3xy}$ is $(0, \infty)$. The range of x^2 is $[0, \infty)$, so the range of the product $x^2 e^{3xy}$ is $[0, \infty)$.

4. (a) $f(1, 1) = \ln(1 + 1 - 1) = \ln 1 = 0$

   (b) $f(e, 1) = \ln(e + 1 - 1) = \ln e = 1$

   (c) $\ln(x + y - 1)$ is defined only when $x + y - 1 > 0$, that is, $y > 1 - x$. So the domain of f is $\{(x, y) \,|\, y > 1 - x\}$.

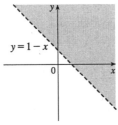

   (d) Since $\ln(x + y - 1)$ can be any real number, the range is $\mathbb{R}$.

5. $\sqrt{x+y}$ is defined only when $x + y \geq 0$, or $y \geq -x$. So the domain of f is $\{(x, y) \mid y \geq -x\}$.

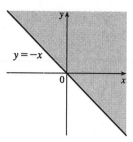

6. We need $x \geq 0$ and $y \geq 0$, so $D = \{(x, y) \mid x \geq 0 \text{ and } y \geq 0\}$, the first quadrant.

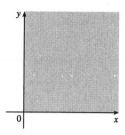

7. $\sqrt{y - x^2}$ is defined only when $y - x^2 \geq 0$, or $y \geq x^2$. In addition, f is not defined if $1 - x^2 = 0 \implies x = \pm 1$. Thus the domain of f is $\{(x, y) \mid y \geq x^2, x \neq \pm 1\}$.

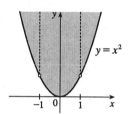

8. f is defined only when $x^2 + y^2 - 1 \geq 0$ $\implies x^2 + y^2 \geq 1$ and $4 - x^2 - y^2 > 0 \implies x^2 + y^2 < 4$. Thus $D = \{(x, y) \mid 1 \leq x^2 + y^2 < 4\}$.

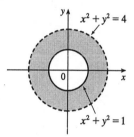

9. $z = 3$, a horizontal plane through the point $(0, 0, 3)$.

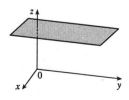

10. $z = x$, a plane which intersects the xz-plane in the line $z = x$, $y = 0$. The portion of this plane that lies in the first octant is shown.

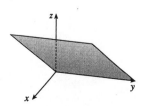

11. $z = 1 - x - y$ or $x + y + z = 1$, a plane with intercepts 1, 1, and 1.

12. $z = \sin y$, a "wave".

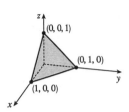

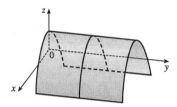

13. $z = 1 - x^2$, a parabolic cylinder.

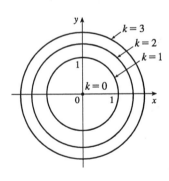

14. (a) The traces in $x = k$ are parabolas of the form $z = k^2 + y^2$, the traces in $y = k$ are parabolas of the form $z = x^2 + k^2$, and the traces in $z = k$ are circles $x^2 + y^2 = k$, $k \geq 0$.

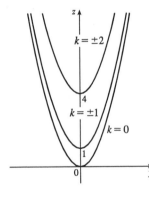

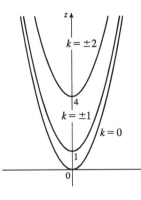

Combining these traces we form the graph.

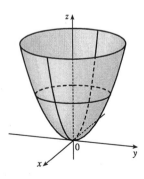

(b)

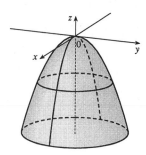

(c)

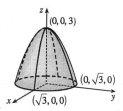

$g(x, y)$ is the graph of $f(x, y)$ reflected in the
xy-plane. [Note that $g(x, y) = -f(x, y)$.]

$h(x, y)$ is the graph of $g(x, y)$ shifted
upward 3 units.

15. All six graphs have different traces in the planes $x = 0$ and $y = 0$, so we investigate these for each function.

(a) $f(x, y) = |x| + |y|$. The trace in $x = 0$ is $z = |y|$, and in $y = 0$ is $z = |x|$, so it must be graph VI.

(b) $f(x, y) = |xy|$. The trace in $x = 0$ is $z = 0$, and in $y = 0$ is $z = 0$, so it must be graph V.

(c) $f(x, y) = \dfrac{1}{1 + x^2 + y^2}$. The trace in $x = 0$ is $z = \dfrac{1}{1 + y^2}$, and in $y = 0$ is $z = \dfrac{1}{1 + x^2}$. In addition, we can
see that f is close to 0 for large values of x and y, so this is graph I.

(d) $f(x, y) = (x^2 - y^2)^2$. The trace in $x = 0$ is $z = y^4$, and in $y = 0$ is $z = x^4$. Both graph II and graph IV seem
plausible; notice the trace in $z = 0$ is $0 = (x^2 - y^2)^2 \;\Rightarrow\; y = \pm x$, so it must be graph IV.

(e) $f(x, y) = (x - y)^2$. The trace in $x = 0$ is $z = y^2$, and in $y = 0$ is $z = x^2$. Both graph II and graph IV seem
plausible; notice the trace in $z = 0$ is $0 = (x - y)^2 \;\Rightarrow\; y = x$, so it must be graph II.

(f) $f(x, y) = \sin(|x| + |y|)$. The trace in $x = 0$ is $z = \sin|y|$, and in $y = 0$ is $z = \sin|x|$. In addition, notice that
the oscillating nature of the graph is characteristic of trigonometric functions. So this is graph III.

16. The equation of the graph is $z = \sqrt{16 - x^2 - 16y^2}$ or equivalently

$x^2 + 16y^2 + z^2 = 16$, $z \geq 0$. Traces in $x = k$ are $16y^2 + z^2 = 16 - k^2$,
$z \geq 0$, a family of ellipses where here we have only the upper halves. Traces in
$y = k$ are $x^2 + z^2 = 16 - 16k^2$, $z \geq 0$, again a family of half-ellipses. Traces
in $z = k$, $k \geq 0$, are another family of ellipses, $x^2 + 16y^2 = 16 - k^2$.

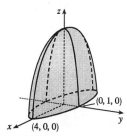

Note that the equation can be written as $\dfrac{x^2}{16} + y^2 + \dfrac{z^2}{16} = 1$, $z \geq 0$, which we recognize as the top half of an
ellipsoid with intercepts ± 4, ± 1, and 4.

17. The equation of the graph is $z = x^2 + 9y^2$. The traces in $x = k$ are

$z = 9y^2 + k$, a family of parabolas opening upward. In $y = k$, we have

$z = x^2 + 9k^2$, again a family of parabolas opening upward. The traces in

$z = k$ are $x^2 + 9y^2 = k$, a family of ellipses. The surface is an elliptic

paraboloid.

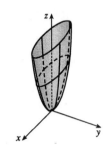

18. The equation of the graph is $z = x^2 - y^2$. The traces in $x = k$ are

$z = -y^2 + k^2$, a family of parabolas opening downward. In $y = k$, we

have $z = x^2 - k^2$, a family of parabolas opening upward. The traces in

$z = k$ are $x^2 - y^2 = k$, a family of hyperbolas. The surface is a

hyperbolic paraboloid with saddle point $(0, 0, 0)$.

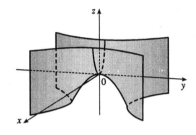

19. $y = z^2 - x^2$. The traces in $x = k$ are the parabolas $y = z^2 - k^2$; the traces in

$y = k$ are $k = z^2 - x^2$, which are hyperbolas (note the hyperbolas are

oriented differently for $k > 0$ than for $k < 0$); and the traces in $z = k$ are the

parabolas $y = k^2 - x^2$. Thus, $\dfrac{y}{1} = \dfrac{z^2}{1^2} - \dfrac{x^2}{1^2}$ is a hyperbolic paraboloid.

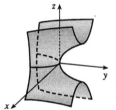

20. For $y = x^2 + z^2$, the traces in $x = k$ are $y = z^2 + k^2$, a family of parabolas

opening in the positive y-direction. The traces in $y = k$ are $x^2 + z^2 = k$,

$k \geq 0$, a family of circles. The traces in $z = k$ are $y = x^2 + k^2$, a family of

parabolas opening in the positive y-direction. We recognize the graph as a

circular paraboloid with axis the y-axis.

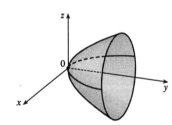

21. Factoring the equation gives $x = 4y^2 + (z - 2)^2$. This corresponds to an elliptic paraboloid with axis parallel to the

x-axis and vertex $(0, 0, 2)$ that opens in the positive x-direction.

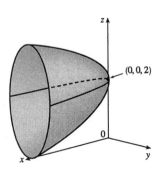

$(0, 0, 2)$

22. Completing the square in x gives $(x - 1)^2 + 4y^2 + z^2 = 1$ or

$(x - 1)^2 + \dfrac{y^2}{(1/2)^2} + z^2 = 1$, an ellipsoid with center $(1, 0, 0)$ and

intercepts $(0, 0, 0)$, $(2, 0, 0)$.

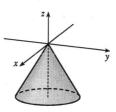

23. (a) In $\mathbb{R}^2$, $x^2 + y^2 = 1$ represents a circle of radius 1 centered at the origin.

(b) In $\mathbb{R}^3$, the equation doesn't involve z, which means that any horizontal plane $z = k$ intersects the surface in a circle $x^2 + y^2 = 1$, $z = k$. Thus the surface is a circular cylinder, made up of infinitely many shifted copies of the circle $x^2 + y^2 = 1$, with axis the z-axis.

(c) In $\mathbb{R}^3$, $x^2 + z^2 = 1$ also represents a circular cylinder of radius 1, this time with axis the y-axis.

24. (a) The traces of $z^2 = x^2 + y^2$ in $x = k$ are $z^2 = y^2 + k^2$, a family of hyperbolas, as are traces in $y = k$, $z^2 = x^2 + k^2$. Traces in $z = k$ are $x^2 + y^2 = k^2$, a family of circles.

(b) The surface is a circular cone with axis the z-axis.

(c) The graph of $f(x, y) = \sqrt{x^2 + y^2}$ is the upper half of the cone in part (b), and the graph of $g(x, y) = -\sqrt{x^2 + y^2}$ is the lower half.

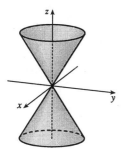

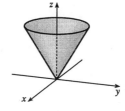

25. (a) The traces of $x^2 + y^2 - z^2 = 1$ in $x = k$ are $y^2 - z^2 = 1 - k^2$, a family of hyperbolas. (Note that the hyperbolas are oriented differently for $-1 < k < 1$ than for $k < -1$ or $k > 1$.) The traces in $y = k$ are $x^2 - z^2 = 1 - k^2$, a similar family of hyperbolas. The traces in $z = k$ are $x^2 + y^2 = 1 + k^2$, a family of circles. For $k = 0$, the trace in the xy-plane, the circle is of radius 1. As $|k|$ increases, so does the radius of the circle. This behavior, combined with the hyperbolic vertical traces, gives the graph of the hyperboloid of one sheet in Table 2.

(b) The shape of the surface is unchanged, but the hyperboloid is rotated so that its axis is the y-axis. Traces in $y = k$ are circles, while traces in $x = k$ and $z = k$ are hyperbolas.

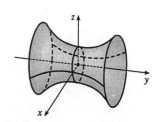

(c) Completing the square in y gives $x^2 + (y+1)^2 - z^2 = 1$. The surface is a hyperboloid identical to the one in part (a) but shifted one unit in the negative y-direction.

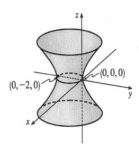

26. (a) The traces of $-x^2 - y^2 + z^2 = 1$ in $x = k$ are $-y^2 + z^2 = 1 + k^2$, a family of hyperbolas, as are the traces in $y = k$, $-x^2 + z^2 = 1 + k^2$. The traces in $z = k$ are $x^2 + y^2 = k^2 - 1$, a family of circles for $|k| > 1$. As $|k|$ increases, the radii of the circles increase; the traces are empty for $|k| < 1$. This behavior, combined with the vertical traces, gives the graph of the hyperboloid of two sheets in Table 2.

(b) The graph has the same shape as the hyperboloid in part (a) but is rotated so that its axis is the x-axis. Traces in $x = k$, $|k| > 1$, are circles, while traces in $y = k$ and $z = k$ are hyperbolas.

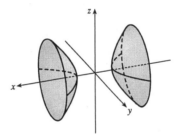

27. $f(x, y) = 3x - x^4 - 4y^2 - 10xy$

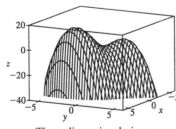

Three-dimensional view

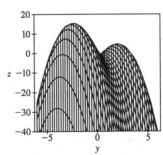

Front view

It does appear that the function has a maximum value, at the higher of the two "hilltops." From the front view graph, the maximum value appears to be approximately 15. Both hilltops could be considered local maximum points, as the values of f there are larger than at the neighboring points. There does not appear to be any local minimum point; although the valley shape between the two peaks looks like a minimum of some kind, some neighboring points have lower function values.

28. $f(x, y) = xye^{-x^2-y^2}$

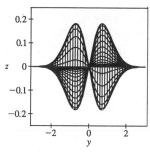

Three-dimensional view   Front view

The function does have a maximum value, which it appears to achieve at two different points (the two "hilltops.") From the front view graph, we can estimate the maximum value to be approximately 0.18. These same two points can also be considered local maximum points. The two "valley bottoms" visible in the graph can be considered local minimum points, as all the neighboring points give greater values of f.

29.

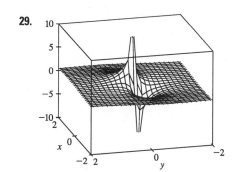

$f(x, y) = \dfrac{x + y}{x^2 + y^2}$. As both x and y become large, the function values appear to approach 0, regardless of which direction is considered. As (x, y) approaches the origin, the graph exhibits asymptotic behavior. From some directions, $f(x, y) \to \infty$, while in others $f(x, y) \to -\infty$. (These are the vertical spikes visible in the graph.) If the graph is examined carefully, however, one can see that $f(x, y)$ approaches 0 along the line $y = -x$.

30.

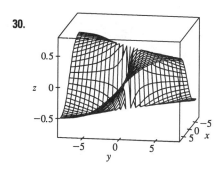

$f(x, y) = \dfrac{xy}{x^2 + y^2}$. The graph exhibits different limiting values as x and y become large or as (x, y) approaches the origin, depending on the direction being examined. For example, although f is undefined at the origin, the function values appear to be $\frac{1}{2}$ along the line $y = x$, regardless of the distance from the origin. Along the line $y = -x$, the value is always $-\frac{1}{2}$. Along the axes, $f(x, y) = 0$ for all values of (x, y) except the origin. Other directions, heading toward the origin or away from the origin, give various limiting values between $-\frac{1}{2}$ and $\frac{1}{2}$.

31.

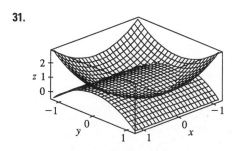

The curve of intersection looks like a bent ellipse. The projection of this curve onto the xy-plane is the set of points $(x, y, 0)$ which satisfy $x^2 + y^2 = 1 - y^2$ $\Leftrightarrow$ $x^2 + 2y^2 = 1$ $\Leftrightarrow$ $x^2 + \dfrac{y^2}{\left(1/\sqrt{2}\right)^2} = 1$. This is an equation of an ellipse.

32. Any point on the curve of intersection must satisfy both $2x^2 + 4y^2 - 2z^2 + 6x = 2$ and
$2x^2 + 4y^2 - 2z^2 - 5y = 0$. Subtracting, we get $6x + 5y = 2$, which is linear and therefore the equation of a plane.
Thus the curve of intersection lies in this plane.

33. If (a, b, c) satisfies $z = y^2 - x^2$, then $c = b^2 - a^2$. $L_1: x = a + t$, $y = b + t$, $z = c + 2(b - a)t$, $L_2: x = a + t$,
$y = b - t$, $z = c - 2(b + a)t$. Substitute the parametric equations of L_1 into the equation of the
hyperbolic paraboloid in order to find the points of intersection: $z = y^2 - x^2 \Rightarrow$
$c + 2(b - a)t = (b + t)^2 - (a + t)^2 = b^2 - a^2 + 2(b - a)t \Rightarrow c = b^2 - a^2$. As this is true for all values of t,
L_1 lies on $z = y^2 - x^2$. Performing similar operations with L_2 gives: $z = y^2 - x^2 \Rightarrow$
$c - 2(b + a)t = (b - t)^2 - (a + t)^2 = b^2 - a^2 - 2(b + a)t \Rightarrow c = b^2 - a^2$. This tells us that all of L_2 also lies
on $z = y^2 - x^2$.

34. Let $P = (x, y, z)$ be an arbitrary point whose distance from the x-axis is twice its distance from the yz-plane. The
distance from P to the x-axis is $\sqrt{(x - x)^2 + y^2 + z^2} = \sqrt{y^2 + z^2}$ and the distance from P to the yz-plance
$(x = 0)$ is $|x|/1 = |x|$. Thus $\sqrt{y^2 + z^2} = 2|x| \Leftrightarrow y^2 + z^2 = 4x^2 \Leftrightarrow x^2 = (y^2/2^2) + (z^2/2^2)$. So the
surface is a right circular cone with vertex the origin and axis the x-axis.

9.7 Cylindrical and Spherical Coordinates · · · · · · · ·

1. See Figure 1 and the accompanying discussion on page 694; see the paragraph preceding Figure 3 on page 695.

2. See Figure 5 and the accompanying discussion on page 696.

3. (a)

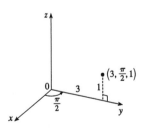

$x = 3\cos\frac{\pi}{2} = 0$, $y = 3\sin\frac{\pi}{2} = 3$, and $z = 1$,
so the point is $(0, 3, 1)$ in rectangular
coordinates.

(b)

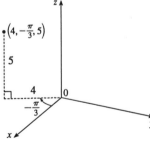

$x = 4\cos\left(-\frac{\pi}{3}\right) = 2$,
$y = 4\sin\left(-\frac{\pi}{3}\right) = -2\sqrt{3}$, and $z = 5$, so the
point is $\left(2, -2\sqrt{3}, 5\right)$ in rectangular
coordinates.

4. (a)

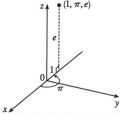

$x = 1\cos\pi = -1$, $y = 1\sin\pi = 0$, and $z = e$, so the point is $(-1, 0, e)$ in rectangular coordinates.

(b)

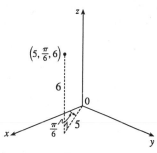

$x = 5\cos\left(\frac{\pi}{6}\right) = \frac{5\sqrt{3}}{2}$, $y = 5\sin\left(\frac{\pi}{6}\right) = \frac{5}{2}$, and $z = 6$, so the point is $\left(\frac{5\sqrt{3}}{2}, \frac{5}{2}, 6\right)$ in rectangular coordinates.

5. (a) $r^2 = x^2 + y^2 = 1^2 + (-1)^2 = 2$ so $r = \sqrt{2}$; $\tan\theta = \frac{y}{x} = \frac{-1}{1} = -1$ and the point $(1, -1)$ is in the fourth quadrant of the xy-plane, so $\theta = \frac{7\pi}{4} + 2n\pi$; $z = 4$. Thus, one set of cylindrical coordinates is $\left(\sqrt{2}, \frac{7\pi}{4}, 4\right)$.

(b) $r^2 = (-1)^2 + \left(-\sqrt{3}\right)^2 = 4$ so $r = 2$; $\tan\theta = \frac{-\sqrt{3}}{-1} = \sqrt{3}$ and the point $\left(-1, -\sqrt{3}\right)$ is in the third quadrant of the xy-plane, so $\theta = \frac{4\pi}{3} + 2n\pi$; $z = 2$. Thus, one set of cylindrical coordinates is $\left(2, \frac{4\pi}{3}, 2\right)$.

6. (a) $r^2 = x^2 + y^2 = 3^2 + 3^2 = 18$ so $r = \sqrt{18} = 3\sqrt{2}$; $\tan\theta = \frac{y}{x} = \frac{3}{3} = 1$ and the point $(3, 3)$ is in the first quadrant of the xy-plane, so $\theta = \frac{\pi}{4} + 2n\pi$; $z = -2$. Thus, one set of cylindrical coordinates is $\left(3\sqrt{2}, \frac{\pi}{4}, -2\right)$.

(b) $r^2 = 3^2 + 4^2 = 25$ so $r = 5$; $\tan\theta = \frac{4}{3}$ and the point $(3, 4)$ is in the first quadrant of the xy-plane, so $\theta = \tan^{-1}\frac{4}{3} + 2n\pi \approx 0.93 + 2n\pi$; $z = 5$. Thus, one set of cylindrical coordinates is $\left(5, \tan^{-1}\frac{4}{3}, 5\right) \approx (5, 0.93, 5)$.

7. (a)

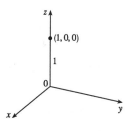

$x = \rho\sin\phi\cos\theta = (1)\sin 0\cos 0 = 0$,
$y = \rho\sin\phi\sin\theta = (1)\sin 0\sin 0 = 0$, and
$z = \rho\cos\phi = (1)\cos 0 = 1$ so the point is
$(0, 0, 1)$ in rectangular coordinates.

(b)

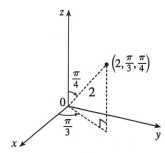

$x = 2\sin\frac{\pi}{4}\cos\frac{\pi}{3} = \frac{\sqrt{2}}{2}$,
$y = 2\sin\frac{\pi}{4}\sin\frac{\pi}{3} = \frac{\sqrt{6}}{2}$, $z = 2\cos\frac{\pi}{4} = \sqrt{2}$
so the point is $\left(\frac{\sqrt{2}}{2}, \frac{\sqrt{6}}{2}, \sqrt{2}\right)$ in rectangular coordinates.

8. (a)

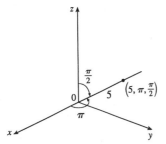

(b)

$x = 5 \sin \frac{\pi}{2} \cos \pi = -5$, $y = 5 \sin \frac{\pi}{2} \sin \pi = 0$,

$z = 5 \cos \frac{\pi}{2} = 0$ so the point is $(-5, 0, 0)$ in

rectangular coordinates.

$x = 2 \sin \frac{\pi}{3} \cos \frac{\pi}{4} = \frac{\sqrt{6}}{2}$,

$y = 2 \sin \frac{\pi}{3} \sin \frac{\pi}{4} = \frac{\sqrt{6}}{2}$, $z = 2 \cos \frac{\pi}{3} = 1$ so

the point is $\left(\frac{\sqrt{6}}{2}, \frac{\sqrt{6}}{2}, 1 \right)$ in rectangular

coordinates.

9. (a) $\rho = \sqrt{x^2 + y^2 + z^2} = \sqrt{9 + 0 + 0} = 3$, $\cos \phi = \frac{z}{\rho} = \frac{0}{3} = 0$ so $\phi = \frac{\pi}{2}$, and

$\cos \theta = \frac{x}{\rho \sin \phi} = \frac{-3}{3 \sin \frac{\pi}{2}} = -1$ so $\theta = \pi$. Thus spherical coordinates are $\left(3, \pi, \frac{\pi}{2} \right)$.

(b) $\rho = \sqrt{0 + 4 + 4} = 2\sqrt{2}$, $\cos \phi = \frac{z}{\rho} = \frac{-2}{2\sqrt{2}} = -\frac{\sqrt{2}}{2}$ so $\phi = \frac{3\pi}{4}$, and $\cos \theta = \frac{x}{\rho \sin \phi} = 0$ so $\theta = \frac{\pi}{2}$ (since

$y > 0$). Thus spherical coordinates are $\left(2\sqrt{2}, \frac{\pi}{2}, \frac{3\pi}{4} \right)$.

10. (a) $\rho = \sqrt{1 + 3 + 4} = 2\sqrt{2}$, $\cos \phi = \frac{z}{\rho} = \frac{2}{2\sqrt{2}} = \frac{\sqrt{2}}{2}$ so $\phi = \frac{\pi}{4}$, and $\cos \theta = \frac{x}{\rho \sin \phi} = \frac{1}{2\sqrt{2} \sin \frac{\pi}{4}} = \frac{1}{2}$ so

$\theta = \frac{\pi}{3}$ (since $y > 0$). Thus spherical coordinates are $\left(2\sqrt{2}, \frac{\pi}{3}, \frac{\pi}{4} \right)$.

(b) $\rho = \sqrt{0 + 0 + 9} = 3$ and $\cos \phi = \frac{-3}{3} = -1$ so $\phi = \pi$. Because the point is on the z-axis, θ can be any angle.

Thus one set of spherical coordinates is $(3, 0, \pi)$.

11. Since $r = 3$, $x^2 + y^2 = 9$ and the surface is a circular cylinder with radius 3 and axis the z-axis.

12. Since $\rho = 3$, $x^2 + y^2 + z^2 = 9$ and the surface is a sphere with center the origin and radius 3.

13. Since $\phi = \frac{\pi}{3}$, the surface is the top half of the right circular cone with vertex at the origin and axis the positive

z-axis.

14. Whether spherical or cylindrical coordinates, since $\theta = \frac{\pi}{3}$ the surface is a half-plane including the z-axis and

intersecting the xy-plane in the half-line $y = \sqrt{3}x$, $x > 0$.

15. $z = r^2 = x^2 + y^2$, so the surface is a circular paraboloid with vertex at the origin and axis the positive z-axis.

16. Since $\rho \sin \phi = 2$ and $x = \rho \sin \phi \cos \theta$, $x = 2 \cos \theta$. Also $y = \rho \sin \phi \sin \theta$ so $y = 2 \sin \theta$. Then

$x^2 + y^2 = 4 \cos^2 \theta + 4 \sin^2 \theta = 4$, a circular cylinder of radius 2 about the z-axis.

17. $r = 2 \cos \theta$ $\Rightarrow$ $r^2 = x^2 + y^2 = 2r \cos \theta = 2x$ $\Leftrightarrow$ $(x - 1)^2 + y^2 = 1$, which is the equation of a circular

cylinder with radius 1, whose axis is the vertical line $x = 1$, $y = 0$, $z = z$.

18. $\rho = 2 \cos \phi$ $\Rightarrow$ $\rho^2 = 2\rho \cos \phi = 2z$ $\Leftrightarrow$ $x^2 + y^2 + z^2 = 2z$ $\Leftrightarrow$ $x^2 + y^2 + (z - 1)^2 = 1$. Therefore, the

surface is a sphere of radius 1 centered at $(0, 0, 1)$.

19. Since $r^2 + z^2 = 25$ and $r^2 = x^2 + y^2$, we have $x^2 + y^2 + z^2 = 25$, a sphere with radius 5 and center at the origin.

20. Since $r^2 - 2z^2 = 4$ and $r^2 = x^2 + y^2$, we have $x^2 + y^2 - 2z^2 = 4$ or $\frac{1}{4}x^2 + \frac{1}{4}y^2 - \frac{1}{2}z^2 = 1$, a hyperboloid of one sheet with axis the z-axis.

21. (a) $r^2 = x^2 + y^2$, so $r^2 + z^2 = 16$.

   (b) $\rho^2 = x^2 + y^2 + z^2$, so $\rho^2 = 16$ or $\rho = 4$.

22. (a) $r^2 - z^2 = 16$

   (b) $x^2 + y^2 - z^2 = x^2 + y^2 + z^2 - 2z^2$, so $\rho^2 - 2\rho^2 \cos^2 \phi = 16$ or $\rho^2 (1 - 2\cos^2 \phi) = 16$.

23. (a) $r^2 = 2r \sin \theta$ or $r = 2 \sin \theta$.

   (b) $\rho^2 \sin^2 \phi (\cos^2 \theta + \sin^2 \theta) = 2\rho \sin \phi \sin \theta$ or $\rho \sin^2 \phi = 2 \sin \phi \sin \theta$ or $\rho \sin \phi = 2 \sin \theta$.

24. (a) $z = r^2 (\cos^2 \theta - \sin^2 \theta)$ or $z = r^2 \cos 2\theta$.

   (b) $\rho \cos \phi = \rho^2 \sin^2 \phi (\cos^2 \theta - \sin^2 \theta)$ or $\cos \phi = \rho \sin^2 \phi \cos 2\theta$.

25.

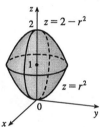

$z = r^2 = x^2 + y^2$ is a circular paraboloid with vertex $(0, 0, 0)$, opening upward. $z = 2 - r^2$ $\Rightarrow$ $z - 2 = -(x^2 + y^2)$ is a circular paraboloid with vertex $(0, 0, 2)$ opening downward. Thus $r^2 \le z \le 2 - r^2$ is the solid region enclosed by these two surfaces.

26.

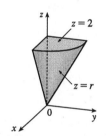

$z = r = \sqrt{x^2 + y^2}$ is a cone that opens upward. Thus $r \le z \le 2$ is the region above this cone and beneath the horizontal plane $z = 2$. $0 \le \theta \le \frac{\pi}{2}$ restricts the solid to that part of this region in the first octant.

27.

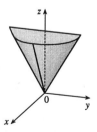

$-\frac{\pi}{2} \le \theta \le \frac{\pi}{2}$ restricts the solid to the 4 octants in which x is positive. $\rho = \sec \phi$ $\Rightarrow$ $\rho \cos \phi = z = 1$, which is the equation of a horizontal plane. $0 \le \phi \le \frac{\pi}{6}$ describes a cone, opening upward. So the solid lies above the cone $\phi = \frac{\pi}{6}$ and below the plane $z = 1$.

28.

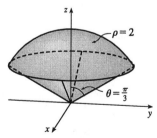

$\rho = 2$ $\Leftrightarrow$ $x^2 + y^2 + z^2 = 4$, which is a sphere of radius 2, centered at the origin. Hence $\rho \le 2$ is this sphere and its interior. $0 \le \phi \le \frac{\pi}{3}$ restricts the solid to that section of this ball that lies above the cone $\phi = \frac{\pi}{3}$.

29. We can position the cylindrical shell vertically so that its axis coincides with the z-axis and its base lies in the xy-plane. If we use centimeters as the unit of measurement, then cylindrical coordinates conveniently describe the shell as $6 \le r \le 7, 0 \le \theta \le 2\pi, 0 \le z \le 20$.

30. (a) The hollow ball is a spherical shell with outer radius 15 cm and inner radius 14.5 cm. If we center the ball at the origin of the coordinate system and use centimeters as the unit of measurement, then spherical coordinates conveniently describe the hollow ball as $14.5 \le \rho \le 15, 0 \le \theta \le 2\pi, 0 \le \phi \le \pi$.

(b) If we position the ball as in part (a), one possibility is to take the half of the ball that is above the xy-plane which is described by $14.5 \le \rho \le 15, 0 \le \theta \le 2\pi, 0 \le \phi \le \pi/2$.

31. $z \ge \sqrt{x^2 + y^2}$ because the solid lies above the cone. Squaring both sides of this inequality gives $z^2 \ge x^2 + y^2$ $\Rightarrow$ $2z^2 \ge x^2 + y^2 + z^2 = \rho^2$ $\Rightarrow$ $z^2 = \rho^2 \cos^2 \phi \ge \frac{1}{2}\rho^2$ $\Rightarrow$ $\cos^2 \phi \ge \frac{1}{2}$. The cone opens upward so that the inequality is $\cos \phi \ge \frac{1}{\sqrt{2}}$, or equivalently $0 \le \phi \le \frac{\pi}{4}$. In spherical coordinates the sphere $z = x^2 + y^2 + z^2$ is $\rho \cos \phi = \rho^2$ $\Rightarrow$ $\rho = \cos \phi$. $0 \le \rho \le \cos \phi$ because the solid lies below the sphere. The solid can therefore be described as the region in spherical coordinates satisfying $0 \le \rho \le \cos \phi, 0 \le \phi \le \frac{\pi}{4}$.

32. In cylindrical coordinates, the equations are $z = r^2$ and $z = 5 - r^2$.

The curve of intersection is $r^2 = 5 - r^2$ or $r = \sqrt{5/2}$. So we graph the surfaces in cylindrical coordinates, with $0 \le r \le \sqrt{5/2}$. In Maple, we can use either the `coords=cylindrical` option in a regular `plot` command, or the `plots[cylinderplot]` command. In Mathematica, we can use `ParametricPlot3d`.

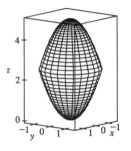

33. In cylindrical coordinates, the equation of the cylinder is $r = 3$, $0 \le z \le 10$. The hemisphere is the upper part of the sphere radius 3, center $(0, 0, 10)$, equation $r^2 + (z - 10)^2 = 3^2, z \ge 10$. In Maple, we can use either the `coords=cylindrical` option in a regular `plot` command, or the `plots[cylinderplot]` command. In Mathematica, we can use `ParametricPlot3d`.

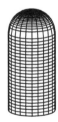

34. We begin by finding the positions of Los Angeles and Montréal in spherical coordinates, using the method described in the exercise:

Montréal	Los Angeles
$\rho = 3960$ mi	$\rho = 3960$ mi
$\theta = 360° - 73.60° = 286.40°$	$\theta = 360° - 118.25° = 241.75°$
$\phi = 90° - 45.50° = 44.50°$	$\phi = 90° - 34.06° = 55.94°$

Now we change the above to Cartesian coordinates using $x = \rho \cos \theta \sin \phi$, $y = \rho \sin \theta \sin \phi$ and $z = \rho \cos \phi$ to get two position vectors of length 3960 mi (since both cities must lie on the surface of the Earth). In particular:

Montréal: $\langle 783.67, -2662.67, 2824.47 \rangle$ Los Angeles: $\langle -1552.80, -2889.91, 2217.84 \rangle$

To find the angle α between these two vectors we use the dot product:

$\langle 783.67, -2662.67, 2824.47 \rangle \cdot \langle -1552.80, -2889.91, 2217.84 \rangle = (3960)^2 \cos \alpha \quad \Rightarrow \quad \cos \alpha \approx 0.8126 \quad \Rightarrow$
$\alpha \approx 0.6223$ rad. The great circle distance between the cities is $s = \rho\theta \approx 3960(0.6223) \approx 2464$ mi.

Laboratory Project | Families of Surfaces

---

1. $f(x, y) = (ax^2 + by^2)e^{-x^2 - y^2}$. There are only three basic shapes which can be obtained (the fourth and fifth graphs are the reflections of the first and second ones in the xy-plane). Interchanging a and b rotates the graph by $90°$ about the z-axis.

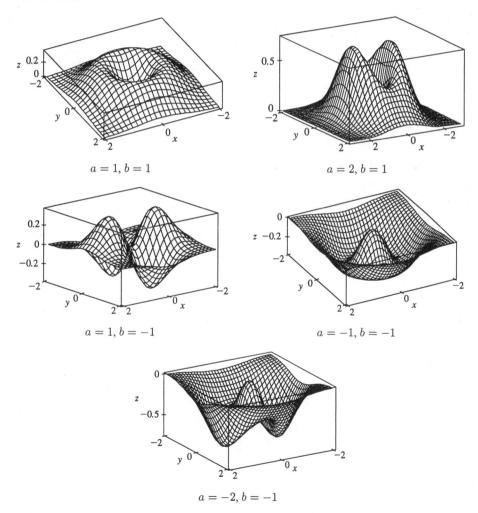

If a and b are both positive ($a \neq b$), we see that the graph has two maximum points whose height increases as a and b increase. If a and b have opposite signs, the graph has two maximum points and two minimum points, and if a and b are both negative, the graph has one maximum point and two minimum points.

2. $z = x^2 + y^2 + cxy$. When $c < -2$, the surface intersects the plane $z = k \neq 0$ in a hyperbola. (See graph below.) It intersects the plane $x = y$ in the parabola $z = (2 + c)x^2$, and the plane $x = -y$ in the parabola $z = (2 - c)x^2$. These parabolas open in opposite directions, so the surface is a hyperbolic paraboloid.

When $c = -2$ the surface is $z = x^2 + y^2 - 2xy = (x - y)^2$. So the surface is constant along each line $x - y = k$. That is, the surface is a cylinder with axis $x - y = 0$, $z = 0$. The shape of the cylinder is determined by its intersection with the plane $x + y = 0$, where $z = 4x^2$, and hence the cylinder is parabolic with minima of 0 on the line $y = x$.

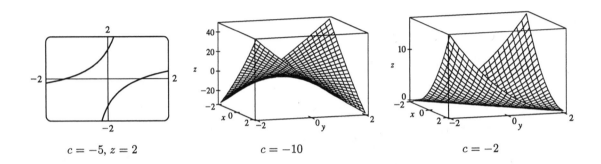

$c = -5,\ z = 2$ \qquad\qquad $c = -10$ \qquad\qquad $c = -2$

When $-2 < c \leq 0$, $z \geq 0$ for all x and y. If x and y have the same sign, then $x^2 + y^2 + cxy \geq x^2 + y^2 - 2xy = (x - y)^2 \geq 0$. If they have opposite signs, then $cxy \geq 0$. The intersection with the surface and the plane $z = k > 0$ is an ellipse (see graph below). The intersection with the surface and the planes $x = 0$ and $y = 0$ are parabolas $z = y^2$ and $z = x^2$ respectively, so the surface is an elliptic paraboloid.

When $c > 0$ the graphs have the same shape, but are reflected in the plane $x = 0$, because $x^2 + y^2 + cxy = (-x)^2 + y^2 + (-c)(-x)y$. That is, the value of z is the same for c at (x, y) as it is for $-c$ at $(-x, y)$.

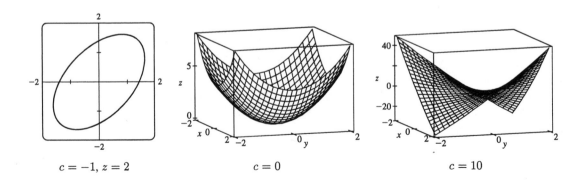

$c = -1,\ z = 2$ \qquad\qquad $c = 0$ \qquad\qquad $c = 10$

So the surface is an elliptic paraboloid for $0 < c < 2$, a parabolic cylinder for $c = 2$, and a hyperbolic paraboloid for $c > 2$.

3. $\rho = 1 + 0.2 \sin m\theta \sin n\phi$. If we start with $m = 1, n = 1$ the equation is $\rho = 1 + 0.2 \sin \theta \sin \phi$, whose graph appears spherical or nearly spherical in shape. First we investigate varying just m. Values of $m > 1$ produce vertical ridges in the sphere, the number of ridges corresponding to the value of m. We graph two examples.

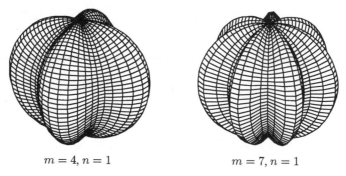

$$m = 4, n = 1 \qquad\qquad m = 7, n = 1$$

If we leave m fixed at 1 and vary n, we see horizontal ridges that span half the sphere arranged in a staggered fashion. Again, the number of "bumps" coincides with the value of n.

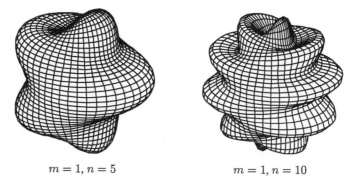

$$m = 1, n = 5 \qquad\qquad m = 1, n = 10$$

If we allow both m and n to vary, we get combinations of the vertical and horizontal bumps.

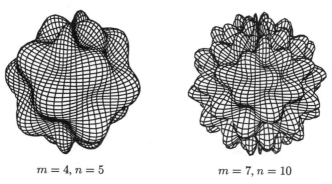

$$m = 4, n = 5 \qquad\qquad m = 7, n = 10$$

The graph on the left shows $m = 4$, $n = 5$. Looking at the top of the bumpy sphere, we can see the 4 vertical ridges which become perturbed horizontally as they progress down the sphere. We can also see the 5 horizontal rows of bumps. (Consequently, there are 20 bumps on the surface.) The graph on the right shows $m = 7, n = 10$ which should have 70 bumps.

Review

1. A scalar is a real number, while a vector is a quantity that has both a real-valued magnitude and a direction.

2. To add two vectors geometrically, we can use either the Triangle Law or the Parallelogram Law, as illustrated in Figures 3 and 4 in Section 9.2. (See also the definition of vector addition on page 653.) Algebraically, we add the corresponding components of the vectors.

3. For $c > 0$, $c\mathbf{a}$ is a vector with the same direction as $\mathbf{a}$ and length c times the length of $\mathbf{a}$. If $c < 0$, $c\mathbf{a}$ points in the opposite direction as $\mathbf{a}$ and has length $|c|$ times the length of $\mathbf{a}$. (See Figure 7 in Section 9.2.) Algebraically, to find $c\mathbf{a}$ we multiply each component of $\mathbf{a}$ by c.

4. See (1) in Section 9.2.

5. See the definition on page 661 and the boxed equation on page 663.

6. The dot product can be used to determine the work done moving an object given the force and displacement vectors. The dot product can also be used to find the angle between two vectors and the scalar projection of one vector onto another. In particular, the dot product can determine if two vectors are orthogonal.

7. See the boxed equations on page 665 as well as Figures 5 and 6 and the accompanying discussion on pages 664-665.

8. See the definition on page 668; use either (2) or (4) in Section 9.4 .

9. The cross product can be used to determine torque if the force and position vectors are known. In addition, the cross product can be used to create a vector orthogonal to two given vectors as well as to determine if two vectors are parallel. The cross product can also be used to find the area of a parallelogram determined by two vectors.

10. (a) The area of the parallelogram determined by $\mathbf{a}$ and $\mathbf{b}$ is the length of the cross product: $|\mathbf{a} \times \mathbf{b}|$.

(b) The volume of the parallelepiped determined by $\mathbf{a}$, $\mathbf{b}$, and $\mathbf{c}$ is the magnitude of their scalar triple product: $|\mathbf{a} \cdot (\mathbf{b} \times \mathbf{c})|$.

11. If an equation of the plane is known, it can be written as $ax + by + cz + d = 0$. A normal vector, which is perpendicular to the plane, is $\langle a, b, c \rangle$ (or any scalar multiple of $\langle a, b, c \rangle$). If an equation is not known, we can use points on the plane to find two non-parallel vectors which lie in the plane. The cross product of these vectors is a vector perpendicular to the plane.

12. The angle between two intersecting planes is defined as the acute angle between their normal vectors. We can find this angle using the definition of the dot product on page 661.

13. See (1), (2), and (3) in Section 9.5.

14. See (4), (5), and (6) in Section 9.5.

15. (a) Two (nonzero) vectors are parallel if and only if one is a scalar multiple of the other. In addition, two nonzero vectors are parallel if and only if their cross product is $\mathbf{0}$.

(b) Two vectors are perpendicular if and only if their dot product is 0.

(c) Two planes are parallel if and only if their normal vectors are parallel.

16. (a) Determine the vectors $\overrightarrow{PQ} = \langle a_1, a_2, a_3 \rangle$ and $\overrightarrow{PR} = \langle b_1, b_2, b_3 \rangle$. If there is a scalar t such that $\langle a_1, a_2, a_3 \rangle = t \langle b_1, b_2, b_3 \rangle$, then the vectors are parallel and the points must all lie on the same line.

Alternatively, if $\overrightarrow{PQ} \times \overrightarrow{PR} = \mathbf{0}$, then $\overrightarrow{PQ}$ and $\overrightarrow{PR}$ are parallel, so P, Q, and R are collinear.

Thirdly, an algebraic method is to determine an equation of the line joining two of the points, and then check whether or not the third point satisfies this equation.

(b) Find the vectors $\overrightarrow{PQ} = \mathbf{a}$, $\overrightarrow{PR} = \mathbf{b}$, $\overrightarrow{PS} = \mathbf{c}$. $\mathbf{a} \times \mathbf{b}$ is normal to the plane formed by P, Q and R, and so S lies on this plane if $\mathbf{a} \times \mathbf{b}$ and $\mathbf{c}$ are orthogonal, that is, if $(\mathbf{a} \times \mathbf{b}) \cdot \mathbf{c} = 0$. (Or use the reasoning in Example 6 in Section 9.4.)

Alternatively, find an equation for the plane determined by three of the points and check whether or not the fourth point satisfies this equation.

17. (a) See Exercise 9.4.27.

(b) See Example 8 in Section 9.5.

(c) See Example 10 in Section 9.5.

18. One method of graphing a function of two variables is to first find traces (see Example 6 in Section 9.6 and the discussion preceding it).

19. See Table 2 in Section 9.6.

20. (a) See (1) and the discussion accompanying Figure 3 in Section 9.7.

(b) See (3) and Figures 6–8, and the accompanying discussion, in Section 9.7.

─────────────── ▲ **TRUE–FALSE QUIZ** ▲ ───────────────

1. True, by Property 2 of the dot product. (See page 664).

2. False. Property 1 of the cross product says that $\mathbf{u} \times \mathbf{v} = -\mathbf{v} \times \mathbf{u}$. (See page 669).

3. True. If θ is the angle between $\mathbf{u}$ and $\mathbf{v}$, then by definition of the cross product,

$|\mathbf{u} \times \mathbf{v}| = |\mathbf{u}|\,|\mathbf{v}| \sin\theta = |\mathbf{v}|\,|\mathbf{u}| \sin\theta = |\mathbf{v} \times \mathbf{u}|.$

(Or, by Properties 1 and 2 of the cross product, $|\mathbf{u} \times \mathbf{v}| = |-\mathbf{v} \times \mathbf{u}| = |-1|\,|\mathbf{v} \times \mathbf{u}| = |\mathbf{v} \times \mathbf{u}|.$)

4. This is true by Property 4 of the dot product.

5. Property 2 of the cross product tells us that this is true.

6. This is true by Property 4 of the cross product.

7. This is true by (6) in Section 9.4.

8. In general, this assertion is false; a counterexample is $\mathbf{i} \times (\mathbf{i} \times \mathbf{j}) \neq (\mathbf{i} \times \mathbf{i}) \times \mathbf{j}$. (See the discussion following Example 2 on page 669.

9. This is true because $\mathbf{u} \times \mathbf{v}$ is orthogonal to $\mathbf{u}$ (see page 668), and the dot product of two orthogonal vectors is 0.

10. $(\mathbf{u} + \mathbf{v}) \times \mathbf{v} = \mathbf{u} \times \mathbf{v} + \mathbf{v} \times \mathbf{v}$ (by Property 4 of the cross product)

$\qquad = \mathbf{u} \times \mathbf{v} + \mathbf{0}$ (by the margin note on page 668)

$\qquad = \mathbf{u} \times \mathbf{v}$, so this is true.

11. If $|\mathbf{u}| = 1$, $|\mathbf{v}| = 1$ and θ is the angle between these two vectors (so $0 \leq \theta \leq \pi$), then by definition of the cross product, $|\mathbf{u} \times \mathbf{v}| = |\mathbf{u}|\,|\mathbf{v}| \sin\theta = \sin\theta$, which is equal to 1 if and only if $\theta = \frac{\pi}{2}$ (that is, if and only if the two vectors are orthogonal). Therefore, the assertion that the cross product of two unit vectors is a unit vector is false.

12. This is false, because according to (7) in Section 9.5, $ax + by + cz + d = 0$ is the general equation of a plane.

13. This is false. In $\mathbb{R}^2$, $x^2 + y^2 = 1$ represents a circle, but $\{(x, y, z) \mid x^2 + y^2 = 1\}$ represents a *three-dimensional surface*, namely, a circular cylinder with axis the z-axis.

14. This is false, as the dot product of two vectors is a scalar, not a vector.

◆ **EXERCISES** ◆

---

1. (a) The radius of the sphere is the distance between the points $(-1, 2, 1)$ and $(6, -2, 3)$, namely

$\sqrt{[6 - (-1)]^2 + (-2 - 2)^2 + (3 - 1)^2} = \sqrt{69}$. By the formula for an equation of a sphere (see page 650), an equation of the sphere with center $(-1, 2, 1)$ and radius $\sqrt{69}$ is $(x + 1)^2 + (y - 2)^2 + (z - 1)^2 = 69$.

(b) The intersection of this sphere with the yz-plane is the set of points on the sphere whose x-coordinate is 0. Putting $x = 0$ into the equation, we have $(y - 2)^2 + (z - 1)^2 = 68, x = 0$ which represents a circle in the yz-plane with center $(0, 2, 1)$ and radius $\sqrt{68}$.

(c) Completing squares gives $(x - 4)^2 + (y + 1)^2 + (z + 3)^2 = -1 + 16 + 1 + 9 = 25$. Thus, the sphere is centered at $(4, -1, -3)$ and has radius 5.

2. (a)

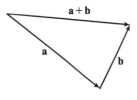

(b)

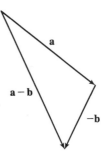

(c)

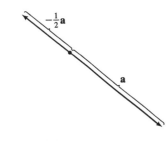

(d)

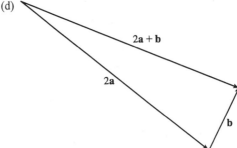

3. $\mathbf{u} \cdot \mathbf{v} = |\mathbf{u}| \, |\mathbf{v}| \cos 45° = (2)(3)\frac{\sqrt{2}}{2} = 3\sqrt{2}$. $|\mathbf{u} \times \mathbf{v}| = |\mathbf{u}| \, |\mathbf{v}| \sin 45° = (2)(3)\frac{\sqrt{2}}{2} = 3\sqrt{2}$. By the right-hand rule, $\mathbf{u} \times \mathbf{v}$ is directed out of the page.

4. (a) $2\mathbf{a} + 3\mathbf{b} = 2\mathbf{i} + 2\mathbf{j} - 4\mathbf{k} + 9\mathbf{i} - 6\mathbf{j} + 3\mathbf{k} = 11\mathbf{i} - 4\mathbf{j} - \mathbf{k}$

(b) $|\mathbf{b}| = \sqrt{9 + 4 + 1} = \sqrt{14}$

(c) $\mathbf{a} \cdot \mathbf{b} = (1)(3) + (1)(-2) + (-2)(1) = -1$

(d) $\mathbf{a} \times \mathbf{b} = \begin{vmatrix} \mathbf{i} & \mathbf{j} & \mathbf{k} \\ 1 & 1 & -2 \\ 3 & -2 & 1 \end{vmatrix} = (1 - 4)\mathbf{i} - (1 + 6)\mathbf{j} + (-2 - 3)\mathbf{k} = -3\mathbf{i} - 7\mathbf{j} - 5\mathbf{k}$

(e) $\mathbf{b} \times \mathbf{c} = \begin{vmatrix} \mathbf{i} & \mathbf{j} & \mathbf{k} \\ 3 & -2 & 1 \\ 0 & 1 & -5 \end{vmatrix} = 9\mathbf{i} + 15\mathbf{j} + 3\mathbf{k}, |\mathbf{b} \times \mathbf{c}| = 3\sqrt{9 + 25 + 1} = 3\sqrt{35}$

(f) $\mathbf{a} \cdot (\mathbf{b} \times \mathbf{c}) = \begin{vmatrix} 1 & 1 & -2 \\ 3 & -2 & 1 \\ 0 & 1 & -5 \end{vmatrix} = \begin{vmatrix} -2 & 1 \\ 1 & -5 \end{vmatrix} - \begin{vmatrix} 3 & 1 \\ 0 & -5 \end{vmatrix} - 2 \begin{vmatrix} 3 & -2 \\ 0 & 1 \end{vmatrix} = 9 + 15 - 6 = 18$

(g) $\mathbf{c} \times \mathbf{c} = \mathbf{0}$ for any $\mathbf{c}$.

(h) From part (e),

$$\mathbf{a} \times (\mathbf{b} \times \mathbf{c}) = \mathbf{a} \times (9\,\mathbf{i} + 15\,\mathbf{j} + 3\,\mathbf{k}) = \begin{vmatrix} \mathbf{i} & \mathbf{j} & \mathbf{k} \\ 1 & 1 & -2 \\ 9 & 15 & 3 \end{vmatrix} = (3 + 30)\,\mathbf{i} - (3 + 18)\,\mathbf{j} + (15 - 9)\,\mathbf{k}$$

$$= 33\,\mathbf{i} - 21\,\mathbf{j} + 6\,\mathbf{k}.$$

(i) The scalar projection is $\operatorname{comp}_{\mathbf{a}} \mathbf{b} = |\mathbf{b}| \cos\theta = \mathbf{a} \cdot \mathbf{b}/|\mathbf{a}| = -\frac{1}{\sqrt{6}}$.

(j) The vector projection is $\operatorname{proj}_{\mathbf{a}} \mathbf{b} = -\frac{1}{\sqrt{6}}(\mathbf{a}/|\mathbf{a}|) = -\frac{1}{6}(\mathbf{i} + \mathbf{j} - 2\,\mathbf{k})$.

(k) $\cos\theta = \dfrac{\mathbf{a} \cdot \mathbf{b}}{|\mathbf{a}|\,|\mathbf{b}|} = \dfrac{-1}{\sqrt{6}\,\sqrt{14}} = \dfrac{-1}{2\sqrt{21}}$ and $\theta = \cos^{-1}\dfrac{-1}{2\sqrt{21}} \approx 96\,°$.

5. For the two vectors to be orthogonal, we need $\langle 3, 2, x \rangle \cdot \langle 2x, 4, x \rangle = 0 \quad \Leftrightarrow$
$(3)(2x) + (2)(4) + (x)(x) = 0 \quad \Leftrightarrow \quad x^2 + 6x + 8 = 0 \quad \Leftrightarrow \quad (x + 2)(x + 4) = 0 \quad \Leftrightarrow \quad x = -2$ or $x = -4$.

6. We know that the cross product of two vectors is orthogonal to both. So we calculate
$(\mathbf{j} + 2\,\mathbf{k}) \times (\mathbf{i} - 2\,\mathbf{j} + 3\,\mathbf{k}) = [3 - (-4)]\,\mathbf{i} - (0 - 2)\,\mathbf{j} + (0 - 1)\,\mathbf{k} = 7\,\mathbf{i} + 2\,\mathbf{j} - \mathbf{k}$. Then two unit vectors
orthogonal to both given vectors are $\pm\dfrac{7\,\mathbf{i} + 2\,\mathbf{j} - \mathbf{k}}{\sqrt{7^2 + 2^2 + (-1)^2}} = \pm\dfrac{1}{3\sqrt{6}}(7\,\mathbf{i} + 2\,\mathbf{j} - \mathbf{k})$, that is,

$\frac{7}{3\sqrt{6}}\mathbf{i} + \frac{2}{3\sqrt{6}}\mathbf{j} - \frac{1}{3\sqrt{6}}\mathbf{k}$ and $-\frac{7}{3\sqrt{6}}\mathbf{i} - \frac{2}{3\sqrt{6}}\mathbf{j} + \frac{1}{3\sqrt{6}}\mathbf{k}$.

7. (a) $(\mathbf{u} \times \mathbf{v}) \cdot \mathbf{w} = \mathbf{u} \cdot (\mathbf{v} \times \mathbf{w}) = 2$

(b) $\mathbf{u} \cdot (\mathbf{w} \times \mathbf{v}) = \mathbf{u} \cdot [-(\mathbf{v} \times \mathbf{w})] = -\mathbf{u} \cdot (\mathbf{v} \times \mathbf{w}) = -2$

(c) $\mathbf{v} \cdot (\mathbf{u} \times \mathbf{w}) = (\mathbf{v} \times \mathbf{u}) \cdot \mathbf{w} = -(\mathbf{u} \times \mathbf{v}) \cdot \mathbf{w} = -2$

(d) $(\mathbf{u} \times \mathbf{v}) \cdot \mathbf{v} = \mathbf{u} \cdot (\mathbf{v} \times \mathbf{v}) = \mathbf{u} \cdot \mathbf{0} = 0$

8. $(\mathbf{a} \times \mathbf{b}) \cdot [(\mathbf{b} \times \mathbf{c}) \times (\mathbf{c} \times \mathbf{a})] = (\mathbf{a} \times \mathbf{b}) \cdot ([(\mathbf{b} \times \mathbf{c}) \cdot \mathbf{a}]\,\mathbf{c} - [(\mathbf{b} \times \mathbf{c}) \cdot \mathbf{c}]\,\mathbf{a})$

(see Exercise 9.4.30)

$= (\mathbf{a} \times \mathbf{b}) \cdot [(\mathbf{b} \times \mathbf{c}) \cdot \mathbf{a}]\,\mathbf{c} = [\mathbf{a} \cdot (\mathbf{b} \times \mathbf{c})]\,(\mathbf{a} \times \mathbf{b}) \cdot \mathbf{c}$

$= [\mathbf{a} \cdot (\mathbf{b} \times \mathbf{c})]\,[\mathbf{a} \cdot (\mathbf{b} \times \mathbf{c})] = [\mathbf{a} \cdot (\mathbf{b} \times \mathbf{c})]^2$

9. For simplicity, consider a unit cube positioned with its back left corner at the origin. Vector representations of the
diagonals joining the points $(0, 0, 0)$ to $(1, 1, 1)$ and $(1, 0, 0)$ to $(0, 1, 1)$ are $\langle 1, 1, 1 \rangle$ and $\langle -1, 1, 1 \rangle$. Let θ be the
angle between these two vectors. $\langle 1, 1, 1 \rangle \cdot \langle -1, 1, 1 \rangle = -1 + 1 + 1 = 1 = |\langle 1, 1, 1 \rangle|\,|\langle -1, 1, 1 \rangle| \cos\theta = 3 \cos\theta$
$\Rightarrow \quad \cos\theta = \frac{1}{3} \quad \Rightarrow \quad \theta = \cos^{-1}\left(\frac{1}{3}\right) \approx 71\,°$.

10. $\overrightarrow{AB} = \langle 1, 3, -1 \rangle$, $\overrightarrow{AC} = \langle -2, 1, 3 \rangle$ and $\overrightarrow{AD} = \langle -1, 3, 1 \rangle$. By Equation 9.4.7,

$$\overrightarrow{AB} \cdot \left(\overrightarrow{AC} \times \overrightarrow{AD} \right) = \begin{vmatrix} 1 & 3 & -1 \\ -2 & 1 & 3 \\ -1 & 3 & 1 \end{vmatrix} = \begin{vmatrix} 1 & 3 \\ 3 & 1 \end{vmatrix} - 3 \begin{vmatrix} -2 & 3 \\ -1 & 1 \end{vmatrix} - \begin{vmatrix} -2 & 1 \\ -1 & 3 \end{vmatrix} = -8 - 3 + 5 = -6.$$ The volume is

$\left| \overrightarrow{AB} \cdot \left(\overrightarrow{AC} \times \overrightarrow{AD} \right) \right| = 6$ cubic units.

11. $\overrightarrow{AB} = \langle 1, 0, -1 \rangle$, $\overrightarrow{AC} = \langle 0, 4, 3 \rangle$, so

(a) a vector perpendicular to the plane is $\overrightarrow{AB} \times \overrightarrow{AC} = \langle 0 + 4, -(3 + 0), 4 - 0 \rangle = \langle 4, -3, 4 \rangle$.

(b) $\frac{1}{2} \left| \overrightarrow{AB} \times \overrightarrow{AC} \right| = \frac{1}{2}\sqrt{16 + 9 + 16} = \frac{\sqrt{41}}{2}$.

12. $\mathbf{D} = 4\mathbf{i} + 3\mathbf{j} + 6\mathbf{k}$, $W = \mathbf{F} \cdot \mathbf{D} = 12 + 15 + 60 = 87$ joules

13. Let F_1 be the magnitude of the force directed $20°$ away from the direction of shore, and let F_2 be the magnitude of the other force. Separating these forces into components parallel to the direction of the resultant force and perpendicular to it gives $F_1 \cos 20° + F_2 \cos 30° = 255$ (1), and $F_1 \sin 20° - F_2 \sin 30° = 0$ $\Rightarrow$ $F_1 = F_2 \dfrac{\sin 30°}{\sin 20°}$ (2). Substituting (2) into (1) gives $F_2(\sin 30° \cot 20° + \cos 30°) = 255$ $\Rightarrow$ $F_2 \approx 114$ N. Substituting this into (2) gives $F_1 \approx 166$ N.

14. $|\tau| = |\mathbf{r}| \, |\mathbf{F}| \sin \theta = (0.40)(50) \sin(90° - 30°) \approx 17.3$ joules

15. $x = 1 + 2t$, $y = 2 - t$, $z = 4 + 3t$

16. $\mathbf{v} = \langle 8, -2, 5 \rangle$, so $x = -6 + 8t$, $y = -1 - 2t$ and $z = 5t$.

17. $\mathbf{v} = \langle 4, -3, 5 \rangle$, so $x = 1 + 4t$, $y = -3t$, $z = 1 + 5t$.

18. $2(x - 4) + 6(y + 1) - 3(z + 1) = 0$ or $2x + 6y - 3z = 5$.

19. Since the two planes are parallel, they will have the same normal vectors. So se can take $\mathbf{n} = \langle 1, 2, 5 \rangle$ and an equation of the plane is $1[x - (-4)] + 2(y - 1) + 5(z - 2) = 0$ or $x + 2y + 5z = 8$.

20. Here the vectors $\mathbf{a} = \langle 2 - (-1), 0 - 2, 1 - 0 \rangle = \langle 3, -2, 1 \rangle$ and $\mathbf{b} = \langle -5 - (-1), 3 - 2, 1 - 0 \rangle = \langle -4, 1, 1 \rangle$ lie in the plane, so $\mathbf{n} = \mathbf{a} \times \mathbf{b} = \langle -3, -7, -5 \rangle$ is a normal vector to the plane and an equation of the plane is $-3[x - (-1)] - 7(y - 2) - 5(z - 0) = 0$ or $3x + 7y + 5z = 11$.

21. $\mathbf{n}_1 = \langle 1, 0, -1 \rangle$ and $\mathbf{n}_2 = \langle 0, 1, 2 \rangle$. Setting $z = 0$, it is easy to see that $(1, 3, 0)$ is a point on the line of intersection of $x - z = 1$ and $y + 2z = 3$. The direction of this line is $\mathbf{v}_1 = \mathbf{n}_1 \times \mathbf{n}_2 = \langle 1, -2, 1 \rangle$. A second vector parallel to the desired plane is $\mathbf{v}_2 = \langle 1, 1, -2 \rangle$, since it is perpendicular to $x + y - 2z = 1$. Therefore, the normal of the plane in question is $\mathbf{n} = \mathbf{v}_1 \times \mathbf{v}_2 = \langle 4 - 1, 1 + 2, 1 + 2 \rangle = 3 \langle 1, 1, 1 \rangle$. Taking $(x_0, y_0, z_0) = (1, 3, 0)$, the equation we are looking for is $(x - 1) + (y - 3) + z = 0$ $\Leftrightarrow$ $x + y + z = 4$.

22. Substitution of the parametric equations into the equation of the plane gives $2x - y + z = 2(2 - t) - (1 + 3t) + 4t = 2$ $\Rightarrow$ $-t + 3 = 2$ $\Rightarrow$ $t = 1$. When $t = 1$, the parametric equations give $x = 2 - 1 = 1$, $y = 1 + 3 = 4$ and $z = 4$. Therefore, the point of intersection is $(1, 4, 4)$.

23. Since the direction vectors $\langle 2, 3, 4 \rangle$ and $\langle 6, -1, 2 \rangle$ aren't parallel, neither are the lines. For the lines to intersect, the three equations $1 + 2t = -1 + 6s$, $2 + 3t = 3 - s$, $3 + 4t = -5 + 2s$ must be satisfied simultaneously. Solving the first two equations gives $t = \frac{1}{5}$, $s = \frac{2}{5}$ and checking we see these values don't satisfy the third equation. Thus the lines aren't parallel and they don't intersect, so they must be skew.

24. (a) The normal vectors are $\langle 1, 1, -1 \rangle$ and $\langle 2, -3, 4 \rangle$. Since these vectors aren't parallel, neither are the planes parallel. Also $\langle 1, 1, -1 \rangle \cdot \langle 2, -3, 4 \rangle = 2 - 3 - 4 = -5 \neq 0$ so the normal vectors, and thus the planes, are not perpendicular.

(b) $\cos\theta = \dfrac{\langle 1,1,-1\rangle \cdot \langle 2,-3,4\rangle}{\sqrt{3}\sqrt{29}} = -\dfrac{5}{\sqrt{87}}$ and $\theta = \cos^{-1}\left(-\dfrac{5}{\sqrt{87}}\right) \approx 122°$ (or we can say $\approx 58°$).

25. By Exercise 9.5.49, $D = \dfrac{|2-24|}{\sqrt{26}} = \dfrac{22}{\sqrt{26}}$.

26. Use the formula proven in Exercise 9.4.27. In the notation used in that exercise, **a** is just the direction of the line; that is, $\mathbf{a} = \langle 1,-1,2\rangle$. A point on the line is $(1,2,-1)$ (setting $t=0$), and therefore $\mathbf{b} = \langle 1-0, 2-0, -1-0\rangle = \langle 1,2,-1\rangle$. Hence

$$d = \frac{|\mathbf{a}\times\mathbf{b}|}{|\mathbf{a}|} = \frac{|\langle 1,-1,2\rangle \times \langle 1,2,-1\rangle|}{\sqrt{1+1+4}} = \frac{|\langle -3,3,3\rangle|}{\sqrt{6}} = \sqrt{\frac{27}{6}} = \frac{3}{\sqrt{2}}.$$

27. $\ln\left(x-y^2\right)$ is defined only when $x-y^2 > 0$, or $x > y^2$, and x is defined for all real numbers, so the domain of the product $x\ln\left(x-y^2\right)$ is $\left\{(x,y) \mid x > y^2\right\}$.

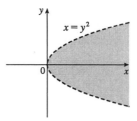

28. We need $\sin\pi\left(x^2+y^2\right) \ge 0 \;\Leftrightarrow\; 2n\pi \le \pi\left(x^2+y^2\right) \le (2n+1)\pi$, n an integer, so $D = \left\{(x,y) \mid 2n \le x^2+y^2 \le 2n+1, n \text{ an integer}\right\}$.

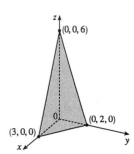

29. The graph is the plane $z = 6 - 2x - 3y \;\Rightarrow\; 2x + 3y + z = 6$. The intercepts with the coordinate axes are $(3,0,0)$, $(0,2,0)$, and $(0,0,6)$ which enable us to sketch the portion of the plane that lies in the first octant.

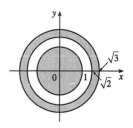

30. The equation is $z = \cos x$, which doesn't involve y. Thus the traces in $y = k$ are the graph $z = \cos x$, $y = k$, giving a cylindrical surface.

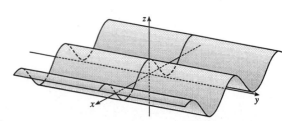

31. The equation is $z = 4 - x^2 - 4y^2$. The traces in $x = k$ are $z = 4 - k^2 - 4y^2$, a family of parabolas opening downward, as are the traces in $y = k$, $z = 4 - 4k^2 - x^2$. The traces in $z = k$ are $x^2 + 4y^2 = 4 - k$, a family of ellipses, so the surface is an elliptic paraboloid.

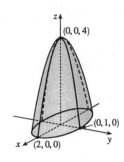

32. The equation is $z = \sqrt{4 - x^2 - 4y^2}$ or $x^2 + 4y^2 + z^2 = 4$, $z \geq 0$. The traces in $x = k$, $y = k$, and $z = k$ are ellipses or portions of ellipses, and the equation can be recognized as that of an ellipsoid $\dfrac{x^2}{4} + y^2 + \dfrac{z^2}{4} = 1$, $z \geq 0$, with intercepts ± 2, ± 1, and 2 for x, y, and z respectively. Since $z \geq 0$, we have only the upper half of the ellipsoid.

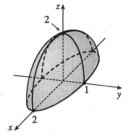

33. An equivalent equation is $\dfrac{x^2}{(1/2)^2} + y^2 + z^2 = 1$, an ellipsoid centered at the origin with intercepts $\pm\frac{1}{2}$, ± 1, and ± 1.

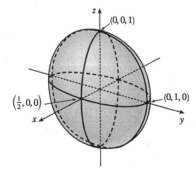

34. $x = y^2 + z^2$ is the equation of a circular paraboloid opening in the direction of the positive x-axis.

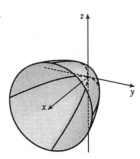

35. $y^2 + z^2 = 1$ is the equation of a circular cylinder with axis the x-axis.

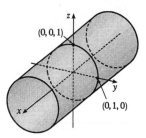

36. An equivalent equation is $-x^2 + y^2 + z^2 = 1$, a hyperboloid of one sheet with axis the x-axis.

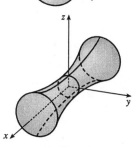

37. $x = 2\cos\frac{\pi}{6} = \sqrt{3}$, $y = 2\sin\frac{\pi}{6} = 1$, $z = 2$, so in rectangular coordinates the point is $\left(\sqrt{3}, 1, 2\right)$. $\rho = \sqrt{3 + 1 + 4} = 2\sqrt{2}$, $\theta = \frac{\pi}{6}$, and $\cos\phi = z/\rho = \frac{1}{\sqrt{2}}$, so $\phi = \frac{\pi}{4}$ and the spherical coordinates are $\left(2\sqrt{2}, \frac{\pi}{6}, \frac{\pi}{4}\right)$.

38. $r = \sqrt{4 + 4} = 2\sqrt{2}$, $z = -1$, $\cos\theta = \frac{2}{2\sqrt{2}} = \frac{\sqrt{2}}{2}$ so $\theta = \frac{\pi}{4}$ and in cylindrical coordinates the point is $\left(2\sqrt{2}, \frac{\pi}{4}, -1\right)$. $\rho = \sqrt{4 + 4 + 1} = 3$, $\cos\phi = -\frac{1}{3}$, so the spherical coordinates are $\left(3, \frac{\pi}{4}, \cos^{-1}\left(-\frac{1}{3}\right)\right)$.

39. $x = 4\sin\frac{\pi}{6}\cos\frac{\pi}{3} = 1$, $y = 4\sin\frac{\pi}{6}\sin\frac{\pi}{3} = \sqrt{3}$, $z = 4\cos\frac{\pi}{6} = 2\sqrt{3}$ so in rectangular coordinates the point is $\left(1, \sqrt{3}, 2\sqrt{3}\right)$. $r^2 = x^2 + y^2 = 4$, $r = 2$, so the cylindrical coordinates are $\left(2, \frac{\pi}{3}, 2\sqrt{3}\right)$.

40. (a) $\theta = \frac{\pi}{4}$. In spherical coordinates, this is a half-plane including the z-axis and intersecting the xy-plane in the half-line $x = y$, $x > 0$.

(b) $\phi = \frac{\pi}{4}$. This is one frustum of a circular cone with vertex the origin and axis the positive z-axis.

41. $x^2 + y^2 + z^2 = 4$. In cylindrical coordinates, this becomes $r^2 + z^2 = 4$. In spherical coordinates, it becomes $\rho^2 = 4$ or $\rho = 2$.

42. $x^2 + y^2 = 4$. In cylindrical coordinates: $r^2 = 4$. In spherical coordinates: $\rho^2 - z^2 = 4$ or $\rho^2 - \rho^2\cos^2\phi = 4$ or $\rho^2\sin^2\phi = 4$ or $\rho\sin\phi = 2$.

43. The resulting surface is a circular paraboloid with equation $z = 4x^2 + 4y^2$. Changing to cylindrical coordinates we have $z = 4\left(x^2 + y^2\right) = 4r^2$.

44. $\rho = 2\cos\phi \;\Rightarrow\; \rho^2 = 2\rho\cos\phi \;\Rightarrow\; x^2 + y^2 + z^2 = 2z \;\Rightarrow$ $x^2 + y^2 + (z-1)^2 = 1$. This is the equation of a sphere with radius 1, centered at $(0, 0, 1)$. Therefore, $0 \le \rho \le 2\cos\phi$ is the solid ball whose boundary is this sphere. $0 \le \theta \le \frac{\pi}{2}$ and $0 \le \phi \le \frac{\pi}{6}$ restrict the solid to the section of this ball that lies above the cone $\phi = \frac{\pi}{6}$ and is in the first octant.

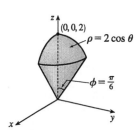

Focus on Problem Solving

1. Since three-dimensional situations are often difficult to visualize and work with, let us first try to find an analogous problem in two dimensions. The analogue of a cube is a square and the analogue of a sphere is a circle. Thus a similar problem in two dimensions is the following: if five circles with the same radius r are contained in a square of side 1 m so that the circles touch each other and four of the circles touch two sides of the square, find r.

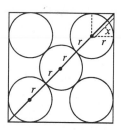

The diagonal of the square is $\sqrt{2}$. The diagonal is also $4r + 2x$. But x is the diagonal of a smaller square of side r. Therefore $x = \sqrt{2}\,r \;\Rightarrow\; \sqrt{2} = 4r + 2x = 4r + 2\sqrt{2}\,r = \left(4 + 2\sqrt{2}\right)r \;\Rightarrow\; r = \frac{\sqrt{2}}{4 + 2\sqrt{2}}$.

Let us use these ideas to solve the original three-dimensional problem. The diagonal of the cube is $\sqrt{1^2 + 1^2 + 1^2} = \sqrt{3}$. The diagonal of the cube is also $4r + 2x$ where x is the diagonal of a smaller cube with edge r. Therefore $x = \sqrt{r^2 + r^2 + r^2} = \sqrt{3}\,r \;\Rightarrow\; \sqrt{3} = 4r + 2x = 4r + 2\sqrt{3}\,r = \left(4 + 2\sqrt{3}\right)r$. Thus

$r = \dfrac{\sqrt{3}}{4 + 2\sqrt{3}} = \dfrac{2\sqrt{3} - 3}{2}$. The radius of each ball is $\left(\sqrt{3} - \frac{3}{2}\right)$ m.

2. Try an analogous problem in two dimensions. Consider a rectangle with length L and width W and find the area of S in terms of L and W. Since S contains B, it has area

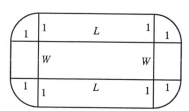

$$A(S) = LW + \text{the area of two } L \times 1 \text{ rectangles}$$

$$+ \text{ the area of two } 1 \times W \text{ rectangles}$$

$$+ \text{ the area of four quarter-circles of radius 1}$$

as seen in the diagram. So $A(S) = LW + 2L + 2W + \pi \cdot 1^2$.
Now in three dimensions, the volume of S is

$$LWH + 2(L \times W \times 1) + 2(1 \times W \times H) + 2(L \times 1 \times H)$$

$$+ \text{ the volume of 4 quarter-cylinders with radius 1 and height } W$$

$$+ \text{ the volume of 4 quarter-cylinders with radius 1 and height } L$$

$$+ \text{ the volume of 4 quarter-cylinders with radius 1 and height } H$$

$$+ \text{ the volume of 8 eighths of a sphere of radius 1}$$

So

$$V(S) = LWH + 2LW + 2WH + 2LH + \pi \cdot 1^2 \cdot W + \pi \cdot 1^2 \cdot L + \pi \cdot 1^2 \cdot H + \tfrac{4}{3}\pi \cdot 1^3$$
$$= LWH + 2(LW + WH + LH) + \pi(L + W + H) + \tfrac{4}{3}\pi.$$

3. (a) We find the line of intersection L as in Example 9.5.7(b). Observe that the point $(-1, c, c)$ lies on both planes. Now since L lies in both planes, it is perpendicular to both of the normal vectors $\mathbf{n}_1$ and $\mathbf{n}_2$, and thus parallel to

$$\text{their cross product } \mathbf{n}_1 \times \mathbf{n}_2 = \begin{vmatrix} \mathbf{i} & \mathbf{j} & \mathbf{k} \\ c & 1 & 1 \\ 1 & -c & c \end{vmatrix} = \langle 2c, -c^2 + 1, -c^2 - 1 \rangle. \text{ So symmetric equations of } L \text{ can be}$$

written as $\dfrac{x+1}{-2c} = \dfrac{y-c}{c^2-1} = \dfrac{z-c}{c^2+1}$, provided that $c \neq 0, \pm 1$.

If $c = 0$, then the two planes are given by $y + z = 0$ and $x = -1$, so symmetric equations of L are $x = -1$, $y = -z$. If $c = -1$, then the two planes are given by $-x + y + z = -1$ and $x + y + z = -1$, and they intersect in the line $x = 0$, $y = -z - 1$. If $c = 1$, then the two planes are given by $x + y + z = 1$ and $x - y + z = 1$, and they intersect in the line $y = 0$, $x = 1 - z$.

(b) If we set $z = t$ in the symmetric equations and solve for x and y separately, we get $x + 1 = \dfrac{(t-c)(-2c)}{c^2+1}$,

$y - c = \dfrac{(t-c)(c^2-1)}{c^2+1} \Rightarrow x = \dfrac{-2ct + (c^2-1)}{c^2+1}$, $y = \dfrac{(c^2-1)t + 2c}{c^2+1}$. Eliminating c from these

equations, we have $x^2 + y^2 = t^2 + 1$. So the curve traced out by L in the plane $z = t$ is a circle with center at $(0, 0, t)$ and radius $\sqrt{t^2 + 1}$.

(c) The area of a horizontal cross-section of the solid is $A(z) = \pi(z^2 + 1)$, so

$$V = \int_0^1 A(z)\,dz = \pi\left[\tfrac{1}{3}z^3 + z\right]_0^1 = \tfrac{4\pi}{3}.$$

4. (a) We consider velocity vectors for the plane and the wind. Let $\mathbf{v}_i$ be the initial, intended velocity for the plane and $\mathbf{v}_g$ the actual velocity relative to the ground. If $\mathbf{w}$ is the velocity of the wind, $\mathbf{v}_g$ is the resultant, that is, the vector sum $\mathbf{v}_i + \mathbf{w}$ as shown in the figure. We know $\mathbf{v}_i = 180\,\mathbf{j}$, and since the plane actually flew 80 km in $\tfrac{1}{2}$ hour, $|\mathbf{v}_g| = 160$. Thus

$\mathbf{v}_g = (160 \cos 85°)\,\mathbf{i} + (160 \sin 85°)\,\mathbf{j} \approx 13.9\,\mathbf{i} + 159.4\,\mathbf{j}$. Finally,

$\mathbf{v}_i + \mathbf{w} = \mathbf{v}_g$, so $\mathbf{w} = \mathbf{v}_g - \mathbf{v}_i \approx 13.9\,\mathbf{i} - 20.6\,\mathbf{j}$. Thus, the wind velocity is about $13.9\,\mathbf{i} - 20.6\,\mathbf{j}$, and the wind speed is

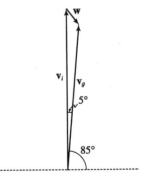

$$|\mathbf{w}| \approx \sqrt{(13.9)^2 + (-20.6)^2} \approx 24.9 \text{ km/h}.$$

(b) Let $\mathbf{v}$ be the velocity the pilot should take. With the effect of wind, the actual velocity (with respect to the ground) will be $\mathbf{v} + \mathbf{w}$, which we want to be $\mathbf{v}_i$. Thus

$\mathbf{v} = \mathbf{v}_i - \mathbf{w} \approx 180\,\mathbf{j} - (13.9\,\mathbf{i} - 20.6\,\mathbf{j}) \approx -13.9\,\mathbf{i} + 200.6\,\mathbf{j}$. The angle for this vector can be found by

$\tan\theta \approx \frac{200.6}{-13.9} \quad \Rightarrow \quad \theta \approx 94.0°$, or $4.0°$ west of north.

5. (a) When $\theta = \theta_s$, the block is not moving, so the sum of the forces on the

block must be $\mathbf{0}$, thus $\mathbf{N} + \mathbf{F} + \mathbf{W} = \mathbf{0}$. This relationship is illustrated

geometrically in the figure. Since the vectors form a right triangle, we have

$$\tan(\theta_s) = \frac{|\mathbf{F}|}{|\mathbf{N}|} = \frac{\mu_s n}{n} = \mu_s.$$

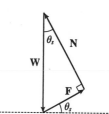

(b) We place the block at the origin and sketch the force vectors acting on the block, including the additional

horizontal force $\mathbf{H}$, with initial points at the origin. We then rotate this system so that $\mathbf{F}$ lies along the positive

x-axis and the inclined plane is parallel to the x-axis.

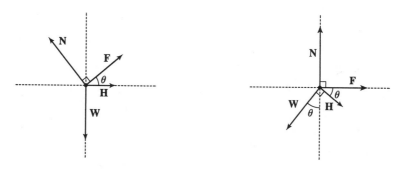

$|\mathbf{F}|$ is maximal, so $|\mathbf{F}| = \mu_s n$ for $\theta > \theta_s$. Then the vectors, in terms of components parallel and perpendicular

to the inclined plane, are

$$\mathbf{N} = n\,\mathbf{j} \qquad\qquad \mathbf{F} = (\mu_s n)\,\mathbf{i}$$

$$\mathbf{W} = (-mg\sin\theta)\,\mathbf{i} + (-mg\cos\theta)\,\mathbf{j}$$

$$\mathbf{H} = (h_{\min}\cos\theta)\,\mathbf{i} + (-h_{\min}\sin\theta)\,\mathbf{j}$$

Equating components, we have

$$\mu_s n - mg\sin\theta + h_{\min}\cos\theta = 0 \quad \Rightarrow \quad h_{\min}\cos\theta + \mu_s n = mg\sin\theta \qquad (1)$$

$$n - mg\cos\theta - h_{\min}\sin\theta = 0 \quad \Rightarrow \quad h_{\min}\sin\theta + mg\cos\theta = n \qquad (2)$$

(c) Since (2) is solved for n, we substitute into (1):

$$h_{\min}\cos\theta + \mu_s(h_{\min}\sin\theta + mg\cos\theta) = mg\sin\theta \quad \Rightarrow$$

$$h_{\min}\cos\theta + h_{\min}\mu_s\sin\theta = mg\sin\theta - mg\mu_s\cos\theta \quad \Rightarrow$$

$$h_{\min} = mg\left(\frac{\sin\theta - \mu_s\cos\theta}{\cos\theta + \mu_s\sin\theta}\right) = mg\left(\frac{\tan\theta - \mu_s}{1 + \mu_s\tan\theta}\right)$$

From part (a) we know $\mu_s = \tan\theta_s$, so this becomes $h_{min} = mg\left(\dfrac{\tan\theta - \tan\theta_s}{1 + \tan\theta_s \tan\theta}\right)$ and using a

trigonometric identity, this is $mg\tan(\theta - \theta_s)$ as desired.

Note for $\theta = \theta_s$, $h_{min} = mg\tan 0 = 0$, which makes sense since the block is at rest for θ_s, thus no additional force **H** is necessary to prevent it from moving. As θ increases, the factor $\tan(\theta - \theta_s)$, and hence the value of h_{min}, increases slowly for small values of $\theta - \theta_s$ but much more rapidly as $\theta - \theta_s$ becomes significant. This seems reasonable, as the steeper the inclined plane, the less the horizontal components of the various forces affect the movement of the block, so we would need a much larger magnitude of horizontal force to keep the block motionless. If we allow $\theta \to 90°$, corresponding to the inclined plane being placed vertically, the value of h_{min} is quite large; this is to be expected, as it takes a great amount of horizontal force to keep an object from moving vertically. In fact, without friction (so $\theta_s = 0$), we would have $\theta \to 90°$ $\Rightarrow$ $h_{min} \to \infty$, and it would be impossible to keep the block from slipping.

(d) Since h_{max} is the largest value of h that keeps the block from slipping, the force of friction is keeping the block from moving *up* the inclined plane; thus, **F** is directed *down* the plane. Our system of forces is similar to that in part (b), then, except that we have $\mathbf{F} = -(\mu_s n)\,\mathbf{i}$. (Note that $|\mathbf{F}|$ is again maximal.) Following our procedure in parts (b) and (c), we equate components:

$$-\mu_s n - mg\sin\theta + h_{max}\cos\theta = 0 \quad \Rightarrow \quad h_{max}\cos\theta - \mu_s n = mg\sin\theta$$

$$n - mg\cos\theta - h_{max}\sin\theta = 0 \quad \Rightarrow \quad h_{max}\sin\theta + mg\cos\theta = n$$

Then substituting,

$$h_{max}\cos\theta - \mu_s(h_{max}\sin\theta + mg\cos\theta) = mg\sin\theta \quad \Rightarrow$$

$$h_{max}\cos\theta - h_{max}\mu_s\sin\theta = mg\sin\theta + mg\mu_s\cos\theta \quad \Rightarrow$$

$$h_{max} = mg\left(\frac{\sin\theta + \mu_s\cos\theta}{\cos\theta - \mu_s\sin\theta}\right) = mg\left(\frac{\tan\theta + \mu_s}{1 - \mu_s\tan\theta}\right)$$

$$= mg\left(\frac{\tan\theta + \tan\theta_s}{1 - \tan\theta_s\tan\theta}\right) = mg\tan(\theta + \theta_s)$$

We would expect h_{max} to increase as θ increases, with similar behavior as we established for h_{min}, but with h_{max} values always larger than h_{min}. We can see that this is the case if we graph h_{max} as a function of θ, as the curve is the graph of h_{min} translated $2\theta_s$ to the left, so the equation does seem reasonable. Notice that the equation predicts $h_{max} \to \infty$ as $\theta \to (90° - \theta_s)$. In fact, as h_{max} increases, the normal force increases as well. When $(90° - \theta_s) \le \theta \le 90°$, the horizontal force is completely counteracted by the sum of the normal and frictional forces, so no part of the horizontal force contributes to moving the block up the plane no matter how large its magnitude.

10   Vector Functions

10.1   Vector Functions and Space Curves   •   •   •   •   •   •   •   •   •

1. The component functions t^2, $\sqrt{t-1}$, and $\sqrt{5-t}$ are all defined when $t-1 \geq 0 \ \Rightarrow \ t \geq 1$ and $5 - t \geq 0 \ \Rightarrow$ $t \leq 5$, so the domain of $\mathbf{r}(t)$ is $[1, 5]$.

2. The component functions $\dfrac{t-2}{t+2}$, $\sin t$, and $\ln(9 - t^2)$ are all defined when $t \neq -2$ and $9 - t^2 > 0 \ \Rightarrow \ -3 < t < 3$, so the domain of $\mathbf{r}(t)$ is $(-3, -2) \cup (-2, 3)$.

3. $\displaystyle\lim_{t \to 0+} \cos t = \cos 0 = 1$, $\displaystyle\lim_{t \to 0+} \sin t = \sin 0 = 0$, $\displaystyle\lim_{t \to 0+} t \ln t = \lim_{t \to 0+} \dfrac{\ln t}{1/t} = \lim_{t \to 0+} \dfrac{1/t}{-1/t^2} = \lim_{t \to 0+} -t = 0$

(by l'Hospital's Rule). Thus $\displaystyle\lim_{t \to 0+} \langle \cos t, \sin t, t \ln t \rangle = \Big\langle \lim_{t \to 0+} \cos t, \lim_{t \to 0+} \sin t, \lim_{t \to 0+} t \ln t \Big\rangle = \langle 1, 0, 0 \rangle$.

4. $\displaystyle\lim_{t \to \infty} \arctan t = \tfrac{\pi}{2}$, $\displaystyle\lim_{t \to \infty} e^{-2t} = 0$, $\displaystyle\lim_{t \to \infty} \dfrac{\ln t}{t} = \lim_{t \to \infty} \dfrac{1/t}{1} = 0$ (by l'Hospital's Rule). Thus

$\displaystyle\lim_{t \to \infty} \Big\langle \arctan t, e^{-2t}, \dfrac{\ln t}{t} \Big\rangle = \langle \tfrac{\pi}{2}, 0, 0 \rangle$.

5. $x = \cos 4t$, $y = t$, $z = \sin 4t$. At any point (x, y, z) on the curve, $x^2 + z^2 = \cos^2 4t + \sin^2 4t = 1$. So the curve lies on a circular cylinder with axis the y-axis. Since $y = t$, this is a helix. So the graph is VI.

6. $x = t$, $y = t^2$, $z = e^{-t}$. At any point on the curve, $y = x^2$. So the curve lies on the parabolic cylinder $y = x^2$. Note that y and z are positive for all t, and the point $(0, 0, 1)$ is on the curve (when $t = 0$). As $t \to \infty$, $(x, y, z) \to (\infty, \infty, 0)$, while as $t \to -\infty$, $(x, y, z) \to (-\infty, \infty, \infty)$, so the graph must be II.

7. $x = t$, $y = 1/(1 + t^2)$, $z = t^2$. Note that y and z are positive for all t. The curve passes through $(0, 1, 0)$ when $t = 0$. As $t \to \infty$, $(x, y, z) \to (\infty, 0, \infty)$, and as $t \to -\infty$, $(x, y, z) \to (-\infty, 0, \infty)$. So the graph is IV.

8. $x = e^{-t} \cos 10t$, $y = e^{-t} \sin 10t$, $z = e^{-t}$.
$x^2 + y^2 = e^{-2t} \cos^2 10t + e^{-2t} \sin^2 10t = e^{-2t} (\cos^2 10t + \sin^2 10t) = e^{-2t} = z^2$, so the curve lies on the cone $x^2 + y^2 = z^2$. Also, z is always positive; the graph must be I.

9. $x = \cos t$, $y = \sin t$, $z = \sin 5t$. $x^2 + y^2 = \cos^2 t + \sin^2 t = 1$, so the curve lies on a circular cylinder with axis the z-axis. Each of x, y and z is periodic, and at $t = 0$ and $t = 2\pi$ the curve passes through the same point, so the curve repeats itself and the graph is V.

10. $x = \cos t$, $y = \sin t$, $z = \ln t$. $x^2 + y^2 = \cos^2 t + \sin^2 t = 1$, so the curve lies on a circular cylinder with axis the z-axis. As $t \to 0$, $z \to -\infty$, so the graph is III.

11. The corresponding parametric equations for this curve are

$x = t^4 + 1$, $y = t$. We can make a table of values, or we can

eliminate the parameter: $t = y \Rightarrow x = y^4 + 1$, with

$y \in \mathbb{R}$. By comparing different values of t, we find the

direction in which t increases as indicated in the graph.

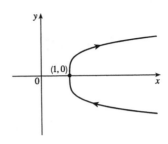

12. The corresponding parametric equations for this curve are

$x = t^3$, $y = t^2$. We can make a table of values, or we can

eliminate the parameter: $x = t^3 \Rightarrow t = \sqrt[3]{x} \Rightarrow$

$y = t^2 = (\sqrt[3]{x})^2 = x^{2/3}$, with $t \in \mathbb{R} \Rightarrow x \in \mathbb{R}$. By

comparing different values of t, we find the direction in

which t increases as indicated in the graph.

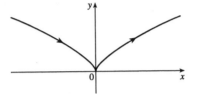

13. The corresponding parametric equations are $x = t$, $y = \cos 2t$, $z = \sin 2t$. Note that

$y^2 + z^2 = \cos^2 2t + \sin^2 2t = 1$, so the curve lies on the circular cylinder $y^2 + z^2 = 1$. Since $x = t$, the curve is a

helix.

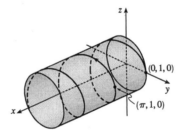

14. The corresponding parametric equations are $x = 1 + t$, $y = 3t$, $z = -t$, which are parametric equations of a line

through the point $(1, 0, 0)$ and with direction vector $\langle 1, 3, -1 \rangle$.

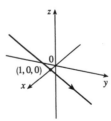

15. The parametric equations give

$x^2 + z^2 = \sin^2 t + \cos^2 t = 1$, $y = 3$, which is a circle of

radius 1, center $(0, 3, 0)$ in the plane $y = 3$.

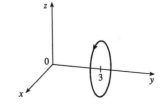

16. The parametric equations are $x = t$, $y = t$, $z = \cos t$. Thus $x = y$, so the curve must lie in the plane $x = y$. Combine this with $z = \cos t$ to determine that the curve traces out the cosine curve in the vertical plane $x = y$.

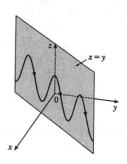

17. The parametric equations are $x = t^2$, $y = t^4$, $z = t^6$. These are positive for $t \neq 0$ and 0 when $t = 0$. So the curve lies entirely in the first quadrant. The projection of the graph onto the xy-plane is $y = x^2$, $y > 0$, a half parabola. On the xz-plane $z = x^3$, $z > 0$, a half cubic, and the yz-plane, $y^3 = z^2$.

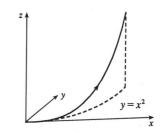

18. The parametric equations give
$$x^2 + y^2 + z^2 = 2\sin^2 t + 2\cos^2 t = 2,$$ so the curve lies on the sphere with radius $\sqrt{2}$ and center $(0, 0, 0)$. Furthermore $x = y = \sin t$, so the curve is the intersection of this sphere with the plane $x = y$, that is, the curve is the circle of radius $\sqrt{2}$, center $(0, 0, 0)$ in the plane $x = y$.

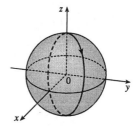

19. If $x = t\cos t$, $y = t\sin t$, and $z = t$, then
$$x^2 + y^2 = t^2 \cos^2 t + t^2 \sin^2 t = t^2 = z^2,$$ so the curve lies on the cone $z^2 = x^2 + y^2$. Since $z = t$, the curve is a spiral on this cone.

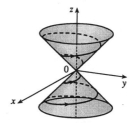

20. Here $x^2 = \sin^2 t = z$ and $x^2 + y^2 = \sin^2 t + \cos^2 t = 1$, so the curve is the intersection of the parabolic cylinder $z = x^2$ with the circular cylinder $x^2 + y^2 = 1$.

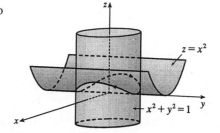

21. $\mathbf{r}(t) = \langle \sin t, \cos t, t^2 \rangle$

22. $\mathbf{r}(t) = \langle t^4 - t^2 + 1, t, t^2 \rangle$

23. $\mathbf{r}(t) = \langle t^2, \sqrt{t-1}, \sqrt{5-t} \rangle$

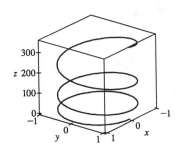
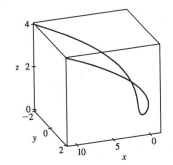

24. We have the computer plot the parametric equations $x = \sin t$, $y = \sin 2t$, $z = \sin 3t$, $0 \le t \le 2\pi$. The shape of the curve is not clear from just one viewpoint, so we include a second plot drawn from a different angle.

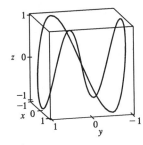
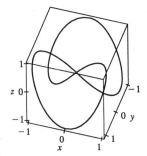

25.

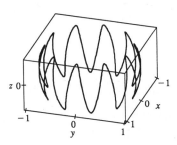

$x = (1 + \cos 16t) \cos t$, $y = (1 + \cos 16t) \sin t$, $z = 1 + \cos 16t$. At any point on the graph,
$$x^2 + y^2 = (1 + \cos 16t)^2 \cos^2 t + (1 + \cos 16t)^2 \sin^2 t$$
$$= (1 + \cos 16t)^2 = z^2,$$ so the graph lies on the cone
$x^2 + y^2 = z^2$. From the graph at left, we see that this curve looks like the projection of a leaved two-dimensional curve onto a cone.

26.

$x = \sqrt{1 - 0.25 \cos^2 10t} \cos t$, $y = \sqrt{1 - 0.25 \cos^2 10t} \sin t$, $z = 0.5 \cos 10t$. At any point on the graph,
$$x^2 + y^2 + z^2 = (1 - 0.25 \cos^2 10t) \cos^2 t$$
$$+ (1 - 0.25 \cos^2 10t) \sin^2 t + 0.25 \cos^2 t$$
$$= 1 - 0.25 \cos^2 10t + 0.25 \cos^2 10t = 1,$$
so the graph lies on the sphere $x^2 + y^2 + z^2 = 1$, and since $z = 0.5 \cos 10t$ the graph resembles a trigonometric curve with ten peaks projected onto the sphere. The graph is generated by $t \in [0, 2\pi]$.

27. If $t = -1$, then $x = 1, y = 4, z = 0$, so the curve passes through the point $(1, 4, 0)$. If $t = 3$, then
$x = 9, y = -8, z = 28$, so the curve passes through the point $(9, -8, 28)$. For the point $(4, 7, -6)$ to be on the
curve, we require $y = 1 - 3t = 7 \Rightarrow t = -2$. But then $z = 1 + (-2)^3 = -7 \neq -6$, so $(4, 7, -6)$ is not on the
curve.

28. The projection of the curve C of intersection onto the xy-plane is the circle $x^2 + y^2 = 4, z = 0$. Then we can write
$x = 2\cos t, y = 2\sin t, 0 \leq t \leq 2\pi$. Since C also lies on the surface $z = xy$, we have
$z = xy = (2\cos t)(2\sin t) = 4\cos t\sin t$, or $2\sin(2t)$. Then parametric equations for C are
$x = 2\cos t, y = 2\sin t, z = 2\sin(2t), 0 \leq t \leq 2\pi$, and the corresponding vector function is
$\mathbf{r}(t) = 2\cos t\,\mathbf{i} + 2\sin t\,\mathbf{j} + 2\sin(2t)\mathbf{k}, 0 \leq t \leq 2\pi$.

29. Both equations are solved for z, so we can substitute to eliminate z: $\sqrt{x^2 + y^2} = 1 + y \Rightarrow$
$x^2 + y^2 = 1 + 2y + y^2 \Rightarrow x^2 = 1 + 2y \Rightarrow y = \frac{1}{2}(x^2 - 1)$. We can form parametric equations for the
curve C of intersection by choosing a parameter $x = t$, then $y = \frac{1}{2}(t^2 - 1)$ and
$z = 1 + y = 1 + \frac{1}{2}(t^2 - 1) = \frac{1}{2}(t^2 + 1)$. Thus a vector function representing C is
$\mathbf{r}(t) = t\,\mathbf{i} + \frac{1}{2}(t^2 - 1)\,\mathbf{j} + \frac{1}{2}(t^2 + 1)\,\mathbf{k}$.

30. The projection of the curve C of intersection onto the xy-plane is the parabola $y = x^2, z = 0$. Then we can choose
the parameter $x = t \Rightarrow y = t^2$. Since C also lies on the surface $z = 4x^2 + y^2$, we have
$z = 4x^2 + y^2 = 4t^2 + (t^2)^2$. Then parametric equations for C are $x = t, y = t^2, z = 4t^2 + t^4$, and the
corresponding vector function is $\mathbf{r}(t) = t\,\mathbf{i} + t^2\,\mathbf{j} + (4t^2 + t^4)\,\mathbf{k}$.

31.

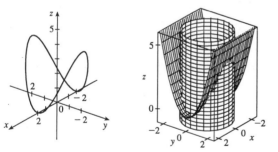

The projection of the curve C of intersection onto
the xy-plane is the circle $x^2 + y^2 = 4, z = 0$.
Then we can write $x = 2\cos t, y = 2\sin t$,
$0 \leq t \leq 2\pi$. Since C also lies on the surface
$z = x^2$, we have $z = x^2 = (2\cos t)^2 = 4\cos^2 t$.
Then parametric equations for C are $x = 2\cos t$,
$y = 2\sin t, z = 4\cos^2 t, 0 \leq t \leq 2\pi$.

32.

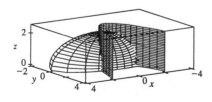

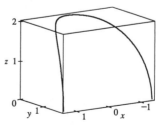

$x = t \Rightarrow y = t^2 \Rightarrow 4z^2 = 16 - x^2 - 4y^2 = 16 - t^2 - 4t^4 \Rightarrow z = \sqrt{4 - \left(\frac{1}{2}t\right)^2 - t^4}$. Note that z is

positive because the intersection is with the top half of the ellipsoid. Hence the curve is given by $x = t, y = t^2$,
$z = \sqrt{4 - \frac{1}{4}t^2 - t^4}$.

33. Let $\mathbf{u}(t) = \langle u_1(t), u_2(t), u_3(t) \rangle$ and $\mathbf{v}(t) = \langle v_1(t), v_2(t), v_3(t) \rangle$. In each part of this problem the basic procedure is to use Equation 1 and then analyze the individual component functions using the limit properties we have already developed for real-valued functions.

(a) $\lim\limits_{t \to a} \mathbf{u}(t) + \lim\limits_{t \to a} \mathbf{v}(t) = \left\langle \lim\limits_{t \to a} u_1(t), \lim\limits_{t \to a} u_2(t), \lim\limits_{t \to a} u_3(t) \right\rangle + \left\langle \lim\limits_{t \to a} v_1(t), \lim\limits_{t \to a} v_2(t), \lim\limits_{t \to a} v_3(t) \right\rangle$ and the limits of these component functions must each exist since the vector functions both possess limits as $t \to a$. Then adding the two vectors and using the addition property of limits for real-valued functions, we have that

$$\lim_{t \to a} \mathbf{u}(t) + \lim_{t \to a} \mathbf{v}(t) = \left\langle \lim_{t \to a} u_1(t) + \lim_{t \to a} v_1(t), \lim_{t \to a} u_2(t) + \lim_{t \to a} v_2(t), \lim_{t \to a} u_3(t) + \lim_{t \to a} v_3(t) \right\rangle$$

$$= \left\langle \lim_{t \to a} [u_1(t) + v_1(t)], \lim_{t \to a} [u_2(t) + v_2(t)], \lim_{t \to a} [u_3(t) + v_3(t)] \right\rangle$$

$$= \lim_{t \to a} \langle u_1(t) + v_1(t), u_2(t) + v_2(t), u_3(t) + v_3(t) \rangle \quad \text{[using (1) backward]}$$

$$= \lim_{t \to a} [\mathbf{u}(t) + \mathbf{v}(t)]$$

(b) $\lim\limits_{t \to a} c\mathbf{u}(t) = \lim\limits_{t \to a} \langle cu_1(t), cu_2(t), cu_3(t) \rangle = \left\langle \lim\limits_{t \to a} cu_1(t), \lim\limits_{t \to a} cu_2(t), \lim\limits_{t \to a} cu_3(t) \right\rangle$

$$= \left\langle c \lim_{t \to a} u_1(t), c \lim_{t \to a} u_2(t), c \lim_{t \to a} u_3(t) \right\rangle = c \left\langle \lim_{t \to a} u_1(t), \lim_{t \to a} u_2(t), \lim_{t \to a} u_3(t) \right\rangle$$

$$= c \lim_{t \to a} \langle u_1(t), u_2(t), u_3(t) \rangle = c \lim_{t \to a} \mathbf{u}(t)$$

(c) $\lim\limits_{t \to a} \mathbf{u}(t) \cdot \lim\limits_{t \to a} \mathbf{v}(t) = \left\langle \lim\limits_{t \to a} u_1(t), \lim\limits_{t \to a} u_2(t), \lim\limits_{t \to a} u_3(t) \right\rangle \cdot \left\langle \lim\limits_{t \to a} v_1(t), \lim\limits_{t \to a} v_2(t), \lim\limits_{t \to a} v_3(t) \right\rangle$

$$= \left[\lim_{t \to a} u_1(t) \right] \left[\lim_{t \to a} v_1(t) \right] + \left[\lim_{t \to a} u_2(t) \right] \left[\lim_{t \to a} v_2(t) \right] + \left[\lim_{t \to a} u_3(t) \right] \left[\lim_{t \to a} v_3(t) \right]$$

$$= \lim_{t \to a} u_1(t)v_1(t) + \lim_{t \to a} u_2(t)v_2(t) + \lim_{t \to a} u_3(t)v_3(t)$$

$$= \lim_{t \to a} [u_1(t)v_1(t) + u_2(t)v_2(t) + u_3(t)v_3(t)] = \lim_{t \to a} [\mathbf{u}(t) \cdot \mathbf{v}(t)]$$

(d) $\lim\limits_{t \to a} \mathbf{u}(t) \times \lim\limits_{t \to a} \mathbf{v}(t) = \left\langle \lim\limits_{t \to a} u_1(t), \lim\limits_{t \to a} u_2(t), \lim\limits_{t \to a} u_3(t) \right\rangle \times \left\langle \lim\limits_{t \to a} v_1(t), \lim\limits_{t \to a} v_2(t), \lim\limits_{t \to a} v_3(t) \right\rangle$

$$= \left\langle \left[\lim_{t \to a} u_2(t) \right] \left[\lim_{t \to a} v_3(t) \right] - \left[\lim_{t \to a} u_3(t) \right] \left[\lim_{t \to a} v_2(t) \right], \right.$$

$$\left[\lim_{t \to a} u_3(t) \right] \left[\lim_{t \to a} v_1(t) \right] - \left[\lim_{t \to a} u_1(t) \right] \left[\lim_{t \to a} v_3(t) \right],$$

$$\left. \left[\lim_{t \to a} u_1(t) \right] \left[\lim_{t \to a} v_2(t) \right] - \left[\lim_{t \to a} u_2(t) \right] \left[\lim_{t \to a} v_1(t) \right] \right\rangle$$

$$= \left\langle \lim_{t \to a} [u_2(t)v_3(t) - u_3(t)v_2(t)], \lim_{t \to a} [u_3(t)v_1(t) - u_1(t)v_3(t)], \right.$$

$$\left. \lim_{t \to a} [u_1(t)v_2(t) - u_2(t)v_1(t)] \right\rangle$$

$$= \lim_{t \to a} \langle u_2(t)v_3(t) - u_3(t)v_2(t), u_3(t)v_1(t) - u_1(t)v_3(t),$$

$$u_1(t)v_2(t) - u_2(t)v_1(t) \rangle$$

$$= \lim_{t \to a} [\mathbf{u}(t) \times \mathbf{v}(t)]$$

34. The projection of the curve onto the xy-plane is given by the parametric equations $x = (2 + \cos 1.5t) \cos t$, $y = (2 + \cos 1.5t) \sin t$. If we convert to polar coordinates, we have

$$r^2 = x^2 + y^2 = [(2 + \cos 1.5t) \cos t]^2 + [(2 + \cos 1.5t) \sin t]^2$$
$$= (2 + \cos 1.5t)^2 (\cos^2 t + \sin^2 t)$$
$$= (2 + \cos 1.5t)^2$$

$\Rightarrow \quad r = 2 + \cos 1.5t$. Also, $\tan \theta = \dfrac{y}{x} = \dfrac{(2 + \cos 1.5t) \sin t}{(2 + \cos 1.5t) \cos t} = \tan t \quad \Rightarrow \quad \theta = t$.

Thus the polar equation of the curve is $r = 2 + \cos 1.5\theta$. At $\theta = 0$, we have $r = 3$, and r decreases to 1 as θ increases to $\frac{2\pi}{3}$. For $\frac{2\pi}{3} \leq \theta \leq \frac{4\pi}{3}$, r increases to 3; r decreases to 1 again at $\theta = 2\pi$, increases to 3 at $\theta = \frac{8\pi}{3}$, decreases to 1 at $\theta = \frac{10\pi}{3}$, and completes the closed curve by increasing to 3 at $\theta = 4\pi$. We sketch an approximate graph as shown in the figure.

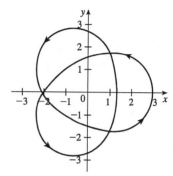

We can determine how the curve passes over itself by investigating the maximum and minimum values of z for $t = \theta \in [0, 4\pi]$. Since $z = \sin 1.5t$, z is maximized where $\sin 1.5t = 1 \quad \Rightarrow \quad 1.5t = \frac{\pi}{2}, \frac{5\pi}{2}, \text{or } \frac{9\pi}{2} \quad \Rightarrow$ $t = \frac{\pi}{3}, \frac{5\pi}{3}, \text{or } 3\pi$. z is minimized where $\sin 1.5t = -1 \quad \Rightarrow$ $1.5t = \frac{3\pi}{2}, \frac{7\pi}{2}, \text{or } \frac{11\pi}{2} \quad \Rightarrow \quad t = \pi, \frac{7\pi}{3}, \text{or } \frac{11\pi}{3}$. Note that these are precisely the values for which $\cos 1.5t = 0 \quad \Rightarrow$ $r = 2$, and on the graph of the projection, these six points appear to be at the three self-intersections we see. Comparing the maximum and minimum values of z at these intersections, we can determine where the curve passes over itself, as indicated in the figure.

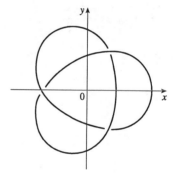

We show a computer-drawn graph of the curve from above, as well as views from the front and from the right side.

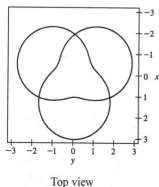

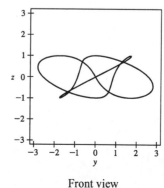

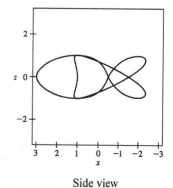

Top view   Front view   Side view

The top view graph shows a more accurate representation of the projection of the trefoil knot on the xy-plane (the axes are rotated 90°). Notice the indentations the graph exhibits at the points corresponding to $r = 1$. Finally, we graph several additional viewpoints of the trefoil knot, along with two plots showing a tube of radius 0.2 around the curve.

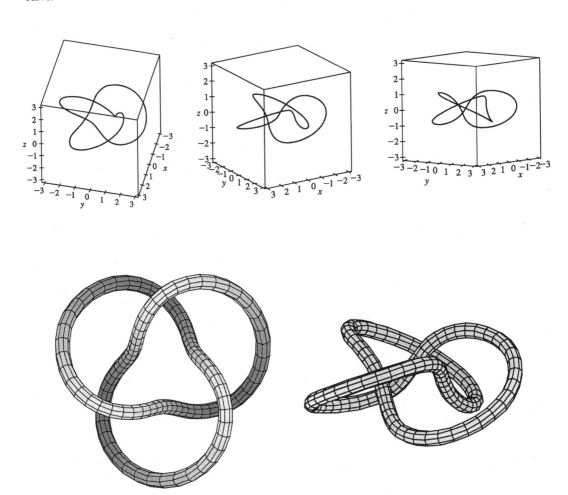

10.2 Derivatives and Integrals of Vector Functions • • • • •

1. (a)

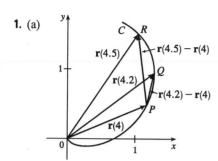

(b) $\dfrac{\mathbf{r}(4.5) - \mathbf{r}(4)}{0.5} = 2\,[\mathbf{r}(4.5) - \mathbf{r}(4)]$, so we draw a vector in the
same direction but with twice the length of the vector

$\mathbf{r}(4.5) - \mathbf{r}(4)$. $\dfrac{\mathbf{r}(4.2) - \mathbf{r}(4)}{0.2} = 5\,[\mathbf{r}(4.2) - \mathbf{r}(4)]$, so we draw a

vector in the same direction but with 5 times the length of the

vector $\mathbf{r}(4.2) - \mathbf{r}(4)$.

(c) By Definition 1, $\mathbf{r}'(4) = \lim\limits_{h \to 0} \dfrac{\mathbf{r}(4 + h) - \mathbf{r}(4)}{h}$.

$\mathbf{T}(4) = \dfrac{\mathbf{r}'(4)}{|\mathbf{r}'(4)|}$.

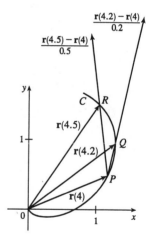

(d) $\mathbf{T}(4)$ is a unit vector in the same direction as $\mathbf{r}'(4)$, that is, parallel to the tangent line to the curve at $\mathbf{r}(4)$ with
length 1.

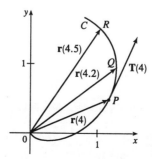

2. (a) The curve can be represented by the parametric equations $x = t^2$, $y = t$, $0 \leq t \leq 2$. Eliminating the parameter, we have $x = y^2$, $0 \leq y \leq 2$, a portion of which we graph here, along with the vectors $\mathbf{r}(1)$, $\mathbf{r}(1.1)$, and $\mathbf{r}(1.1) - \mathbf{r}(1)$.

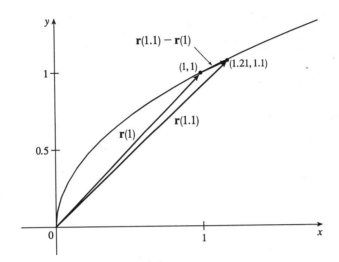

(b) Since $\mathbf{r}(t) = \langle t^2, t \rangle$, we differentiate components, giving $\mathbf{r}'(t) = \langle 2t, 1 \rangle$, so $\mathbf{r}'(1) = \langle 2, 1 \rangle$.

$$\frac{\mathbf{r}(1.1) - \mathbf{r}(1)}{0.1} = \frac{\langle 1.21, 1.1 \rangle - \langle 1, 1 \rangle}{0.1} = 10 \langle 0.21, 0.1 \rangle = \langle 2.1, 1 \rangle.$$

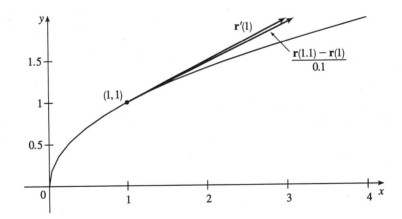

As we can see from the graph, these vectors are very close in length and direction. $\mathbf{r}'(1)$ is defined to be $\lim\limits_{h \to 0} \dfrac{\mathbf{r}(1+h) - \mathbf{r}(1)}{h}$, and we recognize $\dfrac{\mathbf{r}(1.1) - \mathbf{r}(1)}{0.1}$ as the expression after the limit sign with $h = 0.1$.

Since h is close to 0, we would expect $\dfrac{\mathbf{r}(1.1) - \mathbf{r}(1)}{0.1}$ to be a vector close to $\mathbf{r}'(1)$.

3. (a), (c)

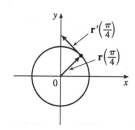

(b) $\mathbf{r}'(t) = \langle -\sin t, \cos t \rangle$

4. (a), (c)

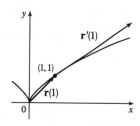

(b) $\mathbf{r}'(t) = \langle 3t^2, 2t \rangle$

5. Since $(x-1)^2 = t^2 = y$, the curve is a parabola.

(a), (c)

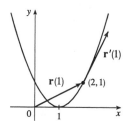

(b) $\mathbf{r}'(t) = \mathbf{i} + 2t\mathbf{j}$

6. $x = 2\sin t$, $y = 3\cos t$, so $(x/2)^2 + (y/3)^2 = \sin^2 t + \cos^2 t = 1$ and the curve is an ellipse.

(a), (c)

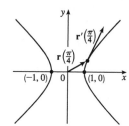

(b) $\mathbf{r}'(t) = 2\cos t\,\mathbf{i} - 3\sin t\,\mathbf{j}$

7. $x^{-2} = e^{-2t} = y$, so $y = 1/x^2$, $x > 0$.

(a), (c)

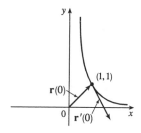

(b) $\mathbf{r}'(t) = e^t\mathbf{i} - 2e^{-2t}\mathbf{j}$

8. $x^2 - y^2 = \sec^2 t - \tan^2 t = 1$, so the curve is a hyperbola.

(a), (c)

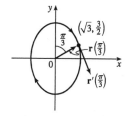

(b) $\mathbf{r}'(t) = \sec t \tan t\,\mathbf{i} + \sec^2 t\,\mathbf{j}$

9. $\mathbf{r}'(t) = \left\langle \dfrac{d}{dt}\,[t^2], \dfrac{d}{dt}\,[1-t], \dfrac{d}{dt}\,[\sqrt{t}] \right\rangle = \left\langle 2t, -1, \dfrac{1}{2\sqrt{t}} \right\rangle$

10. $\mathbf{r}(t) = \langle \cos 3t, t, \sin 3t \rangle \quad \Rightarrow \quad \mathbf{r}'(t) = \langle -3\sin 3t, 1, 3\cos 3t \rangle$

11. $\mathbf{r}(t) = e^{t^2}\mathbf{i} - \mathbf{j} + \ln(1+3t)\,\mathbf{k} \quad \Rightarrow \quad \mathbf{r}'(t) = 2te^{t^2}\mathbf{i} + \dfrac{3}{1+3t}\,\mathbf{k}$

12. $\mathbf{r}(t) = \sin^{-1} t\,\mathbf{i} + \sqrt{1-t^2}\,\mathbf{j} + \mathbf{k} \quad \Rightarrow \quad \mathbf{r}'(t) = \dfrac{1}{\sqrt{1-t^2}}\,\mathbf{i} - \dfrac{t}{\sqrt{1-t^2}}\,\mathbf{j}$

13. $\mathbf{r}'(t) = \mathbf{0} + \mathbf{b} + 2t\,\mathbf{c} = \mathbf{b} + 2t\,\mathbf{c}$ by Formulas 1 and 3 of Theorem 3.

14. To find $\mathbf{r}'(t)$, we first expand $\mathbf{r}(t) = t\,\mathbf{a} \times (\mathbf{b} + t\,\mathbf{c}) = t(\mathbf{a} \times \mathbf{b}) + t^2(\mathbf{a} \times \mathbf{c})$, so $\mathbf{r}'(t) = \mathbf{a} \times \mathbf{b} + 2t(\mathbf{a} \times \mathbf{c})$.

15. $\mathbf{r}'(t) = -\sin t\,\mathbf{i} + 3\,\mathbf{j} + 4\cos 2t\,\mathbf{k} \;\Rightarrow\; \mathbf{r}'(0) = 3\,\mathbf{j} + 4\,\mathbf{k}$. Thus

$$\mathbf{T}(0) = \frac{\mathbf{r}'(0)}{|\mathbf{r}'(0)|} = \frac{1}{\sqrt{0^2 + 3^2 + 4^2}}\,(3\,\mathbf{j} + 4\,\mathbf{k}) = \tfrac{1}{5}(3\,\mathbf{j} + 4\,\mathbf{k}) = \tfrac{3}{5}\,\mathbf{j} + \tfrac{4}{5}\,\mathbf{k}.$$

16. $\mathbf{r}'(t) = \dfrac{2}{\sqrt{t}}\,\mathbf{i} + 2t\,\mathbf{j} + \mathbf{k} \;\Rightarrow\; \mathbf{r}'(1) = 2\,\mathbf{i} + 2\,\mathbf{j} + \mathbf{k}$. Thus

$$\mathbf{T}(1) = \frac{\mathbf{r}'(1)}{|\mathbf{r}'(1)|} = \frac{1}{\sqrt{2^2 + 2^2 + 1^2}}\,(2\,\mathbf{i} + 2\,\mathbf{j} + \mathbf{k}) = \tfrac{1}{3}(2\,\mathbf{i} + 2\,\mathbf{j} + \mathbf{k}) = \tfrac{2}{3}\,\mathbf{i} + \tfrac{2}{3}\,\mathbf{j} + \tfrac{1}{3}\,\mathbf{k}.$$

17. $\mathbf{r}(t) = \langle t, t^2, t^3 \rangle \;\Rightarrow\; \mathbf{r}'(t) = \langle 1, 2t, 3t^2 \rangle$. Then $\mathbf{r}'(1) = \langle 1, 2, 3 \rangle$ and $|\mathbf{r}'(1)| = \sqrt{1^2 + 2^2 + 3^2} = \sqrt{14}$, so

$$\mathbf{T}(1) = \frac{\mathbf{r}'(1)}{|\mathbf{r}'(1)|} = \tfrac{1}{\sqrt{14}}\langle 1, 2, 3 \rangle = \left\langle \tfrac{1}{\sqrt{14}}, \tfrac{2}{\sqrt{14}}, \tfrac{3}{\sqrt{14}} \right\rangle. \quad \mathbf{r}''(t) = \langle 0, 2, 6t \rangle, \text{ so}$$

$$\mathbf{r}'(t) \times \mathbf{r}''(t) = \begin{vmatrix} \mathbf{i} & \mathbf{j} & \mathbf{k} \\ 1 & 2t & 3t^2 \\ 0 & 2 & 6t \end{vmatrix} = \begin{vmatrix} 2t & 3t^2 \\ 2 & 6t \end{vmatrix}\mathbf{i} - \begin{vmatrix} 1 & 3t^2 \\ 0 & 6t \end{vmatrix}\mathbf{j} + \begin{vmatrix} 1 & 2t \\ 0 & 2 \end{vmatrix}\mathbf{k}$$

$$= \left(12t^2 - 6t^2\right)\mathbf{i} - (6t - 0)\mathbf{j} + (2 - 0)\mathbf{k} = \langle 6t^2, -6t, 2 \rangle.$$

18. $\mathbf{r}(t) = \langle e^{2t}, e^{-2t}, te^{2t} \rangle \;\Rightarrow\; \mathbf{r}'(t) = \langle 2e^{2t}, -2e^{-2t}, (2t+1)e^{2t} \rangle \;\Rightarrow$

$\mathbf{r}'(0) = \langle 2e^0, -2e^0, (0+1)e^0 \rangle = \langle 2, -2, 1 \rangle$ and $|\mathbf{r}'(0)| = \sqrt{2^2 + (-2)^2 + 1^2} = 3$. Then

$$\mathbf{T}(0) = \frac{\mathbf{r}'(0)}{|\mathbf{r}'(0)|} = \tfrac{1}{3}\langle 2, -2, 1 \rangle = \langle \tfrac{2}{3}, \tfrac{-2}{3}, \tfrac{1}{3} \rangle. \quad \mathbf{r}''(t) = \langle 4e^{2t}, 4e^{-2t}, (4t+4)e^{2t} \rangle \;\Rightarrow$$

$\mathbf{r}''(0) = \langle 4e^0, 4e^0, (0+4)e^0 \rangle = \langle 4, 4, 4 \rangle.$

$$\mathbf{r}'(t) \cdot \mathbf{r}''(t) = \langle 2e^{2t}, -2e^{-2t}, (2t+1)e^{2t} \rangle \cdot \langle 4e^{2t}, 4e^{-2t}, (4t+4)e^{2t} \rangle$$

$$= \left(2e^{2t}\right)\left(4e^{2t}\right) + \left(-2e^{-2t}\right)\left(4e^{-2t}\right) + \left((2t+1)e^{2t}\right)\left((4t+4)e^{2t}\right)$$

$$= 8e^{4t} - 8e^{-4t} + \left(8t^2 + 12t + 4\right)e^{4t} = \left(8t^2 + 12t + 12\right)e^{4t} - 8e^{-4t}$$

19. The vector equation for the curve is $\mathbf{r}(t) = \langle t^5, t^4, t^3 \rangle$, so $\mathbf{r}'(t) = \langle 5t^4, 4t^3, 3t^2 \rangle$. The point $(1, 1, 1)$ corresponds to $t = 1$, so the tangent vector there is $\mathbf{r}'(1) = \langle 5, 4, 3 \rangle$. Thus, the tangent line goes through the point $(1, 1, 1)$ and is parallel to the vector $\langle 5, 4, 3 \rangle$. Parametric equations are $x = 1 + 5t$, $y = 1 + 4t$, $z = 1 + 3t$.

20. The vector equation for the curve is $\mathbf{r}(t) = \langle t^2 - 1, t^2 + 1, t + 1 \rangle$, so $\mathbf{r}'(t) = \langle 2t, 2t, 1 \rangle$. The point $(-1, 1, 1)$ corresponds to $t = 0$, so the tangent vector there is $\mathbf{r}'(0) = \langle 0, 0, 1 \rangle$. Thus, the tangent line is parallel to the vector $\langle 0, 0, 1 \rangle$ and parametric equations are $x = -1 + 0 \cdot t = -1$, $y = 1 + 0 \cdot t = 1$, $z = 1 + 1 \cdot t = 1 + t$.

21. The vector equation for the curve is $\mathbf{r}(t) = \langle e^{-t}\cos t, e^{-t}\sin t, e^{-t} \rangle$, so

$\mathbf{r}'(t) = \langle e^{-t}(-\sin t) + (\cos t)(-e^{-t}), e^{-t}\cos t + (\sin t)(-e^{-t}), (-e^{-t}) \rangle =$

$\langle -e^{-t}(\cos t + \sin t), e^{-t}(\cos t - \sin t), -e^{-t} \rangle$. The point $(1, 0, 1)$ corresponds to $t = 0$, so the tangent vector

there is $\mathbf{r}'(0) = \langle -e^0(\cos 0 + \sin 0), e^0(\cos 0 - \sin 0), -e^0 \rangle = \langle -1, 1, -1 \rangle$. Thus, the tangent line is parallel to

the vector $\langle -1, 1, -1 \rangle$ and parametric equations are $x = 1 + (-1)t = 1 - t$, $y = 0 + 1 \cdot t = t$,

$z = 1 + (-1)t = 1 - t$.

22. $\mathbf{r}(t) = \langle \ln t, 2\sqrt{t}, t^2 \rangle$, $\mathbf{r}'(t) = \langle 1/t, 1/\sqrt{t}, 2t \rangle$. At $(0, 2, 1)$, $t = 1$ and $\mathbf{r}'(1) = \langle 1, 1, 2 \rangle$. Thus, parametric equations of the tangent line are $x = t$, $y = 2 + t$, $z = 1 + 2t$.

23. $\mathbf{r}(t) = \langle t, \sqrt{2}\cos t, \sqrt{2}\sin t \rangle \Rightarrow$

$\mathbf{r}'(t) = \langle 1, -\sqrt{2}\sin t, \sqrt{2}\cos t \rangle$. At $\left(\frac{\pi}{4}, 1, 1\right)$, $t = \frac{\pi}{4}$ and

$\mathbf{r}'\left(\frac{\pi}{4}\right) = \langle 1, -1, 1 \rangle$. Thus, parametric equations of the tangent line

are $x = \frac{\pi}{4} + t$, $y = 1 - t$, $z = 1 + t$.

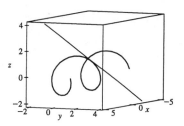

24. $\mathbf{r}(t) = \langle \cos t, 3e^{2t}, 3e^{-2t} \rangle$, $\mathbf{r}'(t) = \langle -\sin t, 6e^{2t}, -6e^{-2t} \rangle$. At

$(1, 3, 3)$, $t = 0$ and $\mathbf{r}'(0) = \langle 0, 6, -6 \rangle$. Thus, parametric equations of

the tangent line are $x = 1$, $y = 3 + 6t$, $z = 3 - 6t$.

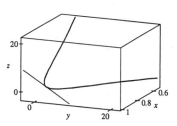

25. (a) $\mathbf{r}(t) = \langle t^3, t^4, t^5 \rangle \Rightarrow \mathbf{r}'(t) = \langle 3t^2, 4t^3, 5t^4 \rangle$, and since $\mathbf{r}'(0) = \langle 0, 0, 0 \rangle = \mathbf{0}$, the curve is not smooth.

(b) $\mathbf{r}(t) = \langle t^3 + t, t^4, t^5 \rangle \Rightarrow \mathbf{r}'(t) = \langle 3t^2 + 1, 4t^3, 5t^4 \rangle$. $\mathbf{r}'(t)$ is continuous since its component functions are
continuous. Also, $\mathbf{r}'(t) \neq \mathbf{0}$, as the y- and z-components are 0 only for $t = 0$, but $\mathbf{r}'(0) = \langle 1, 0, 0 \rangle \neq \mathbf{0}$. Thus,
the curve is smooth.

(c) $\mathbf{r}(t) = \langle \cos^3 t, \sin^3 t \rangle \Rightarrow \mathbf{r}'(t) = \langle -3\cos^2 t \sin t, 3\sin^2 t \cos t \rangle$. Since
$\mathbf{r}'(0) = \langle -3\cos^2 0 \sin 0, 3\sin^2 0 \cos 0 \rangle = \langle 0, 0 \rangle = \mathbf{0}$, the curve is not smooth.

26. (a) The tangent line at $t = 0$ is the line through the point with

position vector $\mathbf{r}(0) = \langle \sin 0, 2\sin 0, \cos 0 \rangle = \langle 0, 0, 1 \rangle$,

and in the direction of the tangent vector,

$\mathbf{r}'(0) = \langle \pi\cos 0, 2\pi\cos 0, -\pi\sin 0 \rangle = \langle \pi, 2\pi, 0 \rangle$.

So an equation of the line is

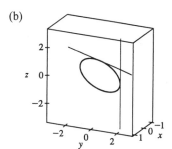

$\langle x, y, z \rangle = \mathbf{r}(0) + u\mathbf{r}'(0) = \langle 0 + \pi u, 0 + 2\pi u, 1 \rangle = \langle \pi u, 2\pi u, 1 \rangle$

$\mathbf{r}\left(\frac{1}{2}\right) = \langle \sin\frac{\pi}{2}, 2\sin\frac{\pi}{2}, \cos\frac{\pi}{2} \rangle = \langle 1, 2, 0 \rangle$, $\mathbf{r}'\left(\frac{1}{2}\right) = \langle \pi\cos\frac{\pi}{2}, 2\pi\cos\frac{\pi}{2}, -\pi\sin\frac{\pi}{2} \rangle = \langle 0, 0, -\pi \rangle$.
So the equation of the second line is $\langle x, y, z \rangle = \langle 1, 2, 0 \rangle + v\langle 0, 0, -\pi \rangle = \langle 1, 2, -\pi v \rangle$. The lines intersect
where $\langle \pi u, 2\pi u, 1 \rangle = \langle 1, 2, -\pi v \rangle$, so the point of intersection is $(1, 2, 1)$.

27. The angle of intersection of the two curves is the angle between the two tangent vectors to the curves at the point of
intersection. Since $\mathbf{r}_1'(t) = \langle 1, 2t, 3t^2 \rangle$ and $t = 0$ at $(0, 0, 0)$, $\mathbf{r}_1'(0) = \langle 1, 0, 0 \rangle$ is a tangent vector to $\mathbf{r}_1$ at $(0, 0, 0)$.
Similarly, $\mathbf{r}_2'(t) = \langle \cos t, 2\cos 2t, 1 \rangle$ and since $\mathbf{r}_2(0) = \langle 0, 0, 0 \rangle$, $\mathbf{r}_2'(0) = \langle 1, 2, 1 \rangle$ is a tangent vector to $\mathbf{r}_2$ at
$(0, 0, 0)$. If θ is the angle between these two tangent vectors, then $\cos\theta = \frac{1}{\sqrt{1}\sqrt{6}}\langle 1, 0, 0 \rangle \cdot \langle 1, 2, 1 \rangle = \frac{1}{\sqrt{6}}$ and
$\theta = \cos^{-1}\left(\frac{1}{\sqrt{6}}\right) \approx 66°$.

28. To find the point of intersection, we must find the values of t and s which satisfy the following three equations simultaneously: $t = 3 - s$, $1 - t = s - 2$, $3 + t^2 = s^2$. Solving the last two equations gives $t = 1$, $s = 2$ (check these in the first equation). Thus the point of intersection is $(1, 0, 4)$. To find the angle θ of intersection, we proceed as in Exercise 27. The tangent vectors to the respective curves at $(1, 0, 4)$ are $\mathbf{r}_1'(1) = \langle 1, -1, 2 \rangle$ and
$\mathbf{r}_2'(2) = \langle -1, 1, 4 \rangle$. So $\cos \theta = \frac{1}{\sqrt{6}\sqrt{18}}(-1 - 1 + 8) = \frac{6}{6\sqrt{3}} = \frac{1}{\sqrt{3}}$ and $\theta = \cos^{-1}\left(\frac{1}{\sqrt{3}}\right) \approx 55\,°$.

Note: In Exercise 27, the curves intersect when the value of both parameters is zero. However, as seen in this exercise, it is not necessary for the parameters to be of equal value at the point of intersection.

29. $\int_0^1 (16t^3\,\mathbf{i} - 9t^2\,\mathbf{j} + 25t^4\,\mathbf{k})\,dt = \left(\int_0^1 16t^3\,dt\right)\mathbf{i} - \left(\int_0^1 9t^2\,dt\right)\mathbf{j} + \left(\int_0^1 25t^4\,dt\right)\mathbf{k}$
$$= \left[4t^4\right]_0^1\mathbf{i} - \left[3t^3\right]_0^1\mathbf{j} + \left[5t^5\right]_0^1\mathbf{k} = 4\,\mathbf{i} - 3\,\mathbf{j} + 5\,\mathbf{k}$$

30. $\displaystyle\int_0^1 \left(\frac{4}{1+t^2}\,\mathbf{j} + \frac{2t}{1+t^2}\,\mathbf{k}\right)dt = \left[4\tan^{-1}t\,\mathbf{j} + \ln\left(1+t^2\right)\mathbf{k}\right]_0^1$
$$= \left[4\tan^{-1}1\,\mathbf{j} + \ln 2\,\mathbf{k}\right] - \left[4\tan^{-1}0\,\mathbf{j} + \ln 1\,\mathbf{k}\right] = 4\left(\tfrac{\pi}{4}\right)\mathbf{j} + \ln 2\,\mathbf{k} - 0\,\mathbf{j} - 0\,\mathbf{k} = \pi\,\mathbf{j} + \ln 2\,\mathbf{k}$$

31. $\int_0^{\pi/4} (\cos 2t\,\mathbf{i} + \sin 2t\,\mathbf{j} + t\sin t\,\mathbf{k})\,dt = \left[\tfrac{1}{2}\sin 2t\,\mathbf{i} - \tfrac{1}{2}\cos 2t\,\mathbf{j}\right]_0^{\pi/4} + \left[[-t\cos t]_0^{\pi/4} + \int_0^{\pi/4}\cos t\,dt\right]\mathbf{k}$
$$= \tfrac{1}{2}\mathbf{i} + \tfrac{1}{2}\mathbf{j} + \left[-\tfrac{\pi}{4}\cos\tfrac{\pi}{4} + \sin\tfrac{\pi}{4}\right]\mathbf{k} = \tfrac{1}{2}\mathbf{i} + \tfrac{1}{2}\mathbf{j} + \tfrac{1}{\sqrt{2}}\left(1 - \tfrac{\pi}{4}\right)\mathbf{k} = \tfrac{1}{2}\mathbf{i} + \tfrac{1}{2}\mathbf{j} + \tfrac{4-\pi}{4\sqrt{2}}\mathbf{k}$$

32. $\int_1^4 \left(\sqrt{t}\,\mathbf{i} + te^{-t}\,\mathbf{j} + t^{-2}\,\mathbf{k}\right)dt = \left[\tfrac{2}{3}t^{3/2}\,\mathbf{i} - t^{-1}\,\mathbf{k}\right]_1^4 + \left([-te^{-t}]_1^4 + \int_1^4 e^{-t}\,dt\right)\mathbf{j}$
$$= \left(\tfrac{16}{3} - \tfrac{2}{3}\right)\mathbf{i} - \left(\tfrac{1}{4} - 1\right)\mathbf{k} + \left(-4e^{-4} + e^{-1} - e^{-4} + e^{-1}\right)\mathbf{j} = \tfrac{14}{3}\mathbf{i} + e^{-1}\left(2 - 5e^{-3}\right)\mathbf{j} + \tfrac{3}{4}\mathbf{k}$$

33. $\int (e^t\,\mathbf{i} + 2t\,\mathbf{j} + \ln t\,\mathbf{k})\,dt = \left(\int e^t\,dt\right)\mathbf{i} + \left(\int 2t\,dt\right)\mathbf{j} + \left(\int \ln t\,dt\right)\mathbf{k}$
$$= e^t\,\mathbf{i} + t^2\,\mathbf{j} + (t\ln t - t)\,\mathbf{k} + \mathbf{C}, \text{ where } \mathbf{C} \text{ is a vector constant of integration.}$$

34. $\int (\cos \pi t\,\mathbf{i} + \sin \pi t\,\mathbf{j} + t\,\mathbf{k})\,dt = \left(\int \cos \pi t\,dt\right)\mathbf{i} + \left(\int \sin \pi t\,dt\right)\mathbf{j} + \left(\int t\,dt\right)\mathbf{k}$
$$= \tfrac{1}{\pi}\sin \pi t\,\mathbf{i} - \tfrac{1}{\pi}\cos \pi t\,\mathbf{j} + \tfrac{1}{2}t^2\,\mathbf{k} + \mathbf{C}$$

35. $\mathbf{r}'(t) = t^2\,\mathbf{i} + 4t^3\,\mathbf{j} - t^2\,\mathbf{k} \ \Rightarrow\ \mathbf{r}(t) = \tfrac{1}{3}t^3\,\mathbf{i} + t^4\,\mathbf{j} - \tfrac{1}{3}t^3\,\mathbf{k} + \mathbf{C}$, where $\mathbf{C}$ is a constant vector. But
$\mathbf{j} = \mathbf{r}(0) = (0)\,\mathbf{i} + (0)\,\mathbf{j} - (0)\,\mathbf{k} + \mathbf{C}$. Thus $\mathbf{C} = \mathbf{j}$ and
$\mathbf{r}(t) = \tfrac{1}{3}t^3\,\mathbf{i} + t^4\,\mathbf{j} - \tfrac{1}{3}t^3\,\mathbf{k} + \mathbf{j} = \tfrac{1}{3}t^3\,\mathbf{i} + (t^4 + 1)\,\mathbf{j} - \tfrac{1}{3}t^3\,\mathbf{k}$.

36. $\mathbf{r}'(t) = \sin t\,\mathbf{i} - \cos t\,\mathbf{j} + 2t\,\mathbf{k} \ \Rightarrow\ \mathbf{r}(t) = (-\cos t)\,\mathbf{i} - (\sin t)\,\mathbf{j} + t^2\,\mathbf{k} + \mathbf{C}$. But
$\mathbf{i} + \mathbf{j} + 2\mathbf{k} = \mathbf{r}(0) = -\mathbf{i} + (0)\,\mathbf{j} + (0)\,\mathbf{k} + \mathbf{C}$. Thus $\mathbf{C} = 2\,\mathbf{i} + \mathbf{j} + 2\,\mathbf{k}$ and
$\mathbf{r}(t) = (2 - \cos t)\,\mathbf{i} + (1 - \sin t)\,\mathbf{j} + (2 + t^2)\,\mathbf{k}$.

For Exercises 37–40, let $\mathbf{u}(t) = \langle u_1(t), u_2(t), u_3(t)\rangle$ and $\mathbf{v}(t) = \langle v_1(t), v_2(t), v_3(t)\rangle$. In each of these exercises, the procedure is to apply Theorem 2 so that the corresponding properties of derivatives of real-valued functions can be used.

37. $\dfrac{d}{dt}[\mathbf{u}(t) + \mathbf{v}(t)] = \dfrac{d}{dt}\langle u_1(t) + v_1(t), u_2(t) + v_2(t), u_3(t) + v_3(t)\rangle$
$$= \left\langle \dfrac{d}{dt}[u_1(t) + v_1(t)], \dfrac{d}{dt}[u_2(t) + v_2(t)], \dfrac{d}{dt}[u_3(t) + v_3(t)]\right\rangle$$
$$= \langle u_1'(t) + v_1'(t), u_2'(t) + v_2'(t), u_3'(t) + v_3'(t)\rangle$$
$$= \langle u_1'(t), u_2'(t), u_3'(t)\rangle + \langle v_1'(t), v_2'(t), v_3'(t)\rangle = \mathbf{u}'(t) + \mathbf{v}'(t).$$

38. $\dfrac{d}{dt}[f(t)\mathbf{u}(t)] = \dfrac{d}{dt}\langle f(t)u_1(t), f(t)u_2(t), f(t)u_3(t)\rangle$

$$= \left\langle \frac{d}{dt}[f(t)u_1(t)], \frac{d}{dt}[f(t)u_2(t)], \frac{d}{dt}[f(t)u_3(t)] \right\rangle$$

$$= \langle f'(t)u_1(t) + f(t)u_1'(t), f'(t)u_2(t) + f(t)u_2'(t), f'(t)u_3(t) + f(t)u_3'(t)\rangle$$

$$= f'(t)\langle u_1(t), u_2(t), u_3(t)\rangle + f(t)\langle u_1'(t), u_2'(t), u_3'(t)\rangle$$

$$= f'(t)\mathbf{u}(t) + f(t)\mathbf{u}'(t)$$

39. $\dfrac{d}{dt}[\mathbf{u}(t) \times \mathbf{v}(t)]$

$$= \frac{d}{dt}\langle u_2(t)v_3(t) - u_3(t)v_2(t), u_3(t)v_1(t) - u_1(t)v_3(t), u_1(t)v_2(t) - u_2(t)v_1(t)\rangle$$

$$= \langle u_2'v_3(t) + u_2(t)v_3'(t) - u_3'(t)v_2(t) - u_3(t)v_2'(t),$$

$$u_3'(t)v_1(t) + u_3(t)v_1'(t) - u_1'(t)v_3(t) - u_1(t)v_3'(t),$$

$$u_1'(t)v_2(t) + u_1(t)v_2'(t) - u_2'(t)v_1(t) - u_2(t)v_1'(t)\rangle$$

$$= \langle u_2'(t)v_3(t) - u_3'(t)v_2(t), u_3'(t)v_1(t) - u_1'(t)v_3(t), u_1'(t)v_2(t) - u_2'(t)v_1(t)\rangle$$

$$+ \langle u_2(t)v_3'(t) - u_3(t)v_2'(t), u_3(t)v_1'(t) - u_1(t)v_3'(t), u_1(t)v_2'(t) - u_2(t)v_1'(t)\rangle$$

$$= \mathbf{u}'(t) \times \mathbf{v}(t) + \mathbf{u}(t) \times \mathbf{v}'(t)$$

Alternate solution: Let $\mathbf{r}(t) = \mathbf{u}(t) \times \mathbf{v}(t)$. Then

$\mathbf{r}(t+h) - \mathbf{r}(t) = [\mathbf{u}(t+h) \times \mathbf{v}(t+h)] - [\mathbf{u}(t) \times \mathbf{v}(t)]$

$$= [\mathbf{u}(t+h) \times \mathbf{v}(t+h)] - [\mathbf{u}(t) \times \mathbf{v}(t)] + [\mathbf{u}(t+h) \times \mathbf{v}(t)] - [\mathbf{u}(t+h) \times \mathbf{v}(t)]$$

$$= \mathbf{u}(t+h) \times [\mathbf{v}(t+h) - \mathbf{v}(t)] + [\mathbf{u}(t+h) - \mathbf{u}(t)] \times \mathbf{v}(t)$$

(Be careful of the order of the cross product.)

Dividing through by h and taking the limit as $h \to 0$ we have

$$\mathbf{r}'(t) = \lim_{h \to 0} \frac{\mathbf{u}(t+h) \times [\mathbf{v}(t+h) - \mathbf{v}(t)]}{h} + \lim_{h \to 0} \frac{[\mathbf{u}(t+h) - \mathbf{u}(t)] \times \mathbf{v}(t)}{h}$$

$$= \mathbf{u}(t) \times \mathbf{v}'(t) + \mathbf{u}'(t) \times \mathbf{v}(t)$$

by Exercise 10.1.33(a) and Definition 1.

40. $\dfrac{d}{dt}[\mathbf{u}(f(t))] = \dfrac{d}{dt}\langle u_1(f(t)), u_2(f(t)), u_3(f(t))\rangle$

$$= \left\langle \frac{d}{dt}[u_1(f(t))], \frac{d}{dt}[u_2(f(t))], \frac{d}{dt}[u_3(f(t))] \right\rangle$$

$$= \langle f'(t)u_1'(f(t)), f'(t)u_2'(f(t)), f'(t)u_3'(f(t))\rangle$$

$$= f'(t)\mathbf{u}'(t)$$

41. $D_t\left[\mathbf{u}(t)\cdot\mathbf{v}(t)\right]=\mathbf{u}'(t)\cdot\mathbf{v}(t)+\mathbf{u}(t)\cdot\mathbf{v}'(t)$ [by Formula 4 of Theorem 3]

$$=\left(-4t\,\mathbf{j}+9t^2\,\mathbf{k}\right)\cdot\left(t\,\mathbf{i}+\cos t\,\mathbf{j}+\sin t\,\mathbf{k}\right)+\left(\mathbf{i}-2t^2\,\mathbf{j}+3t^3\,\mathbf{k}\right)\cdot\left(\mathbf{i}-\sin t\,\mathbf{j}+\cos t\,\mathbf{k}\right)$$

$$=-4t\cos t+9t^2\sin t+1+2t^2\sin t+3t^3\cos t$$

$$=1-4t\cos t+11t^2\sin t+3t^3\cos t$$

42. $D_t\left[\mathbf{u}(t)\times\mathbf{v}(t)\right]=\mathbf{u}'(t)\times\mathbf{v}(t)+\mathbf{u}(t)\times\mathbf{v}'(t)$ [by Formula 5 of Theorem 3]

$$=\left(-4t\,\mathbf{j}+9t^2\,\mathbf{k}\right)\times\left(t\,\mathbf{i}+\cos t\,\mathbf{j}+\sin t\,\mathbf{k}\right)+\left(\mathbf{i}-2t^2\,\mathbf{j}+3t^3\,\mathbf{k}\right)\times\left(\mathbf{i}-\sin t\,\mathbf{j}+\cos t\,\mathbf{k}\right)$$

$$=\left(-4t\sin t-9t^2\cos t\right)\mathbf{i}+\left(9t^3-0\right)\mathbf{j}+\left(0+4t^2\right)\mathbf{k}$$

$$+\left(-2t^2\cos t+3t^3\sin t\right)\mathbf{i}+\left(3t^3-\cos t\right)\mathbf{j}+\left(-\sin t+2t^2\right)\mathbf{k}$$

$$=\left[(\sin t)\left(3t^3-4t\right)-11t^2\cos t\right]\mathbf{i}+\left(12t^3-\cos t\right)\mathbf{j}+\left(6t^2-\sin t\right)\mathbf{k}$$

43. $\dfrac{d}{dt}\left[\mathbf{r}(t)\times\mathbf{r}'(t)\right]=\mathbf{r}'(t)\times\mathbf{r}'(t)+\mathbf{r}(t)\times\mathbf{r}''(t)$ by Formula 5 of Theorem 3. But $\mathbf{r}'(t)\times\mathbf{r}'(t)=\mathbf{0}$ (by the margin

note on page 668). Thus, $\dfrac{d}{dt}\left[\mathbf{r}(t)\times\mathbf{r}'(t)\right]=\mathbf{r}(t)\times\mathbf{r}''(t)$.

44. $\dfrac{d}{dt}\left(\mathbf{u}(t)\cdot\left[\mathbf{v}(t)\times\mathbf{w}(t)\right]\right)=\mathbf{u}'(t)\cdot\left[\mathbf{v}(t)\times\mathbf{w}(t)\right]+\mathbf{u}(t)\cdot\dfrac{d}{dt}\left[\mathbf{v}(t)\times\mathbf{w}(t)\right]$

$$=\mathbf{u}'(t)\cdot\left[\mathbf{v}(t)\times\mathbf{w}(t)\right]+\mathbf{u}(t)\cdot\left[\mathbf{v}'(t)\times\mathbf{w}(t)+\mathbf{v}(t)\times\mathbf{w}'(t)\right]$$

$$=\mathbf{u}'(t)\cdot\left[\mathbf{v}(t)\times\mathbf{w}(t)\right]+\mathbf{u}(t)\cdot\left[\mathbf{v}'(t)\times\mathbf{w}(t)\right]+\mathbf{u}(t)\cdot\left[\mathbf{v}(t)\times\mathbf{w}'(t)\right]$$

$$=\mathbf{u}'(t)\cdot\left[\mathbf{v}(t)\times\mathbf{w}(t)\right]-\mathbf{v}'(t)\cdot\left[\mathbf{u}(t)\times\mathbf{w}(t)\right]+\mathbf{w}'(t)\cdot\left[\mathbf{u}(t)\times\mathbf{v}(t)\right]$$

45. $\dfrac{d}{dt}\left|\mathbf{r}(t)\right|=\dfrac{d}{dt}\left[\mathbf{r}(t)\cdot\mathbf{r}(t)\right]^{1/2}=\tfrac{1}{2}\left[\mathbf{r}(t)\cdot\mathbf{r}(t)\right]^{-1/2}\left[2\mathbf{r}(t)\cdot\mathbf{r}'(t)\right]=\dfrac{\mathbf{r}(t)\cdot\mathbf{r}'(t)}{\left|\mathbf{r}(t)\right|}$

46. Since $\mathbf{r}(t)\cdot\mathbf{r}'(t)=0$, we have $0=2\mathbf{r}(t)\cdot\mathbf{r}'(t)=\dfrac{d}{dt}\left[\mathbf{r}(t)\cdot\mathbf{r}(t)\right]=\dfrac{d}{dt}\left|\mathbf{r}(t)\right|^2$. Thus $\left|\mathbf{r}(t)\right|^2$, and so $\left|\mathbf{r}(t)\right|$, is a

constant, and hence the curve lies on a sphere with center the origin.

47. Since $\mathbf{u}(t)=\mathbf{r}(t)\cdot\left[\mathbf{r}'(t)\times\mathbf{r}''(t)\right]$,

$$\mathbf{u}'(t)=\mathbf{r}'(t)\cdot\left[\mathbf{r}'(t)\times\mathbf{r}''(t)\right]+\mathbf{r}(t)\cdot\dfrac{d}{dt}\left[\mathbf{r}'(t)\times\mathbf{r}''(t)\right]$$

$$=0+\mathbf{r}(t)\cdot\left[\mathbf{r}''(t)\times\mathbf{r}''(t)+\mathbf{r}'(t)\times\mathbf{r}'''(t)\right]\qquad\qquad\text{[since }\mathbf{r}'(t)\perp\mathbf{r}'(t)\times\mathbf{r}''(t)\text{]}$$

$$=\mathbf{r}(t)\cdot\left[\mathbf{r}'(t)\times\mathbf{r}'''(t)\right]\qquad\qquad\qquad\qquad\qquad\text{[since }\mathbf{r}''(t)\times\mathbf{r}''(t)=\mathbf{0}\text{]}$$

Arc Length and Curvature • • • • • • • • • • • •

1. $\mathbf{r}'(t) = \langle 2\cos t, 5, -2\sin t \rangle$ ⟹ $|\mathbf{r}'(t)| = \sqrt{(2\cos t)^2 + 5^2 + (-2\sin t)^2} = \sqrt{29}$. Then using Formula 3, we

have $L = \int_{-10}^{10} |\mathbf{r}'(t)|\, dt = \int_{-10}^{10} \sqrt{29}\, dt = \sqrt{29}\, t\big]_{-10}^{10} = 20\sqrt{29}$.

2. $\mathbf{r}'(t) = \langle 2t, \cos t + t\sin t - \cos t, -\sin t + t\cos t + \sin t \rangle = \langle 2t, t\sin t, t\cos t \rangle$ ⟹

$|\mathbf{r}'(t)| = \sqrt{(2t)^2 + (t\sin t)^2 + (t\cos t)^2} = \sqrt{4t^2 + t^2(\sin^2 t + \cos^2 t)} = \sqrt{5}\,|t| = \sqrt{5}\,t$ for $0 \le t \le \pi$. Then

using Formula 3, we have $L = \int_0^\pi |\mathbf{r}'(t)|\, dt = \int_0^\pi \sqrt{5}\, t\, dt = \sqrt{5}\, \dfrac{t^2}{2}\bigg]_0^\pi = \dfrac{\sqrt{5}}{2}\pi^2$.

3. $\mathbf{r}'(t) = \sqrt{2}\,\mathbf{i} + e^t\mathbf{j} - e^{-t}\mathbf{k}$ ⟹

$|\mathbf{r}'(t)| = \sqrt{\left(\sqrt{2}\right)^2 + (e^t)^2 + (-e^{-t})^2} = \sqrt{2 + e^{2t} + e^{-2t}} = \sqrt{(e^t + e^{-t})^2} = e^t + e^{-t}$ (since $e^t + e^{-t} > 0$).

Then $L = \int_0^1 |\mathbf{r}'(t)|\, dt = \int_0^1 (e^t + e^{-t})\, dt = \left[e^t - e^{-t}\right]_0^1 = e - e^{-1}$.

4. $\mathbf{r}'(t) = \langle 2t, 2, 1/t \rangle$, $|\mathbf{r}'(t)| = \sqrt{4t^2 + 4 + (1/t)^2} = \dfrac{1 + 2t^2}{|t|} = \dfrac{1 + 2t^2}{t}$ for $1 \le t \le e$.

$L = \int_1^e \dfrac{1 + 2t^2}{t}\, dt = \int_1^e \left(\dfrac{1}{t} + 2t\right)\, dt = \left[\ln t + t^2\right]_1^e = e^2$

5. The point $(2, 4, 8)$ corresponds to $t = 2$, so by Equation 2, $L = \int_0^2 \sqrt{(1)^2 + (2t)^2 + (3t^2)^2}\, dt$.

If $f(t) = \sqrt{1 + 4t^2 + 9t^4}$, then Simpson's Rule gives

$L \approx \dfrac{2 - 0}{10 \cdot 3}\left[f(0) + 4f(0.2) + 2f(0.4) + \cdots + 4f(1.8) + f(2)\right] \approx 9.5706$.

6. Here are two views of the curve with parametric equations $x = \cos t$, $y = \sin 3t$, $z = \sin t$:

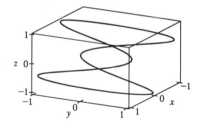 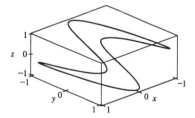

The complete curve is given by the parameter interval $[0, 2\pi]$, so

$L = \int_0^{2\pi} \sqrt{(-\sin t)^2 + (3\cos 3t)^2 + (\cos t)^2}\, dt = \int_0^{2\pi} \sqrt{1 + 9\cos^2 3t}\, dt \approx 13.9744$.

7. $\mathbf{r}'(t) = e^t(\cos t + \sin t)\mathbf{i} + e^t(\cos t - \sin t)\mathbf{j}$,

$ds/dt = |\mathbf{r}'(t)| = e^t\sqrt{(\cos t + \sin t)^2 + (\cos t - \sin t)^2} = e^t\sqrt{2\cos^2 t + 2\sin^2 t} = \sqrt{2}\,e^t$.

$s(t) = \int_0^t |\mathbf{r}'(u)|\, du = \int_0^t \sqrt{2}\,e^u\, du = \sqrt{2}\,(e^t - 1)$ ⟹ $\dfrac{1}{\sqrt{2}}s + 1 = e^t$ ⟹ $t(s) = \ln\left(\dfrac{1}{\sqrt{2}}s + 1\right)$.

Therefore, $\mathbf{r}(t(s)) = \left(\dfrac{1}{\sqrt{2}}s + 1\right)\left[\sin\left(\ln\left(\dfrac{1}{\sqrt{2}}s + 1\right)\right)\mathbf{i} + \cos\left(\ln\left(\dfrac{1}{\sqrt{2}}s + 1\right)\right)\mathbf{j}\right]$.

8. $\mathbf{r}'(t) = 2\mathbf{i} + \mathbf{j} - 5\mathbf{k}$, $ds/dt = |\mathbf{r}'(t)| = \sqrt{4 + 1 + 25} = \sqrt{30}$ and $s(t) = \int_0^t |\mathbf{r}'(u)|\, du = \int_0^t \sqrt{30}\, du = \sqrt{30}\, t$

⟹ $t(s) = \dfrac{1}{\sqrt{30}}s$. Therefore, $\mathbf{r}(t(s)) = \left(1 + \dfrac{2}{\sqrt{30}}s\right)\mathbf{i} + \left(3 + \dfrac{1}{\sqrt{30}}s\right)\mathbf{j} - \dfrac{5}{\sqrt{30}}s\,\mathbf{k}$.

9. $|\mathbf{r}'(t)| = \sqrt{(3\cos t)^2 + 16 + (-3\sin t)^2} = \sqrt{9 + 16} = 5$ and $s(t) = \int_0^t |\mathbf{r}'(u)|\, du = \int_0^t 5\, du = 5t$ ⟹

$t(s) = \dfrac{1}{5}s$. Therefore, $\mathbf{r}(t(s)) = 3\sin\left(\dfrac{1}{5}s\right)\mathbf{i} + \dfrac{4}{5}s\,\mathbf{j} + 3\cos\left(\dfrac{1}{5}s\right)\mathbf{k}$.

10. $\mathbf{r}'(t) = \dfrac{-4t}{(t^2+1)^2}\,\mathbf{i} + \dfrac{-2t^2+2}{(t^2+1)^2}\,\mathbf{j},$

$$\frac{ds}{dt} = |\mathbf{r}'(t)| = \sqrt{\left[\frac{-4t}{(t^2+1)^2}\right]^2 + \left[\frac{-2t^2+2}{(t^2+1)^2}\right]^2} = \sqrt{\frac{4t^4+8t^2+4}{(t^2+1)^4}} = \sqrt{\frac{4(t^2+1)^2}{(t^2+1)^4}}$$

$$= \sqrt{\frac{4}{(t^2+1)^2}} = \frac{2}{t^2+1}$$

Since the initial point $(1,0)$ corresponds to $t = 0$, the arc length function

$$s(t) = \int_0^t |\mathbf{r}'(u)|\, du = \int_0^t \frac{2}{u^2+1}\, du = 2\arctan t. \text{ Then } \arctan t = \tfrac{1}{2}s \;\Rightarrow\; t = \tan \tfrac{1}{2}s. \text{ Substituting, we}$$

have

$$\mathbf{r}(t(s)) = \left[\frac{2}{\tan^2\left(\frac{1}{2}s\right)+1} - 1\right]\mathbf{i} + \frac{2\tan\left(\frac{1}{2}s\right)}{\tan^2\left(\frac{1}{2}s\right)+1}\,\mathbf{j} = \frac{1-\tan^2\left(\frac{1}{2}s\right)}{1+\tan^2\left(\frac{1}{2}s\right)}\,\mathbf{i} + \frac{2\tan\left(\frac{1}{2}s\right)}{\sec^2\left(\frac{1}{2}s\right)}\,\mathbf{j}$$

$$= \frac{1-\tan^2\left(\frac{1}{2}s\right)}{\sec^2\left(\frac{1}{2}s\right)}\,\mathbf{i} + 2\tan\left(\tfrac{1}{2}s\right)\cos^2\left(\tfrac{1}{2}s\right)\mathbf{j}$$

$$= \left[\cos^2\left(\tfrac{1}{2}s\right) - \sin^2\left(\tfrac{1}{2}s\right)\right]\mathbf{i} + 2\sin\left(\tfrac{1}{2}s\right)\cos\left(\tfrac{1}{2}s\right)\mathbf{j} = \cos s\,\mathbf{i} + \sin s\,\mathbf{j}$$

With this parametrization, we recognize the function as representing the unit circle. Note here that the curve approaches, but does not include, the point $(-1, 0)$, since $\cos s = -1$ for $s = \pi + 2k\pi$ (k an integer) but then $t = \tan\left(\frac{1}{2}s\right)$ is undefined.

11. (a) $\mathbf{r}'(t) = \langle 2\cos t, 5, -2\sin t\rangle \;\Rightarrow\; |\mathbf{r}'(t)| = \sqrt{4\cos^2 t + 25 + 4\sin^2 t} = \sqrt{29}.$ Then

$$\mathbf{T}(t) = \frac{\mathbf{r}'(t)}{|\mathbf{r}'(t)|} = \tfrac{1}{\sqrt{29}}\langle 2\cos t, 5, -2\sin t\rangle \text{ or } \left\langle \tfrac{2}{\sqrt{29}}\cos t, \tfrac{5}{\sqrt{29}}, -\tfrac{2}{\sqrt{29}}\sin t\right\rangle.$$

$$\mathbf{T}'(t) = \tfrac{1}{\sqrt{29}}\langle -2\sin t, 0, -2\cos t\rangle \;\Rightarrow\; |\mathbf{T}'(t)| = \tfrac{1}{\sqrt{29}}\sqrt{4\sin^2 t + 0 + 4\cos^2 t} = \tfrac{2}{\sqrt{29}}. \text{ Thus}$$

$$\mathbf{N}(t) = \frac{\mathbf{T}'(t)}{|\mathbf{T}'(t)|} = \frac{1/\sqrt{29}}{2/\sqrt{29}}\langle -2\sin t, 0, -2\cos t\rangle = \langle -\sin t, 0, -\cos t\rangle.$$

(b) $\kappa(t) = \dfrac{|\mathbf{T}'(t)|}{|\mathbf{r}'(t)|} = \dfrac{2/\sqrt{29}}{\sqrt{29}} = \dfrac{2}{29}.$

12. (a) $\mathbf{r}'(t) = \langle 2t, t\sin t, t\cos t\rangle \;\Rightarrow\; |\mathbf{r}'(t)| = \sqrt{4t^2 + t^2\sin^2 t + t^2\cos^2 t} = \sqrt{5t^2} = \sqrt{5}\,t$ (since

$t > 0$). Then $\mathbf{T}(t) = \dfrac{\mathbf{r}'(t)}{|\mathbf{r}'(t)|} = \dfrac{1}{\sqrt{5}\,t}\langle 2t, t\sin t, t\cos t\rangle = \tfrac{1}{\sqrt{5}}\langle 2, \sin t, \cos t\rangle.$

$$\mathbf{T}'(t) = \tfrac{1}{\sqrt{5}}\langle 0, \cos t, -\sin t\rangle \;\Rightarrow\; |\mathbf{T}'(t)| = \tfrac{1}{\sqrt{5}}\sqrt{0 + \cos^2 t + \sin^2 t} = \tfrac{1}{\sqrt{5}}. \text{ Thus}$$

$$\mathbf{N}(t) = \frac{\mathbf{T}'(t)}{|\mathbf{T}'(t)|} = \frac{1/\sqrt{5}}{1/\sqrt{5}}\langle 0, \cos t, -\sin t\rangle = \langle 0, \cos t, -\sin t\rangle.$$

(b) $\kappa(t) = \dfrac{|\mathbf{T}'(t)|}{|\mathbf{r}'(t)|} = \dfrac{1/\sqrt{5}}{\sqrt{5}\,t} = \dfrac{1}{5t}.$

13. (a) $\mathbf{r}'(t) = \langle t^2, 2t, 2 \rangle$ $\Rightarrow$ $|\mathbf{r}'(t)| = \sqrt{t^4 + 4t^2 + 4} = \sqrt{(t^2 + 2)^2} = t^2 + 2$. Then

$$\mathbf{T}(t) = \frac{\mathbf{r}'(t)}{|\mathbf{r}'(t)|} = \frac{1}{t^2 + 2} \langle t^2, 2t, 2 \rangle.$$

$$\mathbf{T}'(t) = \frac{-2t}{(t^2 + 2)^2} \langle t^2, 2t, 2 \rangle + \frac{1}{t^2 + 2} \langle 2t, 2, 0 \rangle \qquad \text{[by Theorem 10.2.3 #3]}$$

$$= \frac{1}{(t^2 + 2)^2} \langle -2t^3, -4t^2, -4t \rangle + \frac{1}{(t^2 + 2)^2} \langle 2t^3 + 4t, 2t^2 + 4, 0 \rangle = \frac{1}{(t^2 + 2)^2} \langle 4t, 4 - 2t^2, -4t \rangle$$

$$|\mathbf{T}'(t)| = \frac{1}{(t^2 + 2)^2} \sqrt{16t^2 + (16 - 16t^2 + 4t^4) + 16t^2} = \frac{1}{(t^2 + 2)^2} \sqrt{4t^4 + 16t^2 + 16}$$

$$= \frac{1}{(t^2 + 2)^2} \sqrt{4(t^2 + 2)^2} = \frac{2(t^2 + 2)}{(t^2 + 2)^2} = \frac{2}{t^2 + 2}$$

Thus $\mathbf{N}(t) = \dfrac{\mathbf{T}'(t)}{|\mathbf{T}'(t)|} = \dfrac{1/(t^2 + 2)^2}{2/(t^2 + 2)} \langle 4t, 4 - 2t^2, -4t \rangle = \dfrac{1}{t^2 + 2} \langle 2t, 2 - t^2, -2t \rangle.$

(b) $\kappa(t) = \dfrac{|\mathbf{T}'(t)|}{|\mathbf{r}'(t)|} = \dfrac{2/(t^2 + 2)}{t^2 + 2} = \dfrac{2}{(t^2 + 2)^2}$

14. (a) $\mathbf{T}(t) = \dfrac{\mathbf{r}'(t)}{|\mathbf{r}'(t)|} = \dfrac{1}{\sqrt{4t^2 + 4 + (1/t)^2}} \langle 2t, 2, 1/t \rangle = \dfrac{|t|}{2t^2 + 1} \langle 2t, 2, 1/t \rangle.$ But since the

k-component is $\ln t$, t is positive, $|t| = t$ and $\mathbf{T}(t) = \dfrac{1}{2t^2 + 1} \langle 2t^2, 2t, 1 \rangle.$ Then

$$\mathbf{T}'(t) = \frac{1}{2t^2 + 1} \langle 4t, 2, 0 \rangle - (2t^2 + 1)^{-2} (4t) \langle 2t^2, 2t, 1 \rangle = \frac{1}{(2t^2 + 1)^2} \langle 4t, 2 - 4t^2, -4t \rangle, \text{ so}$$

$$\mathbf{N}(t) = \frac{\mathbf{T}'(t)}{|\mathbf{T}'(t)|} = \frac{\langle 4t, 2 - 4t^2, -4t \rangle}{\sqrt{(4t)^2 + (2 - 4t^2)^2 + (-4t)^2}} = \frac{1}{2t^2 + 1} \langle 2t, 1 - 2t^2, -2t \rangle.$$

(b) $\kappa(t) = \dfrac{|\mathbf{T}'(t)|}{|\mathbf{r}'(t)|} = \dfrac{2}{2t^2 + 1} \left(\dfrac{t}{2t^2 + 1} \right) = \dfrac{2t}{(2t^2 + 1)^2}$

15. $\mathbf{r}'(t) = 2t\,\mathbf{i} + \mathbf{k}$, $\mathbf{r}''(t) = 2\mathbf{i}$, $|\mathbf{r}'(t)| = \sqrt{(2t)^2 + 0^2 + 1^2} = \sqrt{4t^2 + 1}$, $\mathbf{r}'(t) \times \mathbf{r}''(t) = 2\mathbf{j}$, $|\mathbf{r}'(t) \times \mathbf{r}''(t)| = 2$.

Then $\kappa(t) = \dfrac{|\mathbf{r}'(t) \times \mathbf{r}''(t)|}{|\mathbf{r}'(t)|^3} = \dfrac{2}{\left(\sqrt{4t^2 + 1}\right)^3} = \dfrac{2}{(4t^2 + 1)^{3/2}}.$

16. $\mathbf{r}'(t) = \mathbf{i} + \mathbf{j} + 2t\,\mathbf{k}$, $\mathbf{r}''(t) = 2\mathbf{k}$, $|\mathbf{r}'(t)| = \sqrt{1^2 + 1^2 + (2t)^2} = \sqrt{4t^2 + 2}$,

$\mathbf{r}'(t) \times \mathbf{r}''(t) = 2\mathbf{i} - 2\mathbf{j}$, $|\mathbf{r}'(t) \times \mathbf{r}''(t)| = \sqrt{2^2 + 2^2 + 0^2} = \sqrt{8} = 2\sqrt{2}$. Then

$$\kappa(t) = \frac{|\mathbf{r}'(t) \times \mathbf{r}''(t)|}{|\mathbf{r}'(t)|^3} = \frac{2\sqrt{2}}{\left(\sqrt{4t^2 + 2}\right)^3} = \frac{2\sqrt{2}}{\left(\sqrt{2}\sqrt{2t^2 + 1}\right)^3} = \frac{1}{(2t^2 + 1)^{3/2}}.$$

17. $\mathbf{r}'(t) = \langle \cos t, -\sin t, \cos t \rangle$, $\mathbf{r}''(t) = \langle -\sin t, -\cos t, -\sin t \rangle$, $|\mathbf{r}'(t)|^3 = \left(\sqrt{\cos^2 t + 1}\right)^3$,

$|\mathbf{r}'(t) \times \mathbf{r}''(t)| = |\langle 1, 0, -1 \rangle| = \sqrt{2}$, $\kappa(t) = \dfrac{|\mathbf{r}'(t) \times \mathbf{r}''(t)|}{|\mathbf{r}'(t)|^3} = \dfrac{\sqrt{2}}{(1 + \cos^2 t)^{3/2}}$

18. $\mathbf{r}'(t) = \langle e^t \cos t - e^t \sin t, e^t \cos t + e^t \sin t, 1 \rangle$. The point $(1, 0, 0)$ corresponds to $t = 0$, and $\mathbf{r}'(0) = \langle 1, 1, 1 \rangle$

$\Rightarrow$ $|\mathbf{r}'(0)| = \sqrt{1^2 + 1^2 + 1^2} = \sqrt{3}$.

$\mathbf{r}''(t) = \langle e^t \cos t - e^t \sin t - e^t \cos t - e^t \sin t, e^t \cos t - e^t \sin t + e^t \cos t + e^t \sin t, 0 \rangle$

$= \langle -2e^t \sin t, 2e^t \cos t, 0 \rangle$ $\Rightarrow$ $\mathbf{r}''(0) = \langle 0, 2, 0 \rangle$. $\mathbf{r}'(0) \times \mathbf{r}''(0) = \langle -2, 0, 2 \rangle$.

$|\mathbf{r}'(0) \times \mathbf{r}''(0)| = \sqrt{(-2)^2 + 0^2 + 2^2} = \sqrt{8} = 2\sqrt{2}$. Then $\kappa(0) = \dfrac{|\mathbf{r}'(0) \times \mathbf{r}''(0)|}{|\mathbf{r}'(0)|^3} = \dfrac{2\sqrt{2}}{(\sqrt{3})^3} = \dfrac{2\sqrt{2}}{3\sqrt{3}}$

or $\dfrac{2\sqrt{6}}{9}$.

19. $\mathbf{r}'(t) = \langle \sqrt{2}, e^t, -e^{-t} \rangle$. The point $(0, 1, 1)$ corresponds to $t = 0$, and $\mathbf{r}'(0) = \langle \sqrt{2}, 1, -1 \rangle$ $\Rightarrow$

$|\mathbf{r}'(0)| = \sqrt{(\sqrt{2})^2 + 1^2 + (-1)^2} = 2$. $\mathbf{r}''(t) = \langle 0, e^t, e^{-t} \rangle$ $\Rightarrow$ $\mathbf{r}''(0) = \langle 0, 1, 1 \rangle$.

$\mathbf{r}'(0) \times \mathbf{r}''(0) = \langle 2, -\sqrt{2}, \sqrt{2} \rangle$, $|\mathbf{r}'(0) \times \mathbf{r}''(0)| = \sqrt{2^2 + (-\sqrt{2})^2 + (\sqrt{2})^2} = \sqrt{8} = 2\sqrt{2}$. Then

$\kappa(0) = \dfrac{|\mathbf{r}'(0) \times \mathbf{r}''(0)|}{|\mathbf{r}'(0)|^3} = \dfrac{2\sqrt{2}}{2^3} = \dfrac{\sqrt{2}}{4}$.

20.

$\mathbf{r}(t) = \langle t, 4t^{3/2}, -t^2 \rangle$ $\Rightarrow$ $\mathbf{r}'(t) = \langle 1, 6t^{1/2}, -2t \rangle$,

$\mathbf{r}''(t) = \langle 0, 3t^{-1/2}, -2 \rangle$, $|\mathbf{r}'(t)|^3 = (1 + 36t + 4t^2)^{3/2}$,

$\mathbf{r}'(t) \times \mathbf{r}''(t) = \langle -12t^{1/2} + 6t^{1/2}, 2, 3t^{-1/2} \rangle$ $\Rightarrow$

$|\mathbf{r}'(t) \times \mathbf{r}''(t)| = \sqrt{36t + 4 + 9t^{-1}} = \left[\dfrac{36t^2 + 4t + 9}{t} \right]^{1/2}$

$\kappa(t) = \dfrac{|\mathbf{r}'(t) \times \mathbf{r}''(t)|}{|\mathbf{r}'(t)|^3} = \left(\dfrac{36t^2 + 4t + 9}{t} \right)^{1/2} \dfrac{1}{(1 + 36t + 4t^2)^{3/2}} = \dfrac{\sqrt{36t^2 + 4t + 9}}{t^{1/2}(1 + 36t + 4t^2)^{3/2}}$.

The point $(1, 4, -1)$ corresponds to $t = 1$, so the curvature at this point is $\kappa(1) = \dfrac{\sqrt{36 + 4 + 9}}{(1 + 36 + 4)^{3/2}} = \dfrac{7}{41\sqrt{41}}$.

21. $f(x) = x^3$, $f'(x) = 3x^2$, $f''(x) = 6x$, $\kappa(x) = \dfrac{|f''(x)|}{[1 + (f'(x))^2]^{3/2}} = \dfrac{6|x|}{(1 + 9x^4)^{3/2}}$

22. $f(x) = \cos x$, $f'(x) = -\sin x$, $f''(x) = -\cos x$,

$\kappa(x) = \dfrac{|f''(x)|}{[1 + (f'(x))^2]^{3/2}} = \dfrac{|-\cos x|}{[1 + (-\sin x)^2]^{3/2}} = \dfrac{|\cos x|}{(1 + \sin^2 x)^{3/2}}$

23. $f(x) = 4x^{5/2}$, $f'(x) = 10x^{3/2}$, $f''(x) = 15x^{1/2}$,

$\kappa(x) = \dfrac{|f''(x)|}{[1 + (f'(x))^2]^{3/2}} = \dfrac{|15x^{1/2}|}{[1 + (10x^{3/2})^2]^{3/2}} = \dfrac{15\sqrt{x}}{(1 + 100x^3)^{3/2}}$

24. $y' = \dfrac{1}{x}$, $y'' = -\dfrac{1}{x^2}$,

$$\kappa(x) = \frac{|y''(x)|}{\left[1 + (y'(x))^2\right]^{3/2}} = \left|\frac{-1}{x^2}\right| \frac{1}{(1 + 1/x^2)^{3/2}} = \frac{1}{x^2} \frac{(x^2)^{3/2}}{(x^2 + 1)^{3/2}} = \frac{|x|}{(x^2 + 1)^{3/2}} = \frac{x}{(x^2 + 1)^{3/2}}$$

(since $x > 0$). To find the maximum curvature, we first find the critical numbers of $\kappa(x)$:

$$\kappa'(x) = \frac{(x^2 + 1)^{3/2} - x\left(\frac{3}{2}\right)(x^2 + 1)^{1/2}(2x)}{\left[(x^2 + 1)^{3/2}\right]^2} = \frac{(x^2 + 1)^{1/2}\left[(x^2 + 1) - 3x^2\right]}{(x^2 + 1)^3} = \frac{1 - 2x^2}{(x^2 + 1)^{5/2}};$$

$\kappa'(x) = 0 \Rightarrow 1 - 2x^2 = 0$, so the only critical number in the domain is $x = \frac{1}{\sqrt{2}}$. Since $\kappa'(x) > 0$ for

$0 < x < \frac{1}{\sqrt{2}}$ and $\kappa'(x) < 0$ for $x > \frac{1}{\sqrt{2}}$, $\kappa(x)$ attains its maximum at $x = \frac{1}{\sqrt{2}}$. Thus, the maximum curvature

occurs at $\left(\frac{1}{\sqrt{2}}, \ln \frac{1}{\sqrt{2}}\right)$. Since $\displaystyle\lim_{x \to \infty} \frac{x}{(x^2 + 1)^{3/2}} = 0$, $\kappa(x)$ approaches 0 as $x \to \infty$.

25. Since $y' = y'' = e^x$, the curvature is $\kappa(x) = \dfrac{|y''(x)|}{\left[1 + (y'(x))^2\right]^{3/2}} = \dfrac{e^x}{(1 + e^{2x})^{3/2}} = e^x\left(1 + e^{2x}\right)^{-3/2}$.

To find the maximum curvature, we first find the critical numbers of $\kappa(x)$:

$$\kappa'(x) = e^x\left(1 + e^{2x}\right)^{-3/2} + e^x\left(-\frac{3}{2}\right)\left(1 + e^{2x}\right)^{-5/2}(2e^{2x}) = e^x\frac{1 + e^{2x} - 3e^{2x}}{(1 + e^{2x})^{5/2}} = e^x\frac{1 - 2e^{2x}}{(1 + e^{2x})^{5/2}}.$$

$\kappa'(x) = 0$ when $1 - 2e^{2x} = 0$, so $e^{2x} = \frac{1}{2}$ or $x = -\frac{1}{2}\ln 2$. And since $1 - 2e^{2x} > 0$ for $x < -\frac{1}{2}\ln 2$ and

$1 - 2e^{2x} < 0$ for $x > -\frac{1}{2}\ln 2$, the maximum curvature is attained at the point

$\left(-\frac{1}{2}\ln 2, e^{(-\ln 2)/2}\right) = \left(-\frac{1}{2}\ln 2, \frac{1}{\sqrt{2}}\right)$. Since $\displaystyle\lim_{x \to \infty} e^x\left(1 + e^{2x}\right)^{-3/2} = 0$, $\kappa(x)$ approaches 0 as $x \to \infty$.

26. We can take the parabola as having its vertex at the origin and opening upward, so the equation is

$f(x) = ax^2$, $a > 0$. Then by Equation 11, $\kappa(x) = \dfrac{|f''(x)|}{\left[1 + (f'(x))^2\right]^{3/2}} = \dfrac{|2a|}{\left[1 + (2ax)^2\right]^{3/2}} = \dfrac{2a}{(1 + 4a^2x^2)^{3/2}}$,

thus $\kappa(0) = 2a$. We want $\kappa(0) = 4$, so $a = 2$ and the equation is $y = 2x^2$.

27. (a) C appears to be changing direction more quickly at P than Q, so we would expect the curvature to be greater
at P.

(b) First we sketch approximate osculating circles at P and
Q. Using the axes scale as a guide, we measure the radius
of the osculating circle at P to be approximately 0.8 units,

thus $\rho = \dfrac{1}{\kappa} \Rightarrow \kappa = \dfrac{1}{\rho} \approx \dfrac{1}{0.8} \approx 1.3$. Similarly, we

estimate the radius of the osculating circle at Q to be

1.4 units, so $\kappa = \dfrac{1}{\rho} \approx \dfrac{1}{1.4} \approx 0.7$.

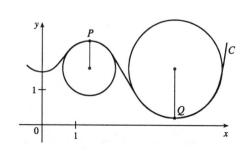

28. $y = xe^{-x}$ $\Rightarrow$ $y' = e^{-x}(1-x), y'' = e^{-x}(x-2)$, and $\kappa(x) = \dfrac{|y''|}{[1+(y')^2]^{3/2}} = \dfrac{e^{-x}|x-2|}{[1+e^{-2x}(1-x)^2]^{3/2}}.$

The graph of the curvature here is what we would expect. The graph of xe^{-x} is bending most sharply slightly to the

right of the origin. As $x \to \infty$, the graph of xe^{-x} is asymptotic to the x-axis, and so the curvature approaches zero.

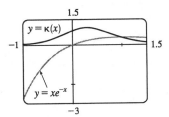

29. $y = x^4$ $\Rightarrow$ $y' = 4x^3, y'' = 12x^2$, and $\kappa(x) = \dfrac{|y''|}{[1+(y')^2]^{3/2}} = \dfrac{12x^2}{(1+16x^6)^{3/2}}.$ The appearance of the two

humps in this graph is perhaps a little surprising, but it is explained by the fact that $y = x^4$ is very flat around the

origin, and so here the curvature is zero.

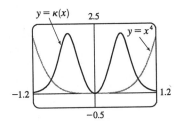

30. Notice that the curve a is highest for the same x-values at which curve b is turning more sharply, and a is 0 or near 0

where b is nearly straight. So, a must be the graph of $y = \kappa(x)$, and b is the graph of $y = f(x)$.

31. Notice that the curve b has two inflection points at which the graph appears almost straight. We would expect the

curvature to be 0 or nearly 0 at these values, but the curve a isn't near 0 there. Thus, a must be the graph of

$y = f(x)$ rather than the graph of curvature, and b is the graph of $y = \kappa(x)$.

32. Here $\mathbf{r}(t) = \langle f(t), g(t) \rangle$, $\mathbf{r}'(t) = \langle f'(t), g'(t) \rangle$, $\mathbf{r}''(t) = \langle f''(t), g''(t) \rangle$,

$$|\mathbf{r}'(t)|^3 = \left[\sqrt{(f'(t))^2 + (g'(t))^2} \right]^3 = \left[(f'(t))^2 + (g'(t))^2 \right]^{3/2} = (\dot{x}^2 + \dot{y}^2)^{3/2}, \text{ and}$$

$$|\mathbf{r}'(t) \times \mathbf{r}''(t)| = |\langle 0, 0, f'(t)g''(t) - f''(t)g'(t) \rangle| = \left[(\dot{x}\ddot{y} - \ddot{x}\dot{y})^2 \right]^{1/2} = |\dot{x}\ddot{y} - \dot{y}\ddot{x}|.$$

Thus $\kappa(t) = \dfrac{|\dot{x}\ddot{y} - \dot{y}\ddot{x}|}{(\dot{x}^2 + \dot{y}^2)^{3/2}}.$

33. $x = e^t \cos t \;\Rightarrow\; \dot{x} = e^t (\cos t - \sin t) \;\Rightarrow\; \ddot{x} = e^t(-\sin t - \cos t) + e^t(\cos t - \sin t) = -2e^t \sin t,$

$y = e^t \sin t \;\Rightarrow\; \dot{y} = e^t(\cos t + \sin t) \;\Rightarrow\; \ddot{y} = e^t(-\sin t + \cos t) + e^t(\cos t + \sin t) = 2e^t \cos t.$ Then

$$\kappa(t) = \frac{|\dot{x}\ddot{y} - \dot{y}\ddot{x}|}{(\dot{x}^2 + \dot{y}^2)^{3/2}} = \frac{\left|e^t(\cos t - \sin t)(2e^t \cos t) - e^t(\cos t + \sin t)(-2e^t \sin t)\right|}{\left([e^t(\cos t - \sin t)]^2 + [e^t(\cos t + \sin t)]^2\right)^{3/2}}$$

$$= \frac{\left|2e^{2t}\left(\cos^2 t - \sin t \cos t + \sin t \cos t + \sin^2 t\right)\right|}{\left[e^{2t}\left(\cos^2 t - 2\cos t \sin t + \sin^2 t + \cos^2 t + 2\cos t \sin t + \sin^2 t\right)\right]^{3/2}}$$

$$= \frac{\left|2e^{2t}(1)\right|}{[e^{2t}(1+1)]^{3/2}} = \frac{2e^{2t}}{e^{3t}(2)^{3/2}} = \frac{1}{\sqrt{2}\,e^t}$$

34. $x = 1 + t^3 \;\Rightarrow\; \dot{x} = 3t^2 \;\Rightarrow\; \ddot{x} = 6t, \quad y = t + t^2 \;\Rightarrow\; \dot{y} = 1 + 2t \;\Rightarrow\; \ddot{y} = 2.$ Then

$$\kappa(t) = \frac{|\dot{x}\ddot{y} - \dot{y}\ddot{x}|}{(\dot{x}^2 + \dot{y}^2)^{3/2}} = \frac{\left|(3t^2)(2) - (1+2t)(6t)\right|}{\left[(3t^2)^2 + (1+2t)^2\right]^{3/2}} = \frac{\left|-6t^2 - 6t\right|}{(9t^4 + 4t^2 + 4t + 1)^{3/2}}$$

$$= \frac{6\left|t^2 + t\right|}{(9t^4 + 4t^2 + 4t + 1)^{3/2}}$$

35. $\left(1, \frac{2}{3}, 1\right)$ corresponds to $t = 1$. $\mathbf{T}(t) = \dfrac{\mathbf{r}'(t)}{|\mathbf{r}'(t)|} = \dfrac{\langle 2t, 2t^2, 1\rangle}{\sqrt{4t^2 + 4t^4 + 1}} = \dfrac{\langle 2t, 2t^2, 1\rangle}{2t^2 + 1}$, so $\mathbf{T}(1) = \left\langle \frac{2}{3}, \frac{2}{3}, \frac{1}{3}\right\rangle$.

$\mathbf{T}'(t) = -4t\left(2t^2 + 1\right)^{-2}\langle 2t, 2t^2, 1\rangle + \left(2t^2 + 1\right)^{-1}\langle 2, 4t, 0\rangle$ [by Theorem 10.2.3 #3]

$\quad = \left(2t^2 + 1\right)^{-2}\left\langle -8t^2 + 4t^2 + 2, -8t^3 + 8t^3 + 4t, -4t\right\rangle = 2\left(2t^2 + 1\right)^{-2}\left\langle 1 - 2t^2, 2t, -2t\right\rangle$

$\mathbf{N}(t) = \dfrac{\mathbf{T}'(t)}{|\mathbf{T}'(t)|} = \dfrac{2\left(2t^2 + 1\right)^{-2}\left\langle 1 - 2t^2, 2t, -2t\right\rangle}{2(2t^2 + 1)^{-2}\sqrt{(1 - 2t^2)^2 + (2t)^2 + (-2t)^2}} = \dfrac{\left\langle 1 - 2t^2, 2t, -2t\right\rangle}{\sqrt{1 - 4t^2 + 4t^4 + 8t^2}}$

$\quad = \dfrac{\left\langle 1 - 2t^2, 2t, -2t\right\rangle}{1 + 2t^2}$

$\mathbf{N}(1) = \left\langle -\frac{1}{3}, \frac{2}{3}, -\frac{2}{3}\right\rangle$ and $\mathbf{B}(1) = \mathbf{T}(1) \times \mathbf{N}(1) = \left\langle -\frac{4}{9} - \frac{2}{9}, -\left(-\frac{4}{9} + \frac{1}{9}\right), \frac{4}{9} + \frac{2}{9}\right\rangle = \left\langle -\frac{2}{3}, \frac{1}{3}, \frac{2}{3}\right\rangle.$

36. $(1, 0, 1)$ corresponds to $t = 0$. $\mathbf{r}(t) = e^t\langle 1, \sin t, \cos t\rangle$, so

$\mathbf{r}'(t) = e^t\langle 1, \sin t, \cos t\rangle + e^t\langle 0, \cos t, -\sin t\rangle = e^t\langle 1, \sin t + \cos t, \cos t - \sin t\rangle$ and

$\mathbf{T}(t) = \dfrac{\mathbf{r}'(t)}{|\mathbf{r}'(t)|} = \dfrac{e^t\langle 1, \sin t + \cos t, \cos t - \sin t\rangle}{e^t\sqrt{1 + \sin^2 t + 2\sin t \cos t + \cos^2 t + \cos^2 t - 2\sin t \cos t + \sin^2 t}}$

$\quad = \dfrac{\langle 1, \sin t + \cos t, \cos t - \sin t\rangle}{\sqrt{3}},$

$\mathbf{T}(0) = \left\langle \frac{1}{\sqrt{3}}, \frac{1}{\sqrt{3}}, \frac{1}{\sqrt{3}} \right\rangle.$ $\mathbf{T}'(t) = \frac{1}{\sqrt{3}} \left\langle 0, \cos t - \sin t, -\sin t - \cos t \right\rangle,$ so

$$\mathbf{N}(t) = \frac{\mathbf{T}'(t)}{|\mathbf{T}'(t)|} = \frac{\frac{1}{\sqrt{3}} \left\langle 0, \cos t - \sin t, -\sin t - \cos t \right\rangle}{\frac{1}{\sqrt{3}} \sqrt{0^2 + \cos^2 t - 2\cos t \sin t + \sin^2 t + \sin^2 t + 2\sin t \cos t + \cos^2 t}}$$

$$= \frac{1}{\sqrt{2}} \left\langle 0, \cos t - \sin t, -\sin t - \cos t \right\rangle.$$

$\mathbf{N}(0) = \left\langle 0, \frac{1}{\sqrt{2}}, -\frac{1}{\sqrt{2}} \right\rangle$ and $\mathbf{B}(0) = \mathbf{T}(0) \times \mathbf{N}(0) = \left\langle -\frac{2}{\sqrt{6}}, \frac{1}{\sqrt{6}}, \frac{1}{\sqrt{6}} \right\rangle.$

37. $(0, \pi, -2)$ corresponds to $t = \pi.$ $\mathbf{r}(t) = \left\langle 2\sin 3t, t, 2\cos 3t \right\rangle$ ⇒

$$\mathbf{T}(t) = \frac{\mathbf{r}'(t)}{|\mathbf{r}'(t)|} = \frac{\left\langle 6\cos 3t, 1, -6\sin 3t \right\rangle}{\sqrt{36\cos^2 3t + 1 + 36\sin^2 3t}} = \frac{1}{\sqrt{37}} \left\langle 6\cos 3t, 1, -6\sin 3t \right\rangle.$$

$\mathbf{T}(\pi) = \frac{1}{\sqrt{37}} \left\langle -6, 1, 0 \right\rangle$ is a normal vector for the normal plane, and so $\left\langle -6, 1, 0 \right\rangle$ is also normal. Thus an equation

for the plane is $-6(x - 0) + 1(y - \pi) + 0(z + 2) = 0$ or $y - 6x = \pi.$

$\mathbf{T}'(t) = \frac{1}{\sqrt{37}} \left\langle -18\sin 3t, 0, -18\cos 3t \right\rangle$ ⇒ $|\mathbf{T}'(t)| = \frac{\sqrt{18^2 \sin^2 3t + 18^2 \cos^2 3t}}{\sqrt{37}} = \frac{18}{\sqrt{37}}$ ⇒

$\mathbf{N}(t) = \frac{\mathbf{T}'(t)}{|\mathbf{T}'(t)|} = \left\langle -\sin 3t, 0, -\cos 3t \right\rangle.$ So $\mathbf{N}(\pi) = \left\langle 0, 0, 1 \right\rangle$ and

$\mathbf{B}(\pi) = \frac{1}{\sqrt{37}} \left\langle -6, 1, 0 \right\rangle \times \left\langle 0, 0, 1 \right\rangle = \frac{1}{\sqrt{37}} \left\langle 1, 6, 0 \right\rangle.$ Since $\mathbf{B}(\pi)$ is a normal to the osculating plane, so is $\left\langle 1, 6, 0 \right\rangle$

and an equation for the plane is $1(x - 0) + 6(y - \pi) + 0(z + 2) = 0$ or $x + 6y = 6\pi.$

38. $t = 1$ at $(1, 1, 1).$ $\mathbf{r}'(t) = \left\langle 1, 2t, 3t^2 \right\rangle.$ $\mathbf{r}'(1) = \left\langle 1, 2, 3 \right\rangle$ is normal to the normal plane, so an equation for this

plane is $1(x - 1) + 2(y - 1) + 3(z - 1) = 0$, or $x + 2y + 3z = 6.$

$\mathbf{T}(t) = \frac{\mathbf{r}'(t)}{|\mathbf{r}'(t)|} = \frac{1}{\sqrt{1 + 4t^2 + 9t^4}} \left\langle 1, 2t, 3t^2 \right\rangle.$ Using the product rule on each term of $\mathbf{T}(t)$ gives

$$\mathbf{T}'(t) = \frac{1}{(1 + 4t^2 + 9t^4)^{3/2}} \left\langle -\frac{1}{2}(8t + 36t^3), 2(1 + 4t^2 + 9t^4) - \frac{1}{2}(8t + 36t^3)2t, \right.$$

$$\left. 6t(1 + 4t^2 + 9t^4) - \frac{1}{2}(8t + 36t^3)3t^2 \right\rangle$$

$$= \frac{1}{(1 + 4t^2 + 9t^4)^{3/2}} \left\langle -4t - 18t^3, 2 - 18t^4, 6t + 12t^3 \right\rangle = \frac{-2}{(14)^{3/2}} \left\langle 11, 8, -9 \right\rangle \text{ when } t = 1.$$

$\mathbf{N}(1) \parallel \mathbf{T}'(1) \parallel \left\langle 11, 8, -9 \right\rangle$ and $\mathbf{T}(1) \parallel \mathbf{r}'(1) = \left\langle 1, 2, 3 \right\rangle$ ⇒ a normal vector to the osculating plane is

$\left\langle 11, 8, -9 \right\rangle \times \left\langle 1, 2, 3 \right\rangle = \left\langle 42, -42, 14 \right\rangle$ or equivalently $\left\langle 3, -3, 1 \right\rangle.$ An equation for the plane is

$3(x - 1) - 3(y - 1) + (z - 1) = 0$ or $3x - 3y + z = 1.$

39. The ellipse is given by the parametric equations $x = 2 \cos t$, $y = 3 \sin t$, so using the result from Exercise 32,

$$\kappa(t) = \frac{|\dot{x}\ddot{y} - \ddot{x}\dot{y}|}{(\dot{x}^2 + \dot{y}^2)^{3/2}} = \frac{|(-2 \sin t)(-3 \sin t) - (3 \cos t)(-2 \cos t)|}{(4 \sin^2 t + 9 \cos^2 t)^{3/2}} = \frac{6}{(4 \sin^2 t + 9 \cos^2 t)^{3/2}}.$$

At $(2, 0)$, $t = 0$. Now $\kappa(0) = \frac{6}{27} = \frac{2}{9}$, so the radius of the osculating circle is $1/\kappa(0) = \frac{9}{2}$ and its center is

$\left(-\frac{5}{2}, 0\right)$. Its equation is therefore $\left(x + \frac{5}{2}\right)^2 + y^2 = \frac{81}{4}$. At $(0, 3)$, $t = \frac{\pi}{2}$, and $\kappa\left(\frac{\pi}{2}\right) = \frac{6}{8} = \frac{3}{4}$. So the radius of the

osculating circle is $\frac{4}{3}$ and its center is $\left(0, \frac{5}{3}\right)$. Hence its equation is $x^2 + \left(y - \frac{5}{3}\right)^2 = \frac{16}{9}$.

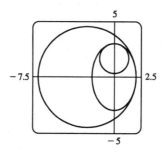

40. $y = \frac{1}{2}x^2 \Rightarrow y' = x$ and $y'' = 1$, so Formula 11 gives $\kappa(x) = \dfrac{1}{(1 + x^2)^{3/2}}$. So the curvature at $(0, 0)$ is

$\kappa(0) = 1$ and the osculating circle has radius 1 and center $(0, 1)$, and hence equation $x^2 + (y - 1)^2 = 1$.

The curvature at $\left(1, \frac{1}{2}\right)$ is $\kappa(1) = \dfrac{1}{(1 + 1^2)^{3/2}} = \dfrac{1}{2\sqrt{2}}$.

The tangent line to the parabola at $\left(1, \frac{1}{2}\right)$ has slope 1, so the normal

line has slope -1. Thus the center of the osculating circle lies in the

direction of the unit vector $\left\langle -\frac{1}{\sqrt{2}}, \frac{1}{\sqrt{2}} \right\rangle$. The circle has radius $2\sqrt{2}$,

so its center has position vector

$\left\langle 1, \frac{1}{2} \right\rangle + 2\sqrt{2} \left\langle -\frac{1}{\sqrt{2}}, \frac{1}{\sqrt{2}} \right\rangle = \left\langle -1, \frac{5}{2} \right\rangle$. So the equation of the circle

is $(x + 1)^2 + \left(y - \frac{5}{2}\right)^2 = 8$.

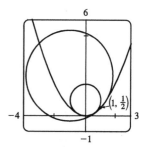

41. The tangent vector is normal to the normal plane, and the vector $\langle 6, 6, -8 \rangle$ is normal to the given plane. But

$\mathbf{T}(t) \parallel \mathbf{r}'(t)$ and $\langle 6, 6, -8 \rangle \parallel \langle 3, 3, -4 \rangle$, so we need to find t such that $\mathbf{r}'(t) \parallel \langle 3, 3, -4 \rangle$. $\mathbf{r}(t) = \langle t^3, 3t, t^4 \rangle \Rightarrow$

$\mathbf{r}'(t) = \langle 3t^2, 3, 4t^3 \rangle \parallel \langle 3, 3, -4 \rangle$ when $t = -1$. So the planes are parallel at the point $\mathbf{r}(-1) = (-1, -3, 1)$.

42. To find the osculating plane, we first calculate the tangent and normal vectors.

In Maple, we set $x:=t\wedge3;\ y:=3*t;$ and $z:=t\wedge4;$ and then calculate the components of the tangent vector

$\mathbf{T}(t)$ using the diff command. We find that $\mathbf{T}(t) = \dfrac{\langle 3t^2, 3, 4t^3\rangle}{\sqrt{16t^6 + 9t^4 + 9}}$. Differentiating the components of $\mathbf{T}(t)$,

we find that $\mathbf{N}(t) = \dfrac{\mathbf{T}'(t)}{|\mathbf{T}'(t)|} = \dfrac{\langle -6t\left(8t^6 - 9\right), 3\left(48t^5 + 18t^3\right), 36t^2\left(t^4 + 3\right)\rangle}{\sqrt{144t^2(8t^6 - 9)^2 + 9(96t^5 + 36t^3)^2 + 5{,}184t^{12} + 31{,}104t^8 + 46{,}656t^4}}$.

In Maple, we can calculate $\mathbf{B}(t) = \mathbf{T}(t) \times \mathbf{N}(t)$ using the linalg package. First we define $\mathbf{T}$

and $\mathbf{N}$ using $\text{T:=array([f,g,h]);}$ and $\text{N:=array([F,G,H]);}$ where f, g, h, F, G, and H are the

components of $\mathbf{T}$ and $\mathbf{N}$. Then we use the command $\text{B:=crossprod(T,N);}$. After normalization and

simplification, we find that $\mathbf{B}(t) = b\langle 6t, -2t^3, -3\rangle$, where

$$b = \frac{t\sqrt{16t^6 + 9t^4 + 9}}{\sqrt{16t^2(8t^6-9)2 + (96t^5 + 36t^3)^2 + 576t^{12} + 3456t^8 + 5184t^4}}$$

In Mathematica, we use the command Dt to differentiate the components of $\mathbf{r}(t)$ and subsequently $\mathbf{T}(t)$, and then
load the vector analysis package with the command <<Calculus`VectorAnalysis`. After setting

$\text{T=\{f,g,h\}}$ and $\text{N=\{F,G,H\}}$, we use CrossProduct[T,N] to find $\mathbf{B}$ (before normalization).

Now $\mathbf{B}(t)$ is parallel to $\langle 6t, -2t^3, -3\rangle$, so if $\mathbf{B}(t)$ is parallel to $\langle 1,1,1\rangle$ for some t, then $6t = 1 \ \Rightarrow \ t = \frac{1}{6}$, but

$-2\left(\frac{1}{6}\right)^3 \neq 1$. So there is no such osculating plane.

43. $\kappa = \left|\dfrac{d\mathbf{T}}{ds}\right| = \left|\dfrac{d\mathbf{T}/dt}{ds/dt}\right| = \dfrac{|d\mathbf{T}/dt|}{ds/dt}$ and $\mathbf{N} = \dfrac{d\mathbf{T}/dt}{|d\mathbf{T}/dt|}$, so $\kappa\mathbf{N} = \dfrac{\left|\dfrac{d\mathbf{T}}{dt}\right|\dfrac{d\mathbf{T}}{dt}}{\left|\dfrac{d\mathbf{T}}{dt}\right|\dfrac{ds}{dt}} = \dfrac{d\mathbf{T}/dt}{ds/dt} = \dfrac{d\mathbf{T}}{ds}$ by the Chain Rule.

44. For a plane curve, $\mathbf{T} = |\mathbf{T}|\cos\phi\,\mathbf{i} + |\mathbf{T}|\sin\phi\,\mathbf{j} = \cos\phi\,\mathbf{i} + \sin\phi\,\mathbf{j}$. Then

$\dfrac{d\mathbf{T}}{ds} = \left(\dfrac{d\mathbf{T}}{d\phi}\right)\left(\dfrac{d\phi}{ds}\right) = (-\sin\phi\,\mathbf{i} + \cos\phi\,\mathbf{j})\left(\dfrac{d\phi}{ds}\right)$ and $\left|\dfrac{d\mathbf{T}}{ds}\right| = |-\sin\phi\,\mathbf{i} + \cos\phi\,\mathbf{j}|\left|\dfrac{d\phi}{ds}\right| = \left|\dfrac{d\phi}{ds}\right|$. Hence for a

plane curve, the curvature is $\kappa = |d\phi/ds|$.

45. (a) $|\mathbf{B}| = 1 \ \Rightarrow \ \mathbf{B}\cdot\mathbf{B} = 1 \ \Rightarrow \ \dfrac{d}{ds}(\mathbf{B}\cdot\mathbf{B}) = 0 \ \Rightarrow \ 2\dfrac{d\mathbf{B}}{ds}\cdot\mathbf{B} = 0 \ \Rightarrow \ \dfrac{d\mathbf{B}}{ds} \perp \mathbf{B}$

(b) $\mathbf{B} = \mathbf{T}\times\mathbf{N} \ \Rightarrow$

$\dfrac{d\mathbf{B}}{ds} = \dfrac{d}{ds}(\mathbf{T}\times\mathbf{N}) = \dfrac{d}{dt}(\mathbf{T}\times\mathbf{N})\dfrac{1}{ds/dt} = \dfrac{d}{dt}(\mathbf{T}\times\mathbf{N})\dfrac{1}{|\mathbf{r}'(t)|}$

$= [(\mathbf{T}'\times\mathbf{N}) + (\mathbf{T}\times\mathbf{N}')]\dfrac{1}{|\mathbf{r}'(t)|} = \left[\left(\mathbf{T}\times\dfrac{\mathbf{T}'}{|\mathbf{T}'|}\right) + (\mathbf{T}\times\mathbf{N}')\right]\dfrac{1}{|\mathbf{r}'(t)|} = \dfrac{\mathbf{T}\times\mathbf{N}'}{|\mathbf{r}'(t)|}$

$\Rightarrow \ \dfrac{d\mathbf{B}}{ds} \perp \mathbf{T}$

(c) $\mathbf{B} = \mathbf{T} \times \mathbf{N} \implies \mathbf{T} \perp \mathbf{N}, \mathbf{B} \perp \mathbf{T}$ and $\mathbf{B} \perp \mathbf{N}$. So $\mathbf{B}, \mathbf{T}$ and $\mathbf{N}$ form an orthogonal set of vectors in the three-dimensional space $\mathbb{R}^3$. From parts (a) and (b), $d\mathbf{B}/ds$ is perpendicular to both $\mathbf{B}$ and $\mathbf{T}$, so $d\mathbf{B}/ds$ is parallel to $\mathbf{N}$. Therefore, $d\mathbf{B}/ds = -\tau(s)\mathbf{N}$, where $\tau(s)$ is a scalar.

(d) Since $\mathbf{B} = \mathbf{T} \times \mathbf{N}, \mathbf{T} \perp \mathbf{N}$ and both $\mathbf{T}$ and $\mathbf{N}$ are unit vectors, $\mathbf{B}$ is a unit vector mutually perpendicular to both $\mathbf{T}$ and $\mathbf{N}$. For a plane curve, $\mathbf{T}$ and $\mathbf{N}$ always lie in the plane of the curve, so that $\mathbf{B}$ is a constant unit vector always perpendicular to the plane. Thus $d\mathbf{B}/ds = \mathbf{0}$, but $d\mathbf{B}/ds = -\tau(s)\mathbf{N}$ and $\mathbf{N} \neq \mathbf{0}$, so $\tau(s) = 0$.

46. $\mathbf{N} = \mathbf{B} \times \mathbf{T} \implies$

$$\frac{d\mathbf{N}}{ds} = \frac{d}{ds}(\mathbf{B} \times \mathbf{T}) = \frac{d\mathbf{B}}{ds} \times \mathbf{T} + \mathbf{B} \times \frac{d\mathbf{T}}{ds} \qquad \text{[by Theorem 10.2.3 \#5]}$$

$$= -\tau\mathbf{N} \times \mathbf{T} + \mathbf{B} \times \kappa\mathbf{N} \qquad \text{[by Formulas 3 and 1]}$$

$$= -\tau(\mathbf{N} \times \mathbf{T}) + \kappa(\mathbf{B} \times \mathbf{N}) \qquad \text{[by Property 2 of the cross product]}$$

But $\mathbf{B} \times \mathbf{N} = \mathbf{B} \times (\mathbf{B} \times \mathbf{T}) = (\mathbf{B} \cdot \mathbf{T})\mathbf{B} - (\mathbf{B} \cdot \mathbf{B})\mathbf{T}$ [by Equation 9.4.8] $= -\mathbf{T} \implies$

$$d\mathbf{N}/ds = \tau(\mathbf{T} \times \mathbf{N}) - \kappa\mathbf{T} = -\kappa\mathbf{T} + \tau\mathbf{B}.$$

47. (a) $\mathbf{r}' = s'\mathbf{T} \implies \mathbf{r}'' = s''\mathbf{T} + s'\mathbf{T}' = s''\mathbf{T} + s'\dfrac{d\mathbf{T}}{ds}s' = s''\mathbf{T} + \kappa(s')^2\mathbf{N}$ by the first Serret-Frenet formula.

(b) Using part (a), we have

$$\mathbf{r}' \times \mathbf{r}'' = (s'\mathbf{T}) \times \left[s''\mathbf{T} + \kappa(s')^2\mathbf{N}\right]$$

$$= \left[(s'\mathbf{T}) \times (s''\mathbf{T})\right] + \left[(s'\mathbf{T}) \times \left(\kappa(s')^2\mathbf{N}\right)\right] \qquad \text{[By Property 3 of the cross product]}$$

$$= (s's'')(\mathbf{T} \times \mathbf{T}) + \kappa(s')^3(\mathbf{T} \times \mathbf{N}) = \mathbf{0} + \kappa(s')^3\mathbf{B} = \kappa(s')^3\mathbf{B}$$

(c) Using part (a), we have

$$\mathbf{r}''' = \left[s''\mathbf{T} + \kappa(s')^2\mathbf{N}\right]' = s'''\mathbf{T} + s''\mathbf{T}' + \kappa'(s')^2\mathbf{N} + 2\kappa s's''\mathbf{N} + \kappa(s')^2\mathbf{N}'$$

$$= s'''\mathbf{T} + s''\frac{d\mathbf{T}}{ds}s' + \kappa'(s')^2\mathbf{N} + 2\kappa s's''\mathbf{N} + \kappa(s')^2\frac{d\mathbf{N}}{ds}s'$$

$$= s'''\mathbf{T} + s''s'\kappa\mathbf{N} + \kappa'(s')^2\mathbf{N} + 2\kappa s's''\mathbf{N} + \kappa(s')^3(-\kappa\mathbf{T} + \tau\mathbf{B}) \qquad \text{[by the second formula]}$$

$$= \left[s''' - \kappa^2(s')^3\right]\mathbf{T} + \left[3\kappa s's'' + \kappa'(s')^2\right]\mathbf{N} + \kappa\tau(s')^3\mathbf{B}$$

(d) Using parts (b) and (c) and the facts that $\mathbf{B} \cdot \mathbf{T} = 0$, $\mathbf{B} \cdot \mathbf{N} = 0$, and $\mathbf{B} \cdot \mathbf{B} = 1$, we get

$$\frac{(\mathbf{r}' \times \mathbf{r}'') \cdot \mathbf{r}'''}{|\mathbf{r}' \times \mathbf{r}''|^2} = \frac{\kappa(s')^3\mathbf{B} \cdot \left\{\left[s''' - \kappa^2(s')^3\right]\mathbf{T} + \left[3\kappa s's'' + \kappa'(s')^2\right]\mathbf{N} + \kappa\tau(s')^3\mathbf{B}\right\}}{|\kappa(s')^3\mathbf{B}|^2}$$

$$= \frac{\kappa(s')^3\kappa\tau(s')^3}{[\kappa(s')^3]^2} = \tau$$

48. First we find the quantities required to compute κ:

$$\mathbf{r}'(t) = \langle -a\sin t, a\cos t, b \rangle \Rightarrow \mathbf{r}''(t) = \langle -a\cos t, -a\sin t, 0 \rangle \Rightarrow \mathbf{r}'''(t) = \langle a\sin t, -a\cos t, 0 \rangle$$

$$\left| \mathbf{r}'(t) \right| = \sqrt{(-a\sin t)^2 + (a\cos t)^2 + b^2} = \sqrt{a^2 + b^2}$$

$$\mathbf{r}'(t) \times \mathbf{r}''(t) = \begin{vmatrix} \mathbf{i} & \mathbf{j} & \mathbf{k} \\ -a\sin t & a\cos t & b \\ -a\cos t & -a\sin t & 0 \end{vmatrix} = ab\sin t\,\mathbf{i} - ab\cos t\,\mathbf{j} + a^2\,\mathbf{k}$$

$$\left| \mathbf{r}'(t) \times \mathbf{r}''(t) \right| = \sqrt{(ab\sin t)^2 + (-ab\cos t)^2 + (a^2)^2} = \sqrt{a^2 b^2 + a^4}$$

$$(\mathbf{r}'(t) \times \mathbf{r}''(t)) \cdot \mathbf{r}'''(t) = (ab\sin t)(a\sin t) + (-ab\cos t)(-a\cos t) + (a^2)(0) = a^2 b$$

Then by Theorem 10,

$$\kappa(t) = \frac{\left| \mathbf{r}'(t) \times \mathbf{r}''(t) \right|}{\left| \mathbf{r}'(t) \right|^3} = \frac{\sqrt{a^2 b^2 + a^4}}{\left(\sqrt{a^2 + b^2} \right)^3} = \frac{a\sqrt{a^2 + b^2}}{\left(\sqrt{a^2 + b^2} \right)^3} = \frac{a}{a^2 + b^2}$$

which is a constant.

From Exercise 47(d), the torsion τ is given by

$$\tau = \frac{(\mathbf{r}' \times \mathbf{r}'') \cdot \mathbf{r}'''}{\left| \mathbf{r}' \times \mathbf{r}'' \right|^2} = \frac{a^2 b}{\left(\sqrt{a^2 b^2 + a^4} \right)^2} = \frac{b}{a^2 + b^2}$$

which is also a constant.

49. For one helix, the vector equation is $\mathbf{r}(t) = \langle 10\cos t, 10\sin t, 34t/(2\pi) \rangle$ (measuring in angstroms), because the radius of each helix is 10 angstroms, and z increases by 34 angstroms for each increase of 2π in t. Using the arc length formula, letting t go from 0 to $2.9 \times 10^8 \times 2\pi$, we find the approximate length of each helix to be

$$L = \int_0^{2.9 \times 10^8 \times 2\pi} \left| \mathbf{r}'(t) \right| dt$$

$$= \int_0^{2.9 \times 10^8 \times 2\pi} \sqrt{(-10\sin t)^2 + (10\cos t)^2 + \left(\tfrac{34}{2\pi} \right)^2}\, dt$$

$$= \sqrt{100 + \left(\tfrac{34}{2\pi} \right)^2}\, t \, \Bigg]_0^{2.9 \times 10^8 \times 2\pi}$$

$$= 2.9 \times 10^8 \times 2\pi \sqrt{100 + \left(\tfrac{34}{2\pi} \right)^2}$$

$$\approx 2.07 \times 10^{10}\,\text{Å} \text{ — more than two meters!}$$

50. (a) For the function $F(x) = \begin{cases} 0 & \text{if } x < 0 \\ P(x) & \text{if } 0 < x < 1 \\ 1 & \text{if } x \geq 1 \end{cases}$ to be continuous, we must have $P(0) = 0$ and $P(1) = 1$.

For F' to be continuous, we must have $P'(0) = P'(1) = 0$. The curvature of the curve $y = F(x)$ at the point

$(x, F(x))$ is $\kappa(x) = \dfrac{|F''(x)|}{\left(1 + [F'(x)]^2\right)^{3/2}}$. For $\kappa(x)$ to be continuous, we must have $P''(0) = P''(1) = 0$.

Write $P(x) = ax^5 + bx^4 + cx^3 + dx^2 + ex + f$. Then $P'(x) = 5ax^4 + 4bx^3 + 3cx^2 + 2dx + e$ and $P''(x) = 20ax^3 + 12bx^2 + 6cx + 2d$. Our six conditions are:

$$P(0) = 0 \quad \Rightarrow \quad f = 0 \tag{1}$$

$$P(1) = 1 \quad \Rightarrow \quad a + b + c + d + e + f = 1 \tag{2}$$

$$P'(0) = 0 \quad \Rightarrow \quad e = 0 \tag{3}$$

$$P'(1) = 0 \quad \Rightarrow \quad 5a + 4b + 3c + 2d + e = 0 \tag{4}$$

$$P''(0) = 0 \quad \Rightarrow \quad d = 0 \tag{5}$$

$$P''(1) = 0 \quad \Rightarrow \quad 20a + 12b + 6c + 2d = 0 \tag{6}$$

From (1), (3), and (5), we have $d = e = f = 0$. Thus (2), (4) and (6) become (7) $a + b + c = 1$,
(8) $5a + 4b + 3c = 0$, and (9) $10a + 6b + 3c = 0$. Subtracting (8) from (9) gives (10) $5a + 2b = 0$.
Multiplying (7) by 3 and subtracting from (8) gives (11) $2a + b = -3$. Multiplying (11) by 2 and subtracting
from (10) gives $a = 6$. By (10), $b = -15$. By (7), $c = 10$. Thus, $P(x) = 6x^5 - 15x^4 + 10x^3$.

(b)

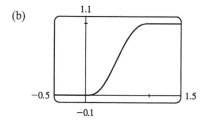

10.4 Motion in Space · · · · · · · · · · · · · · · · ·

1. (a) If $\mathbf{r}(t) = x(t)\,\mathbf{i} + y(t)\,\mathbf{j} + z(t)\,\mathbf{k}$ is the position vector of the particle at time t, then the average velocity over the time interval $[0, 1]$ is

$$\mathbf{v}_{\text{ave}} = \frac{\mathbf{r}(1) - \mathbf{r}(0)}{1 - 0} = \frac{(4.5\,\mathbf{i} + 6.0\,\mathbf{j} + 3.0\,\mathbf{k}) - (2.7\,\mathbf{i} + 9.8\,\mathbf{j} + 3.7\,\mathbf{k})}{1} = 1.8\,\mathbf{i} - 3.8\,\mathbf{j} - 0.7\,\mathbf{k}. \text{ Similarly,}$$

over the other intervals we have

$$[0.5, 1]: \quad \mathbf{v}_{\text{ave}} = \frac{\mathbf{r}(1) - \mathbf{r}(0.5)}{1 - 0.5} = \frac{(4.5\,\mathbf{i} + 6.0\,\mathbf{j} + 3.0\,\mathbf{k}) - (3.5\,\mathbf{i} + 7.2\,\mathbf{j} + 3.3\,\mathbf{k})}{0.5}$$

$$= 2.0\,\mathbf{i} - 2.4\,\mathbf{j} - 0.6\,\mathbf{k}$$

$$[1, 2]: \quad \mathbf{v}_{\text{ave}} = \frac{\mathbf{r}(2) - \mathbf{r}(1)}{2 - 1} = \frac{(7.3\,\mathbf{i} + 7.8\,\mathbf{j} + 2.7\,\mathbf{k}) - (4.5\,\mathbf{i} + 6.0\,\mathbf{j} + 3.0\,\mathbf{k})}{1}$$

$$= 2.8\,\mathbf{i} + 1.8\,\mathbf{j} - 0.3\,\mathbf{k}$$

$$[1, 1.5]: \quad \mathbf{v}_{\text{ave}} = \frac{\mathbf{r}(1.5) - \mathbf{r}(1)}{1.5 - 1} = \frac{(5.9\,\mathbf{i} + 6.4\,\mathbf{j} + 2.8\,\mathbf{k}) - 94.5\,\mathbf{i} + 6.0\,\mathbf{j} + 3.0\,\mathbf{k})}{0.5}$$

$$= 2.8\,\mathbf{i} + 0.8\,\mathbf{j} - 0.4\,\mathbf{k}$$

(b) We can estimate the velocity at $t = 1$ by averaging the average velocities over the time intervals $[0.5, 1]$ and $[1, 1.5]$: $\mathbf{v}(1) \approx \frac{1}{2}[(2\,\mathbf{i} - 2.4\,\mathbf{j} - 0.6\,\mathbf{k}) + (2.8\,\mathbf{i} + 0.8\,\mathbf{j} - 0.4\,\mathbf{k})] = 2.4\,\mathbf{i} - 0.8\,\mathbf{j} - 0.5\,\mathbf{k}.$ Then the speed is $|\mathbf{v}(1)| \approx \sqrt{(2.4)^2 + (-0.8)^2 + (-0.5)^2} \approx 2.58.$

2. (a) The average velocity over $2 \leq t \leq 2.4$ is

$$\frac{\mathbf{r}(2.4) - \mathbf{r}(2)}{2.4 - 2} = 2.5\,[\mathbf{r}(2.4) - \mathbf{r}(2)], \text{ so we sketch a vector}$$

in the same direction but 2.5 times the length of

$$[\mathbf{r}(2.4) - \mathbf{r}(2)].$$

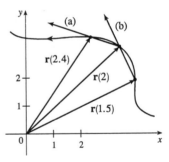

(b) The average velocity over $1.5 \leq t \leq 2$ is $\dfrac{\mathbf{r}(2) - \mathbf{r}(1.5)}{2 - 1.5} = 2[\mathbf{r}(2) - \mathbf{r}(1.5)]$, so we sketch a vector in the same direction but twice the length of $[\mathbf{r}(2) - \mathbf{r}(1.5)]$.

(c) Using Equation 2 we have $\mathbf{v}(2) = \displaystyle\lim_{h \to 0} \frac{\mathbf{r}(2 + h) - \mathbf{r}(2)}{h}.$

(d) $\mathbf{v}(2)$ is tangent to the curve at $\mathbf{r}(2)$ and points in the direction of increasing t. Its length is the speed of the particle at $t = 2$. We can estimate the speed by averaging the lengths of the vectors found in parts (a) and (b) which represent the average speed over $2 \leq t \leq 2.4$ and $1.5 \leq t \leq 2$ respectively. Using the axes scale as a guide, we estimate the vectors to have lengths 2.8 and 2.7. Thus, we estimate the speed at $t = 2$ to be $|\mathbf{v}(2)| \approx \frac{1}{2}(2.8 + 2.7) = 2.75$ and we draw the velocity vector $\mathbf{v}(2)$ with this length.

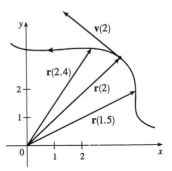

3. $\mathbf{r}(t) = \langle t^2 - 1, t \rangle \Rightarrow$ At $t = 1$:

$\mathbf{v}(t) = \mathbf{r}'(t) = \langle 2t, 1 \rangle,$ $\mathbf{v}(1) = \langle 2, 1 \rangle$

$\mathbf{a}(t) = \mathbf{r}''(t) = \langle 2, 0 \rangle,$ $\mathbf{a}(1) = \langle 2, 0 \rangle$

$|\mathbf{v}(t)| = \sqrt{4t^2 + 1}$

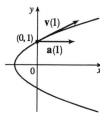

4. $\mathbf{r}(t) = \langle \sqrt{t}, 1 - t \rangle \Rightarrow$ At $t = 1$:

$\mathbf{v}(t) = \langle \frac{1}{2} t^{-1/2}, -1 \rangle,$ $\mathbf{v}(1) = \langle \frac{1}{2}, -1 \rangle$

$\mathbf{a}(t) = \langle -\frac{1}{4} t^{-3/2}, 0 \rangle,$ $\mathbf{a}(1) = \langle -\frac{1}{4}, 0 \rangle$

$|\mathbf{v}(t)| = \sqrt{\frac{1}{4} t^{-1} + 1}$

Since $x^2 = t$, $y = 1 - t = 1 - x^2$, but $x = \sqrt{t}$, so $x \geq 0$.

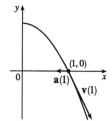

5. $\mathbf{r}(t) = e^t \mathbf{i} + e^{-t} \mathbf{j} \Rightarrow$ At $t = 0$:

$\mathbf{v}(t) = e^t \mathbf{i} - e^{-t} \mathbf{j},$ $\mathbf{v}(0) = \mathbf{i} - \mathbf{j},$

$\mathbf{a}(t) = e^t \mathbf{i} + e^{-t} \mathbf{j}$ $\mathbf{a}(0) = \mathbf{i} + \mathbf{j}$

$|\mathbf{v}(t)| = \sqrt{e^{2t} + e^{-2t}} = e^{-t} \sqrt{e^{4t} + 1}$

Since $x = e^t$, $t = \ln x$ and $y = e^{-t} = e^{-\ln x} = 1/x$, and $x > 0$, $y > 0$.

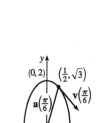

6. $\mathbf{r}(t) = \sin t \, \mathbf{i} + 2 \cos t \, \mathbf{j} \Rightarrow$

$\mathbf{v}(t) = \cos t \, \mathbf{i} - 2 \sin t \, \mathbf{j}, \mathbf{v}\left(\frac{\pi}{6}\right) = \frac{\sqrt{3}}{2} \mathbf{i} - \mathbf{j}$

$\mathbf{a}(t) = -\sin t \, \mathbf{i} - 2 \cos t \, \mathbf{j}, \mathbf{a}\left(\frac{\pi}{6}\right) = -\frac{1}{2} \mathbf{i} - \sqrt{3} \mathbf{j}$

$|\mathbf{v}(t)| = \sqrt{\cos^2 t + 4 \sin^2 t} = \sqrt{1 + 3 \sin^2 t}$

And $x^2 + y^2/4 = \sin^2 t + \cos^2 t = 1$, an ellipse.

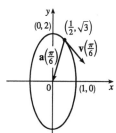

7. $\mathbf{r}(t) = \sin t \, \mathbf{i} + t \, \mathbf{j} + \cos t \, \mathbf{k} \Rightarrow$

$\mathbf{v}(t) = \cos t \, \mathbf{i} + \mathbf{j} - \sin t \, \mathbf{k}, \mathbf{v}(0) = \mathbf{i} + \mathbf{j}$

$\mathbf{a}(t) = -\sin t \, \mathbf{i} - \cos t \, \mathbf{k}, \mathbf{a}(0) = -\mathbf{k}$

$|\mathbf{v}(t)| = \sqrt{\cos^2 t + 1 + \sin^2 t} = \sqrt{2}$

Since $x^2 + z^2 = 1$, $y = t$, the path of the particle is a helix about the y-axis.

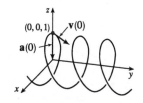

8. $\mathbf{r}(t) = t\,\mathbf{i} + t^2\,\mathbf{j} + t^3\,\mathbf{k} \;\Rightarrow$

$\mathbf{v}(t) = \mathbf{i} + 2t\,\mathbf{j} + 3t^2\,\mathbf{k}, \mathbf{v}(1) = \mathbf{i} + 2\,\mathbf{j} + 3\,\mathbf{k}$

$\mathbf{a}(t) = 2\,\mathbf{j} + 6t\,\mathbf{k}, \mathbf{a}(1) = 2\,\mathbf{j} + 6\,\mathbf{k}$

$|\mathbf{v}(t)| = \sqrt{1 + 4t^2 + 9t^4}$

The path is a "twisted cubic" (see Example 10.1.6).

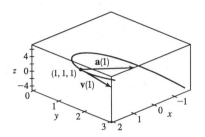

9. $\mathbf{r}(t) = \langle t, t^2, t^3 \rangle \;\Rightarrow\; \mathbf{v}(t) = \mathbf{r}'(t) = \langle 1, 2t, 3t^2 \rangle, \mathbf{a}(t) = \mathbf{v}'(t) = \langle 0, 2, 6t \rangle,$

$|\mathbf{v}(t)| = \sqrt{1^2 + (2t)^2 + (3t^2)^2} = \sqrt{1 + 4t^2 + 9t^4}.$

10. $\mathbf{r}(t) = \langle 2\cos t, 3t, 2\sin t \rangle \;\Rightarrow\; \mathbf{v}(t) = \mathbf{r}'(t) = \langle -2\sin t, 3, 2\cos t \rangle, \mathbf{a}(t) = \mathbf{v}'(t) = \langle -2\cos t, 0, -2\sin t \rangle,$

$|\mathbf{v}(t)| = \sqrt{4\sin^2 t + 9 + 4\cos^2 t} = \sqrt{13}.$

11. $\mathbf{r}(t) = \sqrt{2}\,t\,\mathbf{i} + e^t\,\mathbf{j} + e^{-t}\,\mathbf{k} \;\Rightarrow\; \mathbf{v}(t) = \mathbf{r}'(t) = \sqrt{2}\,\mathbf{i} + e^t\,\mathbf{j} - e^{-t}\,\mathbf{k}, \mathbf{a}(t) = \mathbf{v}'(t) = e^t\,\mathbf{j} + e^{-t}\,\mathbf{k},$

$|\mathbf{v}(t)| = \sqrt{2 + e^{2t} + e^{-2t}} = \sqrt{(e^t + e^{-t})^2} = e^t + e^{-t}.$

12. $\mathbf{r}(t) = t\sin t\,\mathbf{i} + t\cos t\,\mathbf{j} + t^2\,\mathbf{k} \;\Rightarrow\; \mathbf{v}(t) = \mathbf{r}'(t) = (\sin t + t\cos t)\,\mathbf{i} + (\cos t - t\sin t)\,\mathbf{j} + 2t\,\mathbf{k},$

$\mathbf{a}(t) = \mathbf{v}'(t) = (2\cos t - t\sin t)\,\mathbf{i} + (-2\sin t - t\cos t)\,\mathbf{j} + 2\mathbf{k},$

$|\mathbf{v}(t)| = \sqrt{\left(\sin^2 t + 2t\sin t\cos t + t^2\cos^2 t\right) + \left(\cos^2 t - 2t\sin t\cos t + t^2\sin^2 t\right) + 4t^2} = \sqrt{5t^2 + 1}.$

13. $\mathbf{a}(t) = \mathbf{k} \;\Rightarrow\; \mathbf{v}(t) = \int \mathbf{a}(t)\,dt = \int \mathbf{k}\,dt = t\,\mathbf{k} + \mathbf{c}_1$ and $\mathbf{i} - \mathbf{j} = \mathbf{v}(0) = 0\,\mathbf{k} + \mathbf{c}_1$, so $\mathbf{c}_1 = \mathbf{i} - \mathbf{j}$ and

$\mathbf{v}(t) = \mathbf{i} - \mathbf{j} + t\,\mathbf{k}$. $\mathbf{r}(t) = \int \mathbf{v}(t)\,dt = \int (\mathbf{i} - \mathbf{j} + t\,\mathbf{k})\,dt = t\,\mathbf{i} - t\,\mathbf{j} + \frac{1}{2}t^2\,\mathbf{k} + \mathbf{c}_2$. But $0 = \mathbf{r}(0) = 0 + \mathbf{c}_2$, so

$\mathbf{c}_2 = 0$ and $\mathbf{r}(t) = t\,\mathbf{i} - t\,\mathbf{j} + \frac{1}{2}t^2\,\mathbf{k}$.

14. $\mathbf{a}(t) = -10\,\mathbf{k} \;\Rightarrow\; \mathbf{v}(t) = \int (-10\mathbf{k})\,dt = -10t\,\mathbf{k} + \mathbf{c}_1$, and $\mathbf{i} + \mathbf{j} - \mathbf{k} = \mathbf{v}(0) = 0 + \mathbf{c}_1$, so $\mathbf{c}_1 = \mathbf{i} + \mathbf{j} - \mathbf{k}$ and

$\mathbf{v}(t) = \mathbf{i} + \mathbf{j} - (10t + 1)\,\mathbf{k}$.

$\mathbf{r}(t) = \int [\mathbf{i} + \mathbf{j} - (10t + 1)\,\mathbf{k}]\,dt = t\,\mathbf{i} + t\,\mathbf{j} - (5t^2 + t)\,\mathbf{k} + \mathbf{c}_2$. But $2\,\mathbf{i} + 3\,\mathbf{j} = \mathbf{r}(0) = 0 + \mathbf{c}_2$, so $\mathbf{c}_2 = 2\,\mathbf{i} + 3\,\mathbf{j}$

and $\mathbf{r}(t) = (t + 2)\,\mathbf{i} + (t + 3)\,\mathbf{j} - (5t^2 + t)\,\mathbf{k}$.

15. (a) $\mathbf{a}(t) = \mathbf{i} + 2\,\mathbf{j} + 2t\,\mathbf{k} \;\Rightarrow$ (b)

$\mathbf{v}(t) = \int (\mathbf{i} + 2\,\mathbf{j} + 2t\,\mathbf{k})\,dt = t\,\mathbf{i} + 2t\,\mathbf{j} + t^2\,\mathbf{k} + \mathbf{c}_1$, and

$0 = \mathbf{v}(0) = 0 + \mathbf{c}_1$, so $\mathbf{c}_1 = 0$ and $\mathbf{v}(t) = \mathbf{i} + 2t\,\mathbf{j} + t^2\,\mathbf{k}$.

$\mathbf{r}(t) = \int (t\,\mathbf{i} + 2t\,\mathbf{j} + t^2\,\mathbf{k})\,dt = \frac{1}{2}t^2\,\mathbf{i} + t^2\,\mathbf{j} + \frac{1}{3}t^3\,\mathbf{k} + \mathbf{c}_2$.

But $\mathbf{i} + \mathbf{k} = \mathbf{r}(0) = 0 + \mathbf{c}_2$, so $\mathbf{c}_2 = \mathbf{i} + \mathbf{k}$ and

$\mathbf{r}(t) = \left(1 + \frac{1}{2}t^2\right)\mathbf{i} + t^2\,\mathbf{j} + \left(1 + \frac{1}{3}t^3\right)\mathbf{k}.$

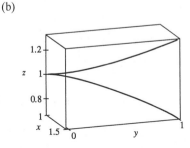

16. (a) $\mathbf{a}(t) = t\,\mathbf{i} + t^2\,\mathbf{j} + \cos 2t\,\mathbf{k} \Rightarrow$

$\mathbf{v}(t) = \int \left(t\,\mathbf{i} + t^2\,\mathbf{j} + \cos 2t\,\mathbf{k} \right) dt$

$\quad = \dfrac{t^2}{2}\,\mathbf{i} + \dfrac{t^3}{3}\,\mathbf{j} + \dfrac{\sin 2t}{2}\,\mathbf{k} + \mathbf{c}_1$

and $\mathbf{i} + \mathbf{k} = \mathbf{v}(0) = 0 + \mathbf{c}_1$, so $\mathbf{c}_1 = \mathbf{i} + \mathbf{k}$ and

$\mathbf{v}(t) = \left(\tfrac{1}{2}t^2 + 1 \right)\mathbf{i} + \tfrac{1}{3}t^3\,\mathbf{j} + \left(1 + \tfrac{1}{2}\sin 2t \right)\mathbf{k}.$

(b)
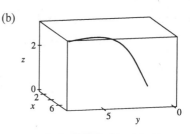

$\mathbf{r}(t) = \int \left[\left(\tfrac{1}{2}t^2 + 1 \right)\mathbf{i} + \tfrac{1}{3}t^3\,\mathbf{j} + \left(1 + \tfrac{1}{2}\sin 2t \right)\mathbf{k} \right] dt$

$\quad = \left(\tfrac{1}{6}t^3 + t \right)\mathbf{i} + \tfrac{1}{12}t^4\,\mathbf{j} + \left(t - \tfrac{1}{4}\cos 2t \right)\mathbf{k} + \mathbf{c}_2$

But $\mathbf{j} = \mathbf{r}(0) = -\tfrac{1}{4}\mathbf{k} + \mathbf{c}_2$, so $\mathbf{c}_2 = \mathbf{j} + \tfrac{1}{4}\mathbf{k}$ and $\mathbf{r}(t) = \left(\tfrac{1}{6}t^3 + t \right)\mathbf{i} + \left(1 + \tfrac{1}{12}t^4 \right)\mathbf{j} + \left(\tfrac{1}{4} + t - \tfrac{1}{4}\cos 2t \right)\mathbf{k}.$

17. $\mathbf{r}(t) = \langle t^2, 5t, t^2 - 16t \rangle \Rightarrow \mathbf{v}(t) = \langle 2t, 5, 2t - 16 \rangle,$

$|\mathbf{v}(t)| = \sqrt{4t^2 + 25 + 4t^2 - 64t + 256} = \sqrt{8t^2 - 64t + 281}$ and

$\dfrac{d}{dt}\,|\mathbf{v}(t)| = \tfrac{1}{2}(8t^2 - 64t + 281)^{-1/2}(16t - 64).$ This is zero if and only if the numerator is zero, that is,

$16t - 64 = 0$ or $t = 4$. Since $\dfrac{d}{dt}\,|\mathbf{v}(t)| < 0$ for $t < 4$ and $\dfrac{d}{dt}\,|\mathbf{v}(t)| > 0$ for $t > 4$, the minimum speed of $\sqrt{153}$ is

attained at $t = 4$ units of time.

18. Since $\mathbf{r}(t) = t^3\,\mathbf{i} + t^2\,\mathbf{j} + t^3\,\mathbf{k},$ $\mathbf{a}(t) = \mathbf{r}''(t) = 6t\,\mathbf{i} + 2\,\mathbf{j} + 6t\,\mathbf{k}.$ By Newton's Second Law,

$\mathbf{F}(t) = m\,\mathbf{a}(t) = 6mt\,\mathbf{i} + 2m\,\mathbf{j} + 6mt\,\mathbf{k}$ is the required force.

19. $|\mathbf{F}(t)| = 20\,\text{N}$ in the direction of the positive z-axis, so $\mathbf{F}(t) = 20\mathbf{k}.$ Also $m = 4\,\text{kg},$ $\mathbf{r}(0) = 0$ and $\mathbf{v}(0) = \mathbf{i} - \mathbf{j}.$

Since $20\mathbf{k} = \mathbf{F}(t) = 4\,\mathbf{a}(t),$ $\mathbf{a}(t) = 5\,\mathbf{k}.$ Then $\mathbf{v}(t) = 5t\,\mathbf{k} + \mathbf{c}_1$ where $\mathbf{c}_1 = \mathbf{i} - \mathbf{j}$ so $\mathbf{v}(t) = \mathbf{i} - \mathbf{j} + 5t\,\mathbf{k}$ and the

speed is $|\mathbf{v}(t)| = \sqrt{1 + 1 + 25t^2} = \sqrt{25t^2 + 2}.$ Also $\mathbf{r}(t) = t\,\mathbf{i} - t\,\mathbf{j} + \tfrac{5}{2}t^2\,\mathbf{k} + \mathbf{c}_2$ and $0 = \mathbf{r}(0),$ so $\mathbf{c}_2 = 0$ and

$\mathbf{r}(t) = t\,\mathbf{i} - t\,\mathbf{j} + \tfrac{5}{2}t^2\,\mathbf{k}.$

20. The argument here is the same as that in Example 10.2.5 with $\mathbf{r}(t)$ replaced by $\mathbf{v}(t)$ and $\mathbf{r}'(t)$ replaced

by $\mathbf{a}(t).$

21. $|\mathbf{v}(0)| = 500\,\text{m/s}$ and since the angle of elevation is $30°$, the direction of the velocity is $\tfrac{1}{2}\left(\sqrt{3}\,\mathbf{i} + \mathbf{j}\right).$ Thus

$\mathbf{v}(0) = 250\left(\sqrt{3}\,\mathbf{i} + \mathbf{j}\right)$ and if we set up the axes so the projectile starts at the origin, then $\mathbf{r}(0) = 0.$ Ignoring air

resistance, the only force is that due to gravity, so $\mathbf{F}(t) = -mg\,\mathbf{j}$ where $g \approx 9.8\,\text{m/s}^2.$ Thus $\mathbf{a}(t) = -g\,\mathbf{j}$ and

$\mathbf{v}(t) = -gt\,\mathbf{j} + \mathbf{c}_1.$ But $250\left(\sqrt{3}\,\mathbf{i} + \mathbf{j}\right) = \mathbf{v}(0) = \mathbf{c}_1,$ so $\mathbf{v}(t) = 250\sqrt{3}\,\mathbf{i} + (250 - gt)\,\mathbf{j}$ and

$\mathbf{r}(t) = 250\sqrt{3}\,t\,\mathbf{i} + \left(250t - \tfrac{1}{2}gt^2 \right)\mathbf{j} + \mathbf{c}_2$ where $0 = \mathbf{r}(0) = \mathbf{c}_2.$ Thus $\mathbf{r}(t) = 250\sqrt{3}\,t\,\mathbf{i} + \left(250t - \tfrac{1}{2}gt^2 \right)\mathbf{j}.$

(a) Setting $250t - \tfrac{1}{2}gt^2 = 0$ gives $t = 0$ or $t = \dfrac{500}{g} \approx 51.0\,\text{s}.$ So the range is $250\sqrt{3} \cdot \dfrac{500}{g} \approx 22\,\text{km}.$

(b) $0 = \dfrac{d}{dt}\left(250t - \tfrac{1}{2}gt^2 \right) = 250 - gt$ implies that the maximum height is attained when $t = 250/g \approx 25.5\,\text{s}.$

Thus, the maximum height is $(250)(250/g) - g(250/g)^2\tfrac{1}{2} = (250)^2/(2g) \approx 3.2\,\text{km}.$

(c) From part (a), impact occurs at $t = 500/g \approx 51.0.$ Thus, the velocity at impact is

$\mathbf{v}(500/g) = 250\sqrt{3}\,\mathbf{i} + [250 - g(500/g)]\,\mathbf{j} = 250\sqrt{3}\,\mathbf{i} - 250\,\mathbf{j}$ and the speed is

$|\mathbf{v}(500/g)| = 250\sqrt{3 + 1} = 500\,\text{m/s}.$

22. As in Exercise 21, $\mathbf{v}(t) = 250\sqrt{3}\,\mathbf{i} + (250 - gt)\,\mathbf{j}$ and $\mathbf{r}(t) = 250\sqrt{3}\,t\,\mathbf{i} + \left(250t - \frac{1}{2}gt^2\right)\mathbf{j} + \mathbf{c}_2$. But
$\mathbf{r}(0) = 200\,\mathbf{j}$, so $\mathbf{c}_2 = 200\,\mathbf{j}$ and $\mathbf{r}(t) = 250\sqrt{3}\,t\,\mathbf{i} + \left(200 + 250t - \frac{1}{2}gt^2\right)\mathbf{j}$.

(a) $200 + 250t - \frac{1}{2}gt^2 = 0$ implies that $gt^2 - 500t - 400 = 0$ or $t = \dfrac{500 \pm \sqrt{500^2 + 1600g}}{2g}$. Taking the

positive t-value gives $t = \dfrac{500 + \sqrt{250{,}000 + 1600g}}{2g} \approx 51.8$ s. Thus the range is

$(250\sqrt{3})\,\dfrac{500 + \sqrt{250{,}000 + 1600g}}{2g} \approx 22.4$ km.

(b) $0 = \dfrac{d}{dt}\left(200 + 250t - \frac{1}{2}gt^2\right) = 250 - gt$ implies that the maximum height is attained

when $t = 250/g \approx 25.5$ s and thus the maximum height is

$\left[200 + (250)\left(\dfrac{250}{g}\right) - \dfrac{g}{2}\left(\dfrac{250}{g}\right)^2\right] = 200 + \dfrac{(250)^2}{2g} \approx 3.4$ km.

Alternate solution: Because the projectile is fired in the same direction and with the same velocity as in
Exercise 21, but from a point 200 m higher, the maximum height reached is 200 m higher than that found in
Exercise 21, that is, 3.2 km + 200 m = 3.4 km.

(c) From part (a), impact occurs at $t = \dfrac{500 + \sqrt{250{,}000 + 1600g}}{2g}$. Thus the velocity at impact is

$250\sqrt{3}\,\mathbf{i} + \left[250 - g\,\dfrac{500 + \sqrt{250{,}000 + 1600g}}{2g}\right]\mathbf{j}$, so $|\mathbf{v}| \approx \sqrt{(250)^2(3) + (250 - 51.8g)^2} \approx 504$ m/s.

23. As in Example 5, $\mathbf{r}(t) = (v_0 \cos 45°)\,t\,\mathbf{i} + \left[(v_0 \sin 45°)\,t - \frac{1}{2}gt^2\right]\mathbf{j} = \frac{1}{2}\left[v_0\sqrt{2}\,t\,\mathbf{i} + \left(v_0\sqrt{2}\,t - gt^2\right)\mathbf{j}\right]$. Then

the ball lands at $t = \dfrac{v_0\sqrt{2}}{g}$ s. Now since it lands 90 m away, $90 = \frac{1}{2}v_0\sqrt{2}\,\dfrac{v_0\sqrt{2}}{g}$ or $v_0^2 = 90g$ and the initial

velocity is $v_0 = \sqrt{90g} \approx 30$ m/s.

24. As in Example 5, $\mathbf{r}(t) = (v_0 \cos 30°)\,t\,\mathbf{i} + \left[(v_0 \sin 30°)\,t - \frac{1}{2}gt^2\right]\mathbf{j} = \frac{1}{2}\left[v_0\sqrt{3}\,t\,\mathbf{i} + \left(v_0 t - gt^2\right)\mathbf{j}\right]$ and then
$\mathbf{v}(t) = \mathbf{r}'(t) = \frac{1}{2}\left[v_0\sqrt{3}\,\mathbf{i} + (v_0 - 2gt)\,\mathbf{j}\right]$. The shell reaches its maximum height when the vertical component of

velocity is zero, so $\frac{1}{2}(v_0 - 2gt) = 0 \;\Rightarrow\; t = \dfrac{v_0}{2g}$. The vertical height of the shell at that time is 500 m, so

$\dfrac{1}{2}\left[v_0\left(\dfrac{v_0}{2g}\right) - g\left(\dfrac{v_0}{2g}\right)^2\right] = 500 \;\Rightarrow\; \dfrac{v_0^2}{8g} = 500 \;\Rightarrow\; v_0 = \sqrt{4000g} = \sqrt{4000\,(9.8)} \approx 198$ m/s.

25. Let α be the angle of elevation. Then $v_0 = 150$ m/s and from Example 5, the horizontal distance traveled by the

projectile is $d = \dfrac{v_0^2 \sin 2\alpha}{g}$. Thus $\dfrac{150^2 \sin 2\alpha}{g} = 800 \;\Rightarrow\; \sin 2\alpha = \dfrac{800g}{150^2} \approx 0.3484 \;\Rightarrow\; 2\alpha \approx 20.4°$ or
$180 - 20.4 = 159.6°$. Two angles of elevation then are $\alpha \approx 10.2°$ and $\alpha \approx 79.8°$.

26. Here $v_0 = 115$ ft/s, the angle of elevation is $\alpha = 50°$, and if we place the origin at home plate, then $\mathbf{r}(0) = 3\,\mathbf{j}$. As
in Example 5, we have $\mathbf{r}(t) = -\frac{1}{2}gt^2\,\mathbf{j} + t\mathbf{v}_0 + \mathbf{D}$ where $\mathbf{D} = \mathbf{r}(0) = 3\,\mathbf{j}$ and $\mathbf{v}_0 = v_0 \cos\alpha\,\mathbf{i} + v_0 \sin\alpha\,\mathbf{j}$, so
$\mathbf{r}(t) = (v_0 \cos\alpha)\,t\,\mathbf{i} + \left[(v_0 \sin\alpha)\,t - \frac{1}{2}gt^2 + 3\right]\mathbf{j}$. Thus, parametric equations for the trajectory of the ball are
$x = (v_0 \cos\alpha)\,t$, $y = (v_0 \sin\alpha)\,t - \frac{1}{2}gt^2 + 3$. The ball reaches the fence when $x = 400 \;\Rightarrow\; (v_0 \cos\alpha)\,t = 400$

$\Rightarrow\; t = \dfrac{400}{v_0 \cos\alpha} = \dfrac{400}{115 \cos 50°} \approx 5.41$ s. At this time, the height of the ball is

$y = (v_0 \sin\alpha)\,t - \frac{1}{2}gt^2 + 3 \approx (115 \sin 50°)(5.41) - \frac{1}{2}(32)(5.41)^2 + 3 \approx 11.2$ ft. Since the fence is 10 ft high,
the ball clears the fence.

27. (a) After t seconds, the boat will be $5t$ meters west of point A. The velocity of the water at that location is
$\frac{3}{400}(5t)(40-5t)\mathbf{j}$. The velocity of the boat in still water is $5\mathbf{i}$, so the resultant velocity of the boat is
$\mathbf{v}(t) = 5\mathbf{i} + \frac{3}{400}(5t)(40-5t)\mathbf{j} = 5\mathbf{i} + \left(\frac{3}{2}t - \frac{3}{16}t^2\right)\mathbf{j}$. Integrating, we obtain
$\mathbf{r}(t) = 5t\mathbf{i} + \left(\frac{3}{4}t^2 - \frac{1}{16}t^3\right)\mathbf{j} + \mathbf{C}$. If we place the origin at A (and consider $\mathbf{i}$ to coincide with the northern
direction) then $\mathbf{r}(0) = \mathbf{0} \Rightarrow \mathbf{C} = \mathbf{0}$ and we have $\mathbf{r}(t) = 5t\mathbf{i} + \left(\frac{3}{4}t^2 - \frac{1}{16}t^3\right)\mathbf{j}$. The boat reaches the east
bank after 8 s, and it is located at $\mathbf{r}(8) = 5(8)\mathbf{i} + \left(\frac{3}{4}(8)^2 - \frac{1}{16}(8)^3\right)\mathbf{j} = 40\mathbf{i} + 16\mathbf{j}$. Thus the boat is 16 m
downstream.

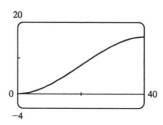

(b) Let α be the angle north of east that the boat heads. Then the velocity of the boat in still water is given by
$5(\cos\alpha)\mathbf{i} + 5(\sin\alpha)\mathbf{j}$. At t seconds, the boat is $5(\cos\alpha)t$ meters from the west bank, at which point the velocity
of the water is $\frac{3}{400}[5(\cos\alpha)t][40 - 5(\cos\alpha)t]\mathbf{j}$. The resultant velocity of the boat is given by

$$\mathbf{v}(t) = 5(\cos\alpha)\mathbf{i} + \left[5\sin\alpha + \frac{3}{400}(5t\cos\alpha)(40 - 5t\cos\alpha)\right]\mathbf{j}$$
$$= (5\cos\alpha)\mathbf{i} + \left(5\sin\alpha + \frac{3}{2}t\cos\alpha - \frac{3}{16}t^2\cos^2\alpha\right)\mathbf{j}.$$

Integrating, $\mathbf{r}(t) = (5t\cos\alpha)\mathbf{i} + \left(5t\sin\alpha + \frac{3}{4}t^2\cos\alpha - \frac{1}{16}t^3\cos^2\alpha\right)\mathbf{j}$ (where we have again placed the
origin at A). The boat will reach the east bank when $5t\cos\alpha = 40 \Rightarrow t = \dfrac{40}{5\cos\alpha} = \dfrac{8}{\cos\alpha}$.
In order to land at point B $(40,0)$ we need $5t\sin\alpha + \frac{3}{4}t^2\cos\alpha - \frac{1}{16}t^3\cos^2\alpha = 0 \Rightarrow$

$5\left(\dfrac{8}{\cos\alpha}\right)\sin\alpha + \dfrac{3}{4}\left(\dfrac{8}{\cos\alpha}\right)^2\cos\alpha - \dfrac{1}{16}\left(\dfrac{8}{\cos\alpha}\right)^3\cos^2\alpha = 0 \Rightarrow \dfrac{1}{\cos\alpha}(40\sin\alpha + 48 - 32) = 0$

$\Rightarrow 40\sin\alpha + 16 = 0 \Rightarrow \sin\alpha = -\frac{2}{5}$. Thus $\alpha = \sin^{-1}\left(-\frac{2}{5}\right) \approx -23.6°$, so the boat should head $23.6°$
south of east (upstream).

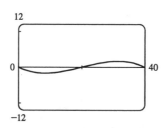

The path does seem realistic. The boat initially heads upstream to counteract the effect of the current. Near the
center of the river, the current is stronger and the boat is pushed downstream. When the boat nears the eastern
bank, the current is slower and the boat is able to progress upstream to arrive at point B.

28. As in Exercise 27(b), let α be the angle north of east that the boat heads, so the velocity of the boat in still water is given by $5(\cos\alpha)\mathbf{i} + 5(\sin\alpha)\mathbf{j}$. At t seconds, the boat is $5(\cos\alpha)t$ meters from the west bank, at which point the velocity of the water is $3\sin(\pi x/40)\mathbf{j} = 3\sin[\pi \cdot 5(\cos\alpha)t/40]\mathbf{j} = 3\sin\left(\frac{\pi}{8}t\cos\alpha\right)\mathbf{j}$. The resultant velocity of the boat then is given by $\mathbf{v}(t) = 5(\cos\alpha)\mathbf{i} + \left[5\sin\alpha + 3\sin\left(\frac{\pi}{8}t\cos\alpha\right)\right]\mathbf{j}$. Integrating,

$$\mathbf{r}(t) = (5t\cos\alpha)\,\mathbf{i} + \left[5t\sin\alpha - \frac{24}{\pi\cos\alpha}\cos\left(\frac{\pi}{8}t\cos\alpha\right)\right]\mathbf{j} + \mathbf{C}.$$

If we place the origin at A then $\mathbf{r}(0) = \mathbf{0} \quad \Rightarrow \quad -\frac{24}{\pi\cos\alpha}\mathbf{j} + \mathbf{C} = \mathbf{0} \quad \Rightarrow \quad \mathbf{C} = \frac{24}{\pi\cos\alpha}\mathbf{j}$ and

$$\mathbf{r}(t) = (5t\cos\alpha)\,\mathbf{i} + \left[5t\sin\alpha - \frac{24}{\pi\cos\alpha}\cos\left(\frac{\pi}{8}t\cos\alpha\right) + \frac{24}{\pi\cos\alpha}\right]\mathbf{j}.$$

The boat will reach the east bank when $5t\cos\alpha = 40 \quad \Rightarrow \quad t = \dfrac{8}{\cos\alpha}$. In order to land

at point $B(40,0)$ we need $5t\sin\alpha - \dfrac{24}{\pi\cos\alpha}\cos\left(\dfrac{\pi}{8}t\cos\alpha\right) + \dfrac{24}{\pi\cos\alpha} = 0$

$$\Rightarrow \quad 5\left(\frac{8}{\cos\alpha}\right)\sin\alpha - \frac{24}{\pi\cos\alpha}\cos\left[\frac{\pi}{8}\left(\frac{8}{\cos\alpha}\right)\cos\alpha\right] + \frac{24}{\pi\cos\alpha} = 0 \quad \Rightarrow$$

$$\frac{1}{\cos\alpha}\left(40\sin\alpha - \frac{24}{\pi}\cos\pi + \frac{24}{\pi}\right) = 0 \quad \Rightarrow \quad 40\sin\alpha + \frac{48}{\pi} = 0 \quad \Rightarrow \quad \sin\alpha = -\frac{6}{5\pi}. \text{ Thus}$$

$\alpha = \sin^{-1}\left(-\dfrac{6}{5\pi}\right) \approx -22.5°$, so the boat should head $22.5°$ south of east.

29. $\mathbf{r}(t) = \left(3t - t^3\right)\mathbf{i} + 3t^2\,\mathbf{j} \quad \Rightarrow \quad \mathbf{r}'(t) = \left(3 - 3t^2\right)\mathbf{i} + 6t\,\mathbf{j}$,

$|\mathbf{r}'(t)| = \sqrt{(3 - 3t^2)^2 + (6t)^2} = \sqrt{9 + 18t^2 + 9t^4} = \sqrt{(3 - 3t^2)^2} = 3 + 3t^2$,

$\mathbf{r}''(t) = -6t\,\mathbf{i} + 6\mathbf{j}$, $\mathbf{r}'(t) \times \mathbf{r}''(t) = (18 + 18t^2)\,\mathbf{k}$. Then Equation 9 gives

$$a_T = \frac{\mathbf{r}'(t) \cdot \mathbf{r}''(t)}{|\mathbf{r}'(t)|} = \frac{(3 - 3t^2)(-6t) + (6t)(6)}{3 + 3t^2} = \frac{18t + 18t^3}{3 + 3t^2} = \frac{18t(1 + t^2)}{3(1 + t^2)} = 6t \quad \text{[or by Equation 8,}$$

$$a_T = v' = \frac{d}{dt}\left[3 + 3t^2\right] = 6t\text{]} \quad \text{and Equation 10 gives } a_N = \frac{|\mathbf{r}'(t) \times \mathbf{r}''(t)|}{|\mathbf{r}'(t)|} = \frac{18 + 18t^2}{3 + 3t^2} = \frac{18(1 + t^2)}{3(1 + t^2)} = 6.$$

30. $\mathbf{r}(t) = t\mathbf{i} + t^2\mathbf{j} + 3t\,\mathbf{k} \quad \Rightarrow \quad \mathbf{r}'(t) = \mathbf{i} + 2t\mathbf{j} + 3\mathbf{k}$, $|\mathbf{r}'(t)| = \sqrt{1^2 + (2t)^2 + 3^2} = \sqrt{4t^2 + 10}$, $\mathbf{r}''(t) = 2\mathbf{j}$,

$\mathbf{r}'(t) \times \mathbf{r}''(t) = -6\mathbf{i} + 2\mathbf{k}$. Then $a_T = \dfrac{\mathbf{r}'(t) \cdot \mathbf{r}''(t)}{|\mathbf{r}'(t)|} = \dfrac{4t}{\sqrt{4t^2 + 10}}$ and $a_N = \dfrac{|\mathbf{r}'(t) \times \mathbf{r}''(t)|}{|\mathbf{r}'(t)|} = \dfrac{2\sqrt{10}}{\sqrt{4t^2 + 10}}$.

31. $\mathbf{r}(t) = \cos t\,\mathbf{i} + \sin t\,\mathbf{j} + t\,\mathbf{k} \quad \Rightarrow \quad \mathbf{r}'(t) = -\sin t\,\mathbf{i} + \cos t\,\mathbf{j} + \mathbf{k}$, $|\mathbf{r}'(t)| = \sqrt{\sin^2 t + \cos^2 t + 1} = \sqrt{2}$,

$\mathbf{r}''(t) = -\cos t\,\mathbf{i} - \sin t\,\mathbf{j}$, $\mathbf{r}'(t) \times \mathbf{r}''(t) = \sin t\,\mathbf{i} - \cos t\,\mathbf{j} + \mathbf{k}$.

Then $a_T = \dfrac{\mathbf{r}'(t) \cdot \mathbf{r}''(t)}{|\mathbf{r}'(t)|} = \dfrac{\sin t\cos t - \sin t\cos t}{\sqrt{2}} = 0$ and

$a_N = \dfrac{|\mathbf{r}'(t) \times \mathbf{r}''(t)|}{|\mathbf{r}'(t)|} = \dfrac{\sqrt{\sin^2 t + \cos^2 t + 1}}{\sqrt{2}} = \dfrac{\sqrt{2}}{\sqrt{2}} = 1$.

32. $\mathbf{r}(t) = t\mathbf{i} + \cos^2 t\,\mathbf{j} + \sin^2 t\,\mathbf{k} \quad \Rightarrow \quad \mathbf{r}'(t) = \mathbf{i} - 2\cos t\sin t\,\mathbf{j} + 2\sin t\cos t\,\mathbf{k} = \mathbf{i} - \sin 2t\,\mathbf{j} + \sin 2t\,\mathbf{k}$,

$|\mathbf{r}'(t)| = \sqrt{1 + 2\sin^2 2t}$, $\mathbf{r}''(t) = 2(\sin^2 t - \cos^2 t)\,\mathbf{j} + 2(\cos^2 t - \sin^2 t)\,\mathbf{k} = -2\cos 2t\,\mathbf{j} + 2\cos 2t\,\mathbf{k}$. So

$$a_T = \frac{2\sin 2t\cos 2t + 2\sin 2t\cos 2t}{\sqrt{1 + 2\sin^2 2t}} = \frac{4\sin 2t\cos 2t}{\sqrt{1 + 2\sin^2 2t}} \text{ and } a_N = \frac{|-2\cos 2t\,\mathbf{j} - 2\cos 2t\,\mathbf{k}|}{\sqrt{1 + 2\sin^2 2t}} = \frac{2\sqrt{2}\,|\cos 2t|}{\sqrt{1 + 2\sin^2 t}}.$$

33. The tangential component of **a** is the length of the projection of **a** onto **T**, so we sketch the scalar projection of **a** in the tangential direction to the curve and estimate its length to be 4.5 (using the fact that **a** has length 10 as a guide).

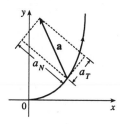

Similarly, the normal component of **a** is the length of the projection of **a** onto **N**, so we sketch the scalar projection of **a** in the normal direction to the curve and estimate its length to be 9.0. Thus $a_T \approx 4.5 \text{ cm/s}^2$ and $a_N \approx 9.0 \text{ cm/s}^2$.

34. $\mathbf{L}(t) = m\,\mathbf{r}(t) \times \mathbf{v}(t) \quad \Rightarrow$
$\mathbf{L}'(t) = m[\mathbf{r}'(t) \times \mathbf{v}(t) + \mathbf{r}(t) \times \mathbf{v}'(t)] \qquad$ [by Theorem 10.2.3 #5]

$\qquad = m[\mathbf{v}(t) \times \mathbf{v}(t) + \mathbf{r}(t) \times \mathbf{v}'(t)] = m[\mathbf{0} + \mathbf{r}(t) \times \mathbf{a}(t)] = \boldsymbol{\tau}(t)$

So if the torque is always **0**, then $\mathbf{L}'(t) = \mathbf{0}$ for all t, and so $\mathbf{L}(t)$ is constant.

35. If the engines are turned off at time t, then the spacecraft will continue to travel in the direction of $\mathbf{v}(t)$, so we need a t such that for some scalar $s > 0$, $\mathbf{r}(t) + s\,\mathbf{v}(t) = \langle 6, 4, 9\rangle$. $\quad \mathbf{v}(t) = \mathbf{r}'(t) = \mathbf{i} + \dfrac{1}{t}\mathbf{j} + \dfrac{8t}{(t^2+1)^2}\mathbf{k} \quad \Rightarrow$

$\mathbf{r}(t) + s\,\mathbf{v}(t) = \left\langle 3 + t + s, 2 + \ln t + \dfrac{s}{t}, 7 - \dfrac{4}{t^2+1} + \dfrac{8st}{(t^2+1)^2} \right\rangle \quad \Rightarrow \quad 3 + t + s = 6 \quad \Rightarrow \quad s = 3 - t$, so

$7 - \dfrac{4}{t^2+1} + \dfrac{8(3-t)t}{(t^2+1)^2} = 9 \quad \Leftrightarrow \quad \dfrac{24t - 12t^2 - 4}{(t^2+1)^2} = 2 \quad \Leftrightarrow \quad t^4 + 8t^2 - 12t + 3 = 0$. It is easily seen that $t = 1$ is a root of this polynomial. Also $2 + \ln 1 + \dfrac{3-1}{1} = 4$, so $t = 1$ is the desired solution.

36. (a) $m\dfrac{d\mathbf{v}}{dt} = \dfrac{dm}{dt}\mathbf{v}_e \quad \Leftrightarrow \quad \dfrac{d\mathbf{v}}{dt} = \dfrac{1}{m}\dfrac{dm}{dt}\mathbf{v}_e$. Integrating both sides of this equation with respect to t gives

$\displaystyle\int_0^t \dfrac{d\mathbf{v}}{du}\,du = \mathbf{v}_e \int_0^t \dfrac{1}{m}\dfrac{dm}{du}\,du \quad \Rightarrow \quad \int_{\mathbf{v}(0)}^{\mathbf{v}(t)} d\mathbf{v} = \mathbf{v}_e \int_{m(0)}^{m(t)} \dfrac{dm}{m} \qquad$ [Substitution Rule] $\quad \Rightarrow$

$\mathbf{v}(t) - \mathbf{v}(0) = \ln\left(\dfrac{m(t)}{m(0)}\right)\mathbf{v}_e \quad \Rightarrow \quad \mathbf{v}(t) = \mathbf{v}(0) - \ln\left(\dfrac{m(0)}{m(t)}\right)\mathbf{v}_e.$

(b) $|\mathbf{v}(t)| = 2\,|\mathbf{v}_e|$, and $|\mathbf{v}(0)| = 0$. Therefore, by part (a), $2\,|\mathbf{v}_e| = \left| -\ln\left(\dfrac{m(0)}{m(t)}\right)\mathbf{v}_e \right| \quad \Rightarrow$

$2\,|\mathbf{v}_e| = \ln\left(\dfrac{m(0)}{m(t)}\right)|\mathbf{v}_e|$. [*Note:* $m(0) > m(t)$ so that $\ln(m(0)/m(t)) > 0$] $\quad \Rightarrow \quad m(t) = e^{-2}m(0)$.

Thus $\dfrac{m(0) - e^{-2}m(0)}{m(0)} = 1 - e^{-2}$ is the fraction of the initial mass that is burned as fuel.

Applied Project	Kepler's Laws

1. With $\mathbf{r} = (r\cos\theta)\,\mathbf{i} + (r\sin\theta)\,\mathbf{j}$ and $\mathbf{h} = \alpha\,\mathbf{k}$ where $\alpha > 0$,

(a) $\mathbf{h} = \mathbf{r} \times \mathbf{r}' = [(r\cos\theta)\,\mathbf{i} + (r\sin\theta)\,\mathbf{j}] \times \left[\left(r'\cos\theta - r\sin\theta\,\dfrac{d\theta}{dt} \right)\mathbf{i} + \left(r'\sin\theta + r\cos\theta\,\dfrac{d\theta}{dt} \right)\mathbf{j} \right]$

$$= \left[rr'\cos\theta\sin\theta + r^2\cos^2\theta\,\frac{d\theta}{dt} - rr'\cos\theta\sin\theta + r^2\sin^2\theta\,\frac{d\theta}{dt} \right]\mathbf{k} = r^2\,\frac{d\theta}{dt}\,\mathbf{k}$$

(b) Since $\mathbf{h} = \alpha\,\mathbf{k}$, $\alpha > 0$, $\alpha = |\mathbf{h}|$. But by part (a), $\alpha = |\mathbf{h}| = r^2\,(d\theta/dt)$.

(c) $A(t) = \frac{1}{2}\int_{\theta_0}^{\theta} |\mathbf{r}|^2\,d\theta = \frac{1}{2}\int_{t_0}^{t} r^2\,(d\theta/dt)\,dt$ in polar coordinates. Thus, by the Fundamental Theorem

of Calculus, $\dfrac{dA}{dt} = \dfrac{r^2}{2}\dfrac{d\theta}{dt}$.

(d) $\dfrac{dA}{dt} = \dfrac{r^2}{2}\dfrac{d\theta}{dt} = \dfrac{h}{2} = $ constant since $\mathbf{h}$ is a constant vector and $h = |\mathbf{h}|$.

2. (a) Since $dA/dt = \frac{1}{2}h$, a constant, $A(t) = \frac{1}{2}ht + c_1$. But $A(0) = 0$, so $A(t) = \frac{1}{2}ht$. But
$A(T) = $ area of the ellipse $= \pi ab$ and $A(T) = \frac{1}{2}hT$, so $T = 2\pi ab/h$.

(b) $h^2/(GM) = ed$ where e is the eccentricity of the ellipse. But $a = ed/(1 - e^2)$ or $ed = a(1 - e^2)$ and
$1 - e^2 = b^2/a^2$. Hence $h^2/(GM) = ed = b^2/a$.

(c) $T^2 = \dfrac{4\pi^2 a^2 b^2}{h^2} = 4\pi^2 a^2 b^2 \dfrac{a}{GMb^2} = \dfrac{4\pi^2}{GM}a^3$.

3. From Problem 2, $T^2 = \dfrac{4\pi^2}{GM}a^3$. $T \approx 365.25$ days $\times\, 24 \cdot 60^2\,\dfrac{\text{seconds}}{\text{day}} \approx 3.1558 \times 10^7$ seconds. Therefore

$a^3 = \dfrac{GMT^2}{4\pi^2} \approx \dfrac{\left(6.67 \times 10^{-11} \right)\left(1.99 \times 10^{30} \right)\left(3.1558 \times 10^7 \right)^2}{4\pi^2} \approx 3.348 \times 10^{33}\ \text{m}^3 \quad\Rightarrow$

$a \approx 1.496 \times 10^{11}$ m. Thus, the length of the major axis of Earth's orbit (that is, $2a$) is approximately
2.99×10^{11} m $= 2.99 \times 10^8$ km.

4. We can adapt the equation $T^2 = \dfrac{4\pi^2}{GM}a^3$ from Problem 2(c) with Earth at the center of the system, so T is the
period of the satellite's orbit about Earth, M is the mass of Earth, and a is the length of the semimajor axis of the
satellite's orbit (measured from Earth's center). Since we want the satellite to remain fixed above a
particular point on Earth's equator, T must coincide with the period of Earth's own
rotation, so $T = 24$ h $= 86{,}400$ s. The mass of Earth is $M = 5.98 \times 10^{24}$ kg, so

$a = \left(\dfrac{T^2 GM}{4\pi^2} \right)^{1/3} \approx \left[\dfrac{(86{,}400)^2\left(6.67 \times 10^{-11} \right)\left(5.98 \times 10^{24} \right)}{4\pi^2} \right]^{1/3} \approx 4.23 \times 10^7$ m. If we assume a circular

orbit, the radius of the orbit is a, and since the radius of Earth is 6.37×10^6 m, the required altitude above Earth's
surface for the satellite is $4.23 \times 10^7 - 6.37 \times 10^6 \approx 3.59 \times 10^7$ m, or 35,900 km.

10.5 **Parametric Surfaces** · · · · · · · · · · · · · · · ·

1. $\mathbf{r}(au, v) = u\cos v\,\mathbf{i} + u\sin v\,\mathbf{j} + u^2\,\mathbf{k}$, so the corresponding parametric equations for the surface are
$x = u\cos v$, $y = u\sin v$, $z = u^2$. For any point (x, y, z) on the surface, we have
$x^2 + y^2 = u^2\cos^2 v + u^2\sin^2 v = u^2 = z$. Since no restrictions are placed on the parameters, the surface is
$z = x^2 + y^2$, which we recognize as a circular paraboloid opening upward whose axis is the z-axis.

2. $\mathbf{r}(u, v) = (1 + 2u)\,\mathbf{i} + (-u + 3v)\,\mathbf{j} + (2 + 4u + 5v)\,\mathbf{k} = \langle 1, 0, 2\rangle + u\,\langle 2, -1, 4\rangle + v\,\langle 0, 3, 5\rangle$. From Example 3,
we recognize this as a vector equation of a plane through the point $(1, 0, 2)$ and containing vectors $\mathbf{a} = \langle 2, -1, 4\rangle$
and $\mathbf{b} = \langle 0, 3, 5\rangle$. If we wish to find a more conventional equation for the plane, a normal vector to the plane

is $\mathbf{a} \times \mathbf{b} = \begin{vmatrix} \mathbf{i} & \mathbf{j} & \mathbf{k} \\ 2 & -1 & 4 \\ 0 & 3 & 5 \end{vmatrix} = -17\mathbf{i} - 10\mathbf{j} + 6\mathbf{k}$ and an equation of the plane is

$-17(x - 1) - 10(y - 0) + 6(z - 2) = 0$ or $-17x - 10y + 6z = -5$.

3. $\mathbf{r}(x, \theta) = \langle x, \cos\theta, \sin\theta\rangle$, so the corresponding parametric equations for the surface are
$x = x$, $y = \cos\theta$, $z = \sin\theta$. For any point (x, y, z) on the surface, we have $y^2 + z^2 = \cos^2\theta + \sin^2\theta = 1$, so any
vertical trace in $x = k$ is the circle $y^2 + z^2 = 1$, $x = k$. Since $x = x$ with no restriction, the surface is a circular
cylinder with radius 1 whose axis is the x-axis.

4. $\mathbf{r}(x, \theta) = \langle x, x\cos\theta, x\sin\theta\rangle$, so the corresponding parametric equations for the surface are
$x = x$, $y = x\cos\theta$, $z = x\sin\theta$. For any point (x, y, z) on the surface, we have
$y^2 + z^2 = x^2\cos^2\theta + x^2\sin^2\theta = x^2$. With $x = x$ and no restrictions on the parameters, the surface is
$x^2 = y^2 + z^2$, which we recognize as a circular cone whose axis is the x-axis.

5. $\mathbf{r}(u, v) = \langle u^2 + 1, v^3 + 1, u + v\rangle$, $-1 \le u \le 1$, $-1 \le v \le 1$.

The surface has parametric equations $x = u^2 + 1$, $y = v^3 + 1$,
$z = u + v$, $-1 \le u \le 1$, $-1 \le v \le 1$. If we keep u constant at
u_0, $x = u_0^2 + 1$, a constant, so the corresponding grid curves must
be the curves parallel to the yz-plane. If v is constant, we have
$y = v_0^3 + 1$, a constant, so these grid curves are the curves parallel
to the xz-plane.

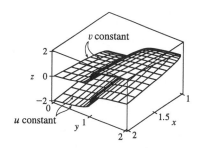

6. $\mathbf{r}(u, v) = \langle u + v, u^2, v^2\rangle$, $-1 \le u \le 1$, $-1 \le v \le 1$.

The surface has parametric equations $x = u + v$, $y = u^2$,
$z = v^2$, $-1 \le u \le 1$, $-1 \le v \le 1$. If $u = u_0$ is constant,
$y = u_0^2 = $ constant, so the corresponding grid curves are the
curves parallel to the xz-plane. If $v = v_0$ is constant,
$z = v_0^2 = $ constant, so the corresponding grid curves are the
curves parallel to the xy-plane.

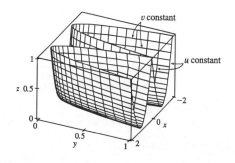

7. $\mathbf{r}(u, v) = \langle \cos^3 u \cos^3 v, \sin^3 u \cos^3 v, \sin^3 v \rangle$.

The surface has parametric equations $x = \cos^3 u \cos^3 v$, $y = \sin^3 u \cos^3 v$, $z = \sin^3 v$, $0 \le u \le \pi$, $0 \le v \le 2\pi$. Note that if $v = v_0$ is constant then $z = \sin^3 v_0$ is constant, so the corresponding grid curves must be the curves parallel to the xy-plane. The vertically oriented grid curves, then, correspond to $u = u_0$ being held constant, giving $x = \cos^3 u_0 \cos^3 v$, $y = \sin^3 u_0 \cos^3 v$, $z = \sin^3 v$. These curves lie in vertical planes that contain the z-axis.

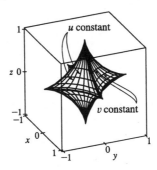

8. $\mathbf{r}(u, v) = \langle \cos u \sin v, \sin u \sin v, \cos v + \ln \tan(v/2) \rangle$.

The surface has parametric equations $x = \cos u \sin v$, $y = \sin u \sin v$, $z = \cos v + \ln \tan(v/2)$, $0 \le u \le 2\pi$, $0.1 \le v \le 6.2$. Note that if $v = v_0$ is constant, the parametric equations become $x = \cos u \sin v_0$, $y = \sin u \sin v_0$, $z = \cos v_0 + \ln \tan(v_0/2)$ which represent a circle of radius $\sin v_0$ in the plane $z = \cos v_0 + \ln \tan(v_0/2)$. So the circular grid curves we see lying horizontally are the grid curves with v constant. The vertically oriented grid curves correspond to $u = u_0$ being held constant, giving $x = \cos u_0 \sin v$, $y = \sin u_0 \sin v$, $z = \cos v + \ln \tan(v/2)$. These curves lie in vertical planes that contain the z-axis.

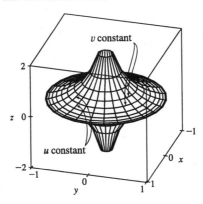

9. $x = \cos u \sin 2v$, $y = \sin u \sin 2v$, $z = \sin v$.

The complete graph of the surface is given by the parametric domain $0 \le u \le \pi$, $0 \le v \le 2\pi$. Note that if $v = v_0$ is constant, the parametric equations become $x = \cos u \sin 2v_0$, $y = \sin u \sin 2v_0$, $z = \sin v_0$ which represent a circle of radius $\sin 2v_0$ in the plane $z = \sin v_0$. So the circular grid curves we see lying horizontally are the grid curves which have v constant. The vertical grid curves, then, correspond to $u = u_0$ being held constant, giving $x = \cos u_0 \sin 2v$ and $y = \sin u_0 \sin 2v$ with $z = \sin v$ which has a "figure-eight" shape.

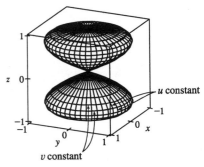

10. $x = u \sin u \cos v$, $y = u \cos u \cos v$, $z = u \sin v$.

We graph the portion of the surface with parametric domain

$0 \le u \le 4\pi, 0 \le v \le 2\pi$. Note that if $v = v_0$ is constant, the

parametric equations become $x = u \sin u \cos v_0$, $y = u \cos u \cos v_0$,

$z = u \sin v_0$. The equations for x and y show that the projections

onto the xy-plane give a spiral shape, so the corresponding grid

curves are the almost-horizontal spiral curves we see. The vertical

grid curves, which look approximately circular, correspond to

$u = u_0$ being held constant, giving $x = u_0 \sin u_0 \cos v$,

$y = u_0 \cos u_0 \cos v$, $z = u_0 \sin v$.

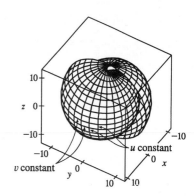

11. $\mathbf{r}(u, v) = \cos v \, \mathbf{i} + \sin v \, \mathbf{j} + u \, \mathbf{k}$. The parametric equations for the surface are $x = \cos v$, $y = \sin v$, $z = u$. Then $x^2 + y^2 = \cos^2 v + \sin^2 v = 1$ and $z = u$ with no restriction on u, so we have a circular cylinder, graph IV. The grid curves with u constant are the horizontal circles we see in the plane $z = u$. If v is constant, both x and y are constant with z free to vary, so the corresponding grid curves are the lines on the cylinder parallel to the z-axis.

12. $\mathbf{r}(u, v) = u \cos v \, \mathbf{i} + u \sin v \, \mathbf{j} + u \, \mathbf{k}$. The parametric equations for the surface are $x = u \cos v$, $y = u \sin v$, $z = u$. Then $x^2 + y^2 = u^2 \cos^2 v + u^2 \sin^2 v = u^2 = z^2$, which represents the equation of a cone with axis the z-axis, graph V. The grid curves with u constant are the horizontal circles we see, corresponding to the equations $x^2 + y^2 = u^2$ in the plane $z = u$. If v is constant, x, y, z are each scalar multiples of u, corresponding to the straight line grid curves through the origin.

13. $\mathbf{r}(u, v) = u \cos v \, \mathbf{i} + u \sin v \, \mathbf{j} + v \, \mathbf{k}$. The parametric equations for the surface are $x = u \cos v$, $y = u \sin v$, $z = v$. We look at the grid curves first; if we fix v, then x and y parametrize a straight line in the plane $z = v$ which intersects the z-axis. If u is held constant, the projection onto the xy-plane is circular; with $z = v$, each grid curve is a helix. The surface is a spiraling ramp, graph I.

14. $x = u^3$, $y = u \sin v$, $z = u \cos v$. Then $y^2 + z^2 = u^2 \sin v^2 + u^2 \cos v^2 = u^2$, so if u is held constant, each grid curve is a circle of radius u in the plane $x = u^3$. The graph then must be graph III. If v is held constant, so $v = v_0$, we have $y = u \sin v_0$ and $z = u \cos v_0$. Then $y = (\tan v_0) z$, so the grid curves we see running lengthwise along the surface in the planes $y = kz$ correspond to keeping v constant.

15. $x = (u - \sin u) \cos v$, $y = (1 - \cos u) \sin v$, $z = u$. If u is held constant, x and y give an equation of an ellipse in the plane $z = u$, thus the grid curves are horizontally oriented ellipses. Note that when $u = 0$, the "ellipse" is the single point $(0, 0, 0)$, and when $u = \pi$, we have $y = 0$ while x ranges from $-\pi$ to π, a line segment parallel to the x-axis in the plane $z = \pi$. This is the upper "seam" we see in graph II. When v is held constant, $z = u$ is free to vary, so the corresponding grid curves are the curves we see running up and down along the surface.

16. $x = (1 - u)(3 + \cos v) \cos 4\pi u$, $y = (1 - u)(3 + \cos v) \sin 4\pi u$, $z = 3u + (1 - u) \sin v$. These equations correspond to graph VI: when $u = 0$, then $x = 3 + \cos v$, $y = 0$, and $z = \sin v$, which are equations of a circle with radius 1 in the xz-plane centered at $(3, 0, 0)$. When $u = \frac{1}{2}$, then $x = \frac{3}{2} + \frac{1}{2} \cos v$, $y = 0$, and $z = \frac{3}{2} + \frac{1}{2} \sin v$, which are equations of a circle with radius $\frac{1}{2}$ in the xz-plane centered at $\left(\frac{3}{2}, 0, \frac{3}{2}\right)$. When $u = 1$, then $x = y = 0$ and $z = 3$, giving the topmost point shown in the graph. This suggests that the grid curves with u constant are the vertically oriented circles visible on the surface. The spiralling grid curves correspond to keeping v constant.

17. From Example 3, parametric equations for the plane through the point $(1, 2, -3)$ that contains the vectors

$\mathbf{a} = \langle 1, 1, -1 \rangle$ and $\mathbf{b} = \langle 1, -1, 1 \rangle$ are $x = 1 + u(1) + v(1) = 1 + u + v$, $y = 2 + u(1) + v(-1) = 2 + u - v$,

$z = -3 + u(-1) + v(1) = -3 - u + v$.

18. Solving the equation for z gives $z^2 = 1 - 2x^2 - 4y^2 \implies z = -\sqrt{1 - 2x^2 - 4y^2}$ (since we want the lower half

of the ellipsoid). If we let x and y be the parameters, parametric equations are $x = x$, $y = y$,

$z = -\sqrt{1 - 2x^2 - 4y^2}$.

Alternate solution: The equation can be rewritten as $\dfrac{x^2}{(1/\sqrt{2})^2} + \dfrac{y^2}{(1/2)^2} + z^2 = 1$, and if we let $x = \dfrac{1}{\sqrt{2}} u \cos v$

and $y = \frac{1}{2} u \sin v$, then $z = -\sqrt{1 - 2x^2 - 4y^2} = -\sqrt{1 - u^2 \cos^2 v - u^2 \sin^2 v} = -\sqrt{1 - u^2}$, where $0 \le u \le 1$

and $0 \le v \le 2\pi$.

19. Solving the equation for y gives $y^2 = 1 - x^2 + z^2 \implies y = \sqrt{1 - x^2 + z^2}$. (We choose the positive root since

we want the part of the hyperboloid that corresponds to $y \ge 0$.) If we let x and z be the parameters, parametric

equations are $x = x$, $z = z$, $y = \sqrt{1 - x^2 + z^2}$.

20. $x = 4 - y^2 - 2z^2$, $y = y$, $z = z$ where $y^2 + 2z^2 \le 4$ since $x \ge 0$. Then the associated vector equation is

$\mathbf{r}(y, z) = (4 - y^2 - 2z^2)\,\mathbf{i} + y\,\mathbf{j} + z\,\mathbf{k}$.

21. Since the cone intersects the sphere in the circle $x^2 + y^2 = 2$, $z = 2$ and we want the portion of the sphere above

this, we can parametrize the surface as $x = x$, $y = y$, $z = \sqrt{4 - x^2 - y^2}$ where $2 \le x^2 + y^2 \le 4$.

Alternate solution: Using spherical coordinates, $x = 2 \sin \phi \cos \theta$, $y = 2 \sin \phi \sin \theta$, $z = 2 \cos \phi$ where $0 \le \phi \le \frac{\pi}{4}$

and $0 \le \theta \le 2\pi$.

22. In cylindrical coordinates, parametric equations are $x = \sin \theta$, $y = y$, $z = \cos \theta$, $0 \le \theta \le 2\pi$, $-1 \le y \le 3$.

23. The surface is a disc with radius 4 and center $(0, 0, 5)$. Thus, $x = r \cos \theta$, $y = r \sin \theta$, $z = 5$ where $0 \le r \le 4$,

$0 \le \theta \le 2\pi$ is a parametric representation of the surface.

Alternate solution: In rectangular coordinates we could represent the surface as $x = x$, $y = y$, $z = 5$ where

$x^2 + y^2 \le 16$.

24. Using x and y as the parameters, $x = x$, $y = y$, $z = x + 3$ where $0 \le x^2 + y^2 \le 1$. Also, since the plane intersects

the cylinder in an ellipse, the surface is a planar ellipse in the plane $z = x + 3$. Thus, parametrizing with respect to s

and θ, we have $x = s \cos \theta$, $y = s \sin \theta$, $z = 3 + s \cos \theta$ where $0 \le s \le 1$ and $0 \le \theta \le 2\pi$.

25. The surface appears to be a portion of a circular cylinder of radius 3 with axis the x-axis. An equation of the

cylinder is $y^2 + z^2 = 9$, and we can impose the restrictions $0 \le x \le 5$, $y \le 0$ to obtain the portion shown. To graph

the surface on a CAS, we can use parametric equations $x = u$, $y = 3 \cos v$, $z = 3 \sin v$ with the parameter domain

$0 \le u \le 5$, $\frac{\pi}{2} \le v \le \frac{3\pi}{2}$. Alternatively, we can regard x and z as parameters. Then parametric equations are

$x = x$, $z = z$, $y = -\sqrt{9 - z^2}$, where $0 \le x \le 5$ and $-3 \le z \le 3$.

26. The surface appears to be a portion of a sphere of radius 1 centered at the origin. In spherical coordinates, the sphere

has equation $\rho = 1$, and imposing the restrictions $\frac{\pi}{2} \le \theta \le 2\pi$, $\frac{\pi}{4} \le \phi \le \pi$ will give only the portion of the sphere

shown. Thus, to graph the surface on a CAS we can either use spherical coordinates with the stated restrictions, or

we can use parametric equations: $x = \sin \phi \cos \theta$, $y = \sin \phi \sin \theta$, $z = \cos \phi$, $\frac{\pi}{2} \le \theta \le 2\pi$, $\frac{\pi}{4} \le \phi \le \pi$.

27. Using Equations 3, we have the parametrization $x = x$, $y = e^{-x} \cos \theta$, $z = e^{-x} \sin \theta$, $0 \le x \le 3$, $0 \le \theta \le 2\pi$.

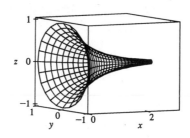

28. Letting θ be the angle of rotation about the y-axis, we have the parametrization $x = \left(4y^2 - y^4\right) \cos \theta$, $y = y$,

$z = \left(4y^2 - y^4\right) \sin \theta$, $-2 \le y \le 2$, $0 \le \theta \le 2\pi$.

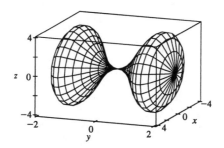

29. (a) $x = a \sin u \cos v$, $y = b \sin u \sin v$, $z = c \cos u$ ⇒ (b)

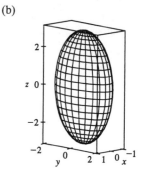

$$\frac{x^2}{a^2} + \frac{y^2}{b^2} + \frac{z^2}{c^2} = \left(\sin u \cos v\right)^2 + \left(\sin u \sin v\right)^2 + \left(\cos u\right)^2$$

$$= \sin^2 u + \cos^2 u = 1$$

and since the ranges of u and v are sufficient to generate the entire graph,
the parametric equations represent an ellipsoid.

30. First we graph the surface as viewed from the front, then from two additional viewpoints.

 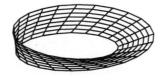 

The surface appears as a twisted sheet, and is unusual because it has only one side. (The Möbius strip is discussed in more detail in Section 13.6.)

31. (a) Replacing $\cos u$ by $\sin u$ and $\sin u$ by $\cos u$ gives parametric equations

$x = (2 + \sin v) \sin u$, $y = (2 + \sin v) \cos u$, $z = u + \cos v$. From the graph, it

appears that the direction of the spiral is reversed. We can verify this observation

by noting that the projection of the spiral grid curves onto the xy-plane, given by

$x = (2 + \sin v) \sin u$, $y = (2 + \sin v) \cos u$, $z = 0$, draws a circle in the

clockwise direction for each value of v. The original equations, on the other hand,

give circular projections drawn in the counterclockwise direction. The equation for

z is identical in both surfaces, so as z increases, these grid curves spiral up in

opposite directions for the two surfaces.

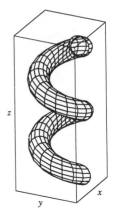

(b) Replacing $\cos u$ by $\cos 2u$ and $\sin u$ by $\sin 2u$ gives parametric equations

$x = (2 + \sin v) \cos 2u$, $y = (2 + \sin v) \sin 2u$, $z = u + \cos v$. From the graph, it

appears that the number of coils in the surface doubles within the same parametric

domain. We can verify this observation by noting that the projection of the spiral

grid curves onto the xy-plane, given by $x = (2 + \sin v) \cos 2u$,

$y = (2 + \sin v) \sin 2u$, $z = 0$ (where v is constant), complete circular revolutions

for $0 \le u \le \pi$ while the original surface requires $0 \le u \le 2\pi$ for a complete

revolution. Thus, the new surface winds around twice as fast as the original

surface, and since the equation for z is identical in both surfaces, we observe twice

as many circular coils in the same z-interval.

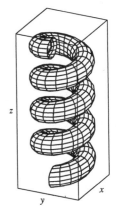

32. (a)

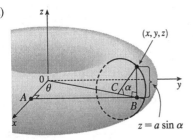

Here $z = a \sin \alpha$, $y = |AB|$, and $x = |OA|$. But $|OB| = |OC| + |CB| = b + a \cos \alpha$ and $\sin \theta = \dfrac{|AB|}{|OB|}$ so

that $y = |OB| \sin \theta = (b + a \cos \alpha) \sin \theta$. Similarly $\cos \theta = \dfrac{|OA|}{|OB|}$ so $x = (b + a \cos \alpha) \cos \theta$. Hence a

parametric representation for the torus is $x = b \cos \theta + a \cos \alpha \cos \theta$, $y = b \sin \theta + a \cos \alpha \sin \theta$, $z = a \sin \alpha$,

where $0 \le \alpha \le 2\pi$, $0 \le \theta \le 2\pi$.

(b)

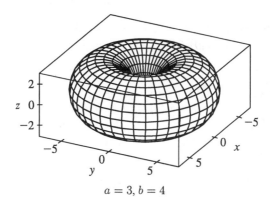

$a = 1, b = 8$

$a = 3, b = 8$

$a = 3, b = 4$

10 Review

— • **CONCEPT CHECK** • —

1. A vector function is a function whose domain is a set of real numbers and whose range is a set of vectors. To find the derivative or integral, we can differentiate or integrate each component of the vector function.

2. The tip of the moving vector $\mathbf{r}(t)$ of a continuous vector function traces out a space curve.

3. (a) A curve represented by the vector function $\mathbf{r}(t)$ is smooth if $\mathbf{r}'(t)$ is continuous and $\mathbf{r}'(t) \neq \mathbf{0}$ on its parametric domain (except possibly at the endpoints).

(b) The tangent vector to a smooth curve at a point P with position vector $\mathbf{r}(t)$ is the vector $\mathbf{r}'(t)$. The tangent line at P is the line through P parallel to the tangent vector $\mathbf{r}'(t)$. The unit tangent vector is $\mathbf{T}(t) = \dfrac{\mathbf{r}'(t)}{|\mathbf{r}'(t)|}$.

4. (a) – (f) See Theorem 10.2.3.

5. Use Formula 10.3.2, or equivalently 10.3.3.

6. (a) The curvature of a curve is $\kappa = \left| \dfrac{d\mathbf{T}}{ds} \right|$ where $\mathbf{T}$ is the unit tangent vector.

(b) $\kappa(t) = \left| \dfrac{\mathbf{T}'(t)}{\mathbf{r}'(t)} \right|$ (c) $\kappa(t) = \dfrac{|\mathbf{r}'(t) \times \mathbf{r}''(t)|}{|\mathbf{r}'(t)|^3}$ (d) $\kappa(x) = \dfrac{|f''(x)|}{[1 + (f'(x))^2]^{3/2}}$

7. (a) The unit normal vector: $\mathbf{N}(t) = \dfrac{\mathbf{T}'(t)}{|\mathbf{T}'(t)|}$. The binormal vector: $\mathbf{B}(t) = \mathbf{T}(t) \times \mathbf{N}(t)$.

(b) See the discussion preceding Example 7 in Section 10.3.

8. (a) If $\mathbf{r}(t)$ is the position vector of the particle on the space curve, the velocity $\mathbf{v}(t) = \mathbf{r}'(t)$, the speed is given by $|\mathbf{v}(t)|$, and the acceleration $\mathbf{a}(t) = \mathbf{v}'(t) = \mathbf{r}''(t)$.

(b) $\mathbf{a} = a_T\mathbf{T} + a_N\mathbf{N}$ where $a_T = v'$ and $a_N = \kappa v^2$.

9. See the statement of Kepler's Laws on page 731.

10. See the discussion on pages 736 and 737.

───────────────── ▲ **TRUE–FALSE QUIZ** ▲ ─────────────────

1. True. If we reparametrize the curve by replacing $u = t^3$, we have $\mathbf{r}(u) = u\,\mathbf{i} + 2u\,\mathbf{j} + 3u\,\mathbf{k}$, which is a line through the origin with direction vector $\mathbf{i} + 2\,\mathbf{j} + 3\,\mathbf{k}$.

2. True. $\mathbf{r}'(t) = \langle 1, 3t^2, 5t^4 \rangle$ is continuous for all t (since its component functions are each continuous) and since $x'(t) = 1$, we have $\mathbf{r}'(t) \neq \mathbf{0}$ for all t.

3. False. $\mathbf{r}'(t) = \langle -\sin t, 2t, 4t^3 \rangle$, and since $\mathbf{r}'(0) = \langle 0, 0, 0 \rangle = \mathbf{0}$, the curve is not smooth.

4. True. See Theorem 10.2.2.

5. False. By Formula 5 of Theorem 10.2.3, $\dfrac{d}{dt}\,[\mathbf{u}(t) \times \mathbf{v}(t)] = \mathbf{u}'(t) \times \mathbf{v}(t) + \mathbf{u}(t) \times \mathbf{v}'(t)$.

6. False. For example, let $\mathbf{r}(t) = \langle \cos t, \sin t \rangle$. Then $|\mathbf{r}(t)| = \sqrt{\cos^2 t + \sin^2 t} = 1 \Rightarrow \dfrac{d}{dt}\,|\mathbf{r}(t)| = 0$, but $|\mathbf{r}'(t)| = |\langle -\sin t, \cos t \rangle| = \sqrt{(-\sin t)^2 + \cos^2 t} = 1$.

7. False. κ is the magnitude of the rate of change of the unit tangent vector $\mathbf{T}$ with respect to arc length s, not with respect to t.

8. False. The binormal vector, by the definition given in Section 10.3, is $\mathbf{B}(t) = \mathbf{T}(t) \times \mathbf{N}(t) = -[\mathbf{N}(t) \times \mathbf{T}(t)]$.

9. True. See the discussion preceding Example 7 in Section 10.3.

10. False. For example, $\mathbf{r}_1(t) = \langle t, t \rangle$ and $\mathbf{r}_2(t) = \langle 2t, 2t \rangle$ both represent the same plane curve (the line $y = x$), but the tangent vector $\mathbf{r}_1'(t) = \langle 1, 1 \rangle$ for all t, while $\mathbf{r}_2'(t) = \langle 2, 2 \rangle$. In fact, different parametrizations give parallel tangent vectors at a point, but their magnitudes may differ.

───────────────── ◆ **EXERCISES** ◆ ─────────────────

1. (a) The corresponding parametric equations for the curve are $x = t$, $y = \cos \pi t$, $z = \sin \pi t$. Since $y^2 + z^2 = 1$, the curve is contained in a circular cylinder with axis the x-axis. Since $x = t$, the curve is a helix.

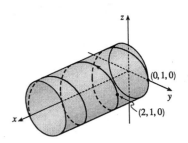

(b) $\mathbf{r}(t) = t\,\mathbf{i} + \cos \pi t\,\mathbf{j} + \sin \pi t\,\mathbf{k} \Rightarrow \mathbf{r}'(t) = \mathbf{i} - \pi \sin \pi t\,\mathbf{j} + \pi \cos \pi t\,\mathbf{k} \Rightarrow$
$\mathbf{r}''(t) = -\pi^2 \cos \pi t\,\mathbf{j} - \pi^2 \sin \pi t\,\mathbf{k}$

2. (a) The expressions $\sqrt{2-t}$, $(e^t - 1)/t$, and $\ln(t+1)$ are all defined when $2 - t \geq 0$ $\Rightarrow$ $t \leq 2, t \neq 0$, and
$t + 1 > 0$ $\Rightarrow$ $t > -1$. Thus the domain of $\mathbf{r}$ is $(-1, 0) \cup (0, 2]$.

(b) $\lim_{t \to 0} \mathbf{r}(t) = \left\langle \lim_{t \to 0} \sqrt{2-t}, \lim_{t \to 0} \frac{e^t - 1}{t}, \lim_{t \to 0} \ln(t+1) \right\rangle = \left\langle \sqrt{2-0}, \lim_{t \to 0} \frac{e^t}{1}, \ln(0+1) \right\rangle = \langle \sqrt{2}, 1, 0 \rangle$

(using l'Hospital's Rule in the y-component).

(c) $\mathbf{r}'(t) = \left\langle \frac{d}{dt} \sqrt{2-t}, \frac{d}{dt} \frac{e^t - 1}{t}, \frac{d}{dt} \ln(t+1) \right\rangle = \left\langle -\frac{1}{2\sqrt{2-t}}, \frac{te^t - e^t + 1}{t^2}, \frac{1}{t+1} \right\rangle$

3. The projection of the curve C of intersection onto the xy-plane is the circle $x^2 + y^2 = 16, z = 0$. So we can write
$x = 4\cos t, y = 4\sin t, 0 \leq t \leq 2\pi$. From the equation of the plane, we have $z = 5 - x = 5 - 4\cos t$, so
parametric equations for C are $x = 4\cos t, y = 4\sin t, z = 5 - 4\cos t, 0 \leq t \leq 2\pi$, and the corresponding vector
function is $\mathbf{r}(t) = 4\cos t\,\mathbf{i} + 4\sin t\,\mathbf{j} + (5 - 4\cos t)\,\mathbf{k}, 0 \leq t \leq 2\pi$.

4. The curve is given by $\mathbf{r}(t) = \langle t^2, t^4, t^3 \rangle$, so $\mathbf{r}'(t) = \langle 2t, 4t^3, 3t^2 \rangle$.
The point $(1, 1, 1)$ corresponds to $t = 1$, so the tangent vector there
is $\mathbf{r}'(1) = \langle 2, 4, 3 \rangle$. Then the tangent line has direction vector
$\langle 2, 4, 3 \rangle$ and includes the point $(1, 1, 1)$, so parametric equations are
$x = 1 + 2t, y = 1 + 4t, z = 1 + 3t$.

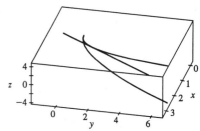

5. $\int_0^1 (t^2\,\mathbf{i} + t\cos \pi t\,\mathbf{j} + \sin \pi t\,\mathbf{k})\,dt = \left(\int_0^1 t^2\,dt \right) \mathbf{i} + \left(\int_0^1 t\cos \pi t\,dt \right) \mathbf{j} + \left(\int_0^1 \sin \pi t\,dt \right) \mathbf{k}$

$= \left[\frac{1}{3} t^3 \right]_0^1 \mathbf{i} + \left(\frac{t}{\pi} \sin \pi t \big]_0^1 - \int_0^1 \frac{1}{\pi} \sin \pi t\,dt \right) \mathbf{j} + \left[-\frac{1}{\pi} \cos \pi t \right]_0^1 \mathbf{k}$

$= \frac{1}{3}\mathbf{i} + \left[\frac{1}{\pi^2} \cos \pi t \right]_0^1 \mathbf{j} + \frac{2}{\pi}\mathbf{k} = \frac{1}{3}\mathbf{i} - \frac{2}{\pi^2}\mathbf{j} + \frac{2}{\pi}\mathbf{k}$

where we integrated by parts in the y-component.

6. (a) C intersects the xz-plane where $y = 0$ $\Rightarrow$ $2t - 1 = 0$ $\Rightarrow$ $t = \frac{1}{2}$, so the point is
$\left(2 - \left(\frac{1}{2} \right)^3, 0, \ln \frac{1}{2} \right) = \left(\frac{15}{8}, 0, -\ln 2 \right)$.

(b) The curve is given by $\mathbf{r}(t) = \langle 2 - t^3, 2t - 1, \ln t \rangle$, so $\mathbf{r}'(t) = \langle -3t^2, 2, 1/t \rangle$. The point $(1, 1, 0)$ corresponds
to $t = 1$, so the tangent vector there is $\mathbf{r}'(1) = \langle -3, 2, 1 \rangle$. Then the tangent line has direction vector $\langle -3, 2, 1 \rangle$
and includes the point $(1, 1, 0)$, so parametric equations are $x = 1 - 3t, y = 1 + 2t, z = t$.

(c) The normal plane has normal vector $\mathbf{r}'(1) = \langle -3, 2, 1 \rangle$ and equation $-3(x - 1) + 2(y - 1) + z = 0$ or
$3x - 2y - z = 1$.

7. $t = 1$ at $(1, 4, 2)$ and $t = 4$ at $(2, 1, 17)$, so

$L = \int_1^4 \sqrt{\frac{1}{4t} + \frac{16}{t^4} + 4t^2}\,dt$

$\approx \frac{4 - 1}{3 \cdot 4} \left[\sqrt{\frac{1}{4} + 16 + 4} + 4 \cdot \sqrt{\frac{1}{4 \cdot \frac{7}{4}} + \frac{16}{\left(\frac{7}{4} \right)^4} + 4 \left(\frac{7}{4} \right)^2} + 2 \cdot \sqrt{\frac{1}{4 \cdot \frac{10}{4}} + \frac{16}{\left(\frac{10}{4} \right)^4} + 4 \left(\frac{10}{4} \right)^2} \right.$

$\left. + 4 \cdot \sqrt{\frac{1}{4 \cdot \frac{13}{4}} + \frac{16}{\left(\frac{13}{4} \right)^4} + 4 \left(\frac{13}{4} \right)^2} + \sqrt{\frac{1}{4 \cdot 4} + \frac{16}{4^4} + 4 \cdot 4^2} \right]$

≈ 15.9241

8. $\mathbf{r}'(t) = \left\langle 3t^{1/2}, -2\sin 2t, 2\cos 2t \right\rangle$, $|\mathbf{r}'(t)| = \sqrt{9t + 4(\sin^2 2t + \cos^2 2t)} = \sqrt{9t + 4}$. Thus

$$L = \int_0^1 \sqrt{9t+4}\,dt = \int_4^{13} \tfrac{1}{9} u^{1/2}\,du = \tfrac{1}{9}\cdot\tfrac{2}{3} u^{3/2}\Big]_4^{13} = \tfrac{2}{27}\left(13^{3/2} - 8\right).$$

9. The angle of intersection of the two curves, θ, is the angle between their respective tangents at the point of intersection. For both curves the point $(1, 0, 0)$ occurs when $t = 0$. $\mathbf{r}_1'(t) = -\sin t\,\mathbf{i} + \cos t\,\mathbf{j} + \mathbf{k}$ $\Rightarrow$ $\mathbf{r}_1'(0) = \mathbf{j} + \mathbf{k}$ and $\mathbf{r}_2'(t) = \mathbf{i} + 2t\mathbf{j} + 3t^2\,\mathbf{k}$ $\Rightarrow$ $\mathbf{r}_2'(0) = \mathbf{i}$. $\mathbf{r}_1'(0)\cdot\mathbf{r}_2'(0) = (\mathbf{j}+\mathbf{k})\cdot\mathbf{i} = 0$. Therefore, the curves intersect in a right angle, that is, $\theta = \frac{\pi}{2}$.

10. The parametric value corresponding to the point $(1, 0, 1)$ is $t = 0$.

$\mathbf{r}'(t) = e^t\,\mathbf{i} + e^t(\cos t + \sin t)\mathbf{j} + e^t(\cos t - \sin t)\mathbf{k}$

$\Rightarrow$ $|\mathbf{r}'(t)| = e^t\sqrt{1 + (\cos t + \sin t)^2 + (\cos t - \sin t)^2} = \sqrt{3}\,e^t$

and $s(t) = \int_0^t e^u\sqrt{3}\,du = \sqrt{3}(e^t - 1)$ $\Rightarrow$ $t = \ln\left(1 + \frac{1}{\sqrt{3}}s\right)$. Therefore,

$\mathbf{r}(t(s)) = \left(1 + \frac{1}{\sqrt{3}}s\right)\mathbf{i} + \left(1 + \frac{1}{\sqrt{3}}s\right)\sin\ln\left(1 + \frac{1}{\sqrt{3}}s\right)\mathbf{j} + \left(1 + \frac{1}{\sqrt{3}}s\right)\cos\ln\left(1 + \frac{1}{\sqrt{3}}s\right)\mathbf{k}$.

11. (a) $\mathbf{T}(t) = \dfrac{\mathbf{r}'(t)}{|\mathbf{r}'(t)|} = \dfrac{\langle t^2, t, 1\rangle}{|\langle t^2, t, 1\rangle|} = \dfrac{\langle t^2, t, 1\rangle}{\sqrt{t^4 + t^2 + 1}}$

(b) $\mathbf{T}'(t) = -\tfrac{1}{2}\left(t^4 + t^2 + 1\right)^{-3/2}\left(4t^3 + 2t\right)\langle t^2, t, 1\rangle + \left(t^4 + t^2 + 1\right)^{-1/2}\langle 2t, 1, 0\rangle$

$$= \dfrac{-2t^3 - t}{\left(t^4 + t^2 + 1\right)^{3/2}}\langle t^2, t, 1\rangle + \dfrac{1}{\left(t^4 + t^2 + 1\right)^{1/2}}\langle 2t, 1, 0\rangle$$

$$= \dfrac{\langle -2t^5 - t^3, -2t^4 - t^2, -2t^3 - t\rangle + \langle 2t^5 + 2t^3 + 2t, t^4 + t^2 + 1, 0\rangle}{\left(t^4 + t^2 + 1\right)^{3/2}}$$

$$= \dfrac{\langle 2t, -t^4 + 1, -2t^3 - t\rangle}{\left(t^4 + t^2 + 1\right)^{3/2}}$$

$$|\mathbf{T}'(t)| = \dfrac{\sqrt{4t^2 + t^8 - 2t^4 + 1 + 4t^6 + 4t^4 + t^2}}{\left(t^4 + t^2 + 1\right)^{3/2}} = \dfrac{\sqrt{t^8 + 4t^6 + 2t^4 + 5t^2}}{\left(t^4 + t^2 + 1\right)^{3/2}},\text{ and}$$

$$\mathbf{N}(t) = \dfrac{\langle 2t, 1 - t^4, -2t^3 - t\rangle}{\sqrt{t^8 + 4t^6 + 2t^4 + 5t^2}}.$$

(c) $\kappa(t) = \dfrac{|\mathbf{T}'(t)|}{|\mathbf{r}'(t)|} = \dfrac{\sqrt{t^8 + 4t^6 + 2t^4 + 5t^2}}{\left(t^4 + t^2 + 1\right)^2}$

12. Using Exercise 10.3.32, we have $\mathbf{r}'(t) = \langle -3\sin t, 4\cos t\rangle$, $\mathbf{r}''(t) = \langle -3\cos t, -4\sin t\rangle$,

$|\mathbf{r}'(t)|^3 = \left(\sqrt{9\sin^2 t + 4\cos^2 t}\right)^3$ and then

$$\kappa(t) = \dfrac{|(-3\sin t)(-4\sin t) - (4\cos t)(-3\cos t)|}{\left(9\sin^2 t + 16\cos^2 t\right)^{3/2}} = \dfrac{12}{\left(9\sin^2 t + 16\cos^2 t\right)^{3/2}}.$$

At $(3, 0)$, $t = 0$ and $\kappa(0) = 12/(16)^{3/2} = \frac{12}{64} = \frac{3}{16}$. At $(0, 4)$, $t = \frac{\pi}{2}$ and $\kappa\left(\frac{\pi}{2}\right) = 12/9^{3/2} = \frac{12}{27} = \frac{4}{9}$.

13. $y' = 4x^3$, $y'' = 12x^2$ and $\kappa(x) = \dfrac{|y''|}{\left[1 + (y')^2\right]^{3/2}} = \dfrac{|12x^2|}{(1 + 16x^6)^{3/2}}$, so $\kappa(1) = \dfrac{12}{17^{3/2}}$.

14. $\kappa(x) = \dfrac{|12x^2 - 2|}{\left[1 + (4x^3 - 2x)^2\right]^{3/2}}$ ⟹ $\kappa(0) = 2$. So the osculating

circle has radius $\frac{1}{2}$ and center $\left(0, -\frac{1}{2}\right)$. Thus its equation is

$x^2 + \left(y + \frac{1}{2}\right)^2 = \frac{1}{4}$.

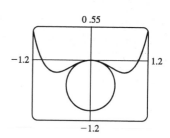

15. $\mathbf{r}(t) = \langle \sin 2t, t, \cos 2t \rangle$ ⟹ $\mathbf{r}'(t) = \langle 2\cos 2t, 1, -2\sin 2t \rangle$ ⟹ $\mathbf{T}(t) = \frac{1}{\sqrt{5}} \langle 2\cos 2t, 1, -2\sin 2t \rangle$ ⟹

$\mathbf{T}'(t) = \frac{1}{\sqrt{5}} \langle -4\sin 2t, 0, -4\cos 2t \rangle$ ⟹ $\mathbf{N}(t) = \langle -\sin 2t, 0, -\cos 2t \rangle$. So $\mathbf{N} = \mathbf{N}(\pi) = \langle 0, 0, -1 \rangle$ and

$\mathbf{B} = \mathbf{T} \times \mathbf{N} = \frac{1}{\sqrt{5}} \langle -1, 2, 0 \rangle$. So a normal to the osculating plane is $\langle -1, 2, 0 \rangle$ and an equation is

$-1(x - 0) + 2(y - \pi) + 0(z - 1) = 0$ or $x - 2y + 2\pi = 0$.

16. (a) The average velocity over $[3, 3.2]$ is given by $\dfrac{\mathbf{r}(3.2) - \mathbf{r}(3)}{3.2 - 3} = 5[\mathbf{r}(3.2) - \mathbf{r}(3)]$, so we draw a vector with the

same direction but 5 times the length of the vector $[\mathbf{r}(3.2) - \mathbf{r}(3)]$.

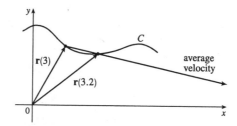

(b) $\mathbf{v}(3) = \mathbf{r}'(3) = \lim\limits_{h \to 0} \dfrac{\mathbf{r}(3 + h) - \mathbf{r}(3)}{h}$.

(c) $\mathbf{T}(3) = \dfrac{\mathbf{r}'(3)}{|\mathbf{r}'(3)|}$, a unit vector in the same direction as $\mathbf{r}'(3)$, that is,

parallel to the tangent line to the curve at $\mathbf{r}(3)$, pointing in the

direction corresponding to increasing t, and with length 1.

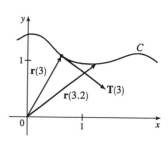

17. $\mathbf{r}(t) = t \ln t\, \mathbf{i} + t\, \mathbf{j} + e^{-t}\, \mathbf{k}$, $\mathbf{v}(t) = \mathbf{r}'(t) = (1 + \ln t)\, \mathbf{i} + \mathbf{j} - e^{-t}\, \mathbf{k}$,

$|\mathbf{v}(t)| = \sqrt{(1 + \ln t)^2 + 1^2 + (-e^{-t})^2} = \sqrt{2 + 2\ln t + (\ln t)^2 + e^{-2t}}$, $\mathbf{a}(t) = \mathbf{v}'(t) = \frac{1}{t}\, \mathbf{i} + e^{-t}\, \mathbf{k}$.

18. $\mathbf{v}(t) = \int \mathbf{a}(t)\, dt = \int (6t\, \mathbf{i} + 12t^2\, \mathbf{j} - 6t\, \mathbf{k})\, dt = 3t^2\, \mathbf{i} + 4t^3\, \mathbf{j} - 3t^2\, \mathbf{k} + \mathbf{C}$, but

$\mathbf{i} - \mathbf{j} + 3\mathbf{k} = \mathbf{v}(0) = \mathbf{0} + \mathbf{C}$, so $\mathbf{C} = \mathbf{i} - \mathbf{j} + 3\mathbf{k}$ and $\mathbf{v}(t) = (3t^2 + 1)\, \mathbf{i} + (4t^3 - 1)\, \mathbf{j} + (3 - 3t^2)\, \mathbf{k}$.

$\mathbf{r}(t) = \int \mathbf{v}(t)\, dt = (t^3 + t)\, \mathbf{i} + (t^4 - t)\, \mathbf{j} + (3t - t^3)\, \mathbf{k} + \mathbf{D}$. But $\mathbf{r}(0) = \mathbf{0}$, so $\mathbf{D} = \mathbf{0}$ and

$\mathbf{r}(t) = (t^3 + t)\, \mathbf{i} + (t^4 - t)\, \mathbf{j} + (3t - t^3)\, \mathbf{k}$.

19. We set up the axes so that the shot leaves the athlete's hand 7 ft above the origin. Then we are given $\mathbf{r}(0) = 7\mathbf{j}$, $|\mathbf{v}(0)| = 43$ ft/s, and $\mathbf{v}(0)$ has direction given by a 45° angle of elevation. Then a unit vector in the direction of $\mathbf{v}(0)$ is $\frac{1}{\sqrt{2}}(\mathbf{i}+\mathbf{j})$ $\Rightarrow$ $\mathbf{v}(0) = \frac{43}{\sqrt{2}}(\mathbf{i}+\mathbf{j})$. Assuming air resistance is negligible, the only external force is due to gravity, so as in Example 10.4.5 we have $\mathbf{a} = -g\mathbf{j}$ where here $g \approx 32$ ft/s². Since $\mathbf{v}'(t) = \mathbf{a}(t)$, we integrate, giving $\mathbf{v}(t) = -gt\,\mathbf{j} + \mathbf{C}$ where $\mathbf{C} = \mathbf{v}(0) = \frac{43}{\sqrt{2}}(\mathbf{i}+\mathbf{j})$ $\Rightarrow$ $\mathbf{v}(t) = \frac{43}{\sqrt{2}}\mathbf{i} + \left(\frac{43}{\sqrt{2}} - gt\right)\mathbf{j}$. Since $\mathbf{r}'(t) = \mathbf{v}(t)$ we integrate again, so $\mathbf{r}(t) = \frac{43}{\sqrt{2}}t\,\mathbf{i} + \left(\frac{43}{\sqrt{2}}t - \frac{1}{2}gt^2\right)\mathbf{j} + \mathbf{D}$. But $\mathbf{D} = \mathbf{r}(0) = 7\mathbf{j}$ $\Rightarrow$ $\mathbf{r}(t) = \frac{43}{\sqrt{2}}t\,\mathbf{i} + \left(\frac{43}{\sqrt{2}}t - \frac{1}{2}gt^2 + 7\right)\mathbf{j}$.

(a) At 2 seconds, the shot is at $\mathbf{r}(2) = \frac{43}{\sqrt{2}}(2)\mathbf{i} + \left(\frac{43}{\sqrt{2}}(2) - \frac{1}{2}g(2)^2 + 7\right)\mathbf{j} \approx 60.8\,\mathbf{i} + 3.8\,\mathbf{j}$, so the shot is about 3.8 ft above the ground, at a horizontal distance of 60.8 ft from the athlete.

(b) The shot reaches its maximum height when the vertical component of velocity is 0: $\frac{43}{\sqrt{2}} - gt = 0$ $\Rightarrow$ $t = \dfrac{43}{\sqrt{2}g} \approx 0.95$ s. Then $\mathbf{r}(0.95) \approx 28.9\,\mathbf{i} + 21.4\,\mathbf{j}$, so the maximum height is approximately 21.4 ft.

(c) The shot hits the ground when the vertical component of $\mathbf{r}(t)$ is 0, so $\frac{43}{\sqrt{2}}t - \frac{1}{2}gt^2 + 7 = 0$ $\Rightarrow$ $-16t^2 + \frac{43}{\sqrt{2}}t + 7 = 0$ $\Rightarrow$ $t \approx 2.11$ s. $\mathbf{r}(2.11) \approx 64.2\,\mathbf{i} - 0.08\,\mathbf{j}$, thus the shot lands approximately 64.2 ft from the athlete.

20. $\mathbf{r}'(t) = \mathbf{i} + 2\mathbf{j} + 2t\,\mathbf{k}$, $\mathbf{r}''(t) = 2\mathbf{k}$, $|\mathbf{r}'(t)| = \sqrt{1 + 4 + 4t^2} = \sqrt{4t^2 + 5}$.

Then $a_T = \dfrac{\mathbf{r}'(t) \cdot \mathbf{r}''(t)}{|\mathbf{r}'(t)|} = \dfrac{4t}{\sqrt{4t^2 + 5}}$ and $a_N = \dfrac{|\mathbf{r}'(t) \times \mathbf{r}''(t)|}{|\mathbf{r}'(t)|} = \dfrac{|4\mathbf{i} - 2\mathbf{j}|}{\sqrt{4t^2 + 5}} = \dfrac{2\sqrt{5}}{\sqrt{4t^2 + 5}}$.

21. From Example 4 in Section 10.5, a parametric representation of the sphere $x^2 + y^2 + z^2 = 4$ is $x = 2\sin\phi\cos\theta$, $y = 2\sin\phi\sin\theta$, $z = 2\cos\phi$ with $0 \le \theta \le 2\pi$ and $0 \le \phi \le \pi$. We can restrict the surface to that portion between the planes $z = 1$ and $z = -1$ by restricting $-1 \le z \le 1$ $\Rightarrow$ $-1 \le 2\cos\phi \le 1$ $\Rightarrow$ $\frac{\pi}{3} \le \phi \le \frac{2\pi}{3}$.

22. $x = (1 - \cos u)\sin v$, $y = u$, $z = (u - \sin u)\cos v$. We plot the portion of the surface corresponding to the parametric domain $-4\pi \le u \le 4\pi$, $0 \le v \le 2\pi$. If u is held constant, x and z give the equation of an ellipse in the plane $y = u$, thus the grid curves are the vertically oriented ellipses we see. Note that when $u = 2k\pi$, k an integer, we have $x = 0$ and z ranges from $-2k\pi$ to $2k\pi$, representing a line segment parallel to the z-axis

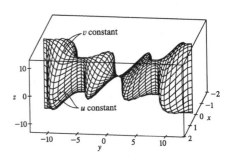

in the plane $y = 2k\pi$. These are the vertical "seams" we see on the surface. If v is held constant, y is free to vary, so the grid curves running lengthwise along the surface correspond to keeping v constant.

23. (a) Instead of proceeding directly, we use Formula 3 of Theorem 10.2.3: $r(t) = t\,\mathbf{R}(t) \Rightarrow$
$\mathbf{v} = \mathbf{r}'(t) = \mathbf{R}(t) + t\,\mathbf{R}'(t) = \cos\omega t\,\mathbf{i} + \sin\omega t\,\mathbf{j} + t\,\mathbf{v}_d$.

(b) Using the same method as in part (a) and starting with $\mathbf{v} = \mathbf{R}(t) + t\,\mathbf{R}'(t)$, we have
$\mathbf{a} = \mathbf{v}' = \mathbf{R}'(t) + \mathbf{R}'(t) + t\,\mathbf{R}''(t) = 2\,\mathbf{R}'(t) + t\,\mathbf{R}''(t) = 2\,\mathbf{v}_d + t\,\mathbf{a}_d$.

(c) Here we have $\mathbf{r}(t) = e^{-t}\cos\omega t\,\mathbf{i} + e^{-t}\sin\omega t\,\mathbf{j} = e^{-t}\,\mathbf{R}(t)$. So, as in parts (a) and (b),
$\mathbf{v} = \mathbf{r}'(t) = e^{-t}\,\mathbf{R}'(t) - e^{-t}\,\mathbf{R}(t) = e^{-t}\,[\mathbf{R}'(t) - \mathbf{R}(t)] \Rightarrow$
$\mathbf{a} = \mathbf{v}' = e^{-t}\,[\mathbf{R}''(t) - \mathbf{R}'(t)] - e^{-t}\,[\mathbf{R}'(t) - \mathbf{R}(t)] = e^{-t}\,[\mathbf{R}''(t) - 2\,\mathbf{R}'(t) + \mathbf{R}(t)]$
$= e^{-t}\,\mathbf{a}_d - 2e^{-t}\,\mathbf{v}_d + e^{-t}\,\mathbf{R}$

Thus, the Coriolis acceleration (the sum of the "extra" terms not involving $\mathbf{a}_d$) is $-2e^{-t}\,\mathbf{v}_d + e^{-t}\,\mathbf{R}$.

24. By the Fundamental Theorem of Calculus, $\mathbf{r}'(t) = \langle\sin(\pi t^2/2), \cos(\pi t^2/2)\rangle$, $|\mathbf{r}'(t)| = 1$ and so $\mathbf{T}(t) = \mathbf{r}'(t)$.

Thus $\mathbf{T}'(t) = \pi t\,\langle\sin(\pi t^2/2), \cos(\pi t^2/2)\rangle$ and the curvature is $\kappa = |\mathbf{T}'(t)| = \sqrt{(\pi t)^2(1)} = \pi\,|t|$.

25. (a) $F(x) = \begin{cases} 1 & \text{if } x \le 0 \\ \sqrt{1-x^2} & \text{if } 0 < x < \frac{1}{\sqrt{2}} \\ -x + \sqrt{2} & \text{if } x \ge \frac{1}{\sqrt{2}} \end{cases} \Rightarrow F'(x) = \begin{cases} 0 & \text{if } x < 0 \\ -x/\sqrt{1-x^2} & \text{if } 0 < x < \frac{1}{\sqrt{2}} \\ -1 & \text{if } x > \frac{1}{\sqrt{2}} \end{cases} \Rightarrow$

$F''(x) = \begin{cases} 0 & \text{if } x < 0 \\ -1/(1-x^2)^{3/2} & \text{if } 0 < x < \frac{1}{\sqrt{2}} \\ 0 & \text{if } x > \frac{1}{\sqrt{2}} \end{cases}$

since $\dfrac{d}{dx}\left[-x\,(1-x^2)^{-1/2}\right] = -(1-x^2)^{-1/2} - x^2\,(1-x^2)^{-3/2} = -(1-x^2)^{-3/2}$.

Now $\lim\limits_{x\to 0^+}\sqrt{1-x^2} = 1 = F(0)$ and $\lim\limits_{x\to(1/\sqrt{2})^-}\sqrt{1-x^2} = \frac{1}{\sqrt{2}} = F\!\left(\frac{1}{\sqrt{2}}\right)$, so F is continuous. Also, since

$\lim\limits_{x\to 0^+}F'(x) = 0 = \lim\limits_{x\to 0^-}F'(x)$ and $\lim\limits_{x\to(1/\sqrt{2})^-}F'(x) = -1 = \lim\limits_{x\to(1/\sqrt{2})^+}F'(x)$, F' is continuous. But

$\lim\limits_{x\to 0^+}F''(x) = -1 \ne 0 = \lim\limits_{x\to 0^-}F''(x)$, so F'' is not continuous at $x = 0$. (The same is true at $x = \frac{1}{\sqrt{2}}$.)

So F does not have continuous curvature.

(b) Set $P(x) = ax^5 + bx^4 + cx^3 + dx^2 + ex + f$. The continuity conditions on P are $P(0) = 0$, $P(1) = 1$,
$P'(0) = 0$ and $P'(1) = 1$. Also the curvature must be continuous. For $x \le 0$ and $x \ge 1$, $\kappa(x) = 0$; elsewhere

$\kappa(x) = \dfrac{|P''(x)|}{\left(1 + [P'(x)]^2\right)^{3/2}}$, so we need $P''(0) = 0$ and $P''(1) = 0$.

The conditions $P(0) = P'(0) = P''(0) = 0$ imply that $d = e = f = 0$.

The other conditions imply that $a + b + c = 1$, $5a + 4b + 3c = 1$, and

$10a + 6b + 3c = 0$. From these, we find that $a = 3$, $b = -8$, and $c = 6$.

Therefore $P(x) = 3x^5 - 8x^4 + 6x^3$. Since there was no solution with

$a = 0$, this could not have been done with a polynomial of degree 4.

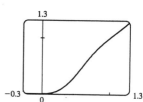

1. (a) $r(t) = R\cos\omega t\,\mathbf{i} + R\sin\omega t\,\mathbf{j}$ $\Rightarrow$ $\mathbf{v} = \mathbf{r}'(t) = -\omega R\sin\omega t\,\mathbf{i} + \omega R\cos\omega t\,\mathbf{j}$, so $\mathbf{r} = R(\cos\omega t\,\mathbf{i} + \sin\omega t\,\mathbf{j})$ and $\mathbf{v} = \omega R(-\sin\omega t\,\mathbf{i} + \cos\omega t\,\mathbf{j})$. $\mathbf{v}\cdot\mathbf{r} = \omega R^2(-\cos\omega t\sin\omega t + \sin\omega t\cos\omega t) = 0$, so $\mathbf{v}\perp\mathbf{r}$. Since $\mathbf{r}$ points along a radius of the circle, and $\mathbf{v}\perp\mathbf{r}$, $\mathbf{v}$ is tangent to the circle. Because it is a velocity vector, $\mathbf{v}$ points in the direction of motion.

(b) In (a), we wrote $\mathbf{v}$ in the form $\omega R\,\mathbf{u}$, where $\mathbf{u}$ is the unit vector $-\sin\omega t\,\mathbf{i} + \cos\omega t\,\mathbf{j}$. Clearly $|\mathbf{v}| = \omega R\,|\mathbf{u}| = \omega R$. At speed ωR, the particle completes one revolution, a distance $2\pi R$, in time
$$T = \frac{2\pi R}{\omega R} = \frac{2\pi}{\omega}.$$

(c) $\mathbf{a} = \dfrac{d\mathbf{v}}{dt} = -\omega^2 R\cos\omega t\,\mathbf{i} - \omega^2 R\sin\omega t\,\mathbf{j} = -\omega^2 R(\cos\omega t\,\mathbf{i} + \sin\omega t\,\mathbf{j})$, so $\mathbf{a} = -\omega^2\mathbf{r}$. This shows that $\mathbf{a}$ is proportional to $\mathbf{r}$ and points in the opposite direction (toward the origin). Also, $|\mathbf{a}| = \omega^2\,|\mathbf{r}| = \omega^2 R$.

(d) By Newton's Second Law (see Section 10.4), $\mathbf{F} = m\mathbf{a}$, so $|\mathbf{F}| = m\,|\mathbf{a}| = mR\omega^2 = \dfrac{m\,(\omega R)^2}{R} = \dfrac{m\,|\mathbf{v}|^2}{R}$.

2. (a) Dividing the equation $|\mathbf{F}|\sin\theta = \dfrac{mv_R^2}{R}$ by the equation $|\mathbf{F}|\cos\theta = mg$, we obtain $\tan\theta = \dfrac{v_R^2}{Rg}$, so $v_R^2 = Rg\tan\theta$.

(b) $R = 400$ ft and $\theta = 12°$, so $v_R = \sqrt{Rg\tan\theta} \approx \sqrt{400\cdot32\cdot\tan12°} \approx 52.16$ ft/s ≈ 36 mi/h.

(c) We want to choose a new radius R_1 for which the new rated speed is $\frac{3}{2}$ of the old one:
$\sqrt{R_1 g\tan12°} = \frac{3}{2}\sqrt{Rg\tan12°}$. Squaring, we get $R_1 g\tan12° = \frac{9}{4}Rg\tan12°$, so $R_1 = \frac{9}{4}R = \frac{9}{4}(400) = 900$ ft.

3. (a) The projectile reaches maximum height when $0 = \dfrac{dy}{dt} = \dfrac{d}{dt}\left[(v_0\sin\alpha)\,t - \frac{1}{2}gt^2\right] = v_0\sin\alpha - gt$; that is, when $t = \dfrac{v_0\sin\alpha}{g}$ and $y = (v_0\sin\alpha)\left(\dfrac{v_0\sin\alpha}{g}\right) - \dfrac{1}{2}g\left(\dfrac{v_0\sin\alpha}{g}\right)^2 = \dfrac{v_0^2\sin^2\alpha}{2g}$. This is the maximum height attained when the projectile is fired with an angle of elevation α. This maximum height is largest when $\alpha = \frac{\pi}{2}$. In that case, $\sin\alpha = 1$ and the maximum height is $\dfrac{v_0^2}{2g}$.

(b) Let $R = v_0^2/g$. We are asked to consider the parabola $x^2 + 2Ry - R^2 = 0$ which can be rewritten as $y = -\dfrac{1}{2R}x^2 + \dfrac{R}{2}$. The points on or inside this parabola are those for which $-R \le x \le R$ and $0 \le y \le \dfrac{-1}{2R}x^2 + \dfrac{R}{2}$. When the projectile is fired at angle of elevation α, the points (x,y) along its path satisfy the relations $x = (v_0\cos\alpha)\,t$ and $y = (v_0\sin\alpha)\,t - \frac{1}{2}gt^2$, where $0 \le t \le (2v_0\sin\alpha)/g$ (as in Example 5 in Section 10.4). Thus $|x| \le \left|v_0\cos\alpha\left(\dfrac{2v_0\sin\alpha}{g}\right)\right| = \left|\dfrac{v_0^2}{g}\sin2\alpha\right| \le \left|\dfrac{v_0^2}{g}\right| = |R|$. This shows that $-R \le x \le R$.

For t in the specified range, we also have $y = t\left(v_0 \sin \alpha - \frac{1}{2}gt\right) = \frac{1}{2}gt\left(\dfrac{2v_0 \sin \alpha}{g} - t\right) \geq 0$ and

$$y = (v_0 \sin \alpha)\frac{x}{v_0 \cos \alpha} - \frac{g}{2}\left(\frac{x}{v_0 \cos \alpha}\right)^2 = (\tan \alpha)\, x - \frac{g}{2v_0^2 \cos^2 \alpha}x^2 = -\frac{1}{2R \cos^2 \alpha}x^2 + (\tan \alpha)\, x. \text{ Thus}$$

$$\begin{aligned}
y - \left(\frac{-1}{2R}x^2 + \frac{R}{2}\right) &= \frac{-1}{2R \cos^2 \alpha}x^2 + \frac{1}{2R}x^2 + (\tan \alpha)\, x - \frac{R}{2}\\
&= \frac{x^2}{2R}\left(1 - \frac{1}{\cos^2 \alpha}\right) + (\tan \alpha)\, x - \frac{R}{2} = \frac{x^2\left(1 - \sec^2 \alpha\right) + 2R\left(\tan \alpha\right)x - R^2}{2R}\\
&= \frac{-\left(\tan^2 \alpha\right)x^2 + 2R\left(\tan \alpha\right)x - R^2}{2R} = \frac{-[(\tan \alpha)\, x - R]^2}{2R} \leq 0
\end{aligned}$$

We have shown that every target that can be hit by the projectile lies on or inside the parabola $y = -\dfrac{1}{2R}x^2 + \dfrac{R}{2}$. Now let (a, b) be any point on or inside the parabola $y = -\dfrac{1}{2R}x^2 + \dfrac{R}{2}$. Then $-R \leq a \leq R$ and $0 \leq b \leq -\dfrac{1}{2R}a^2 + \dfrac{R}{2}$. We seek an angle α such that (a, b) lies in the path of the projectile; that is, we wish to find an angle α such that $b = -\dfrac{1}{2R \cos^2 \alpha}a^2 + (\tan \alpha)\, a$ or equivalently $b = \dfrac{-1}{2R}\left(\tan^2 \alpha + 1\right)a^2 + (\tan \alpha)\, a$. Rearranging this equation we get

$$\frac{a^2}{2R}\tan^2 \alpha - a \tan \alpha + \left(\frac{a^2}{2R} + b\right) = 0 \text{ or } a^2\left(\tan \alpha\right)^2 - 2aR\left(\tan \alpha\right) + \left(a^2 + 2bR\right) = 0 \ (\bigstar). \text{ This}$$

quadratic equation for $\tan \alpha$ has real solutions exactly when the discriminant is nonnegative. Now

$$B^2 - 4AC \geq 0 \iff (-2aR)^2 - 4a^2\left(a^2 + 2bR\right) \geq 0 \iff 4a^2\left(R^2 - a^2 - 2bR\right) \geq 0 \iff$$

$$-a^2 - 2bR + R^2 \geq 0 \iff b \leq \frac{1}{2R}\left(R^2 - a^2\right) \iff b \leq \frac{-1}{2R}a^2 + \frac{R}{2}. \text{ This condition is satisfied since}$$

(a, b) is on or inside the parabola $y = -\dfrac{1}{2R}x^2 + \dfrac{R}{2}$. It follows that (a, b) lies in the path of the projectile when $\tan \alpha$ satisfies $(\bigstar)$, that is, when $\tan \alpha = \dfrac{2aR \pm \sqrt{4a^2\left(R^2 - a^2 - 2bR\right)}}{2a^2} = \dfrac{R \pm \sqrt{R^2 - 2bR - a^2}}{a}$.

(c)

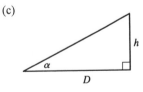

If the gun is pointed at a target with height h at a distance D downrange, then $\tan \alpha = h/D$. When the projectile reaches a distance D downrange (remember we are assuming that it doesn't hit the ground first), we have

$$D = x = (v_0 \cos \alpha)\, t, \text{ so } t = \frac{D}{v_0 \cos \alpha} \text{ and}$$

$y = (v_0 \sin \alpha)\, t - \frac{1}{2}gt^2 = D \tan \alpha - \dfrac{gD^2}{2v_0^2 \cos^2 \alpha}$. Meanwhile, the target, whose x-coordinate is also D, has

fallen from height h to height $h - \frac{1}{2}gt^2 = D \tan \alpha - \dfrac{gD^2}{2v_0^2 \cos^2 \alpha}$. Thus the projectile hits the target.

4. (a) As in Problem 3, $\mathbf{r}(t) = (v_0 \cos\alpha)\, t\, \mathbf{i} + \left[(v_0 \sin\alpha)\, t - \frac{1}{2}gt^2\right] \mathbf{j}$, so $x = (v_0 \cos\alpha)\, t$ and

$y = (v_0 \sin\alpha)\, t - \frac{1}{2}gt^2$. The difference here is that the projectile travels until it reaches a point where $x > 0$

and $y = -(\tan\theta)\, x$. (Here $0 \le \theta \le \frac{\pi}{2}$.) From the parametric equations, we obtain $t = \dfrac{x}{v_0 \cos\alpha}$ and

$$y = \frac{(v_0 \sin\alpha)\, x}{v_0 \cos\alpha} - \frac{gx^2}{2v_0^2 \cos^2\alpha} = (\tan\alpha)\, x - \frac{gx^2}{2v_0^2 \cos^2\alpha}.$$

Thus the projectile hits the inclined plane at the point where $(\tan\alpha)\, x - \dfrac{gx^2}{2v_0^2 \cos^2\alpha} = -(\tan\theta)\, x$. Since

$\dfrac{gx^2}{2v_0^2 \cos^2\alpha} = (\tan\alpha + \tan\theta)\, x$ and $x > 0$, we must have $\dfrac{gx}{2v_0^2 \cos^2\alpha} = \tan\alpha + \tan\theta$. It follows that

$x = \dfrac{2v_0^2 \cos^2\alpha}{g} (\tan\alpha + \tan\theta)$ and $t = \dfrac{x}{v_0 \cos\alpha} = \dfrac{2v_0 \cos\alpha}{g} (\tan\alpha + \tan\theta)$. This means that the

parametric equations are defined for t in the interval $\left[0, \dfrac{2v_0 \cos\alpha}{g} (\tan\alpha + \tan\theta)\right]$.

(b) The downhill range (that is, the distance to the projectile's landing point as

measured along the inclined plane) is $R(\alpha) = x \sec\theta$, where x is the

coordinate of the landing point calculated in part (a). Thus

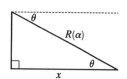

$$R(\alpha) = \frac{2v_0^2 \cos^2\alpha}{g} (\tan\alpha + \tan\theta) \sec\theta = \frac{2v_0^2}{g} \left(\frac{\sin\alpha \cos\alpha}{\cos\theta} + \frac{\cos^2\alpha \sin\theta}{\cos^2\theta}\right)$$

$$= \frac{2v_0^2 \cos\alpha}{g \cos^2\theta} (\sin\alpha \cos\theta + \cos\alpha \sin\theta) = \frac{2v_0^2 \cos\alpha \sin(\alpha + \theta)}{g \cos^2\theta}$$

$R(\alpha)$ is maximized when

$$0 = R'(\alpha) = \frac{2v_0^2}{g \cos^2\theta} [-\sin\alpha \sin(\alpha + \theta) + \cos\alpha \cos(\alpha + \theta)]$$

$$= \frac{2v_0^2}{g \cos^2\theta} \cos[(\alpha + \theta) + \alpha] = \frac{2v_0^2 \cos(2\alpha + \theta)}{g \cos^2\theta}$$

This condition implies that $\cos(2\alpha + \theta) = 0 \;\;\Rightarrow\;\; 2\alpha + \theta = \frac{\pi}{2} \;\;\Rightarrow\;\; \alpha = \frac{1}{2}\left(\frac{\pi}{2} - \theta\right)$.

(c) The solution is similar to the solutions to parts (a) and (b). This time the projectile travels until it reaches a point

where $x > 0$ and $y = (\tan\theta)\, x$. Since $\tan\theta = -\tan(-\theta)$, we obtain the solution from the previous one by

replacing θ with $-\theta$. The desired angle is $\alpha = \frac{1}{2}\left(\frac{\pi}{2} + \theta\right)$.

(d) As observed in part (c), firing the projectile up an inclined plane with angle of inclination θ involves the same

equations as in parts (a) and (b) but with θ replaced by $-\theta$. So if R is the distance up an inclined plane, we know

from part (b) that $R = \dfrac{2v_0^2 \cos\alpha \sin(\alpha - \theta)}{g \cos^2(-\theta)} \;\;\Rightarrow\;\; v_0^2 = \dfrac{Rg \cos^2\theta}{2 \cos\alpha \sin(\alpha - \theta)}$. v_0^2 is minimized (and hence v_0

is minimized) with respect to α when

$$0 = \frac{d}{d\alpha}(v_0^2) = \frac{Rg \cos^2\theta}{2} \cdot \frac{-(\cos\alpha \cos(\alpha - \theta) - \sin\alpha \sin(\alpha - \theta))}{[\cos\alpha \sin(\alpha - \theta)]^2}$$

$$= \frac{-Rg \cos^2\theta}{2} \cdot \frac{\cos[\alpha + (\alpha - \theta)]}{[\cos\alpha \sin(\alpha - \theta)]^2} = \frac{-Rg \cos^2\theta}{2} \cdot \frac{\cos(2\alpha - \theta)}{[\cos\alpha \sin(\alpha - \theta)]^2}$$

Since $\theta < \alpha < \frac{\pi}{2}$, this implies $\cos(2\alpha - \theta) = 0$ ⟺ $2\alpha - \theta = \frac{\pi}{2}$ ⟹ $\alpha = \frac{1}{2}\left(\frac{\pi}{2} + \theta\right)$. Thus the initial speed, and hence the energy required, is minimized for $\alpha = \frac{1}{2}\left(\frac{\pi}{2} + \theta\right)$.

5. (a) $m\dfrac{d^2\mathbf{R}}{dt^2} = -mg\mathbf{j} - k\dfrac{d\mathbf{R}}{dt}$ ⟹ $\dfrac{d}{dt}\left(m\dfrac{d\mathbf{R}}{dt} + k\mathbf{R} + mgt\,\mathbf{j}\right) = 0$ ⟹ $m\dfrac{d\mathbf{R}}{dt} + k\mathbf{R} + mgt\,\mathbf{j} = \mathbf{c}$ (**c** is a constant vector in the xy-plane). At $t = 0$, this says that $m\mathbf{v}(0) + k\mathbf{R}(0) = \mathbf{c}$. Since $\mathbf{v}(0) = \mathbf{v}_0$ and $\mathbf{R}(0) = \mathbf{0}$, we have $\mathbf{c} = m\mathbf{v}_0$. Therefore $\dfrac{d\mathbf{R}}{dt} + \dfrac{k}{m}\mathbf{R} + gt\,\mathbf{j} = \mathbf{v}_0$, or $\dfrac{d\mathbf{R}}{dt} + \dfrac{k}{m}\mathbf{R} = \mathbf{v}_0 - gt\,\mathbf{j}$.

(b) Multiplying by $e^{(k/m)t}$ gives $e^{(k/m)t}\dfrac{d\mathbf{R}}{dt} + \dfrac{k}{m}e^{(k/m)t}\mathbf{R} = e^{(k/m)t}\mathbf{v}_0 - gte^{(k/m)t}\,\mathbf{j}$ or

$\dfrac{d}{dt}\left(e^{(k/m)t}\mathbf{R}\right) = e^{(k/m)t}\mathbf{v}_0 - gte^{(k/m)t}\,\mathbf{j}$. Integrating gives

$e^{(k/m)t}\mathbf{R} = \dfrac{m}{k}e^{(k/m)t}\mathbf{v}_0 - \left[\dfrac{mg}{k}te^{(k/m)t} - \dfrac{m^2g}{k^2}e^{(k/m)t}\right]\mathbf{j} + \mathbf{b}$ for some constant vector $\mathbf{b}$. Setting $t = 0$

yields the relation $\mathbf{R}(0) = \dfrac{m}{k}\mathbf{v}_0 + \dfrac{m^2g}{k^2}\mathbf{j} + \mathbf{b}$, so $\mathbf{b} = -\dfrac{m}{k}\mathbf{v}_0 - \dfrac{m^2g}{k^2}\mathbf{j}$. Thus

$e^{(k/m)t}\mathbf{R} = \dfrac{m}{k}\left[e^{(k/m)t} - 1\right]\mathbf{v}_0 - \left[\dfrac{mg}{k}te^{(k/m)t} - \dfrac{m^2g}{k^2}\left(e^{(k/m)t} - 1\right)\right]\mathbf{j}$ and

$\mathbf{R}(t) = \dfrac{m}{k}\left[1 - e^{-kt/m}\right]\mathbf{v}_0 + \dfrac{mg}{k}\left[\dfrac{m}{k}\left(1 - e^{-kt/m}\right) - t\right]\mathbf{j}$.

6. The surface given by $x = \sin u$, $y = \sin v$, $z = \sin(u + v)$ is difficult to visualize, so we first graph the surface from three different points of view.

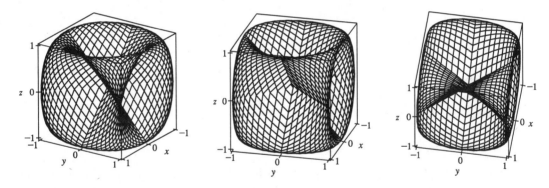

The trace in the horizontal plane $z = 0$ is given by $z = \sin(u + v) = 0$ ⟹ $u + v = k\pi$ (k an integer). Then we can write $v = k\pi - u$, and the trace is given by the parametric equations $x = \sin u$, $y = \sin v = \sin(k\pi - u) = \sin k\pi \cos u - \cos k\pi \sin u = \pm\sin u$, and since $\sin u = x$, the trace consists of the two lines $y = \pm x$.

If $z = 1$, $z = \sin(u + v) = 1$ ⟹ $u + v = \frac{\pi}{2} + 2k\pi$. So $v = \left(\frac{\pi}{2} + 2k\pi\right) - u$ and the trace in $z = 1$ is given by the parametric equations $x = \sin u$, $y = \sin v = \sin\left(\left(\frac{\pi}{2} + 2k\pi\right) - u\right) = \sin\left(\frac{\pi}{2} + 2k\pi\right)\cos u - \cos\left(\frac{\pi}{2} + 2k\pi\right)\sin u = \cos u$. This curve is equivalent to $x^2 + y^2 = 1$, $z = 1$, a circle of radius 1. Similarly, in $z = -1$ we have $z = \sin(u + v) = -1$ ⟹ $u + v = \frac{3\pi}{2} + 2k\pi$ ⟹ $v = \left(\frac{3\pi}{2} + 2k\pi\right) - u$, so the trace is given by the parametric equations $x = \sin u$, $y = \sin v = \sin\left(\left(\frac{3\pi}{2} + 2k\pi\right) - u\right) = \sin\left(\frac{3\pi}{2} + 2k\pi\right)\cos u - \cos\left(\frac{3\pi}{2} + 2k\pi\right)\sin u = -\cos u$, which again is a circle, $x^2 + y^2 = 1$, $z = -1$.

If $z = \frac{1}{2}$, $z = \sin(u+v) = \frac{1}{2}$ $\Rightarrow$ $u + v = \alpha + 2k\pi$ where $\alpha = \frac{\pi}{6}$ or $\frac{5\pi}{6}$. Then

$v = (\alpha + 2k\pi) - u$ and the trace in $z = \frac{1}{2}$ is given by the parametric equations $x = \sin u$,

$y = \sin v = \sin[(\alpha + 2k\pi) - u] = \sin(\alpha + 2k\pi)\cos u - \cos(\alpha + 2k\pi)\sin u = \frac{1}{2}\cos u \pm \frac{\sqrt{3}}{2}\sin u$. In

rectangular coordinates, $x = \sin u$ so $y = \frac{1}{2}\cos u \pm \frac{\sqrt{3}}{2}x$ $\Rightarrow$ $y \pm \frac{\sqrt{3}}{2}x = \frac{1}{2}\cos u$ $\Rightarrow$ $2y \pm \sqrt{3}x = \cos u$.

But then $x^2 + (2y \pm \sqrt{3}x)^2 = \sin^2 u + \cos^2 u = 1$ $\Rightarrow$ $x^2 + 4y^2 \pm 4\sqrt{3}xy + 3x^2 = 1$ $\Rightarrow$

$4x^2 \pm 4\sqrt{3}xy + 4y^2 = 1$, which may be recognized as a conic section. In particular, each equation is an ellipse

rotated $\pm 45°$ from the standard orientation (see the graph below). The trace in $z = -\frac{1}{2}$ is similar:

$z = \sin(u+v) = -\frac{1}{2}$ $\Rightarrow$ $u + v = \beta + 2k\pi$ where $\beta = \frac{7\pi}{6}$ or $\frac{11\pi}{6}$. Then

$v = (\beta + 2k\pi) - u$ and the trace is given by the parametric equations $x = \sin u$,

$y = \sin v = \sin[(\beta + 2k\pi) - u] = \sin(\beta + 2k\pi)\cos u - \cos(\beta + 2k\pi)\sin u = -\frac{1}{2}\cos u \pm \frac{\sqrt{3}}{2}\sin u$. If we

convert to rectangular coordinates, we arrive at the same pair of equations, $4x^2 \pm 4\sqrt{3}xy + 4y^2 = 1$, so the trace is

identical to the trace in $z = \frac{1}{2}$.

Graphing each of these, we have the following 5 traces.

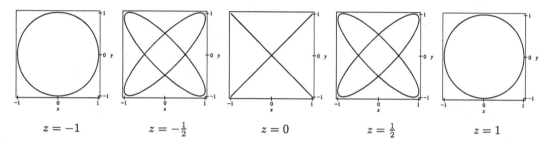

| $z = -1$ | $z = -\frac{1}{2}$ | $z = 0$ | $z = \frac{1}{2}$ | $z = 1$ |

Visualizing these traces on the surface reveals that horizontal cross sections are pairs of intersecting ellipses whose
major axes are perpendicular to each other. At the bottom of the surface, $z = -1$, the ellipses coincide as circles of
radius 1. As we move up the surface, the ellipses become narrower until at $z = 0$ they collapse into line segments,
after which the process is reversed, and the ellipses widen to again coincide as circles at $z = 1$.

7. (a) $\mathbf{a} = -g\mathbf{j}$ $\Rightarrow$ $\mathbf{v} = \mathbf{v}_0 - gt\mathbf{j} = 2\mathbf{i} - gt\mathbf{j}$ $\Rightarrow$ $\mathbf{s} = \mathbf{s}_0 + 2t\mathbf{i} - \frac{1}{2}gt^2\mathbf{j} = 3.5\mathbf{j} + 2t\mathbf{i} - \frac{1}{2}gt^2\mathbf{j}$ $\Rightarrow$

$\mathbf{s} = 2t\mathbf{i} + (3.5 - \frac{1}{2}gt^2)\mathbf{j}$. Therefore $y = 0$ when $t = \sqrt{7/g}$ seconds. At that instant, the ball is

$2\sqrt{7/g} \approx 0.94$ ft to the right of the table top. Its coordinates (relative to an origin on the floor directly under the

table's edge) are $(0.94, 0)$. At impact, the velocity is $\mathbf{v} = 2\mathbf{i} - \sqrt{7g}\,\mathbf{j}$, so the speed is

$|\mathbf{v}| = \sqrt{4 + 7g} \approx 15$ ft/s.

(b) The slope of the curve when $t = \sqrt{\dfrac{7}{g}}$ is $\dfrac{dy}{dx} = \dfrac{dy/dt}{dx/dt} = \dfrac{-gt}{2} = \dfrac{-g\sqrt{7/g}}{2} = \dfrac{-\sqrt{7g}}{2}$. Thus $\cot\theta = \sqrt{7g}/2$

and $\theta \approx 7.6°$.

(c) From (a), $|\mathbf{v}| = \sqrt{4 + 7g}$. So the ball rebounds with speed $0.8\sqrt{4+7g} \approx 12.08$ ft/s at angle of inclination

$90° - \theta \approx 82.3886°$. By Example 10.4.5, the horizontal distance traveled between bounces is $d = \dfrac{v_0^2 \sin 2\alpha}{g}$,

where $v_0 \approx 12.08$ ft/s and $\alpha \approx 82.3886°$. Therefore, $d \approx 1.197$ ft. So the ball strikes the floor at about

$2\sqrt{7/g} + 1.197 \approx 2.13$ ft to the right of the table's edge.

8. As the cable is wrapped around the spool, think of the top or bottom of the cable forming a helix of radius $R + r$. Let h be the vertical distance between coils. Then, from similar triangles,

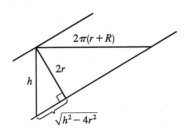

$$\frac{2r}{\sqrt{h^2 - 4r^2}} = \frac{2\pi (r + R)}{h} \implies h^2 r^2 = \pi^2 (r + R)^2 (h^2 - 4r^2)$$

$$\implies h = \frac{2\pi r (r + R)}{\sqrt{\pi^2 (r + R)^2 - r^2}}.$$

If we parametrize the helix by $x(t) = (R + r)\cos t$, $y(t) = (R + r)\sin t$, then we must have $z(t) = [h/(2\pi)]\, t$. The length of one complete cycle is

$$\ell = \int_0^{2\pi} \sqrt{[x'(t)]^2 + [y'(t)]^2 + [z'(t)]^2}\, dt = \int_0^{2\pi} \sqrt{(R + r)^2 + \left(\frac{h}{2\pi}\right)^2}\, dt = 2\pi \sqrt{(R + r)^2 + \left(\frac{h}{2\pi}\right)^2}$$

$$= 2\pi \sqrt{(R + r)^2 + \frac{r^2 (R + r)^2}{\pi^2 (R + r)^2 - r^2}} = 2\pi (R + r)\sqrt{1 + \frac{r^2}{\pi^2 (R + r)^2 - r^2}} = \frac{2\pi^2 (R + r)^2}{\sqrt{\pi^2 (R + r)^2 - r^2}}$$

The number of complete cycles is $[\![L/\ell]\!]$, and so the shortest length along the spool is

$$h\left[\!\!\left[\frac{L}{\ell}\right]\!\!\right] = \frac{2\pi r (R + r)}{\sqrt{\pi^2 (R + r)^2 - r^2}} \left[\!\!\left[\frac{L\sqrt{\pi^2 (R + r)^2 - r^2}}{2\pi^2 (R + r)^2}\right]\!\!\right]$$

Partial Derivatives

11.1 Functions of Several Variables · · · · · · · · · · ·

1. (a) From Table 1, $f(8, 60) = -7$, which means that if the temperature is $8\,°C$ and the wind speed is 60 km/h, then the air would feel equivalent to approximately $-7\,°C$ without wind.

(b) The question is asking: when the temperature is $-12\,°C$, what wind speed gives a wind-chill index of $-26\,°C$? From Table 1, the speed is 20 km/h.

(c) The question is asking: when the wind speed is 80 km/h, what temperature gives a wind-chill index of $-14\,°C$? From Table 1, the temperature is $4\,°C$.

(d) The function $I = f(-4, v)$ means that we fix T at -4 and allow v to vary, resulting in a function of one variable. In other words, the function gives wind-chill index values for different wind speeds when the temperature is $-4\,°C$. From Table 1 (look at the row corresponding to $T = -4$), the function decreases and appears to approach a constant value as v increases.

(e) The function $I = f(T, 50)$ means that we fix v at 50 and allow T to vary, again giving a function of one variable. In other words, the function gives wind-chill index values for different temperatures when the wind speed is 50 km/h. From Table 1 (look at the column corresponding to $v = 50$), the function increases almost linearly as T increases.

2. (a) From the table, $f(95, 70) = 124$, which means that when the actual temperature is $95\,°F$ and the relative humidity is 70%, the perceived air temperature is approximately $124\,°F$.

(b) Looking at the row corresponding to $T = 90$, we see that $f(90, h) = 100$ when $h = 60$.

(c) Looking at the column corresponding to $h = 50$, we see that $f(T, 50) = 88$ when $T = 85$.

(d) $I = f(80, h)$ means that T is fixed at 80 and h is allowed to vary, resulting in a function of h that gives the humidex values for different relative humidities when the actual temperature is $80\,°F$. Similarly, $I = f(100, h)$ is a function of one variable that gives the humidex values for different relative humidities when the actual temperature is $100\,°F$. Looking at the rows of the table corresponding to $T = 80$ and $T = 100$, we see that $f(80, h)$ increases at a relatively constant rate of approximately $1\,°F$ per 10% relative humidity, while $f(100, h)$ increases more quickly (at first with an average rate of change of $5\,°F$ per 10% relative humidity) and at an increasing rate (approximately $12\,°F$ per 10% relative humidity for larger values of h).

3. If the amounts of labor and capital are both doubled, we replace L, K in the function with $2L, 2K$, giving

$$P(2L, 2K) = 1.01(2L)^{0.75}(2K)^{0.25} = 1.01\left(2^{0.75}\right)\left(2^{0.25}\right)L^{0.75}K^{0.25} = \left(2^1\right)1.01L^{0.75}K^{0.25}$$
$$= 2P(L, K)$$

Thus, the production is doubled. It is also true for the general case $P(L, K) = bL^{\alpha}K^{1-\alpha}$:

$$P(2L, 2K) = b(2L)^{\alpha}(2K)^{1-\alpha} = b\left(2^{\alpha}\right)\left(2^{1-\alpha}\right)L^{\alpha}K^{1-\alpha} = \left(2^{\alpha+1-\alpha}\right)bL^{\alpha}K^{1-\alpha} = 2P(L, K).$$

4. We compare the values for the temperature-humidity index given by Table 3 with those given by the model function:

Modeled Humidex Values $I\,(T, h)$

Relative humidity (%)

$\begin{smallmatrix}&h\\T&\end{smallmatrix}$	20	30	40	50	60	70
80	78.6	79.2	79.9	80.8	81.8	83.0
85	82.0	82.9	84.3	86.5	89.3	92.7
90	86.3	87.9	90.7	94.6	99.7	105.9
95	91.5	94.4	99.0	105.2	113.1	122.6
100	97.5	102.3	109.3	118.3	129.5	142.8

(Actual temperature (°F) along left vertical axis.)

Although the model is not a perfect fit, the values it gives appear to be fairly close to the values in Table 3, usually within $2\,°\text{F}$. For most purposes, the numerical representation of the function is much more convenient.

5. $\ln\left(9 - x^2 - 9y^2\right)$ is defined only when $9 - x^2 - 9y^2 > 0$, or $\frac{1}{9}x^2 + y^2 < 1$. So the domain of f is $\left\{(x, y)\mid \frac{1}{9}x^2 + y^2 < 1\right\}$, the interior of an ellipse.

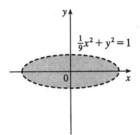

$\frac{1}{9}x^2 + y^2 = 1$

6. $\sqrt{1 + x - y^2}$ is defined only when $1 + x - y^2 \geq 0 \;\Rightarrow\; x \geq y^2 - 1$, so the domain of f is $\left\{(x, y)\mid x \geq y^2 - 1\right\}$, all those points on or to the right of the parabola $x = y^2 - 1$.

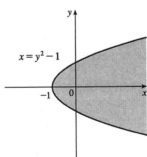

$x = y^2 - 1$

The range of f is $[0, \infty)$.

7. (a) $f\,(2, -1, 6) = e^{\sqrt{6 - 2^2 - (-1)^2}} = e^{\sqrt{1}} = e$.

(b) $e^{\sqrt{z - x^2 - y^2}}$ is defined when $z - x^2 - y^2 \geq 0 \;\Rightarrow\; z \geq x^2 + y^2$. Thus the domain of f is $\left\{(x, y, z)\mid z \geq x^2 + y^2\right\}$.

(c) Since $\sqrt{z - x^2 - y^2} \geq 0$, we have $e^{\sqrt{z - x^2 - y^2}} \geq 1$. Thus the range of f is $[1, \infty)$.

8. (a) $g(2, -2, 4) = \ln(25 - 2^2 - (-2)^2 - 4^2) = \ln 1 = 0.$

(b) For the logarithmic function to be defined, we need $25 - x^2 - y^2 - z^2 > 0$. Thus the domain of g is
$\{(x, y, z) \mid x^2 + y^2 + z^2 < 25\}$, the interior of the sphere $x^2 + y^2 + z^2 = 25$.

(c) Since $0 < 25 - x^2 - y^2 - z^2 \le 25$ for (x, y, z) in the domain of g, $\ln(25 - x^2 - y^2 - z^2) \le \ln 25$. Thus the
range of g is $(-\infty, \ln 25]$.

9. The point $(-3, 3)$ lies between the level curves with z-values 50 and 60. Since the point is a little closer to the level
curve with $z = 60$, we estimate that $f(-3, 3) \approx 56$. The point $(3, -2)$ appears to be just about halfway between
the level curves with z-values 30 and 40, so we estimate $f(3, -2) \approx 35$. The graph rises as we approach the origin,
gradually from above, steeply from below.

10. If we start at the origin and move along the x-axis, for example, the z-values of a cone centered at the origin
increase at a constant rate, so we would expect its level curves to be equally spaced. A paraboloid with vertex the
origin, on the other hand, has z-values which change slowly near the origin and more quickly as we move farther
away. Thus, we would expect its level curves near the origin to be spaced more widely apart than those farther from
the origin. Therefore contour map I must correspond to the paraboloid, and contour map II the cone.

11. Near A, the level curves are very close together,
indicating that the terrain is quite steep. At B, the
level curves are much farther apart, so we would
expect the terrain to be much less steep than
near A, perhaps almost flat.

12.

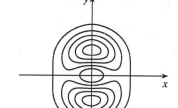

13.

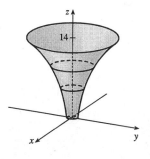

14.

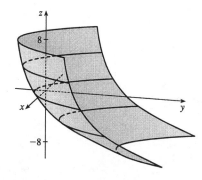

15. The level curves are $xy = k$. For $k = 0$ the curves are the coordinate axis; if $k > 0$, they are hyperbolas in the first and third quadrants; if $k < 0$, they are hyperbolas in the second and fourth quadrants.

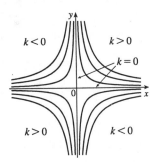

16. The level curves are $k = x^2 - y^2$. When $k = 0$, these are the lines $y = \pm x$. When $k > 0$, the curves are hyperbolas with axis the x-axis and when $k < 0$, they are hyperbolas with axis the y-axis.

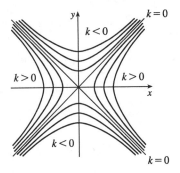

17. The level curves are $y - \ln x = k$ or $y = \ln x + k$.

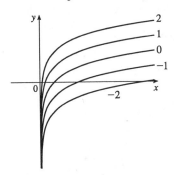

18. The level curves are $e^{y/x} = k$ or equivalently $y = x \ln k$ $(x \neq 0)$, a family of lines with slope $\ln k$ $(k > 0)$ without the origin.

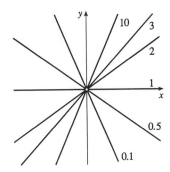

19. $k = \sqrt{x + y}$ or for $x + y \geq 0$, $k^2 = x + y$, or $y = -x + k^2$.

Note: $k \geq 0$ since $k = \sqrt{x + y}$.

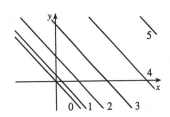

20. $k = y \sec x$ or $y = k \cos x$, $x \neq \frac{\pi}{2} + n\pi$ (n an integer)

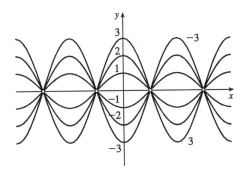

21. $k = x - y^2$, or $x - k = y^2$, a family of parabolas with vertex $(k, 0)$.

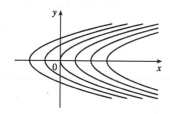

22. For $k \neq 0$ and $(x, y) \neq (0, 0)$, $k = \dfrac{y}{x^2 + y^2}$ ⇔

$$x^2 + y^2 - \frac{y}{k} = 0 \quad \Leftrightarrow \quad x^2 + \left(y - \frac{1}{2k}\right)^2 = \frac{1}{4k^2},$$

a family of circles with center $\left(0, \frac{1}{2k}\right)$ and radius $\frac{1}{2k}$ (without the origin). If $k = 0$, the level curve is the x-axis.

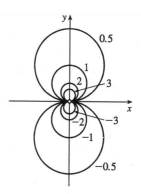

23. The contour map consists of the level curves $k = x^2 + 9y^2$, a family of ellipses with major axis the x-axis. (Or, if $k = 0$, the origin.)

The graph of $f(x, y)$ is the surface $z = x^2 + 9y^2$, an elliptic paraboloid.

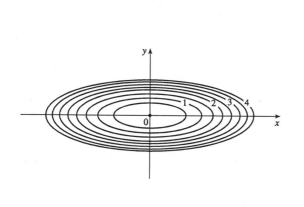

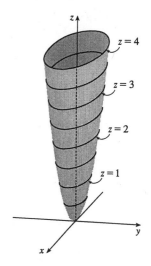

If we visualize lifting each ellipse $k = x^2 + 9y^2$ of the contour map to the plane $z = k$, we have horizontal traces that indicate the shape of the graph of f.

24. The contour map consists of the level curves $k = \sqrt{36 - 9x^2 - 4y^2}$ $\Rightarrow$ $9x^2 + 4y^2 = 36 - k^2$, $k \geq 0$, a family of ellipses with major axis the y-axis. (Or, if $k = 6$, the origin.)

The graph of $f(x, y)$ is the surface $z = \sqrt{36 - 9x^2 - 4y^2}$, or equivalently the upper half of the ellipsoid $9x^2 + 4y^2 + z^2 = 36$.

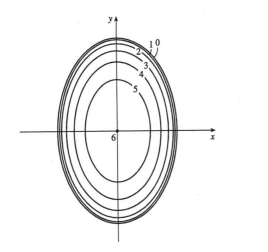
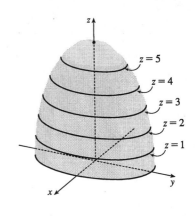

If we visualize lifting each ellipse $k = \sqrt{36 - 9x^2 - 4y^2}$ of the contour map to the plane $z = k$, we have horizontal traces that indicate the shape of the graph of f.

25. The isothermals are given by $k = 100/(1 + x^2 + 2y^2)$ or $x^2 + 2y^2 = (100 - k)/k$ $(0 < k \leq 100)$, a family of ellipses.

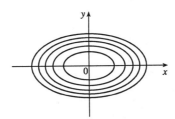

26. The equipotential curves are $k = c / \sqrt{r^2 - x^2 - y^2}$ or $x^2 + y^2 = r^2 - (c/k)^2$, a family of circles $(k \geq c/r)$.

Note: As $k \to \infty$, the radius of the circle approaches r.

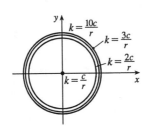

27. $f(x, y) = e^x \cos y$

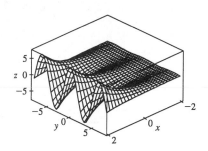

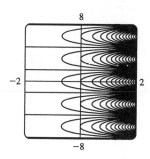

Traces parallel to the yz-plane (such as the left-front trace in the first graph above) are cosine curves.
The amplitudes of these curves decrease as x decreases.

28. $f(x, y) = (1 - 3x^2 + y^2)e^{1 - x^2 - y^2}$

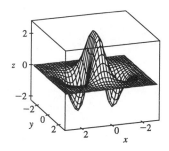

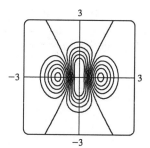

29. $f(x, y) = xy^2 - x^3$

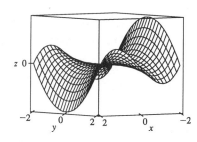

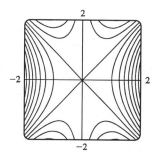

The traces parallel to the yz-plane (such as the left-front trace in the graph above) are parabolas; those parallel to the
xz-plane (such as the right-front trace) are cubic curves. The surface is called a monkey saddle because a monkey
sitting on the surface near the origin has places for both legs and tail to rest.

30. $f(x, y) = xy^3 - yx^3$

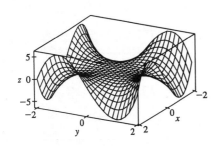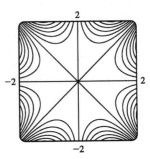

The traces parallel to either the yz-plane or the xz-plane are cubic curves.

31. (a) B   *Reasons:* This function is constant on any circle centered at the origin, a description which matches
   (b) III   only B and III.

32. (a) C   *Reasons:* This function is the same if x is interchanged with y, so its graph is symmetric about the
   (b) II   plane $x = y$. Also, $z(0,0) = 0$ and the values of z approach 0 as we use points farther
   from the origin. These conditions are satisfied only by C and II.

33. (a) F   *Reasons:* z increases without bound as we use points closer to the origin, a condition satisfied only
   (b) V   by F and V.

34. (a) A   *Reasons:* Along the lines $y = \pm\frac{1}{\sqrt{3}}x$ and $x = 0$, this function is 0.
   (b) VI

35. (a) D   *Reasons:* This function is periodic in both x and y, with period 2π in each variable.
   (b) IV

36. (a) E   *Reasons:* This function is periodic along the x-axis, and increases as $|y|$ increases.
   (b) I

37. $k = x + 3y + 5z$ is a family of parallel planes with normal vector $\langle 1, 3, 5 \rangle$.

38. $k = x^2 + 3y^2 + 5z^2$ is a family of ellipsoids for $k > 0$ and the origin for $k = 0$.

39. $k = x^2 - y^2 + z^2$ are the equations of the level surfaces. For $k = 0$, the surface is a right circular cone with vertex
the origin and axis the y-axis. For $k > 0$, we have a family of hyperboloids of one sheet with axis the y-axis. For
$k < 0$, we have a family of hyperboloids of two sheets with axis the y-axis.

40. $k = x^2 - y^2$ is a family of hyperbolic cylinders. The cross section of this family in the xy-plane has the same graph
as the level curves in Exercise 16.

41. (a) The graph of g is the graph of f shifted upward 2 units.

   (b) The graph of g is the graph of f stretched vertically by a factor of 2.

   (c) The graph of g is the graph of f reflected about the xy-plane.

   (d) The graph of $g(x, y) = -f(x, y) + 2$ is the graph of f reflected about the xy-plane and then shifted upward
   2 units.

42. (a) The graph of g is the graph of f shifted 2 units in the positive x-direction.

(b) The graph of g is the graph of f shifted 2 units in the negative y-direction.

(c) The graph of g is the graph of f shifted 3 units in the negative x-direction and 4 units in the positive y-direction.

43. $f(x,y) = e^{cx^2+y^2}$. First, if $c = 0$, the graph is the cylindrical surface $z = e^{y^2}$ (whose level curves are parallel lines). When $c > 0$, the vertical trace above the y-axis remains fixed while the sides of the surface in the x-direction "curl" upward, giving the graph a shape resembling an elliptic paraboloid. The level curves of the surface are ellipses centered at the origin.

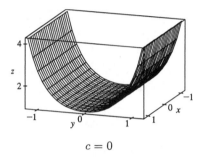

$c = 0$

For $0 < c < 1$, the ellipses have major axis the x-axis and the eccentricity increases as $c \to 0$.

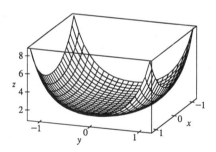 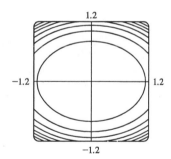

$c = 0.5$ (level curves in increments of 1)

For $c = 1$ the level curves are circles centered at the origin.

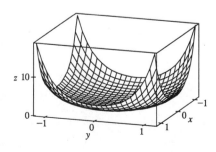 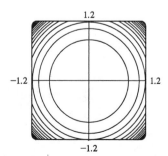

$c = 1$ (level curves in increments of 1)

When $c > 1$, the level curves are ellipses with major axis the y-axis, and the eccentricity increases as c increases.

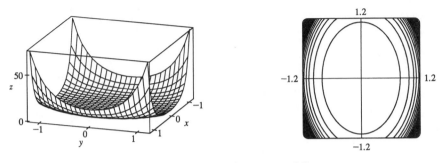

$c = 2$ (level curves in increments of 4)

For values of $c < 0$, the sides of the surface in the x-direction curl downward and approach the xy-plane (while the vertical trace $x = 0$ remains fixed), giving a saddle-shaped appearance to the graph near the point $(0, 0, 1)$. The level curves consist of a family of hyperbolas. As c decreases, the surface becomes flatter in the x-direction and the surface's approach to the curve in the trace $x = 0$ becomes steeper, as the graphs demonstrate.

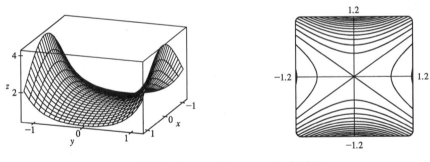

$c = -0.5$ (level curves in increments of 0.25)

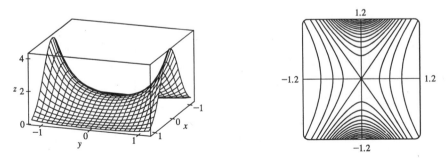

$c = -2$ (level curves in increments of 0.25)

44. First, we graph $f(x, y) = \sqrt{x^2 + y^2}$. As an alternative, the $x^2 + y^2$ expression suggests that cylindrical coordinates may be appropriate, giving the equivalent equation $z = \sqrt{r^2} = r, r \geq 0$ which we graph as well. Notice that the graph in cylindrical coordinates better demonstrates the symmetry of the surface.

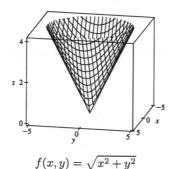

$$f(x, y) = \sqrt{x^2 + y^2}$$

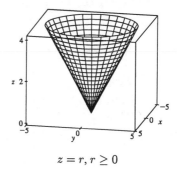

$$z = r, r \geq 0$$

Graphs of the other four functions follow.

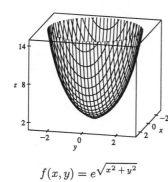

$$f(x, y) = e^{\sqrt{x^2 + y^2}}$$

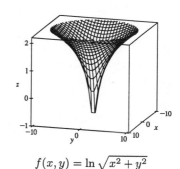

$$f(x, y) = \ln \sqrt{x^2 + y^2}$$

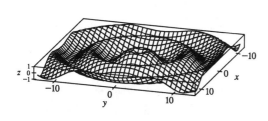

$$f(x, y) = \sin\left(\sqrt{x^2 + y^2}\right)$$

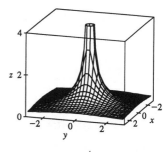

$$f(x, y) = 1 \Big/ \sqrt{x^2 + y^2}$$

Notice that each graph $f(x, y) = g\left(\sqrt{x^2 + y^2}\right)$ exhibits radial symmetry about the z-axis and the trace in the xz-plane for $x \geq 0$ is the graph of $z = g(x)$, $x \geq 0$. This suggests that the graph of $f(x, y) = g\left(\sqrt{x^2 + y^2}\right)$ is obtained from the graph of g by graphing $z = g(x)$ in the xz-plane and rotating the curve about the z-axis.

45. (a) $P = bL^\alpha K^{1-\alpha}$ $\Rightarrow$ $\dfrac{P}{K} = bL^\alpha K^{-\alpha}$ $\Rightarrow$ $\dfrac{P}{K} = b\left(\dfrac{L}{K}\right)^\alpha$ $\Rightarrow$ $\ln\dfrac{P}{K} = \ln\left(b\left(\dfrac{L}{K}\right)^\alpha\right)$ $\Rightarrow$

$\ln\dfrac{P}{K} = \ln b + \alpha\ln\left(\dfrac{L}{K}\right)$

(b) We list the values for $\ln(L/K)$ and $\ln(P/K)$ for the years 1899-1922. (Historically, these values were rounded to 2 decimal places.)

Year	$x = \ln(L/K)$	$y = \ln(P/K)$	Year	$x = \ln(L/K)$	$y = \ln(P/K)$
1899	0	0	1911	−0.38	−0.34
1900	−0.02	−0.06	1912	−0.38	−0.24
1901	−0.04	−0.02	1913	−0.41	−0.25
1902	−0.04	0	1914	−0.47	−0.37
1903	−0.07	−0.05	1915	−0.53	−0.34
1904	−0.13	−0.12	1916	−0.49	−0.28
1905	−0.18	−0.04	1917	−0.53	−0.39
1906	−0.20	−0.07	1918	−0.60	−0.50
1907	−0.23	−0.15	1919	−0.68	−0.57
1908	−0.41	−0.38	1920	−0.74	−0.57
1909	−0.33	−0.24	1921	−1.05	−0.85
1910	−0.35	−0.27	1922	−0.98	−0.59

After entering the (x, y) pairs into a calculator or CAS, the resulting least squares regression line through the points is approximately $y = 0.75136x + 0.01053$, which we round to $y = 0.75x + 0.01$.

(c) Comparing the regression line from part (b) to the equation $y = \ln b + \alpha x$ with $x = \ln(L/K)$ and $y = \ln(P/K)$, we have $\alpha = 0.75$ and $\ln b = 0.01$ $\Rightarrow$ $b = e^{0.01} \approx 1.01$. Thus, the Cobb-Douglas production function is $P = bL^\alpha K^{1-\alpha} = 1.01L^{0.75}K^{0.25}$.

11.2 Limits and Continuity • • • • • • • • • • •

1. In general, we can't say anything about $f(3, 1)$! $\displaystyle\lim_{(x,y)\to(3,1)} f(x, y) = 6$ means that the values of $f(x, y)$ approach 6 as (x, y) approaches, but is not equal to, $(3, 1)$. If f is continuous, we know that $\displaystyle\lim_{(x,y)\to(a,b)} f(x, y) = f(a, b)$, so $\displaystyle\lim_{(x,y)\to(3,1)} f(x, y) = f(3, 1) = 6$.

2. (a) The outdoor temperature as a function of longitude, latitude, and time is continuous. Small changes in longitude, latitude, or time can produce only small changes in temperature, as the temperature doesn't jump abruptly from one value to another.

(b) Elevation is not necessarily continuous. If we think of a cliff with a sudden drop-off, a very small change in longitude or latitude can produce a comparatively large change in elevation, without all the intermediate values being attained. Elevation *can* jump from one value to another.

(c) The cost of a taxi ride is usually discontinuous. The cost normally increases in jumps, so small changes in distance traveled or time can produce a jump in cost. A graph of the function would show breaks in the surface.

3. We make a table of values of $f(x,y) = \dfrac{x^2y^3 + x^3y^2 - 5}{2 - xy}$ for a set of (x,y) points near the origin.

x \ y	−0.2	−0.1	−0.05	0	0.05	0.1	0.2
−0.2	−2.551	−2.525	−2.513	−2.500	−2.488	−2.475	−2.451
−0.1	−2.525	−2.513	−2.506	−2.500	−2.494	−2.488	−2.475
−0.05	−2.513	−2.506	−2.503	−2.500	−2.497	−2.494	−2.488
0	−2.500	−2.500	−2.500		−2.500	−2.500	−2.500
0.05	−2.488	−2.494	−2.497	−2.500	−2.503	−2.506	−2.513
0.1	−2.475	−2.488	−2.494	−2.500	−2.506	−2.513	−2.525
0.2	−2.451	−2.475	−2.488	−2.500	−2.513	−2.525	−2.551

As the table shows, the values of $f(x,y)$ seem to approach -2.5 as (x,y) approaches the origin from a variety of different directions. This suggests that $\lim\limits_{(x,y)\to(0,0)} f(x,y) = -2.5$.

Since f is a rational function, it is continuous on its domain. f is defined at $(0,0)$, so we can use direct substitution to establish that $\lim\limits_{(x,y)\to(0,0)} f(x,y) = \dfrac{0^2 0^3 + 0^3 0^2 - 5}{2 - 0\cdot 0} = -\dfrac{5}{2}$, verifying our guess.

4. We make a table of values of $f(x,y) = \dfrac{2xy}{x^2 + 2y^2}$ for a set of (x,y) points near the origin.

x \ y	−0.3	−0.2	−0.1	0	0.1	0.2	0.3
−0.3	0.667	0.706	0.545	0.000	−0.545	−0.706	−0.667
−0.2	0.545	0.667	0.667	0.000	−0.667	−0.667	−0.545
−0.1	0.316	0.444	0.667	0.000	−0.667	−0.444	−0.316
0	0.000	0.000	0.000		0.000	0.000	0.000
0.1	−0.316	−0.444	−0.667	0.000	0.667	0.444	0.316
0.2	−0.545	−0.667	−0.667	0.000	0.667	0.667	0.545
0.3	−0.667	−0.706	−0.545	0.000	0.545	0.706	0.667

It appears from the table that the values of $f(x,y)$ are not approaching a single value as (x,y) approaches the origin. For verification, if we first approach $(0,0)$ along the x-axis, we have $f(x,0) = 0$, so $f(x,y) \to 0$. But if we approach $(0,0)$ along the line $y = x$, $f(x,x) = \dfrac{2x^2}{x^2 + 2x^2} = \dfrac{2}{3}$ $(x \neq 0)$, so $f(x,y) \to \frac{2}{3}$. Since f approaches different values along different paths to the origin, this limit does not exist.

5. $f(x,y) = x^5 + 4x^3y - 5xy^2$ is a polynomial, and hence continuous, so
$$\lim\limits_{(x,y)\to(5,-2)} f(x,y) = f(5,-2) = 5^5 + 4(5)^3(-2) - 5(5)(-2)^2 = 2025.$$

6. $x - 2y$ is a polynomial and therefore continuous. Since $\cos t$ is a continuous function, the composition $\cos(x - 2y)$ is also continuous. xy is also a polynomial, and hence continuous, so the product $f(x,y) = xy\cos(x - 2y)$ is a continuous function. Then $\lim\limits_{(x,y)\to(6,3)} f(x,y) = f(6,3) = (6)(3)\cos(6 - 2\cdot 3) = 18.$

7. $f(x, y) = x^2/(x^2 + y^2)$. First approach $(0, 0)$ along the x-axis. Then $f(x, 0) = x^2/x^2 = 1$ for $x \neq 0$, so
$f(x, y) \to 1$. Now approach $(0, 0)$ along the y-axis. Then for $y \neq 0$, $f(0, y) = 0$, so $f(x, y) \to 0$. Since f has two
different limits along two different lines, the limit does not exist.

8. $f(x, y) = (x + y)^2/(x^2 + y^2)$. As $(x, y) \to (0, 0)$ along the x-axis, $f(x, y) \to 1$. But as $(x, y) \to (0, 0)$ along
the line $y = x$, $f(x, x) = 4x^2/(2x^2) = 2$ for $x \neq 0$, so $f(x, y) \to 2$. Thus, the limit does not exist.

9. $f(x, y) = 8x^2 y^2/(x^4 + y^4)$. Approaching $(0, 0)$ along the x-axis gives $f(x, y) \to 0$. Approaching $(0, 0)$ along the
line $y = x$, $f(x, x) = 8x^4/2x^4 = 4$ for $x \neq 0$, so along this line $f(x, y) \to 4$ as $(x, y) \to (0, 0)$. Thus the limit
doesn't exist.

10. $\lim\limits_{(x,y)\to(0,0)} (x^3 + xy^2)/(x^2 + y^2) = \lim\limits_{(x,y)\to(0,0)} x = 0$

11. $f(x, y) = \dfrac{xy}{\sqrt{x^2 + y^2}}$. We can see that the limit along any line through $(0, 0)$ is 0, as well as along other paths

through $(0, 0)$ such as $x = y^2$ and $y = x^2$. So we suspect that the limit exists and equals 0; we use the Squeeze

Theorem to prove our assertion. $0 \leq \left| \dfrac{xy}{\sqrt{x^2 + y^2}} \right| \leq |x|$ since $|y| \leq \sqrt{x^2 + y^2}$, and $|x| \to 0$ as $(x, y) \to (0, 0)$.

So $\lim\limits_{(x,y)\to(0,0)} f(x, y) = 0$.

12. We can use the Squeeze Theorem to show that $\lim\limits_{(x,y)\to(0,0)} \dfrac{x^2 \sin^2 y}{x^2 + 2y^2} = 0$:

$0 \leq \dfrac{x^2 \sin^2 y}{x^2 + 2y^2} \leq \sin^2 y$ since $\dfrac{x^2}{x^2 + 2y^2} \leq 1$, and $\sin^2 y \to 0$ as $(x, y) \to (0, 0)$, so $\lim\limits_{(x,y)\to(0,0)} \dfrac{x^2 \sin^2 y}{x^2 + 2y^2} = 0$.

13. Let $f(x, y) = \dfrac{2x^2 y}{x^4 + y^2}$. Then $f(x, 0) = 0$ for $x \neq 0$, so $f(x, y) \to 0$ as $(x, y) \to (0, 0)$ along the x-axis. But

$f(x, x^2) = \dfrac{2x^4}{2x^4} = 1$ for $x \neq 0$, so $f(x, y) \to 1$ as $(x, y) \to (0, 0)$ along the parabola $y = x^2$. Thus the limit
doesn't exist.

14. $f(x, y) = \dfrac{xy - 2y}{x^2 + y^2 - 4x + 4} = \dfrac{y(x - 2)}{y^2 + (x - 2)^2}$. Then $f(x, 0) = 0$ for $x \neq 2$, so $f(x, y) \to 0$ as $(x, y) \to (2, 0)$

along the x-axis. But $f(x, x - 2) = \dfrac{(x - 2)(x - 2)}{(x - 2)^2 + (x - 2)^2} = \dfrac{(x - 2)^2}{2(x - 2)^2} = \dfrac{1}{2}$ for $x \neq 2$, so $f(x, y) \to \dfrac{1}{2}$ as

$(x, y) \to (2, 0)$ along the line $y = x - 2$ ($x \neq 2$). Thus, the limit doesn't exist.

15. $\lim\limits_{(x,y)\to(0,0)} \dfrac{x^2 + y^2}{\sqrt{x^2 + y^2 + 1} - 1} = \lim\limits_{(x,y)\to(0,0)} \dfrac{x^2 + y^2}{\sqrt{x^2 + y^2 + 1} - 1} \cdot \dfrac{\sqrt{x^2 + y^2 + 1} + 1}{\sqrt{x^2 + y^2 + 1} + 1}$

$$= \lim\limits_{(x,y)\to(0,0)} \dfrac{(x^2 + y^2)\left(\sqrt{x^2 + y^2 + 1} + 1\right)}{x^2 + y^2}$$

$$= \lim\limits_{(x,y)\to(0,0)} \left(\sqrt{x^2 + y^2 + 1} + 1\right) = 2$$

16. $e^{x^2 z} \cos(y + z)$ is a continuous function, so

$\lim\limits_{(x,y,z)\to(3,-2,2)} e^{x^2 z} \cos(y + z) = e^{3^2 \cdot 2} \cos(-2 + 2) = e^{18} \cos 0 = e^{18}$.

17. $f(x,y,z) = \dfrac{xy + yz^2 + xz^2}{x^2 + y^2 + z^4}$. Then $f(x,0,0) = 0/x^2 = 0$ for $x \neq 0$, so as $(x,y,z) \to (0,0,0)$ along the x-axis,

$f(x,y,z) \to 0$. But $f(x,x,0) = x^2/(2x^2) = \frac{1}{2}$ for $x \neq 0$, so as $(x,y,z) \to (0,0,0)$ along the line $y = x$, $z = 0$,

$f(x,y,z) \to \frac{1}{2}$. Thus the limit doesn't exist.

18. $f(x,y,z) = \dfrac{x^2 + 2y^2 + 3z^2}{x^2 + y^2 + z^2}$. Then $f(x,0,0) = \dfrac{x^2 + 0 + 0}{x^2 + 0 + 0} = 1$ for $x \neq 0$, so $f(x,y,z) \to 1$ as

$(x,y,z) \to (0,0,0)$ along the x-axis. But $f(0,y,0) = \dfrac{0 + 2y^2 + 0}{0 + y^2 + 0} = 2$ for $y \neq 0$, so $f(x,y,z) \to 2$ as

$(x,y,z) \to (0,0,0)$ along the y-axis. Thus, the limit doesn't exist.

19.

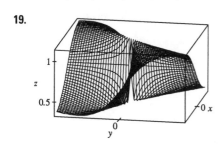

From the ridges on the graph, we see that as $(x,y) \to (0,0)$ along the lines under the two ridges, $f(x,y)$ approaches different values. So the limit does not exist.

20.

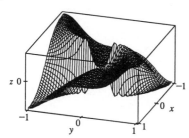

From the graph, it appears that as we approach the origin along the lines $x = 0$ or $y = 0$, the function is everywhere 0, whereas if we approach the origin along a certain curve it has a constant value of about $\frac{1}{2}$. [In fact, $f(y^3, y) = y^6/(2y^6) = \frac{1}{2}$ for $y \neq 0$, so $f(x,y) \to \frac{1}{2}$ as $(x,y) \to (0,0)$ along the curve $x = y^3$.] Since the function approaches different values depending on the path of approach, the limit does not exist.

21. $h(x,y) = g(f(x,y)) = (2x + 3y - 6)^2 + \sqrt{2x + 3y - 6}$. Since f is a polynomial, it is continuous on $\mathbb{R}^2$ and g is continuous on its domain $\{t \mid t \geq 0\}$. Thus h is continuous on its domain

$D = \{(x,y) \mid 2x + 3y - 6 \geq 0\} = \{(x,y) \mid y \geq -\frac{2}{3}x + 2\}$, which consists of all points on and above the line $y = -\frac{2}{3}x + 2$.

22. $h(x,y) = g(f(x,y)) = \sin(y \ln x)$. Since $f(x,y) = y \ln x$ it is continuous on its domain $\{(x,y) \mid x > 0\}$ and g is continuous throughout $\mathbb{R}$. Thus h is continuous on its domain $D = \{(x,y) \mid x > 0\}$, the right half-plane excluding the y-axis.

23.

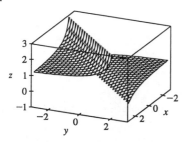

From the graph, it appears that f is discontinuous along the line $y = x$. If we consider $f(x,y) = e^{1/(x-y)}$ as a composition of functions, $g(x,y) = 1/(x-y)$ is a rational function and therefore continuous except where $x - y = 0 \;\Rightarrow\; y = x$. Since the function $h(t) = e^t$ is continuous everywhere, the composition $h(g(x,y)) = e^{1/(x-y)} = f(x,y)$ is continuous except along the line $y = x$, as we suspected.

24.

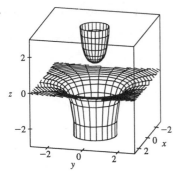

We can see a circular break in the graph, corresponding approximately to the unit circle, where f is discontinuous. [*Note:* For a more accurate graph, try converting to cylindrical coordinates first.] Since $f(x, y) = \dfrac{1}{1 - x^2 - y^2}$ is a rational function, it is continuous except where $1 - x^2 - y^2 = 0 \quad \Rightarrow$ $x^2 + y^2 = 1$, confirming our observation that f is discontinuous on the circle $x^2 + y^2 = 1$.

25. $F(x, y) = \dfrac{1}{x^2 - y}$ is a rational function and thus is continuous on its domain

$\{(x, y) \mid x^2 - y \neq 0\} = \{(x, y) \mid y \neq x^2\}$, so F is continuous on $\mathbb{R}^2$ except the parabola $y = x^2$.

26. $F(x, y) = \dfrac{x - y}{1 + x^2 + y^2}$ is a rational function and thus is continuous on its domain $\mathbb{R}^2$ (since the denominator is never zero).

27. $F(x, y) = \arctan(x + \sqrt{y}) = g(f(x, y))$ where $f(x, y) = x + \sqrt{y}$, continuous on its domain $\{(x, y) \mid y \geq 0\}$, and $g(t) = \arctan t$ is continuous everywhere. Thus F is continuous on its domain $\{(x, y) \mid y \geq 0\}$.

28. $G(x, y) = g(f(x, y))$ where $f(x, y) = x^2 + y^2$, continuous on $\mathbb{R}^2$, and $g(t) = \sin^{-1} t$, continuous on its domain $\{t \mid -1 \leq t \leq 1\}$. Thus G is continuous on its domain $D = \{(x, y) \mid -1 \leq x^2 + y^2 \leq 1\} = \{(x, y) \mid x^2 + y^2 \leq 1\}$, inside and on the circle $x^2 + y^2 = 1$.

29. $f(x, y, z) = \dfrac{xyz}{x^2 + y^2 - z}$ is a rational function and thus is continuous on its domain

$\{(x, y, z) \mid x^2 + y^2 - z \neq 0\} = \{(x, y, z) \mid z \neq x^2 + y^2\}$, so f is continuous on $\mathbb{R}^3$ except on the circular paraboloid $z = x^2 + y^2$.

30. $f(x, y, z) = \sqrt{x + y + z} = h(g(x, y, z))$ where $g(x, y, z) = x + y + z$, continuous everywhere, and $h(t) = \sqrt{t}$ is continuous on its domain $\{t \mid t \geq 0\}$. Thus f is continuous on its domain $\{(x, y, z) \mid x + y + z \geq 0\}$, so f is continuous on and above the plane $z = -x - y$.

31. $f(x, y) = \begin{cases} \dfrac{x^2 y^3}{2x^2 + y^2} & \text{if } (x, y) \neq (0, 0) \\ 1 & \text{if } (x, y) = (0, 0) \end{cases}$ The first piece of f is a rational function defined everywhere except

at the origin, so f is continuous on $\mathbb{R}^2$ except possibly at the origin. Since $x^2 \leq 2x^2 + y^2$, we have $|x^2 y^3 / (2x^2 + y^2)| \leq |y^3|$. We know that $|y^3| \to 0$ as $(x, y) \to (0, 0)$. So, by the Squeeze Theorem,

$\displaystyle \lim_{(x,y) \to (0,0)} f(x, y) = \lim_{(x,y) \to (0,0)} \dfrac{x^2 y^3}{2x^2 + y^2} = 0$. But $f(0, 0) = 1$, so f is discontinuous at $(0, 0)$. Therefore, f is

continuous on the set $\{(x, y) \mid (x, y) \neq (0, 0)\}$.

32. $f(x, y) = \begin{cases} \dfrac{xy}{x^2 + xy + y^2} & \text{if } (x, y) \neq (0, 0) \\ 0 & \text{if } (x, y) = (0, 0) \end{cases}$ The first piece of f is a rational function defined everywhere

except at the origin, so f is continuous on $\mathbb{R}^2$ except possibly at the origin. $f(x, 0) = 0/x^2 = 0$ for $x \neq 0$, so

$f(x,y) \to 0$ as $(x,y) \to (0,0)$ along the x-axis. But $f(x,x) = x^2/(3x^2) = \frac{1}{3}$ for $x \neq 0$, so $f(x,y) \to \frac{1}{3}$ as $(x,y) \to (0,0)$ along the line $y = x$. Thus $\lim\limits_{(x,y)\to(0,0)} f(x,y)$ doesn't exist, so f is not continuous at $(0,0)$ and the largest set on which f is continuous is $\{(x,y) \mid (x,y) \neq (0,0)\}$.

33. $\lim\limits_{(x,y)\to(0,0)} \dfrac{x^3 + y^3}{x^2 + y^2} = \lim\limits_{r\to0+} \dfrac{(r\cos\theta)^3 + (r\sin\theta)^3}{r^2} = \lim\limits_{r\to0+} (r\cos^3\theta + r\sin^3\theta) = 0$

34. $\lim\limits_{(x,y)\to(0,0)} (x^2 + y^2)\ln(x^2 + y^2) = \lim\limits_{r\to0+} r^2\ln r^2 = \lim\limits_{r\to0+} \dfrac{\ln r^2}{1/r^2}$

$\qquad\qquad\qquad = \lim\limits_{r\to0+} \dfrac{(1/r^2)(2r)}{-2/r^3}$ (using l'Hospital's Rule) $= \lim\limits_{r\to0+} (-r^2) = 0$

35. $\lim\limits_{(x,y,z)\to(0,0,0)} \dfrac{xyz}{x^2 + y^2 + z^2} = \lim\limits_{\rho\to0+} \dfrac{(\rho\sin\phi\cos\theta)(\rho\sin\phi\sin\theta)(\rho\cos\phi)}{\rho^2}$

$\qquad\qquad\qquad = \lim\limits_{\rho\to0+} (\rho\sin^2\phi\cos\phi\sin\theta\cos\theta) = 0$

36. $\lim\limits_{(x,y)\to(0,0)} \dfrac{\sin(x^2 + y^2)}{x^2 + y^2} = \lim\limits_{r\to0+} \dfrac{\sin(r^2)}{r^2}$, which is an

indeterminate form of type 0/0. Using l'Hospital's Rule, we get

$\lim\limits_{r\to0+} \dfrac{\sin(r^2)}{r^2} \overset{\text{H}}{=} \lim\limits_{r\to0+} \dfrac{2r\cos(r^2)}{2r} = \lim\limits_{r\to0+} \cos(r^2) = 1$.

Or: Use the fact that $\lim\limits_{\theta\to0} \dfrac{\sin\theta}{\theta} = 1$.

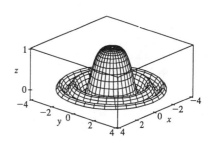

 Partial Derivatives • • • • • • • • • • • • • • •

1. (a) $\partial T/\partial x$ represents the rate of change of T when we fix y and t and consider T as a function of the single variable x, which describes how quickly the temperature changes when longitude changes but latitude and time are constant. $\partial T/\partial y$ represents the rate of change of T when we fix x and t and consider T as a function of y, which describes how quickly the temperature changes when latitude changes but longitude and time are constant. $\partial T/\partial t$ represents the rate of change of T when we fix x and y and consider T as a function of t, which describes how quickly the temperature changes over time for a constant longitude and latitude.

(b) $f_x(158, 21, 9)$ represents the rate of change of temperature at longitude $158\,°$ W, latitude $21\,°$ N at 9:00 A.M. when only longitude varies. Since the air is warmer to the west than to the east, increasing longitude results in an increased air temperature, so we would expect $f_x(158, 21, 9)$ to be positive. $f_y(158, 21, 9)$ represents the rate of change of temperature at the same time and location when only latitude varies. Since the air is warmer to the south and cooler to the north, increasing latitude results in a decreased air temperature, so we would expect $f_y(158, 21, 9)$ to be negative. $f_t(158, 21, 9)$ represents the rate of change of temperature at the same time and location when only time varies. Since typically air temperature increases from the morning to the afternoon as the sun warms it, we would expect $f_t(158, 21, 9)$ to be positive.

2. By Definition 4, $f_T(92, 60) = \lim\limits_{h \to 0} \dfrac{f(92 + h, 60) - f(92, 60)}{h}$, which we can approximate by considering $h = 2$

and $h = -2$ and using the values given in Table 1: $f_T(92, 60) \approx \dfrac{f(94, 60) - f(92, 60)}{2} = \dfrac{111 - 105}{2} = 3,$

$f_T(92, 60) \approx \dfrac{f(90, 60) - f(92, 60)}{-2} = \dfrac{100 - 105}{-2} = 2.5.$ Averaging these values, we estimate $f_T\,(92, 60)$ to be

approximately 2.75. Thus, when the actual temperature is 92 °F and the relative humidity is 60%, the apparent

temperature rises by about 2.75 °F for every degree that the actual temperature rises.

Similarly, $f_H(92, 60) = \lim\limits_{h \to 0} \dfrac{f(92, 60 + h) - f(92, 60)}{h}$ which we can approximate by considering

$h = 5$ and $h = -5$: $f_H(92, 60) \approx \dfrac{f(92, 65) - f(92, 60)}{5} = \dfrac{108 - 105}{5} = 0.6,$

$f_H(92, 60) \approx \dfrac{f(92, 55) - f(92, 60)}{-5} = \dfrac{103 - 105}{-5} = 0.4.$ Averaging these values, we estimate $f_H(92, 60)$ to be

approximately 0.5. Thus, when the actual temperature is 92 °F and the relative humidity is 60%, the apparent

temperature rises by about 0.5 °F for every percent that the relative humidity increases.

3. (a) By Definition 4, $f_T(12, 20) = \lim\limits_{h \to 0} \dfrac{f(12 + h, 20) - f(12, 20)}{h}$, which we can approximate by considering

  $h = 4$ and $h = -4$ and using the values given in the table:

  $f_T(12, 20) \approx \dfrac{f(16, 20) - f(12, 20)}{4} = \dfrac{11 - 5}{4} = 1.5,\ f_T(12, 20) \approx \dfrac{f(8, 20) - f(12, 20)}{-4} = \dfrac{0 - 5}{-4} = 1.25.$

  Averaging these values, we estimate $f_T(12, 20)$ to be approximately 1.375. Thus, when the actual temperature

  is 12 °C and the wind speed is 20 km/h, the apparent temperature rises by about 1.375 °C for every degree that

  the actual temperature rises.

  Similarly, $f_v(12, 20) = \lim\limits_{h \to 0} \dfrac{f(12, 20 + h) - f(12, 20)}{h}$ which we can approximate by considering

  $h = 10$ and $h = -10$: $f_v(12, 20) \approx \dfrac{f(12, 30) - f(12, 20)}{10} = \dfrac{3 - 5}{10} = -0.2,$

  $f_v(12, 20) \approx \dfrac{f(12, 10) - f(12, 20)}{-10} = \dfrac{9 - 5}{-10} = -0.4.$ Averaging these values, we estimate $f_v(12, 20)$ to be

  approximately -0.3. Thus, when the actual temperature is 12 °C and the wind speed is 20 km/h, the apparent

  temperature decreases by about 0.3 °C for every km/h that the wind speed increases.

  (b) For a fixed wind speed v, the values of the wind-chill index I increase as temperature T increases (look at a

  column of the table), so $\dfrac{\partial I}{\partial T}$ is positive. For a fixed temperature T, the values of I decrease (or remain constant)

  as v increases (look at a row of the table), so $\dfrac{\partial I}{\partial v}$ is negative (or perhaps 0).

  (c) For fixed values of T, the function values $f(T, v)$ appear to become constant (or nearly constant) as v increases,

  so the corresponding rate of change is 0 or near 0 as v increases. This suggests that $\lim\limits_{v \to \infty} \left(\dfrac{\partial I}{\partial v}\right) = 0.$

4. (a) $\partial h/\partial v$ represents the rate of change of h when we fix t and consider h as a function of v, which describes how

  quickly the wave heights change when the wind speed changes for a fixed time duration. $\partial h/\partial t$ represents the

  rate of change of h when we fix v and consider h as a function of t, which describes how quickly the wave

  heights change when the duration of time changes, but the wind speed is constant.

(b) By Definition 4, $f_v(40, 15) = \lim\limits_{h \to 0} \dfrac{f(40 + h, 15) - f(40, 15)}{h}$ which we can approximate by considering

$h = 10$ and $h = -10$ and using the values given in the table:

$$f_v(40, 15) \approx \frac{f(50, 15) - f(40, 15)}{10} = \frac{36 - 25}{10} = 1.1,$$

$$f_v(40, 15) \approx \frac{f(30, 15) - f(40, 15)}{-10} = \frac{16 - 25}{-10} = 0.9.$$ Averaging these values, we have $f_v(40, 15) \approx 1.0$.

Thus, when a 40-knot wind has been blowing for 15 hours, the wave heights should increase by about 1 foot for every knot that the wind speed increases (with the same time duration). Similarly,

$$f_t(40, 15) = \lim\limits_{h \to 0} \frac{f(40, 15 + h) - f(40, 15)}{h}$$ which we can approximate by considering

$h = 5$ and $h = -5$: $f_t(40, 15) \approx \dfrac{f(40, 20) - f(40, 15)}{5} = \dfrac{28 - 25}{5} = 0.6$,

$$f_t(40, 15) \approx \frac{f(40, 10) - f(40, 15)}{-5} = \frac{21 - 25}{-5} = 0.8.$$ Averaging these values, we have $f_t(40, 15) \approx 0.7$.

Thus, when a 40-knot wind has been blowing for 15 hours, the wave heights increase by about 0.7 feet for every additional hour that the wind blows.

(c) For fixed values of v, the function values $f(v, t)$ appear to increase in smaller and smaller increments, becoming nearly constant as t increases. Thus, the corresponding rate of change is nearly 0 as t increases, suggesting that $\lim\limits_{t \to \infty} (\partial h / \partial t) = 0$.

5. (a) If we start at $(1, 2)$ and move in the positive x-direction, the graph of f increases. Thus $f_x(1, 2)$ is positive.

(b) If we start at $(1, 2)$ and move in the positive y-direction, the graph of f decreases. Thus $f_y(1, 2)$ is negative.

6. (a) The graph of f decreases if we start at $(-1, 2)$ and move in the positive x-direction, so $f_x(-1, 2)$ is negative.

(b) The graph of f decreases if we start at $(-1, 2)$ and move in the positive y-direction, so $f_y(-1, 2)$ is negative.

(c) $f_{xx} = \frac{\partial}{\partial x}(f_x)$, so f_{xx} is the rate of change of f_x in the x-direction. f_x is negative at $(-1, 2)$ and if we move in the positive x-direction, the surface becomes less steep. Thus the values of f_x are increasing and $f_{xx}(-1, 2)$ is positive.

(d) f_{yy} is the rate of change of f_y in the y-direction. f_y is negative at $(-1, 2)$ and if we move in the positive y-direction, the surface becomes steeper. Thus the values of f_y are decreasing, and $f_{yy}(-1, 2)$ is negative.

7. First of all, if we start at the point $(3, -3)$ and move in the positive y-direction, we see that both b and c decrease, while a increases. Both b and c have a low point at about $(3, -1.5)$, while a is 0 at this point. So a is definitely the graph of f_y, and one of b and c is the graph of f. To see which is which, we start at the point $(-3, -1.5)$ and move in the positive x-direction. b traces out a line with negative slope, while c traces out a parabola opening downward. This tells us that b is the x-derivative of c. So c is the graph of f, b is the graph of f_x, and a is the graph of f_y.

8. $f_x(2, 1)$ is the rate of change of f at $(2, 1)$ in the x-direction. If we start at $(2, 1)$, where $f(2, 1) = 10$, and move in the positive x-direction, we reach the next contour line (where $f(x, y) = 12$) after approximately 0.6 units. This represents an average rate of change of about $\frac{2}{0.6}$. If we approach the point $(2, 1)$ from the left (moving in the positive x-direction) the output values increase from 8 to 10 with an increase in x of approximately 0.9 units, corresponding to an average rate of change of $\frac{2}{0.9}$. A good estimate for $f_x(2, 1)$ would be the average of these two, so $f_x(2, 1) \approx 2.8$. Similarly, $f_y(2, 1)$ is the rate of change of f at $(2, 1)$ in the y-direction. If we approach $(2, 1)$ from below, the output values decrease from 12 to 10 with a change in y of approximately 1 unit, corresponding to an average rate of change of -2. If we start at $(2, 1)$ and move in the positive y-direction, the output values decrease from 10 to 8 after approximately 0.9 units, a rate of change of $\frac{-2}{0.9}$. Averaging these two results, we estimate $f_y(2, 1) \approx -2.1$.

9. $f(x, y) = 16 - 4x^2 - y^2 \Rightarrow f_x(x, y) = -8x$ and $f_y(x, y) = -2y \Rightarrow f_x(1, 2) = -8$ and $f_y(1, 2) = -4$. The graph of f is the paraboloid $z = 16 - 4x^2 - y^2$ and the vertical plane $y = 2$ intersects it in the parabola $z = 12 - 4x^2$, $y = 2$ (the curve C_1 in the first figure).
The slope of the tangent line to this parabola at $(1, 2, 8)$ is $f_x(1, 2) = -8$. Similarly the plane $x = 1$ intersects the paraboloid in the parabola $z = 12 - y^2$, $x = 1$ (the curve C_2 in the second figure) and the slope of the tangent line at $(1, 2, 8)$ is $f_y(1, 2) = -4$.

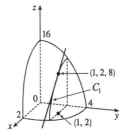
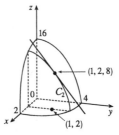

10. $f(x, y) = \left(4 - x^2 - 4y^2\right)^{1/2} \Rightarrow f_x(x, y) = -x\left(4 - x^2 - 4y^2\right)^{-1/2}$ and
$f_y(x, y) = -4y\left(4 - x^2 - 4y^2\right)^{-1/2} \Rightarrow f_x(1, 0) = -\frac{1}{\sqrt{3}}$, $f_y(1, 0) = 0$. The graph of f is the upper half of the ellipsoid $z^2 + x^2 + 4y^2 = 4$ and the plane $y = 0$ intersects the graph in the semicircle $x^2 + z^2 = 4$, $z \geq 0$ and the slope of the tangent line T_1 to this semicircle at $\left(1, 0, \sqrt{3}\right)$ is $f_x(1, 0) = -\frac{1}{\sqrt{3}}$. Similarly the plane $x = 1$ intersects the graph in the semi-ellipse $z^2 + 4y^2 = 3$, $z \geq 0$ and the slope of the tangent line T_2 to this semi-ellipse at $\left(1, 0, \sqrt{3}\right)$ is $f_y(1, 0) = 0$.

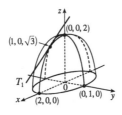
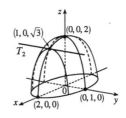

11. $f(x,y) = x^2 + y^2 + x^2y \Rightarrow f_x = 2x + 2xy,\ f_y = 2y + x^2$

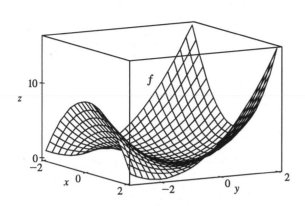
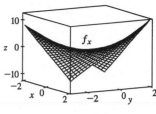
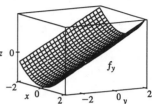
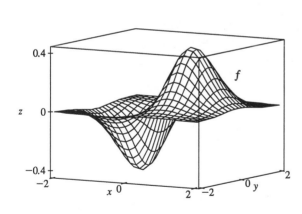
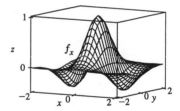
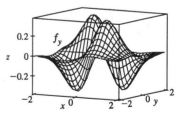

Note that the traces of f in planes parallel to the xz-plane are parabolas which open downward for $y < -1$ and upward for $y > -1$, and the traces of f_x in these planes are straight lines, which have negative slopes for $y < -1$ and positive slopes for $y > -1$. The traces of f in planes parallel to the yz-plane are parabolas which always open upward, and the traces of f_y in these planes are straight lines with positive slopes.

12. $f(x,y) = xe^{-x^2-y^2} \Rightarrow f_x = xs\left(-2xe^{-x^2-y^2}\right) + e^{-x^2-y^2} = e^{-x^2-y^2}\left(1 - 2x^2\right),\ f_y = -2xye^{-x^2-y^2}$

Note that traces of f in planes parallel to the xz-plane have two extreme values, while traces of f_x in these planes have two zeros. Traces of f in planes parallel to the yz-plane have only one extreme value (a minimum if $x < 0$, a maximum if $x > 0$), and traces of f_y in these planes have only one zero (going from negative to positive if $x < 0$ and from positive to negative if $x > 0$).

13. $f(x,y) = 3x - 2y^4 \Rightarrow f_x(x,y) = 3 - 0 = 3,\ f_y(x,y) = 0 - 8y^3 = -8y^3$

14. $f(x,y) = x^5 + 3x^3y^2 + 3xy^4 \Rightarrow f_x(x,y) = 5x^4 + 3\cdot 3x^2\cdot y^2 + 3\cdot 1\cdot y^4 = 5x^4 + 9x^2y^2 + 3y^4,$
$f_y(x,y) = 0 + 3x^3\cdot 2y + 3x\cdot 4y^3 = 6x^3y + 12xy^3.$

15. $z = xe^{3y}$ $\Rightarrow$ $\dfrac{\partial z}{\partial x} = e^{3y}, \dfrac{\partial z}{\partial y} = 3xe^{3y}$

16. $z = y \ln x$ $\Rightarrow$ $\dfrac{\partial z}{\partial x} = \dfrac{y}{x}, \dfrac{\partial z}{\partial y} = \ln x$

17. $f(x, y) = \dfrac{x - y}{x + y}$ $\Rightarrow$ $f_x(x, y) = \dfrac{(1)(x + y) - (x - y)(1)}{(x + y)^2} = \dfrac{2y}{(x + y)^2}$,

$f_y(x, y) = \dfrac{(-1)(x + y) - (x - y)(1)}{(x + y)^2} = -\dfrac{2x}{(x + y)^2}$

18. $f(x, y) = x^y$ $\Rightarrow$ $f_x(x, y) = yx^{y-1}, f_y(x, y) = x^y \ln x$

19. $w = \sin \alpha \cos \beta$ $\Rightarrow$ $\dfrac{\partial w}{\partial \alpha} = \cos \alpha \cos \beta, \dfrac{\partial w}{\partial \beta} = -\sin \alpha \sin \beta$

20. $f(s, t) = \dfrac{st^2}{s^2 + t^2}$ $\Rightarrow$ $f_s(s, t) = \dfrac{t^2(s^2 + t^2) - st^2(2t)}{(s^2 + t^2)^2} = \dfrac{t^4 - s^2t^2}{(s^2 + t^2)^2}$,

$f_t(s, t) = \dfrac{2st(s^2 + t^2) - st^2(2t)}{(s^2 + t^2)^2} = \dfrac{2s^3t}{(s^2 + t^2)^2}$

21. $f(u, v) = \tan^{-1}\left(\dfrac{u}{v}\right)$ $\Rightarrow$ $f_u(u, v) = \dfrac{1}{1 + (u/v)^2}\left(\dfrac{1}{v}\right) = \dfrac{1}{v}\left(\dfrac{v^2}{u^2 + v^2}\right) = \dfrac{v}{u^2 + v^2}$,

$f_v(u, v) = \dfrac{1}{1 + (u/v)^2}\left(-\dfrac{u}{v^2}\right) = -\dfrac{u}{v^2}\left(\dfrac{v^2}{u^2 + v^2}\right) = -\dfrac{u}{u^2 + v^2}$

22. $f(x, t) = e^{\sin(t/x)}$ $\Rightarrow$ $f_x(x, t) = e^{\sin(t/x)} \cos\left(\dfrac{t}{x}\right)\left(-\dfrac{t}{x^2}\right) = -t \cos\left(\dfrac{t}{x}\right)\dfrac{e^{\sin(t/x)}}{x^2}$,

$f_t(x, t) = e^{\sin(t/x)} \cos\left(\dfrac{t}{x}\right)\left(\dfrac{1}{x}\right) = \dfrac{e^{\sin(t/x)}}{x} \cos\left(\dfrac{t}{x}\right)$

23. $z = \ln\left(x + \sqrt{x^2 + y^2}\right)$ $\Rightarrow$

$\dfrac{\partial z}{\partial x} = \dfrac{1}{x + \sqrt{x^2 + y^2}}\left[1 + \tfrac{1}{2}(x^2 + y^2)^{-1/2}(2x)\right] = \dfrac{\left(\sqrt{x^2 + y^2} + x\right)/\sqrt{x^2 + y^2}}{\left(x + \sqrt{x^2 + y^2}\right)} = \dfrac{1}{\sqrt{x^2 + y^2}}$

$\dfrac{\partial z}{\partial y} = \dfrac{1}{x + \sqrt{x^2 + y^2}}\left(\dfrac{1}{2}\right)(x^2 + y^2)^{-1/2}(2y) = \dfrac{y}{x\sqrt{x^2 + y^2} + x^2 + y^2}$

24. $f(x, y) = \displaystyle\int_y^x \cos(t^2)\, dt$ $\Rightarrow$ $f_x(x, y) = \dfrac{\partial}{\partial x}\displaystyle\int_y^x \cos(t^2)\, dt = \cos(x^2)$ by the Fundamental Theorem of

Calculus, Part 1; $f_y(x, y) = \dfrac{\partial}{\partial y}\displaystyle\int_y^x \cos(t^2)\, dt = -\dfrac{\partial}{\partial y}\displaystyle\int_x^y \cos(t^2)\, dt = -\cos(y^2)$.

25. $f(x, y, z) = xy^2z^3 + 3yz$ $\Rightarrow$ $f_x(x, y, z) = y^2z^3, f_y(x, y, z) = 2xyz^3 + 3z, f_z(x, y, z) = 3xy^2z^2 + 3y$

26. $f(x, y, z) = x^2e^{yz}$ $\Rightarrow$ $f_x(x, y, z) = 2xe^{yz}, f_y(x, y, z) = x^2e^{yz}(z) = x^2ze^{yz}$,

$f_z(x, y, z) = x^2e^{yz}(y) = x^2ye^{yz}$.

27. $w = \ln(x + 2y + 3z)$ $\Rightarrow$ $\dfrac{\partial w}{\partial x} = \dfrac{1}{x + 2y + 3z}, \dfrac{\partial w}{\partial y} = \dfrac{2}{x + 2y + 3z}, \dfrac{\partial w}{\partial z} = \dfrac{3}{x + 2y + 3z}$

28. $w = \sqrt{r^2 + s^2 + t^2} \quad \Rightarrow \quad \dfrac{\partial w}{\partial r} = \dfrac{1}{2}\left(r^2 + s^2 + t^2\right)^{-1/2}(2r) = \dfrac{r}{\sqrt{r^2 + s^2 + t^2}}, \dfrac{\partial w}{\partial s} = \dfrac{s}{\sqrt{r^2 + s^2 + t^2}},$

$\dfrac{\partial w}{\partial t} = \dfrac{t}{\sqrt{r^2 + s^2 + t^2}}.$

29. $u = xe^{-t}\sin\theta \quad \Rightarrow \quad \dfrac{\partial u}{\partial x} = e^{-t}\sin\theta, \dfrac{\partial u}{\partial t} = -xe^{-t}\sin\theta, \dfrac{\partial u}{\partial\theta} = xe^{-t}\cos\theta$

30. $u = x^{y/z} \quad \Rightarrow \quad u_x = \dfrac{y}{z}x^{(y/z)-1}, u_y = x^{y/z}\ln x \cdot \dfrac{1}{z} = \dfrac{x^{y/z}}{z}\ln x, u_z = x^{y/z}\ln x \cdot \dfrac{-y}{z^2} = -\dfrac{yx^{y/z}}{z^2}\ln x$

31. $f(x,y,z,t) = \dfrac{x-y}{z-t} \quad \Rightarrow \quad f_x(x,y,z,t) = \dfrac{1}{z-t}, f_y(x,y,z,t) = -\dfrac{1}{z-t},$

$f_z(x,y,z,t) = (x-y)(-1)(z-t)^{-2} = \dfrac{y-x}{(z-t)^2}, \text{ and}$

$f_t(x,y,z,t) = (x-y)(-1)(z-t)^{-2}(-1) = \dfrac{x-y}{(z-t)^2}.$

32. $f(x,y,z,t) = xy^2z^3t^4 \quad \Rightarrow \quad f_x(x,y,z,t) = y^2z^3t^4, f_y(x,y,z,t) = 2xyz^3t^4, f_z(x,y,z,t) = 3xy^2z^2t^4,$
and $f_t(x,y,z,t) = 4xy^2z^3t^3.$

33. $u = \sqrt{x_1^2 + x_2^2 + \cdots + x_n^2}.$ For each $i = 1, \ldots, n,$

$u_{x_i} = \dfrac{1}{2}\left(x_1^2 + x_2^2 + \cdots + x_n^2\right)^{-1/2}(2x_i) = \dfrac{x_i}{\sqrt{x_1^2 + x_2^2 + \cdots + x_n^2}}.$

34. $u = \sin(x_1 + 2x_2 + \cdots + nx_n).$ For each $i = 1, \ldots, n, u_{x_i} = i\cos(x_1 + 2x_2 + \cdots + nx_n).$

35. $f(x,y) = \sqrt{x^2 + y^2} \quad \Rightarrow \quad f_x(x,y) = \dfrac{1}{2}\left(x^2 + y^2\right)^{-1/2}(2x) = \dfrac{x}{\sqrt{x^2 + y^2}},$ so $f_x(3,4) = \dfrac{3}{\sqrt{3^2 + 4^2}} = \dfrac{3}{5}.$

36. $f(x,y) = \sin(2x + 3y) \quad \Rightarrow \quad f_y(x,y) = \cos(2x + 3y) \cdot 3 = 3\cos(2x + 3y),$ so
$f_y(-6,4) = 3\cos[2(-6) + 3(4)] = 3\cos 0 = 3.$

37. $f(x,y,z) = \dfrac{x}{y+z} = x(y+z)^{-1} \quad \Rightarrow \quad f_z(x,y,z) = x(-1)(y+z)^{-2} = -\dfrac{x}{(y+z)^2},$ so

$f_z(3,2,1) = -\dfrac{3}{(2+1)^2} = -\dfrac{1}{3}.$

38. $f(u,v,w) = w\tan(uv) \quad \Rightarrow \quad f_v(u,v,w) = w\sec^2(uv) \cdot u = uw\sec^2(uv),$ so
$f_v(2,0,3) = (2)(3)\sec^2(2 \cdot 0) = 6.$

39. $f(x,y) = x^2 - xy + 2y^2 \quad \Rightarrow$

$$f_x(x,y) = \lim_{h \to 0}\dfrac{f(x+h,y) - f(x,y)}{h} = \lim_{h \to 0}\dfrac{(x+h)^2 - (x+h)y + 2y^2 - (x^2 - xy + 2y^2)}{h}$$

$$= \lim_{h \to 0}\dfrac{h(2x - y + h)}{h} = \lim_{h \to 0}(2x - y + h) = 2x - y$$

$$f_y(x,y) = \lim_{h \to 0}\dfrac{f(x,y+h) - f(x,y)}{h} = \lim_{h \to 0}\dfrac{x^2 - x(y+h) + 2(y+h)^2 - (x^2 - xy + 2y^2)}{h}$$

$$= \lim_{h \to 0}\dfrac{h(4y - x + 2h)}{h} = \lim_{h \to 0}(4y - x + 2h) = 4y - x$$

40. $f(x, y) = \sqrt{3x - y}$ ⇒

$$f_x(x, y) = \lim_{h \to 0} \frac{f(x + h, y) - f(x, y)}{h}$$

$$= \lim_{h \to 0} \frac{\sqrt{3(x + h) - y} - \sqrt{3x - y}}{h} \cdot \frac{\sqrt{3(x + h) - y} + \sqrt{3x - y}}{\sqrt{3(x + h) - y} + \sqrt{3x - y}}$$

$$= \lim_{h \to 0} \frac{3}{\sqrt{3(x + h) - y} + \sqrt{3x - y}} = \frac{3}{2\sqrt{3x - y}}$$

$$f_y(x, y) = \lim_{h \to 0} \frac{f(x, y + h) - f(x, y)}{h}$$

$$= \lim_{h \to 0} \frac{\sqrt{3x - (y + h)} - \sqrt{3x - y}}{h} \cdot \frac{\sqrt{3x - (y + h)} + \sqrt{3x - y}}{\sqrt{3x - (y + h)} + \sqrt{3x - y}}$$

$$= \lim_{h \to 0} \frac{-1}{\sqrt{3x - (y + h)} + \sqrt{3x - y}} = \frac{-1}{2\sqrt{3x - y}}$$

41. $xy + yz = xz$ ⇒ $\dfrac{\partial}{\partial x}(xy + yz) = \dfrac{\partial}{\partial x}(xz)$ ⇔ $y + y\dfrac{\partial z}{\partial x} = z + x\dfrac{\partial z}{\partial x}$ ⇔ $(y - x)\dfrac{\partial z}{\partial x} = z - y$, so

$$\frac{\partial z}{\partial x} = \frac{z - y}{y - x}. \quad \frac{\partial}{\partial y}(xy + yz) = \frac{\partial}{\partial y}(xz) \quad \Leftrightarrow \quad x + z + y\frac{\partial z}{\partial y} = x\frac{\partial z}{\partial y} \quad \Leftrightarrow \quad (y - x)\frac{\partial z}{\partial y} = -(x + z),$$

so $\dfrac{\partial z}{\partial y} = \dfrac{x + z}{x - y}.$

42. $xyz = \cos(x + y + z)$ ⇒ $\dfrac{\partial}{\partial x}(xyz) = \dfrac{\partial}{\partial x}[\cos(x + y + z)]$ ⇔

$$yz + xy\frac{\partial z}{\partial x} = [-\sin(x + y + z)]\left(1 + \frac{\partial z}{\partial x}\right), [xy + \sin(x + y + z)]\frac{\partial z}{\partial x} = -[yz + \sin(x + y + z)], \text{ so}$$

$$\frac{\partial z}{\partial x} = -\frac{yz + \sin(x + y + z)}{xy + \sin(x + y + z)}, \frac{\partial}{\partial y}(xyz) = \frac{\partial}{\partial y}(\cos(x + y + z)), \text{ and so by symmetry,}$$

$$\frac{\partial z}{\partial y} = -\frac{xz + \sin(x + y + z)}{xy + \sin(x + y + z)}.$$

43. $x^2 + y^2 - z^2 = 2x(y + z)$ ⇔ $\dfrac{\partial}{\partial x}(x^2 + y^2 - z^2) = \dfrac{\partial}{\partial x}[2x(y + z)]$ ⇔ $2x - 2z\dfrac{\partial z}{\partial x} = 2(y + z) + 2x\dfrac{\partial z}{\partial x}$

⇔ $2(x + z)\dfrac{\partial z}{\partial x} = 2(x - y - z)$, so $\dfrac{\partial z}{\partial x} = \dfrac{x - y - z}{x + z}.$

$$\frac{\partial}{\partial y}(x^2 + y^2 - z^2) = \frac{\partial}{\partial y}[2x(y + z)] \quad \Leftrightarrow \quad 2y - 2z\frac{\partial z}{\partial y} = 2x\left(1 + \frac{\partial z}{\partial y}\right) \quad \Leftrightarrow \quad 2(x + z)\frac{\partial z}{\partial y} = 2(y - x),$$

so $\dfrac{\partial z}{\partial y} = \dfrac{y - x}{x + z}.$

44. $xy^2z^3 + x^3y^2z = x + y + z$ ⇒ $\dfrac{\partial}{\partial x}(xy^2z^3 + x^3y^2z) = \dfrac{\partial}{\partial x}(x + y + z)$ ⇔

$$y^2z^3 + 3xy^2z^2\frac{\partial z}{\partial x} + 3x^2y^2z + x^3y^2\frac{\partial z}{\partial x} = 1 + \frac{\partial z}{\partial x}, \text{ so } (3xy^2z^2 + x^3y^2 - 1)\frac{\partial z}{\partial x} = 1 - y^2z^3 - 3x^2y^2z$$

and $\dfrac{\partial z}{\partial x} = \dfrac{1 - y^2z^3 - 3x^2y^2z}{3xy^2z^2 + x^3y^2 - 1}.$

$$\frac{\partial}{\partial y}(xy^2z^3 + x^3y^2z) = \frac{\partial}{\partial y}(x + y + z) \quad \Leftrightarrow \quad 2xyz^3 + 3xy^2z^2\frac{\partial z}{\partial y} + 2x^3yz + x^3y^2\frac{\partial z}{\partial y} = 1 + \frac{\partial z}{\partial y},$$

so $(3xy^2z^2 + x^3y^2 - 1)\dfrac{\partial z}{\partial y} = 1 - 2xyz^3 - 2x^3yz$ and $\dfrac{\partial z}{\partial y} = \dfrac{1 - 2xyz^3 - 2x^3yz}{3xy^2z^2 + x^3y^2 - 1}.$

45. (a) $z = f(x) + g(y)$ $\Rightarrow$ $\dfrac{\partial z}{\partial x} = f'(x), \dfrac{\partial z}{\partial y} = g'(y)$

(b) $z = f(x+y)$. Let $u = x+y$. Then $\dfrac{\partial z}{\partial x} = \dfrac{df}{du}\dfrac{\partial u}{\partial x} = \dfrac{df}{du}(1) = f'(u) = f'(x+y)$,

$\dfrac{\partial z}{\partial y} = \dfrac{df}{du}\dfrac{\partial u}{\partial y} = \dfrac{df}{du}(1) = f'(u) = f'(x+y)$.

46. (a) $z = f(x)g(y)$ $\Rightarrow$ $\dfrac{\partial z}{\partial x} = f'(x)g(y), \dfrac{\partial z}{\partial y} = f(x)g'(y)$

(b) $z = f(xy)$. Let $u = xy$. Then $\dfrac{\partial u}{\partial x} = y$ and $\dfrac{\partial u}{\partial y} = x$. Hence $\dfrac{\partial z}{\partial x} = \dfrac{df}{du}\dfrac{\partial u}{\partial x} = \dfrac{df}{du} \cdot y = yf'(u) = yf'(xy)$ and

$\dfrac{\partial z}{\partial y} = \dfrac{df}{du}\dfrac{\partial u}{\partial y} = \dfrac{df}{du} \cdot x = xf'(u) = xf'(xy)$.

(c) $z = f\left(\dfrac{x}{y}\right)$. Let $u = \dfrac{x}{y}$. Then $\dfrac{\partial u}{\partial x} = \dfrac{1}{y}$ and $\dfrac{\partial u}{\partial y} = -\dfrac{x}{y^2}$. Hence $\dfrac{\partial z}{\partial x} = \dfrac{df}{du}\dfrac{\partial u}{\partial x} = f'(u)\dfrac{1}{y} = \dfrac{f'(x/y)}{y}$ and

$\dfrac{\partial z}{\partial y} = \dfrac{df}{du}\dfrac{\partial u}{\partial y} = f'(u)\left(-\dfrac{x}{y^2}\right) = -\dfrac{xf'(x/y)}{y^2}$.

47. $f(x,y) = x^4 - 3x^2y^3$ $\Rightarrow$ $f_x(x,y) = 4x^3 - 6xy^3$, $f_y(x,y) = -9x^2y^2$. Then $f_{xx}(x,y) = 12x^2 - 6y^3$, $f_{xy}(x,y) = -18xy^2$, $f_{yx}(x,y) = -18xy^2$, and $f_{yy}(x,y) = -18x^2y$.

48. $f(x,y) = \ln(3x+5y)$ $\Rightarrow$ $f_x(x,y) = \dfrac{3}{3x+5y}$, $f_y(x,y) = \dfrac{5}{3x+5y}$. Then

$f_{xx}(x,y) = 3(-1)(3x+5y)^{-2}(3) = -\dfrac{9}{(3x+5y)^2}$, $f_{xy}(x,y) = -\dfrac{15}{(3x+5y)^2}$, $f_{yx}(x,y) = -\dfrac{15}{(3x+5y)^2}$,

and $f_{yy}(x,y) = -\dfrac{25}{(3x+5y)^2}$.

49. $u = e^{-s}\sin t$ $\Rightarrow$ $u_s = -e^{-s}\sin t$, $u_t = e^{-s}\cos t$. Then $u_{ss} = e^{-s}\sin t$, $u_{st} = -e^{-s}\cos t$, $u_{ts} = -e^{-s}\cos t$, and $u_{tt} = -e^{-s}\sin t$.

50. $z = y\tan 2x$ $\Rightarrow$ $z_x = y\sec^2(2x) \cdot 2 = 2y\sec^2(2x)$, $z_y = \tan 2x$. Then

$z_{xx} = 2y(2)\sec(2x) \cdot \sec(2x)\tan(2x) \cdot 2 = 8y\sec^2(2x)\tan(2x)$, $z_{xy} = 2\sec^2(2x)$,

$z_{yx} = \sec^2(2x) \cdot 2 = 2\sec^2(2x)$, and $z_{yy} = 0$.

51. $u = \ln\sqrt{x^2+y^2} = \ln(x^2+y^2)^{1/2} = \tfrac{1}{2}\ln(x^2+y^2)$ $\Rightarrow$ $u_x = \dfrac{1}{2}\dfrac{1}{x^2+y^2} \cdot 2x = \dfrac{x}{x^2+y^2}$,

$u_{xy} = x(-1)(x^2+y^2)^{-2}(2y) = -\dfrac{2xy}{(x^2+y^2)^2}$ and $u_y = \dfrac{1}{2}\dfrac{1}{x^2+y^2} \cdot 2y = \dfrac{y}{x^2+y^2}$,

$u_{yx} = y(-1)(x^2+y^2)^{-2}(2x) = -\dfrac{2xy}{(x^2+y^2)^2}$. Thus $u_{xy} = u_{yx}$.

52. $u = xye^y$ $\Rightarrow$ $u_x = ye^y$, $u_{xy} = ye^y + e^y = (y+1)e^y$ and $u_y = x(ye^y + e^y) = x(y+1)e^y$, $u_{yx} = (y+1)e^y$. Thus $u_{xy} = u_{yx}$.

53. $f(x,y) = x^2y^3 - 2x^4y$ $\Rightarrow$ $f_x = 2xy^3 - 8x^3y$, $f_{xx} = 2y^3 - 24x^2y$, $f_{xxx} = -48xy$

54. $f(x,y) = e^{xy^2}$ $\Rightarrow$ $f_x = y^2e^{xy^2}$, $f_{xx} = y^4e^{xy^2}$, $f_{xxy} = 4y^3e^{xy^2} + 2xy^5e^{xy^2} = 2y^3e^{xy^2}(2+xy^2)$

55. $f(x,y,z) = x^5 + x^4y^4z^3 + yz^2$ $\Rightarrow$ $f_x = 5x^4 + 4x^3y^4z^3$, $f_{xy} = 16x^3y^3z^3$, and $f_{xyz} = 48x^3y^3z^2$

56. $f(x,y,z) = e^{xyz}$ $\Rightarrow$ $f_y = xze^{xyz}$, $f_{yz} = xe^{xyz} + xz(xy)e^{xyz} = xe^{xyz}(1+yxz)$, and $f_{yzy} = x(xz)e^{xyz}(1+yxz) + xe^{xyz}(xz) = x^2z(2+xyz)e^{xyz}$.

57. $z = x \sin y \Rightarrow \dfrac{\partial z}{\partial x} = \sin y, \ \dfrac{\partial^2 z}{\partial y \partial x} = \cos y$, and $\dfrac{\partial^3 z}{\partial y^2 \partial x} = -\sin y$.

58. $u = x^a y^b z^c$. If $a = 0$, or if $b = 0$ or 1, or if $c = 0$, 1, or 2, then $\dfrac{\partial^6 u}{\partial x \, \partial y^2 \, \partial z^3} = 0$. Otherwise $\dfrac{\partial u}{\partial z} = cx^a y^b z^{c-1}$,

$\dfrac{\partial^2 u}{\partial z^2} = c(c-1)x^a y^b z^{c-2}, \ \dfrac{\partial^3 u}{\partial z^3} = c(c-1)(c-2)x^a y^b z^{c-3}, \ \dfrac{\partial^4 u}{\partial y \, \partial z^3} = bc(c-1)(c-2)x^a y^{b-1} z^{c-3}$,

$\dfrac{\partial^5 u}{\partial y^2 \, \partial z^3} = b(b-1)c(c-1)(c-2)x^a y^{b-2} z^{c-3}$, and $\dfrac{\partial^6 u}{\partial x \, \partial y^2 \, \partial z^3} = ab(b-1)c(c-1)(c-2)x^{a-1} y^{b-2} z^{c-3}$.

59. By Definition 4, $f_x(3, 2) = \lim\limits_{h \to 0} \dfrac{f(3+h, 2) - f(3, 2)}{h}$ which we can approximate by considering $h = 0.5$

and $h = -0.5$: $f_x(3, 2) \approx \dfrac{f(3.5, 2) - f(3, 2)}{0.5} = \dfrac{22.4 - 17.5}{0.5} = 9.8$,

$f_x(3, 2) \approx \dfrac{f(2.5, 2) - f(3, 2)}{-0.5} = \dfrac{10.2 - 17.5}{-0.5} = 14.6$. Averaging these values, we estimate $f_x(3, 2)$ to be

approximately 12.2. Similarly, $f_x(3, 2.2) = \lim\limits_{h \to 0} \dfrac{f(3+h, 2.2) - f(3, 2.2)}{h}$ which we can approximate by

considering $h = 0.5$ and $h = -0.5$: $f_x(3, 2.2) \approx \dfrac{f(3.5, 2.2) - f(3, 2.2)}{0.5} = \dfrac{26.1 - 15.9}{0.5} = 20.4$,

$f_x(3, 2.2) \approx \dfrac{f(2.5, 2.2) - f(3, 2.2)}{-0.5} = \dfrac{9.3 - 15.9}{-0.5} = 13.2$. Averaging these values, we have $f_x(3, 2.2) \approx 16.8$.

To estimate $f_{xy}(3, 2)$, we first need an estimate for $f_x(3, 1.8)$:

$f_x(3, 1.8) \approx \dfrac{f(3.5, 1.8) - f(3, 1.8)}{0.5} = \dfrac{20.0 - 18.1}{0.5} = 3.8$,

$f_x(3, 1.8) \approx \dfrac{f(2.5, 1.8) - f(3, 1.8)}{-0.5} = \dfrac{12.5 - 18.1}{-0.5} = 11.2$. Averaging these values, we get $f_x(3, 1.8) \approx 7.5$.

Now $f_{xy}(x, y) = \dfrac{\partial}{\partial y} \left[f_x(x, y) \right]$ and $f_x(x, y)$ is itself a function of 2 variables, so Definition 4 says that

$f_{xy}(x, y) = \dfrac{\partial}{\partial y} \left[f_x(x, y) \right] = \lim\limits_{h \to 0} \dfrac{f_x(x, y+h) - f_x(x, y)}{h} \ \Rightarrow \ f_{xy}(3, 2) = \lim\limits_{h \to 0} \dfrac{f_x(3, 2+h) - f_x(3, 2)}{h}$.

We can estimate this value using our previous work with $h = 0.2$ and $h = -0.2$:

$f_{xy}(3, 2) \approx \dfrac{f_x(3, 2.2) - f_x(3, 2)}{0.2} = \dfrac{16.8 - 12.2}{0.2} = 23$,

$f_{xy}(3, 2) \approx \dfrac{f_x(3, 1.8) - f_x(3, 2)}{-0.2} = \dfrac{7.5 - 12.2}{-0.2} = 23.5$. Averaging these values, we estimate $f_{xy}(3, 2)$ to be

approximately 23.25.

60. (a) If we fix y and allow x to vary, the level curves indicate that the value of f decreases as we move through P in the positive x-direction, so f_x is negative at P.

(b) If we fix x and allow y to vary, the level curves indicate that the value of f increases as we move through P in the positive y-direction, so f_y is positive at P.

(c) $f_{xx} = \dfrac{\partial}{\partial x} (f_x)$, so if we fix y and allow x to vary, f_{xx} is the rate of change of f_x as x increases. Note that at points to the right of P the level curves are spaced farther apart (in the x-direction) than at points to the left of P, demonstrating that f decreases less quickly with respect to x to the right of P. So as we move through P in the positive x-direction the (negative) value of f_x increases, hence $\dfrac{\partial}{\partial x} (f_x) = f_{xx}$ is positive at P.

(d) $f_{xy} = \dfrac{\partial}{\partial y}(f_x)$, so if we fix x and allow y to vary, f_{xy} is the rate of change of f_x as y increases. The level curves are closer together (in the x-direction) at points above P than at those below P, demonstrating that f decreases more quickly with respect to x for y-values above P. So as we move through P in the positive y-direction, the (negative) value of f_x decreases, hence f_{xy} is negative.

(e) $f_{yy} = \dfrac{\partial}{\partial y}(f_y)$, so if we fix x and allow y to vary, f_{yy} is the rate of change of f_y as y increases. The level curves are closer together (in the y-direction) at points above P than at those below P, demonstrating that f increases more quickly with respect to y above P. So as we move through P in the positive y-direction the (positive) value of f_y increases, hence $\dfrac{\partial}{\partial y}(f_y) = f_{yy}$ is positive at P.

61. $u = e^{-\alpha^2 k^2 t}\sin kx \;\Rightarrow\; u_x = ke^{-\alpha^2 k^2 t}\cos kx,\; u_{xx} = -k^2 e^{-\alpha^2 k^2 t}\sin kx$, and $u_t = -\alpha^2 k^2 e^{-\alpha^2 k^2 t}\sin kx$. Thus $\alpha^2 u_{xx} = u_t$.

62. (a) $u = x^2 + y^2 \;\Rightarrow\; u_x = 2x,\, u_{xx} = 2;\, u_y = 2y,\, u_{yy} = 2$. Thus $u_{xx} + u_{yy} \neq 0$ and $u = x^2 + y^2$ does not satisfy Laplace's Equation.

(b) $u = x^2 - y^2$ is a solution: $u_{xx} = 2,\, u_{yy} = -2$ so $u_{xx} + u_{yy} = 0$.

(c) $u = x^3 + 3xy^2$ is not a solution: $u_x = 3x^2 + 3y^2,\, u_{xx} = 6x;\, u_y = 6xy,\, u_{yy} = 6x$.

(d) $u = \ln\sqrt{x^2 + y^2}$ is a solution: $u_x = \dfrac{1}{\sqrt{x^2 + y^2}}\left(\dfrac{1}{2}\right)(x^2 + y^2)^{-1/2}(2x) = \dfrac{x}{x^2 + y^2}$,

$u_{xx} = \dfrac{(x^2 + y^2) - x(2x)}{(x^2 + y^2)^2} = \dfrac{y^2 - x^2}{(x^2 + y^2)^2}$. By symmetry, $u_{yy} = \dfrac{x^2 - y^2}{(x^2 + y^2)^2}$, so $u_{xx} + u_{yy} = 0$.

(e) $u = e^{-x}\cos y - e^{-y}\cos x$ is a solution: $u_x = -e^{-x}\cos y + e^{-y}\sin x,\, u_{xx} = e^{-x}\cos y + e^{-y}\cos x$, and $u_y = -e^{-x}\sin y + e^{-y}\cos x,\, u_{yy} = -e^{-x}\cos y - e^{-y}\cos x$.

63. $u = \dfrac{1}{\sqrt{x^2 + y^2 + z^2}} \;\Rightarrow\; u_x = \left(-\tfrac{1}{2}\right)(x^2 + y^2 + z^2)^{-3/2}(2x) = -x(x^2 + y^2 + z^2)^{-3/2}$ and

$u_{xx} = -(x^2 + y^2 + z^2)^{-3/2} - x\left(-\tfrac{3}{2}\right)(x^2 + y^2 + z^2)^{-5/2}(2x) = \dfrac{2x^2 - y^2 - z^2}{(x^2 + y^2 + z^2)^{5/2}}$.

By symmetry, $u_{yy} = \dfrac{2y^2 - x^2 - z^2}{(x^2 + y^2 + z^2)^{5/2}}$ and $u_{zz} = \dfrac{2z^2 - x^2 - y^2}{(x^2 + y^2 + z^2)^{5/2}}$. Thus

$u_{xx} + u_{yy} + u_{zz} = \dfrac{2x^2 - y^2 - z^2 + 2y^2 - x^2 - z^2 + 2z^2 - x^2 - y^2}{(x^2 + y^2 + z^2)^{5/2}} = 0$.

64. (a) $u = \sin(kx)\sin(akt) \;\Rightarrow\; u_t = ak\sin(kx)\cos(akt),\, u_{tt} = -a^2 k^2 \sin(kx)\sin(akt)$, $u_x = k\cos(kx)\sin(akt),\, u_{xx} = -k^2 \sin(kx)\sin(akt)$. Thus $u_{tt} = a^2 u_{xx}$.

(b) $u = \dfrac{t}{a^2 t^2 - x^2} \;\Rightarrow\; u_t = \dfrac{(a^2 t^2 - x^2) - t(2a^2 t)}{(a^2 t^2 - x^2)^2} = -\dfrac{a^2 t^2 + x^2}{(a^2 t^2 - x^2)^2}$,

$u_{tt} = \dfrac{-2a^2 t(a^2 t^2 - x^2)^2 + (a^2 t^2 + x^2)(2)(a^2 t^2 - x^2)(2a^2 t)}{(a^2 t^2 - x^2)^4} = \dfrac{2a^4 t^3 + 6a^2 tx^2}{a^2 t^2 - x^2}$,

$u_x = t(-1)(a^2 t^2 - x^2)^{-2}(2x) = \dfrac{2tx}{(a^2 t^2 - x^2)^2}$,

$u_{xx} = \dfrac{2t(a^2 t^2 - x^2)^2 - 2tx(2)(a^2 t^2 - x^2)(-2x)}{(a^2 t^2 - x^2)^4} = \dfrac{2a^2 t^3 - 2tx^2 + 8tx^2}{(a^2 t^2 - x^2)^3} = \dfrac{2a^2 t^3 + 6tx^2}{(a^2 t^2 - x^2)^4}$.

Thus $u_{tt} = a^2 u_{xx}$.

(c) $u = (x - at)^6 + (x + at)^6 \Rightarrow u_t = -6a(x - at)^5 + 6a(x + at)^5$,

$u_{tt} = 30a^2(x - at)^4 + 30a^2(x + at)^4$, $u_x = 6(x - at)^5 + 6(x + at)^5$, $u_{xx} = 30(x - at)^4 + 30(x + at)^4$.

Thus $u_{tt} = a^2 u_{xx}$.

(d) $u = \sin(x - at) + \ln(x + at) \Rightarrow u_t = -a\cos(x - at) + \dfrac{a}{x + at}$, $u_{tt} = -a^2\sin(x - at) - \dfrac{a^2}{(x + at)^2}$,

$u_x = \cos(x - at) + \dfrac{1}{x + at}$, $u_{xx} = -\sin(x - at) - \dfrac{1}{(x + at)^2}$. Thus $u_{tt} = a^2 u_{xx}$.

65. Let $v = x + at$, $w = x - at$. Then $u_t = \dfrac{\partial[f(v) + g(w)]}{\partial t} = \dfrac{df(v)}{dv}\dfrac{\partial v}{\partial t} + \dfrac{dg(w)}{dw}\dfrac{\partial w}{\partial t} = af'(v) - ag'(w)$ and

$u_{tt} = \dfrac{\partial[af'(v) - ag'(w)]}{\partial t} = a[af''(v) + ag''(w)] = a^2[f''(v) + g''(w)]$. Similarly, by using the Chain Rule

we have $u_x = f'(v) + g'(w)$ and $u_{xx} = f''(v) + g''(w)$. Thus $u_{tt} = a^2 u_{xx}$.

66. $P = bL^\alpha K^\beta$, so $\dfrac{\partial P}{\partial L} = \alpha b L^{\alpha-1}K^\beta$ and $\dfrac{\partial P}{\partial K} = \beta b L^\alpha K^{\beta-1}$. Then

$$L\dfrac{\partial P}{\partial L} + K\dfrac{\partial P}{\partial K} = L\left(\alpha b L^{\alpha-1}K^\beta\right) + K\left(\beta b L^\alpha K^{\beta-1}\right) = \alpha b L^{1+\alpha-1}K^\beta + \beta b L^\alpha K^{1+\beta-1}$$

$$= (\alpha + \beta)bL^\alpha K^\beta = (\alpha + \beta)vP$$

67. If we fix $K = K_0$, $P(L, K_0)$ is a function of a single variable L, and $\dfrac{dP}{dL} = \alpha\dfrac{P}{L}$ is a separable differential

equation. Then $\dfrac{dP}{P} = \alpha\dfrac{dL}{L} \Rightarrow \displaystyle\int\dfrac{dP}{P} = \int\alpha\dfrac{dL}{L} \Rightarrow \ln|P| = \alpha\ln|L| + C(K_0)$, where $C(K_0)$ can

depend on K_0. Then $|P| = e^{\alpha\ln|L| + C(K_0)}$, and since $P > 0$ and $L > 0$, we have

$P = e^{\alpha\ln L}e^{C(K_0)} = e^{C(K_0)}e^{\ln L^\alpha} = C_1(K_0)L^\alpha$ where $C_1(K_0) = e^{C(K_0)}$.

68. (a) $\partial T/\partial x = -60(2x)/\left(1 + x^2 + y^2\right)^2$, so at $(2, 1)$, $T_x = -240/(1 + 4 + 1)^2 = -\frac{20}{3}$.

(b) $\partial T/\partial y = -60(2y)/\left(1 + x^2 + y^2\right)^2$, so at $(2, 1)$, $T_y = -120/36 = -\frac{10}{3}$. Thus from the point $(2, 1)$ the

temperature is decreasing at a rate of $\frac{20}{3}\,°\text{C}/\text{m}$ in the x-direction and is decreasing at a rate of $\frac{10}{3}\,°\text{C}/\text{m}$ in the

y-direction.

69. By the Chain Rule, taking the partial derivative of both sides with respect to R_1 gives

$\dfrac{\partial R^{-1}}{\partial R}\dfrac{\partial R}{\partial R_1} = \dfrac{\partial[(1/R_1) + (1/R_2) + (1/R_3)]}{\partial R_1}$ or $-R^{-2}\dfrac{\partial R}{\partial R_1} = -R_1^{-2}$. Thus $\dfrac{\partial R}{\partial R_1} = \dfrac{R^2}{R_1^2}$.

70. $P = \dfrac{mRT}{V}$ so $\dfrac{\partial P}{\partial V} = \dfrac{-mRT}{V^2}$; $V = \dfrac{mRT}{P}$, so $\dfrac{\partial V}{\partial T} = \dfrac{mR}{P}$; $T = \dfrac{PV}{mR}$, so $\dfrac{\partial T}{\partial P} = \dfrac{V}{mR}$. Thus

$\dfrac{\partial P}{\partial V}\dfrac{\partial V}{\partial T}\dfrac{\partial T}{\partial P} = \dfrac{-mRT}{V^2}\dfrac{mR}{P}\dfrac{V}{mR} = \dfrac{-mRT}{PV} = -1$, since $PV = mRT$.

71. $\dfrac{\partial K}{\partial m} = \frac{1}{2}V^2$, $\dfrac{\partial K}{\partial V} = mV$, $\dfrac{\partial^2 K}{\partial V^2} = m$. Thus $\dfrac{\partial K}{\partial m}\cdot\dfrac{\partial^2 K}{\partial V^2} = \frac{1}{2}V^2 m = K$.

72. The Law of Cosines says that $a^2 = b^2 + c^2 - 2bc\cos A$. Thus $\dfrac{\partial(a^2)}{\partial a} = \dfrac{\partial(b^2 + c^2 - 2ab\cos A)}{\partial a}$ or

$2a = -2bc\,(-\sin A)\dfrac{\partial A}{\partial a}$, implying that $\dfrac{\partial A}{\partial a} = \dfrac{a}{bc\sin A}$. Taking the partial derivative of both sides with respect to

b gives $0 = 2b - 2c\,(\cos A) - 2bc\,(-\sin A)\dfrac{\partial A}{\partial b}$. Thus $\dfrac{\partial A}{\partial b} = \dfrac{c\cos A - b}{bc\sin A}$. By symmetry $\dfrac{\partial A}{\partial c} = \dfrac{b\cos A - c}{bc\sin A}$.

73. $f_x(x, y) = x + 4y \Rightarrow f_{xy}(x, y) = 4$ and $f_y(x, y) = 3x - y \Rightarrow f_{yx}(x, y) = 3$. Since f_{xy} and f_{yx} are continuous everywhere but $f_{xy}(x, y) \neq f_{yx}(x, y)$, Clairaut's Theorem implies that such a function $f(x, y)$ does not exist.

74. Setting $x = 1$, the equation of the parabola of

intersection is $z = 6 - 1 - 1 - 2y^2 = 4 - 2y^2$.

The slope of the tangent is $\partial z / \partial y = -4y$, so at

$(1, 2, -4)$ the slope is -8. Parametric equations

for the line are therefore $x = 1$, $y = 2 + t$,

$z = -4 - 8t$.

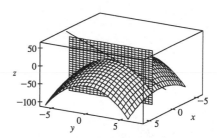

75. By the geometry of partial derivatives, the slope of the tangent line is $f_x(1, 2)$. By implicit differentiation of $4x^2 + 2y^2 + z^2 = 16$, we get $8x + 2z (\partial z / \partial x) = 0 \Rightarrow \partial z / \partial x = -4x/z$, so when $x = 1$ and $z = 2$ we have $\partial z / \partial x = -2$. So the slope is $f_x(1, 2) = -2$. Thus the tangent line is given by $z - 2 = -2(x - 1)$, $y = 2$. Taking the parameter to be $t = x - 1$, we can write parametric equations for this line: $x = 1 + t$, $y = 2$, $z = 2 - 2t$.

76. $T(x, t) = T_0 + T_1 e^{-\lambda x} \sin(\omega t - \lambda x)$

(a) $\partial T / \partial x = T_1 e^{-\lambda x} [\cos(\omega t - \lambda x) (-\lambda)] + T_1 (-\lambda e^{-\lambda x}) \sin(\omega t - \lambda x)$

$= -\lambda T_1 e^{-\lambda x} [\sin(\omega t - \lambda x) + \cos(\omega t - \lambda x)]$

This quantity represents the rate of change of temperature with respect to depth below the surface, at a given time t.

(b) $\partial T / \partial t = T_1 e^{-\lambda x} [\cos(\omega t - \lambda x) (\omega)] = \omega T_1 e^{-\lambda x} \cos(\omega t - \lambda x)$. This quantity represents the rate of change of temperature with respect to time at a fixed depth x.

(c) $T_{xx} = \dfrac{\partial}{\partial x} \left(\dfrac{\partial T}{\partial x} \right)$

$= -\lambda T_1 (e^{-\lambda x} [\cos(\omega t - \lambda x) (-\lambda) - \sin(\omega t - \lambda x) (-\lambda)]$

$+ e^{-\lambda x} (-\lambda) [\sin(\omega t - \lambda x) + \cos(\omega t - \lambda x)])$

$= 2\lambda^2 T_1 e^{-\lambda x} \cos(\omega t - \lambda x)$

But from part (b), $T_t = \omega T_1 e^{-\lambda x} \cos(\omega t - \lambda x) = \dfrac{\omega}{2\lambda^2} T_{xx}$. So with $k = \dfrac{\omega}{2\lambda^2}$, the function T satisfies the heat equation.

(d)

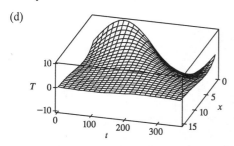

Note that near the surface (that is, for small x) the temperature varies greatly as t changes, but deeper (for large x) the temperature is more stable.

(e) The term $-\lambda x$ is a phase shift: it represents the fact that since heat diffuses slowly through soil, it takes time for changes in the surface temperature to affect the temperature at deeper points. As x increases, the phase shift also increases. For example, at the surface the highest temperature is reached at $t \approx 100$, whereas at a depth of 5 feet the peak temperature is attained at $t \approx 150$, and at a depth of 10 feet, at $t \approx 220$.

77. Let $g(x) = f(x, 0) = x(x^2)^{-3/2} e^0 = x|x|^{-3}$. But we are using the point $(1, 0)$, so near $(1, 0)$, $g(x) = x^{-2}$.

Then $g'(x) = -2x^{-3}$ and $g'(1) = -2$, so using (1) we have $f_x(1, 0) = g'(1) = -2$.

78. $f_x(0, 0) = \lim\limits_{h \to 0} \dfrac{f(0 + h, 0) - f(0, 0)}{h} = \lim\limits_{h \to 0} \dfrac{(h^3 + 0)^{1/3} - 0}{h} = \lim\limits_{h \to 0} \dfrac{h}{h} = 1$.

Or: Let $g(x) = f(x, 0) = \sqrt[3]{x^3 + 0} = x$. Then $g'(x) = 1$ and $g'(0) = 1$ so, by (1), $f_x(0, 0) = g'(0) = 1$.

79. (a)

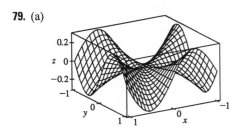

(b) For $(x, y) \neq (0, 0)$, $f_x(x, y) = \dfrac{(3x^2 y - y^3)(x^2 + y^2) - (x^3 y - xy^3)(2x)}{(x^2 + y^2)^2} = \dfrac{x^4 y + 4x^2 y^3 - y^5}{(x^2 + y^2)^2}$, and by

symmetry $f_y(x, y) = \dfrac{x^5 - 4x^3 y^2 - xy^4}{(x^2 + y^2)^2}$.

(c) $f_x(0, 0) = \lim\limits_{h \to 0} \dfrac{f(h, 0) - f(0, 0)}{h} = \lim\limits_{h \to 0} \dfrac{(0/h^2) - 0}{h} = 0$ and $f_y(0, 0) = \lim\limits_{h \to 0} \dfrac{f(0, h) - f(0, 0)}{h} = 0$.

(d) By (3), $f_{xy}(0, 0) = \dfrac{\partial f_x}{\partial y} = \lim\limits_{h \to 0} \dfrac{f_x(0, h) - f_x(0, 0)}{h} = \lim\limits_{h \to 0} \dfrac{(-h^5 - 0)/h^4}{h} = -1$ while by (2),

$f_{yx}(0, 0) = \dfrac{\partial f_y}{\partial x} = \lim\limits_{h \to 0} \dfrac{f_y(h, 0) - f_y(0, 0)}{h} = \lim\limits_{h \to 0} \dfrac{h^5/h^4}{h} = 1$.

(e) For $(x, y) \neq (0, 0)$, we use a CAS to compute $f_{xy}(x, y) = \dfrac{x^6 + 9x^4 y^2 - 4x^2 y^4 + 4y^6}{(x^2 + y^2)^3}$. Now as

$(x, y) \to (0, 0)$ along the x-axis, $f_{xy}(x, y) \to 1$ while as $(x, y) \to (0, 0)$ along the y-axis, $f_{xy}(x, y) \to 4$.

Thus f_{xy} isn't continuous at $(0, 0)$ and Clairaut's Theorem doesn't apply, so there is no contradiction. The

graphs of f_{xy} and f_{yx} are identical except at the origin, where we observe the discontinuity.

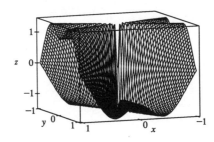

11.4   Tangent Planes and Linear Approximations   •   •   •   •   •   •

1. $z = f(x,y) = 4x^2 - y^2 + 2y$ $\Rightarrow$ $f_x(x,y) = 8x$, $f_y(x,y) = -2y + 2$, so $f_x(-1,2) = -8$, $f_y(-1,2) = -2$. By Equation 2, an equation of the tangent plane is $z - 4 = f_x(-1,2)[x - (-1)] + f_y(-1,2)(y - 2)$ $\Rightarrow$ $z - 4 = -8(x+1) - 2(y-2)$ or $z = -8x - 2y$.

2. $z = f(x,y) = e^{x^2 - y^2}$ $\Rightarrow$ $f_x(x,y) = 2xe^{x^2 - y^2}$, $f_y(x,y) = -2ye^{x^2 - y^2}$, so $f_x(1,-1) = 2$, $f_y(1,-1) = 2$. By Equation 2, an equation of the tangent plane is $z - 1 = f_x(1,-1)(x-1) + f_y(1,-1)[y - (-1)]$ $\Rightarrow$ $z - 1 = 2(x-1) + 2(y+1)$ or $z = 2x + 2y + 1$.

3. $z = f(x,y) = \sqrt{4 - x^2 - 2y^2}$ $\Rightarrow$ $f_x(x,y) = \frac{1}{2}\left(4 - x^2 - 2y^2\right)^{-1/2}(-2x) = -\dfrac{x}{\sqrt{4 - x^2 - 2y^2}}$, $f_y(x,y) = \frac{1}{2}\left(4 - x^2 - 2y^2\right)^{-1/2}(-4y) = -\dfrac{2y}{\sqrt{4 - x^2 - 2y^2}}$, so $f_x(1,-1) = -1$ and $f_y(1,-1) = 2$. Thus, an equation of the tangent plane is $z - 1 = f_x(1,-1)(x-1) + f_y(1,-1)\left[y - (-1)\right]$ $\Rightarrow$ $z - 1 = -1(x-1) + 2(y+1)$ or $x - 2y + z = 4$.

4. $z = f(x,y) = y \ln x$ $\Rightarrow$ $f_x(x,y) = y/x$, $f_y(x,y) = \ln x$, so $f_x(1,4) = 4$, $f_y(1,4) = 0$, and an equation of the tangent plane is $z - 0 = f_x(1,4)(x-1) + f_y(1,4)(y-4)$ $\Rightarrow$ $z = 4(x-1) + 0(y-4)$ or $z = 4x - 4$.

5. $z = f(x,y) = x^2 + xy + 3y^2$, so $f_x(x,y) = 2x + y$ $\Rightarrow$ $f_x(1,1) = 3$, $f_y(x,y) = x + 6y$ $\Rightarrow$ $f_y(1,1) = 7$ and an equation of the tangent plane is $z - 5 = 3(x-1) + 7(y-1)$ or $z = 3x + 7y - 5$. After zooming in, the surface and the tangent plane become almost indistinguishable. (Here, the tangent plane is below the surface.) If we zoom in farther, the surface and the tangent plane will appear to coincide.

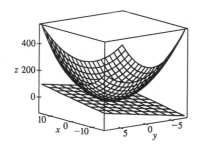
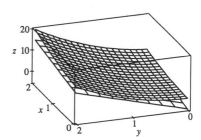

6. $z = f(x,y) = \sqrt{x - y}$, so $f_x(x,y) = \frac{1}{2}(x-y)^{-1/2}$, $f_x(5,1) = \frac{1}{4}$, $f_y(x,y) = -\frac{1}{2}(x-y)^{-1/2}$, $f_y(5,1) = -\frac{1}{4}$, and an equation of the tangent plane is $z - 2 = \frac{1}{4}(x-5) - \frac{1}{4}(y-1)$ or $z = \frac{1}{4}x - \frac{1}{4}y + 1$. After zooming in, the surface and the tangent plane become almost indistinguishable. (Here, the tangent plane is above the surface.) If we zoom in farther, the surface and the tangent plane will appear to coincide.

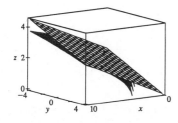
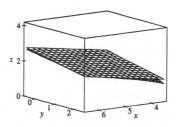

7. $f(x, y) = e^{-(x^2+y^2)/15} \left(\sin^2 x + \cos^2 y\right)$. A CAS gives

$f_x = -\frac{2}{15}e^{-(x^2+y^2)/15} \left(x \sin^2 x + x \cos^2 y - 15 \sin x \cos x\right)$ and

$f_y = -\frac{2}{15}e^{-(x^2+y^2)/15} \left(y \sin^2 x + y \cos^2 y + 15 \sin y \cos y\right)$. We use the CAS to evaluate these at $(2, 3)$, and

then substitute the results into Equation 2 in order to plot the tangent plane. After zooming in, the surface and the

tangent plane become almost indistinguishable. (Here, the tangent plane is above the surface.) If we zoom in farther,

the surface and the tangent plane will appear to coincide.

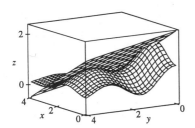

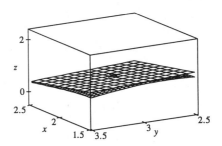

8. $f(x, y) = \dfrac{\sqrt{1 + 4x^2 + 4y^2}}{1 + x^4 + y^4}$. A CAS gives $f_x = \dfrac{4x\left(1 - 3x^4 + y^4 - x^2 - 4x^2y^2\right)}{\sqrt{1 + 4x^2 + 4y^2}\left(1 + x^4 + y^4\right)^2}$ and

$f_y = \dfrac{4y\left(1 - 3y^4 + x^4 - y^2 - 4x^2y^2\right)}{\sqrt{1 + 4x^2 + 4y^2}\left(1 + x^4 + y^4\right)^2}$. We use the CAS to evaluate these at $(1, 1)$, and then substitute the results

into Equation 2 to get an equation of the tangent plane: $z = \dfrac{25 - 8x - 8y}{9}$. After zooming in, the surface and the

tangent plane become almost indistinguishable. (Here, the tangent plane is shown with fewer traces than the

surface.) If we zoom in farther, the surface and the tangent plane will appear to coincide.

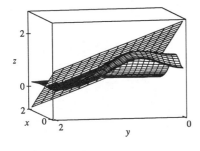

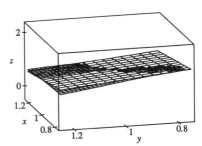

9. $f(x, y) = x\sqrt{y}$. The partial derivatives are $f_x(x, y) = \sqrt{y}$ and $f_y(x, y) = \dfrac{x}{2\sqrt{y}}$, so $f_x(1, 4) = 2$ and

$f_y(1, 4) = \frac{1}{4}$. Both f_x and f_y are continuous functions for $y > 0$, so by Theorem 8, f is

differentiable at $(1, 4)$. By Equation 3, the linearization of f at $(1, 4)$ is given by

$L(x, y) = f(1, 4) + f_x(1, 4)(x - 1) + f_y(1, 4)(y - 4) = 2 + 2(x - 1) + \frac{1}{4}(y - 4) = 2x + \frac{1}{4}y - 1$.

10. $f(x, y) = \dfrac{x}{y}$. The partial derivatives are $f_x(x, y) = \dfrac{1}{y}$ and $f_y(x, y) = -\dfrac{x}{y^2}$, so $f_x(6, 3) = \frac{1}{3}$ and $f_y(6, 3) = -\frac{2}{3}$.

Both f_x and f_y are continuous functions for $y \neq 0$, so f is differentiable at $(6, 3)$ by Theorem 8. The linearization

of f at $(6, 3)$ is given by

$L(x, y) = f(6, 3) + f_x(6, 3)(x - 6) + f_y(6, 3)(y - 3) = 2 + \frac{1}{3}(x - 6) - \frac{2}{3}(y - 3) = \frac{1}{3}x - \frac{2}{3}y + 2$

11. $f(x, y) = \tan^{-1}(x + 2y)$. The partial derivatives are $f_x(x, y) = \dfrac{1}{1 + (x + 2y)^2}$ and

$f_y(x, y) = \dfrac{2}{1 + (x + 2y)^2}$, so $f_x(1, 0) = \frac{1}{2}$ and $f_y(1, 0) = 1$. Both f_x and f_y are continuous

functions, so f is differentiable at $(1, 0)$, and the linearization of f at $(1, 0)$ is

$L(x, y) = f(1, 0) + f_x(1, 0)(x - 1) + f_y(1, 0)(y - 0) = \frac{\pi}{4} + \frac{1}{2}(x - 1) + 1(y) = \frac{1}{2}x + y + \frac{\pi}{4} - \frac{1}{2}$.

12. $f(x, y) = \sin(2x + 3y)$. The partial derivatives are $f_x(x, y) = 2\cos(2x + 3y)$ and

$f_y(x, y) = 3\cos(2x + 3y)$, so $f_x(-3, 2) = 2$ and $f_y(-3, 2) = 3$. Both f_x and f_y are continuous

functions, so f is differentiable at $(-3, 2)$, and the linearization of f at $(-3, 2)$ is

$L(x, y) = f(-3, 2) + f_x(-3, 2)(x + 3) + f_y(-3, 2)(y - 2) = 0 + 2(x + 3) + 3(y - 2) = 2x + 3y$.

13. $f(x, y) = \sqrt{20 - x^2 - 7y^2} \Rightarrow f_x(x, y) = -\dfrac{x}{\sqrt{20 - x^2 - 7y^2}}$ and $f_y(x, y) = -\dfrac{7y}{\sqrt{20 - x^2 - 7y^2}}$, so

$f_x(2, 1) = -\frac{2}{3}$ and $f_y(2, 1) = -\frac{7}{3}$. Then the linear approximation of f at $(2, 1)$ is given by

$$f(x, y) \approx f(2, 1) + f_x(2, 1)(x - 2) + f_y(2, 1)(y - 1) = 3 - \frac{2}{3}(x - 2) - \frac{7}{3}(y - 1)$$

$$= -\frac{2}{3}x - \frac{7}{3}y + \frac{20}{3}$$

Thus $f(1.95, 1.08) \approx -\frac{2}{3}(1.95) - \frac{7}{3}(1.08) + \frac{20}{3} = 2.84\overline{6}$.

14. $f(x, y) = \ln(x - 3y) \Rightarrow f_x(x, y) = \dfrac{1}{x - 3y}$ and $f_y(x, y) = -\dfrac{3}{x - 3y}$, so $f_x(7, 2) = 1$ and $f_y(7, 2) = -3$.

Then the linear approximation of f at $(7, 2)$ is given by

$$f(x, y) \approx f(7, 2) + f_x(7, 2)(x - 7) + f_y(7, 2)(y - 2)$$

$$= 0 + 1(x - 7) - 3(y - 2) = x - 3y - 1$$

Thus $f(6.9, 2.06) \approx 6.9 - 3(2.06) - 1 = -0.28$. The graph shows that our approximated value is slightly greater

than the actual value.

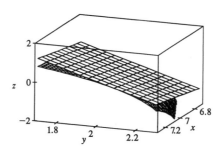

15. $f(x, y, z) = \sqrt{x^2 + y^2 + z^2} \Rightarrow f_x(x, y, z) = \dfrac{x}{\sqrt{x^2 + y^2 + z^2}}$, $f_y(x, y, z) = \dfrac{y}{\sqrt{x^2 + y^2 + z^2}}$, and

$f_z(x, y, z) = \dfrac{z}{\sqrt{x^2 + y^2 + z^2}}$, so $f_x(3, 2, 6) = \frac{3}{7}$, $f_y(3, 2, 6) = \frac{2}{7}$, and $f_z(3, 2, 6) = \frac{6}{7}$. Then the linear

approximation of f at $(3, 2, 6)$ is given by

$$f(x, y, z) \approx f(3, 2, 6) + f_x(3, 2, 6)(x - 3) + f_y(3, 2, 6)(y - 2) + f_z(3, 2, 6)(z - 6)$$

$$= 7 + \frac{3}{7}(x - 3) + \frac{2}{7}(y - 2) + \frac{6}{7}(z - 6) = \frac{3}{7}x + \frac{2}{7}y + \frac{6}{7}z$$

Thus $\sqrt{(3.02)^2 + (1.97)^2 + (5.99)^2} = f(3.02, 1.97, 5.99) \approx \frac{3}{7}(3.02) + \frac{2}{7}(1.97) + \frac{6}{7}(5.99) \approx 6.9914$.

16. From the table, $f(40, 20) = 28$. To estimate $f_v(40, 20)$ and $f_t(40, 20)$ we follow the procedure used in

Exercise 11.3.4. Since $f_v(40, 20) = \lim\limits_{h \to 0} \dfrac{f(40 + h, 20) - f(40, 20)}{h}$, we approximate this quantity with $h = \pm 10$

and use the values given in the table: $f_v(40, 20) \approx \dfrac{f(50, 20) - f(40, 20)}{10} = \dfrac{40 - 28}{10} = 1.2$,

$f_v(40, 20) \approx \dfrac{f(30, 20) - f(40, 20)}{-10} = \dfrac{17 - 28}{-10} = 1.1$. Averaging these values gives $f_v(40, 20) \approx 1.15$.

Similarly, $f_t(40, 20) = \lim\limits_{h \to 0} \dfrac{f(40, 20) - f(40, 20)}{h}$, so we use $h = 10$ and $h = -5$:

$f_t(40, 20) \approx \dfrac{f(40, 30) - f(40, 20)}{10} = \dfrac{31 - 28}{10} = 0.3$, $f_t(40, 20) \approx \dfrac{f(40, 15) - f(40, 20)}{-5} = \dfrac{25 - 28}{-5} = 0.6$.

Averaging these values gives $f_t(40, 15) \approx 0.45$. The linear approximation, then, is

$$f(v, t) \approx f(40, 20) + f_v(40, 20)(v - 40) + f_t(40, 20)(t - 20)$$
$$\approx 28 + 1.15(v - 40) + 0.45(t - 20)$$

When $v = 43$ and $t = 24$, we estimate $f(43, 24) \approx 28 + 1.15(43 - 40) + 0.45(24 - 20) = 33.25$, so we would expect the wave heights to be approximately 33.25 ft.

17. From the table, $f(94, 80) = 127$. To estimate $f_T(94, 80)$ and $f_H(94, 80)$ we follow the procedure used in

Section 11.3. Since $f_T(94, 80) = \lim\limits_{h \to 0} \dfrac{f(94 + h, 80) - f(94, 80)}{h}$, we approximate this quantity with $h = \pm 2$ and

use the values given in the table: $f_T(94, 80) \approx \dfrac{f(96, 80) - f(94, 80)}{2} = \dfrac{135 - 127}{2} = 4$,

$f_T(94, 80) \approx \dfrac{f(92, 80) - f(94, 80)}{-2} = \dfrac{119 - 127}{-2} = 4$.

Averaging these values gives $f_T(94, 80) \approx 4$. Similarly, $f_H(94, 80) = \lim\limits_{h \to 0} \dfrac{f(94, 80) - f(94, 80)}{h}$,

so we use $h = \pm 5$: $f_H(94, 80) \approx \dfrac{f(94, 85) - f(94, 80)}{5} = \dfrac{132 - 127}{5} = 1$,

$f_H(94, 80) \approx \dfrac{f(94, 75) - f(94, 80)}{-5} = \dfrac{122 - 127}{-5} = 1$. Averaging these values gives $f_H(94, 80) \approx 1$. The

linear approximation, then, is

$$f(T, H) \approx f(94, 80) + f_T(94, 80)(T - 94) + f_H(94, 80)(H - 80)$$
$$\approx 127 + 4(T - 94) + 1(H - 80)$$

Thus when $T = 95$ and $H = 78$, $f(95, 78) \approx 127 + 4(95 - 94) + 1(78 - 80) = 129$, so we estimate the heat index to be approximately $129 \, ^\circ$F.

18. From the table, $f(16, 30) = 9$. To estimate $f_T(16, 30)$ and $f_v(16, 30)$ we follow the procedure used in

Section 11.3. Since $f_T(16, 30) = \lim\limits_{h \to 0} \dfrac{f(16 + h, 30) - f(16, 30)}{h}$, we approximate this quantity with $h = \pm 4$ and

use the values given in the table: $f_T(16, 30) \approx \dfrac{f(20, 30) - f(16, 30)}{4} = \dfrac{14 - 9}{4} = 1.25$,

$f_T(16, 30) \approx \dfrac{f(12, 30) - f(16, 30)}{-4} = \dfrac{3 - 9}{-4} = 1.5$.

Averaging these values gives $f_T(16, 30) \approx 1.375$. Similarly, $f_v(16, 30) = \lim\limits_{h \to 0} \dfrac{f(16, 30) - f(16, 30)}{h}$,

so we use $h = \pm 10$: $f_v(16, 30) \approx \dfrac{f(16, 40) - f(16, 30)}{10} = \dfrac{7 - 9}{10} = -0.2$,

$f_v(16, 30) \approx \dfrac{f(16, 20) - f(16, 30)}{-10} = \dfrac{11 - 9}{-10} = -0.2$. Averaging these values gives $f_v(16, 30) \approx -0.2$. The

linear approximation, then, is

$$f(T, v) \approx f(16, 30) + f_T(16, 30)(T - 16) + f_v(16, 30)(v - 30)$$
$$\approx 9 + 1.375(T - 16) - 0.2(v - 30)$$

Thus when $T = 14$ and $v = 27$, $f(14, 27) \approx 9 + 1.375(14 - 16) - 0.2(27 - 30) = 6.85$, so we estimate the wind-chill index to be approximately $6.85\,°\mathrm{C}$.

19. $u = e^t \sin \theta \;\; \Rightarrow \;\; du = \dfrac{\partial u}{\partial t}\, dt + \dfrac{\partial u}{\partial \theta}\, d\theta = e^t \sin \theta\, dt + e^t \cos \theta\, d\theta$

20. $v = y \cos xy \;\; \Rightarrow$

$dv = \dfrac{\partial v}{\partial x}\, dx + \dfrac{\partial v}{\partial y}\, dy = y(-\sin xy)y\, dx + [y(-\sin xy)x + \cos xy]\, dy = -y^2 \sin xy\, dx + (\cos xy - xy \sin xy)\, dy$

21. $w = \ln \sqrt{x^2 + y^2 + z^2} \;\; \Rightarrow$

$dw = \dfrac{\partial w}{\partial x}\, dx + \dfrac{\partial w}{\partial y}\, dy + \dfrac{\partial w}{\partial z}\, dz$

$= \left(\dfrac{1}{2}\right) \dfrac{2x\left(x^2 + y^2 + z^2\right)^{-1/2} dx + 2y\left(x^2 + y^2 + z^2\right)^{-1/2} dy + 2z\left(x^2 + y^2 + z^2\right)^{-1/2} dz}{(x^2 + y^2 + z^2)^{1/2}}$

$= \dfrac{x\, dx + y\, dy + z\, dz}{x^2 + y^2 + z^2}$

22. $u = \dfrac{r}{s + 2t} \;\; \Rightarrow$

$du = \dfrac{\partial u}{\partial r}\, dr + \dfrac{\partial u}{\partial s}\, ds + \dfrac{\partial u}{\partial t}\, dt = \dfrac{1}{s + 2t}\, dr + r(-1)(s + 2t)^{-2}\, ds + r(-1)(s + 2t)^{-2}(2)\, dt$

$= \dfrac{1}{s + 2t}\, dr - \dfrac{r}{(s + 2t)^2}\, ds - \dfrac{2r}{(s + 2t)^2}\, dt$

23. $dx = \Delta x = 0.05$, $dy = \Delta y = 0.1$, $z = 5x^2 + y^2$, $z_x = 10x$, $z_y = 2y$. Thus when $x = 1$ and $y = 2$, $dz = z_x(1, 2)\, dx + z_y(1, 2)\, dy = (10)(0.05) + (4)(0.1) = 0.9$ while $\Delta z = f(1.05, 2.1) - f(1, 2) = 5(1.05)^2 + (2.1)^2 - 5 - 4 = 0.9225$.

24. $dx = \Delta x = -0.04$, $dy = \Delta y = 0.05$, $z = x^2 - xy + 3y^2$, $z_x = 2x - y$, $z_y = 6y - x$. Thus when $x = 3$ and $y = -1$, $dz = (7)(-0.04) + (-9)(0.05) = -0.73$ while $\Delta z = (2.96)^2 - (2.96)(-0.95) + 3(-0.95)^2 - (9 + 3 + 3) = -0.7189$.

25. $dA = \dfrac{\partial A}{\partial x}\, dx + \dfrac{\partial A}{\partial y}\, dy = y\, dx + x\, dy$ and $|\Delta x| \le 0.1$, $|\Delta y| \le 0.1$. We use $dx = 0.1$, $dy = 0.1$ with $x = 30$, $y = 24$; then the maximum error in the area is about $dA = 24(0.1) + 30(0.1) = 5.4 \text{ cm}^2$.

26. Let S be surface area. Then $S = 2(xy + xz + yz)$ and $dS = 2(y + z)\, dx + 2(x + z)\, dy + 2(x + y)\, dz$. The maximum error occurs with $\Delta x = \Delta y = \Delta z = 0.2$. Using $dx = \Delta x$, $dy = \Delta y$, $dz = \Delta z$ we find the maximum error in calculated surface area to be about $dS = (220)(0.2) + (260)(0.2) + (280)(0.2) = 152 \text{ cm}^2$.

27. The volume of a can is $V = \pi r^2 h$ and $\Delta V \approx dV$ is an estimate of the amount of tin. Here

$dV = 2\pi r h\, dr + \pi r^2\, dh$, so put $dr = 0.04$, $dh = 0.08$ (0.04 on top, 0.04 on bottom) and then

$\Delta V \approx dV = 2\pi\,(48)\,(0.04) + \pi\,(16)\,(0.08) \approx 16.08\text{ cm}^3$. Thus the amount of tin is about 16 cm³.

28. Let V be the volume. Then $V = \pi r^2 h$ and $\Delta V \approx dV = 2\pi r h\, dr + \pi r^2\, dh$ is an estimate of the amount of metal.

With $dr = 0.05$ and $dh = 0.2$ we get $dV = 2\pi\,(2)\,(10)\,(0.05) + \pi\,(2)^2\,(0.2) = 2.80\pi \approx 8.8\text{ cm}^3$.

29. The area of the rectangle is $A = xy$, and $\Delta A \approx dA$ is an estimate of the area of paint in the stripe. Here

$dA = y\, dx + x\, dy$, so with $dx = dy = \frac{3+3}{12} = \frac{1}{2}$, $\Delta A \approx dA = (100)\left(\frac{1}{2}\right) + (200)\left(\frac{1}{2}\right) = 150\text{ ft}^2$. Thus there are

approximately 150 ft² of paint in the stripe.

30. Here $dV = \Delta V = 0.3$, $dT = \Delta T = -5$, $P = 8.31\dfrac{T}{V}$, so

$$dP = \left(\frac{8.31}{V}\right) dT - \frac{8.31 \cdot T}{V^2}\, dV = 8.31\left[-\frac{5}{12} - \frac{310}{144} \cdot \frac{3}{10}\right] \approx -8.83.$$

Thus the pressure will drop by about 8.83 kPa.

31. First we find $\dfrac{\partial R}{\partial R_1}$ implicitly by taking partial derivatives of both sides with respect to R_1:

$$\frac{\partial}{\partial R_1}\left[\frac{1}{R}\right] = \frac{\partial\,[(1/R_1) + (1/R_2) + (1/R_3)]}{\partial R_1} \;\Rightarrow\; -R^{-2}\frac{\partial R}{\partial R_1} = -R_1^{-2} \;\Rightarrow\; \frac{\partial R}{\partial R_1} = \frac{R^2}{R_1^2}.\; \text{Then by}$$

symmetry, $\dfrac{\partial R}{\partial R_2} = \dfrac{R^2}{R_2^2}$, $\dfrac{\partial R}{\partial R_3} = \dfrac{R^2}{R_3^2}$. When $R_1 = 25$, $R_2 = 40$ and $R_3 = 50$, $\dfrac{1}{R} = \dfrac{17}{200} \;\Leftrightarrow\; R = \dfrac{200}{17}$ ohms.

Since the possible error for each R_i is 0.5%, the maximum error of R is attained by setting $\Delta R_i = 0.005 R_i$. So

$$\Delta R \approx dR = \frac{\partial R}{\partial R_1}\Delta R_1 + \frac{\partial R}{\partial R_2}\Delta R_2 + \frac{\partial R}{\partial R_3}\Delta R_3 = (0.005)\,R^2\left[\frac{1}{R_1} + \frac{1}{R_2} + \frac{1}{R_3}\right]$$

$$= (0.005)R = \frac{1}{17} \approx 0.059\text{ ohms}$$

32. Let x, y, z and w be the four numbers with $p(x, y, z, w) = xyzw$. Since the largest error due to rounding for each number is 0.05, the maximum error in the calculated product is approximated by

$dp = (yzw)(0.05) + (xzw)(0.05) + (xyw)(0.05) + (xyz)(0.05)$. Furthermore, each of the numbers is positive but less than 50, so the product of any three is between 0 and $(50)^3$. Thus $dp \leq 4(50)^3(0.05) = 25{,}000$.

33. $\mathbf{r}(u, v) = (u + v)\,\mathbf{i} + 3u^2\,\mathbf{j} + (u - v)\,\mathbf{k}$

$\mathbf{r}_u = \mathbf{i} + 6u\,\mathbf{j} + \mathbf{k}$ and $\mathbf{r}_v = \mathbf{i} - \mathbf{k}$, so

$\mathbf{r}_u \times \mathbf{r}_v = -6u\,\mathbf{i} + 2\,\mathbf{j} - 6u\,\mathbf{k}$. Since the point $(2, 3, 0)$

corresponds to $u = 1$, $v = 1$, a normal vector to the surface at

$(2, 3, 0)$ is $-6\,\mathbf{i} + 2\,\mathbf{j} - 6\,\mathbf{k}$, and an equation of the tangent plane is

$-6x + 2y - 6z = -6$ or $3x - y + 3z = 3$.

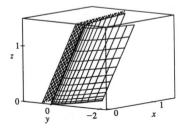

34. $(u, v) = \langle u^2, u - v^2, v^2 \rangle$

$\mathbf{r}_u = \langle 2u, 1, 0 \rangle$ and $\mathbf{r}_v = \langle 0, -2v, 2v \rangle$, so

$\mathbf{r}_u \times \mathbf{r}_v = \langle 2v, -4uv, -4uv \rangle$. The point $(1, 0, 1)$ corresponds to

$u = 1$, $v = \pm 1$. So a normal vector to the surface at $(1, 0, 1)$ is

$\pm\langle 2, -4, -4 \rangle$ and an equation of the tangent plane is

$2x - 4y - 4z = -2$ or $x - 2y - 2z + 1 = 0$.

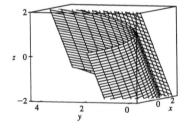

35. $\mathbf{r}(u, v) = uv\,\mathbf{i} + ue^v\,\mathbf{j} + ve^u\,\mathbf{k}$

$\mathbf{r}_u = \langle v, e^v, ve^u \rangle$, $\mathbf{r}_v = \langle u, ue^v, e^u \rangle$, and

$\mathbf{r}_u \times \mathbf{r}_v = e^{u+v}(1 - uv)\,\mathbf{i} + e^u S\,(uv - v)\,\mathbf{j} + e^v\,(uv - u)\,\mathbf{k}$.

The point $(0, 0, 0)$ corresponds to $u = 0$, $v = 0$. Thus a normal
vector to the surface at $(0, 0, 0)$ is $\mathbf{i}$, and an equation of the
tangent plane is $x = 0$.

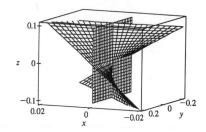

36. $\mathbf{r}(u, v) = (u + v)\,\mathbf{i} + u\cos v\,\mathbf{j} + v\sin u\,\mathbf{k}$

$\mathbf{r}_u = \langle 1, \cos v, v\cos u \rangle$, $\mathbf{r}_v = \langle 1, -u\sin v, \sin u \rangle$, and

$\mathbf{r}_u \times \mathbf{r}_v = \langle \cos v\sin u + uv\cos u\sin v,$

$v\cos u - \sin u, -u\sin v - \cos v \rangle$

The point $(1, 1, 0)$ corresponds to $u = 1$, $v = 0$. Thus a normal
vector to the surface at $(1, 1, 0)$ is $\langle \sin 1, -\sin 1, -1 \rangle$, and an
equation of the tangent plane is $(\sin 1)x - (\sin 1)y - z = 0$.

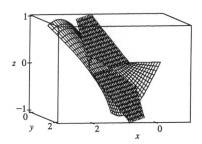

37. $\Delta z = f(a + \Delta x, b + \Delta y) - f(a, b) = (a + \Delta x)^2 + (b + \Delta y)^2 - (a^2 + b^2)$

$= a^2 + 2a\,\Delta x + (\Delta x)^2 + b^2 + 2b\,\Delta y + (\Delta y)^2 - a^2 - b^2 = 2a\,\Delta x + (\Delta x)^2 + 2b\,\Delta y + (\Delta y)^2$

But $f_x(a, b) = 2a$ and $f_y(a, b) = 2b$ and so $\Delta z = f_x(a, b)\,\Delta x + f_y(a, b)\,\Delta y + \Delta x\,\Delta x + \Delta y\,\Delta y$, which is
Definition 7 with $\epsilon_1 = \Delta x$ and $\epsilon_2 = \Delta y$. Hence f is differentiable.

38. $\Delta z = f(a + \Delta x, b + \Delta y) - f(a, b) = (a + \Delta x)(b + \Delta y) - 5(b + \Delta y)^2 - (ab - 5b^2)$

$= ab + a\,\Delta y + b\,\Delta x + \Delta x\,\Delta y - 5b^2 - 10b\,\Delta y - 5\,(\Delta y)^2 - ab + 5b^2$

$= (a - 10b)\,\Delta y + b\,\Delta x + \Delta x\,\Delta y - 5\,\Delta y\,\Delta y,$

but $f_x(a, b) = b$ and $f_y(a, b) = a - 10b$ and so $\Delta z = f_x(a, b)\,\Delta x + f_y(a, b)\,\Delta y + \Delta x\,\Delta y - 5\Delta y\,\Delta y$, which is
Definition 7 with $\epsilon_1 = \Delta y$ and $\epsilon_2 = -5\,\Delta y$. Hence f is differentiable.

39. To show that f is continuous at (a, b) we need to show that $\displaystyle\lim_{(x,y)\to(a,b)} f(x, y) = f(a, b)$ or equivalently

$\displaystyle\lim_{(\Delta x, \Delta y)\to(0,0)} f(a + \Delta x, b + \Delta y) = f(a, b)$. Since f is differentiable at (a, b),

$f(a + \Delta x, b + \Delta y) - f(a, b) = \Delta z = f_x(a, b)\,\Delta x + f_y(a, b)\,\Delta y + \epsilon_1\,\Delta x + \epsilon_2\,\Delta y$, where ϵ_1 and $\epsilon_2 \to 0$ as
$(\Delta x, \Delta y) \to (0, 0)$. Thus $f(a + \Delta x, b + \Delta y) = f(a, b) + f_x(a, b)\,\Delta x + f_y(a, b)\,\Delta y + \epsilon_1\,\Delta x + \epsilon_2\,\Delta y$. Taking
the limit of both sides as $(\Delta x, \Delta y) \to (0, 0)$ gives $\displaystyle\lim_{(\Delta x, \Delta y)\to(0,0)} f(a + \Delta x, b + \Delta y) = f(a, b)$. Thus f is

continuous at (a, b).

40. (a) $\displaystyle\lim_{h\to 0} \frac{f(h, 0) - f(0, 0)}{h} = \lim_{h\to 0}\frac{0 - 0}{h} = 0$ and $\displaystyle\lim_{h\to 0}\frac{f(0, h) - f(0, 0)}{h} = \lim_{h\to 0}\frac{0 - 0}{h} = 0$. Thus

$f_x(0, 0) = f_y(0, 0) = 0$. To show that f isn't differentiable at $(0, 0)$ we need only show that f is not continuous
at $(0, 0)$ and apply Exercise 39. As $(x, y) \to (0, 0)$ along the x-axis $f(x, y) = 0/x^2 = 0$ for $x \neq 0$ so
$f(x, y) \to 0$ as $(x, y) \to (0, 0)$ along the x-axis. But as $(x, y) \to (0, 0)$ along the line $y = x$,
$f(x, x) = x^2/(2x^2) = \frac{1}{2}$ for $x \neq 0$ so $f(x, y) \to \frac{1}{2}$ as $(x, y) \to (0, 0)$ along this line. Thus $\displaystyle\lim_{(x,y)\to(0,0)} f(x, y)$

doesn't exist, so f is discontinuous at $(0, 0)$ and thus not differentiable there.

(b) For $(x, y) \neq (0, 0)$, $f_x(x, y) = \dfrac{(x^2 + y^2)\, sy - xy(2x)}{(x^2 + y^2)^2} = \dfrac{y(y^2 - x^2)}{(x^2 + y^2)^2}$. If we approach $(0, 0)$ along the

y-axis, then $f_x(x, y) = f_x(0, y) = \dfrac{y^3}{y^4} = \dfrac{1}{y}$, so $f_x(x, y) \to \pm\infty$ as $(x, y) \to (0, 0)$. Thus

$\lim\limits_{(x,y) \to (0,0)} f_x(x, y)$ does not exist and $f_x(x, y)$ is not continuous at $(0, 0)$. Similarly,

$f_y(x, y) = \dfrac{(x^2 + y^2)x - xy(2y)}{(x^2 + y^2)^2} = \dfrac{x(x^2 - y^2)}{(x^2 + y^2)^2}$ for $(x, y) \neq (0, 0)$, and if we approach $(0, 0)$ along the

x-axis, then $f_y(x, y) = f_x(x, 0) = \dfrac{x^3}{x^4} = \dfrac{1}{x}$. Thus $\lim\limits_{(x,y) \to (0,0)} f_y(x, y)$ does not exist and $f_y(x, y)$ is not

continuous at $(0, 0)$.

◆11.5 The Chain Rule · · · · · · · · · · · · ·

1. $z = \sin x \cos y$, $x = \pi t$, $y = \sqrt{t}$ $\Rightarrow$

$\dfrac{dz}{dt} = \dfrac{\partial z}{\partial x}\dfrac{dx}{dt} + \dfrac{\partial z}{\partial y}\dfrac{dy}{dt} = \cos x \cos y \cdot \pi + \sin x \,(-\sin y) \cdot \tfrac{1}{2}t^{-1/2} = \pi \cos x \cos y - \dfrac{1}{2\sqrt{t}} \sin x \sin y$

2. $z = x \ln(x + 2y)$, $x = \sin t$, $y = \cos t$ $\Rightarrow$

$\dfrac{dz}{dt} = \dfrac{\partial z}{\partial x}\dfrac{dx}{dt} + \dfrac{\partial z}{\partial y}\dfrac{dy}{dt} = \left[x \cdot \dfrac{1}{x + 2y} + 1 \cdot \ln(x + 2y) \right] \cos t + x \cdot \dfrac{1}{x + 2y}\, (2) \cdot (-\sin t)$

$= \left[\dfrac{x}{x + 2y} + \ln(x + 2y) \right] \cos t - \dfrac{2x}{x + 2y}\, (\sin t)$

3. $w = xe^{y/z}$, $x = t^2$, $y = 1 - t$, $z = 1 + 2t$ $\Rightarrow$

$\dfrac{dw}{dt} = \dfrac{\partial w}{\partial x}\dfrac{dx}{dt} + \dfrac{\partial w}{\partial y}\dfrac{dy}{dt} + \dfrac{\partial w}{\partial z}\dfrac{dz}{dt} = e^{y/z} \cdot 2t + xe^{y/z}\left(\dfrac{1}{z}\right) \cdot (-1) + xe^{y/z}\left(-\dfrac{y}{z^2}\right) \cdot 2 = e^{y/z}\left(2t - \dfrac{x}{z} - \dfrac{2xy}{z^2}\right)$

4. $w = xy + yz^2$, $x = e^t$, $y = e^t \sin t$, $z = e^t \cos t$ $\Rightarrow$

$\dfrac{dw}{dt} = \dfrac{\partial w}{\partial x}\dfrac{dx}{dt} + \dfrac{\partial w}{\partial y}\dfrac{dy}{dt} + \dfrac{\partial w}{\partial z}\dfrac{dz}{dt} = y \cdot e^t + (x + z^2) \cdot (e^t \cos t + e^t \sin t) + 2yz \cdot (-e^t \sin t + e^t \cos t)$

$= e^t \left[y + (x + z^2)(\cos t + \sin t) + 2yz(\cos t - \sin t) \right]$

5. $z = x^2 + xy + y^2$, $x = s + t$, $y = st$ $\Rightarrow$

$\dfrac{\partial z}{\partial s} = \dfrac{\partial z}{\partial x}\dfrac{\partial x}{\partial s} + \dfrac{\partial z}{\partial y}\dfrac{\partial y}{\partial s} = (2x + y)(1) + (x + 2y)(t) = 2x + y + xt + 2yt$

$\dfrac{\partial z}{\partial t} = \dfrac{\partial z}{\partial x}\dfrac{\partial x}{\partial t} + \dfrac{\partial z}{\partial y}\dfrac{\partial y}{\partial t} = (2x + y)(1) + (x + 2y)(s) = 2x + y + xs + 2ys$

6. $z = \dfrac{x}{y}$, $x = se^t$, $y = 1 + se^{-t}$ $\Rightarrow$

$\dfrac{\partial z}{\partial s} = \dfrac{\partial z}{\partial x}\dfrac{\partial x}{\partial s} + \dfrac{\partial z}{\partial y}\dfrac{\partial y}{\partial s} = \dfrac{1}{y}\,(e^t) + \left(-\dfrac{x}{y^2}\right)(e^{-t}) = \dfrac{1}{y}e^t - \dfrac{x}{y^2}e^{-t}$

$\dfrac{\partial z}{\partial t} = \dfrac{\partial z}{\partial x}\dfrac{\partial x}{\partial t} + \dfrac{\partial z}{\partial y}\dfrac{\partial y}{\partial t} = \dfrac{1}{y}\,(se^t) + \left(-\dfrac{x}{y^2}\right)(-se^{-t}) = \dfrac{s}{y}e^t + \dfrac{xs}{y^2}e^{-t}$

7. $z = e^r \cos\theta$, $r = st$, $\theta = \sqrt{s^2 + t^2}$ $\Rightarrow$

$$\frac{\partial z}{\partial s} = \frac{\partial z}{\partial r}\frac{\partial r}{\partial s} + \frac{\partial z}{\partial \theta}\frac{\partial \theta}{\partial s} = e^r \cos\theta \cdot t + e^r(-\sin\theta) \cdot \tfrac{1}{2}(s^2+t^2)^{-1/2}(2s)$$

$$= te^r \cos\theta - e^r \sin\theta \cdot \frac{s}{\sqrt{s^2+t^2}} = e^r\left(t\cos\theta - \frac{s}{\sqrt{s^2+t^2}}\sin\theta\right)$$

$$\frac{\partial z}{\partial t} = \frac{\partial z}{\partial r}\frac{\partial r}{\partial t} + \frac{\partial z}{\partial \theta}\frac{\partial \theta}{\partial t} = e^r\cos\theta \cdot s + e^r(-\sin\theta) \cdot \tfrac{1}{2}(s^2+t^2)^{-1/2}(2t)$$

$$= se^r\cos\theta - e^r\sin\theta \cdot \frac{t}{\sqrt{s^2+t^2}} = e^r\left(s\cos\theta - \frac{t}{\sqrt{s^2+t^2}}\sin\theta\right)$$

8. $z = \sin\alpha \tan\beta$, $\alpha = 3s+t$, $\beta = s-t$ $\Rightarrow$

$$\frac{\partial z}{\partial s} = \frac{\partial z}{\partial \alpha}\frac{\partial \alpha}{\partial s} + \frac{\partial z}{\partial \beta}\frac{\partial \beta}{\partial s} = \cos\alpha\tan\beta \cdot 3 + \sin\alpha\sec^2\beta \cdot 1 = 3\cos\alpha\tan\beta + \sin\alpha\sec^2\beta$$

$$\frac{\partial z}{\partial t} = \frac{\partial z}{\partial \alpha}\frac{\partial \alpha}{\partial t} + \frac{\partial z}{\partial \beta}\frac{\partial \beta}{\partial t} = \cos\alpha\tan\beta \cdot 1 + \sin\alpha\sec^2\beta \cdot (-1) = \cos\alpha\tan\beta - \sin\alpha\sec^2\beta$$

9. When $t = 3$, $x = g(3) = 2$ and $y = h(3) = 7$. By the Chain Rule (2),

$$\frac{dz}{dt} = \frac{\partial f}{\partial x}\frac{dx}{dt} + \frac{\partial f}{\partial y}\frac{dy}{dt} = f_x(2,7)g'(3) + f_y(2,7)h'(3) = (6)(5) + (-8)(-4) = 62.$$

10. By the Chain Rule (3), $\dfrac{\partial W}{\partial s} = \dfrac{\partial W}{\partial u}\dfrac{\partial u}{\partial s} + \dfrac{\partial W}{\partial v}\dfrac{\partial v}{\partial s}$. Then

$$W_s(1,0) = F_u\left(u(1,0), v(1,0)\right)u_s(1,0) + F_v\left(u(1,0), v(1,0)\right)v_s(1,0)$$
$$= F_u(2,3)u_s(1,0) + F_v(2,3)v_s(1,0) = (-1)(-2) + (10)(5) = 52$$

Similarly, $\dfrac{\partial W}{\partial t} = \dfrac{\partial W}{\partial u}\dfrac{\partial u}{\partial t} + \dfrac{\partial W}{\partial v}\dfrac{\partial v}{\partial t}$ $\Rightarrow$

$$W_t(1,0) = F_u\left(u(1,0), v(1,0)\right)u_t(1,0) + F_v\left(u(1,0), v(1,0)\right)v_t(1,0)$$
$$= F_u(2,3)u_t(1,0) + F_v(2,3)v_t(1,0) = (-1)(6) + (10)(4) = 34$$

11.

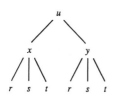

$u = f(x,y)$, $x = x(r,s,t)$, $y = y(r,s,t)$ $\Rightarrow$

$$\frac{\partial u}{\partial r} = \frac{\partial u}{\partial x}\frac{\partial x}{\partial r} + \frac{\partial u}{\partial y}\frac{\partial y}{\partial r}, \quad \frac{\partial u}{\partial s} = \frac{\partial u}{\partial x}\frac{\partial x}{\partial s} + \frac{\partial u}{\partial y}\frac{\partial y}{\partial s},$$

$$\frac{\partial u}{\partial t} = \frac{\partial u}{\partial x}\frac{\partial x}{\partial t} + \frac{\partial u}{\partial y}\frac{\partial y}{\partial t}$$

12.

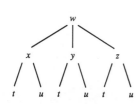

$w = f(x,y,z)$, $x = x(t,u)$, $y = y(t,u)$, $z = z(t,u)$ $\Rightarrow$

$$\frac{\partial w}{\partial t} = \frac{\partial w}{\partial x}\frac{\partial x}{\partial t} + \frac{\partial w}{\partial y}\frac{\partial y}{\partial t} + \frac{\partial w}{\partial z}\frac{\partial z}{\partial t},$$

$$\frac{\partial w}{\partial u} = \frac{\partial w}{\partial x}\frac{\partial x}{\partial u} + \frac{\partial w}{\partial y}\frac{\partial y}{\partial u} + \frac{\partial w}{\partial z}\frac{\partial z}{\partial u}$$

13.

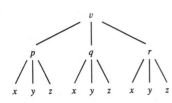

$$v = f(p, q, r), p = p(x, y, z), q = q(x, y, z), r = r(x, y, z) \Rightarrow$$
$$\frac{\partial v}{\partial x} = \frac{\partial v}{\partial p}\frac{\partial p}{\partial x} + \frac{\partial v}{\partial q}\frac{\partial q}{\partial x} + \frac{\partial v}{\partial r}\frac{\partial r}{\partial x}, \frac{\partial v}{\partial y} = \frac{\partial v}{\partial p}\frac{\partial p}{\partial y} + \frac{\partial v}{\partial q}\frac{\partial q}{\partial y} + \frac{\partial v}{\partial r}\frac{\partial r}{\partial y},$$
$$\frac{\partial v}{\partial z} = \frac{\partial v}{\partial p}\frac{\partial p}{\partial z} + \frac{\partial v}{\partial q}\frac{\partial q}{\partial z} + \frac{\partial v}{\partial r}\frac{\partial r}{\partial z}$$

14.

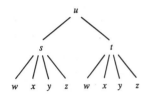

$$u = f(s, t), s = s(w, x, y, z), t = t(w, x, y, z) \Rightarrow$$
$$\frac{\partial u}{\partial w} = \frac{\partial u}{\partial s}\frac{\partial s}{\partial w} + \frac{\partial u}{\partial t}\frac{\partial t}{\partial w}, \frac{\partial u}{\partial x} = \frac{\partial u}{\partial s}\frac{\partial s}{\partial x} + \frac{\partial u}{\partial t}\frac{\partial t}{\partial x},$$
$$\frac{\partial u}{\partial y} = \frac{\partial u}{\partial s}\frac{\partial s}{\partial y} + \frac{\partial u}{\partial t}\frac{\partial t}{\partial y}, \frac{\partial u}{\partial z} = \frac{\partial u}{\partial s}\frac{\partial s}{\partial z} + \frac{\partial u}{\partial t}\frac{\partial t}{\partial z}$$

15. $w = x^2 + y^2 + z^2$, $x = st$, $y = s\cos t$, $z = s\sin t$ $\Rightarrow$
$$\frac{\partial w}{\partial s} = \frac{\partial w}{\partial x}\frac{\partial x}{\partial s} + \frac{\partial w}{\partial y}\frac{\partial y}{\partial s} + \frac{\partial w}{\partial z}\frac{\partial z}{\partial s} = 2xt + 2y\cos t + 2z\sin t.$$ When $s = 1$, $t = 0$, we have $x = 0$, $y = 1$ and
$z = 0$, so $\partial w/\partial s = 2\cos 0 = 2$. Similarly $\partial w/\partial t = 2xs + 2y(-s\sin t) + 2z(s\cos t) = 0 + (-2)\sin 0 + 0 = 0$
when $s = 1$ and $t = 0$.

16. $u = xy + yz + zx$, $x = st$, $y = e^{st}$, $z = t^2$ $\Rightarrow$
$\partial u/\partial s = (y + z)t + (x + z)ste^{st} + (x + y)s(0)$ and $\partial u/\partial t = (y + z)s + (x + z)se^{st} + (x + y)(2t)$. When
$s = 0$, $t = 1$, we have $x = 0$, $y = 1$, $z = 1$, so $\partial u/\partial s = 2 + 1 + 0 = 3$ and $\partial u/\partial t = 0 + 0 + (1)(2) = 2$.

17. $z = y^2\tan x$, $x = t^2uv$, $y = u + tv^2$ $\Rightarrow$
$\partial z/\partial t = (y^2\sec^2 x)\,2tuv + (2y\tan x)\,v^2$, $\partial z/\partial u = (y^2\sec^2 x)\,t^2v + 2y\tan x$,
$\partial z/\partial v = (y^2\sec^2 x)\,t^2u + (2y\tan x)\,2tv$. When $t = 2$, $u = 1$ and $v = 0$, we have $x = 0$, $y = 1$, so $\partial z/\partial t = 0$,
$\partial z/\partial u = 0$, $\partial z/\partial v = 4$.

18. $z = \dfrac{x}{y}$, $x = re^{st}$, $y = rse^{t}$ $\Rightarrow$
$$\frac{\partial z}{\partial r} = \frac{1}{y}e^{st} + \frac{-x}{y^2}se^t, \frac{\partial z}{\partial s} = \frac{1}{y}rte^{st} - \frac{x}{y^2}re^t, \frac{\partial z}{\partial t} = \frac{1}{y}rse^{st} - \frac{x}{y^2}rse^t.$$ When $r = 1$, $s = 2$ and $t = 0$, we
have $x = 1$, $y = 2$, so $\partial z/\partial r = \frac{1}{2} + \frac{-1}{4}\cdot 2 = 0$, $\partial z/\partial s = 0 - \frac{1}{4} = -\frac{1}{4}$ and $\partial z/\partial t = \frac{1}{2}\cdot 2 - \frac{1}{4}\cdot 2 = \frac{1}{2}$.

19. $u = \dfrac{x + y}{y + z}$, $x = p + r + t$, $y = p - r + t$, $z = p + r - t$ $\Rightarrow$
$$\frac{\partial u}{\partial p} = \frac{1}{y + z} + \frac{(y + z) - (x + y)}{(y + z)^2} - \frac{x + y}{(y + z)^2} = \frac{(y + z) + (z - x) - (x + y)}{(y + z)^2} = 2\frac{z - x}{(y + z)^2}$$
$$= 2\frac{-2t}{4p^2} = -\frac{t}{p^2},$$
$$\frac{\partial u}{\partial r} = \frac{1}{y + z} + \frac{z - x}{(y + z)^2}(-1) - \frac{x + y}{(y + z)^2} = 0, \text{ and}$$
$$\frac{\partial u}{\partial t} = \frac{1}{y + z} + \frac{z - x}{(y + z)^2} + \frac{x + y}{(y + z)^2} = 2\frac{y + z}{(y + z)^2} = \frac{2}{2p} = \frac{1}{p}.$$

20. $y^5 + x^2y^3 = 1 + ye^{x^2}$, so let $F(x, y) = y^5 + x^2y^3 - 1 - ye^{x^2} = 0$. Then
$$\frac{dy}{dx} = -\frac{F_x}{F_y} = -\frac{2xy^3 - 2xye^{x^2}}{5y^4 + 3x^2y^2 - e^{x^2}} = \frac{2xye^{x^2} - 2xy^3}{5y^4 + 3x^2y^2 - e^{x^2}}.$$

21. $\cos(x - y) = xe^y$, so let $F(x, y) = \cos(x - y) - xe^y = 0$.

Then $\dfrac{dy}{dx} = -\dfrac{F_x}{F_y} = -\dfrac{-\sin(x-y) - e^y}{-\sin(x-y)(-1) - xe^y} = \dfrac{\sin(x-y) + e^y}{\sin(x-y) - xe^y}$.

22. $\sin x + \cos y = \sin x \cos y$, so let $F(x, y) = \sin x + \cos y - \sin x \cos y = 0$. Then

$\dfrac{dy}{dx} = -\dfrac{F_x}{F_y} = -\dfrac{\cos x - \cos x \cos y}{-\sin y + \sin x \sin y} = \dfrac{\cos x(\cos y - 1)}{\sin y(\sin x - 1)}$.

23. $xy^2 + yz^2 + zx^2 = 3$, so let $F(x, y) = xy^2 + yz^2 + zx^2 - 3 = 0$.

Then $\dfrac{\partial z}{\partial x} = -\dfrac{F_x}{F_z} = -\dfrac{y^2 + 2zx}{2yz + x^2}$ and $\dfrac{\partial z}{\partial y} = -\dfrac{F_y}{F_z} = -\dfrac{2xy + z^2}{2yz + x^2}$.

24. $xyz = \cos(x + y + z)$. Let $F(x, y, z) = xyz - \cos(x + y + z) = 0$, so

$\dfrac{\partial z}{\partial x} = -\dfrac{F_x}{F_z} = -\dfrac{yz + \sin(x+y+z)}{xy + \sin(x+y+z)}$, $\dfrac{\partial z}{\partial y} = -\dfrac{F_y}{F_z} = -\dfrac{xz + \sin(x+y+z)}{xy + \sin(x+y+z)}$.

25. Let $F(x, y, z) = xe^y + yz + ze^x = 0$. Then $\dfrac{\partial z}{\partial x} = -\dfrac{F_x}{F_z} = -\dfrac{e^y + ze^x}{y + e^x}$, $\dfrac{\partial z}{\partial y} = -\dfrac{F_y}{F_z} = -\dfrac{xe^y + z}{y + e^x}$.

26. $\ln(x + yz) = 1 + xy^2z^3$, so let $F(x, y) = \ln(x + yz) - 1 - xy^2z^3 = 0$. Then

$$\dfrac{\partial z}{\partial x} = -\dfrac{F_x}{F_z} = -\dfrac{1/(x+yz) - y^2z^3}{y/(x+yz) - 3xy^2z^2} = \dfrac{y^2z^3(x+yz) - 1}{y - 3xy^2z^2(x+yz)}$$

$$\dfrac{\partial z}{\partial y} = -\dfrac{F_y}{F_z} = -\dfrac{z/(x+yz) - 2xyz^3}{y/(x+yz) - 3xy^2z^2} = \dfrac{2xyz^3(x+yz) - z}{y - 3xy^2z^2(x+yz)}$$

27. Since x and y are each functions of t, $T(x, y)$ is a function of t, so by the Chain Rule, $\dfrac{dT}{dt} = \dfrac{\partial T}{\partial x}\dfrac{dx}{dt} + \dfrac{\partial T}{\partial y}\dfrac{dy}{dt}$.

After 3 seconds, $x = \sqrt{1+t} = \sqrt{1+3} = 2$, $y = 2 + \frac{1}{3}t = 2 + \frac{1}{3}(3) = 3$, $\dfrac{dx}{dt} = \dfrac{1}{2\sqrt{1+t}} = \dfrac{1}{2\sqrt{1+3}} = \dfrac{1}{4}$,

and $\dfrac{dy}{dt} = \dfrac{1}{3}$. Then $\dfrac{dT}{dt} = T_x(2, 3)\dfrac{dx}{dt} + T_y(2, 3)\dfrac{dy}{dt} = 4\left(\frac{1}{4}\right) + 3\left(\frac{1}{3}\right) = 2$. Thus the temperature is rising at a rate of $2\,°C/s$.

28. (a) Since $\partial W/\partial T$ is negative, a rise in average temperature (while annual rainfall remains constant) causes a decrease in wheat production at the current production levels. Since $\partial W/\partial R$ is positive, an increase in annual rainfall (while the average temperature remains constant) causes an increase in wheat production.

(b) Since the average temperature is rising at a rate of $0.15\,°C/\text{year}$, we know that $dT/dt = 0.15$. Since rainfall is decreasing at a rate of $0.1\,\text{cm/year}$, we know $dR/dt = -0.1$. Then, by the Chain Rule,

$\dfrac{dW}{dt} = \dfrac{\partial W}{\partial T}\dfrac{dT}{dt} + \dfrac{\partial W}{\partial R}\dfrac{dR}{dt} = (-2)(0.15) + (8)(-0.1) = -1.1$. Thus we estimate that wheat production will

decrease at a rate of 1.1 units/year.

29. $C = 1449.2 + 4.6T - 0.055T^2 + 0.00029T^3 + 0.016D$, so $\dfrac{\partial C}{\partial T} = 4.6 - 0.11T + 0.00087T^2$ and

$\dfrac{\partial C}{\partial D} = 0.016$. According to the graph, the diver is experiencing a temperature of approximately $12.5\,°C$ at

$t = 20$ minutes, so $\dfrac{\partial C}{\partial T} = 4.6 - 0.11(12.5) + 0.00087(12.5)^2 \approx 3.36$. By sketching tangent lines at $t = 20$ to the

graphs given, we estimate $\dfrac{dD}{dt} \approx \dfrac{1}{2}$ and $\dfrac{dT}{dt} \approx -\dfrac{1}{10}$. Then, by the Chain Rule,

$\dfrac{dC}{dt} = \dfrac{\partial C}{\partial T}\dfrac{dT}{dt} + \dfrac{\partial C}{\partial D}\dfrac{dD}{dt} \approx (3.36)\left(-\frac{1}{10}\right) + (0.016)\left(\frac{1}{2}\right) \approx -0.33$. Thus the speed of sound experienced by the

diver is decreasing at a rate of approximately 0.33 m/s per minute.

30. $V = \pi r^2 h/3$, so $\dfrac{dV}{dt} = \dfrac{\partial V}{\partial r}\dfrac{dr}{dt} + \dfrac{\partial V}{\partial h}\dfrac{dh}{dt} = \dfrac{2\pi r h}{3}\,1.8 + \dfrac{\pi r^2}{3}(-2.5) = 20{,}160\pi - 12{,}000\pi = 8160\pi \text{ in}^3/\text{s}.$

31. (a) $V = \ell w h$, so by the Chain Rule,

$$\frac{dV}{dt} = \frac{\partial V}{\partial \ell}\frac{d\ell}{dt} + \frac{\partial V}{\partial w}\frac{dw}{dt} + \frac{\partial V}{\partial h}\frac{dh}{dt} = wh\frac{d\ell}{dt} + \ell h\frac{dw}{dt} + \ell w\frac{dh}{dt}$$

$$= 2 \cdot 2 \cdot 2 + 1 \cdot 2 \cdot 2 + 1 \cdot 2 \cdot (-3) = 6 \text{ m}^3/\text{s}$$

(b) $S = 2(\ell w + \ell h + wh)$, so by the Chain Rule,

$$\frac{dS}{dt} = \frac{\partial S}{\partial \ell}\frac{d\ell}{dt} + \frac{\partial S}{\partial w}\frac{dw}{dt} + \frac{\partial S}{\partial h}\frac{dh}{dt} = 2(w + h)\frac{d\ell}{dt} + 2(\ell + h)\frac{dw}{dt} + 2(\ell + w)\frac{dh}{dt}$$

$$= 2(2 + 2)2 + 2(1 + 2)2 + 2(1 + 2)(-3) = 10 \text{ m}^2/\text{s}$$

(c) $L^2 = \ell^2 + w^2 + h^2 \;\Rightarrow\; 2L\dfrac{dL}{dt} = 2\ell\dfrac{d\ell}{dt} + 2w\dfrac{dw}{dt} + 2h\dfrac{dh}{dt} = 2(1)(2) + 2(2)(2) + 2(2)(-3) = 0 \;\Rightarrow$

$dL/dt = 0$ m/s.

32. $I = \dfrac{V}{R} \;\Rightarrow\; \dfrac{dI}{dt} = \dfrac{\partial I}{\partial V}\dfrac{dV}{dt} + \dfrac{\partial I}{\partial R}\dfrac{dR}{dt} = \dfrac{1}{R}\dfrac{dV}{dt} - \dfrac{V}{R^2}\dfrac{dR}{dt} = \dfrac{1}{R}\dfrac{dV}{dt} - \dfrac{I}{R}\dfrac{dR}{dt}$

$= \frac{1}{400}(-0.01) - \frac{0.08}{400}(0.03) = -0.000031$ A/s

33. $\dfrac{dP}{dt} = 0.05$, $\dfrac{dT}{dt} = 0.15$, $V = 8.31\dfrac{T}{P}$ and $\dfrac{dV}{dt} = \dfrac{8.31}{P}\dfrac{dT}{dt} - 8.31\dfrac{T}{P^2}\dfrac{dP}{dt}$. Thus when $P = 20$ and $T = 320$,

$\dfrac{dV}{dt} = 8.31\left[\dfrac{0.15}{20} - \dfrac{(0.05)(320)}{400}\right] \approx -0.27$ L/s.

34. Let x and y be the respective distances of car A and car B from the intersection and let z be the distance between the two cars. Then $dx/dt = -90$, $dy/dt = -80$ and $z^2 = x^2 + y^2$. When $x = 0.3$ and $y = 0.4$, $z = \sqrt{0.25} = 0.5$ and $2z\,(dz/dt) = 2x\,(dx/dt) + 2y\,(dy/dt)$ or $dz/dt = 0.6(-90) + 0.8(-80) = -118$ km/h.

35. (a) By the Chain Rule, $\dfrac{\partial z}{\partial r} = \dfrac{\partial z}{\partial x}\cos\theta + \dfrac{\partial z}{\partial y}\sin\theta$, $\dfrac{\partial z}{\partial \theta} = \dfrac{\partial z}{\partial x}(-r\sin\theta) + \dfrac{\partial z}{\partial y}r\cos\theta$.

(b) $\left(\dfrac{\partial z}{\partial r}\right)^2 = \left(\dfrac{\partial z}{\partial x}\right)^2 \cos^2\theta + 2\dfrac{\partial z}{\partial x}\dfrac{\partial z}{\partial y}\cos\theta\sin\theta + \left(\dfrac{\partial z}{\partial y}\right)^2 \sin^2\theta,$

$\left(\dfrac{\partial z}{\partial \theta}\right)^2 = \left(\dfrac{\partial z}{\partial x}\right)^2 r^2\sin^2\theta - 2\dfrac{\partial z}{\partial x}\dfrac{\partial z}{\partial y}r^2\cos\theta\sin\theta + \left(\dfrac{\partial z}{\partial y}\right)^2 r^2\cos^2\theta.$ Thus

$\left(\dfrac{\partial z}{\partial r}\right)^2 + \dfrac{1}{r^2}\left(\dfrac{\partial z}{\partial \theta}\right)^2 = \left[\left(\dfrac{\partial z}{\partial x}\right)^2 + \left(\dfrac{\partial z}{\partial y}\right)^2\right](\cos^2\theta + \sin^2\theta) = \left(\dfrac{\partial z}{\partial x}\right)^2 + \left(\dfrac{\partial z}{\partial y}\right)^2.$

36. By the Chain Rule, $\dfrac{\partial u}{\partial s} = \dfrac{\partial u}{\partial x}e^s\cos t + \dfrac{\partial u}{\partial y}e^s\sin t$, $\dfrac{\partial u}{\partial t} = \dfrac{\partial u}{\partial x}(-e^s\sin t) + \dfrac{\partial u}{\partial y}e^s\cos t$. Then

$\left(\dfrac{\partial u}{\partial s}\right)^2 = \left(\dfrac{\partial u}{\partial x}\right)^2 e^{2s}\cos^2 t + 2\dfrac{\partial u}{\partial x}\dfrac{\partial u}{\partial y}e^{2s}\cos t\sin t + \left(\dfrac{\partial u}{\partial y}\right)^2 e^{2t}\sin^2 t$ and

$\left(\dfrac{\partial u}{\partial t}\right)^2 = \left(\dfrac{\partial u}{\partial x}\right)^2 e^{2s}\sin^2 t - 2\dfrac{\partial u}{\partial x}\dfrac{\partial u}{\partial y}e^{2s}\cos t\sin t + \left(\dfrac{\partial u}{\partial y}\right)^2 e^{2t}\sin^2 t.$ Thus

$\left[\left(\dfrac{\partial u}{\partial s}\right)^2 + \left(\dfrac{\partial u}{\partial t}\right)^2\right]e^{-2t} = \left(\dfrac{\partial u}{\partial x}\right)^2 + \left(\dfrac{\partial u}{\partial y}\right)^2.$

37. Let $u = x - y$. Then $\dfrac{\partial z}{\partial x} = \dfrac{dz}{du}\dfrac{\partial u}{\partial x} = \dfrac{dz}{du}$ and $\dfrac{\partial z}{\partial y} = \dfrac{dz}{du}(-1)$. Thus $\dfrac{\partial z}{\partial x} + \dfrac{\partial z}{\partial y} = 0$.

38. $\dfrac{\partial z}{\partial s} = \dfrac{\partial z}{\partial x} + \dfrac{\partial z}{\partial y}$ and $\dfrac{\partial z}{\partial t} = \dfrac{\partial z}{\partial x} - \dfrac{\partial z}{\partial y}$. Thus $\dfrac{\partial z}{\partial s}\dfrac{\partial z}{\partial t} = \left(\dfrac{\partial z}{\partial x}\right)^2 - \left(\dfrac{\partial z}{\partial y}\right)^2$.

39. Let $u = x + at$, $v = x - at$. Then $z = f(u) + g(v)$, so $\partial z/\partial u = f'(u)$ and $\partial z/\partial v = g'(v)$.

Thus $\dfrac{\partial z}{\partial t} = \dfrac{\partial z}{\partial u}\dfrac{\partial u}{\partial t} + \dfrac{\partial z}{\partial v}\dfrac{\partial v}{\partial t} = af'(u) - ag'(v)$ and

$$\frac{\partial^2 z}{\partial t^2} = a\frac{\partial}{\partial t}[f'(u) - g'(v)] = a\left(\frac{df'(u)}{du}\frac{\partial u}{\partial t} - \frac{dg'(v)}{dv}\frac{\partial v}{\partial t}\right) = a^2 f''(u) + a^2 g''(v).$$

Similarly $\dfrac{\partial z}{\partial x} = f'(u) + g'(v)$ and $\dfrac{\partial^2 z}{\partial x^2} = f''(u) + g''(v)$. Thus $\dfrac{\partial^2 z}{\partial t^2} = a^2\dfrac{\partial^2 z}{\partial x^2}$.

40. By the Chain Rule, $\dfrac{\partial u}{\partial s} = e^s\cos t\,\dfrac{\partial u}{\partial x} + e^s\sin t\,\dfrac{\partial u}{\partial y}$ and $\dfrac{\partial u}{\partial t} = -e^s\sin t\,\dfrac{\partial u}{\partial x} + e^s\cos t\,\dfrac{\partial u}{\partial y}$. Then

$$\frac{\partial^2 u}{\partial s^2} = e^s\cos t\,\frac{\partial u}{\partial x} + e^s\cos t\,\frac{\partial}{\partial s}\left(\frac{\partial u}{\partial x}\right) + e^s\sin t\,\frac{\partial u}{\partial y} + e^s\sin t\,\frac{\partial}{\partial s}\left(\frac{\partial u}{\partial y}\right).$$

But $\dfrac{\partial}{\partial s}\left(\dfrac{\partial u}{\partial x}\right) = \dfrac{\partial^2 u}{\partial x^2}\dfrac{\partial x}{\partial s} + \dfrac{\partial^2 u}{\partial y\,\partial x}\dfrac{\partial y}{\partial s} = e^s\cos t\,\dfrac{\partial^2 u}{\partial x^2} + e^s\sin t\,\dfrac{\partial^2 u}{\partial y\,\partial x}$ and

$\dfrac{\partial}{\partial s}\left(\dfrac{\partial u}{\partial y}\right) = \dfrac{\partial^2 u}{\partial y^2}\dfrac{\partial y}{\partial s} + \dfrac{\partial^2 u}{\partial x\,\partial y}\dfrac{\partial x}{\partial s} = e^s\sin t\,\dfrac{\partial^2 u}{\partial y^2} + e^s\cos t\,\dfrac{\partial^2 u}{\partial x\,\partial y}$. Also, by continuity of the partials,

$\dfrac{\partial^2 u}{\partial x\,\partial y} = \dfrac{\partial^2 u}{\partial y\,\partial x}$. Thus

$$\frac{\partial^2 u}{\partial s^2} = e^s\cos t\,\frac{\partial u}{\partial x} + e^s\cos t\left(e^s\cos t\,\frac{\partial^2 u}{\partial x^2} + e^s\sin t\,\frac{\partial^2 u}{\partial x\,\partial y}\right) + e^s\sin t\,\frac{\partial u}{\partial y}$$

$$+ e^s\sin t\left(e^s\sin t\,\frac{\partial^2 u}{\partial y^2} + e^s\cos t\,\frac{\partial^2 u}{\partial x\,\partial y}\right)$$

$$= e^s\cos t\,\frac{\partial u}{\partial x} + e^s\sin t\,\frac{\partial u}{\partial y} + e^{2s}\cos^2 t\,\frac{\partial^2 u}{\partial x^2} + 2e^{2s}\cos t\sin t\,\frac{\partial^2 u}{\partial x\,\partial y} + e^{2s}\sin^2 t\,\frac{\partial^2 u}{\partial y^2}$$

Similarly

$$\frac{\partial^2 u}{\partial t^2} = -e^s\cos t\,\frac{\partial u}{\partial x} - e^s\sin t\,\frac{\partial}{\partial t}\left(\frac{\partial u}{\partial x}\right) - e^s\sin t\,\frac{\partial u}{\partial y} + e^s\cos t\,\frac{\partial}{\partial t}\left(\frac{\partial u}{\partial y}\right)$$

$$= -e^s\cos t\,\frac{\partial u}{\partial x} - e^s\sin t\left(-e^s\sin t\,\frac{\partial^2 u}{\partial x^2} + e^s\cos t\,\frac{\partial^2 u}{\partial x\,\partial y}\right)$$

$$- e^s\sin t\,\frac{\partial u}{\partial y} + e^s\cos t\left(e^s\cos t\,\frac{\partial^2 u}{\partial y^2} - e^s\sin t\,\frac{\partial^2 u}{\partial x\,\partial y}\right)$$

$$= -e^s\cos t\,\frac{\partial u}{\partial x} - e^s\sin t\,\frac{\partial u}{\partial y} + e^{2s}\sin^2 t\,\frac{\partial^2 u}{\partial x^2} - 2e^{2s}\cos t\sin t\,\frac{\partial^2 u}{\partial x\,\partial y} + e^{2s}\cos^2 t\,\frac{\partial^2 u}{\partial y^2}$$

Thus $e^{-2s}\left(\dfrac{\partial^2 u}{\partial s^2} + \dfrac{\partial^2 u}{\partial t^2}\right) = (\cos^2 t + \sin^2 t)\left(\dfrac{\partial^2 u}{\partial x^2} + \dfrac{\partial^2 u}{\partial y^2}\right) = \dfrac{\partial^2 u}{\partial x^2} + \dfrac{\partial^2 u}{\partial y^2}$, as desired.

41. $\dfrac{\partial z}{\partial s} = \dfrac{\partial z}{\partial x}\,2s + \dfrac{\partial z}{\partial y}\,2r.$ Then

$$\frac{\partial^2 z}{\partial r \partial s} = \frac{\partial}{\partial r}\left(\frac{\partial z}{\partial x}2s\right) + \frac{\partial}{\partial r}\left(\frac{\partial z}{\partial y}2r\right)$$

$$= \frac{\partial^2 z}{\partial x^2}\frac{\partial x}{\partial r}2s + \frac{\partial}{\partial y}\left(\frac{\partial z}{\partial x}\right)\frac{\partial y}{\partial r}2s + \frac{\partial z}{\partial x}\frac{\partial}{\partial r}2s + \frac{\partial^2 z}{\partial y^2}\frac{\partial y}{\partial r}2r + \frac{\partial}{\partial x}\left(\frac{\partial z}{\partial y}\right)\frac{\partial x}{\partial r}2r + \frac{\partial z}{\partial y}2$$

$$= 4rs\,\frac{\partial^2 z}{\partial x^2} + \frac{\partial^2 z}{\partial y\,\partial x}4s^2 + 0 + 4rs\,\frac{\partial^2 z}{\partial y^2} + \frac{\partial^2 z}{\partial x\,\partial y}4r^2 + 2\,\frac{\partial z}{\partial y}$$

By the continuity of the partials, $\dfrac{\partial^2 z}{\partial r \partial s} = 4rs\,\dfrac{\partial^2 z}{\partial x^2} + 4rs\,\dfrac{\partial^2 z}{\partial y^2} + \left(4r^2 + 4s^2\right)\dfrac{\partial^2 z}{\partial x\,\partial y} + 2\dfrac{\partial z}{\partial y}.$

42. By the Chain Rule,

(a) $\dfrac{\partial z}{\partial r} = \dfrac{\partial z}{\partial x}\cos\theta + \dfrac{\partial z}{\partial y}\sin\theta$

(b) $\dfrac{\partial z}{\partial \theta} = -\dfrac{\partial z}{\partial x}\,r\sin\theta + \dfrac{\partial z}{\partial y}\,r\cos\theta$

(c) $\dfrac{\partial^2 z}{\partial r \partial \theta} = \dfrac{\partial^2 z}{\partial \theta \partial r} = \dfrac{\partial}{\partial \theta}\left(\dfrac{\partial z}{\partial x}\cos\theta + \dfrac{\partial z}{\partial y}\sin\theta\right)$

$$= -\sin\theta\,\frac{\partial z}{\partial x} + \cos\theta\,\frac{\partial}{\partial \theta}\left(\frac{\partial z}{\partial x}\right) + \cos\theta\,\frac{\partial z}{\partial y} + \sin\theta\,\frac{\partial}{\partial \theta}\left(\frac{\partial z}{\partial y}\right)$$

$$= -\sin\theta\,\frac{\partial z}{\partial x} + \cos\theta\left(\frac{\partial^2 z}{\partial x^2}\frac{\partial x}{\partial \theta} + \frac{\partial^2 z}{\partial y \partial x}\frac{\partial y}{\partial \theta}\right) + \cos\theta\,\frac{\partial z}{\partial y} + \sin\theta\,\frac{\partial^2 z}{\partial y^2}\frac{\partial y}{\partial \theta} + \frac{\partial^2 z}{\partial x \partial y}\frac{\partial x}{\partial \theta}$$

$$= -\sin\theta\,\frac{\partial z}{\partial x} + \cos\theta\left(-r\sin\theta\,\frac{\partial^2 z}{\partial x^2} + r\cos\theta\,\frac{\partial^2 z}{\partial y \partial x}\right) + \cos\theta\,\frac{\partial z}{\partial y}$$

$$+ \sin\theta\left(r\cos\theta\,\frac{\partial^2 z}{\partial y^2} - r\sin\theta\,\frac{\partial^2 z}{\partial x \partial y}\right)$$

$$= -\sin\theta\,\frac{\partial z}{\partial x} - r\cos\theta\sin\theta\,\frac{\partial^2 z}{\partial x^2} + r\cos^2\theta\,\frac{\partial^2 z}{\partial y \partial x} + \cos\theta\,\frac{\partial z}{\partial y}$$

$$+ r\cos\theta\sin\theta\,\frac{\partial^2 z}{\partial y^2} - r\sin^2\theta\,\frac{\partial^2 z}{\partial y \partial x}$$

$$= \cos\theta\,\frac{\partial z}{\partial y} - \sin\theta\,\frac{\partial z}{\partial x} + r\cos\theta\sin\theta\left(\frac{\partial^2 z}{\partial y^2} - \frac{\partial^2 z}{\partial x^2}\right) + r\left(\cos^2\theta - \sin^2\theta\right)\frac{\partial^2 z}{\partial y \partial x}$$

43. $\dfrac{\partial z}{\partial r} = \dfrac{\partial z}{\partial x}\cos\theta + \dfrac{\partial z}{\partial y}\sin\theta$ and $\dfrac{\partial z}{\partial \theta} = -\dfrac{\partial z}{\partial x}\,r\sin\theta + \dfrac{\partial z}{\partial y}\,r\cos\theta.$ Then

$$\frac{\partial^2 z}{\partial r^2} = \cos\theta\left(\frac{\partial^2 z}{\partial x^2}\cos\theta + \frac{\partial^2 z}{\partial y \partial x}\sin\theta\right) + \sin\theta\left(\frac{\partial^2 z}{\partial y^2}\sin\theta + \frac{\partial^2 z}{\partial x \partial y}\cos\theta\right)$$

$$= \cos^2\theta\,\frac{\partial^2 z}{\partial x^2} + 2\cos\theta\sin\theta\,\frac{\partial^2 z}{\partial x \partial y} + \sin^2\theta\,\frac{\partial^2 z}{\partial y^2}$$

and

$$\frac{\partial^2 z}{\partial \theta^2} = -r \cos \theta \, \frac{\partial z}{\partial x} + (-r \sin \theta) \left(\frac{\partial^2 z}{\partial x^2} (-r \sin \theta) + \frac{\partial^2 z}{\partial y \, \partial x} r \cos \theta \right)$$

$$-r \sin \theta \, \frac{\partial z}{\partial y} + r \cos \theta \left(\frac{\partial^2 z}{\partial y^2} r \cos \theta + \frac{\partial^2 z}{\partial x \, \partial y} (-r \sin \theta) \right)$$

$$= -r \cos \theta \, \frac{\partial z}{\partial x} - r \sin \theta \, \frac{\partial z}{\partial y} + r^2 \sin^2 \theta \, \frac{\partial^2 z}{\partial x^2} - 2r^2 \cos \theta \sin \theta \, \frac{\partial^2 z}{\partial x \, \partial y} + r^2 \cos^2 \theta \, \frac{\partial^2 z}{\partial y^2}$$

Thus

$$\frac{\partial^2 z}{\partial r^2} + \frac{1}{r^2} \frac{\partial^2 z}{\partial \theta^2} + \frac{1}{r} \frac{\partial z}{\partial r} = (\cos^2 \theta + \sin^2 \theta) \frac{\partial^2 z}{\partial x^2} + (\sin^2 \theta + \cos^2 \theta) \frac{\partial^2 z}{\partial y^2} - \frac{1}{r} \cos \theta \, \frac{\partial z}{\partial x}$$

$$- \frac{1}{r} \sin \theta \, \frac{\partial z}{\partial y} + \frac{1}{r} \left(\cos \theta \, \frac{\partial z}{\partial x} + \sin \theta \, \frac{\partial z}{\partial y} \right)$$

$$= \frac{\partial^2 z}{\partial x^2} + \frac{\partial^2 z}{\partial y^2} \text{ as desired.}$$

44. (a) $\dfrac{\partial z}{\partial t} = \dfrac{\partial z}{\partial x} \dfrac{\partial x}{\partial t} + \dfrac{\partial z}{\partial y} \dfrac{\partial y}{\partial t}$. Then

$$\frac{\partial^2 z}{\partial t^2} = \frac{\partial}{\partial t} \left(\frac{\partial z}{\partial x} \frac{\partial x}{\partial t} \right) + \frac{\partial}{\partial t} \left(\frac{\partial z}{\partial y} \frac{\partial y}{\partial t} \right)$$

$$= \frac{\partial}{\partial t} \left(\frac{\partial z}{\partial x} \right) \frac{\partial x}{\partial t} + \frac{\partial^2 x}{\partial t^2} \frac{\partial z}{\partial x} + \frac{\partial}{\partial t} \left(\frac{\partial z}{\partial y} \right) \frac{\partial y}{\partial t} + \frac{\partial^2 y}{\partial t^2} \frac{\partial z}{\partial y}$$

$$= \frac{\partial^2 z}{\partial x^2} \left(\frac{\partial x}{\partial t} \right)^2 + \frac{\partial^2 z}{\partial y \, \partial x} \frac{\partial x}{\partial t} \frac{\partial y}{\partial t} + \frac{\partial^2 x}{\partial t^2} \frac{\partial z}{\partial x} + \frac{\partial^2 z}{\partial y^2} \left(\frac{\partial y}{\partial t} \right)^2 + \frac{\partial^2 z}{\partial x \, \partial y} \frac{\partial y}{\partial t} \frac{\partial x}{\partial t} + \frac{\partial^2 y}{\partial t^2} \frac{\partial z}{\partial y}$$

$$= \frac{\partial^2 z}{\partial x^2} \left(\frac{\partial x}{\partial t} \right)^2 + 2 \frac{\partial^2 z}{\partial x \, \partial y} \frac{\partial x}{\partial t} \frac{\partial y}{\partial t} + \frac{\partial^2 z}{\partial y^2} \left(\frac{\partial y}{\partial t} \right)^2 + \frac{\partial^2 x}{\partial t^2} \frac{\partial z}{\partial x} + \frac{\partial^2 y}{\partial t^2} \frac{\partial z}{\partial y}$$

(b)

$$\frac{\partial^2 z}{\partial s \, \partial t} = \frac{\partial}{\partial s} \left(\frac{\partial z}{\partial x} \frac{\partial x}{\partial t} + \frac{\partial z}{\partial y} \frac{\partial y}{\partial t} \right)$$

$$= \left(\frac{\partial^2 z}{\partial x^2} \frac{\partial x}{\partial s} + \frac{\partial^2 z}{\partial y \, \partial x} \frac{\partial y}{\partial s} \right) \frac{\partial x}{\partial t} + \frac{\partial z}{\partial x} \frac{\partial^2 x}{\partial s \, \partial t} + \left(\frac{\partial^2 z}{\partial y^2} \frac{\partial y}{\partial s} + \frac{\partial^2 z}{\partial x \, \partial y} \frac{\partial x}{\partial s} \right) \frac{\partial y}{\partial t} + \frac{\partial z}{\partial y} \frac{\partial^2 y}{\partial s \, \partial t}$$

$$= \frac{\partial^2 z}{\partial x^2} \frac{\partial x}{\partial s} \frac{\partial x}{\partial t} + \frac{\partial^2 z}{\partial x \, \partial y} \left(\frac{\partial y}{\partial s} \frac{\partial x}{\partial t} + \frac{\partial y}{\partial t} \frac{\partial x}{\partial s} \right) + \frac{\partial z}{\partial x} \frac{\partial^2 x}{\partial s \, \partial t} + \frac{\partial z}{\partial y} \frac{\partial^2 y}{\partial s \, \partial t} + \frac{\partial^2 z}{\partial y^2} \frac{\partial y}{\partial s} \frac{\partial y}{\partial t}$$

45. $F(x, y, z) = 0$ is assumed to define z as a function of x and y, that is, $z = f(x, y)$. So by (7), $\dfrac{\partial z}{\partial x} = -\dfrac{F_x}{F_z}$ since

$F_z \neq 0$. Similarly, it is assumed that $F(x, y, z) = 0$ defines x as a function of y and z, that is $x = h(x, z)$. Then

$F(h(y, z), y, z) = 0$ and by the Chain Rule, $F_x \dfrac{\partial x}{\partial y} + F_y \dfrac{\partial y}{\partial y} + F_z \dfrac{\partial z}{\partial y} = 0$. But $\dfrac{\partial z}{\partial y} = 0$ and $\dfrac{\partial y}{\partial y} = 1$, so

$F_x \dfrac{\partial x}{\partial y} + F_y = 0 \implies \dfrac{\partial x}{\partial y} = -\dfrac{F_y}{F_x}$. A similar calculation shows that $\dfrac{\partial y}{\partial z} = -\dfrac{F_z}{F_y}$. Thus

$$\frac{\partial z}{\partial x} \frac{\partial x}{\partial y} \frac{\partial y}{\partial z} = \left(-\frac{F_x}{F_z} \right) \left(-\frac{F_y}{F_x} \right) \left(-\frac{F_z}{F_y} \right) = -1.$$

11.6 Directional Derivatives and the Gradient Vector · · · · · ·

1. First we draw a line passing through Raleigh and the eye of the hurricane. We can approximate the directional derivative at Raleigh in the direction of the eye of the hurricane by the average rate of change of pressure between the points where this line intersects the contour lines closest to Raleigh. In the direction of the eye of the hurricane, the pressure changes from 996 millibars to 992 millibars. We estimate the distance between these two points to be approximately 40 miles, so the rate of change of pressure in the direction given is approximately $\frac{992 - 996}{40} = -0.1$ millibar/mi.

2. First we draw a line passing through Muskegon and Ludington. We approximate the directional derivative at Muskegon in the direction of Ludington by the average rate of change of snowfall between the points where the line intersects the contour lines closest to Muskegon. In the direction of Ludington, the snowfall changes from 60 to 70 inches. We estimate the distance between these two points to be approximately 28 miles, so the rate of change of annual snowfall in the direction given is approximately $\frac{70 - 60}{28} \approx 0.36$ in/mi. [If we talk of snowfall (rather than annual snowfall), the units are (in/year)/mi.]

3. $\mathbf{u} = \left\langle \frac{1}{\sqrt{2}}, \frac{1}{\sqrt{2}} \right\rangle$ is a unit vector, so by Theorem 3, $D_{\mathbf{u}}f(16, 30) = f_T(16, 30) \cdot \frac{1}{\sqrt{2}} + f_v(16, 30) \cdot \frac{1}{\sqrt{2}}$. We can estimate the value of $f_T(16, 30)$ following the technique used in Exercise 11.3.3.

$$f_T(16, 30) = \lim_{h \to 0} \frac{f(16 + h, 30) - f(16, 30)}{h}, \text{ and taking } h = 4 \text{ and } h = -4 \text{ we have}$$

$$f_T(16, 30) \approx \frac{f(20, 30) - f(16, 30)}{4} = \frac{14 - 9}{4} = 1.25, \ f_T(16, 30) \approx \frac{f(12, 30) - f(16, 30)}{-4} = \frac{3 - 9}{-4} = 1.5.$$

Averaging these values, we estimate $f_T(16, 30) \approx 1.375$. Similarly,

$$f_v(16, 30) = \lim_{h \to 0} \frac{f(16, 30 + h) - f(16, 30)}{h}, \text{ and taking } h = 10 \text{ and } h = -10 \text{ gives}$$

$$f_v(16, 30) \approx \frac{f(16, 40) - f(16, 30)}{10} = \frac{7 - 9}{10} = -0.2, \ f_v(16, 30) \approx \frac{f(16, 20) - f(16, 30)}{-10} = \frac{11 - 9}{-10} = -0.2.$$

Averaging these values, we estimate $f_v(16, 30) \approx -0.2$. Thus

$$D_{\mathbf{u}}f(16, 30) = f_T(16, 30) \cdot \frac{1}{\sqrt{2}} + f_v(16, 30) \cdot \frac{1}{\sqrt{2}} \approx (1.375)\frac{1}{\sqrt{2}} + (-0.2)\frac{1}{\sqrt{2}} \approx 0.83.$$

4. $f(x, y) = \sin(x + 2y) \ \Rightarrow \ f_x(x, y) = \cos(x + 2y)$ and $f_y(x, y) = 2\cos(x + 2y)$. If $\mathbf{u}$ is a unit vector in the direction of $\theta = \frac{3\pi}{4}$, then from Equation 6,

$$D_{\mathbf{u}}f(4, -2) = f_x(4, -2)\cos\frac{3\pi}{4} + f_y(4, -2)\sin\frac{3\pi}{4} = (\cos 0)\left(-\frac{\sqrt{2}}{2}\right) + 2(\cos 0)\left(\frac{\sqrt{2}}{2}\right) = \frac{\sqrt{2}}{2}.$$

5. $f(x, y) = \sqrt{5x - 4y} \ \Rightarrow \ f_x(x, y) = \frac{1}{2}(5x - 4y)^{-1/2}(5) = \frac{5}{2\sqrt{5x - 4y}}$ and

$f_y(x, y) = \frac{1}{2}(5x - 4y)^{-1/2}(-4) = -\frac{2}{\sqrt{5x - 4y}}$. If $\mathbf{u}$ is a unit vector in the direction of $\theta = -\frac{\pi}{6}$, then from

Equation 6, $D_{\mathbf{u}}f(4, 1) = f_x(4, 1)\cos\left(-\frac{\pi}{6}\right) + f_y(4, 1)\sin\left(-\frac{\pi}{6}\right) = \frac{5}{8} \cdot \frac{\sqrt{3}}{2} + \left(-\frac{1}{2}\right)\left(-\frac{1}{2}\right) = \frac{5\sqrt{3}}{16} + \frac{1}{4}.$

6. $f(x, y) = xe^{-2y} \ \Rightarrow \ f_x(x, y) = e^{-2y}$ and $f_y(x, y) = -2xe^{-2y}$. If $\mathbf{u}$ is a unit vector in the direction of $\theta = \frac{\pi}{2}$, then $D_{\mathbf{u}}f(5, 0) = f_x(5, 0)\cos\frac{\pi}{2} + f_y(5, 0)\sin\frac{\pi}{2} = 1 \cdot 0 + (-10)1 = -10.$

7. $f(x,y) = 5xy^2 - 4x^3y$

(a) $\nabla f(x,y) = \langle f_x(x,y), f_y(x,y)\rangle = \langle 5y^2 - 12x^2y, 10xy - 4x^3\rangle$

(b) $\nabla f(1,2) = \langle 5(2)^2 - 12(1)^2(2), 10(1)(2) - 4(1)^3\rangle = \langle -4, 16\rangle$

(c) By Equation 9, $D_{\mathbf{u}}f(1,2) = \nabla f(1,2) \cdot \mathbf{u} = \langle -4, 16\rangle \cdot \langle \frac{5}{13}, \frac{12}{13}\rangle = (-4)\left(\frac{5}{13}\right) + (16)\left(\frac{12}{13}\right) = \frac{172}{13}.$

8. $f(x,y) = y \ln x$

(a) $\nabla f(x,y) = \langle f_x(x,y), f_y(x,y)\rangle = \langle y/x, \ln x\rangle$ (b) $\nabla f(1,-3) = \langle \frac{-3}{1}, \ln 1\rangle = \langle -3, 0\rangle$

(c) By Equation 9, $D_{\mathbf{u}}f(1,-3) = \nabla f(1,-3) \cdot \mathbf{u} = \langle -3, 0\rangle \cdot \langle -\frac{4}{5}, \frac{3}{5}\rangle = \frac{12}{5}.$

9. $f(x,y,z) = xy^2z^3$

(a) $\nabla f(x,y,z) = \langle f_x(x,y,z), f_y(x,y,z), f_z(x,y,z)\rangle = \langle y^2z^3, 2xyz^3, 3xy^2z^2\rangle$

(b) $\nabla f(1,-2,1) = \langle 4, -4, 12\rangle$

(c) $\nabla f(1,-2,1) \cdot \mathbf{u} = \frac{4}{\sqrt{3}} + \frac{4}{\sqrt{3}} + \frac{12}{\sqrt{3}} = \frac{20}{\sqrt{3}}$

10. $f(x,y,z) = xy + yz^2 + xz^3$

(a) $\nabla f(x,y,z) = \langle f_x(x,y,z), f_y(x,y,z), f_z(x,y,z)\rangle = \langle y + z^3, x + z^2, 2yz + 3xz^2\rangle$

(b) $\nabla f(2,0,3) = \langle 27, 11, 54\rangle$

(c) $\nabla f(2,0,3) \cdot \mathbf{u} = \frac{1}{3}(-54 - 11 + 108) = \frac{43}{3}$

11. $f(x,y) = 1 + 2x\sqrt{y}$ $\Rightarrow$ $\nabla f(x,y) = \left\langle 2\sqrt{y}, 2x \cdot \frac{1}{2}y^{-1/2}\right\rangle = \langle 2\sqrt{y}, x/\sqrt{y}\rangle$, $\nabla f(3,4) = \langle 4, \frac{3}{2}\rangle$,

and a unit vector in the direction of $\mathbf{v}$ is $\mathbf{u} = \frac{1}{\sqrt{4^2 + (-3)^2}}\langle 4, -3\rangle = \langle \frac{4}{5}, -\frac{3}{5}\rangle$, so

$D_{\mathbf{u}}f(3,4) = \nabla f(3,4) \cdot \mathbf{u} = \langle 4, \frac{3}{2}\rangle \cdot \langle \frac{4}{5}, -\frac{3}{5}\rangle = \frac{23}{10}.$

12. $g(r,\theta) = e^{-r}\sin\theta$ $\Rightarrow$ $\nabla g(r,\theta) = (-e^{-r}\sin\theta)\mathbf{i} + (e^{-r}\cos\theta)\mathbf{j}$, $\nabla g(0, \frac{\pi}{3}) = -\frac{\sqrt{3}}{2}\mathbf{i} + \frac{1}{2}\mathbf{j}$,

and a unit vector in the direction of $\mathbf{v}$ is $\mathbf{u} = \frac{1}{\sqrt{13}}(3\mathbf{i} - 2\mathbf{j})$, so

$D_{\mathbf{u}}g(0, \frac{\pi}{3}) = \nabla g(0, \frac{\pi}{3}) \cdot \mathbf{u} = \left(-\frac{\sqrt{3}}{2}\mathbf{i} + \frac{1}{2}\mathbf{j}\right) \cdot \frac{1}{\sqrt{13}}(3\mathbf{i} - 2\mathbf{j}) = -\frac{3\sqrt{3}}{2\sqrt{13}} - \frac{1}{\sqrt{13}} = -\frac{3\sqrt{3}+2}{2\sqrt{13}}.$

13. $f(x,y,z) = \sqrt{x^2 + y^2 + z^2}$ $\Rightarrow$ $\nabla f(x,y,z) = \left\langle \frac{x}{\sqrt{x^2 + y^2 + z^2}}, \frac{y}{\sqrt{x^2 + y^2 + z^2}}, \frac{z}{\sqrt{x^2 + y^2 + z^2}}\right\rangle$,

$\nabla f(1,2,-2) = \langle \frac{1}{3}, \frac{2}{3}, -\frac{2}{3}\rangle$, and a unit vector in the direction of $\mathbf{v}$ is $\mathbf{u} = \frac{1}{9}\langle -6, 6, -3\rangle = \langle -\frac{2}{3}, \frac{2}{3}, -\frac{1}{3}\rangle$, so

$D_{\mathbf{u}}f(1,2,-2) = \nabla f(1,2,-2) \cdot \mathbf{u} = \langle \frac{1}{3}, \frac{2}{3}, -\frac{2}{3}\rangle \cdot \langle -\frac{2}{3}, \frac{2}{3}, -\frac{1}{3}\rangle = \frac{4}{9}.$

14. $f(x,y,z) = \frac{x}{y+z}$ $\Rightarrow$ $\nabla f(x,y,z) = \left\langle \frac{1}{y+z}, -\frac{x}{(y+z)^2}, -\frac{x}{(y+z)^2}\right\rangle$,

$\nabla f(4,1,1) = \langle \frac{1}{2}, -1, -1\rangle$, and a unit vector in the direction of $\mathbf{v}$ is $\mathbf{u} = \frac{1}{\sqrt{14}}\langle 1, 2, 3\rangle$, so

$D_{\mathbf{u}}f(4,1,1) = \nabla f(4,1,1) \cdot \mathbf{u} = \langle \frac{1}{2}, -1, -1\rangle \cdot \frac{1}{\sqrt{14}}\langle 1, 2, 3\rangle = -\frac{9}{2\sqrt{14}}.$

15. $g(x,y,z) = x\tan^{-1}(y/z)$ $\Rightarrow$ $\nabla g(x,y,z) = \langle \tan^{-1}(y/z), xz/(y^2 + z^2), -xy/(y^2 + z^2)\rangle$,

$\nabla g(1,2,-2) = \langle -\frac{\pi}{4}, -\frac{1}{4}, -\frac{1}{4}\rangle$, $\mathbf{u} = \frac{1}{\sqrt{3}}\langle 1, 1, -1\rangle$ and

$D_{\mathbf{u}}g(1,2,-2) = \frac{(-\pi)(1)}{4\sqrt{3}} + \frac{(-1)(1)}{4\sqrt{3}} + \frac{(-1)(-1)}{4\sqrt{3}} = -\frac{\pi}{4\sqrt{3}}.$

16. $D_{\mathbf{u}}f(2,2) = \nabla f(2,2) \cdot \mathbf{u}$, the scalar projection of $\nabla f(2,2)$ onto $\mathbf{u}$, so we draw a perpendicular from the tip of $\nabla f(2,2)$ to the line containing $\mathbf{u}$. We can use the point $(2,2)$ to determine the scale of the axes, and we estimate the length of the projection to be approximately 3.0 units. Since the angle between $\nabla f(2,2)$ and $\mathbf{u}$ is greater than $90°$, the scalar projection is negative. Thus $D_{\mathbf{u}}f(2,2) \approx -3$.

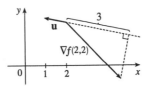

17. $f(x,y) = \sqrt{xy} \;\Rightarrow\; \nabla f(x,y) = \left\langle \frac{1}{2}(xy)^{-1/2}(y), \frac{1}{2}(xy)^{-1/2}(x) \right\rangle = \left\langle \frac{y}{2\sqrt{xy}}, \frac{x}{2\sqrt{xy}} \right\rangle$, so

$\nabla f(2,8) = \langle 1, \frac{1}{4} \rangle$. The unit vector in the direction of $\overrightarrow{PQ} = \langle 5-2, 4-8 \rangle = \langle 3, -4 \rangle$ is $\mathbf{u} = \langle \frac{3}{5}, -\frac{4}{5} \rangle$, so $D_{\mathbf{u}}f(2,8) = \nabla f(2,8) \cdot \mathbf{u} = \langle 1, \frac{1}{4} \rangle \cdot \langle \frac{3}{5}, -\frac{4}{5} \rangle = \frac{2}{5}$.

18. $f(x,y,z) = x^2 + y^2 + z^2 \;\Rightarrow\; \nabla f(x,y,z) = \langle 2x, 2y, 2z \rangle$, so $\nabla f(2,1,3) = \langle 4, 2, 6 \rangle$. The unit vector in the direction of $\overrightarrow{PO} = \langle -2, -1, -3 \rangle$ is $\mathbf{u} = \frac{1}{\sqrt{14}}\langle -2, -1, -3 \rangle$, so

$D_{\mathbf{u}}f(2,1,3) = \nabla f(2,1,3) \cdot \mathbf{u} = \langle 4, 2, 6 \rangle \cdot \frac{1}{\sqrt{14}}\langle -2, -1, -3 \rangle = -\frac{28}{\sqrt{14}} = -2\sqrt{14}$.

19. $f(x,y) = \sin(xy) \;\Rightarrow\; \nabla f(x,y) = \langle y\cos(xy), x\cos(xy) \rangle$, $\nabla f(1,0) = \langle 0, 1 \rangle$. Thus the maximum rate of change is $|\nabla f(1,0)| = 1$ in the direction $\langle 0, 1 \rangle$.

20. $f(x,y) = \ln(x^2 + y^2) \;\Rightarrow\; \nabla f(x,y) = \left\langle \frac{2x}{x^2+y^2}, \frac{2y}{x^2+y^2} \right\rangle$, $\nabla f(1,2) = \langle \frac{2}{5}, \frac{4}{5} \rangle$. Thus the maximum rate of change is $|\nabla f(1,2)| = \frac{2\sqrt{5}}{5}$ in the direction $\langle \frac{2}{5}, \frac{4}{5} \rangle$ or $\langle 2, 4 \rangle$.

21. $f(x,y,z) = x + y/z \;\Rightarrow\; \nabla f(x,y,z) = \left\langle 1, \frac{1}{z}, -\frac{y}{z^2} \right\rangle$, so the maximum rate of change is

$|\nabla f(4,3,-1)| = \sqrt{11}$ in the direction $\langle 1, -1, -3 \rangle$.

22. $f(x,y,z) = x^2 y^3 z^4 \;\Rightarrow\; \nabla f(x,y,z) = \langle 2xy^3 z^4, 3x^2 y^2 z^4, 4x^2 y^3 z^3 \rangle$, $\nabla f(1,1,1) = \langle 2, 3, 4 \rangle$. Thus the maximum rate of change is $|\nabla f(1,1,1)| = \sqrt{29}$ in the direction $\langle 2, 3, 4 \rangle$.

23. (a) As in the proof of Theorem 15, $D_{\mathbf{u}}f = |\nabla f|\cos\theta$. Since the minimum value of $\cos\theta$ is -1 occurring when $\theta = \pi$, the minimum value of $D_{\mathbf{u}}f$ is $-|\nabla f|$ occurring when $\theta = \pi$, that is when $\mathbf{u}$ is in the opposite direction of ∇f (assuming $\nabla f \neq \mathbf{0}$).

(b) $f(x,y) = x^4 y - x^2 y^3 \;\Rightarrow\; \nabla f(x,y) = \langle 4x^3 y - 2xy^3, x^4 - 3x^2 y^2 \rangle$, so f decreases fastest at the point $(2,-3)$ in the direction $-\nabla f(2,-3) = -\langle 12, -92 \rangle = \langle -12, 92 \rangle$.

24. $f(x,y) = x^2 + \sin xy \;\Rightarrow\; f_x(x,y) = 2x + y\cos xy$, $f_y(x,y) = x\cos xy$ and $f_x(1,0) = 2(1) + (0)\cos 0 = 2$, $f_y(1,0) = (1)\cos 0 = 1$. If $\mathbf{u}$ is a unit vector which makes an angle θ with the positive x-axis, then $D_{\mathbf{u}}f(1,0) = f_x(1,0)\cos\theta + f_y(1,0)\sin\theta = 2\cos\theta + \sin\theta$. We want $D_{\mathbf{u}}f(1,0) = 1$, so $2\cos\theta + \sin\theta = 1 \;\Rightarrow\; \sin\theta = 1 - 2\cos\theta \;\Rightarrow\; \sin^2\theta = (1 - 2\cos\theta)^2 \;\Rightarrow\; 1 - \cos^2\theta = 1 - 4\cos\theta + 4\cos^2\theta \;\Rightarrow\; 5\cos^2\theta - 4\cos\theta = 0 \;\Rightarrow\; \cos\theta(5\cos\theta - 4) = 0 \;\Rightarrow\; \cos\theta = 0$ or $\cos\theta = \frac{4}{5} \;\Rightarrow\; \theta = \frac{\pi}{2}$ or $\theta = 2\pi - \cos^{-1}\left(\frac{4}{5}\right) \approx 5.64$.

25. The direction of fastest change is $\nabla f(x,y) = (2x-2)\mathbf{i} + (2y-4)\mathbf{j}$, so we need to find all points (x,y) where $\nabla f(x,y)$ is parallel to $\mathbf{i} + \mathbf{j} \;\Leftrightarrow\; (2x-2)\mathbf{i} + (2y-4)\mathbf{j} = k(\mathbf{i} + \mathbf{j}) \;\Leftrightarrow\; k = 2x - 2$ and $k = 2y - 4$. Then $2x - 2 = 2y - 4 \;\Rightarrow\; y = x + 1$, so the direction of fastest change is $\mathbf{i} + \mathbf{j}$ at all points on the line $y = x + 1$.

26. The fisherman is traveling in the direction $\langle -80, -60 \rangle$. A unit vector in this direction is

$\mathbf{u} = \frac{1}{100}\langle -80, -60 \rangle = \langle -\frac{4}{5}, -\frac{3}{5} \rangle$, and if the depth of the lake is given by $f(x, y) = 200 + 0.02x^2 - 0.001y^3$,

then $\nabla f(x, y) = \langle 0.04x, -0.003y^2 \rangle$. $D_\mathbf{u} f(80, 60) = \nabla f(80, 60) \cdot \mathbf{u} = \langle 3.2, -10.8 \rangle \cdot \langle -\frac{4}{5}, -\frac{3}{5} \rangle = 3.92$. Since

$D_\mathbf{u} f(80, 60)$ is positive, the depth of the lake is increasing near $(80, 60)$ in the direction toward the buoy.

27. $T = \dfrac{k}{\sqrt{x^2 + y^2 + z^2}}$ and $120 = T(1, 2, 2) = \dfrac{k}{3}$ so $k = 360$.

(a) $\mathbf{u} = \dfrac{\langle 1, -1, 1 \rangle}{\sqrt{3}}$,

$$D_\mathbf{u} T(1, 2, 2) = \nabla T(1, 2, 2) \cdot \mathbf{u} = \left[-360(x^2 + y^2 + z^2)^{-3/2} \langle x, y, z \rangle \right]_{(1,2,2)} \cdot \mathbf{u}$$

$$= -\frac{40}{3} \langle 1, 2, 2 \rangle \cdot \frac{1}{\sqrt{3}} \langle 1, -1, 1 \rangle = -\frac{40}{3\sqrt{3}}$$

(b) From (a), $\nabla T = -360(x^2 + y^2 + z^2)^{-3/2} \langle x, y, z \rangle$, and since $\langle x, y, z \rangle$ is the position vector of the point

(x, y, z), the vector $- \langle x, y, z \rangle$, and thus ∇T, always points toward the origin.

28. $\nabla T = -400 e^{-x^2 - 3y^2 - 9z^2} \langle x, 3y, 9z \rangle$

(a) $\mathbf{u} = \frac{1}{\sqrt{6}} \langle 1, -2, 1 \rangle$, $\nabla T(2, -1, 2) = -400 e^{-43} \langle 2, -3, 18 \rangle$ and

$$D_\mathbf{u} T(2, -1, 2) = \left(-\frac{400 e^{-43}}{\sqrt{6}} \right)(26) = -\frac{5200 \sqrt{6}}{3 e^{43}} \, °C/m.$$

(b) $\nabla T(2, -1, 2) = 400 e^{-43} \langle -2, 3, -18 \rangle$ or equivalently $\langle -2, 3, -18 \rangle$.

(c) $|\nabla T| = 400 e^{-x^2 - 3y^2 - 9z^2} \sqrt{x^2 + 9y^2 + 8z^2} \, °C/m$ is the maximum rate of increase. At $(2, -1, 2)$ the

maximum rate of increase is $400 e^{-43} \sqrt{337} \, °C/m$.

29. $\nabla V(x, y, z) = \langle 10x - 3y + yz, xz - 3x, xy \rangle$, $\nabla V(3, 4, 5) = \langle 38, 6, 12 \rangle$

(a) $D_\mathbf{u} V(3, 4, 5) = \langle 38, 6, 12 \rangle \cdot \frac{1}{\sqrt{3}} \langle 1, 1, -1 \rangle = \frac{32}{\sqrt{3}}$

(b) $\nabla V(3, 4, 5) = \langle 38, 6, 12 \rangle$ or equivalently $\langle 19, 3, 6 \rangle$.

(c) $|\nabla V(3, 4, 5)| = \sqrt{38^2 + 6^2 + 12^2} = \sqrt{1624} = 2\sqrt{406}$

30. (a) Let $z = f(x, y) = 1000 - 0.01x^2 - 0.02y^2$. Then $\nabla f(x, y) = \langle -0.02x, -0.04y \rangle$. Proceed in the direction

$\nabla f(60, 100) = \langle -1.2, -4 \rangle$.

(b) The maximum slope is equal to the maximum directional derivative, which is $|\langle -1.2, -4 \rangle| = \sqrt{17.44}$ and

$\theta = \tan^{-1} \sqrt{17.44} \approx 76.5°$.

31. A unit vector in the direction of $\overrightarrow{AB}$ is $\mathbf{i}$ and a unit vector in the direction of $\overrightarrow{AC}$ is $\mathbf{j}$.

Thus $D_{\overrightarrow{AB}} f(1, 3) = f_x(1, 3) = 3$ and $D_{\overrightarrow{AC}} f(1, 3) = f_y(1, 3) = 26$. Therefore

$\nabla f(1, 3) = \langle f_x(1, 3), f_y(1, 3) \rangle = \langle 3, 26 \rangle$, and by definition, $D_{\overrightarrow{AD}} f(1, 3) = \nabla f \cdot \mathbf{u}$ where $\mathbf{u}$ is a unit vector in the

direction of $\overrightarrow{AD}$, which is $\langle \frac{5}{13}, \frac{12}{13} \rangle$. Therefore, $D_{\overrightarrow{AD}} f(1, 3) = \langle 3, 26 \rangle \cdot \langle \frac{5}{13}, \frac{12}{13} \rangle = 3 \cdot \frac{5}{13} + 26 \cdot \frac{12}{13} = \frac{327}{13}$.

32. The curve of steepest ascent is perpendicular to all of the contour lines.

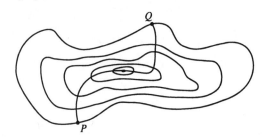

33. (a) $\nabla(au + bv) = \left\langle \dfrac{\partial(au + bv)}{\partial x}, \dfrac{\partial(au + bv)}{\partial y} \right\rangle = \left\langle a\dfrac{\partial u}{\partial x} + b\dfrac{\partial v}{\partial x}, a\dfrac{\partial u}{\partial y} + b\dfrac{\partial v}{\partial y} \right\rangle$

$\qquad = a\left\langle \dfrac{\partial u}{\partial x}, \dfrac{\partial u}{\partial y} \right\rangle + b\left\langle \dfrac{\partial v}{\partial x}, \dfrac{\partial v}{\partial y} \right\rangle = a\,\nabla u + b\,\nabla v$

(b) $\nabla(uv) = \left\langle v\dfrac{\partial u}{\partial x} + u\dfrac{\partial v}{\partial x}, v\dfrac{\partial u}{\partial y} + u\dfrac{\partial v}{\partial y} \right\rangle = v\left\langle \dfrac{\partial u}{\partial x}, \dfrac{\partial u}{\partial y} \right\rangle + u\left\langle \dfrac{\partial v}{\partial x}, \dfrac{\partial v}{\partial y} \right\rangle = v\,\nabla u + u\,\nabla v$

(c) $\nabla\!\left(\dfrac{u}{v}\right) = \left\langle \dfrac{v\dfrac{\partial u}{\partial x} - u\dfrac{\partial v}{\partial x}}{v^2}, \dfrac{v\dfrac{\partial u}{\partial y} - u\dfrac{\partial v}{\partial y}}{v^2} \right\rangle = \dfrac{v\left\langle \dfrac{\partial u}{\partial x}, \dfrac{\partial u}{\partial y} \right\rangle - u\left\langle \dfrac{\partial v}{\partial x}, \dfrac{\partial v}{\partial y} \right\rangle}{v^2} = \dfrac{v\,\nabla u - u\,\nabla v}{v^2}$

(d) $\nabla u^n = \left\langle \dfrac{\partial(u^n)}{\partial x}, \dfrac{\partial(u^n)}{\partial y} \right\rangle = \left\langle nu^{n-1}\dfrac{\partial u}{\partial x}, nu^{n-1}\dfrac{\partial u}{\partial y} \right\rangle = nu^{n-1}\,\nabla u.$

34. If we place the initial point of the gradient vector $\nabla f(4, 6)$ at $(4, 6)$, the vector is perpendicular to the level curve of f that includes $(4, 6)$, so we sketch a portion of the level curve through $(4, 6)$ (using the nearby level curves as a guideline) and draw a line perpendicular to the curve at $(4, 6)$. The gradient vector is parallel to this line, pointing in the direction of increasing function values, and with length equal to the maximum value of the directional derivative of f at $(4, 6)$. We can estimate this length by finding the average rate of change in the direction of the gradient. The line intersects the contour lines

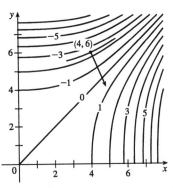

corresponding to -2 and -3 with an estimated distance of 0.5 units. Thus the rate of change is approximately

$\dfrac{-2 - (-3)}{0.5} = 2$, and we sketch the gradient vector with length 2.

35. Let $F(x, y, z) = x^2 + 2y^2 + 3z^2$. Then $x^2 + 2y^2 + 3z^2 = 21$ is a level surface of F.

$F_x(x, y, z) = 2x \quad \Rightarrow \quad F_x(4, -1, 1) = 8$, $F_y(x, y, z) = 4y \quad \Rightarrow \quad F_y(4, -1, 1) = -4$, and

$F_z(x, y, z) = 6z \quad \Rightarrow \quad F_z(4, -1, 1) = 6$.

(a) Equation 19 gives an equation of the tangent plane at $(4, -1, 1)$ as $8(x - 4) - 4[y - (-1)] + 6(z - 1) = 0$ or $4x - 2y + 3z = 21$.

(b) By Equation 20, the normal line has symmetric equations $\dfrac{x - 4}{8} = \dfrac{y + 1}{-4} = \dfrac{z - 1}{6}$

or $\dfrac{x - 4}{4} = \dfrac{y + 1}{-2} = \dfrac{z - 1}{3}$.

36. Let $F(x, y, z) = y^2 + z^2 - x$. Then $x = y^2 + z^2 - 2$ is the level surface $F(x, y, z) = 2$.

$F_x(x, y, z) = -1 \Rightarrow F_x(-1, 1, 0) = -1$, $F_y(x, y, z) = 2y \Rightarrow F_y(-1, 1, 0) = 2$,

and $F_z(x, y, z) = 2z \Rightarrow F_z(-1, 1, 0) = 0$.

(a) An equation of the tangent plane is $-1(x + 1) + 2(y - 1) + 0(z - 0) = 0$ or $-x + 2y = 3$.

(b) The normal line has symmetric equations $\dfrac{x + 1}{-1} = \dfrac{y - 1}{2}$, $z = 0$.

37. $F(x, y, z) = -z + xe^y \cos z \Rightarrow \nabla F(x, y, z) = \langle e^y \cos z, xe^y \cos z, -1 - xe^y \sin z \rangle$,

$\nabla F(1, 0, 0) = \langle 1, 1, -1 \rangle$

(a) $1(x - 1) + 1(y - 0) - 1(z - 0) = 0$ or $x + y - z = 1$ (b) $x - 1 = y = -z$

38. $F(x, y, z) = xe^{yz} \Rightarrow \nabla F(x, y, z) = \langle e^{yz}, xze^{yz}, xye^{yz} \rangle$, $\nabla F(1, 0, 5) = \langle 1, 5, 0 \rangle$

(a) $1(x - 1) + 5(y - 0) + 0(z - 5) = 0$ or $x + 5y = 1$ (b) $x - 1 = \dfrac{y}{5}$, $z = 5$

39. $F(x, y, z) = xy + yz + zx$,

$\nabla F(x, y, z) = \langle y + z, x + z, y + x \rangle$,

$\nabla F(1, 1, 1) = \langle 2, 2, 2 \rangle$, so an equation of the

tangent plane is $2x + 2y + 2z = 6$ or

$x + y + z = 3$, and the normal line is given by

$x - 1 = y - 1 = z - 1$ or $x = y = z$.

40. $F(x, y, z) = xyz$, $\nabla F(x, y, z) = \langle yz, xz, yx \rangle$,

$\nabla F(1, 2, 3) = \langle 6, 3, 2 \rangle$, so an equation of the

tangent plane is $6x + 3y + 2z = 18$, and the

normal line is given by $\dfrac{x - 1}{6} = \dfrac{y - 2}{3} = \dfrac{z - 3}{2}$

or $x = 1 + 6t$, $y = 2 + 3t$, $z = 3 + 2t$.

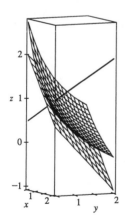

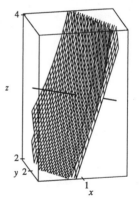

41. $\nabla f(x, y) = \langle 2x, 8y \rangle$, $\nabla f(2, 1) = \langle 4, 8 \rangle$. The tangent line has

equation $\nabla f(2, 1) \cdot \langle x - 2, y - 1 \rangle = 0 \Rightarrow$

$4(x - 2) + 8(y - 1) = 0$, which simplifies to $x + 2y = 4$.

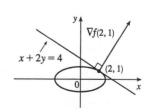

42. $\nabla g(x, y) = \langle 1, -2y \rangle$, $\nabla g(3, -1) = \langle 1, 2 \rangle$. The tangent line has

equation $\nabla g(3, -1) \cdot \langle x - 3, y + 1 \rangle = 0 \Rightarrow$

$1(x - 3) + 2(y + 1) = 0$, which simplifies to $x + 2y = 1$.

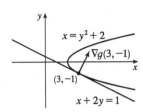

43. $\nabla F(x_0, y_0, z_0) = \left\langle \dfrac{2x_0}{a^2}, \dfrac{2y_0}{b^2}, \dfrac{2z_0}{c^2} \right\rangle$. Thus an equation of the tangent plane at (x_0, y_0, z_0) is

$\dfrac{2x_0}{a^2} x + \dfrac{2y_0}{b^2} y + \dfrac{2z_0}{c^2} z = 2 \left(\dfrac{x_0^2}{a^2} + \dfrac{y_0^2}{b^2} + \dfrac{z_0^2}{c^2} \right) = 2(1) = 2$ since (x_0, y_0, z_0) is a point on the ellipsoid. Hence

$\dfrac{x_0}{a^2} x + \dfrac{y_0}{b^2} y + \dfrac{z_0}{c^2} z = 1$ is an equation of the tangent plane.

44. Since $\nabla f(x_0, y_0, z_0) = \langle 2x_0, 4y_0, 6z_0 \rangle$ and $\langle 3, -1, 3 \rangle$ are both normal vectors to the surface at (x_0, y_0, z_0), we

need $\langle 2x_0, 4y_0, 6z_0 \rangle = c \langle 3, -1, 3 \rangle$ or $\langle x_0, 2y_0, 3z_0 \rangle = k \langle 3, -1, 3 \rangle$. Thus $x_0 = 3k$, $y_0 = -\frac{1}{2}k$ and $z_0 = k$. But

$x_0^2 + 2y_0^2 + 3z_0^2 = 1$ or $\left(9 + \frac{1}{2} + 3 \right) k^2 = 1$, so $k = \pm \frac{\sqrt{2}}{5}$ and there are two such points: $\left(\pm \frac{3\sqrt{2}}{5}, \mp \frac{1}{5\sqrt{2}}, \pm \frac{\sqrt{2}}{5} \right)$.

45. $\nabla f(x_0, y_0, z_0) = \langle 2x_0, -2y_0, 4z_0 \rangle$ and the given line has direction numbers $2, 4, 6$, so

$\langle 2x_0, -2y_0, 4z_0 \rangle = k \langle 2, 4, 6 \rangle$ or $x_0 = k$, $y_0 = -2k$ and $z_0 = \frac{3}{2}k$. But $x_0^2 - y_0^2 + 2z_0^2 = 1$ or $\left(1 - 4 + \frac{9}{2} \right) k^2 = 1$,

so $k = \pm \sqrt{\frac{2}{3}} = \pm \frac{\sqrt{6}}{3}$ and there are two such points: $\left(\pm \frac{\sqrt{6}}{3}, \mp \frac{2\sqrt{6}}{3}, \pm \frac{\sqrt{6}}{2} \right)$.

46. First note that the point $(1, 1, 2)$ is on both surfaces. For the ellipsoid, an equation of the tangent plane at $(1, 1, 2)$ is

$6x + 4y + 4z = 18$ or $3x + 2y + 2z = 9$, and for the sphere, an equation of the tangent plane at $(1, 1, 2)$ is

$(2 - 8)x + (2 - 6)y + (4 - 8)z = -18$ or $-6x - 4y - 4z = -18$ or $3x + 2y + 2z = 9$. Since these tangent

planes are the same, the surfaces are tangent to each other at the point $(1, 1, 2)$.

47. Let (x_0, y_0, z_0) be a point on the surface. Then an equation of the tangent plane at the point is

$\dfrac{x}{2\sqrt{x_0}} + \dfrac{y}{2\sqrt{y_0}} + \dfrac{z}{2\sqrt{z_0}} = \dfrac{\sqrt{x_0} + \sqrt{y_0} + \sqrt{z_0}}{2}$. But $\sqrt{x_0} + \sqrt{y_0} + \sqrt{z_0} = \sqrt{c}$, so the equation is

$\dfrac{x}{\sqrt{x_0}} + \dfrac{y}{\sqrt{y_0}} + \dfrac{z}{\sqrt{z_0}} = \sqrt{c}$. The x-, y-, and z-intercepts are $\sqrt{cx_0}$, $\sqrt{cy_0}$ and $\sqrt{cz_0}$ respectively. (The x-intercept

is found by setting $y = z = 0$ and solving the resulting equation for x, and the y- and z-intercepts are found

similarly.) So the sum of the intercepts is $\sqrt{c} \left(\sqrt{x_0} + \sqrt{y_0} + \sqrt{z_0} \right) = c$, a constant.

48. Let (x_0, y_0, z_0) be a point on the sphere. Then the normal line is given by $\dfrac{x - x_0}{2x_0} = \dfrac{y - y_0}{2y_0} = \dfrac{z - z_0}{2z_0}$. For the

center $(0, 0, 0)$ to be on the line, we need $-\dfrac{x_0}{2x_0} = -\dfrac{y_0}{2y_0} = -\dfrac{z_0}{2z_0}$ or equivalently $1 = 1 = 1$, which is true.

49. If $f(x, y, z) = z - x^2 - y^2$ and $g(x, y, z) = 4x^2 + y^2 + z^2$, then the tangent line is perpendicular to both ∇f and

∇g at $(-1, 1, 2)$. The vector $\mathbf{v} = \nabla f \times \nabla g$ will therefore be parallel to the tangent line. We have:

$\nabla f(x, y, z) = \langle -2x, -2y, 1 \rangle \Rightarrow \nabla f(-1, 1, 2) = \langle 2, -2, 1 \rangle$, and $\nabla g(x, y, z) = \langle 8x, 2y, 2z \rangle \Rightarrow$

$\nabla g(-1, 1, 2) = \langle -8, 2, 4 \rangle$. Hence $\mathbf{v} = \nabla f \times \nabla g = \begin{vmatrix} \mathbf{i} & \mathbf{j} & \mathbf{k} \\ 2 & -2 & 1 \\ -8 & 2 & 4 \end{vmatrix} = -10\,\mathbf{i} - 16\,\mathbf{j} - 12\,\mathbf{k}$. Parametric equations

are: $x = -1 - 10t$, $y = 1 - 16t$, $z = 2 - 12t$.

50. (a) Let $f(x, y, z) = y + z$ and $g(x, y, z) = x^2 + y^2$. Then the required

tangent line is perpendicular to both ∇f and ∇g at $(1, 2, 1)$ and the

vector $\mathbf{v} = \nabla f \times \nabla g$ is parallel to the tangent line. We have

$\nabla f(x, y, z) = \langle 0, 1, 1 \rangle \quad \Rightarrow \quad \nabla f(1, 2, 1) = \langle 0, 1, 1 \rangle$, and
$\nabla g(x, y, z) = \langle 2x, 2y, 0 \rangle \quad \Rightarrow \quad \nabla g(1, 2, 1) = \langle 2, 4, 0 \rangle$. Hence

$$\mathbf{v} = \nabla f \times \nabla g = \begin{vmatrix} \mathbf{i} & \mathbf{j} & \mathbf{k} \\ 0 & 1 & 1 \\ 2 & 4 & 0 \end{vmatrix} = -4\mathbf{i} + 2\mathbf{j} - 2\mathbf{k}. \text{ So parametric}$$

(b)

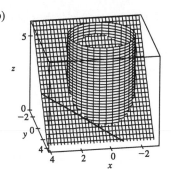

equations of the desired tangent line are $x = 1 - 4t$, $y = 2 + 2t$,
$z = 1 - 2t$.

51. (a) The direction of the normal line of F is given by ∇F, and that of G by ∇G. Assuming that
$\nabla F \neq 0 \neq \nabla G$, the two normal lines are perpendicular at P if $\nabla F \cdot \nabla G = 0$ at $P \quad \Leftrightarrow$
$\langle \partial F/\partial x, \partial F/\partial y, \partial F/\partial z \rangle \cdot \langle \partial G/\partial x, \partial G/\partial y, \partial G/\partial z \rangle = 0$ at $P \quad \Leftrightarrow \quad F_x G_x + F_y G_y + F_z G_z = 0$ at P.

(b) Here $F = x^2 + y^2 - z^2$ and $G = x^2 + y^2 + z^2 - r^2$, so
$\nabla F \cdot \nabla G = \langle 2x, 2y, -2z \rangle \cdot \langle 2x, 2y, 2z \rangle = 4x^2 + 4y^2 - 4z^2 = 4F = 0$, since the point $\langle x, y, z \rangle$ lies on the
graph of $F = 0$. To see that this is true without using calculus, note that $G = 0$ is the equation of a sphere
centered at the origin and $F = 0$ is the equation of a right circular cone with vertex at the origin (which is
generated by lines through the origin). At any point of intersection, the sphere's normal line (which passes
through the origin) lies on the cone, and thus is perpendicular to the cone's normal line. So the surfaces with
equations $F = 0$ and $G = 0$ are everywhere orthogonal.

52. (a) The function $f(x, y) = (xy)^{1/3}$ is continuous on $\mathbb{R}^2$ since it is a composition of a polynomial and the cube root
function, both of which are continuous. (See the text just after Example 8 on page 764.)

$$f_x(0, 0) = \lim_{h \to 0} \frac{f(0 + h, 0) - f(0, 0)}{h} = \lim_{h \to 0} \frac{(h \cdot 0)^{1/3} - 0}{h} = 0,$$

$f_y(0, 0) = \lim_{h \to 0} \dfrac{f(0, 0 + h) - f(0, 0)}{h} = \lim_{h \to 0} \dfrac{(0 \cdot h)^{1/3} - 0}{h} = 0$. Therefore, $f_x(0, 0)$ and $f_y(0, 0)$ do exist

and are equal to 0. Now let $\mathbf{u}$ be any unit vector other than $\mathbf{i}$ and $\mathbf{j}$ (these correspond to f_x and f_y respectively.)
Then $\mathbf{u} = a\mathbf{i} + b\mathbf{j}$ where $a \neq 0$ and $b \neq 0$. Thus

$$D_\mathbf{u} f(0, 0) = \lim_{h \to 0} \frac{f(0 + ha, 0 + hb) - f(0, 0)}{h} = \lim_{h \to 0} \frac{\sqrt[3]{(ha)(hb)}}{h} = \lim_{h \to 0} \frac{\sqrt[3]{ab}}{h^{1/3}} \text{ and this limit does not}$$

exist, so $D_\mathbf{u} f(0, 0)$ does not exist.

(b)

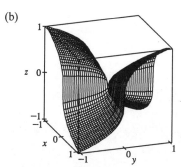

Notice that if we start at the origin and proceed in the direction of
the x- or y-axis, then the graph is flat. But if we proceed in any
other direction, then the graph is extremely steep.

53. Let $\mathbf{u} = \langle a, b \rangle$ and $\mathbf{v} = \langle c, d \rangle$. Then we know that at the given point, $D_{\mathbf{u}} f = \nabla f \cdot \mathbf{u} = a f_x + b f_y$ and $D_{\mathbf{v}} f = \nabla f \cdot \mathbf{v} = c f_x + d f_y$. But these are just two linear equations in the two unknowns f_x and f_y, and since $\mathbf{u}$ and $\mathbf{v}$ are not parallel, we can solve the equations to find $\nabla f = \langle f_x, f_y \rangle$ at the given point. In fact,

$$\nabla f = \left\langle \frac{d D_{\mathbf{u}} f - b D_{\mathbf{v}} f}{ad - bc}, \frac{a D_{\mathbf{v}} f - c D_{\mathbf{u}} f}{ad - bc} \right\rangle.$$

54. Since $z = f(x, y)$ is differentiable at $\mathbf{x}_0 = (x_0, y_0)$, by Definition 11.4.7 we have

$\Delta z = f_x(x_0, y_0) \Delta x + f_y(x_0, y_0) \Delta y + \epsilon_1 \Delta x + \epsilon_2 \Delta y$ where $\epsilon_1, \epsilon_2 \to 0$ as $(\Delta x, \Delta y) \to (0, 0)$. Now $\Delta z = f(\mathbf{x}) - f(\mathbf{x}_0)$, $\langle \Delta x, \Delta y \rangle = \mathbf{x} - \mathbf{x}_0$ so $(\Delta x, \Delta y) \to (0, 0)$ is equivalent to $\mathbf{x} \to \mathbf{x}_0$ and $\langle f_x(x_0, y_0), f_y(x_0, y_0) \rangle = \nabla f(\mathbf{x}_0)$. Substituting into (11.4.7) gives $f(\mathbf{x}) - f(\mathbf{x}_0) = \nabla f(\mathbf{x}_0) \cdot (\mathbf{x} - \mathbf{x}_0) + \langle \epsilon_1, \epsilon_2 \rangle \cdot \langle \Delta x, \Delta y \rangle$ or $\langle \epsilon_1, \epsilon_2 \rangle \cdot (\mathbf{x} - \mathbf{x}_0) = f(\mathbf{x}) - f(\mathbf{x}_0) - \nabla f(\mathbf{x}_0) \cdot (\mathbf{x} - \mathbf{x}_0)$, and so

$$\frac{f(\mathbf{x}) - f(\mathbf{x}_0) - \nabla f(\mathbf{x}_0) \cdot (\mathbf{x} - \mathbf{x}_0)}{|\mathbf{x} - \mathbf{x}_0|} = \frac{\langle \epsilon_1, \epsilon_2 \rangle \cdot (\mathbf{x} - \mathbf{x}_0)}{|\mathbf{x} - \mathbf{x}_0|}. \text{ But } \frac{\mathbf{x} - \mathbf{x}_0}{|\mathbf{x} - \mathbf{x}_0|} \text{ is a}$$

unit vector so $\displaystyle\lim_{\mathbf{x} \to \mathbf{x}_0} \frac{\langle \epsilon_1, \epsilon_2 \rangle \cdot (\mathbf{x} - \mathbf{x}_0)}{|\mathbf{x} - \mathbf{x}_0|} = 0$ since $\epsilon_1, \epsilon_2 \to 0$ as $\mathbf{x} \to \mathbf{x}_0$. Hence

$$\lim_{\mathbf{x} \to \mathbf{x}_0} \frac{f(\mathbf{x}) - f(\mathbf{x}_0) - \nabla f(\mathbf{x}_0) \cdot (\mathbf{x} - \mathbf{x}_0)}{|\mathbf{x} - \mathbf{x}_0|} = 0.$$

11.7 Maximum and Minimum Values · · · · · · · · · ·

1. (a) First we compute $D(1, 1) = f_{xx}(1, 1) f_{yy}(1, 1) - [f_{xy}(1, 1)]^2 = (4)(2) - (1)^2 = 7$. Since $D(1, 1) > 0$ and $f_{xx}(1, 1) > 0$, f has a local minimum at $(1, 1)$ by the Second Derivatives Test.

(b) $D(1, 1) = f_{xx}(1, 1) f_{yy}(1, 1) - [f_{xy}(1, 1)]^2 = (4)(2) - (3)^2 = -1$. Since $D(1, 1) < 0$, f has a saddle point at $(1, 1)$ by the Second Derivatives Test.

2. (a) $D = g_{xx}(0, 2) g_{yy}(0, 2) - [g_{xy}(0, 2)]^2 = (-1)(1) - (6)^2 = -37$. Since $D < 0$, g has a saddle point at $(0, 2)$ by the Second Derivatives Test.

(b) $D = g_{xx}(0, 2) g_{yy}(0, 2) - [g_{xy}(0, 2)]^2 = (-1)(-8) - (2)^2 = 4$. Since $D > 0$ and $g_{xx}(0, 2) < 0$, g has a local maximum at $(0, 2)$ by the Second Derivatives Test.

(c) $D = g_{xx}(0, 2) g_{yy}(0, 2) - [g_{xy}(0, 2)]^2 = (4)(9) - (6)^2 = 0$. In this case the Second Derivatives Test gives no information about g at the point $(0, 2)$.

3. In the figure, a point at approximately $(1, 1)$ is enclosed by level curves which are oval in shape and indicate that as we move away from the point in any direction the values of f are increasing. Hence we would expect a local minimum at or near $(1, 1)$. The level curves near $(0, 0)$ resemble hyperbolas, and as we move away from the origin, the values of f increase in some directions and decrease in others, so we would expect to find a saddle point there.

To verify our predictions, we have $f(x, y) = 4 + x^3 + y^3 - 3xy \Rightarrow f_x(x, y) = 3x^2 - 3y$, $f_y(x, y) = 3y^2 - 3x$. We have critical points where these partial derivatives are equal to 0: $3x^2 - 3y = 0$, $3y^2 - 3x = 0$. Substituting $y = x^2$ from the first equation into the second equation gives $3(x^2)^2 - 3x = 0 \Rightarrow 3x(x^3 - 1) = 0 \Rightarrow x = 0$ or $x = 1$. Then we have two critical points, $(0, 0)$ and $(1, 1)$. The second partial derivatives are $f_{xx}(x, y) = 6x$, $f_{xy}(x, y) = -3$, and $f_{yy}(x, y) = 6y$, so $D(x, y) = f_{xx}(x, y) f_{yy}(x, y) - [f_{xy}(x, y)]^2 = (6x)(6y) - (-3)^2 = 36xy - 9$. Then $D(0, 0) = 36(0)(0) - 9 = -9$, and $D(1, 1) = 36(1)(1) - 9 = 27$. Since $D(0, 0) < 0$, f has a saddle point at $(0, 0)$ by the Second Derivatives Test. Since $D(1, 1) > 0$ and $f_{xx}(1, 1) > 0$, f has a local minimum at $(1, 1)$.

4. In the figure, points at approximately $(-1, 1)$ and $(-1, -1)$ are enclosed by oval-shaped level curves which indicate that as we move away from either point in any direction, the values of f are increasing. Hence we would expect local minima at or near $(-1, \pm 1)$. Similarly, the point $(1, 0)$ appears to be enclosed by oval-shaped level curves which indicate that as we move away from the point in any direction the values of f are decreasing, so we should have a local maximum there. We also show hyperbola-shaped level curves near the points $(-1, 0)$, $(1, 1)$, and $(1, -1)$. The values of f increase along some paths leaving these points and decrease in others, so we should have a saddle point at each of these points.

To confirm our predictions, we have $f(x, y) = 3x - x^3 - 2y^2 + y^4 \Rightarrow f_x(x, y) = 3 - 3x^2$, $f_y(x, y) = -4y + 4y^3$. Setting these partial derivatives equal to 0, we have $3 - 3x^2 = 0 \Rightarrow x = \pm 1$ and $-4y + 4y^3 = 0 \Rightarrow y(y^2 - 1) = 0 \Rightarrow y = 0, \pm 1$. So our critical points are $(\pm 1, 0)$, $(\pm 1, \pm 1)$. The second partial derivatives are $f_{xx}(x, y) = -6x$, $f_{xy}(x, y) = 0$, and $f_{yy}(x, y) = 12y^2 - 4$, so $D(x, y) = f_{xx}(x, y) f_{yy}(x, y) - [f_{xy}(x, y)]^2 = (-6x)(12y^2 - 4) - (0)^2 = -72xy^2 + 24x$. We use the Second Derivatives Test to classify the 6 critical points:

Critical Point	D	f_{xx}	Conclusion
$(1, 0)$	24	-6	$D > 0$, $f_{xx} < 0 \Rightarrow f$ has a local maximum at $(1, 0)$
$(1, 1)$	-48		$D < 0 \Rightarrow f$ has a saddle point at $(1, 1)$
$(1, -1)$	-48		$D < 0 \Rightarrow f$ has a saddle point at $(1, -1)$
$(-1, 0)$	-24		$D < 0 \Rightarrow f$ has a saddle point at $(-1, 0)$
$(-1, 1)$	48	6	$D > 0$, $f_{xx} > 0 \Rightarrow f$ has a local minimum at $(-1, 1)$
$(-1, -1)$	48	6	$D > 0$, $f_{xx} > 0 \Rightarrow f$ has a local minimum at $(-1, -1)$

5. $f(x, y) = 9 - 2x + 4y - x^2 - 4y^2 \Rightarrow f_x = -2 - 2x$, $f_y = 4 - 8y$, $f_{xx} = -2$, $f_{xy} = 0$, $f_{yy} = -8$. Then $f_x = 0$ and $f_y = 0$ imply $x = -1$ and $y = \frac{1}{2}$, and the only critical point is $(-1, \frac{1}{2})$. $D(x, y) = f_{xx} f_{yy} - (f_{xy})^2 = (-2)(-8) - 0^2 = 16$, and since $D(-1, \frac{1}{2}) = 16 > 0$ and $f_{xx}(-1, \frac{1}{2}) = -2 < 0$, $f(-1, \frac{1}{2}) = 11$ is a local maximum by the Second Derivatives Test.

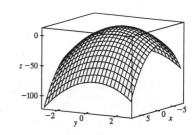

6. $f(x, y) = x^3 y + 12x^2 - 8y$ $\Rightarrow$ $f_x = 3x^2 y + 24x$, $f_y = x^3 - 8$,

$f_{xx} = 6xy + 24$, $f_{xy} = 3x^2$, $f_{yy} = 0$. Then $f_y = 0$ implies $x = 2$,

and substitution into $f_x = 0$ gives $12y + 48 = 0$ $\Rightarrow$ $y = -4$.

Thus, the only critical point is $(2, -4)$.

$D(2, -4) = (-24)(0) - 12^2 = -144 < 0$, so $(2, -4)$ is a saddle

point.

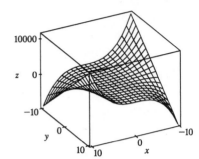

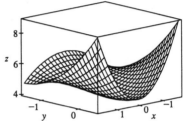

7. $f(x, y) = x^2 + y^2 + x^2 y + 4$ $\Rightarrow$ $f_x = 2x + 2xy$, $f_y = 2y + x^2$,

$f_{xx} = 2 + 2y$, $f_{yy} = 2$, $f_{xy} = 2x$. Then $f_y = 0$ implies $y = -\frac{1}{2}x^2$,

substituting into $f_x = 0$ gives $2x - x^3 = 0$ so $x = 0$ or $x = \pm\sqrt{2}$.

Thus the critical points are $(0, 0)$, $(\sqrt{2}, -1)$ and $(-\sqrt{2}, -1)$. Now

$D(0, 0) = 4$, $D(\sqrt{2}, -1) = -8 = Ds\,(-\sqrt{2}, -1)$, $f_{xx}(0, 0) = 2$,

$f_{xx}(\pm\sqrt{2}, -1) = 0$.

Thus $f(0, 0) = 4$ is a local minimum and $(\pm\sqrt{2}, -1)$ are saddle points.

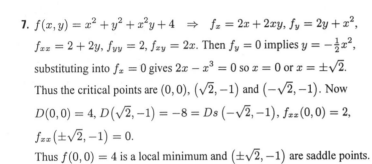

8. $f(x, y) = e^{4y - x^2 - y^2}$ $\Rightarrow$ $f_x = -2xe^{4y - x^2 - y^2}$,

$f_y = (4 - 2y)e^{4y - x^2 - y^2}$, $f_{xx} = (4x^2 - 2)e^{4y - x^2 - y^2}$,

$f_{xy} = -2x(4 - 2y)e^{4y - x^2 - y^2}$,

$f_{yy} = (4y^2 - 16y + 14)e^{4y - x^2 - y^2}$. Then $f_x = 0$ and $f_y = 0$

implies $x = 0$ and $y = 2$, so the only critical point is $(0, 2)$.

$D(0, 2) = (-2e^4)(-2e^4) - 0^2 = 4e^8 > 0$ and

$f_{xx}(0, 2) = -2e^4 < 0$, so $f(0, 2) = e^4$ is a local maximum.

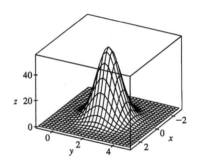

9. $f(x, y) = xy - 2x - y$ $\Rightarrow$ $f_x = y - 2$, $f_y = x - 1$,

$f_{xx} = f_{yy} = 0$, $f_{xy} = 1$ and the only critical point is $(1, 2)$. Now

$D(1, 2) = -1$, so $(1, 2)$ is a saddle point and f has no local

maximum or minimum.

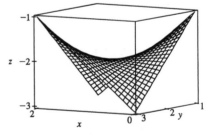

10. $f(x, y) = 2x^3 + xy^2 + 5x^2 + y^2$ $\Rightarrow$ $f_x = 6x^2 + y^2 + 10x$,

$f_y = 2xy + 2y$, $f_{xx} = 12x + 10$, $f_{yy} = 2x + 2$, $f_{xy} = 2y$. Then

$f_y = 0$ implies $y = 0$ or $x = -1$. Substituting into $f_x = 0$ gives the

critical points $(0, 0)$, $\left(-\frac{5}{3}, 0\right)$, $(-1, \pm 2)$. Now $D(0, 0) = 20 > 0$

and $f_{xx}(0, 0) = 10 > 0$, so $f(0, 0) = 0$ is a local minimum. Also

$f_{xx}\left(-\frac{5}{3}, 0\right) < 0$, $D\left(-\frac{5}{3}, 0\right) > 0$, and $D(-1, \pm 2) < 0$. Hence

$f\left(-\frac{5}{3}, 0\right) = \frac{125}{27}$ is a local maximum while $(-1, \pm 2)$ are saddle

points.

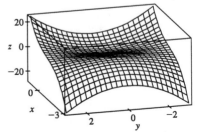

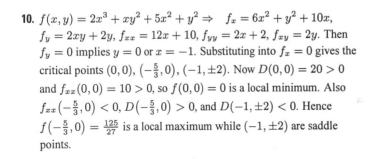

11. $f(x, y) = e^x \cos y$ ⇒ $f_x = e^x \cos y$, $f_y = -e^x \sin y$. Now
$f_x = 0$ implies $\cos y = 0$ or $y = \frac{\pi}{2} + n\pi$ for n an integer. But
$\sin\left(\frac{\pi}{2} + n\pi\right) \neq 0$, so there are no critical points.

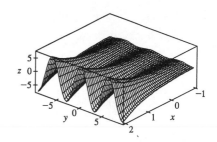

12. $f(x, y) = x^2 + y^2 + \dfrac{1}{x^2 y^2}$ ⇒ $f_x = 2x - 2x^{-3}y^{-2}$,

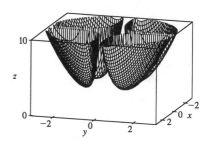

$f_y = 2y - 2x^{-2}y^{-3}$, $f_{xx} = 2 + 6x^{-4}y^{-2}$, $f_{yy} = 2 + 6x^{-2}y^{-4}$,

$f_{xy} = 4x^{-3}y^{-3}$. Then $f_x = 0$ implies $2x^4 y^2 - 2 = 0$ or $x^4 y^2 = 1$

or $y^2 = x^{-4}$. Note that neither x nor y can be zero. Now $f_y = 0$

implies $2x^2 y^4 - 2 = 0$, and with $y^2 = x^{-4}$ this implies

$2x^{-6} - 2 = 0$ or $x^6 = 1$. Thus $x = \pm 1$ and if $x = 1$, $y = \pm 1$; if

$x = -1$, $y = \pm 1$. So the critical points are $(1, 1)$, $(1, -1)$,
$(-1, 1)$ and $(-1, -1)$. Now $D(\pm 1, \pm 1) = D(\pm 1, \mp 1) = 64 - 16 > 0$ and $f_{xx} > 0$ always, so
$f(\pm 1, \pm 1) = f(\pm 1, \mp 1) = 3$ are local minima.

13. $f(x, y) = x \sin y$ ⇒ $f_x = \sin y$, $f_y = x \cos y$, $f_{xx} = 0$,
$f_{yy} = -x \sin y$ and $f_{xy} = \cos y$. Then $f_x = 0$ if and only if
$y = n\pi$, n an integer, and substituting into $f_y = 0$ requires $x = 0$
for each of these y-values. Thus the critical points are $(0, n\pi)$, n
an integer. But $D(0, n\pi) = -\cos^2(n\pi) < 0$ so each critical point
is a saddle point.

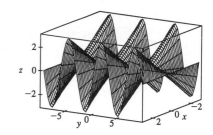

14. $f(x, y) = (2x - x^2)(2y - y^2)$ ⇒ $f_x = (2 - 2x)(2y - y^2)$,
$f_y = (2x - x^2)(2 - 2y)$, $f_{xx} = -2(2y - y^2)$,
$f_{yy} = -2(2x - x^2)$ and $f_{xy} = (2 - 2x)(2 - 2y)$. Then
$f_x = 0$ implies $x = 1$ or $y = 0$ or $y = 2$ and when $x = 1$,
$f_y = 0$ implies $y = 1$, when $y = 0$, $f_y = 0$ implies $x = 0$ or
$x = 2$ and when $y = 2$, $f_y = 0$ implies $x = 0$ or $x = 2$. Thus the

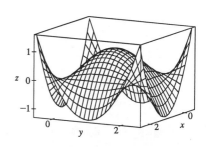

critical points are $(1, 1)$, $(0, 0)$, $(2, 0)$, $(0, 2)$ and $(2, 2)$.

Now $D(0, 0) = D(2, 0) = D(0, 2) = D(2, 2) = -16$ so these critical points are saddle points, and $D(1, 1) = 4$
with $f_{xx}(1, 1) = -2$, so $f(1, 1) = 1$ is a local maximum.

15. $f(x, y) = 3x^2y + y^3 - 3x^2 - 3y^2 + 2$

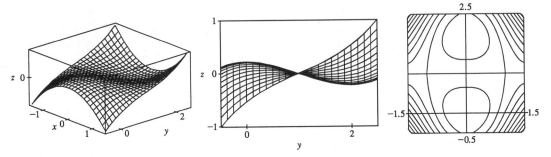

From the graphs, it appears that f has a local maximum $f(0,0) \approx 2$ and a local minimum $f(0,2) \approx -2$. There appear to be saddle points near $(\pm 1, 1)$.

$f_x = 6xy - 6x$, $f_y = 3x^2 + 3y^2 - 6y$. Then $f_x = 0$ implies $x = 0$ or $y = 1$ and when $x = 0$, $f_y = 0$ implies $y = 0$ or $y = 2$; when $y = 1$, $f_y = 0$ implies $x^2 = 1$ or $x = \pm 1$. Thus the critical points are $(0,0)$, $(0,2)$, $(\pm 1, 1)$. Now $f_{xx} = 6y - 6$, $f_{yy} = 6y - 6$ and $f_{xy} = 6x$, so $D(0,0) = D(0,2) = 36 > 0$ while $D(\pm 1, 1) = -36 < 0$ and $f_{xx}(0,0) = -6$, $f_{xx}(0,2) = 6$. Hence $(\pm 1, 1)$ are saddle points while $f(0,0) = 2$ is a local maximum and $f(0,2) = -2$ is a local minimum.

16. $f(x, y) = xye^{-x^2 - y^2}$

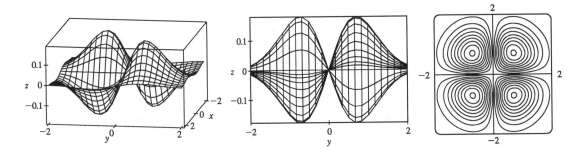

There appear to be local maxima of about $f(\pm 0.7, \pm 0.7) \approx 0.18$ and local minima of about $f(\pm 0.7, \mp 0.7) \approx -0.18$. Also, there seems to be a saddle point at the origin.

$f_x = ye^{-x^2 - y^2}(1 - 2x^2)$, $f_y = xe^{-x^2 - y^2}(1 - 2y^2)$, $f_{xx} = 2xye^{-x^2 - y^2}(2x^2 - 3)$,

$f_{yy} = 2xye^{-x^2 - y^2}(2y^2 - 3)$, $f_{xy} = (1 - 2x^2)e^{-x^2 - y^2}(1 - 2y^2)$. Then $f_x = 0$ implies $y = 0$ or $x = \pm \frac{1}{\sqrt{2}}$.

Substituting these values into $f_y = 0$ gives the critical points $(0,0)$, $\left(\frac{1}{\sqrt{2}}, \pm \frac{1}{\sqrt{2}}\right)$, $\left(-\frac{1}{\sqrt{2}}, \pm \frac{1}{\sqrt{2}}\right)$. Then

$D(x, y) = e^{2(-x^2 - y^2)}\left[4x^2y^2(2x^2 - 3)(2y^2 - 3) - (1 - 2x^2)^2(1 - 2y^2)^2\right]$, so $D(0,0) = -1$, while

$D\left(\frac{1}{\sqrt{2}}, \pm \frac{1}{\sqrt{2}}\right) > 0$ and $D\left(-\frac{1}{\sqrt{2}}, \pm \frac{1}{\sqrt{2}}\right) > 0$. But $f_{xx}\left(\frac{1}{\sqrt{2}}, \frac{1}{\sqrt{2}}\right) < 0$, $f_{xx}\left(\frac{1}{\sqrt{2}}, -\frac{1}{\sqrt{2}}\right) > 0$,

$f_{xx}\left(-\frac{1}{\sqrt{2}}, \frac{1}{\sqrt{2}}\right) > 0$ and $f_{xx}\left(-\frac{1}{\sqrt{2}}, -\frac{1}{\sqrt{2}}\right) < 0$. Hence $(0,0)$ is a saddle point;

$f\left(\frac{1}{\sqrt{2}}, -\frac{1}{\sqrt{2}}\right) = f\left(-\frac{1}{\sqrt{2}}, \frac{1}{\sqrt{2}}\right) = -\frac{1}{2e}$ are local minima and $f\left(\frac{1}{\sqrt{2}}, \frac{1}{\sqrt{2}}\right) = f\left(-\frac{1}{\sqrt{2}}, -\frac{1}{\sqrt{2}}\right) = \frac{1}{2e}$ are local maxima.

17. $f(x, y) = \sin x + \sin y + \sin(x + y)$, $0 \le x \le 2\pi$, $0 \le y \le 2\pi$

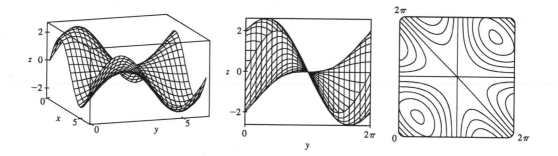

From the graphs it appears that f has a local maximum at about $(1, 1)$ with value approximately 2.6, a local minimum at about $(5, 5)$ with value approximately -2.6, and a saddle point at about $(3, 3)$.
$f_x = \cos x + \cos(x + y)$, $f_y = \cos y + \cos(x + y)$, $f_{xx} = -\sin x - \sin(x + y)$, $f_{yy} = -\sin y - \sin(x + y)$,
$f_{xy} = -\sin(x + y)$. Setting $f_x = 0$ and $f_y = 0$ and subtracting gives $\cos x - \cos y = 0$ or $\cos x = \cos y$. Thus
$x = y$ or $x = 2\pi - y$. If $x = y$, $f_x = 0$ becomes $\cos x + \cos 2x = 0$ or $2\cos^2 x + \cos x - 1 = 0$, a quadratic in
$\cos x$. Thus $\cos x = -1$ or $\frac{1}{2}$ and $x = \pi$, $\frac{\pi}{3}$, or $\frac{5\pi}{3}$, yielding the critical points (π, π), $\left(\frac{\pi}{3}, \frac{\pi}{3}\right)$ and $\left(\frac{5\pi}{3}, \frac{5\pi}{3}\right)$.
Similarly if $x = 2\pi - y$, $f_x = 0$ becomes $(\cos x) + 1 = 0$ and the resulting critical point is (π, π). Now
$D(x, y) = \sin x \sin y + \sin x \sin(x + y) + \sin y \sin(x + y)$. So $D(\pi, \pi) = 0$ and the Second Derivatives Test
doesn't apply. $D\left(\frac{\pi}{3}, \frac{\pi}{3}\right) = \frac{9}{4} > 0$ and $f_{xx}\left(\frac{\pi}{3}, \frac{\pi}{3}\right) < 0$ so $f\left(\frac{\pi}{3}, \frac{\pi}{3}\right) = \frac{3\sqrt{3}}{2}$ is a local maximum while
$D\left(\frac{5\pi}{3}, \frac{5\pi}{3}\right) = \frac{9}{4} > 0$ and $f_{xx}\left(\frac{5\pi}{3}, \frac{5\pi}{3}\right) > 0$, so $f\left(\frac{5\pi}{3}, \frac{5\pi}{3}\right) = -\frac{3\sqrt{3}}{2}$ is a local minimum.

18. $f(x, y) = \sin x + \sin y + \cos(x + y)$, $0 \le x \le \frac{\pi}{4}$, $0 \le y \le \frac{\pi}{4}$

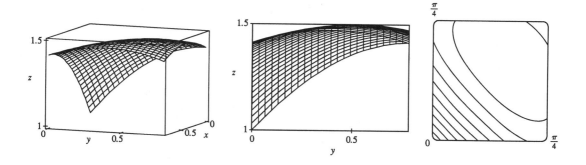

From the graphs, it seems that f has a local maximum at about $(0.5, 0.5)$.
$f_x = \cos x - \sin(x + y)$, $f_y = \cos y - \sin(x + y)$, $f_{xx} = -\sin x - \cos(x + y)$, $f_{yy} = -\sin y - \cos(x + y)$,
$f_{xy} = -\cos(x + y)$. Setting $f_x = 0$ and $f_y = 0$ and subtracting gives $\cos x = \cos y$. Thus $x = y$. Substituting
$x = y$ into $f_x = 0$ gives $\cos x - \sin 2x = 0$ or $\cos x (1 - 2 \sin x) = 0$. But $\cos x \ne 0$ for $0 \le x \le \frac{\pi}{4}$ and
$1 - 2 \sin x = 0$ implies $x = \frac{\pi}{6}$, so the only critical point is $\left(\frac{\pi}{6}, \frac{\pi}{6}\right)$. Here $f_{xx}\left(\frac{\pi}{6}, \frac{\pi}{6}\right) = -1 < 0$ and
$D\left(\frac{\pi}{6}, \frac{\pi}{6}\right) = (-1)^2 - \frac{1}{4} > 0$. Thus $f\left(\frac{\pi}{6}, \frac{\pi}{6}\right) = \frac{3}{2}$ is a local maximum.

19. $f(x,y) = x^4 - 5x^2 + y^2 + 3x + 2 \Rightarrow f_x(x,y) = 4x^3 - 10x + 3$ and $f_y(x,y) = 2y$. $f_y = 0 \Rightarrow y = 0$,

and the graph of f_x shows that the roots of $f_x = 0$ are approximately $x = -1.714, 0.312$ and 1.402. (Alternatively,

we could have used a calculator or a CAS to find these roots.) So to three decimal places, the critical points are

$(-1.714, 0)$, $(1.402, 0)$, and $(0.312, 0)$. Now since $f_{xx} = 12x^2 - 10$, $f_{xy} = 0$, $f_{yy} = 2$, and $D = 24x^2 - 20$, we

have $D(-1.714, 0) > 0$, $f_{xx}(-1.714, 0) > 0$, $D(1.402, 0) > 0$, $f_{xx}(1.402, 0) > 0$, and $D(0.312, 0) < 0$.

Therefore $f(-1.714, 0) \approx -9.200$ and $f(1.402, 0) \approx 0.242$ are local minima, and $(0.312, 0)$ is a saddle point.

The lowest point on the graph is approximately $(-1.714, 0, -9.200)$.

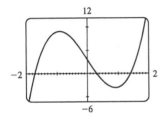
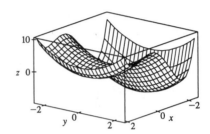

20. $f(x,y) = 5 - 10xy - 4x^2 + 3y - y^4 \Rightarrow f_x(x,y) = -10y - 8x$, $f_y(x,y) = -10x + 3 - 4y^3$. Now

$f_x = 0 \Rightarrow x = -\frac{5}{4}y$, so using a graph, we find solutions to

$0 = f_y\left(-\frac{5}{4}y, y\right) = -10\left(-\frac{5}{4}y\right) + 3 - 4y^3 = -4y^3 + \frac{25}{2}y + 3$. (Alternatively, we could have found the roots of

$f_x = f_y = 0$ directly, using a calculator or a CAS.) To three decimal places, the solutions are $y \approx 1.877, -0.245$

and -1.633, so f has critical points at approximately $(-2.347, 1.877)$, $(0.306, -0.245)$, and $(2.041, -1.633)$.

Now since $f_{xx} = -8$, $f_{xy} = -10$, $f_{yy} = -12y^2$, and $D = 96y^2 - 100$, we have $D(-2.347, 1.877) > 0$,

$D(0.306, -0.245) < 0$, and $D(2.041, -1.633) > 0$. Therefore, since $f_{xx} < 0$ everywhere,

$f(-2.347, 1.877) \approx 20.238$ and $f(2.041, -1.633) \approx 9.657$ are local maxima, and $(0.306, -0.245)$ is a saddle

point. The highest point on the graph is approximately $(-2.347, 1.877, 20.238)$.

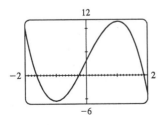
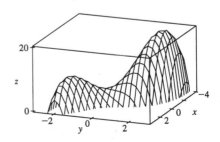

21. $f(x, y) = 2x + 4x^2 - y^2 + 2xy^2 - x^4 - y^4 \Rightarrow f_x(x, y) = 2 + 8x + 2y^2 - 4x^3$,

$f_y(x, y) = -2y + 4xy - 4y^3$. Now $f_y = 0 \Leftrightarrow 2y(2y^2 - 2x + 1) = 0 \Leftrightarrow y = 0$ or $y^2 = x - \frac{1}{2}$.

The first of these implies that $f_x = -4x^3 + 8x + 2$, and the second implies that

$f_x = 2 + 8x + 2(x - \frac{1}{2}) - 4x^3 = -4x^3 + 10x + 1$. From the graphs, we see that the first possibility for f_x has

roots at approximately -1.267, -0.259, and 1.526, and the second has a root at approximately 1.629 (the negative

roots do not give critical points, since $y^2 = x - \frac{1}{2}$ must be positive). So to three decimal places, f has critical points

at $(-1.267, 0)$, $(-0.259, 0)$, $(1.526, 0)$, and $(1.629, \pm 1.063)$. Now since $f_{xx} = 8 - 12x^2$, $f_{xy} = 4y$,

$f_{yy} = 4x - 12y^2$, and $D = (8 - 12x^2)(4x - 12y^2) - 16y^2$, we have $D(-1.267, 0) > 0$, $f_{xx}(-1.267, 0) > 0$,

$D(-0.259, 0) < 0$, $D(1.526, 0) < 0$, $D(1.629, \pm 1.063) > 0$, and $f_{xx}(1.629, \pm 1.063) < 0$. Therefore, to three

decimal places, $f(-1.267, 0) \approx 1.310$ and $f(1.629, \pm 1.063) \approx 8.105$ are local maxima, and $(-0.259, 0)$ and

$(1.526, 0)$ are saddle points. The highest points on the graph are approximately $(1.629, \pm 1.063, 8.105)$.

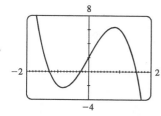 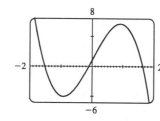 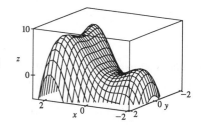

22. $f(x, y) = e^x + y^4 - x^3 + 4 \cos y \Rightarrow f_x(x, y) = e^x - 3x^2$ and $f_y(x, y) = 4y^3 - 4 \sin y$. From the graphs, we

see that to three decimal places, $f_x = 0$ when $x \approx -0.459$, 0.910, or 3.733, and $f_y = 0$ when $y \approx 0$ or ± 0.929.

(Alternatively, we could have used a calculator or a CAS to find the roots of $f_x = 0$ and $f_y = 0$.) So, to three

decimal places, f has critical points at $(-0.459, 0)$, $(-0.459, \pm 0.929)$, $(0.910, 0)$, $(0.910, \pm 0.929)$, $(3.733, 0)$,

and $(3.733, \pm 0.929)$. Now $f_{xx} = e^x - 6x$, $f_{xy} = 0$, $f_{yy} = 12y^2 - 4 \cos y$, and $D = (e^x - 6x)(12y^2 - 4 \cos y)$.

Therefore $D(-0.459, 0) < 0$, $D(-0.459, \pm 0.929) > 0$, $f_{xx}(-0.459, \pm 0.929) > 0$, $D(0.910, 0) > 0$,

$f_{xx}(0.910, 0) < 0$, $D(0.910, \pm 0.929) < 0$, $D(3.733, 0) < 0$, $D(3.733, \pm 0.929) > 0$, and

$f_{xx}(3.733, \pm 0.929) > 0$. So $f(-0.459, \pm 0.929) \approx 3.868$ and $f(3.733, \pm 0.929) \approx -7.077$ are local minima,

$f(0.910, 0) \approx 5.731$ is a local maximum, and $(-0.459, 0)$, $(0.910, \pm 0.929)$, and $(3.733, 0)$ are saddle points. The

lowest points on the graph are approximately $(3.733, \pm 0.929, -7.077)$.

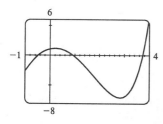 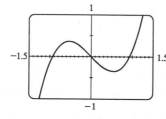 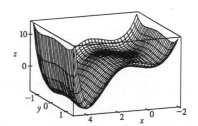

23. Since f is a polynomial it is continuous on D, so an absolute maximum and minimum exist. Here $f_x = 4$, $f_y = -5$ so there are no critical points inside D. Thus the absolute extrema must both occur on the boundary. Along L_1, $x = 0$ and $f(0, y) = 1 - 5y$ for $0 \le y \le 3$, a decreasing function in y, so the maximum value is $f(0, 0) = 1$ and the minimum value is $f(0, 3) = -14$. Along L_2, $y = 0$ and $f(x, 0) = 1 + 4x$ for $0 \le x \le 2$, an increasing function in x, so the minimum value is $f(0, 0) = 1$ and the maximum value is $f(2, 0) = 9$. Along L_3, $y = -\frac{3}{2}x + 3$ and $f\left(x, -\frac{3}{2}x + 3\right) = \frac{23}{2}x - 14$ for $0 \le x \le 2$, an increasing function in x, so the minimum value is $f(0, 3) = -14$ and the maximum value is $f(2, 0) = 9$. Thus the absolue maximum of f on D is $f(2, 0) = 9$ and the absolute minimum is $f(0, 3) = -14$.

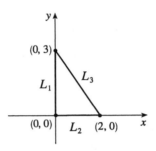

24. Since f is a polynomial it is continuous on D, so an absolute maximum and minimum exist. $f_x = y - 1$, $f_y = x - 2$, and setting $f_x = f_y = 0$ gives $(2, 1)$ as the only critical point, where $f(2, 1) = 1$. Along L_1: $x = 1$ and $f(1, y) = 2 - y$ for $0 \le y \le 4$, a decreasing function in y, so the maximum value is $f(1, 0) = 2$ and the minimum value is $f(1, 4) = -2$. Along L_2: $y = 0$ and $f(x, 0) = 3 - x$ for $1 \le x \le 5$, a decreasing function in x, so the maximum value is $f(1, 0) = 2$ and the minimum value is

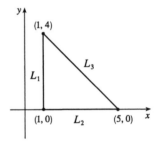

$f(5, 0) = -2$. Along L_3, $y = 5 - x$ and $f(x, 5 - x) = -x^2 + 6x - 7 = -(x - 3)^2 + 2$ for $1 \le x \le 5$, which has a maximum at $x = 3$ where $f(3, 2) = 2$ and a minimum at both $x = 1$ and $x = 5$, where $f(1, 4) = f(5, 0) = -2$. Thus the absolute maximum of f on D is $(1, 0) = f(3, 2) = 2$ and the absolute minimum is $f(1, 4) = f(5, 0) = -2$.

25. In Exercise 7, we found the critical points of f; only $(0, 0)$ with $f(0, 0) = 4$ is in D. On L_1: $y = -1$, $f(x, -1) = 5$, a constant. On L_2: $x = 1$, $f(1, y) = y^2 + y + 5$, a quadratic in y which attains its maximum at $(1, 1)$, $f(1, 1) = 7$ and its minimum at $\left(1, -\frac{1}{2}\right)$, $f\left(1, -\frac{1}{2}\right) = \frac{17}{4}$. On L_3: $f(x, 1) = 2x^2 + 5$ which attains its maximum at $(-1, 1)$ and $(1, 1)$ with $f(\pm 1, 1) = 7$ and its minimum at $(0, 1)$, $f(0, 1) = 5$. On L_4: $f(-1, y) = y^2 + y + 5$ with maximum at $(-1, 1)$, $f(-1, 1) = 7$ and

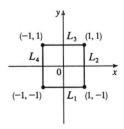

minimum at $\left(-1, -\frac{1}{2}\right)$, $f\left(-1, -\frac{1}{2}\right) = \frac{17}{4}$. Thus the absolute maximum is attained at both $(\pm 1, 1)$ with $f(\pm 1, 1) = 7$ and the absolute minimum on D is attained at $(0, 0)$ with $f(0, 0) = 4$.

26. $f_x(x, y) = 4 - 2x$ and $f_y(x, y) = 6 - 2y$, so the only critical point is $(2, 3)$ (which is in D) where $f(2, 3) = 13$.

Along L_1: $y = 0$, so $f(x, 0) = 4x - x^2 = -(x - 2)^2 + 4$, $0 \le x \le 4$, which has a maximum value when $x = 2$ where $f(2, 0) = 4$ and a minimum value both when $x = 0$ and $x = 4$, where $f(0, 0) = f(4, 0) = 0$. Along L_2: $x = 4$, so $f(4, y) = 6y - y^2 = -(y - 3)^2 + 9$, $0 \le y \le 5$, which has a maximum value when $y = 3$ where $f(4, 3) = 9$ and a minimum value when $y = 0$ where $f(4, 0) = 0$. Along L_3: $y = 5$, so $f(x, 5) = -x^2 + 4x + 5 = -(x - 2)^2 + 9$, $0 \le x \le 4$, which has a maximum value when $x = 2$ where $f(2, 5) = 9$ and a minimum value both when $x = 0$ and $x = 4$, where $f(0, 5) = f(4, 5) = 5$. Along L_4: $x = 0$, so $f(0, y) = 6y - y^2 = -(y - 3)^2 + 9$, $0 \le y \le 5$, which has a maximum value when $y = 3$ where $f(0, 3) = 9$ and a minimum value when $y = 0$ where $f(0, 0) = 0$. Thus the absolute maximum is $f(2, 3) = 13$ and the absolute minimum is attained at both $(0, 0)$ and $(4, 0)$, where $f(0, 0) = f(4, 0) = 0$.

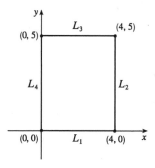

27. $f_x(x, y) = y - 1$ and $f_y(x, y) = x - 1$ and so the critical point is $(1, 1)$ (in D), where $f(1, 1) = 0$. Along L_1: $y = 4$, so $f(x, 4) = 1 + 4x - x - 4 = 3x - 3$, $-2 \le x \le 2$, which is an increasing function and has a maximum value when $x = 2$ where $f(2, 4) = 3$ and a minimum of $f(-2, 4) = -9$.

Along L_2: $y = x^2$, so let $g(x) = f(x, x^2) = x^3 - x^2 - x + 1$. Then $g'(x) = 3x^2 - 2x - 1 = 0 \iff x = -\frac{1}{3}$ or $x = 1$.

$f(-\frac{1}{3}, \frac{1}{9}) = \frac{32}{27}$ and $f(1, 1) = 0$. As a result, the absolute maximum and minimum values of f on D are $f(2, 4) = 3$ and $f(-2, 4) = -9$.

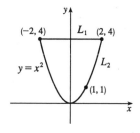

28. $f_x = y^2$ and $f_y = 2xy$, and since $f_x = 0 \iff y = 0$, there are no critical points in the interior of D. Along L_1, $y = 0$ and $f(x, 0) = 0$.

Along L_2, $x = 0$ and $f(0, y) = 0$. Along L_3, $y = \sqrt{3 - x^2}$, so let $g(x) = f(x, \sqrt{3 - x^2}) = 3x - x^3$ for $0 \le x \le \sqrt{3}$. Then $g'(x) = 3 - 3x^2 = 0 \iff x = 1$. The maximum value is $f(1, \sqrt{2}) = 2$ and the minimum occurs both at $x = 0$ and $x = \sqrt{3}$ where $f(0, \sqrt{3}) = f(\sqrt{3}, 0) = 0$.

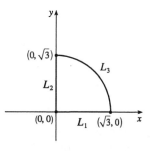

Thus the absolute maximum of f on D is $f(1, \sqrt{2}) = 2$, and the absolute minimum is 0 which occurs at all points along L_1 and L_2.

29. $f(x,y) = -(x^2-1)^2 - (x^2y-x-1)^2$ $\Rightarrow$ $f_x(x,y) = -2(x^2-1)(2x) - 2(x^2y-x-1)(2xy-1)$ and

$f_y(x,y) = -2(x^2y-x-1)x^2$. Setting $f_y(x,y) = 0$ gives either $x = 0$ or $x^2y-x-1 = 0$. There are no

critical points for $x = 0$, since $f_x(0,y) = -2$, so we set $x^2y-x-1 = 0$ $\Leftrightarrow$ $y = \dfrac{x+1}{x^2}$ $(x \neq 0)$, so

$f_x\left(x, \dfrac{x+1}{x^2}\right) = -2(x^2-1)(2x) - 2\left(x^2\dfrac{x+1}{x^2} - x - 1\right)\left(2x\dfrac{x+1}{x^2} - 1\right) = -4x(x^2-1)$. Therefore

$f_x(x,y) = f_y(x,y) = 0$ at the points $(1,2)$ and $(-1,0)$.

To classify these critical points, we calculate

$f_{xx}(x,y) = -12x^2 - 12x^2y^2 + 12xy + 4y + 2$,

$f_{yy}(x,y) = -2x^4$, and $f_{xy}(x,y) = -8x^3y + 6x^2 + 4x$. In order

to use the Second Derivatives Test we calculate

$D(-1,0) = f_{xx}(-1,0)f_{yy}(-1,0) - [f_{xy}(-1,0)]^2$

$= 16 > 0$,

$f_{xx}(-1,0) = -10 < 0$, $D(1,2) = 16 > 0$, and

$f_{xx}(1,2) = -26 < 0$, so both $(-1,0)$ and $(1,2)$ give local

maxima.

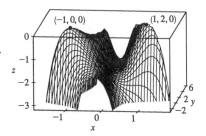

30. $f(x,y) = 3xe^y - x^3 - e^{3y}$ is differentiable everywhere, so the

requirement for critical points is that (1) $f_x = 3e^y - 3x^2 = 0$ and

(2) $f_y = 3xe^y - 3e^{3y} = 0$. From (1) we obtain $e^y = x^2$, and

then (2) gives $3x^3 - 3x^6 = 0$ $\Rightarrow$ $x = 1$ or 0, but only $x = 1$ is

valid, since $x = 0$ makes (1) impossible. So substituting $x = 1$

into (1) gives $y = 0$, and the only critical point is $(1,0)$.

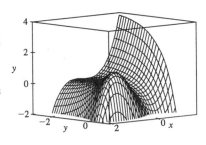

The Second Derivatives Test shows that this gives a local maximum, since

$D(1,0) = \left[-6x(3xe^y - 9e^{3y}) - (3e^y)^2\right]_{(1,0)} = 27 > 0$ and $f_{xx}(1,0) = [-6x]_{(1,0)} = -6 < 0$. But $f(1,0) = 1$

is not an absolute maximum because, for instance, $f(-3,0) = 17$. This can also be seen from the graph.

31. Let d be the distance from $(2,1,-1)$ to any point (x,y,z) on the plane $x + y - z = 1$, so

$d = \sqrt{(x-2)^2 + (y-1)^2 + (z+1)^2}$ where $z = x + y - 1$, and we minimize

$d^2 = f(x,y) = (x-2)^2 + (y-1)^2 + (x+y)^2$. Then $f_x(x,y) = 2(x-2) + 2(x+y) = 4x + 2y - 4$,

$f_y(x,y) = 2(y-1) + 2(x+y) = 2x + 4y - 2$. Solving $4x + 2y - 4 = 0$ and $2x + 4y - 2 = 0$ simultaneously

gives $x = 1$, $y = 0$. An absolute minimum exists (since there is a minimum distance from the point to the plane)

and it must occur at a critical point, so the shortest distance occurs for $x = 1$, $y = 0$ for which

$d = \sqrt{(1-2)^2 + (0-1)^2 + (1+0)^2} = \sqrt{3}$.

32. Here the distance d from a point on the plane to the point $(1, 2, 3)$ is $d = \sqrt{(x-1)^2 + (y-2)^2 + (z-3)^2}$,

where $z = 4 - x + y$. We can minimize $d^2 = f(x, y) = (x-1)^2 + (y-2)^2 + (1-x+y)^2$, so

$f_x(x, y) = 2(x-1) + 2(1 - x + y)(-1) = 4x - 2y - 4$ and

$f_y(x, y) = 2(y-2) + 2(1 - x + y) = 4y - 2x - 2$. Solving $4x - 2y - 4 = 0$ and $4y - 2x - 2 = 0$

simultaneously gives $x = \frac{5}{3}$ and $y = \frac{4}{3}$, so the only critical point is $\left(\frac{5}{3}, \frac{4}{3}\right)$. This point must correspond to the

minimum distance, so the point on the plane closest to $(1, 2, 3)$ is $\left(\frac{5}{3}, \frac{4}{3}, \frac{11}{3}\right)$.

33. Minimize $d^2 = x^2 + y^2 + z^2 = x^2 + y^2 + xy + 1$. Then $f_x = 2x + y$, $f_y = 2y + x$ so the critical point is $(0, 0)$

and $D(0, 0) = 4 - 1 > 0$ with $f_{xx}(0, 0) = 2$ so this is a minimum. Thus $z^2 = 1$ or $z = \pm 1$ and the points on the

surface are $(0, 0, \pm 1)$.

34. Since $z = 1/(x^2 y^2)$ on the surface, we minimize $d^2 = x^2 + y^2 + z^2 = x^2 + y^2 + x^{-4} y^{-4} = f(x, y)$.

$f_x = 2x - \dfrac{4}{x^5 y^4}$, $f_y = 2y - \dfrac{4}{x^4 y^5}$, so the critical points occur when $2x = \dfrac{4}{x^5 y^4}$ and $2y = \dfrac{4}{x^4 y^5}$ or

$x^6 y^4 = 2 = x^4 y^6$, so $x^2 = y^2 \;\Rightarrow\; x = \pm y$ and $x^{10} = 2 \;\Rightarrow\; x = \pm 2^{1/10}, y = \pm 2^{1/10}$. The four critical

points are $\left(\pm 2^{1/10}, \pm 2^{1/10}\right)$. The absolute minimum must occur at these points (there is no maximum since the

surface is infinite in extent). Thus the points on the surface closest to the origin are $\left(\pm 2^{1/10}, \pm 2^{1/10}, 2^{-2/5}\right)$.

35. $x + y + z = 100$, so maximize $f(x, y) = xy(100 - x - y)$. $f_x = 100y - 2xy - y^2$, $f_y = 100x - x^2 - 2xy$,

$f_{xx} = -2y$, $f_{yy} = -2x$, $f_{xy} = 100 - 2x - 2y$. Then $f_x = 0$ implies $y = 0$ or $y = 100 - 2x$. Substituting $y = 0$

into $f_y = 0$ gives $x = 0$ or $x = 100$ and substituting $y = 100 - 2x$ into $f_y = 0$ gives $3x^2 - 100x = 0$ so $x = 0$ or

$\frac{100}{3}$. Thus the critical points are $(0, 0)$, $(100, 0)$, $(0, 100)$ and $\left(\frac{100}{3}, \frac{100}{3}\right)$.

$D(0, 0) = D(100, 0) = D(0, 100) = -10{,}000$ while $D\left(\frac{100}{3}, \frac{100}{3}\right) = \frac{10{,}000}{3}$ and $f_{xx}\left(\frac{100}{3}, \frac{100}{3}\right) = -\frac{200}{3} < 0$.

Thus $(0, 0)$, $(100, 0)$ and $(0, 100)$ are saddle points whereas $f\left(\frac{100}{3}, \frac{100}{3}\right)$ is a local maximum. Thus the numbers are

$x = y = z = \frac{100}{3}$.

36. Maximize $f(x, y) = x^a y^b (100 - x - y)^c$.

$f_x = ax^{a-1} y^b (100 - x - y)^c - cx^a y^b (100 - x - y)^{c-1} = x^{a-1} y^b (100 - x - y)^{c-1} [a(100 - x - y) - cx]$

and $f_y = x^a y^{b-1} (100 - x - y)^{c-1} [b(100 - x - y) - cy]$. Since x, y and z are all positive, the only critical point

occurs when $x = a\dfrac{100 - y}{a + c}$ and $y = \dfrac{100b}{a + b + c}$. Thus the point is $\left(\dfrac{100a}{a + b + c}, \dfrac{100b}{a + b + c}\right)$ and the numbers are

$x = \dfrac{100a}{a + b + c}, y = \dfrac{100b}{a + b + c}, z = \dfrac{100c}{a + b + c}$.

37. Maximize $f(x, y) = xy\left(36 - 9x^2 - 36y^2\right)^{1/2}/2$ with (x, y, z) in first octant. Then

$$f_x = \frac{y\left(36 - 9x^2 - 36y^2\right)^{1/2}}{2} + \frac{-9x^2y\left(36 - 9x^2 - 36y^2\right)^{-1/2}}{2} = \frac{\left(36y - 18x^2y - 36y^3\right)}{2\left(36 - 9x^2 - 36y^2\right)^{1/2}}\ \text{and}$$

$$f_y = \frac{36x - 9x^3 - 72xy^2}{2\left(36 - 9x^2 - 36y^2\right)^{1/2}}.\ \text{Setting } f_x = 0 \text{ gives } y = 0 \text{ or } y^2 = \frac{2 - x^2}{2}\ \text{but } y > 0, \text{ so only the latter solution}$$

applies. Substituting this y into $f_y = 0$ gives $x^2 = \frac{4}{3}$ or $x = \frac{2}{\sqrt{3}}$, $y = \frac{1}{\sqrt{3}}$ and then $z^2 = (36 - 12 - 12)/4 = 3$.

The fact that this gives a maximum volume follows from the geometry. This maximum volume is

$$V = (2x)(2y)(2z) = 8\left(\frac{2}{\sqrt{3}}\right)\left(\frac{1}{\sqrt{3}}\right)\left(\sqrt{3}\right) = \frac{16}{\sqrt{3}}.$$

38. Here maximize $f(x, y) = xy\dfrac{\left(a^2b^2c^2 - b^2c^2x^2 - a^2c^2y^2\right)^{1/2}}{a^2b^2}$. Then

$$f_x = yc^2 \frac{a^2b^2 - 2b^2x^2 - a^2y^2}{a^2b^2\left(a^2b^2c^2 - b^2c^2x^2 - a^2c^2y^2\right)^{1/2}}\ \text{and}\ f_y = xc^2 \frac{a^2b^2 - 2a^2y^2 - b^2x^2}{a^2b^2\left(a^2b^2c^2 - b^2c^2x^2 - a^2c^2y^2\right)^{1/2}}.\ \text{Then}$$

$f_x = 0$ (with $x, y > 0$) implies $y^2 = \dfrac{a^2b^2 - 2b^2x^2}{a^2}$ and substituting into $f_y = 0$ implies $3b^2x^2 = a^2b^2$ or

$x = \frac{1}{\sqrt{3}}\,a$, $y = \frac{1}{\sqrt{3}}\,b$ and then $z = \frac{1}{\sqrt{3}}\,c$. Thus the maximum volume of such a rectangle is

$$V = (2x)(2y)(2z) = \frac{8}{3\sqrt{3}}\,abc.$$

39. Maximize $f(x, y) = \dfrac{xy}{3}\,(6 - x - 2y)$, then the maximum volume is $V = xyz$.

$f_x = \frac{1}{3}\left(6y - 2xy - y^2\right) = \frac{1}{3}y\left(6 - 2x - 2y\right)$ and $f_y = \frac{1}{3}x\left(6 - x - 4y\right)$. Setting $f_x = 0$ and $f_y = 0$ gives the

critical point $(2, 1)$ which geometrically must yield a maximum. Thus the volume of the largest such box is

$$V = (2)(1)\left(\tfrac{2}{3}\right) = \tfrac{4}{3}.$$

40. Surface area $= 2(xy + xz + yz) = 64\ \text{cm}^2$, so $xy + xz + yz = 32$ or $z = \dfrac{32 - xy}{x + y}$. Maximize the volume

$$f(x, y) = xy\frac{32 - xy}{x + y}.\ \text{Then } f_x = \frac{32y^2 - 2xy^3 - x^2y^2}{(x + y)^2} = y^2\frac{32 - 2xy - x^2}{(x + y)^2}\ \text{and}$$

$$f_y = x^2\frac{32 - 2xy - y^2}{(x + y)^2}.\ \text{Setting } f_x = 0 \text{ implies } y = \frac{32 - x^2}{2x}\ \text{and substituting into } f_y = 0 \text{ gives}$$

$32\left(4x^2\right) - \left(32 - x^2\right)\left(4x^2\right) - \left(32 - x^2\right)^2 = 0$ or $3x^4 + 64x^2 - (32)^2 = 0$. Thus $x^2 = \frac{64}{6}$ or $x = \frac{8}{\sqrt{6}}$,

$y = \frac{64/3}{16/\sqrt{6}} = \frac{8}{\sqrt{6}}$ and $z = \frac{8}{\sqrt{6}}$. Thus the box is a cube with edge length $\frac{8}{\sqrt{6}}$ cm.

41. Let the dimensions be x, y, and z; then $4x + 4y + 4z = c$ and the volume is

$V = xyz = xy\left(\frac{1}{4}c - x - y\right) = \frac{1}{4}cxy - x^2y - xy^2$, $x > 0$, $y > 0$. Then $V_x = \frac{1}{4}cy - 2xy - y^2$ and

$V_y = \frac{1}{4}cx - x^2 - 2xy$, so $V_x = 0 = V_y$ when $2x + y = \frac{1}{4}c$ and $x + 2y = \frac{1}{4}c$. Solving, we get $x = \frac{1}{12}c$, $y = \frac{1}{12}c$

and $z = \frac{1}{4}c - x - y = \frac{1}{12}c$. From the geometrical nature of the problem, this critical point must give an absolute

maximum. Thus the box is a cube with edge length $\frac{1}{12}c$.

42. The cost equals $5xy + 2(xz + yz)$ and $xyz = V$, so

$C(x,y) = 5xy + 2V(x+y)/(xy) = 5xy + 2V\left(x^{-1} + y^{-1}\right)$. Then $C_x = 5y - 2Vx^{-2}$, $C_y = 5x - 2Vy^{-2}$,

$f_x = 0$ implies $y = 2V/(5x^2)$, $f_y = 0$ implies $x = \sqrt[3]{\frac{2}{5}V} = y$. Thus the dimensions of the box which minimize

the cost are $x = y = \sqrt[3]{\frac{2}{5}V}$ units, $z = V^{1/3}\left(\frac{5}{2}\right)^{2/3}$.

43. Let the dimensions be x, y and z, then minimize $xy + 2(xz + yz)$ if $xyz = 32{,}000 \text{ m}^3$. Then

$f(x,y) = xy + [64{,}000(x+y)/xy] = xy + 64{,}000\left(x^{-1} + y^{-1}\right)$, $f_x = y - 64{,}000x^{-2}$, $f_y = x - 64{,}000y^{-2}$.

And $f_x = 0$ implies $y = 64{,}000/x^2$; substituting into $f_y = 0$ implies $x^3 = 64{,}000$ or $x = 40$ and then $y = 40$.

Now $D(x,y) = [(2)(64{,}000)]^2\, x^{-3}y^{-3} - 1 > 0$ for $(40, 40)$ and $f_{xx}(40, 40) > 0$ so this is indeed a minimum.

Thus the dimensions of the box are $x = y = 40$ cm, $z = 20$ cm.

44. Since $p + q + r = 1$ we can substitute $p = 1 - r - q$ into P giving

$P = P(q,r) = 2(1 - r - q)q + 2(1 - r - q)r + 2rq = 2q - 2q^2 + 2r - 2r^2 - 2rq$. Since p, q and r represent

proportions and $p + q + r = 1$, we know $q \geq 0$, $r \geq 0$, and $q + r \leq 1$. Thus, we want to find the absolute

maximum of the continuous function $P(q,r)$ on the closed set D enclosed by the lines $q = 0$, $r = 0$, and

$q + r = 1$. To find any critical points, we set the partial derivatives equal to zero: $P_q\,(q,r) = 2 - 4q - 2r = 0$ and

$P_r(q,r) = 2 - 4r - 2q = 0$. The first equation gives $r = 1 - 2q$, and substituting into the second equation we have

$2 - 4(1 - 2q) - 2q = 0 \;\Rightarrow\; q = \frac{1}{3}$. Then we have one critical point, $\left(\frac{1}{3}, \frac{1}{3}\right)$, where $P\left(\frac{1}{3}, \frac{1}{3}\right) = \frac{2}{3}$. Next we find

the maximum values of P on the boundary of D which consists of three line segments. For the segment given by

$r = 0, 0 \leq q \leq 1$, $P(q,r) = P(q,0) = 2q - 2q^2, 0 \leq q \leq 1$. This represents a parabola with maximum value

$P\left(\frac{1}{2}, 0\right) = \frac{1}{2}$. On the segment $q = 0, 0 \leq r \leq 1$ we have $P(0,r) = 2r - 2r^2, 0 \leq r \leq 1$. This represents a

parabola with maximum value $P\left(0, \frac{1}{2}\right) = \frac{1}{2}$. Finally, on the segment $q + r = 1, 0 \leq q \leq 1$,

$P(q,r) = P(q, 1 - q) = 2q - 2q^2, 0 \leq q \leq 1$ which has a maximum value of $P\left(\frac{1}{2}, \frac{1}{2}\right) = \frac{1}{2}$. Comparing these

values with the value of P at the critical point, we see that the absolute maximum value of $P(q,r)$ on D is $\frac{2}{3}$.

45. Note that here the variables are m and b, and $f(m,b) = \sum\limits_{i=1}^{n} [y_i - (mx_i + b)]^2$. Then

$f_m = \sum\limits_{i=1}^{n} -2x_i[y_i - (mx_i + b)] = 0$ implies $\sum\limits_{i=1}^{n} \left(x_iy_i - mx_i^2 - bx_i\right) = 0$ or $\sum\limits_{i=1}^{n} x_iy_i = m\sum\limits_{i=1}^{n} x_i^2 + b\sum\limits_{i=1}^{n} x_i$

and $f_b = \sum\limits_{i=1}^{n} -2[y_i - (mx_i + b)] = 0$ implies $\sum\limits_{i=1}^{n} y_i = m\sum\limits_{i=1}^{n} x_i + \sum\limits_{i=1}^{n} b = m\left(\sum\limits_{i=1}^{n} x_i\right) + nb$. Thus we have

the two desired equations. Now $f_{mm} = \sum\limits_{i=1}^{n} 2x_i^2$, $f_{bb} = \sum\limits_{i=1}^{n} 2 = 2n$ and $f_{mb} = \sum\limits_{i=1}^{n} 2x_i$. And $f_{mm}(m,b) > 0$

always and $D(m,b) = 4n\left(\sum\limits_{i=1}^{n} x_i^2\right) - 4\left(\sum\limits_{i=1}^{n} x_i\right)^2 = 4\left[n\left(\sum\limits_{i=1}^{n} x_i^2\right) - \left(\sum\limits_{i=1}^{n} x_i\right)^2\right] > 0$ always so the

solutions of these two equations do indeed minimize $\sum\limits_{i=1}^{n} d_i^2$.

46. Any such plane must cut out a tetrahedron in the first octant. We need to minimize the volume of the tetrahedron

that passes through the point $(1, 2, 3)$. Writing the equation of the plane as $\dfrac{x}{a} + \dfrac{y}{b} + \dfrac{z}{c} = 1$, the volume of the

tetrahedron is given by $V = \dfrac{abc}{6}$. But $(1, 2, 3)$ must lie on the plane, so we need $\dfrac{1}{a} + \dfrac{2}{b} + \dfrac{3}{c} = 1$ (★) and thus can

think of c as a function of a and b. Then $V_a = \dfrac{b}{6}\left(c + a\,\dfrac{\partial c}{\partial a}\right)$ and $V_b = \dfrac{a}{6}\left(c + b\,\dfrac{\partial c}{\partial b}\right)$. Differentiating (★) with

respect to a we get $-a^{-2} - 3c^{-2}\,\dfrac{\partial c}{\partial a} = 0 \;\Rightarrow\; \dfrac{\partial c}{\partial a} = \dfrac{-c^2}{3a^2}$, and differentiating (★) with respect to b gives

$-2b^{-2} - 3c^{-2}\,\dfrac{\partial c}{\partial b} = 0 \;\Rightarrow\; \dfrac{\partial c}{\partial b} = \dfrac{-2c^2}{3b^2}$. Then $V_a = \dfrac{b}{6}\left(c + a\,\dfrac{-c^2}{3a^2}\right) = 0 \;\Rightarrow\; c = 3a$, and

$V_b = \dfrac{a}{6}\left(c + b\,\dfrac{-2c^2}{3b^2}\right) = 0 \;\Rightarrow\; c = \tfrac{3}{2}b$. Thus $3a = \tfrac{3}{2}b$ or $b = 2a$. Putting these into (★) gives $\tfrac{3}{a} = 1$ or $a = 3$

and then $b = 6$, $c = 9$. Thus the equation of the required plane is $\dfrac{x}{3} + \dfrac{y}{6} + \dfrac{z}{9} = 1$ or $6x + 3y + 2z = 18$.

| **Applied Project** | **Designing a Dumpster** |

Note: The difficulty and results of this project vary widely with the type of container studied. In addition to the variation of basic shapes of containers, dumpsters may include additional constructed parts such as supports, lift pockets, wheels, etc. Also, a CAS or graphing utility may be needed to solve the resulting equations.
Here we present a typical solution for one particular trash dumpster.

1. The basic shape and dimensions (in inches) of an actual trash dumpster are as shown in the figure.

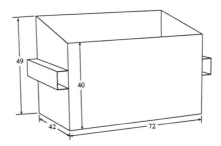

The front and back, as well as both sides, have an extra one-inch-wide flap that is folded under and welded to the base. In addition, the side panels each fold over one inch onto the front and back pieces where they are welded. Each side has a rectangular lift pocket, with cross-section 5 by 8 inches, made of the same material. These are attached with an extra one-inch width of steel on both top and bottom where each pocket is welded to the side sheet. All four sides have a "lip" at the top; the front and back panels have an extra 5 inches of steel at the top which is folded outward in three creases to form a rectangular tube. The edge is then welded back to the main sheet. The two sides form a top lip with separate sheets of steel 5 inches wide, similarly bent into three sides and welded to the main sheets (requiring two welds each). These extend beyond the main side sheets by 1.5 inches at each end in order to join with the lips on the front and back panels. The container has a hinged lid, extra steel supports on the base at each corner, metal "fins" serving as extra support for the side lift pockets, and wheels underneath. The volume of the container is $V = \tfrac{1}{2}(40 + 49) \times 42 \times 72 = 134{,}568 \text{ in}^3$ or 77.875 ft^3.

2. First, we assume that some aspects of the construction do not change with different dimensions, so they may be considered fixed costs. This includes the lid (with hinges), wheels, and extra steel supports. Also, the upper "lip" we previously described extends beyond the side width to connect to the other pieces. We can safely assume that this extra portion, including any associated welds, costs the same regardless of the container's dimensions, so we will consider just the portion matching the measurement of the side panels in our calculations. We will further assume that the angle of the top of the container should be preserved. Then to compute the variable costs, let x be the width, y the length, and z the height of the front of the container. The back of the container is 9 inches, or $\frac{3}{4}$ ft, taller than the front, so using similar triangles we can say the back panel has height $z + \frac{3}{14}x$. Measuring in feet, we want the volume to remain constant, so $V = \frac{1}{2}\left(z + z + \frac{3}{14}x\right)(x)(y) = xyz + \frac{3}{28}x^2y = 77.875$. To determine a function for the variable cost, we first find the area of each sheet of metal needed. The base has area xy ft^2. The front panel has visible area yz plus $\frac{1}{12}y$ for the portion folded onto the base and $\frac{5}{12}y$ for the steel at the top used to form the lip, so $\left(yz + \frac{1}{2}y\right)$ ft^2 in total. Similarly, the back sheet has area $y\left(z + \frac{3}{14}x\right) + \frac{1}{12}y + \frac{5}{12}y = yz + \frac{3}{14}xy + \frac{1}{2}y$. Each side has visible area $\frac{1}{2}s\left[z + \left(z + \frac{3}{14}x\right)\right](x)$, and the sheet includes one-inch flaps folding onto the front and back panels, so with area $\frac{1}{12}z$ and $\frac{1}{12}\left(z + \frac{3}{14}x\right)$, and a one-inch flap to fold onto the base with area $\frac{1}{12}x$. The lift pocket is constructed of a piece of steel 20 inches by x ft (including the 2 extra inches used by the welds). The additional metal used to make the lip at the top of the panel has width 5 inches and length that we can determine using the Pythagorean Theorem: $x^2 + \left(\frac{3}{14}x\right)^2 = \text{length}^2$, so $\text{length} = \frac{\sqrt{205}}{14}x \approx 1.0227x$. Thus the area of steel needed for each side panel is approximately

$$\frac{1}{2}\left[z + \left(z + \frac{3}{14}x\right)\right](x) + \frac{1}{12}z + \frac{1}{12}\left(z + \frac{3}{14}x\right) + \frac{1}{12}x + \frac{5}{3}x + \frac{5}{12}(1.0227x) \approx xz + \frac{3}{28}x^2 + \frac{1}{6}z + 2.194x$$

We also have the following welds:

Weld	Length
Front, back welded to base	$2y$
Sides welded to base	$2x$
Sides welded to front	$2z$
Sides welded to back	$2\left(z + \frac{3}{14}x\right)$
Weld on front and back lip	$2y$
Two welds on each side lip	$4(1.0227x)$
Two welds for each lift pocket	$4x$

Thus the total length of welds needed is

$$2y + 2x + 2z + 2\left(z + \frac{3}{14}x\right) + 2y + 4(1.0227x) + 4x \approx 10.519x + 4y + 4z$$

Finally, the total variable cost is approximately

$$0.90(xy) + 0.70\left[(yz + \tfrac{1}{2}y) + \left(yz + \tfrac{3}{14}xy + \tfrac{1}{2}y\right) + 2\left(xz + \tfrac{3}{28}x^2 + \tfrac{1}{6}z + 2.194x\right)\right]$$

$$+ 0.18(10.519x + 4y + 4z)$$

$$\approx 1.05xy + 1.4yz + 1.42y + 1.4xz + 0.15x^2 + 0.953z + 4.965x$$

We would like to minimize this function while keeping volume constant, so since $xyz + \tfrac{3}{28}x^2y = 77.875$ we

can substitute $z = \dfrac{77.875}{xy} - \dfrac{3}{28}x$ giving variable cost as a function of x and y:

$$C(x, y) \approx 0.9xy + \dfrac{109.0}{x} + 1.42y + \dfrac{109.0}{y} + \dfrac{74.2}{xy} + 4.86x. \text{ Using a CAS, we solve the system of equations}$$

$C_x(x, y) = 0$ and $C_y(x, y) = 0$; the only critical point within an appropriate domain is approximately $(3.58, 5.29)$.

From the nature of the function C (or from a graph) we can determine that C has an absolute minimum at

$(3.58, 5.29)$, and so the minimum cost is attained for $x \approx 3.58$ ft (or 43.0 in), $y \approx 5.29$ ft (or 63.5 in), and

$z \approx \frac{77.875}{3.58(5.29)} - \frac{3}{28}(3.58) \approx 3.73$ ft (or 44.8 in).

3. The fixed cost aspects of the container which we did not include in our calculations, such as the wheels and lid, don't affect the validity of our results. Some of our other assumptions, however, may influence the accuracy of our findings. We simplified the price of the steel sheets to include cuts and bends, and we simplified the price of welding to include the labor and materials. This may not be accurate for areas of the container, such as the lip and lift pockets, that require several cuts, bends, and welds in a relatively small surface area. Consequently, increasing some dimensions of the container may not increase the cost in the same manner as our computations predict. If we do not assume that the angle of the sloped top of the container must be preserved, it is likely that we could farther improve our cost. Finally, our results show that the length of the container should be changed to minimize cost; this may not be possible if the two lift pockets must remain a fixed distance apart for handling by machinery.

4. The minimum variable cost using our values found in Problem 2 is $C(3.58, 5.29) \approx \$96.95$, while the current dimensions give an estimated variable cost of $C(3.5, 6.0) \approx \$97.30$. If we determine that our assumptions and simplifications are acceptable, our work shows that a slight savings can be gained by adjusting the dimensions of the container. However, the difference in cost is modest, and may not justify changes in the manufacturing process.

Discovery Project	**Quadratic Approximations and Critical Points**

1. $Q(x, y) = f(a, b) + f_x(a, b)(x - a) + f_y(a, b)(y - b) + \tfrac{1}{2}f_{xx}(a, b)(x - a)^2$

$$+ f_{xy}(a, b)(x - a)(y - b) + \tfrac{1}{2}f_{yy}(a, b)(y - b)^2,$$

so

$$Q_x(x, y) = f_x(a, b) + \tfrac{1}{2}f_{xx}(a, b)(2)(x - a) + f_{xy}(a, b)(y - b)$$

$$= f_x(a, b) + f_{xx}(a, b)(x - a) + f_{xy}(a, b)(y - b)$$

At (a, b) we have $Q_x(a, b) = f_x(a, b) + f_{xx}(a, b)(a - a) + f_{xy}(a, b)(b - b) = f_x(a, b)$. Similarly,
$Q_y(x, y) = f_y(a, b) + f_{xy}(a, b)(x - a) + f_{yy}(a, b)(y - b)$ $\Rightarrow$
$Q_y(a, b) = f_y(a, b) + f_{xy}(a, b)(a - a) + f_{yy}(a, b)(b - b) = f_y(a, b)$. For the second-order partial derivatives we have

$$Q_{xx}(x, y) = \frac{\partial}{\partial x}\left[f_x(a, b) + f_{xx}(a, b)(x - a) + f_{xy}(a, b)(y - b)\right] = f_{xx}(a, b)$$

$$\Rightarrow Q_{xx}(a, b) = f_{xx}(a, b)$$

$$Q_{xy}(x, y) = \frac{\partial}{\partial y}\left[f_x(a, b) + f_{xx}(a, b)(x - a) + f_{xy}(a, b)(y - b)\right] = f_{xy}(a, b)$$

$$\Rightarrow Q_{xy}(a, b) = f_{xy}(a, b)$$

$$Q_{yy}(x, y) = \frac{\partial}{\partial y}\left[f_y(a, b) + f_{xy}(a, b)(x - a) + f_{yy}(a, b)(y - b)\right] = f_{yy}(a, b)$$

$$\Rightarrow Q_{yy}(a, b) = f_{yy}(a, b)$$

2. (a) First we find the partial derivatives and values that will be needed:

$$f(x, y) = e^{-x^2 - y^2} \qquad\qquad f(0, 0) = 1$$

$$f_x(x, y) = -2xe^{-x^2 - y^2} \qquad\qquad f_x(0, 0) = 0$$

$$f_y(x, y) = -2ye^{-x^2 - y^2} \qquad\qquad f_y(0, 0) = 0$$

$$f_{xx}(x, y) = \left(4x^2 - 2\right)e^{-x^2 - y^2} \qquad f_{xx}(0, 0) = -2$$

$$f_{xy}(x, y) = 4xye^{-x^2 - y^2} \qquad\qquad f_{xy}(0, 0) = 0$$

$$f_{yy}(x, y) = \left(4y^2 - 2\right)e^{-x^2 - y^2} \qquad f_{yy}(0, 0) = -2$$

Then the first-degree Taylor polynomial of f at $(0, 0)$ is

$$L(x, y) = f(0, 0) + f_x(0, 0)(x - 0) + f_y(0, 0)(y - 0) = 1 + (0)(x - 0) + (0)(y - 0)$$

$$= 1$$

The second-degree Taylor polynomial is given by

$$Q(x, y) = f(0, 0) + f_x(0, 0)(x - 0) + f_y(0, 0)(y - 0) + \tfrac{1}{2}f_{xx}(0, 0)(x - 0)^2$$

$$+ f_{xy}(0, 0)(x - 0)(y - 0) + \tfrac{1}{2}f_{yy}(0, 0)(y - 0)^2$$

$$= 1 - x^2 - y^2$$

(b)

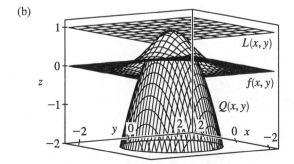

As we see from the graph, L approximates f well only for points (x, y) extremely close to the origin. Q is a much better approximation; the shape of its graph looks similar to that of the graph of f near the origin, and the values of Q appear to be good estimates for the values of f within a significant radius of the origin.

3. (a) First we find the partial derivatives and values that will be needed:

$$f(x, y) = xe^y \qquad f(1, 0) = 1 \qquad\qquad f_{xx}(x, y) = 0 \qquad f_{xx}(1, 0) = 0$$

$$f_x(x, y) = e^y \qquad f_x(1, 0) = 1 \qquad\qquad f_{xy}(x, y) = e^y \qquad f_{xy}(1, 0) = 1$$

$$f_y(x, y) = xe^y \qquad f_y(1, 0) = 1 \qquad\qquad f_{yy}(x, y) = xe^y \qquad f_{yy}(1, 0) = 1$$

Then the first-degree Taylor polynomial of f at $(1, 0)$ is

$$L(x, y) = f(1, 0) + f_x(1, 0)(x - 1) + f_y(1, 0)(y - 0)$$
$$= 1 + (1)(x - 1) + (1)(y - 0)$$
$$= x + y$$

The second-degree Taylor polynomial is given by

$$Q(x, y) = f(1, 0) + f_x(1, 0)(x - 1) + f_y(1, 0)(y - 0) + \tfrac{1}{2} f_{xx}(1, 0)(x - 1)^2$$
$$\qquad\qquad + f_{xy}(1, 0)(x - 1)(y - 0) + \tfrac{1}{2} f_{yy}(1, 0)(y - 0)^2$$
$$= \tfrac{1}{2}y^2 + x + xy$$

(b)
$$L(0.9, 0.1) = 0.9 + 0.1 = 1.0$$
$$Q(0.9, 0.1) = \tfrac{1}{2}(0.1)^2 + 0.9 + (0.9)(0.1) = 0.995$$
$$f(0.9, 0.1) = 0.9e^{0.1} \approx 0.9947$$

(c)

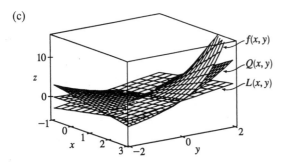

As we see from the graph, L and Q both approximate f reasonably well near the point $(1, 0)$. As we venture farther from the point, the graph of Q follows the shape of the graph of f more closely than L.

4. (a) $f(x, y) = ax^2 + bxy + cy^2 = a\left[x^2 + \dfrac{b}{a} xy + \dfrac{c}{a} y^2 \right]$

$$= a\left[x^2 + \dfrac{b}{a} xy + \left(\dfrac{b}{2a} y \right)^2 - \left(\dfrac{b}{2a} y \right)^2 + \dfrac{c}{a} y^2 \right]$$

$$= a\left[\left(x + \dfrac{b}{2a} y \right)^2 - \dfrac{b^2}{4a^2} y^2 + \dfrac{c}{a} y^2 \right] = a\left[\left(x + \dfrac{b}{2a} y \right)^2 + \left(\dfrac{4ac - b^2}{4a^2} \right) y^2 \right]$$

(b) For $D = 4ac - b^2$, from part (a) we have $f(x, y) = a\left[\left(x + \dfrac{b}{2a} y \right)^2 + \left(\dfrac{D}{4a^2} \right) y^2 \right]$. If $D > 0$,

$\left(\dfrac{D}{4a^2} \right) y^2 \geq 0$ and $\left(x + \dfrac{b}{2a} y \right)^2 \geq 0$, so $\left[\left(x + \dfrac{b}{2a} y \right)^2 + \left(\dfrac{D}{4a^2} \right) y^2 \right] \geq 0$. Here $a > 0$, thus

$f(x,y) = a \left[\left(x + \dfrac{b}{2a}\,y \right)^2 + \left(\dfrac{D}{4a^2} \right)y^2 \right] \geq 0$. We know $f(0,0) = 0$, so $f(0,0) \leq f(x,y)$ for all (x,y), and by definition f has a local minimum at $(0,0)$.

(c) As in part (b), $\left[\left(x + \dfrac{b}{2a}\,y \right)^2 + \left(\dfrac{D}{4a^2} \right)y^2 \right] \geq 0$, and since $a < 0$ we have

$f(x,y) = a \left[\left(x + \dfrac{b}{2a}\,y \right)^2 + \left(\dfrac{D}{4a^2} \right)y^2 \right] \leq 0$. Since $f(0,0) = 0$, we must have $f(0,0) \geq f(x,y)$ for all (x,y), so by definition f has a local maximum at $(0,0)$.

(d) $f(x,y) = ax^2 + bxy + cy^2$, so $f_x(x,y) = 2ax + by \Rightarrow f_x(0,0) = 0$ and $f_y(x,y) = bx + 2cy \Rightarrow f_y(0,0) = 0$. Since $f(0,0) = 0$ and f and its partial derivatives are continuous, we know from Equation 11.4.2 that the tangent plane to the graph of f at $(0,0)$ is the plane $z = 0$. Then f has a saddle point at $(0,0)$ if the graph of f crosses the tangent plane at $(0,0)$, or equivalently, if some paths to the origin have positive function values while other paths have negative function values. Suppose we approach the origin along the x-axis; then we have $y = 0 \Rightarrow f(x,0) = ax^2$ which has the same sign as a. We must now find at least one path to the origin where $f(x,y)$ gives values with sign opposite that of a. Since

$f(x,y) = a \left[\left(x + \dfrac{b}{2a}\,y \right)^2 + \left(\dfrac{D}{4a^2} \right)y^2 \right]$, if we approach the origin along the line $x = -\dfrac{b}{2a}\,y$, we have

$f\left(-\dfrac{b}{2a}\,y, y \right) = a \left[\left(-\dfrac{b}{2a}\,y + \dfrac{b}{2a}\,y \right)^2 + \left(\dfrac{D}{4a^2} \right)y^2 \right] = \dfrac{D}{4a}\,y^2$. Since $D < 0$, these values have signs opposite that of a. Thus, f has a saddle point at $(0,0)$.

5. (a) Since the partial derivatives of f exist at $(0,0)$ and $(0,0)$ is a critical point, we know $f_x(0,0) = 0$ and $f_y(0,0) = 0$. Then the second-degree Taylor polynomial of f at $(0,0)$ can be expressed as

$$Q(x,y) = f(0,0) + f_x(0,0)(x - 0) + f_y(0,0)(y - 0) + \tfrac{1}{2} f_{xx}(0,0)(x - 0)^2$$
$$+ f_{xy}(0,0)(x - 0)(y - 0) + \tfrac{1}{2} f_{yy}(0,0)(y - 0)^2$$
$$= \tfrac{1}{2} f_{xx}(0,0)x^2 + f_{xy}(0,0)xy + \tfrac{1}{2} f_{yy}(0,0)y^2.$$

(b) $Q(x,y) = \tfrac{1}{2} f_{xx}(0,0)x^2 + f_{xy}(0,0)xy + \tfrac{1}{2} f_{yy}(0,0)y^2$ fits the form of the polynomial function in Problem 4 with $a = \tfrac{1}{2} f_{xx}(0,0)$, $b = f_{xy}(0,0)$, and $c = \tfrac{1}{2} f_{yy}(0,0)$. Then we know Q is a paraboloid, and that Q has a local maximum, local minimum, or saddle point at $(0,0)$. Here, $D = 4ac - b^2 = 4\left(\tfrac{1}{2}\right)f_{xx}(0,0)\left(\tfrac{1}{2}\right)f_{yy}(0,0) - [f_{xy}(0,0)]^2 = f_{xx}(0,0)f_{yy}(0,0) - [f_{xy}(0,0)]^2$, and if $D > 0$ with $a = \tfrac{1}{2} f_{xx}(0,0) > 0 \Rightarrow f_{xx}(0,0) > 0$, we know from Problem 4 that Q has a local minimum at $(0,0)$. Similarly, if $D > 0$ and $a < 0 \Rightarrow f_{xx}(0,0) < 0$, Q has a local maximum at $(0,0)$, and if $D < 0$, Q has a saddle point at $(0,0)$.

(c) Since $f(x,y) \approx Q(x,y)$ near $(0,0)$, part (b) suggests that for $D = f_{xx}(0,0)f_{yy}(0,0) - [f_{xy}(0,0)]^2$, if $D > 0$ and $f_{xx}(0,0) > 0$, f has a local minimum at $(0,0)$. If $D > 0$ and $f_{xx}(0,0) < 0$, f has a local maximum at $(0,0)$, and if $D < 0$, f has a saddle point at $(0,0)$. Together with the conditions given in part (a), this is precisely the Second Derivatives Test from Section 11.7.

11.8 Lagrange Multipliers • • • • • • • • • • • • • •

1. At the extreme values of f, the level curves of f just touch the curve $g(x, y) = 8$ with a common tangent line. (See Figure 1 and the accompanying discussion.) We can observe several such occurrences on the contour map, but the level curve $f(x, y) = c$ with the largest value of c which still intersects the curve $g(x, y) = 8$ is approximately $c = 59$, and the smallest value of c corresponding to a level curve which intersects $g(x, y) = 8$ appears to be $c = 30$. Thus we estimate the maximum value of f subject to the constraint $g(x, y) = 8$ to be about 59 and the minimum to be 30.

2. (a) The values $c = \pm 1$ and $c = 1.25$ seem to give curves which are tangent to the circle. These values represent possible extreme values of the function $x^2 + y$ subject to the constraint $x^2 + y^2 = 1$.

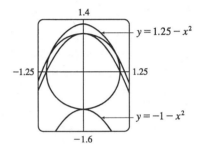

(b) $\nabla f = \langle 2x, 1 \rangle$, $\lambda \nabla g = \langle 2\lambda x, 2\lambda y \rangle$. So $2x = 2\lambda x \implies$ either $\lambda = 1$ or $x = 0$. If $\lambda = 1$, then $y = \frac{1}{2}$ and so $x = \pm \frac{\sqrt{3}}{2}$ (from the constraint). If $x = 0$, then $y = \pm 1$. Therefore f has possible extreme values at the

points $(0, \pm 1)$ and $\left(\pm \frac{\sqrt{3}}{2}, \frac{1}{2} \right)$. We calculate $f\left(\pm \frac{\sqrt{3}}{2}, \frac{1}{2} \right) = \frac{5}{4}$ (the maximum value), $f(0, 1) = 1$, and $f(0, -1) = -1$ (the minimum value). These are our answers from (a).

3. $f(x, y) = x^2 - y^2$, $g(x, y) = x^2 + y^2 = 1 \implies \nabla f = \langle 2x, -2y \rangle$, $\lambda \nabla g = \langle 2\lambda x, 2\lambda y \rangle$. Then $2x = 2\lambda x$ implies $x = 0$ or $\lambda = 1$. If $x = 0$, then $x^2 + y^2 = 1$ implies $y = \pm 1$ and if $\lambda = 1$, then $-2y = 2\lambda y$ implies $y = 0$ and thus $x = \pm 1$. Thus the possible points for the extreme values of f are $(\pm 1, 0)$, $(0, \pm 1)$. But $f(\pm 1, 0) = 1$ while $f(0, \pm 1) = -1$ so the maximum value of f on $x^2 + y^2 = 1$ is $f(\pm 1, 0) = 1$ and the minimum value is $f(0, \pm 1) = -1$.

4. $f(x, y) = 4x + 6y$, $g(x, y) = x^2 + y^2 = 13 \implies \nabla f = \langle 4, 6 \rangle$, $\lambda \nabla g = \langle 2\lambda x, 2\lambda y \rangle$. Then $2\lambda x = 4$ and $2\lambda y = 6$ imply $x = \frac{2}{\lambda}$ and $y = \frac{3}{\lambda}$. But $13 = x^2 + y^2 = \left(\frac{2}{\lambda} \right)^2 + \left(\frac{3}{\lambda} \right)^2 \implies 13 = \frac{13}{\lambda^2} \implies \lambda = \pm 1$, so f has possible extreme values at the points $(2, 3)$, $(-2, -3)$. We compute $f(2, 3) = 26$ and $f(-2, -3) = -26$, so the maximum value of f on $x^2 + y^2 = 13$ is $f(2, 3) = 26$ and the minimum value is $f(-2, -3) = -26$.

5. $f(x, y) = x^2 y$, $g(x, y) = x^2 + 2y^2 = 6 \implies \nabla f = \langle 2xy, x^2 \rangle$, $\lambda \nabla g = \langle 2\lambda x, 4\lambda y \rangle$. Then $2xy = 2\lambda x$ implies $x = 0$ or $\lambda = y$. If $x = 0$, then $x^2 = 4\lambda y$ implies $\lambda = 0$ or $y = 0$. However, if $y = 0$ then $g(x, y) = 0$, a contradiction. So $\lambda = 0$ and then $g(x, y) = 6 \implies y = \pm \sqrt{3}$. If $\lambda = y$, then $x^2 = 4\lambda y$ implies $x^2 = 4y^2$, and so $g(x, y) = 6 \implies 4y^2 + 2y^2 = 6 \implies y^2 = 1 \implies y = \pm 1$. Thus f has possible extreme values at the points $(0, \pm\sqrt{3})$, $(\pm 2, 1)$, and $(\pm 2, -1)$. After evaluating f at these points, we find the maximum value to be $f(\pm 2, 1) = 4$ and the minimum to be $f(\pm 2, -1) = -4$.

6. $f(x, y) = x^2 + y^2$, $g(x, y) = x^4 + y^4 = 1$ $\Rightarrow$ $\nabla f = \langle 2x, 2y \rangle$, $\lambda \nabla g = \langle 4\lambda x^3, 4\lambda y^3 \rangle$. Then $x = 2\lambda x^3$ implies

$x = 0$ or $\lambda = \dfrac{1}{2x^2}$. If $x = 0$, then $x^4 + y^4 = 1$ implies $y = \pm 1$. But $y = 2\lambda y^3$ implies $y = 0$ so $x = \pm 1$ or

$\lambda = \dfrac{1}{2y^2}$ and $x^2 = y^2$ and $2x^4 = 1$ so $x = \pm \frac{1}{\sqrt[4]{2}}$. Hence the possible points are $(0, \pm 1)$, $(\pm 1, 0)$, $\left(\pm \frac{1}{\sqrt[4]{2}}, \pm \frac{1}{\sqrt[4]{2}} \right)$,

with the maximum value of f on $x^4 + y^4 = 1$ being $f\left(\pm \frac{1}{\sqrt[4]{2}}, \pm \frac{1}{\sqrt[4]{2}} \right) = \frac{2}{\sqrt{2}} = \sqrt{2}$ and the minimum value being

$f(0, \pm 1) = f(\pm 1, 0) = 1$.

7. $f(x, y, z) = 2x + 6y + 10z$, $g(x, y, z) = x^2 + y^2 + z^2 = 35$ $\Rightarrow$ $\nabla f = \langle 2, 6, 10 \rangle$,

$\lambda \nabla g = \langle 2\lambda x, 2\lambda y, 2\lambda z \rangle$. Then $2\lambda x = 2$, $2\lambda y = 6$, $2\lambda z = 10$ imply $x = \dfrac{1}{\lambda}$, $y = \dfrac{3}{\lambda}$, and $z = \dfrac{5}{\lambda}$. But

$35 = x^2 + y^2 + z^2 = \left(\dfrac{1}{\lambda} \right)^2 + \left(\dfrac{3}{\lambda} \right)^2 + \left(\dfrac{5}{\lambda} \right)^2$ $\Rightarrow$ $35 = \dfrac{35}{\lambda^2}$ $\Rightarrow$ $\lambda = \pm 1$, so f has possible extreme

values at the points $(1, 3, 5)$, $(-1, -3, -5)$. The maximum value of f on $x^2 + y^2 + z^2 = 35$ is $f(1, 3, 5) = 70$,

and the minimum is $f(-1, -3, -5) = -70$.

8. $f(x, y, z) = 8x - 4z$, $g(x, y, z) = x^2 + 10y^2 + z^2 = 5$ $\Rightarrow$ $\nabla f = \langle 8, 0, -4 \rangle$, $\lambda \nabla g = \langle 2\lambda x, 20\lambda y, 2\lambda z \rangle$.

Then $2\lambda x = 8$, $20\lambda y = 0$, $2\lambda z = -4$ imply $x = \dfrac{4}{\lambda}$, $y = 0$, and $z = -\dfrac{2}{\lambda}$. But

$5 = x^2 + 10y^2 + z^2 = \left(\dfrac{4}{\lambda} \right)^2 + 10\,(0)^2 + \left(-\dfrac{2}{\lambda} \right)^2$ $\Rightarrow$ $5 = \dfrac{20}{\lambda^2}$ $\Rightarrow$ $\lambda = \pm 2$, so f has possible extreme

values at the points $(2, 0, -1)$, $(-2, 0, 1)$. The maximum of f on $x^2 + 10y^2 + z^2 = 5$ is $f(2, 0, -1) = 20$, and the

minimum is $f(-2, 0, 1) = -20$.

9. $f(x, y, z) = xyz$, $g(x, y, z) = x^2 + 2y^2 + 3z^2 = 6$ $\Rightarrow$ $\nabla f = \langle yz, xz, xy \rangle$, $\lambda \nabla g = \langle 2\lambda x, 4\lambda y, 6\lambda z \rangle$. Then

$\nabla f = \lambda \nabla g$ implies $\lambda = (yz)/(2x) = (xz)/(4y) = (xy)/96z)$ or $x^2 = 2y^2$ and $z^2 = \frac{2}{3}y^2$. Thus

$x^2 + 2y^2 + 3z^2 = 6$ implies $6y^2 = 6$ or $y = \pm 1$. Then the possible points are $\left(\sqrt{2}, \pm 1, \sqrt{\frac{2}{3}} \right)$, $\left(\sqrt{2}, \pm 1, -\sqrt{\frac{2}{3}} \right)$,

$\left(-\sqrt{2}, \pm 1, \sqrt{\frac{2}{3}} \right)$, $\left(-\sqrt{2}, \pm 1, -\sqrt{\frac{2}{3}} \right)$. The maximum value of f on the ellipsoid is $\frac{2}{\sqrt{3}}$, occurring when all

coordinates are positive or exactly two are negative and the minimum is $-\frac{2}{\sqrt{3}}$ occurring when 1 or 3 of the

coordinates are negative.

10. $f(x, y, z) = x^2 y^2 z^2$, $g(x, y, z) = x^2 + y^2 + z^2 = 1$ $\Rightarrow$ $\nabla f = \langle 2xy^2 z^2, 2yx^2 z^2, 2zx^2 y^2 \rangle$,

$\lambda \nabla g = \langle 2\lambda x, 2\lambda y, 2\lambda z \rangle$. Then $\nabla f = \lambda \nabla g$ implies (1) $\lambda = y^2 z^2 = x^2 z^2 = x^2 y^2$ and $\lambda \neq 0$, or (2) $\lambda = 0$ and

one or two (but not three) of the coordinates are 0. If (1) then $x^2 = y^2 = z^2 = \frac{1}{3}$. The minimum value of f on the

sphere occurs in case (2) with a value of 0 and the maximum value is $\frac{1}{27}$ which arises from all the points from (1),

that is, the points $\left(\pm \frac{1}{\sqrt{3}}, \frac{1}{\sqrt{3}}, \frac{1}{\sqrt{3}} \right)$, $\left(\pm \frac{1}{\sqrt{3}}, -\frac{1}{\sqrt{3}}, \frac{1}{\sqrt{3}} \right)$, $\left(\pm \frac{1}{\sqrt{3}}, -\frac{1}{\sqrt{3}}, -\frac{1}{\sqrt{3}} \right)$.

11. $f(x, y, z) = x^2 + y^2 + z^2$, $g(x, y, z) = x^4 + y^4 + z^4 = 1$ $\Rightarrow$ $\nabla f = \langle 2x, 2y, 2z \rangle$,

$\lambda \nabla g = \langle 4\lambda x^3, 4\lambda y^3, 4\lambda z^3 \rangle$.

Case 1: If $x \neq 0$, $y \neq 0$ and $z \neq 0$, then $\nabla f = \lambda \nabla g$ implies $\lambda = 1/(2x^2) = 1/s\,(2y^2) = 1/(2z^2)$ or

$x^2 = y^2 = z^2$ and $3x^4 = 1$ or $x = \pm \frac{1}{\sqrt[4]{3}}$ giving the points $\left(\pm \frac{1}{\sqrt[4]{3}}, \frac{1}{\sqrt[4]{3}}, \frac{1}{\sqrt[4]{3}} \right)$, $\left(\pm \frac{1}{\sqrt[4]{3}}, -\frac{1}{\sqrt[4]{3}}, \frac{1}{\sqrt[4]{3}} \right)$,

$\left(\pm \frac{1}{\sqrt[4]{3}}, \frac{1}{\sqrt[4]{3}}, -\frac{1}{\sqrt[4]{3}} \right)$, $\left(\pm \frac{1}{\sqrt[4]{3}}, -\frac{1}{\sqrt[4]{3}}, -\frac{1}{\sqrt[4]{3}} \right)$ all with an f-value of $\sqrt{3}$.

Case 2: If one of the variables equals zero and the other two are not zero, then the squares of the two nonzero coordinates are equal with common value $\frac{1}{\sqrt{2}}$ and corresponding f value of $\sqrt{2}$.

Case 3: If exactly two of the variables are zero, then the third variable has value ± 1 with the corresponding f value of 1. Thus on $x^4 + y^4 + z^4 = 1$, the maximum value of f is $\sqrt{3}$ and the minimum value is 1.

12. $f(x, y, z) = x^4 + y^4 + z^4$, $g(x, y, z) = x^2 + y^2 + z^2 = 1$ $\Rightarrow$ $\nabla f = \langle 4x^3, 4y^3, 4z^3 \rangle$,

$\lambda \nabla g = \langle 2\lambda x, 2\lambda y, 2\lambda z \rangle$.

Case 1: If $x \neq 0$, $y \neq 0$ and $z \neq 0$ then $\nabla f = \lambda \nabla g$ implies $\lambda = 2x^2 = 2y^2 = 2z^2$ or $x^2 = y^2 = z^2 = \frac{1}{3}$

yielding 8 points each with an f-value of $\frac{1}{3}$.

Case 2: If one of the variables is 0 and the other two are not, then the squares of the two nonzero coordinates are equal with common value $\frac{1}{2}$ and the corresponding f-value is $\frac{1}{2}$.

Case 3: If exactly two of the variables are 0, then the third variable has value ± 1 with corresponding f-value of 1. Thus on $x^2 + y^2 + z^2 = 1$, the maximum value of f is 1 and the minimum value is $\frac{1}{3}$.

13. $f(x, y, z, t) = x + y + z + t$, $g(x, y, z, t) = x^2 + y^2 + z^2 + t^2 = 1$ $\Rightarrow$ $\langle 1, 1, 1, 1 \rangle = \langle 2\lambda x, 2\lambda y, 2\lambda z, 2\lambda t \rangle$, so $\lambda = 1/(2x) = 1/(2y) = 1/(2z) = 1/(2t)$ and $x = y = z = t$. But $x^2 + y^2 + z^2 + t^2 = 1$, so the possible points are $\left(\pm \frac{1}{2}, \pm \frac{1}{2}, \pm \frac{1}{2}, \pm \frac{1}{2} \right)$. Thus the maximum value of f is $f \left(\frac{1}{2}, \frac{1}{2}, \frac{1}{2}, \frac{1}{2} \right) = 2$ and the minimum value is $f \left(-\frac{1}{2}, -\frac{1}{2}, -\frac{1}{2}, -\frac{1}{2} \right) = -2$.

14. $f(x_1, x_2, \ldots, x_n) = x_1 + x_2 + \cdots + x_n$, $g(x_1, x_2, \ldots, x_n) = x_1^2 + x_2^2 + \cdots + x_n^2 = 1$ $\Rightarrow$ $\langle 1, 1, \ldots, 1 \rangle = \langle 2\lambda x_1, 2\lambda x_2, \ldots, 2\lambda x_n \rangle$, so $\lambda = 1/(2x_1) = 1/(2x_2) = \cdots = 1/(2x_n)$ and $x_1 = x_2 = \cdots = x_n$. But $x_1^2 + x_2^2 + \cdots + x_n^2 = 1$, so $x_i = \pm 1/\sqrt{n}$ for $i = 1, \ldots, n$. Thus the maximum value of f is $f \left(1/\sqrt{n}, 1/\sqrt{n}, \ldots, 1/\sqrt{n} \right) = \sqrt{n}$ and the minimum value is $f \left(-1/\sqrt{n}, -1/\sqrt{n}, \ldots, -1/\sqrt{n} \right) = -\sqrt{n}$.

15. $f(x, y, z) = x + 2y$, $g(x, y, z) = x + y + z = 1$, $h(x, y, z) = y^2 + z^2 = 4$ $\Rightarrow$ $\nabla f = \langle 1, 2, 0 \rangle$,

$\lambda \nabla g = \langle \lambda, \lambda, \lambda \rangle$ and $\mu \nabla h = \langle 0, 2\mu y, 2\mu z \rangle$. Then $1 = \lambda$, $2 = \lambda + 2\mu y$ and $0 = \lambda + 2\mu z$ so $\mu y = \frac{1}{2} = -\mu z$ or $y = 1/(2\mu)$, $z = -1/(2\mu)$. Thus $x + y + z = 1$ implies $x = 1$ and $y^2 + z^2 = 4$ implies $\mu = \pm \frac{1}{2\sqrt{2}}$. Then the possible points are $\left(1, \pm\sqrt{2}, \mp\sqrt{2} \right)$ and the maximum value is $f \left(1, \sqrt{2}, -\sqrt{2} \right) = 1 + 2\sqrt{2}$ and the minimum value is $f \left(1, -\sqrt{2}, \sqrt{2} \right) = 1 - 2\sqrt{2}$.

16. $f(x, y, z) = 3x - y - 3z$, $g(x, y, z) = x + y - z = 0$, $h(x, y, z) = x^2 + 2z^2 = 1$ $\Rightarrow$ $\nabla f = \langle 3, -1, -3 \rangle$,

$\lambda \nabla g = \langle \lambda, \lambda, -\lambda \rangle$, $\mu \nabla h = \langle 2\mu x, 0, 4\mu z \rangle$. Then $3 = \lambda + 2\mu x$, $-1 = \lambda$ and $-3 = -\lambda + 4\mu z$, so $\lambda = -1$,

$\mu z = -1$, $\mu x = 2$. Thus $h(x, y, z) = 1$ implies $\dfrac{4}{\mu^2} + 2 \left(\dfrac{1}{\mu^2} \right) = 1$ or $\mu = \pm\sqrt{6}$, so $z = \mp\frac{1}{\sqrt{6}}$; $x = \pm\frac{2}{\sqrt{6}}$; and

$g(x, y, z) = 0$ implies $y = \mp\frac{3}{\sqrt{6}}$. Hence the maximum of f subject to the constraints is

$f \left(\frac{\sqrt{6}}{3}, -\frac{\sqrt{6}}{2}, -\frac{\sqrt{6}}{6} \right) = 2\sqrt{6}$ and the minimum is $f \left(-\frac{\sqrt{6}}{3}, \frac{\sqrt{6}}{2}, \frac{\sqrt{6}}{6} \right) = -2\sqrt{6}$.

17. $f(x, y, z) = yz + xy,\, g(x, y, z) = xy = 1,\, h(x, y, z) = y^2 + z^2 = 1\ \Rightarrow\ \nabla f = \langle y, x + z, y \rangle,$
$\lambda\nabla g = \langle \lambda y, \lambda x, 0 \rangle,\, \mu\nabla h = \langle 0, 2\mu y, 2\mu z \rangle.$ Then $y = \lambda y$ implies $\lambda = 1$ [$y \neq 0$ since $g(x, y, z) = 1$],
$x + z = \lambda x + 2\mu y$ and $y = 2\mu z$. Thus $\mu = z/(2y) = y/(2y)$ or $y^2 = z^2$, and so $y^2 + z^2 = 1$ implies $y = \pm\frac{1}{\sqrt{2}}$,
$z = \pm\frac{1}{\sqrt{2}}$. Then $xy = 1$ implies $x = \pm\sqrt{2}$ and the possible points are $\left(\pm\sqrt{2}, \pm\frac{1}{\sqrt{2}}, \frac{1}{\sqrt{2}} \right),\, \left(\pm\sqrt{2}, \pm\frac{1}{\sqrt{2}}, -\frac{1}{\sqrt{2}} \right).$
Hence the maximum of f subject to the constraints is $f\left(\pm\sqrt{2}, \pm\frac{1}{\sqrt{2}}, \pm\frac{1}{\sqrt{2}} \right) = \frac{3}{2}$ and the minimum is
$f\left(\pm\sqrt{2}, \pm\frac{1}{\sqrt{2}}, \mp\frac{1}{\sqrt{2}} \right) = \frac{1}{2}.$
Note: Since $xy = 1$ is one of the constraints we could have solved the problem by solving $f(y, z) = yz + 1$ subject
to $y^2 + z^2 = 1$.

18. $f(x, y) = 2x^2 + 3y^2 - 4x - 5\ \Rightarrow\ \nabla f = \langle 4x - 4, 6y \rangle = \langle 0, 0 \rangle\ \Rightarrow\ x = 1, y = 0.$ Thus $(1, 0)$ is the only
critical point of f, and it lies in the region $x^2 + y^2 < 16$. On the boundary, $g(x, y) = x^2 + y^2 = 16\ \Rightarrow$
$\lambda\nabla g = \langle 2\lambda x, 2\lambda y \rangle,$ so $6y = 2\lambda y\ \Rightarrow$ either $y = 0$ or $\lambda = 3$. If $y = 0$, then $x = \pm 4$; if $\lambda = 3$, then
$4x - 4 = 2\lambda x\ \Rightarrow\ x = -2$ and $y = \pm 2\sqrt{3}$. Now $f(1, 0) = -7,\, f(4, 0) = 11,\, f(-4, 0) = 43,$ and
$f\left(-2, \pm 2\sqrt{3} \right) = 47.$ Thus the maximum value of $f(x, y)$ on the disk $x^2 + y^2 \leq 16$ is $f\left(-2, \pm 2\sqrt{3} \right) = 47,$ and
the minimum value is $f(1, 0) = -7.$

19. $f(x, y) = e^{-xy}.$ For the interior of the region, we find the critical points: $f_x = -ye^{-xy},\, f_y = -xe^{-xy},$ so the
only critical point is $(0, 0),$ and $f(0, 0) = 1.$ For the boundary, we use Lagrange multipliers.
$g(x, y) = x^2 + 4y^2 = 1\ \Rightarrow\ \lambda\nabla g = \langle 2\lambda x, 8\lambda y \rangle,$ so setting $\nabla f = \lambda\nabla g$ we get $-ye^{-xy} = 2\lambda x$ and
$-xe^{-xy} = 8\lambda y.$ The first of these gives $e^{-xy} = -2\lambda x/y,$ and then the second gives $-x(-2\lambda x/y) = 8\lambda y\ \Rightarrow$
$x^2 = 4y^2.$ Solving this last equation with the constraint $x^2 + 4y^2 = 1$ gives $x = \pm\frac{1}{\sqrt{2}}$ and $y = \pm\frac{1}{2\sqrt{2}}.$ Now
$f\left(\pm\frac{1}{\sqrt{2}}, \mp\frac{1}{2\sqrt{2}} \right) = e^{1/4} \approx 1.284$ and $f\left(\pm\frac{1}{\sqrt{2}}, \pm\frac{1}{2\sqrt{2}} \right) = e^{-1/4} \approx 0.779.$ The former are the maxima on the
region and the latter are the minima.

20. (a) The graphs of $f(x, y) = 3.7$ and $f(x, y) = 350$ seem to be tangent
to the circle, and so 3.7 and 350 are the approximate minimum and
maximum values of the function $f(x, y)$ subject to the constraint
$(x - 3)^2 + (y - 3)^2 = 9.$

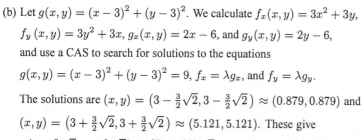

(b) Let $g(x, y) = (x - 3)^2 + (y - 3)^2.$ We calculate $f_x(x, y) = 3x^2 + 3y,$
$f_y(x, y) = 3y^2 + 3x,\, g_x(x, y) = 2x - 6,$ and $g_y(x, y) = 2y - 6,$
and use a CAS to search for solutions to the equations
$g(x, y) = (x - 3)^2 + (y - 3)^2 = 9,\, f_x = \lambda g_x,$ and $f_y = \lambda g_y.$
The solutions are $(x, y) = \left(3 - \frac{3}{2}\sqrt{2}, 3 - \frac{3}{2}\sqrt{2} \right) \approx (0.879, 0.879)$ and
$(x, y) = \left(3 + \frac{3}{2}\sqrt{2}, 3 + \frac{3}{2}\sqrt{2} \right) \approx (5.121, 5.121).$ These give
$f\left(3 - \frac{3}{2}\sqrt{2}, 3 - \frac{3}{2}\sqrt{2} \right) = \frac{351}{2} - \frac{243}{2}\sqrt{2} \approx 3.673$ and $f\left(3 + \frac{3}{2}\sqrt{2}, 3 + \frac{3}{2}\sqrt{2} \right) = \frac{351}{2} + \frac{243}{2}\sqrt{2} \approx 347.33,$ in
accordance with part (a).

21. $P(L, K) = bL^\alpha K^{1-\alpha}$, $g(L, K) = mL + nK = p$ $\Rightarrow$ $\nabla P = \langle \alpha bL^{\alpha-1}K^{1-\alpha}, (1-\alpha)bL^\alpha K^{-\alpha} \rangle$,

$\lambda \nabla g = \langle \lambda m, \lambda n \rangle$. Then $\alpha b(K/L)^{1-\alpha} = \lambda m$ and $(1-\alpha)b(L/K)^\alpha = \lambda n$ and $mL + nK = p$, so

$\alpha b(K/L)^{1-\alpha}/m = (1-\alpha)b(L/K)^\alpha/n$ or $n\alpha/[m(1-\alpha)] = (L/K)^{\alpha(L/K)1-\alpha}$ or $L = Kn\alpha/[m(1-\alpha)]$.

Substituting into $mL + nK = p$ gives $K = (1-\alpha)p/n$ and $L = \alpha p/m$ for the maximum production.

22. $C(L, K) = mL + nK$, $g(L, K) = bL^\alpha K^{1-\alpha} = Q$ $\Rightarrow$ $\nabla C = \langle m, n \rangle$,

$\lambda \nabla g = \langle \lambda \alpha b L^{\alpha-1}K^{1-\alpha}, \lambda(1-\alpha)bL^\alpha K^{-\alpha} \rangle$. Then $\dfrac{m}{\alpha b}\left(\dfrac{L}{K}\right)^{1-\alpha} = \dfrac{n}{(1-\alpha)b}\left(\dfrac{K}{L}\right)^\alpha$ and $bL^\alpha K^{1-\alpha} = Q$

$\Rightarrow$ $\dfrac{n\alpha}{m(1-\alpha)} = \left(\dfrac{L}{K}\right)^{1-\alpha}\left(\dfrac{L}{K}\right)^\alpha$ $\Rightarrow$ $L = \dfrac{Kn\alpha}{m(1-\alpha)}$ and so $b\left[\dfrac{Kn\alpha}{m(1-\alpha)}\right]^\alpha K^{1-\alpha} = Q$. Hence

$K = \dfrac{Q}{b\,(n\alpha/[m(1-\alpha)])^\alpha} = \dfrac{Qm^\alpha(1-\alpha)^\alpha}{bn^\alpha \alpha^\alpha}$ and $L = \dfrac{Qm^{\alpha-1}(1-\alpha)^{\alpha-1}}{bn^{\alpha-1}\alpha^{\alpha-1}} = \dfrac{Qn^{1-\alpha}\alpha^{1-\alpha}}{bm^{1-\alpha}(1-\alpha)^{1-\alpha}}$ minimizes

cost.

23. Let the sides of the rectangle be x and y. Then $f(x, y) = xy$, $g(x, y) = 2x + 2y = p$ $\Rightarrow$ $\nabla f(x, y) = \langle y, x \rangle$,

$\lambda \nabla g = \langle 2\lambda, 2\lambda \rangle$. Then $\lambda = \frac{1}{2}y = \frac{1}{2}x$ implies $x = y$ and the rectangle with maximum area is a square with side

length $\frac{1}{4}p$.

24. Let $f(x, y, z) = s(s-x)(s-y)(s-z)$, $g(x, y, z) = x + y + z$. Then

$\nabla f = \langle -s(s-y)(s-z), -s(s-x)(s-z), -s(s-x)(s-y) \rangle$, $\lambda \nabla g = \langle \lambda, \lambda, \lambda \rangle$. Thus

(1) $(s-y)(s-z) = (s-x)(s-z)$ and (2) $(s-x)(s-z) = (s-x)(s-y)$. (1) implies $x = y$ while (2)

implies $y = z$, so $x = y = z = p/3$ and the triangle with maximum area is equilateral.

25. Let $f(x, y, z) = d^2 = (x-2)^2 + (y-1)^2 + (z+1)^2$, then we want to minimize f subject to the constraint

$g(x, y, z) = x + y - z = 1$. $\nabla f = \lambda \nabla g$ $\Rightarrow$ $\langle 2(x-2), 2(y-1), 2(z+1) \rangle = \lambda \langle 1, 1, -1 \rangle$, so

$x = (\lambda + 4)/2$, $y = (\lambda + 2)/2$, $z = -(\lambda + 2)/2$. Substituting into the constraint equation gives

$\dfrac{\lambda + 4}{2} + \dfrac{\lambda + 2}{2} + \dfrac{\lambda + 2}{2} = 1$ $\Rightarrow$ $3\lambda + 8 = 2$ $\Rightarrow$ $\lambda = -2$, so $x = 1$, $y = 0$, and $z = 0$. This must

correspond to a minimum, so the shortest distance is $d = \sqrt{(1-2)^2 + (0-1)^2 + (0+1)^2} = \sqrt{3}$.

26. Let $f(x, y, z) = d^2 = (x-1)^2 + (y-2)^2 + (z-3)^2$, then we want to minimize f subject to the constraint

$g(x, y, z) = x - y + z = 4$. $\nabla f = \lambda \nabla g$ $\Rightarrow$ $\langle 2(x-1), 2(y-2), 2(z-3) \rangle = \lambda \langle 1, -1, 1 \rangle$, so

$x = (\lambda + 2)/2$, $y = (4-\lambda)/2$, $z = (\lambda + 6)/2$. Substituting into the constraint equation gives

$\dfrac{\lambda + 2}{2} - \dfrac{4 - \lambda}{2} + \dfrac{\lambda + 6}{2} = 4$ $\Rightarrow$ $\lambda = \frac{4}{3}$, so $x = \frac{5}{3}$, $y = \frac{4}{3}$, and $z = \frac{11}{3}$. This must correspond to a minimum,

so the point on the plane closest to the point $(1, 2, 3)$ is $\left(\frac{5}{3}, \frac{4}{3}, \frac{11}{3}\right)$.

27. $f(x, y, z) = x^2 + y^2 + z^2$, $g(x, y, z) = z^2 - xy - 1 = 0$ $\Rightarrow$ $\nabla f = \langle 2x, 2y, 2z \rangle = \lambda \nabla g = \langle -\lambda y, -\lambda x, 2\lambda z \rangle$.

Then $2z = 2\lambda z$ implies $z = 0$ or $\lambda = 1$. If $z = 0$ then $g(x, y, z) = 1$ implies $xy = -1$ or $x = -1/y$. Thus

$2x = -\lambda y$ and $2y = -\lambda x$ imply $\lambda = 2/y^2 = 2y^2$ or $y = \pm 1$, $x = \pm 1$. If $\lambda = 1$, then $2x = -y$ and $2y = -x$

imply $x = y = 0$, so $z = \pm 1$. Hence the possible points are $(\pm 1, \mp 1, 0)$, $(0, 0, \pm 1)$ and the minimum value of f is

$f(0, 0, \pm 1) = 1$, so the points closest to the origin are $(0, 0, \pm 1)$.

28. $f(x, y, z) = x^2 + y^2 + z^2$, $g(x, y, z) = x^2 y^2 z = 1$ $\Rightarrow$

$\nabla f = \langle 2x, 2y, 2z \rangle = \lambda \nabla g = \langle 2\lambda x y^2 z, 2\lambda x^2 y z, \lambda x^2 y^2 \rangle$. Then $\lambda y^2 z = 1$, $\lambda x^2 z = 1$ and $\lambda x^2 y^2 = 2z$ so

$y^2 z = x^2 z$ and $x = \pm y$. Also $2z/1 = \lambda x^2 y^2 / (\lambda x^2 z)$ so $2z^2 = y^2$ and $y = \pm\sqrt{2}\, z$. But $x^2 y^2 z = 1$ implies

$z > 0$ and $4z^5 = 1$. Thus the points are $\left(\pm 2^{1/10}, \pm 2^{1/10}, 2^{-2/5} \right)$, and the minimum distance is attained at each

of these.

29. $f(x, y, z) = xyz$, $g(x, y, z) = x + y + z = 100$ $\Rightarrow$ $\nabla f = \langle yz, xz, xy \rangle = \lambda \nabla g = \langle \lambda, \lambda, \lambda \rangle$. Then

$\lambda = yz = xz = xy$ implies $x = y = z = \frac{100}{3}$.

30. $f(x, y, z) = x^a y^b z^c$, $g(x, y, z) = x + y + z = 100$

$\Rightarrow$ $\nabla f = \langle ax^{a-1} y^b z^c, bx^a y^{b-1} z^c, cx^a y^b z^{c-1} \rangle = \lambda \nabla g = \langle \lambda, \lambda, \lambda \rangle$. Then

$\lambda = ax^{a-1} y^b z^c = bx^a y^{b-1} z^c = cx^a y^b z^{c-1}$ or $ayz = bxz = cxy$. Thus $x = \dfrac{ay}{b}$, $z = \dfrac{cy}{b}$, and

$\dfrac{ay}{b} + y + \dfrac{cy}{b} = 100$ implies that $y = \dfrac{100b}{a+b+c}$, $x = \dfrac{100a}{a+b+c}$ and $z = \dfrac{100c}{a+b+c}$ gives the maximum.

31. If the dimensions are $2x$, $2y$ and $2z$, then $f(x, y, z) = 8xyz$ and $g(x, y, z) = 9x^2 + 36y^2 + 4z^2 = 36$ $\Rightarrow$

$\nabla f = \langle 8yz, 8xz, 8xy \rangle = \lambda \nabla g = \langle 18\lambda x, 72\lambda y, 8\lambda z \rangle$. Thus $18\lambda x = 8yz$, $72\lambda y = 8xz$, $8\lambda z = 8xy$ so $x^2 = 4y^2$,

$z^2 = 9y^2$ and $36y^2 + 36y^2 + 36y^2 = 36$ or $y = \frac{1}{\sqrt{3}}$ $(y > 0)$. Thus the volume of the largest such rectangle is

$8 \left(\frac{1}{\sqrt{3}} \right) \left(\frac{2}{\sqrt{3}} \right) \left(\frac{3}{\sqrt{3}} \right) = 16\sqrt{3}$.

32. $f(x, y, z) = 8xyz$, $g(x, y, z) = a^2 b^2 c^2$ $\Rightarrow$ $\nabla f = \langle 8yz, 8xz, 8xy \rangle = \lambda \nabla g = \langle 2\lambda b^2 c^2 x, 2\lambda a^2 c^2 y, 2\lambda a^2 b^2 z \rangle$.

Then $4yz = \lambda b^2 c^2 x$, $4xz = \lambda a^2 c^2 y$, $4xy = \lambda a^2 b^2 z$ imply $\lambda = \dfrac{4yz}{b^2 c^2 x} = \dfrac{4xz}{a^2 c^2 y} = \dfrac{4xy}{a^2 b^2 z}$ or $\dfrac{y}{b^2 x} = \dfrac{x}{a^2 y}$ and

$\dfrac{z}{c^2 y} = \dfrac{y}{b^2 z}$. Thus $x = \dfrac{ay}{b}$, $z = \dfrac{cy}{b}$, and $a^2 c^2 y^2 + c^2 a^2 y^2 + a^2 c^2 y^2 = a^2 b^2 c^2$, or $y = \dfrac{b}{\sqrt{3}}$, $x = \dfrac{a}{\sqrt{3}}$, $z = \dfrac{c}{\sqrt{3}}$

and the volume is $\dfrac{8}{3\sqrt{3}} abc$.

33. $f(x, y, z) = xyz$, $g(x, y, z) = x + 2y + 3z = 6$ $\Rightarrow$ $\nabla f = \langle yz, xz, xy \rangle = \lambda \nabla g = \langle \lambda, 2\lambda, 3\lambda \rangle$.

Then $\lambda = yz = \frac{1}{2}xz = \frac{1}{3}xy$ implies $x = 2y$, $z = \frac{2}{3}y$. But $2y + 2y + 2y = 6$ so $y = 1$, $x = 2$, $z = \frac{2}{3}$ and the

volume is $V = \frac{4}{3}$.

34. $f(x, y, z) = xyz$, $g(x, y, z) = xy + yz + xz = 32$ $\Rightarrow$

$\nabla f = \langle yz, xz, xy \rangle = \lambda \nabla g = \langle \lambda(y + z), \lambda(x + z), \lambda(x + y) \rangle$. Then (1) $\lambda(y + z) = yz$, (2) $\lambda(x + z) = xz$ and

(3) $\lambda(x + y) = xy$. And (1) minus (2) implies $\lambda(y - x) = z(y - x)$ so $x = y$ or $\lambda = z$. If $\lambda = z$, then (1) implies

$z(y + z) = yz$ or $z = 0$ which is false. Thus $x = y$. Similarly (2) minus (3) implies $\lambda(z - y) = x(z - y)$ so $y = z$

or $\lambda = x$. As above, $\lambda \neq x$, so $x = y = z$ and $3x^2 = 32$ or $x = y = z = \frac{8}{\sqrt{6}}$ cm.

35. $f(x, y, z) = xyz$, $g(x, y, z) = 4(x + y + z) = c$ $\Rightarrow$ $\nabla f = \langle yz, xz, xy \rangle$, $\lambda \nabla g = \langle 4\lambda, 4\lambda, 4\lambda \rangle$. Thus

$4\lambda = yz = xz = xy$ or $x = y = z = \frac{1}{12}c$ are the dimensions giving the maximum volume.

36. Let the dimensions of the box be x, y, and z, so its volume is $f(x, y, z) = xyz$, its surface area is

$g(x, y, z) = xy + yz + xz = 750$ and its total edge length is $h(x, y, z) = x + y + z = 50$. Then

$\nabla f = \langle yz, xz, xy \rangle = \lambda \nabla g + \mu \nabla h = \langle \lambda(y + z), \lambda(x + z), \lambda(x + y) \rangle + \langle \mu, \mu, \mu \rangle$. So (1) $yz = \lambda(y + z) + \mu$,

(2) $xz = \lambda(x + z) + \mu$, and (3) $xy = \lambda(x + y) + \mu$. Notice that the box can't be a cube or else $x = y = z = \frac{50}{3}$

but then $xy + yz + xz = \frac{2500}{3} \neq 750$. Assume x is the distinct side, that is, $x \neq y$, $x \neq z$. Then (1) minus (2)

implies $z(y - x) = \lambda(y - x)$ or $\lambda = z$, and (1) minus (3) implies $y(z - x) = \lambda(z - x)$ or $\lambda = y$. So $y = z = \lambda$

and $x + y + z = 50$ implies $x = 50 - 2\lambda$; also $xy + yz + xz = 750$ implies $x(2\lambda) + \lambda^2 = 750$. Hence

$50 - 2\lambda = \dfrac{750 - \lambda^2}{2\lambda}$ or $3\lambda^2 - 100\lambda + 750 = 0$ and $\lambda = \dfrac{50 \pm 5\sqrt{10}}{3}$, giving the points

$\left(\frac{1}{3}(50 \mp 10\sqrt{10}), \frac{1}{3}(50 \pm 5\sqrt{10}), \frac{1}{3}(50 \pm 5\sqrt{10}) \right)$. Thus the minimum of f is

$f \left(\frac{1}{3}(50 - 10\sqrt{3}), \frac{1}{3}(50 + 5\sqrt{10}), \frac{1}{3}(50 + 5\sqrt{10}) \right) = \frac{1}{27}(87{,}500 - 2500\sqrt{10})$, and its maximum is

$f \left(\frac{1}{3}(50 + 10\sqrt{10}), \frac{1}{3}(50 - 5\sqrt{10}), \frac{1}{3}(50 - 5\sqrt{10}) \right) = \frac{1}{27}(87{,}500 + 2500\sqrt{10})$.

Note: If either y or z is the distinct side, then symmetry gives the same result.

37. We need to find the extreme values of $f(x, y, z) = x^2 + y^2 + z^2$ subject to the two constraints

$g(x, y, z) = x + y + 2z = 2$ and $h(x, y, z) = x^2 + y^2 - z = 0$. $\nabla f = \langle 2x, 2y, 2z \rangle$, $\lambda \nabla g = \langle \lambda, \lambda, 2\lambda \rangle$ and

$\mu \nabla h = \langle 2\mu x, 2\mu y, -\mu \rangle$. Thus we need (1) $2x = \lambda + 2\mu x$, (2) $2y = \lambda + 2\mu y$, (3) $2z = 2\lambda - \mu$,

(4) $x + y + 2z = 2$, and (5) $x^2 + y^2 - z = 0$. From (1) and (2), $2(x - y) = 2\mu(x - y)$, so if $x \neq y$, $\mu = 1$.

Putting this in (3) gives $2z = 2\lambda - 1$ or $\lambda = z + \frac{1}{2}$, but putting $\mu = 1$ into (1) says $\lambda = 0$. Hence $z + \frac{1}{2} = 0$ or

$z = -\frac{1}{2}$. Then (4) and (5) become $x + y - 3 = 0$ and $x^2 + y^2 + \frac{1}{2} = 0$. The last equation cannot be true, so this

case gives no solution. So we must have $x = y$. Then (4) and (5) become $2x + 2z = 2$ and $2x^2 - z = 0$ which

imply $z = 1 - x$ and $z = 2x^2$. Thus $2x^2 = 1 - x$ or $2x^2 + x - 1 = (2x - 1)(x + 1) = 0$ so $x = \frac{1}{2}$ or $x = -1$.

The two points to check are $\left(\frac{1}{2}, \frac{1}{2}, \frac{1}{2} \right)$ and $(-1, -1, 2)$: $f\left(\frac{1}{2}, \frac{1}{2}, \frac{1}{2} \right) = \frac{3}{4}$ and $f(-1, -1, 2) = 6$. Thus $\left(\frac{1}{2}, \frac{1}{2}, \frac{1}{2} \right)$ is

the point on the ellipse nearest the origin and $(-1, -1, 2)$ is the one farthest from the origin.

38. (a) Parametric equations for the ellipse are easiest to determine

using cylindrical coordinates. The cone is given by $z = r$, and

the plane is $4r \cos \theta - 3r \sin \theta + 8z = 5$. Substituting $z = r$

into the plane equation gives $4r \cos \theta - 3r \sin \theta + 8r = 5$ $\Rightarrow$

$r = \dfrac{5}{4 \cos \theta - 3 \sin \theta + 8}$. Since $z = r$ on the ellipse,

parametric equations (in cylindrical coordinates) are $\theta = t$,

$r = z = \dfrac{5}{4 \cos t - 3 \sin t + 8}$, $0 \leq t \leq 2\pi$.

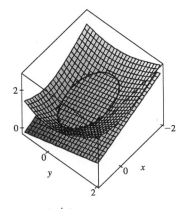

(b) We need to find the extreme values of $f(x, y, z) = z$ subject to the two constraints

$g(x, y, z) = 4x - 3y + 8z = 5$ and $h(x, y, z) = x^2 + y^2 - z^2 = 0$. $\nabla f = \lambda \nabla g + \mu \nabla h$ $\Rightarrow$

$\langle 0, 0, 1 \rangle = \lambda \langle 4, -3, 8 \rangle + \mu \langle 2x, 2y, -2z \rangle$, so we need (1) $4\lambda + 2\mu x = 0$ $\Rightarrow$ $x = -\frac{2\lambda}{\mu}$,

(2) $-3\lambda + 2\mu y = 0$ $\Rightarrow$ $y = \frac{3\lambda}{2\mu}$, (3) $8\lambda - 2\mu z = 1$ $\Rightarrow$ $z = \frac{8\lambda - 1}{2\mu}$, (4) $4x - 3y + 8z = 5$, and

(5) $x^2 + y^2 = z^2$. [Note that $\mu \neq 0$, else $\lambda = 0$ from (1), but substitution into (3) gives a contradiction.]

Substituting (1), (2), and (3) into (4) gives $4\left(-\frac{2\lambda}{\mu}\right) - 3\left(\frac{3\lambda}{2\mu}\right) + 8\left(\frac{8\lambda-1}{2\mu}\right) = 5 \;\Rightarrow\; \mu = \frac{39\lambda-8}{10}$ and into (5)

gives $\left(-\frac{2\lambda}{\mu}\right)^2 + \left(\frac{3\lambda}{2\mu}\right)^2 = \left(\frac{8\lambda-1}{2\mu}\right)^2 \;\Rightarrow\; 16\lambda^2 + 9\lambda^2 = (8\lambda-1)^2 \;\Rightarrow\; 39\lambda^2 - 16\lambda + 1 = 0 \;\Rightarrow$

$\lambda = \frac{1}{13}$ or $\lambda = \frac{1}{3}$. If $\lambda = \frac{1}{13}$ then $\mu = -\frac{1}{2}$ and $x = \frac{4}{13}$, $y = -\frac{3}{13}$, $z = \frac{5}{13}$. If $\lambda = \frac{1}{3}$ then $\mu = \frac{1}{2}$ and $x = -\frac{4}{3}$,

$y = 1$, $z = \frac{5}{3}$. Thus the highest point on the ellipse is $\left(-\frac{4}{3}, 1, \frac{5}{3}\right)$ and the lowest point is $\left(\frac{4}{13}, -\frac{3}{13}, \frac{5}{13}\right)$.

39. $f(x, y, z) = ye^{x-z}$, $g(x, y, z) = 9x^2 + 4y^2 + 36z^2 = 36$, $h(x, y, z) = xy + yz = 1$.

$\nabla f = \lambda \nabla g + \mu \nabla h \;\Rightarrow\; \left\langle ye^{x-z}, e^{x-z}, -ye^{x-z}\right\rangle = \lambda \left\langle 18x, 8y, 72z\right\rangle + \mu \left\langle y, x+z, y\right\rangle$, so

$ye^{x-z} = 18\lambda x + \mu y$, $e^{x-z} = 8\lambda y + \mu(x+z)$, $-ye^{x-z} = 72\lambda z + \mu y$, $9x^2 + 4y^2 + 36z^2 = 36$, $xy + yz = 1$.

Using a CAS to solve these 5 equations simultaneously for x, y, z, λ, and μ (in Maple, use the allvalues

command), we get 4 real-valued solutions:

$$x \approx 0.222444, \quad y \approx -2.157012, \quad z \approx -0.686049, \quad \lambda \approx -0.200401, \quad \mu \approx 2.108584$$

$$x \approx -1.951921, \quad y \approx -0.545867, \quad z \approx 0.119973, \quad \lambda \approx 0.003141, \quad \mu \approx -0.076238$$

$$x \approx 0.155142, \quad y \approx 0.904622, \quad z \approx 0.950293, \quad \lambda \approx -0.012447, \quad \mu \approx 0.489938$$

$$x \approx 1.138731, \quad y \approx 1.768057, \quad z \approx -0.573138, \quad \lambda \approx 0.317141, \quad \mu \approx 1.862675$$

Substituting these values into f gives $f(0.222444, -2.157012, -0.686049) \approx -5.3506$,

$f(-1.951921, -0.545867, 0.119973) \approx -0.0688$, $f(0.155142, 0.904622, 0.950293) \approx 0.4084$,

$f(1.138731, 1.768057, -0.573138) \approx 9.7938$. Thus the maximum is approximately 9.7938, and the mininum is

approximately -5.3506.

40. $f(x, y, z) = x + y + z$, $g(x, y, z) = x^2 - y^2 - z = 0$, $h(x, y, z) = x^2 + z^2 = 4$.

$\nabla f = \lambda \nabla g + \mu \nabla h \;\Rightarrow\; \langle 1, 1, 1\rangle = \lambda \langle 2x, -2y, -1\rangle + \mu \langle 2x, 0, 2z\rangle$, so $1 = 2\lambda x + 2\mu x$, $1 = -2\lambda y$,

$1 = -\lambda + 2\mu z$, $x^2 - y^2 = z$, $x^2 + z^2 = 4$. Using a CAS to solve these 5 equations simultaneously for x, y, z, λ,

and μ, we get 4 real-valued solutions:

$$x \approx -1.652878, \quad y \approx -1.964194, \quad z \approx -1.126052, \quad \lambda \approx 0.254557, \quad \mu \approx -0.557060$$

$$x \approx -1.502800, \quad y \approx 0.968872, \quad z \approx 1.319694, \quad \lambda \approx -0.516064, \quad \mu \approx 0.183352$$

$$x \approx -0.992513, \quad y \approx 1.649677, \quad z \approx -1.736352, \quad \lambda \approx -0.303090, \quad \mu \approx -0.200682$$

$$x \approx 1.895178, \quad y \approx 1.718347, \quad z \approx 0.638984, \quad \lambda \approx -0.290977, \quad \mu \approx 0.554805$$

Substituting these values into f gives $f(-1.652878, -1.964194, -1.126052) \approx -4.7431$,

$f(-1.502800, 0.968872, 1.319694) \approx 0.7858$, $f(-0.992513, 1.649677, -1.736352) \approx -1.0792$,

$f(1.895178, 1.718347, 0.638984) \approx 4.2525$. Thus the maximum is approximately 4.2525, and the mininum is

approximately -4.7431.

41. (a) We wish to maximize $f(x_1, x_2, \ldots, x_n) = \sqrt[n]{x_1 x_2 \cdots x_n}$ subject to

$g(x_1, x_2, \ldots, x_n) = x_1 + x_2 + \cdots + x_n = c$ and $x_i > 0$.

$$\nabla f = \left\langle \frac{1}{n}(x_1 x_2 \cdots x_n)^{\frac{1}{n}-1}(x_2 \cdots x_n), \frac{1}{n}(x_1 x_2 \cdots x_n)^{\frac{1}{n}-1}(x_1 x_3 \cdots x_n), \ldots, \right.$$

$$\left. \frac{1}{n}(x_1 x_2 \cdots x_n)^{\frac{1}{n}-1}(x_1 \cdots x_{n-1}) \right\rangle$$

and $\lambda \nabla g = \langle \lambda, \lambda, \ldots, \lambda \rangle$, so we need to solve the system of equations

$$\frac{1}{n}(x_1 x_2 \cdots x_n)^{\frac{1}{n}-1}(x_2 \cdots x_n) = \lambda \quad \Rightarrow \quad x_1^{1/n} x_2^{1/n} \cdots x_n^{1/n} = n\lambda x_1$$

$$\frac{1}{n}(x_1 x_2 \cdots x_n)^{\frac{1}{n}-1}(x_1 x_3 \cdots x_n) = \lambda \quad \Rightarrow \quad x_1^{1/n} x_2^{1/n} \cdots x_n^{1/n} = n\lambda x_2$$

$$\vdots$$

$$\frac{1}{n}(x_1 x_2 \cdots x_n)^{\frac{1}{n}-1}(x_1 \cdots x_{n-1}) = \lambda \quad \Rightarrow \quad x_1^{1/n} x_2^{1/n} \cdots x_n^{1/n} = n\lambda x_n$$

This implies $n\lambda x_1 = n\lambda x_2 = \cdots = n\lambda x_n$. Note $\lambda \neq 0$, otherwise we can't have all $x_i > 0$. Thus $x_1 = x_2 = \cdots = x_n$. But $x_1 + x_2 + \cdots + x_n = c \quad \Rightarrow \quad nx_1 = c \quad \Rightarrow \quad x_1 = \dfrac{c}{n} = x_2 = x_3 = \cdots = x_n$.

Then the only point where f can have an extreme value is $\left(\dfrac{c}{n}, \dfrac{c}{n}, \ldots, \dfrac{c}{n}\right)$. Since we can choose values for $(x_1, x_2, \ldots, x_n)$ that make f as close to zero (but not equal) as we like, f has no minimum value. Thus the maximum value is $f\left(\dfrac{c}{n}, \dfrac{c}{n}, \ldots, \dfrac{c}{n}\right) = \sqrt[n]{\dfrac{c}{n} \cdot \dfrac{c}{n} \cdots \dfrac{c}{n}} = \dfrac{c}{n}$.

(b) From part (a), $\dfrac{c}{n}$ is the maximum value of f. Thus $f(x_1, x_2, \ldots, x_n) = \sqrt[n]{x_1 x_2 \cdots x_n} \leq \dfrac{c}{n}$. But $x_1 + x_2 + \cdots + x_n = c$, so $\sqrt[n]{x_1 x_2 \cdots x_n} \leq \dfrac{x_1 + x_2 + \cdots + x_n}{n}$. These two means are equal when f attains its maximum value $\dfrac{c}{n}$, but this can occur only at the point $\left(\dfrac{c}{n}, \dfrac{c}{n}, \ldots, \dfrac{c}{n}\right)$ we found in part (a). So the means are equal only when $x_1 = x_2 = x_3 = \cdots = x_n = \dfrac{c}{n}$.

42. (a) Let $f(x_1, \ldots, x_n, y_1, \ldots, y_n) = \sum\limits_{i=1}^{n} x_i y_i$, $g(x_1, \ldots, x_n) = \sum\limits_{i=1}^{n} x_i^2$, and $h(x_1, \ldots, x_n) = \sum\limits_{i=1}^{n} y_i^2$. Then

$$\nabla f = \nabla \sum_{i=1}^{n} x_i y_i = \langle y_1, y_2, \ldots, y_n, x_1, x_2, \ldots, x_n \rangle, \quad \nabla g = \nabla \sum_{i=1}^{n} x_i^2 = \langle 2x_1, 2x_2, \ldots, 2x_n, 0, 0, \ldots, 0 \rangle$$

and $\nabla h = \nabla \sum\limits_{i=1}^{n} y_i^2 = \langle 0, 0, \ldots, 0, 2y_1, 2y_2, \ldots, 2y_n \rangle$. So $\nabla f = \lambda \nabla g + \mu \nabla h \iff y_i = 2\lambda x_i$ and

$x_i = 2\mu y_i$, $1 \leq i \leq n$. Then $1 = \sum\limits_{i=1}^{n} y_i^2 = \sum\limits_{i=1}^{n} 4\lambda^2 x_i^2 = 4\lambda^2 \sum\limits_{i=1}^{n} x_i^2 = 4\lambda^2 \quad \Rightarrow \quad \lambda = \pm\frac{1}{2}$.

If $\lambda = \frac{1}{2}$ then $y_i = 2\left(\frac{1}{2}\right)x_i = x_i$, $1 \leq i \leq n$. Thus $\sum\limits_{i=1}^{n} x_i y_i = \sum\limits_{i=1}^{n} x_i^2 = 1$. Similarly if $\lambda = -\frac{1}{2}$ we get

$y_i = -x_i$ and $\sum\limits_{i=1}^{n} x_i y_i = -1$. Similarly we get $\mu = \pm\frac{1}{2}$ giving $y_i = \pm x_i$, $1 \leq i \leq n$, and $\sum\limits_{i=1}^{n} x_i y_i = \pm 1$.

Thus the maximum value of $\sum\limits_{i=1}^{n} x_i y_i$ is 1.

(b) Here we assume $\sum\limits_{i=1}^{n} a_i^2 \neq 0$ and $\sum\limits_{i=1}^{n} b_i^2 \neq 0$. (If $\sum\limits_{i=1}^{n} a_i^2 = 0$, then each $a_i = 0$ and so the inequality is trivially

true.) $x_i = \dfrac{a_i}{\sqrt{\sum a_i^2}} \quad \Rightarrow \quad \sum x_i^2 = \dfrac{\sum a_i^2}{\sum a_i^2} = 1$, and $y_i = \dfrac{b_i}{\sqrt{\sum b_i^2}} \quad \Rightarrow \quad \sum y_i^2 = \dfrac{\sum b_i^2}{\sum b_i^2} = 1$. Therefore,

from (a), $\sum x_i y_i = \sum \dfrac{a_i b_i}{\sqrt{\sum a_i^2} \sqrt{\sum b_i^2}} \leq 1 \iff \sum a_i b_i \leq \sqrt{\sum a_i^2} \sqrt{\sum b_i^2}$.

Applied Project	**Rocket Science**

1. Initially the rocket engine has mass $M_r = M_1$ and payload mass $P = M_2 + M_3 + A$. Then the change in velocity resulting from the first stage is $\Delta V_1 = -c \ln\left(1 - \dfrac{(1-S)M_1}{M_2 + M_3 + A + M_1}\right)$. After the first stage is jettisoned we can consider the rocket engine to have mass $M_r = M_2$ and the payload to have mass $P = M_3 + A$. The resulting change in velocity from the second stage is $\Delta V_2 = -c \ln\left(1 - \dfrac{(1-S)M_2}{M_3 + A + M_2}\right)$. When only the third stage remains, we have $M_r = M_3$ and $P = A$, so the resulting change in velocity is $\Delta V_3 = -c \ln\left(1 - \dfrac{(1-S)M_3}{A + M_3}\right)$. Since the rocket started from rest, the final velocity attained is

$$v_f = \Delta V_1 + \Delta V_2 + \Delta V_3$$

$$= -c\ln\left(1 - \frac{(1-S)M_1}{M_2 + M_3 + A + M_1}\right) + (-c)\ln\left(1 - \frac{(1-S)M_2}{M_3 + A + M_2}\right)$$

$$+ (-c)\ln\left(1 - \frac{(1-S)M_3}{A + M_3}\right)$$

$$= -c\left[\ln\left(\frac{M_1 + M_2 + M_3 + A - (1-S)M_1}{M_1 + M_2 + M_3 + A}\right) + \ln\left(\frac{M_2 + M_3 + A - (1-S)M_2}{M_2 + M_3 + A}\right)\right.$$

$$\left. + \ln\left(\frac{M_3 + A - (1-S)M_3}{M_3 + A}\right)\right]$$

$$= c\left[\ln\left(\frac{M_1 + M_2 + M_3 + A}{SM_1 + M_2 + M_3 + A}\right) + \ln\left(\frac{M_2 + M_3 + A}{SM_2 + M_3 + A}\right) + \ln\left(\frac{M_3 + A}{SM_3 + A}\right)\right]$$

2. Define $N_1 = \dfrac{M_1 + M_2 + M_3 + A}{SM_1 + M_2 + M_3 + A}$, $N_2 = \dfrac{M_2 + M_3 + A}{SM_2 + M_3 + A}$, and $N_3 = \dfrac{M_3 + A}{SM_3 + A}$. Then

$$\frac{(1-S)N_1}{1 - SN_1} = \frac{(1-S)\dfrac{M_1 + M_2 + M_3 + A}{SM_1 + M_2 + M_3 + A}}{1 - S\dfrac{M_1 + M_2 + M_3 + A}{SM_1 + M_2 + M_3 + A}}$$

$$= \frac{(1-S)(M_1 + M_2 + M_3 + A)}{SM_1 + M_2 + M_3 + A - S(M_1 + M_2 + M_3 + A)}$$

$$= \frac{(1-S)(M_1 + M_2 + M_3 + A)}{(1-S)(M_2 + M_3 + A)} = \frac{M_1 + M_2 + M_3 + A}{M_2 + M_3 + A}$$

as desired.

Similarly,

$$\frac{(1-S)N_2}{1 - SN_2} = \frac{(1-S)(M_2 + M_3 + A)}{SM_2 + M_3 + A - S(M_2 + M_3 + A)} = \frac{(1-S)(M_2 + M_3 + A)}{(1-S)(M_3 + A)} = \frac{M_2 + M_3 + A}{M_3 + A}$$

and

$$\frac{(1-S)N_3}{1 - SN_3} = \frac{(1-S)(M_3 + A)}{SM_3 + A - S(M_3 + A)} = \frac{(1-S)(M_3 + A)}{(1-S)(A)} = \frac{M_3 + A}{A}$$

Then

$$\frac{M+A}{A} = \frac{M_1 + M_2 + M_3 + A}{A} = \frac{M_1 + M_2 + M_3 + A}{M_2 + M_3 + A} \cdot \frac{M_2 + M_3 + A}{M_3 + A} \cdot \frac{M_3 + A}{A}$$

$$= \frac{(1-S)N_1}{1 - SN_1} \cdot \frac{(1-S)N_2}{1 - SN_2} \cdot \frac{(1-S)N_3}{1 - SN_3} = \frac{(1-S)^3 N_1 N_2 N_3}{(1-S)(1-S)(1-S)}$$

3. Since $A > 0$, $M + A$ and consequently $\dfrac{M+A}{A}$ is minimized for the same values as M. $\ln x$ is a strictly increasing

function, so $\ln\left(\dfrac{M+A}{A}\right)$ must give a minimum for the same values as $\dfrac{M+A}{A}$ and hence M. We then wish to

minimize $\ln\left(\dfrac{M+A}{A}\right)$ subject to the constraint $c\,(\ln N_1 + \ln N_2 + \ln N_3) = v_f$. From Problem 2,

$$\ln\left(\frac{M+A}{A}\right) = \ln\left(\frac{(1-S)^3 N_1 N_2 N_3}{(1-SN_1)(1-SN_2)(1-SN_3)}\right)$$

$$= 3\ln(1-S) + \ln N_1 + \ln N_2 + \ln N_3 - \ln(1-SN_1) - \ln(1-SN_2) - \ln(1-SN_3)$$

Using the method of Lagrange multipliers, we need to solve $\nabla\left[\ln\left(\dfrac{M+A}{A}\right)\right] = \lambda\nabla[c(\ln N_1 + \ln N_2 + \ln N_3)]$

with $c(\ln N_1 + \ln N_2 + \ln N_3) = v_f$ in terms of N_1, N_2, and N_3. The resulting system is

$$\frac{1}{N_1} + \frac{S}{1 - SN_1} = \lambda\frac{c}{N_1} \qquad \frac{1}{N_2} + \frac{S}{1 - SN_2} = \lambda\frac{c}{N_2} \qquad \frac{1}{N_3} + \frac{S}{1 - SN_3} = \lambda\frac{c}{N_3}$$

$$c\,(\ln N_1 + \ln N_2 + \ln N_3) = v_f$$

One approach to solving the system is isolating $c\lambda$ in the first three equations which gives

$$1 + \frac{SN_1}{1 - SN_1} = c\lambda = 1 + \frac{SN_2}{1 - SN_2} = 1 + \frac{SN_3}{1 - SN_3} \quad\Rightarrow\quad \frac{N_1}{1 - SN_1} = \frac{N_2}{1 - SN_2} = \frac{N_3}{1 - SN_3} \quad\Rightarrow$$

$N_1 = N_2 = N_3$ (Verify!). This says the fourth equation can be expressed as $c(\ln N_1 + \ln N_1 + \ln N_1) = v_f \quad\Rightarrow$

$3c\ln N_1 = v_f \quad\Rightarrow\quad \ln N_1 = \dfrac{v_f}{3c}$. Thus the minimum mass M of the rocket engine is attained for

$N_1 = N_2 = N_3 = e^{v_f/(3c)}$.

4. Using the previous results,

$$\frac{M+A}{A} = \frac{(1-S)^3 N_1 N_2 N_3}{(1-SN_1)(1-SN_2)(1-SN_3)} = \frac{(1-S)^3\left[e^{v_f/(3c)}\right]^3}{\left[1 - Se^{v_f/(3c)}\right]^3} = \frac{(1-S)^3 e^{v_f/c}}{\left[1 - Se^{v_f/(3c)}\right]^3}. \text{ Then}$$

$$M = \frac{A(1-S)^3 e^{v_f/c}}{\left[1 - Se^{v_f/(3c)}\right]^3} - A.$$

5. (a) From Problem 4, $M = \dfrac{A(1-0.2)^3 e^{(17{,}500/6000)}}{\left(1 - 0.2e^{[17{,}500/(3\cdot6000)]}\right)^3} - A \approx 90.4A - A = 89.4A.$

(b) First, $N_3 = \dfrac{M_3 + A}{SM_3 + A} \quad\Rightarrow\quad e^{[17{,}500/(3\cdot6000)]} = \dfrac{M_3 + A}{0.2M_3 + A} \quad\Rightarrow\quad M_3 = \dfrac{A\left(1 - e^{35/36}\right)}{0.2e^{35/36} - 1} \approx 3.49A.$ Then

$$N_2 = \frac{M_2 + M_3 + A}{SM_2 + M_3 + A} = \frac{M_2 + 3.49A + A}{0.2M_2 + 3.49A + A} \quad\Rightarrow\quad M_2 = \frac{4.49A\left(1 - e^{35/36}\right)}{0.2e^{35/36} - 1} \approx 15.67A$$

and $N_3 = \dfrac{M_1 + M_2 + M_3 + A}{SM_1 + M_2 + M_3 + A} = \dfrac{M_1 + 15.67A + 3.49A + A}{0.2M_1 + 15.67A + 3.49A + A}$ $\Rightarrow$

$M_1 = \dfrac{20.16A\left(1 - e^{35/36}\right)}{0.2e^{35/36} - 1} \approx 70.36A.$

6. As in Problem 5, $N_3 = \dfrac{M_3 + A}{SM_3 + A}$ $\Rightarrow$ $e^{24,700/(3 \cdot 6000)} = \dfrac{M_3 + A}{0.2M_3 + A}$ $\Rightarrow$

$M_3 = \dfrac{A\left(1 - e^{247/180}\right)}{0.2e^{247/180} - 1} \approx 13.9A, \quad N_2 = \dfrac{M_2 + M_3 + A}{SM_2 + M_3 + A} = \dfrac{M_2 + 13.9A + A}{0.2M_2 + 13.9A + A}$ $\Rightarrow$

$M_2 = \dfrac{14.9A\left(1 - e^{247/180}\right)}{0.2e^{247/180} - 1} \approx 208A, \text{ and } N_3 = \dfrac{M_1 + M_2 + M_3 + A}{SM_1 + M_2 + M_3 + A} = \dfrac{M_1 + 208A + 13.9A + A}{0.2M_1 + 208A + 13.9A + A}$ $\Rightarrow$

$M_1 = \dfrac{222.9A\left(1 - e^{247/180}\right)}{0.2e^{247/180} - 1} \approx 3110A.$ Here $A = 500$, so the mass of each stage of the rocket engine is

approximately $M_1 = 3110(500) = 1{,}550{,}000$ lb, $M_2 = 208(500) = 104{,}000$ lb, and
$M_3 = 13.9(500) = 6950$ lb.

Applied Project	**Hydro-Turbine Optimization**

1. We wish to maximize the total energy production for a given total flow, so we can say Q_T is fixed and we want to
maximize $KW_1 + KW_2 + KW_3$. Notice each KW_i has a constant factor $\left(170 - 1.6 \cdot 10^{-6}Q_T^2\right)$, so to simplify
the computations we can equivalently maximize

$$f(Q_1, Q_2, Q_3) = \frac{KW_1 + KW_2 + KW_3}{170 - 1.6 \cdot 10^{-6}Q_T^2}$$

$$= \left(-18.89 + 0.1277Q_1 - 4.08 \cdot 10^{-5}Q_1^2\right)$$

$$+ \left(-24.51 + 0.1358Q_2 - 4.69 \cdot 10^{-5}Q_2^2\right)$$

$$+ \left(-27.02 + 0.1380Q_3 - 3.84 \cdot 10^{-5}Q_3^2\right)$$

subject to the constraint $g(Q_1, Q_2, Q_3) = Q_1 + Q_2 + Q_3 = Q_T$. So first we find the values of Q_1, Q_2, Q_3 where
$\nabla f(Q_1, Q_2, Q_3) = \lambda \nabla g(Q_1, Q_2, Q_3)$ and $Q_1 + Q_2 + Q_3 = Q_T$ which is equivalent to solving the system

$$0.1277 - 2\left(4.08 \cdot 10^{-5}\right)Q_1 = \lambda$$

$$0.1358 - 2\left(4.69 \cdot 10^{-5}\right)Q_2 = \lambda$$

$$0.1380 - 2\left(3.84 \cdot 10^{-5}\right)Q_3 = \lambda$$

$$Q_1 + Q_2 + Q_3 = Q_T$$

Comparing the first and third equations, we have $0.1277 - 2\left(4.08 \cdot 10^{-5}\right)Q_1 = 0.1380 - 2\left(3.84 \cdot 10^{-5}\right)Q_3$ $\Rightarrow$
$Q_1 = -126.2255 + 0.9412Q_3$. From the second and third equations,
$0.1358 - 2\left(4.69 \cdot 10^{-5}\right)Q_2 = 0.1380 - 2\left(3.84 \cdot 10^{-5}\right)Q_3$ $\Rightarrow$ $Q_2 = -23.4542 + 0.8188Q_3$. Substituting

into $Q_1 + Q_2 + Q_3 = Q_T$ gives $(-126.2255 + 0.9412Q_3) + (-23.4542 + 0.8188Q_3) + Q_3 = Q_T \Rightarrow$

$2.76Q_3 = Q_T + 149.6797 \Rightarrow Q_3 = 0.3623Q_T + 54.23$. Then

$Q_1 = -126.2255 + 0.9412Q_3 = -126.2255 + 0.9412(0.3623Q_T + 54.23) = 0.3410Q_T - 75.18$ and

$Q_2 = -23.4542 + 0.8188(0.3623Q_T + 54.23) = 0.2967Q_T + 20.95$. As long as we maintain

$250 \leq Q_1 \leq 1110$, $250 \leq Q_2 \leq 1110$, and $250 \leq Q_3 \leq 1225$, we can reason from the nature of the functions

KW_i that these values give a maximum of f, and hence a maximum energy production, and not a minimum.

2. From Problem 1, the value of Q_1 that maximizes energy production is $0.3410Q_T - 75.18$, but since

$250 \leq Q_1 \leq 1110$, we must have $250 \leq 0.3410Q_T - 75.18 \leq 1110 \Rightarrow 325.18 \leq 0.3410Q_T \leq 1185.18 \Rightarrow$

$953.6 \leq Q_T \leq 3475.6$. Similarly, $250 \leq Q_2 \leq 1110 \Rightarrow 250 \leq 0.2967Q_T + 20.95 \leq 1110 \Rightarrow$

$772.0 \leq Q_T \leq 3670.5$, and $250 \leq Q_3 \leq 1225 \Rightarrow 250 \leq 0.3623Q_T + 54.23 \leq 1225 \Rightarrow$

$540.4 \leq Q_T \leq 3231.5$. Consolidating these results, we see that the values from Problem 1 are applicable only for

$953.6 \leq Q_T \leq 3231.5$.

3. If $Q_T = 2500$, the results from Problem 1 show that the maximum energy production occurs for

$$Q_1 = 0.3410Q_T - 75.18 = 0.3410(2500) - 75.18 = 777.3$$

$$Q_2 = 0.2967Q_T + 20.95 = 0.2967(2500) + 20.95 = 762.7$$

$$Q_3 = 0.3623Q_T + 54.23 = 0.3623(2500) + 54.23 = 960.0$$

The energy produced for these values is $KW_1 + KW_2 + KW_3 \approx 8915.2 + 8285.1 + 11,211.3 \approx 28,411.6$. We

compute the energy production for a nearby distribution, $Q_1 = 770$, $Q_2 = 760$, and $Q_3 = 970$:

$KW_1 + KW_2 + KW_3 \approx 8839.8 + 8257.4 + 11,313.5 = 28,410.7$. For another example, we take $Q_1 = 780$,

$Q_2 = 765$, and $Q_3 = 955$: $KW_1 + KW_2 + KW_3 \approx 8942.9 + 8308.8 + 11,159.7 = 28,411.4$. These

distributions are both close to the distribution from Problem 1 and both give slightly lower energy productions,

suggesting that $Q_1 = 777.3$, $Q_2 = 762.7$, and $Q_3 = 960.0$ is indeed the optimal distribution.

4. First we graph each power function in its domain if all of the
flow is directed to that turbine (so $Q_i = Q_T$).

If we use only one turbine, the graph indicates that for a

water flow of 1000 ft³/s, Turbine 3 produces the most power,

approximately 12,200 kW. In comparison, if we use all three

turbines, the results of Problem 1 with $Q_T = 1000$ give

$Q_1 = 265.8$, $Q_2 = 317.7$, and $Q_3 = 416.5$, resulting in a

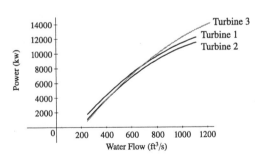

total energy production of $KW_1 + KW_2 + KW_3 \approx 8397.4$ kW. Here, using only one turbine produces

significantly more energy! If the flow is only 600 ft³/s, we do not have the option of using all three turbines, as the

domain restrictions require a minimum of 250 ft³/s in each turbine. We can use just one turbine, then, and from the

graph Turbine 1 produces the most energy for a water flow of 600 ft³.

5. If we examine the graph from Problem 4, we see that for water flows above approximately 450 ft³/s, Turbine 2 produces the least amount of power. Therefore it seems reasonable to assume that we should distribute the incoming flow of 1500 ft³/s between Turbines 1 and 3. (This can be verified by computing the power produced with the other pairs of turbines for comparison.) So now we wish to maximize $KW_1 + KW_3$ subject to the constraint $Q_1 + Q_3 = Q_T$ where $Q_T = 1500$.

As in Problem 1, we can equivalently maximize

$$f(Q_1, Q_3) = \frac{KW_1 + KW_3}{170 - 1.6 \cdot 10^{-6} Q_T^2}$$

$$= \left(-18.89 + 0.1277 Q_1 - 4.08 \cdot 10^{-5} Q_1^2\right) + \left(-27.02 + 0.1380 Q_3 - 3.84 \cdot 10^{-5} Q_3^2\right)$$

subject to the constraint $g(Q_1, Q_3) = Q_1 + Q_3 = Q_T$.

Then we solve $\nabla f(Q_1, Q_3) = \lambda \nabla g(Q_1, Q_3)$ ⇒ $0.1277 - 2\left(4.08 \cdot 10^{-5}\right) Q_1 = \lambda$ and $0.1380 - 2\left(3.84 \cdot 10^{-5}\right) Q_3 = \lambda$, thus $0.1277 - 2\left(4.08 \cdot 10^{-5}\right) Q_1 = 0.1380 - 2\left(3.84 \cdot 10^{-5}\right) Q_3$ ⇒ $Q_1 = -126.2255 + 0.9412 Q_3$. Substituting into $Q_1 + Q_3 = Q_T$ gives $-126.2255 + 0.9412 Q_3 + Q_3 = 1500$ ⇒ $Q_3 \approx 837.7$, and then $Q_1 = Q_T - Q_3 \approx 1500 - 837.7 = 662.3$. So we should apportion approximately 662.3 ft³/s to Turbine 1 and the remaining 837.7 ft³/s to Turbine 3. The resulting energy production is $KW_1 + KW_3 \approx 7952.1 + 10{,}256.2 = 18{,}208.3$ kW. (We can verify that this is indeed a maximum energy production by checking nearby distributions.) In comparison, if we use all three turbines with $Q_T = 1500$ we get $Q_1 = 436.3$, $Q_2 = 466.0$, and $Q_3 = 597.7$, resulting in a total energy production of $KW_1 + KW_2 + KW_3 \approx 16{,}538.7$ kW. Clearly, for this flow level it is beneficial to use only two turbines.

6. Note that an incoming flow of 3400 ft³/s is not within the domain we established in Problem 2, so we cannot simply use our previous work to give the optimal distribution. We will need to use all three turbines, due to the capacity limitations of each individual turbine, but 3400 is less than the maximum combined capacity of 3445 ft³/s, so we still must decide how to distribute the flows. From the graph in Problem 4, Turbine 3 produces the most power for the higher flows, so it seems reasonable to use Turbine 3 at its maximum capacity of 1225 and distribute the remaining 2175 ft³/s flow between Turbines 1 and 2. We can again use the technique of Lagrange multipliers to determine the optimal distribution. Following the procedure we used in Problem 5, we wish to maximize $KW_1 + KW_2$ subject to the constraint $Q_1 + Q_2 = Q_T$ where $Q_T = 2175$. We can equivalently maximize

$$f(Q_1, Q_2) = \frac{KW_1 + KW_2}{170 - 1.6 \cdot 10^{-6} Q_T^2}$$

$$= \left(-18.89 + 0.1277 Q_1 - 4.08 \cdot 10^{-5} Q_1^2\right) + \left(-24.51 + 0.1358 Q_2 - 4.69 \cdot 10^{-5} Q_2^2\right)$$

subject to the constraint $g(Q_1, Q_2) = Q_1 + Q_2 = Q_T$. Then we solve $\nabla f(Q_1, Q_2) = \lambda \nabla g(Q_1, Q_2)$ ⇒ $0.1277 - 2\left(4.08 \cdot 10^{-5}\right) Q_1 = \lambda$ and $0.1358 - 2\left(4.69 \cdot 10^{-5}\right) Q_2 = \lambda$, thus $0.1277 - 2\left(4.08 \cdot 10^{-5}\right) Q_1 = 0.1358 - 2\left(4.69 \cdot 10^{-5}\right) Q_2$ ⇒ $Q_1 = -99.2647 + 1.1495 Q_2$. Substituting into $Q_1 + Q_2 = Q_T$ gives $-99.2647 + 1.1495 Q_2 + Q_2 = 2175 \Rightarrow Q_2 \approx 1058.0$, and then $Q_1 \approx 1117.0$. This value for Q_1 is larger than the allowable maximum flow to Turbine 1, but the result indicates that the flow to Turbine 1 should be maximized. Thus we should recommend that the company apportion the maximum allowable flows to Turbines 1 and 3, 1110 and 1225 ft^3/s, and the remaining 1065 ft^3/s to Turbine 2. Checking nearby distributions within the domain verifies that we have indeed found the optimal distribution.

 Review

━━━━━━━━━━━━ **• CONCEPT CHECK •** ━━━━━━━━━━━━

1. (a) A function f of two variables is a rule that assigns to each ordered pair (x, y) of real numbers in its domain a unique real number denoted by $f(x, y)$.

(b) One way to visualize a function of two variables is by graphing it, resulting in the surface $z = f(x, y)$. Another method for visualizing a function of two variables is a contour map. The contour map consists of level curves of the function which are horizontal traces of the graph of the function projected onto the xy-plane.

2. A function f of three variables is a rule that assigns to each ordered triple (x, y, z) in its domain a unique real number $f(x, y, z)$. We can visualize a function of three variables by examining its level surfaces $f(x, y, z) = k$, where k is a constant.

3. $\lim\limits_{(x,y) \to (a,b)} f(x, y) = L$ means the values of $f(x, y)$ approach the number L as the point (x, y) approaches the point (a, b) along any path that is within the domain of f. We can show that a limit at a point does not exist by finding two different paths approaching the point along which $f(x, y)$ has different limits.

4. (a) See Definition 11.2.3.

(b) If f is continuous on $\mathbb{R}^2$, its graph will appear as a surface without holes or breaks.

5. (a) See (2) and (3) in Section 11.3.

(b) See the discussion preceding Example 2 on page 769.

(c) To find f_x, regard y as a constant and differentiate $f(x, y)$ with respect to x. To find f_y, regard x as a constant and differentiate $f(x, y)$ with respect to y.

6. See the statement of Clairaut's Theorem on page 773.

7. (a) See (2) in Section 11.4.

(b) See (19) and the preceding discussion in Section 11.6.

(c) See the discussion following Example 6 on page 787.

8. See (3) and (4) and the accompanying discussion in Section 11.4. We can interpret the linearization of f at (a, b) geometrically as the linear function whose graph is the tangent plane to the graph of f at (a, b). Thus it is the linear function which best approximates f near (a, b).

9. (a) See Definition 11.4.7.

(b) Use Theorem 11.4.8.

10. See (10) and the associated discussion in Section 11.4.

11. See (2) and (3) in Section 11.5.

12. See (7) and the preceding discussion in Section 11.5.

13. (a) See Definition 11.6.2. We can interpret it as the rate of change of f at (x_0, y_0) in the direction of $\mathbf{u}$. Geometrically, if P is the point $(x_0, y_0, f(x_0, y_0))$ on the graph of f and C is the curve of intersection of the graph of f with the vertical plane that passes through P in the direction $\mathbf{u}$, the directional derivative of f at (x_0, y_0) in the direction of $\mathbf{u}$ is the slope of the tangent line to C at P. (See Figure 5 in Section 11.6.)

(b) See Theorem 11.6.3.

14. (a) See (8) and (13) in Section 11.6.

(b) $D_{\mathbf{u}} f(x, y) = \nabla f(x, y) \cdot \mathbf{u}$ or $D_{\mathbf{u}} f(x, y, z) = \nabla f(x, y, z) \cdot \mathbf{u}$

(c) The gradient vector of a function points in the direction of maximum rate of increase of the function. On a graph of the function, the gradient points in the direction of steepest ascent.

15. (a) f has a local maximum at (a, b) if $f(x, y) \leq f(a, b)$ when (x, y) is near (a, b).

(b) f has an absolute maximum at (a, b) if $f(x, y) \leq f(a, b)$ for all points (x, y) in the domain of f.

(c) f has a local minimum at (a, b) if $f(x, y) \geq f(a, b)$ when (x, y) is near (a, b).

(d) f has an absolute minimum at (a, b) if $f(x, y) \geq f(a, b)$ for all points (x, y) in the domain of f.

(e) f has a saddle point at (a, b) if $f(a, b)$ is a local maximum in one direction but a local minimum in another.

16. (a) By Theorem 11.7.2, if f has a local maximum at (a, b) and the first-order partial derivatives of f exist there, then $f_x(a, b) = 0$ and $f_y(a, b) = 0$.

(b) A critical point of f is a point (a, b) such that $f_x(a, b) = 0$ and $f_y(a, b) = 0$ or one of these partial derivatives does not exist.

17. See (3) in Section 11.7.

18. (a) See Figure 11 and the accompanying discussion in Section 11.7.

(b) See Theorem 11.7.8.

(c) See the procedure outlined in (9) in Section 11.7.

19. See the discussion beginning on page 822; see the discussion preceding Example 5 on page 826.

───────────────────────────── ▲ **TRUE–FALSE QUIZ** ▲ ─────────────

1. True. $f_y(a, b) = \lim\limits_{h \to 0} \dfrac{f(a, b+h) - f(a, b)}{h}$ from Equation 11.3.3. Let $h = y - b$. As $h \to 0$, $y \to b$. Then by substituting, we get $f_y(a, b) = \lim\limits_{y \to b} \dfrac{f(a, y) - f(a, b)}{y - b}$.

2. False. If there were such a function, then $f_{xy} = 2y$ and $f_{yx} = 1$. So $f_{xy} \neq f_{yx}$, which contradicts Clairaut's Theorem.

3. False. $f_{xy} = \dfrac{\partial^2 f}{\partial y \partial x}$.

4. True. From Equation 11.6.14 we get $D_{\mathbf{k}} f(x, y, z) = \nabla f(x, y, z) \cdot \langle 0, 0, 1 \rangle = f_z(x, y, z)$.

5. False. See Example 11.2.3.

6. False. See Exercise 11.4.40(a).

7. True. If f has a local minimum and f is differentiable at (a, b) then by Theorem 11.7.2, $f_x(a, b) = 0$ and $f_y(a, b) = 0$, so $\nabla f(a, b) = \langle f_x(a, b), f_y(a, b) \rangle = \langle 0, 0 \rangle = \mathbf{0}$.

8. False. The limit does not exist because the function is not defined on the line $y = x$, and so we have a path approaching the point $(1, 1)$ along which f does not approach $\frac{1}{2}$.

9. False. $\nabla f(x, y) = \langle 0, 1/y \rangle$.

10. True. This is part (c) of the Second Derivatives Test (11.7.3).

11. True. $\nabla f = \langle \cos x, \cos y \rangle$, so $|\nabla f| = \sqrt{\cos^2 x + \cos^2 y}$. But $|\cos \theta| \leq 1$, so $|\nabla f| \leq \sqrt{2}$. Now $D_{\mathbf{u}} f(x, y) = \nabla f \cdot \mathbf{u} = |\nabla f| |\mathbf{u}| \cos \theta$, but $\mathbf{u}$ is a unit vector, so $|D_{\mathbf{u}} f(x, y)| \leq \sqrt{2} \cdot 1 \cdot 1 = \sqrt{2}$.

12. False. See Exercise 11.7.29.

◆ **EXERCISES** ◆

1. The domain of $\sin^{-1} x$ is $-1 \leq x \leq 1$ while the domain of $\tan^{-1} y$ is all real numbers, so the domain of $f(x, y) = \sin^{-1} x + \tan^{-1} y$ is $\{(x, y) \mid -1 \leq x \leq 1\}$.

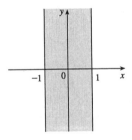

2. $D = \{(x, y, z) \mid z \geq x^2 + y^2\}$, the points on and above the paraboloid $z = x^2 + y^2$.

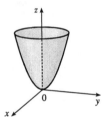

3. $z = f(x, y) = 1 - x^2 - y^2$, a paraboloid with vertex $(0, 0, 1)$.

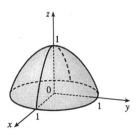

4. $z = f(x, y) = \sqrt{x^2 + y^2 - 1}$, so $z \geq 0$ and $1 = x^2 + y^2 - z^2$. Thus the graph is the upper half of a hyperboloid of one sheet.

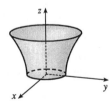

5. Let $k = e^{-c} = e^{-(x^2+y^2)}$ be the level curves. Then
$-\ln k = c = x^2 + y^2$, so we have a family of
concentric circles.

6. $k = x^2 + 4y$ or $4(y - k/4) = -x^2$, a family of
parabolas with vertex at $(0, k/4)$.

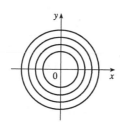

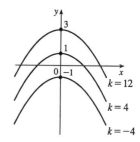

7.

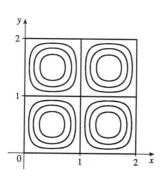

8.

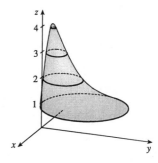

9. f is a rational function, so it is continuous on its domain. Since f is defined at $(1, 1)$, we use direct substitution to

evaluate the limit: $\displaystyle\lim_{(x,y)\to(1,1)} \frac{2xy}{x^2 + 2y^2} = \frac{2(1)(1)}{1^2 + 2(1)^2} = \frac{2}{3}$.

10. As $(x, y) \to (0, 0)$ along the x-axis, $f(x, 0) = 0/x^2 = 0$ for $x \neq 0$, so $f(x, y) \to 0$ along this line. But
$f(x, x) = 2x^2/(3x^2) = \frac{2}{3}$, so as $(x, y) \to (0, 0)$ along the line $x = y$, $f(x, y) \to \frac{2}{3}$. Thus the limit doesn't exist.

11. (a) $T_x(6, 4) = \displaystyle\lim_{h\to 0} \frac{T(6 + h, 4) - T(6, 4)}{h}$, so we can approximate $T_x(6, 4)$ by considering $h = \pm 2$ and using the

values given in the table: $T_x(6, 4) \approx \dfrac{T(8, 4) - T(6, 4)}{2} = \dfrac{86 - 80}{2} = 3$,

$T_x(6, 4) \approx \dfrac{T(4, 4) - T(6, 4)}{-2} = \dfrac{72 - 80}{-2} = 4$. Averaging these values, we estimate $T_x(6, 4)$ to be

approximately $3.5\,^\circ$C$/$m. Similarly, $T_y(6, 4) = \displaystyle\lim_{h\to 0} \frac{T(6, 4 + h) - T(6, 4)}{h}$, which we can

approximate with $h = \pm 2$: $T_y(6, 4) \approx \dfrac{T(6, 6) - T(6, 4)}{2} = \dfrac{75 - 80}{2} = -2.5$,

$T_y(6, 4) \approx \dfrac{T(6, 2) - T(6, 4)}{-2} = \dfrac{87 - 80}{-2} = -3.5$. Averaging these values, we estimate $T_y(6, 4)$ to be

approximately $-3.0\,^\circ$C$/$m.

(b) Here $\mathbf{u} = \left\langle \frac{1}{\sqrt{2}}, \frac{1}{\sqrt{2}} \right\rangle$, so by Equation 11.6.9, $D_{\mathbf{u}}T(6,4) = \nabla T(6,4) \cdot \mathbf{u} = T_x(6,4)\frac{1}{\sqrt{2}} + T_y(6,4)\frac{1}{\sqrt{2}}$. Using our estimates from part (a), we have $D_{\mathbf{u}}T(6,4) \approx (3.5)\frac{1}{\sqrt{2}} + (-3.0)\frac{1}{\sqrt{2}} = \frac{1}{2\sqrt{2}} \approx 0.35$. This means that as we move through the point $(6,4)$ in the direction of $\mathbf{u}$, the temperature increases at a rate of approximately $0.35\,^\circ\mathrm{C}/\mathrm{m}$.

Alternatively, we can use Definition 11.6.2: $D_{\mathbf{u}}T(6,4) = \lim\limits_{h \to 0} \dfrac{T\left(6 + h\frac{1}{\sqrt{2}}, 4 + h\frac{1}{\sqrt{2}}\right) - T(6,4)}{h}$, which we can estimate with $h = \pm 2\sqrt{2}$. Then $D_{\mathbf{u}}T(6,4) \approx \dfrac{T(8,6) - T(6,4)}{2\sqrt{2}} = \dfrac{80 - 80}{2\sqrt{2}} = 0$,

$D_{\mathbf{u}}T(6,4) \approx \dfrac{T(4,2) - T(6,4)}{-2\sqrt{2}} = \dfrac{74 - 80}{-2\sqrt{2}} = \dfrac{3}{\sqrt{2}}$. Averaging these values, we have

$D_{\mathbf{u}}T(6,4) \approx \frac{3}{2\sqrt{2}} \approx 1.1\,^\circ\mathrm{C}/\mathrm{m}$.

(c) $T_{xy}(x,y) = \dfrac{\partial}{\partial y}[T_x(x,y)] = \lim\limits_{h \to 0} \dfrac{T_x(x, y+h) - T_x(x,y)}{h}$, so $T_{xy}(6,4) = \lim\limits_{h \to 0} \dfrac{T_x(6, 4+h) - T_x(6,4)}{h}$

which we can estimate with $h = \pm 2$. We have $T_x(6,4) \approx 3.5$ from part (a), but we will also need values for $T_x(6,6)$ and $T_x(6,2)$. If we use $h = \pm 2$ and the values given in the table, we have

$T_x(6,6) \approx \dfrac{T(8,6) - T(6,6)}{2} = \dfrac{80 - 75}{2} = 2.5$, $T_x(6,6) \approx \dfrac{T(4,6) - T(6,6)}{-2} = \dfrac{68 - 75}{-2} = 3.5$.

Averaging these values, we estimate $T_x(6,6) \approx 3.0$. Similarly,

$T_x(6,2) \approx \dfrac{T(8,2) - T_x(6,2)}{2} = \dfrac{90 - 87}{2} = 1.5$, $T_x(6,2) \approx \dfrac{T(4,2) - T(6,2)}{-2} = \dfrac{74 - 87}{-2} = 6.5$.

Averaging these values, we estimate $T_{xx}(6,2) \approx 4.0$. Finally, we estimate $T_{xy}(6,4)$:

$T_{xy}(6,4) \approx \dfrac{T_x(6,6) - T_x(6,4)}{2} = \dfrac{3.0 - 3.5}{2} = -0.25$,

$T_{xy}(6,4) \approx \dfrac{T_{xx}(6,2) - T_x(6,4)}{-2} = \dfrac{4.0 - 3.5}{-2} = -0.25$. Averaging these values, we have

$T_{xy}(6,4) \approx -0.25$.

12. From the table, $T(6,4) = 80$, and from Exercise 11 we estimated $T_x(6,4) \approx 3.5$ and $T_y(6,4) \approx -3.0$. The linear approximation then is

$$T(x,y) \approx T(6,4) + T_x(6,4)(x-6) + T_y(6,4)(y-4) \approx 80 + 3.5(x-6) - 3(y-4)$$
$$= 3.5x - 3y + 71$$

Thus at the point $(5, 3.8)$, we can use the linear approximation to estimate
$T(5, 3.8) \approx 3.5(5) - 3(3.8) + 71 \approx 77.1\,^\circ\mathrm{C}$.

13. $f(x,y) = \sqrt{2x + y^2}$ $\Rightarrow$ $f_x = \frac{1}{2}\left(2x + y^2\right)^{-1/2}(2) = \dfrac{1}{\sqrt{2x + y^2}}$,

$f_y = \frac{1}{2}\left(2x + y^2\right)^{-1/2}(2y) = \dfrac{y}{\sqrt{2x + y^2}}$

14. $u = e^{-r}\sin 2\theta$ $\Rightarrow$ $u_r = -e^{-r}\sin 2\theta$, $u_\theta = 2e^{-r}\cos 2\theta$

15. $g(u,v) = u\tan^{-1} v$ $\Rightarrow$ $g_u = \tan^{-1} v$, $g_v = \dfrac{u}{1 + v^2}$

16. $w = \dfrac{x}{y-z}$ $\Rightarrow$ $w_x = \dfrac{1}{y-z}$, $w_y = x(-1)(y-z)^{-2} = -\dfrac{x}{(y-z)^2}$,

$w_z = x(-1)(y-z)^{-2}(-1) = \dfrac{x}{(y-z)^2}$

17. $T(p,q,r) = p\ln(q+e^r)$ $\Rightarrow$ $T_p = \ln(q+e^r)$, $T_q = \dfrac{p}{q+e^r}$, $T_r = \dfrac{pe^r}{q+e^r}$

18. $C = 1449.2 + 4.6T - 0.055T^2 + 0.00029T^3 + (1.34 - 0.01T)(S-35) + 0.016D$ $\Rightarrow$
$\partial C/\partial T = 4.6 - 0.11T + 0.00087T^2 - 0.01(S-35)$, $\partial C/\partial S = 1.34 - 0.01T$, and $\partial C/\partial D = 0.016$. When
$T = 10$, $S = 35$, and $D = 100$ we have $\partial C/\partial T = 4.6 - 0.11(10) + 0.00087(10)^2 - 0.01(35-35) \approx 3.587$,
thus in $10\,^\circ$C water with salinity 35 parts per thousand and a depth of 100 m, the speed of sound increases by about
3.59 m/s for every degree Celsius that the water temperature rises. Similarly, $\partial C/\partial S = 1.34 - 0.01(10) = 1.24$,
so the speed of sound increases by about 1.24 m/s for every part per thousand the salinity of the water increases.
$\partial C/\partial D = 0.016$, so the speed of sound increases by about 0.016 m/s for every meter that the depth is increased.

19. $f(x,y) = 4x^3 - xy^2$ $\Rightarrow$ $f_x = 12x^2 - y^2$, $f_y = -2xy$, $f_{xx} = 24x$, $f_{yy} = -2x$, and $f_{xy} = f_{yx} = -2y$.

20. $z = xe^{-2y}$ $\Rightarrow$ $z_x = e^{-2y}$, $z_y = -2xe^{-2y}$, $z_{xx} = 0$, $z_{yy} = 4xe^{-2y}$, and $z_{xy} = z_{yx} = -2e^{-2y}$.

21. $f(x,y,z) = x^k y^l z^m$ $\Rightarrow$ $f_x = kx^{k-1}y^l z^m$, $f_y = lx^k y^{l-1} z^m$, $f_z = mx^k y^l z^{m-1}$,
$f_{xx} = k(k-1)x^{k-2}y^l z^m$, $f_{yy} = l(l-1)x^k y^{l-2} z^m$, $f_{zz} = m(m-1)x^k y^l z^{m-2}$, $f_{xy} = f_{yx} = klx^{k-1}y^{l-1}z^m$,
$f_{xz} = f_{zx} = kmx^{k-1}y^l z^{m-1}$, and $f_{yz} = f_{zy} = lmx^k y^{l-1} z^{m-1}$.

22. $v = r\cos(s+2t)$ $\Rightarrow$ $v_r = \cos(s+2t)$, $v_s = -r\sin(s+2t)$, $v_t = -2r\sin(s+2t)$, $v_{rr} = 0$,
$v_{ss} = -r\cos(s+2t)$, $v_{tt} = -4r\cos(s+2t)$, $v_{rs} = v_{sr} = -\sin(s+2t)$, $v_{rt} = v_{tr} = -2\sin(s+2t)$, and
$v_{st} = v_{ts} = -2r\cos(s+2t)$.

23. $u = x^y$ $\Rightarrow$ $u_x = yx^{y-1}$, $u_y = x^y \ln x$ and $(x/y)u_x + (\ln x)^{-1}u_y = x^y + x^y = 2u$.

24. $\rho = \sqrt{x^2+y^2+z^2}$ $\Rightarrow$ $\rho_x = \dfrac{x}{\sqrt{x^2+y^2+z^2}}$, $\rho_{xx} = \dfrac{y^2+z^2}{(x^2+y^2+z^2)^{3/2}}$.

By symmetry, $\rho_{yy} = \dfrac{x^2+z^2}{(x^2+y^2+z^2)^{3/2}}$ and $\rho_{zz} = \dfrac{x^2+y^2}{(x^2+y^2+z^2)^{3/2}}$. Thus

$\rho_{xx} + \rho_{yy} + \rho_{zz} = 2\dfrac{x^2+y^2+z^2}{(x^2+y^2+z^2)^{3/2}} = \dfrac{2}{(x^2+y^2+z^2)^{1/2}} = \dfrac{2}{\rho}$.

25. (a) $z_x = 6x + 2$ $\Rightarrow$ $z_x(1,-2) = 8$ and $z_y = -2y$ $\Rightarrow$ $z_y(1,-2) = 4$, so an equation of the tangent plane is
$z - 1 = 8(x-1) + 4(y+2)$ or $z = 8x + 4y + 1$.

(b) A normal vector to the tangent plane (and the surface) at $(1,-2,1)$ is $\langle 8, 4, -1 \rangle$. Then parametric equations for
the normal line there are $x = 1 + 8t$, $y = -2 + 4t$, $z = 1 - t$, and symmetric equations are
$\dfrac{x-1}{8} = \dfrac{y+2}{4} = \dfrac{z-1}{-1}$.

26. (a) $z_x = e^x \cos y$ $\Rightarrow$ $z_x(0,0) = 1$ and $z_y = -e^x \sin y$ $\Rightarrow$ $z_y(0,0) = 0$, so an equation of the tangent plane
is $z - 1 = 1(x-0) + 0(y-0)$ or $z = x + 1$.

(b) A normal vector to the tangent plane (and the surface) at $(0,0,1)$ is $\langle 1, 0, -1 \rangle$. Then parametric equations for
the normal line there are $x = t$, $y = 0$, $z = 1 - t$, and symmetric equations are $x = 1 - z$, $y = 0$.

27. (a) Let $F(x, y, z) = x^2 + 2y^2 - 3z^2$. Then $F_x = 2x$, $F_y = 4y$, $F_z = -6z$, so $F_x(2, -1, 1) = 4$,
$F_y(2, -1, 1) = -4$, $F_z(2, -1, 1) = -6$. From Equation 11.6.19, an equation of the tangent plane is
$4(x - 2) - 4(y + 1) - 6(z - 1) = 0$ or equivalently $2x - 2y - 3z = 3$.

(b) From Equation 11.6.20, symmetric equations for the normal line are $\dfrac{x - 2}{4} = \dfrac{y + 1}{-4} = \dfrac{z - 1}{-6}$.

28. (a) Let $F(x, y, z) = xy + yz + zx$. Then $F_x = y + z$, $F_y = x + z$, $F_z = x + y$, so
$F_x(1, 1, 1) = F_y(1, 1, 1) = F_z(1, 1, 1) = 2$. From Equation 11.6.19, an equation of the tangent plane is
$2(x - 1) + 2(y - 1) + 2(z - 1) = 0$ or equivalently $x + y + z = 3$.

(b) From Equations 11.6.20, symmetric equations for the normal line are $\dfrac{x - 1}{2} = \dfrac{y - 1}{2} = \dfrac{z - 1}{2}$ or equivalently
$x = y = z$.

29. (a) $\mathbf{r}(u, v) = (u + v)\,\mathbf{i} + u^2\,\mathbf{j} + v^2\,\mathbf{k}$ and the point $(3, 4, 1)$ corresponds to $u = 2$, $v = 1$. Then $\mathbf{r}_u = \mathbf{i} + 2u\,\mathbf{j} \;\Rightarrow$
$\mathbf{r}_u(2, 1) = \mathbf{i} + 4\,\mathbf{j}$ and $\mathbf{r}_v = \mathbf{i} + 2v\,\mathbf{k} \;\Rightarrow\; \mathbf{r}_v(2, 1) = \mathbf{i} + 2\,\mathbf{j}$. A normal vector to the surface at $(3, 4, 1)$ is
$\mathbf{r}_u \times \mathbf{r}_v = 8\,\mathbf{i} - 2\,\mathbf{j} - 4\,\mathbf{k}$, so an equation of the tangent plane there is $8(x - 3) - 2(y - 4) - 4(z - 1) = 0$ or
equivalently $4x - y - 2z = 6$.

(b) A direction vector for the normal line through $(3, 4, 1)$ is $8\,\mathbf{i} - 2\,\mathbf{j} - 4\,\mathbf{k}$, so a vector equation is
$\mathbf{r}(t) = (3\,\mathbf{i} + 4\,\mathbf{j} + \mathbf{k}) + t\,(8\,\mathbf{i} - 2\,\mathbf{j} - 4\,\mathbf{k})$, and the corresponding parametric equations are $x = 3 + 8t$,
$y = 4 - 2t$, $z = 1 - 4t$.

30. Let $f(x, y) = x^3 + 2xy$. Then $f_x(x, y) = 3x^2 + 2y$ and
$f_y(x, y) = 2x$, so $f_x(1, 2) = 7$, $f_y(1, 2) = 2$ and an
equation of the tangent plane is $z - 5 = 7(x - 1) + 2(y - 2)$
or $7x + 2y - z = 6$. The normal line is given by
$\dfrac{x - 1}{7} = \dfrac{y - 2}{2} = \dfrac{z - 5}{-1}$ or $x = 7t + 1$, $y = 2t + 2$,
$z = -t + 5$.

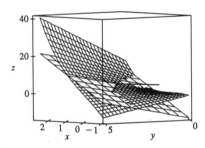

31. $F(x, y, z) = x^2 + y^2 + z^2$, $\nabla F(x_0, y_0, z_0) = \langle 2x_0, 2y_0, 2z_0 \rangle = k\langle 2, 1, -3 \rangle$ or $x_0 = k$, $y_0 = \frac{1}{2}k$ and $z_0 = -\frac{3}{2}k$.
But $x_0^2 + y_0^2 + z_0^2 = 1$, so $\frac{7}{2}k^2 = 1$ and $k = \pm\sqrt{\frac{2}{7}}$. Hence there are two such points: $\left(\pm\sqrt{\frac{2}{7}}, \pm\frac{1}{\sqrt{14}}, \mp\frac{3}{\sqrt{14}}\right)$.

32. $z = x^2 \tan^{-1} y \;\Rightarrow\; dz = \left(2x \tan^{-1} y\right) dx + \left[x^2/(y^2 + 1)\right] dy$

33. $f(x, y, z) = x^3\sqrt{y^2 + z^2} \;\Rightarrow\; f_x(x, y, z) = 3x^2\sqrt{y^2 + z^2}$, $f_y(x, y, z) = \dfrac{yx^3}{\sqrt{y^2 + z^2}}$, and

$f_z(x, y, z) = \dfrac{zx^3}{\sqrt{y^2 + z^2}}$, so $f(2, 3, 4) = 8(5) = 40$, $f_x(2, 3, 4) = 3(4)\sqrt{25} = 60$, $f_y(2, 3, 4) = \frac{3(8)}{\sqrt{25}} = \frac{24}{5}$, and

$f_z(2, 3, 4) = \frac{4(8)}{\sqrt{25}} = \frac{32}{5}$. Then the linear approximation of f at $(2, 3, 4)$ is

$$f(x, y, z) \approx f(2, 3, 4) + f_x(2, 3, 4)(x - 2) + f_y(2, 3, 4)(y - 3) + f_z(2, 3, 4)(z - 4)$$
$$= 40 + 60(x - 2) + \tfrac{24}{5}(y - 3) + \tfrac{32}{5}(z - 4) = 60x + \tfrac{24}{5}y + \tfrac{32}{5}z - 120$$

Then

$$(1.98)^3\sqrt{(3.01)^2 + (3.97)^2} = f(1.98, 3.01, 3.97) \approx 60(1.98) + \tfrac{24}{5}(3.01) + \tfrac{32}{5}(3.97) - 120$$
$$= 38.656$$

34. (a) $dA = \dfrac{\partial A}{\partial x}\,dx + \dfrac{\partial A}{\partial y}\,dy = \tfrac{1}{2}y\,dx + \tfrac{1}{2}x\,dy$ and $|\Delta x| \le 0.002$, $|\Delta y| \le 0.002$. Thus the maximum error in the

calculated area is about $dA = 6(0.002) + \tfrac{5}{2}(0.002) = 0.017$ m^2 or 170 cm^2.

(b) $z = \sqrt{x^2 + y^2}$, $dz = \dfrac{x}{\sqrt{x^2 + y^2}}\,dx + \dfrac{y}{\sqrt{x^2 + y^2}}\,dy$ and $|\Delta x| \le 0.002$, $|\Delta y| \le 0.002$. Thus the maximum

error in the calculated hypotenuse length is about $dz = \tfrac{5}{13}(0.002) + \tfrac{12}{13}(0.002) = \tfrac{0.17}{65} \approx 0.0026$ m or
0.26 cm.

35. $\dfrac{dw}{dt} = \dfrac{1}{2\sqrt{x}}\left(2e^{2t}\right) + \dfrac{2y}{z}\left(3t^2 + 4\right) + \dfrac{-y^2}{z^2}\left(2t\right) = e^t + \dfrac{2y}{z}\left(3t^2 + 4\right) - 2t\,\dfrac{y^2}{z^2}$

36. $\dfrac{\partial z}{\partial u} = (-y\sin xy - y\sin x)(2u) + (-x\sin xy + \cos x) = \cos x - 2uy\sin x - (\sin xy)(x + 2uy)$,

$\dfrac{\partial z}{\partial v} = (-y\sin xy - y\sin x)(1) + (-x\sin xy + \cos x)(-2v) = -2v\cos x + (\sin xy)(2vx - y) - y\sin x$

37. By the Chain Rule, $\dfrac{\partial z}{\partial s} = \dfrac{\partial z}{\partial x}\dfrac{\partial x}{\partial s} + \dfrac{\partial z}{\partial y}\dfrac{\partial y}{\partial s}$. When $s = 1$ and $t = 2$, $x = g(1,2) = 3$ and $y = h(1,2) = 6$, so

$\dfrac{\partial z}{\partial s} = f_x(3,6)g_s(1,2) + f_y(3,6)h_s(1,2) = (7)(-1) + (8)(-5) = -47$. Similarly, $\dfrac{\partial z}{\partial t} = \dfrac{\partial z}{\partial x}\dfrac{\partial x}{\partial t} + \dfrac{\partial z}{\partial y}\dfrac{\partial y}{\partial t}$, so

$\dfrac{\partial z}{\partial t} = f_x(3,6)g_t(1,2) + f_y(3,6)h_t(1,2) = (7)(4) + (8)(10) = 108$.

38.

Using the tree diagram as a guide, we have

$\dfrac{\partial w}{\partial p} = \dfrac{\partial w}{\partial t}\dfrac{\partial t}{\partial p} + \dfrac{\partial w}{\partial u}\dfrac{\partial u}{\partial p} + \dfrac{\partial w}{\partial v}\dfrac{\partial v}{\partial p}$

$\dfrac{\partial w}{\partial q} = \dfrac{\partial w}{\partial t}\dfrac{\partial t}{\partial q} + \dfrac{\partial w}{\partial u}\dfrac{\partial u}{\partial q} + \dfrac{\partial w}{\partial v}\dfrac{\partial v}{\partial q}$

$\dfrac{\partial w}{\partial r} = \dfrac{\partial w}{\partial t}\dfrac{\partial t}{\partial r} + \dfrac{\partial w}{\partial u}\dfrac{\partial u}{\partial r} + \dfrac{\partial w}{\partial v}\dfrac{\partial v}{\partial r}$

$\dfrac{\partial w}{\partial s} = \dfrac{\partial w}{\partial t}\dfrac{\partial t}{\partial s} + \dfrac{\partial w}{\partial u}\dfrac{\partial u}{\partial s} + \dfrac{\partial w}{\partial v}\dfrac{\partial v}{\partial s}$

39. $\dfrac{\partial z}{\partial x} = 2xf'\left(x^2 - y^2\right)$, $\dfrac{\partial z}{\partial y} = 1 - 2yf'\left(x^2 - y^2\right)$ $\left[\text{where } f' = \dfrac{df}{d\left(x^2 - y^2\right)}\right]$. Then

$y\dfrac{\partial z}{\partial x} + x\dfrac{\partial z}{\partial y} = 2xyf'\left(x^2 - y^2\right) + x - 2xyf'\left(x^2 - y^2\right) = x$.

40. $A = \tfrac{1}{2}xy\sin\theta$, $dx/dt = 3$, $dy/dt = -2$, $d\theta/dt = 0.05$, and

$\dfrac{dA}{dt} = \dfrac{1}{2}\left[(y\sin\theta)\dfrac{dx}{dt} + (x\sin\theta)\dfrac{dy}{dt} + (xy\cos\theta)\dfrac{d\theta}{dt}\right]$. So when $x = 40$, $y = 50$ and $\theta = \tfrac{\pi}{6}$,

$\dfrac{dA}{dt} = \dfrac{1}{2}\left[(25)(3) + (20)(-2) + \left(1000\sqrt{3}\right)(0.05)\right] = \dfrac{35 + 50\sqrt{3}}{2} \approx 60.8$ in^2/s.

41. $\dfrac{\partial z}{\partial x} = \dfrac{\partial z}{\partial u}\,y + \dfrac{\partial z}{\partial v}\dfrac{-y}{x^2}$ and

$$\dfrac{\partial^2 z}{\partial x^2} = y\,\dfrac{\partial}{\partial x}\left(\dfrac{\partial z}{\partial u}\right) + \dfrac{2y}{x^3}\dfrac{\partial z}{\partial v} + \dfrac{-y}{x^2}\dfrac{\partial}{\partial x}\left(\dfrac{\partial z}{\partial v}\right)$$

$$= \dfrac{2y}{x^3}\dfrac{\partial z}{\partial v} + y\left(\dfrac{\partial^2 z}{\partial u^2}y + \dfrac{\partial^2 z}{\partial v\partial u}\dfrac{-y}{x^2}\right) + \dfrac{-y}{x^2}\left(\dfrac{\partial^2 z}{\partial v^2}\dfrac{-y}{x^2} + \dfrac{\partial^2 z}{\partial u\partial v}y\right)$$

$$= \dfrac{2y}{x^3}\dfrac{\partial z}{\partial v} + y^2\dfrac{\partial^2 z}{\partial u^2} - \dfrac{2y^2}{x^2}\dfrac{\partial^2 z}{\partial u\partial v} + \dfrac{y^2}{x^4}\dfrac{\partial^2 z}{\partial v^2}$$

Also $\dfrac{\partial z}{\partial y} = x\,\dfrac{\partial z}{\partial u} + \dfrac{1}{x}\dfrac{\partial z}{\partial v}$ and

$$\dfrac{\partial^2 z}{\partial y^2} = x\,\dfrac{\partial}{\partial y}\left(\dfrac{\partial z}{\partial u}\right) + \dfrac{1}{x}\dfrac{\partial}{\partial y}\left(\dfrac{\partial z}{\partial v}\right) = x\left(\dfrac{\partial^2 z}{\partial u^2}x + \dfrac{\partial^2 z}{\partial v\partial u}\dfrac{1}{x}\right) + \dfrac{1}{x}\left(\dfrac{\partial^2 z}{\partial v^2}\dfrac{1}{x} + \dfrac{\partial^2 z}{\partial u\partial v}x\right)$$

$$= x^2\dfrac{\partial^2 z}{\partial u^2} + 2\dfrac{\partial^2 z}{\partial u\partial v} + \dfrac{1}{x^2}\dfrac{\partial^2 z}{\partial v^2}$$

Thus

$$x^2\dfrac{\partial^2 z}{\partial x^2} - y^2\dfrac{\partial^2 z}{\partial y^2} = \dfrac{2y}{x}\dfrac{\partial z}{\partial v} + x^2 y^2\dfrac{\partial^2 z}{\partial u^2} - 2y^2\dfrac{\partial^2 z}{\partial u\partial v} + \dfrac{y^2}{x^2}\dfrac{\partial^2 z}{\partial v^2} - x^2 y^2\dfrac{\partial^2 z}{\partial u^2} - 2y^2\dfrac{\partial^2 z}{\partial u\partial v} - \dfrac{y^2}{x^2}\dfrac{\partial^2 z}{\partial v^2}$$

$$= \dfrac{2y}{x}\dfrac{\partial z}{\partial v} - 4y^2\dfrac{\partial^2 z}{\partial u\partial v} = 2v\dfrac{\partial z}{\partial v} - 4uv\dfrac{\partial^2 z}{\partial u\partial v}$$

since $y = xv = \dfrac{uv}{y}$ or $y^2 = uv$.

42. $F(x,y,z) = e^{xyz} - yz^4 - x^2 z^3 = 0$, so $\dfrac{\partial z}{\partial x} = -\dfrac{F_x}{F_z} = -\dfrac{yze^{xyz} - 2xz^3}{xye^{xyz} - 4yz^3 - 3x^2 z^2} = \dfrac{2xz^3 - yze^{xyz}}{xye^{xyz} - 4yz^3 - 3x^2 z^2}$

and $\dfrac{\partial z}{\partial y} = -\dfrac{F_y}{F_z} = -\dfrac{xze^{xyz} - z^4}{xye^{xyz} - 4yz^3 - 3x^2 z^2} = \dfrac{z^4 - xze^{xyz}}{xye^{xyz} - 4yz^3 - 3x^2 z^2}.$

43. $\nabla f = \left\langle z^2\sqrt{y}\,e^{x\sqrt{y}}, \dfrac{xz^2 e^{x\sqrt{y}}}{2\sqrt{y}}, 2ze^{x\sqrt{y}}\right\rangle = ze^{x\sqrt{y}}\left\langle z\sqrt{y}, \dfrac{xz}{2\sqrt{y}}, 2\right\rangle$

44. (a) By Theorem 11.6.15, the maximum value of the directional derivative occurs when **u** has the same direction as the gradient vector.

   (b) It is a minimum when **u** is in the direction opposite to that of the gradient vector (that is, **u** is in the direction of $-\nabla f$), since $D_{\mathbf{u}}f = |\nabla f|\cos\theta$ (see the proof of Theorem 11.6.15) has a minimum when $\theta = \pi$.

   (c) The directional derivative is 0 when **u** is perpendicular to the gradient vector, since then $D_{\mathbf{u}}f = \nabla f \cdot \mathbf{u} = 0$.

   (d) The directional derivative is half of its maximum value when $D_{\mathbf{u}}f = |\nabla f|\cos\theta = \tfrac{1}{2}|\nabla f| \;\Leftrightarrow\;$ $\cos\theta = \tfrac{1}{2} \;\Leftrightarrow\; \theta = \tfrac{\pi}{3}.$

45. $\nabla f = \langle 1/\sqrt{x}, -2y\rangle$, $\nabla f(1,5) = \langle 1, -10\rangle$, $\mathbf{u} = \tfrac{1}{5}\langle 3, -4\rangle$. Then $D_{\mathbf{u}}f(1,5) = \tfrac{43}{5}.$

46. $\nabla f = \left\langle 2xy + \sqrt{1+z}, x^2, x/(2\sqrt{1+z})\right\rangle$, $\nabla f(1,2,3) = \langle 6, 1, \tfrac{1}{4}\rangle$, and $\mathbf{u} = \langle \tfrac{2}{3}, \tfrac{1}{3}, -\tfrac{2}{3}\rangle$. Then $D_{\mathbf{u}}f(1,2,3) = \tfrac{25}{6}.$

47. $\nabla f = \langle 2xy, x^2 + 1/(2\sqrt{y})\rangle$, $|\nabla f(2,1)| = |\langle 4, \tfrac{9}{2}\rangle|$. Thus the maximum rate of change of f at $(2,1)$ is $\dfrac{\sqrt{145}}{2}$ in the direction $\langle 4, \tfrac{9}{2}\rangle.$

48. $\nabla f = \langle zye^{xy}, zxe^{xy}, e^{xy} \rangle$, $\nabla f(0,1,2) = \langle 2,0,1 \rangle$ is the direction of most rapid increase while the rate is
$|\langle 2,0,1 \rangle| = \sqrt{5}$.

49. First we draw a line passing through Homestead and the eye of the hurricane. We can approximate the directional
derivative at Homestead in the direction of the eye of the hurricane by the average rate of change of wind speed
between the points where this line intersects the contour lines closest to Homestead. In the direction of the eye of
the hurricane, the wind speed changes from 45 to 50 knots. We estimate the distance between these two points to be
approximately 8 miles, so the rate of change of wind speed in the direction given is approximately
$\frac{50 - 45}{8} = \frac{5}{8} = 0.625$ knot/mi.

50. The surfaces are $f(x,y,z) = z - 2x^2 + y^2 = 0$ and $g(x,y,z) = z - 4 = 0$. The tangent line is perpendicular to
both ∇f and ∇g at $(-2,2,4)$. The vector $\mathbf{v} = \nabla f \times \nabla g$ is therefore parallel to the line.
$\nabla f(x,y,z) = \langle -4x, 2y, 1 \rangle \quad \Rightarrow \quad \nabla f(-2,2,4) = \langle 8,4,1 \rangle$, $\nabla g(x,y,z) = \langle 0,0,1 \rangle \quad \Rightarrow$

$\nabla g \langle -2,2,4 \rangle = \langle 0,0,1 \rangle$. Hence $\mathbf{v} = \nabla f \times \nabla g = \begin{vmatrix} \mathbf{i} & \mathbf{j} & \mathbf{k} \\ 8 & 4 & 1 \\ 0 & 0 & 1 \end{vmatrix} = 4\,\mathbf{i} - 8\,\mathbf{j}$. Thus, parametric equations are:

$x = -2 + 4t$, $y = 2 - 8t$, and $z = 4$.

51. $f(x,y) = x^2 - xy + y^2 + 9x - 6y + 10 \quad \Rightarrow \quad f_x = 2x - y + 9$,
$f_y = -x + 2y - 6$, $f_{xx} = 2 = f_{yy}$, $f_{xy} = -1$. Then $f_x = 0$ and
$f_y = 0$ imply $y = 1$, $x = -4$. Thus the only critical point is $(-4, 1)$
and $f_{xx}(-4,1) > 0$, $D(-4,1) = 3 > 0$, so $f(-4,1) = -11$ is a
local minimum.

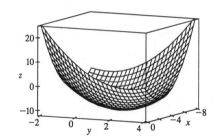

52. $f(x,y) = x^3 - 6xy + 8y^3 \quad \Rightarrow \quad f_x = 3x^2 - 6y$, $f_y = -6x + 24y^2$,
$f_{xx} = 6x$, $f_{yy} = 48y$, $f_{xy} = -6$. Then $f_x = 0$ implies $y = x^2/2$,
substituting into $f_y = 0$ implies $6x(x^3 - 1) = 0$, so the critical points are
$(0,0)$, $\left(1, \frac{1}{2}\right)$. $D(0,0) = -36 < 0$ so $(0,0)$ is a saddle point while
$f_{xx}\left(1, \frac{1}{2}\right) = 6 > 0$ and $D\left(1, \frac{1}{2}\right) = 108 > 0$ so $f\left(1, \frac{1}{2}\right) = -1$ is a local
minimum.

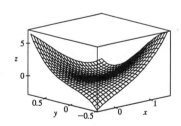

53. $f(x,y) = 3xy - x^2y - xy^2 \quad \Rightarrow \quad f_x = 3y - 2xy - y^2$,
$f_y = 3x - x^2 - 2xy$, $f_{xx} = -2y$, $f_{yy} = -2x$, $f_{xy} = 3 - 2x - 2y$. Then
$f_x = 0$ implies $y(3 - 2x - y) = 0$ so $y = 0$ or $y = 3 - 2x$. Substituting into
$f_y = 0$ implies $x(3 - x) = 0$ or $3x(-1 + x) = 0$. Hence the critical points
are $(0,0)$, $(3,0)$, $(0,3)$ and $(1,1)$. $D(0,0) = D(3,0) = D(0,3) = -9 < 0$
so $(0,0)$, $(3,0)$, and $(0,3)$ are saddle points. $D(1,1) = 3 > 0$ and
$f_{xx}(1,1) = -2 < 0$, so $f(1,1) = 1$ is a local maximum.

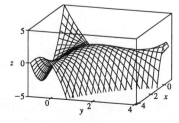

54. $f(x, y) = (x^2 + y) e^{y/2}$ $\Rightarrow$ $f_x = 2xe^{y/2}$, $f_y = e^{y/2} (2 + x^2 + y)/2$, $f_{xx} = 2e^{y/2}$, $f_{yy} = e^{y/2} (4 + x^2 + y)/4$, $f_{xy} = xe^{y/2}$. Then $f_x = 0$ implies $x = 0$, so $f_y = 0$ implies $y = -2$. But $f_{xx}(0, -2) > 0$, $D(0, -2) = e^{-2} - 0 > 0$ so $f(0, -2) = -2/e$ is a local minimum.

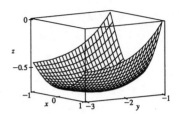

55. First solve inside D. Here $f_x = 4y^2 - 2xy^2 - y^3$, $f_y = 8xy - 2x^2y - 3xy^2$. Then $f_x = 0$ implies $y = 0$ or $y = 4 - 2x$, but $y = 0$ isn't inside D. Substituting $y = 4 - 2x$ into $f_y = 0$ implies $x = 0$, $x = 2$ or $x = 1$, but $x = 0$ isn't inside D, and when $x = 2$, $y = 0$ but $(2, 0)$ isn't inside D. Thus the only critical point inside D is $(1, 2)$ and $f(1, 2) = 4$. Secondly we consider the boundary of D. On L_1, $f(x, 0) = 0$ and so $f = 0$ on L_1. On L_2, $x = -y + 6$ and $f9 - y + 6, y) = y^2(6 - y)(-2) = -2(6y^2 - y^3)$ which has

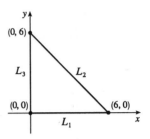

critical points at $y = 0$ and $y = 4$. Then $f(6, 0) = 0$ while $f(2, 4) = -64$. On L_3, $f(0, y) = 0$, so $f = 0$ on L_3. Thus on D the absolute maximum of f is $f(1, 2) = 4$ while the absolute minimum is $f(2, 4) = -64$.

56. Inside D: $f_x = 2xe^{-x^2-y^2} (1 - x^2 - 2y^2) = 0$ implies $x = 0$ or $x^2 + 2y^2 = 1$. Then if $x = 0$, $f_y = 2ye^{-x^2-y^2} (2 - x^2 - 2y^2) = 0$ implies $y = 0$ or $2 - 2y^2 = 0$ giving the critical points $(0, 0)$, $(0, \pm 1)$. If $x^2 + 2y^2 = 1$, then $f_y = 0$ implies $y = 0$ giving the critical points $(\pm 1, 0)$. Now $f(0, 0) = 0$, $f((\pm 1, 0) = e^{-1}$ and $f(0, \pm 1) = 2e^{-1}$. On the boundary of D: $x^2 + y^2 = 4$, so $f(x, y) = e^{-4}(4 + y^2)$ and f is smallest when $y = 0$ and largest when $y^2 = 4$. But $f(\pm 2, 0) = 4e^{-4}$, $f(0, \pm 2) = 8e^{-4}$. Thus on D the absolute maximum of f is $f(0, \pm 1) = 2e^{-1}$ and the absolute minimum is $f(0, 0) = 0$.

57. $f(x, y) = x^3 - 3x + y^4 - 2y^2$

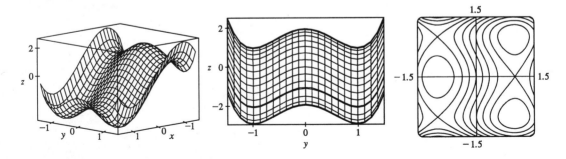

From the graphs, it appears that f has a local maximum $f(-1, 0) \approx 2$, local minima $f(1, \pm 1) \approx -3$, and saddle points at $(-1, \pm 1)$ and $(1, 0)$.

To find the exact quantities, we calculate $f_x = 3x^2 - 3 = 0$ ⇔ $x = \pm 1$ and $f_y = 4y^3 - 4y = 0$ ⇔ $y = 0, \pm 1$, giving the critical points estimated above. Also $f_{xx} = 6x$, $f_{xy} = 0$, $f_{yy} = 12y^2 - 4$, so using the Second Derivatives Test, $D(-1, 0) = 24 > 0$ and $f_{xx}(-1, 0) = -6 < 0$ indicating a local maximum $f(-1, 0) = 2$; $D(1, \pm 1) = 48 > 0$ and $f_{xx}(1, \pm 1) = 6 > 0$ indicating local minima $f(1, \pm 1) = -3$; and $D(-1, \pm 1) = -48$ and $D(1, 0) = -24$, indicating saddle points.

58. $f(x, y) = 12 + 10y - 2x^2 - 8xy - y^4$ ⇒ $f_x(x, y) = -4x - 8y$, $f_y(x, y) = 10 - 8x - 4y^3$. Now $f_x(x, y) = 0$ ⇒ $x = -2x$, and substituting this into $f_y(x, y) = 0$ gives $10 + 16y - 4y^3 = 0$ ⇔ $5 + 8y - 2y^3 = 0$.

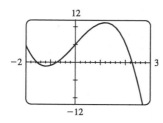

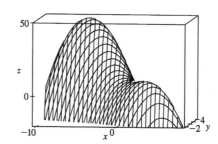

From the first graph, we see that this is true when $y \approx -1.542, -0.717$, or 2.260. (Alternatively, we could have found the solutions to $f_x = f_y = 0$ using a CAS.) So to three decimal places, the critical points are $(3.085, -1.542)$, $(1.434, -0.717)$, and $(-4.519, 2.260)$. Now in order to use the Second Derivatives Test, we calculate $f_{xx} = -4$, $f_{xy} = -8$, $f_{yy} = -12y^2$, and $D = 48y^2 - 64$. So since $D(3.085, -1.542) > 0$, $D(1.434, -0.717) < 0$, and $D(-4.519, 2.260) > 0$, and f_{xx} is always negative, $f(x, y)$ has local maxima $f(-4.519, 2.260) \approx 49.373$ and $f(3.085, -1.542) \approx 9.948$, and a saddle point at approximately $(1.434, -0.717)$. The highest point on the graph is approximately $(-4.519, 2.260, 49.373)$.

59. $f(x, y) = x^2 y$, $g(x, y) = x^2 + y^2 = 1$ ⇒ $\nabla f = \langle 2xy, x^2 \rangle = \lambda \nabla g = \langle 2\lambda x, 2\lambda y \rangle$. Then $2xy = 2\lambda x$ and $x^2 = 2\lambda y$ imply $\lambda = x^2/(2y)$ and $\lambda = y$ if $x \neq 0$ and $y \neq 0$. Hence $x^2 = 2y^2$. Then $x^2 + y^2 = 1$ implies $3y^2 = 1$ so $y = \pm\frac{1}{\sqrt{3}}$ and $x = \pm\sqrt{\frac{2}{3}}$. [Note if $x = 0$ then $x^2 = 2\lambda y$ implies $y = 0$ and $f(0, 0) = 0$.] Thus the possible points are $\left(\pm\sqrt{\frac{2}{3}}, \pm\frac{1}{\sqrt{3}}\right)$ and the absolute maxima are $f\left(\pm\sqrt{\frac{2}{3}}, \frac{1}{\sqrt{3}}\right) = \frac{2}{3\sqrt{3}}$ while the absolute minima are $f\left(\pm\sqrt{\frac{2}{3}}, -\frac{1}{\sqrt{3}}\right) = -\frac{2}{3\sqrt{3}}$.

60. $f(x, y) = 1/x + 1/y$, $g(x, y) = 1/x^2 + 1/y^2 = 1$ ⇒ $\nabla f = \langle -x^{-2}, -y^{-2} \rangle = \lambda \nabla g = \langle -2\lambda x^{-3}, -2\lambda y^{-3} \rangle$. Then $-x^{-2} = -2\lambda x^{-3}$ or $x = 2\lambda$ and $-y^{-2} = -2\lambda y^{-3}$ or $y = 2\lambda$. Thus $x = y$, so $1/x^2 + 1/y^2 = 2/x^2 = 1$ implies $x = \pm\sqrt{2}$ and the possible points are $(\pm\sqrt{2}, \pm\sqrt{2})$. The absolute maximum of f subject to $x^{-2} + y^{-2} = 1$ is then $f(\sqrt{2}, \sqrt{2}) = \sqrt{2}$ and the absolute minimum is $f(-\sqrt{2}, -\sqrt{2}) = -\sqrt{2}$.

61. $f(x,y,z) = xyz$, $g(x,y,z) = x^2 + y^2 + z^2 = 3$. $\nabla f = \lambda \nabla g \Rightarrow \langle yz, xz, xy \rangle = \lambda \langle 2x, 2y, 2z \rangle$. If any of x,

y, or z is zero, then $x = y = z = 0$ which contradicts $x^2 + y^2 + z^2 = 3$. Then $\lambda = \dfrac{yz}{2x} = \dfrac{xz}{2y} = \dfrac{xy}{2z} \Rightarrow$

$2y^2 z = 2x^2 z \Rightarrow y^2 = x^2$, and similarly $2yz^2 = 2x^2 y \Rightarrow z^2 = x^2$. Substituting into the constraint equation

gives $x^2 + x^2 + x^2 = 3 \Rightarrow x^2 = 1 = y^2 = z^2$. Thus the possible points are

$(1, 1, \pm 1)$, $(1, -1, \pm 1)$, $(-1, 1, \pm 1)$, $(-1, -1, \pm 1)$. The absolute maximum is

$f(1, 1, 1) = f(1, -1, -1) = f(-1, 1, -1) = f(-1, -1, 1) = 1$ and the absolute minimum is

$f(1, 1, -1) = f(1, -1, 1) = f(-1, 1, 1) = f(-1, -1, -1) = -1$.

62. $f(x,y,z) = x^2 + 2y^2 + 3z^2$, $g(x,y,z) = x + y + z = 1$, $h(x,y,z) = x - y + 2z = 2 \Rightarrow$

$\nabla f = \langle 2x, 4y, 6z \rangle = \lambda \nabla g + \mu \nabla h = \langle \lambda + \mu, \lambda - \mu, \lambda + 2\mu \rangle$ and (1) $2x = \lambda + \mu$, (2) $4y = \lambda - \mu$,

(3) $6z = \lambda + 2\mu$, (4) $x + y + z = 1$, (5) $x - y + 2z = 2$. Then six times (1) plus three times (2) plus two times

(3) implies $12(x + y + z) = 11\lambda + 7\mu$, so (4) gives $11\lambda + 7\mu = 12$. Also six times (1) minus three times (2) plus

four times (3) implies $12(x - y + 2z) = 7\lambda + 17\mu$, so (5) gives $7\lambda + 17\mu = 24$. Solving $11\lambda + 7\mu = 12$,

$7\lambda + 17\mu = 24$ simultaneously gives $\lambda = \frac{6}{23}$, $\mu = \frac{30}{23}$. Substituting into (1), (2) and (3) implies $x = \frac{18}{23}$, $y = -\frac{6}{23}$,

$z = \frac{11}{23}$ giving only one point. Then $f\left(\frac{18}{23}, -\frac{6}{23}, \frac{11}{23}\right) = \frac{33}{23}$. Now since $(0, 0, 1)$ satisfies both constraints and

$f(0, 0, 1) = 3 > \frac{33}{23}$, $f\left(\frac{18}{23}, -\frac{6}{23}, \frac{11}{23}\right) = \frac{33}{23}$ is an absolute minimum, and there is no absolute maximum.

63. $f(x,y,z) = x^2 + y^2 + z^2$, $g(x,y,z) = xy^2 z^3 = 2 \Rightarrow$

$\nabla f = \langle 2x, 2y, 2z \rangle = \lambda \nabla g = \langle \lambda y^2 z^3, 2\lambda xyz^3, 3\lambda xy^2 z^2 \rangle$. Since $xy^2 z^3 = 2$, $x \neq 0$, $y \neq 0$ and $z \neq 0$, so

(1) $2x = \lambda y^2 z^3$, (2) $1 = \lambda xz^3$, (3) $2 = 3\lambda xy^2 z$. Then (2) and (3) imply $\dfrac{1}{xz^3} = \dfrac{2}{3xy^2 z}$ or $y^2 = \frac{2}{3} z^2$ so

$y = \pm z \sqrt{\frac{2}{3}}$. Similarly (1) and (3) imply $\dfrac{2x}{y^2 z^3} = \dfrac{2}{3xy^2 z}$ or $3x^2 = z^2$ so $x = \pm \frac{1}{\sqrt{3}} z$. But $xy^2 z^3 = 2$ so x and z

must have the same sign, that is, $x = \frac{1}{\sqrt{3}} z$. Thus $g(x,y,z) = 2$ implies $\frac{1}{\sqrt{3}} z \left(\frac{2}{3} z^2\right) z^3 = 2$ or $z = \pm 3^{1/4}$ and the

possible points are $\left(\pm 3^{-1/4}, 3^{-1/4} \sqrt{2}, \pm 3^{1/4}\right)$, $\left(\pm 3^{-1/4}, -3^{-1/4} \sqrt{2}, \pm 3^{1/4}\right)$. However at each of these points

f takes on the same value, $2\sqrt{3}$. But $(2, 1, 1)$ also satisfies $g(x,y,z) = 2$ and $f(2, 1, 1) = 6 > 2\sqrt{3}$. Thus f has

an absolute minimum value of $2\sqrt{3}$ and no absolute maximum subject to the constraint $xy^2 z^3 = 2$.

Alternate solution: $g(x,y,z) = xy^2 z^3 = 2$ implies $y^2 = \dfrac{2}{xz^3}$, so minimize $f(x,z) = x^2 + \dfrac{2}{xz^3} + z^2$. Then

$f_x = 2x - \dfrac{2}{x^2 z^3}$, $f_z = -\dfrac{6}{xz^4} + 2z$, $f_{xx} = 2 + \dfrac{4}{x^3 z^3}$, $f_{zz} = \dfrac{24}{xz^5} + 2$ and $f_{xz} = \dfrac{6}{x^2 z^4}$. Now $f_x = 0$ implies

$2x^3 z^3 - 2 = 0$ or $z = 1/x$. Substituting into $f_y = 0$ implies $-6x^3 + 2x^{-1} = 0$ or $x = \frac{1}{\sqrt[4]{3}}$, so the two critical

points are $\left(\pm \frac{1}{\sqrt[4]{3}}, \pm \sqrt[4]{3}\right)$. Then $D\left(\pm \frac{1}{\sqrt[4]{3}}, \pm \sqrt[4]{3}\right) = (2 + 4)\left(2 + \frac{24}{3}\right) - \left(\frac{6}{\sqrt{3}}\right)^2 > 0$ and

$f_{xx}\left(\pm \frac{1}{\sqrt[4]{3}}, \pm \sqrt[4]{3}\right) = 6 > 0$, so each point is a minimum. Finally, $y^2 = \dfrac{2}{xz^3}$, so the four points closest to the

origin are $\left(\pm \frac{1}{\sqrt[4]{3}}, \frac{\sqrt{2}}{\sqrt[4]{3}}, \pm \sqrt[4]{3}\right)$, $\left(\pm \frac{1}{\sqrt[4]{3}}, -\frac{\sqrt{2}}{\sqrt[4]{3}}, \pm \sqrt[4]{3}\right)$.

64. $V = xyz$, say x is the length and $x + 2y + 2z \le 108$, $x > 0$, $y > 0$, $z > 0$. First maximize V subject to

$x + 2y + 2z = 108$ with x, y, z all positive. Then $\langle yz, xz, xy \rangle = \langle \lambda, 2\lambda, 2\lambda \rangle$ implies $2yz = xz$ or $x = 2y$ and

$xz = xy$ or $z = y$. Thus $g(x, y, z) = 108$ implies $6y = 108$ or $y = 18 = z$, $x = 36$, so the volume is

$V = 11{,}664$ cubic units. Since $(104, 1, 1)$ also satisfies $g(x, y, z) = 108$ and $V(104, 1, 1) = 104$ cubic units,

$(36, 18, 18)$ gives an absolute maximum of V subject to $g(x, y, z) = 108$. But if $x + 2y + 2z < 108$, there exists

$\alpha > 0$ such that $x + 2y + 2z = 108 - \alpha$ and as above $6y = 108 - \alpha$ implies $y = (108 - \alpha)/6 = z$,

$x = (108 - \alpha)/3$ with $V = (108 - \alpha)^3/(6^2 \cdot 3) < (108)^3/(6^2 \cdot 3) = 11{,}664$. Hence we have shown that the

maximum of V subject to $g(x, y, z) \le 108$ is the maximum of V subject to $g(x, y, z) = 108$ (an intuitively obvious

fact).

65.

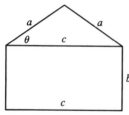

The area of the triangle is $\frac{1}{2}ca \sin\theta$ and the area of the rectangle is bc.

Thus, the area of the whole object is $f(a, b, c) = \frac{1}{2}ca \sin\theta + bc$. The

perimeter of the object is $g(a, b, c) = 2a + 2b + c = P$. To simplify $\sin\theta$

in terms of a, b, and c notice that $a^2 \sin^2\theta + \left(\frac{1}{2}c\right)^2 = a^2 \Rightarrow$

$\sin\theta = \dfrac{1}{2a}\sqrt{4a^2 - c^2}$. Thus $f(a, b, c) = \dfrac{c}{4}\sqrt{4a^2 - c^2} + bc$.

(Instead of using θ, we could just have used the Pythagorean Theorem.) As a result, by Lagrange's method, we must

find a, b, c, and λ by solving $\nabla f = \lambda \nabla g$ which gives the following equations: (1) $ca(4a^2 - c^2)^{-1/2} = 2\lambda$,

(2) $c = 2\lambda$, (3) $\frac{1}{4}(4a^2 - c^2)^{1/2} - \frac{1}{4}c^2(4a^2 - c^2)^{-1/2} + b = \lambda$, and (4) $2a + 2b + c = P$. From (2), $\lambda = \frac{1}{2}c$

and so (1) produces $ca(4a^2 - c^2)^{-1/2} = c \Rightarrow (4a^2 - c^2)^{1/2} = a \Rightarrow 4a^2 - c^2 = a^2 \Rightarrow$ (5) $c = \sqrt{3}\,a$.

Similarly, since $(4a^2 - c^2)^{1/2} = a$ and $\lambda = \frac{1}{2}c$, (3) gives $\dfrac{a}{4} - \dfrac{c^2}{4a} + b = \dfrac{c}{2}$, so from (5), $\dfrac{a}{4} - \dfrac{3a}{4} + b = \dfrac{\sqrt{3}\,a}{2}$

$\Rightarrow \quad -\dfrac{a}{2} - \dfrac{\sqrt{3}\,a}{2} = -b \quad \Rightarrow \quad$ (6) $b = \dfrac{a}{2}(1 + \sqrt{3})$. Substituting (5) and (6) into (4) we get:

$2a + a(1 + \sqrt{3}) + \sqrt{3}\,a = P \quad \Rightarrow \quad 3a + 2\sqrt{3}\,a = P \quad \Rightarrow \quad a = \dfrac{P}{3 + 2\sqrt{3}} = \dfrac{2\sqrt{3} - 3}{3}P$ and thus

$b = \dfrac{(2\sqrt{3} - 3)(1 + \sqrt{3})}{6}P = \dfrac{3 - \sqrt{3}}{6}P$ and $c = (2 - \sqrt{3})\,P$.

66. (a) $\mathbf{r}(t) = x(t)\,\mathbf{i} + y(t)\,\mathbf{j} + f(x(t), y(t))\,\mathbf{k} \quad \Rightarrow \quad \mathbf{v} = \dfrac{d\mathbf{r}}{dt} = \dfrac{dx}{dt}\,\mathbf{i} + \dfrac{dy}{dt}\,\mathbf{j} + \left(f_x\dfrac{dx}{dt} + f_y\dfrac{dy}{dt}\right)\mathbf{k}$ (by the Chain

Rule). Therefore

$$K = \tfrac{1}{2}m\,|\mathbf{v}|^2 = \dfrac{m}{2}\left[\left(\dfrac{dx}{dt}\right)^2 + \left(\dfrac{dy}{dt}\right)^2 + \left(f_x\dfrac{dx}{dt} + f_y\dfrac{dy}{dt}\right)^2\right]$$

$$= \dfrac{m}{2}\left[(1 + f_x^2)\left(\dfrac{dx}{dt}\right)^2 + 2f_x f_y\left(\dfrac{dx}{dt}\right)\left(\dfrac{dy}{dt}\right) + (1 + f_y^2)\left(\dfrac{dy}{dt}\right)^2\right]$$

(b) $\mathbf{a} = \dfrac{d\mathbf{v}}{dt} = \dfrac{d^2x}{dt^2}\mathbf{i} + \dfrac{d^2y}{dt^2}\mathbf{j} + \left[f_{xx}\left(\dfrac{dx}{dt}\right)^2 + 2f_{xy}\dfrac{dx}{dt}\dfrac{dy}{dt} + f_{yy}\left(\dfrac{dy}{dt}\right)^2 + f_x\dfrac{d^2x}{dt^2} + f_y\dfrac{d^2y}{dt^2} \right]\mathbf{k}$

(c) If $z = x^2 + y^2$, where $x = t\cos t$ and $y = t\sin t$, then $z = f(x, y) = t^2$.

$\mathbf{r} = t\cos t\,\mathbf{i} + t\sin t\,\mathbf{j} + t^2\,\mathbf{k} \quad \Rightarrow \quad \mathbf{v} = (\cos t - t\sin t)\,\mathbf{i} + (\sin t + t\cos t)\,\mathbf{j} + 2t\,\mathbf{k},$

$K = \dfrac{m}{2}\left[(\cos t - t\sin t)^2 + (\sin t + t\cos t)^2 + (2t)^2\right] = \dfrac{m}{2}(1 + t^2 + 4t^2) = \dfrac{m}{2}(1 + 5t^2)$, and

$\mathbf{a} = (-2\sin t - t\cos t)\,\mathbf{i} + (2\cos t - t\sin t)\,\mathbf{j} + 2\,\mathbf{k}$. Notice that it is easier not to use the formulas in

(a) and (b).

Focus on Problem Solving

1. The areas of the smaller rectangles are $A_1 = xy$, $A_2 = (L - x)y$, $A_3 = (L - x)(W - y)$, $A_4 = x(W - y)$. For $0 \leq x \leq L$, $0 \leq y \leq W$, let

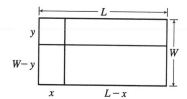

$$f(x, y) = A_1^2 + A_2^2 + A_3^2 + A_4^2$$
$$= x^2 y^2 + (L - x)^2 y^2 + (L - x)^2 (W - y)^2 + x^2 (W - y)^2$$
$$= \left[x^2 + (L - x)^2 \right] \left[y^2 + (W - y)^2 \right]$$

Then we need to find the maximum and minimum values of $f(x, y)$. Here
$f_x(x, y) = [2x - 2(L - x)] \left[y^2 + (W - y)^2 \right] = 0 \; \Rightarrow \; 4x - 2L = 0$ or $x = \frac{1}{2}L$, and
$f_y(x, y) = \left[x^2 + (L - x)^2 \right] [2y - 2(W - y)] = 0 \; \Rightarrow \; 4y - 2W = 0$ or $y = W/2$. Also
$f_{xx} = 4 \left[y^2 + (W - y)^2 \right]$, $f_{yy} = 4 \left[x^2 + (L - x)^2 \right]$, and $f_{xy} = (4x - 2L)(4y - 2W)$. Then
$D = 16 \left[y^2 + (W - y)^2 \right] \left[x^2 + (L - x)^2 \right] - (4x - 2L)^2 (4y - 2W)^2$. Thus when $x = \frac{1}{2}L$ and $y = \frac{1}{2}W$,
$D > 0$ and $f_{xx} = 2W^2 > 0$. Thus a minimum of f occurs at $\left(\frac{1}{2}L, \frac{1}{2}W \right)$ and this minimum value is
$f\left(\frac{1}{2}L, \frac{1}{2}W \right) = \frac{1}{4}L^2 W^2$. There are no other critical points, so the maximum must occur on the boundary. Now
along the width of the rectangle let $g(y) = f(0, y) = f(L, y) = L^2 \left[y^2 + (W - y)^2 \right]$, $0 \leq y \leq W$. Then
$g'(y) = L^2 [2y - 2(W - y)] = 0 \; \Leftrightarrow \; y = \frac{1}{2}W$. And $g\left(\frac{1}{2} \right) = \frac{1}{2}L^2 W^2$. Checking the endpoints, we get
$g(0) = g(W) = L^2 W^2$. Along the length of the rectangle let $h(x) = f(x, 0) = f(x, W) = W^2 \left[x^2 + (L - x)^2 \right]$,
$0 \leq x \leq L$. By symmetry $h'(x) = 0 \; \Leftrightarrow \; x = \frac{1}{2}L$ and $h\left(\frac{1}{2}L \right) = \frac{1}{2}L^2 W^2$. At the endpoints we have
$h(0) = h(L) = L^2 W^2$. Therefore $L^2 W^2$ is the maximum value of f. This maximum value of f occurs when the
"cutting" lines correspond to sides of the rectangle.

2. (a) The level curves of the function $C(x, y) = e^{-(x^2 + 2y^2)/10^4}$

are the curves $e^{-(x^2 + 2y^2)/10^4} = k$ (k is a positive constant).

This equation is equivalent to $x^2 + 2y^2 = K \; \Rightarrow$

$$\frac{x^2}{\left(\sqrt{K} \right)^2} + \frac{y^2}{\left(\sqrt{K/2} \right)^2} = 1, \text{ where } K = -10^4 \ln k,$$

a family of ellipses. We sketch level curves for $K = 1, 2$,

3, and 4. If the shark always swims in the direction of

maximum increase of blood concentration, its direction

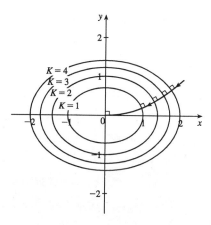

at any point would coincide with the gradient vector. Then we know the shark's path is perpendicular to the level curves it intersects. We sketch one example of such a path.

(b) $\nabla C = -\frac{2}{10^4} e^{-(x^2+2y^2)/10^4}(x\,\mathbf{i}+2y\,\mathbf{j})$. And ∇C points in the direction of most rapid increase in concentration; that is, ∇C is tangent to the most rapid increase curve. If $r(t) = x(t)\,\mathbf{i} + y(t)\,\mathbf{j}$ is a

parametrization of the most rapid increase curve, then $\dfrac{d\mathbf{r}}{dt} = \dfrac{dx}{dt}\,\mathbf{i} + \dfrac{dy}{dt}\,\mathbf{j}$ is tangent to the curve, so $\dfrac{d\mathbf{r}}{dt} = \lambda \nabla C$

$\Rightarrow \quad \dfrac{dx}{dt} = \lambda \left[-\dfrac{2}{10^4} e^{-(x^2+2y^2)/10^4} \right] x$ and $\dfrac{dy}{dt} = \lambda \left[-\dfrac{2}{10^4} e^{-(x^2+2y^2)/10^4} \right](2y)$. Therefore

$\dfrac{dy}{dx} = \dfrac{dy/dt}{dx/dt} = 2\dfrac{y}{x} \quad \Rightarrow \quad \dfrac{dy}{y} = 2\dfrac{dx}{x} \quad \Rightarrow \quad \ln|y| = 2\ln|x|$ so that $y = kx^2$ for some constant k. But

$y(x_0) = y_0 \quad \Rightarrow \quad y_0 = kx_0^2 \quad \Rightarrow \quad k = y_0/x_0^2 \quad (x_0 = 0 \quad \Rightarrow \quad y_0 = 0 \quad \Rightarrow \quad$ the shark is already at the origin, so we can assume $x_0 \neq 0$.) Therefore the path the shark will follow is along the parabola $y = y_0(x/x_0)^2$.

3. (a) The area of a trapezoid is $\frac{1}{2}h(b_1 + b_2)$, where h is the height (the distance between the two parallel sides) and b_1, b_2 are the lengths of the bases (the parallel sides). From the figure in the text, we see that $h = x\sin\theta$, $b_1 = w - 2x$, and $b_2 = w - 2x + 2x\cos\theta$. Therefore the cross-sectional area of the rain gutter is

$$A(x, \theta) = \tfrac{1}{2}x\sin\theta\,[(w - 2x) + (w - 2x + 2x\cos\theta)] = (x\sin\theta)(w - 2x + x\cos\theta)$$
$$= wx\sin\theta - 2x^2\sin\theta + x^2\sin\theta\cos\theta, \ 0 < x \leq \tfrac{1}{2}w, 0 < \theta \leq \tfrac{\pi}{2}$$

We look for the critical points of A: $\partial A/\partial x = w\sin\theta - 4x\sin\theta + 2x\sin\theta\cos\theta$ and
$\partial A/\partial\theta = wx\cos\theta - 2x^2\cos\theta + x^2(\cos^2\theta - \sin^2\theta)$, so $\partial A/\partial x = 0 \iff \sin\theta(w - 4x + 2x\cos\theta) = 0$

$\iff \quad \cos\theta = \dfrac{4x - w}{2x} = 2 - \dfrac{w}{2x} \quad (0 < \theta \leq \tfrac{\pi}{2} \quad \Rightarrow \quad \sin\theta > 0)$. If, in addition, $\partial A/\partial\theta = 0$, then

$$0 = wx\cos\theta - 2x^2\cos\theta + x^2(2\cos^2\theta - 1)$$
$$= wx\left(2 - \dfrac{w}{2x}\right) - 2x^2\left(2 - \dfrac{w}{2x}\right) + x^2\left[2\left(2 - \dfrac{w}{2x}\right)^2 - 1\right]$$
$$= 2wx - \tfrac{1}{2}w^2 - 4x^2 + wx + x^2\left[8 - \dfrac{4w}{x} + \dfrac{w^2}{2x^2} - 1\right] = -wx + 3x^2 = x(3x - w)$$

Since $x > 0$, we must have $x = \tfrac{1}{3}w$, in which case $\cos\theta = \tfrac{1}{2}$, so $\theta = \tfrac{\pi}{3}$, $\sin\theta = \tfrac{\sqrt{3}}{2}$, $k = \tfrac{\sqrt{3}}{6}w$, $b_1 = \tfrac{1}{3}w$,
$b_2 = \tfrac{2}{3}w$, and $A = \tfrac{\sqrt{3}}{12}w^2$. As in Example 11.7.6, we can argue from the physical nature of this problem that we
have found a relative maximum of A. Now checking the boundary of A, let
$g(\theta) = A(w/2, \theta) = \tfrac{1}{2}w^2\sin\theta - \tfrac{1}{2}w^2\sin\theta + \tfrac{1}{4}w^2\sin\theta\cos\theta = \tfrac{1}{8}w^2\sin 2\theta, 0 < \theta \leq \tfrac{\pi}{2}$. Clearly g is
maximized when $\sin 2\theta = 1$ in which case $A = \tfrac{1}{8}w^2$. Also along the line $\theta = \tfrac{\pi}{2}$, let
$h(x) = A\left(x, \tfrac{\pi}{2}\right) = wx - 2x^2, 0 < x < \tfrac{1}{2}w \quad \Rightarrow \quad h'(x) = w - 4x = 0 \iff x = \tfrac{1}{4}w$, and
$h\left(\tfrac{1}{4}w\right) = w\left(\tfrac{1}{4}w\right) - 2\left(\tfrac{1}{4}w\right)^2 = \tfrac{1}{8}w^2$. Since $\tfrac{1}{8}w^2 < \tfrac{\sqrt{3}}{12}w^2$, we conclude that the relative maximum found
earlier was an absolute maximum.

(b) If the metal were bent into a semi-circular gutter of radius r, we would have $w = \pi r$ and

$$A = \tfrac{1}{2}\pi r^2 = \tfrac{1}{2}\pi\left(\frac{w}{\pi}\right)^2 = \frac{w^2}{2\pi}. \text{ Since } \frac{w^2}{2\pi} > \frac{\sqrt{3}\,w^2}{12}, \text{ it } would \text{ be better to bend the metal into a gutter with a}$$

semicircular cross-section.

4. Since $(x + y + z)^r / (x^2 + y^2 + z^2)$ is a rational function with domain $\{(x, y, z) \mid (x, y, z) \neq (0, 0, 0)\}$, f is

continuous on $\mathbb{R}^3$ if and only if $\displaystyle\lim_{(x,y,z)\to(0,0,0)} f(x, y, z) = f(0, 0, 0) = 0$. Recall that

$(a + b)^2 \leq 2a^2 + 2b^2$ and a double application of this inequality to $(x + y + z)^2$

gives $(x + y + z)^2 \leq 4x^2 + 4y^2 + 2z^2 \leq 4(x^2 + y^2 + z^2)$. Now for each r,

$|(x + y + z)^r| = (|x + y + z|^2)^{r/2} = [(x + y + z)^2]^{r/2} \leq [4(x^2 + y^2 + z^2)]^{r/2} = 2^r (x^2 + y^2 + z^2)^{r/2}$ for

$(x, y, z) \neq (0, 0, 0)$. Thus

$$|f(x, y, z) - 0| = \left|\frac{(x + y + z)^r}{x^2 + y^2 + z^2}\right| = \frac{|(x + y + z)^r|}{x^2 + y^2 + z^2} \leq 2^r \frac{(x^2 + y^2 + z^2)^{r/2}}{x^2 + y^2 + z^2} = 2^r (x^2 + y^2 + z^2)^{(r/2)-1} \text{ for }$$

$(x, y, z) \neq (0, 0, 0)$. Thus if $(r/2) - 1 > 0$, that is $r > 2$, then $2^r (x^2 + y^2 + z^2)^{(r/2)-1} \to 0$ as

$(x, y, z) \to (0, 0, 0)$ and so $\displaystyle\lim_{(x,y,z)\to(0,0,0)} (x + y + z)^r / (x^2 + y^2 + z^2) = 0$. Hence for $r > 2$, f is continuous

on $\mathbb{R}^3$. Now if $r \leq 2$, then as $(x, y, z) \to (0, 0, 0)$ along the x-axis, $f(x, 0, 0) = x^r/x^2 = x^{r-2}$ for $x \neq 0$. So

when $r = 2$, $f(x, y, z) \to 1 \neq 0$ as $(x, y, z) \to (0, 0, 0)$ along the x-axis and when $r < 2$ the limit of $f(x, y, z)$ as

$(x, y, z) \to (0, 0, 0)$ along the x-axis doesn't exist and thus can't be zero. Hence for $r \leq 2$ f isn't continuous at

$(0, 0, 0)$ and thus is not continuous on $\mathbb{R}^3$.

5. Let $g(x, y) = xf\left(\dfrac{y}{x}\right)$. Then $g_x(x, y) = f\left(\dfrac{y}{x}\right) + xf'\left(\dfrac{y}{x}\right)\left(-\dfrac{y}{x^2}\right) = f\left(\dfrac{y}{x}\right) - \dfrac{y}{x}f'\left(\dfrac{y}{x}\right)$ and

$g_y(x, y) = xf'\left(\dfrac{y}{x}\right)\left(\dfrac{1}{x}\right) = f'\left(\dfrac{y}{x}\right)$. Thus the tangent plane at (x_0, y_0, z_0) on the surface has equation

$$z - x_0 f\left(\frac{y_0}{x_0}\right) = \left[f\left(\frac{y_0}{x_0}\right) - y_0 x_0^{-1} f'\left(\frac{y_0}{x_0}\right)\right](x - x_0) + f'\left(\frac{y_0}{x_0}\right)(y - y_0) \Rightarrow$$

$$\left[f\left(\frac{y_0}{x_0}\right) - y_0 x_0^{-1} f'\left(\frac{y_0}{x_0}\right)\right]x + \left[f'\left(\frac{y_0}{x_0}\right)\right]y - z = 0. \text{ But any plane whose equation is of the form}$$

$ax + by + cz = 0$ passes through the origin. Thus the origin is the common point of intersection.

6. (a) At $(x_1, y_1, 0)$ the equations of the tangent planes to $z = f(x, y)$ and $z = g(x, y)$ are

P_1: $z - f(x_1, y_1) = f_x(x_1, y_1)(x - x_1) + f_y(x_1, y_1)(y - y_1)$ and

P_2: $z - g(x_1, y_1) = g_x(x_1, y_1)(x - x_1) + g_y(x_1, y_1)(y - y_1)$, respectively. P_1 intersects the xy-plane in the

line given by $f_x(x_1, y_1)(x - x_1) + f_y(x_1, y_1)(y - y_1) = -f(x_1, y_1)$, $z = 0$; and P_2 intersects the xy-plane

in the line given by $g_x(x_1, y_1)(x - x_1) + g_y(x_1, y_1)(y - y_1) = -g(x_1, y_1)$, $z = 0$. The point $(x_2, y_2, 0)$ is the

point of intersection of these two lines, since $(x_2, y_2, 0)$ is the point where the line of intersection of the two

tangent planes intersects the xy-plane. Thus (x_2, y_2) is the solution of the simultaneous

equations $f_x(x_1, y_1)(x_2 - x_1) + f_y(x_1, y_1)(y_2 - y_1) = -f(x_1, y_1)$ and

$g_x(x_1, y_1)(x_2 - x_1) + g_y(x_1, y_1)(y_2 - y_1) = -g(x_1, y_1)$. For simplicity, rewrite $f_x(x_1, y_1)$ as f_x and

similarly for f_y, g_x, g_y, f and g and solve the equations $(f_x)(x_2 - x_1) + (f_y)(y_2 - y_1) = -f$ and

$(g_x)(x_2 - x_1) + (g_y)(y_2 - y_1) = -g$ simultaneously for $(x_2 - x_1)$ and $(y_2 - y_1)$. Then

$$y_2 - y_1 = \frac{gf_x - fg_x}{g_x f_y - f_x g_y} \text{ or } y_2 = y_1 - \frac{gf_x - fg_x}{f_x g_y - g_x f_y} \text{ and } (f_x)(x_2 - x_1) + \frac{(f_y)(gf_x - fg_x)}{g_x f_y - f_x g_y} = -f \text{ so}$$

$$x_2 - x_1 = \frac{-f - [(f_y)(gf_x - fg_x)/(g_x f_y - f_x g_y)]}{f_x} = \frac{fg_y - f_y g}{g_x f_y - f_x g_y}. \text{ Hence } x_2 = x_1 - \frac{fg_y - f_y g}{f_x g_y - g_x f_y}.$$

(b) Let $f(x, y) = x^x + y^y - 1000$ and $g(x, y) = x^y + y^x - 100$. Then we wish to solve the system of equations $f(x, y) = 0$, $g(x, y) = 0$. Recall $\dfrac{d}{dx} [x^x] = x^x(1 + \ln x)$ (differentiate logarithmically), so

$f_x(x, y) = x^x(1 + \ln x)$, $f_y(x, y) = y^y(1 + \ln y)$, $g_x(x, y) = yx^{y-1} + y^x \ln y$, and

$g_y(x, y) = x^y \ln x + xy^{x-1}$. Looking at the graph, we estimate the first point of intersection of the curves, and thus the solution to the system, to be approximately $(2.5, 4.5)$. Then following the method of part (a), $x_1 = 2.5$, $y_1 = 4.5$ and

$$x_2 = 2.5 - \frac{f(2.5, 4.5)\, g_y(2.5, 4.5) - f_y(2.5, 4.5)\, g(2.5, 4.5)}{f_x(2.5, 4.5)\, g_y(2.5, 4.5) - f_y(2.5, 4.5)\, g_x(2.5, 4.5)} \approx 2.447674117$$

$$y_2 = 4.5 - \frac{f_x(2.5, 4.5)\, g(2.5, 4.5) - f(2.5, 4.5)\, g_x(2.5, 4.5)}{f_x(2.5, 4.5)\, g_y(2.5, 4.5) - f_y(2.5, 4.5)\, g_x(2.5, 4.5)} \approx 4.555657467$$

Continuing this procedure, we arrive at the following values. (If you use a CAS, you may need to increase its computational precision.)

$x_1 = 2.5$	$y_1 = 4.5$
$x_2 = 2.447674117$	$y_2 = 4.555657467$
$x_3 = 2.449614877$	$y_3 = 4.551969333$
$x_4 = 2.449624628$	$y_4 = 4.551951420$
$x_5 = 2.449624628$	$y_5 = 4.551951420$

Thus, to six decimal places, the point of intersection is $(2.449625, 4.551951)$. The second point of intersection can be found similarly, or, by symmetry it is approximately $(4.551951, 2.449625)$.

7. (a) $x = r \cos\theta$, $y = r \sin\theta$, $z = z$. Then $\dfrac{\partial u}{\partial r} = \dfrac{\partial u}{\partial x}\dfrac{\partial x}{\partial r} + \dfrac{\partial u}{\partial y}\dfrac{\partial y}{\partial r} + \dfrac{\partial u}{\partial z}\dfrac{\partial z}{\partial r} = \dfrac{\partial u}{\partial x}\cos\theta + \dfrac{\partial u}{\partial y}\sin\theta$ and

$$\frac{\partial^2 u}{\partial r^2} = \cos\theta \left[\frac{\partial^2 u}{\partial x^2}\frac{\partial x}{\partial r} + \frac{\partial^2 u}{\partial y\partial x}\frac{\partial y}{\partial r} + \frac{\partial^2 u}{\partial z\partial x}\frac{\partial z}{\partial r} \right] + \sin\theta \left[\frac{\partial^2 u}{\partial y^2}\frac{\partial y}{\partial r} + \frac{\partial^2 u}{\partial x\partial y}\frac{\partial x}{\partial r} + \frac{\partial^2 u}{\partial z\partial y}\frac{\partial z}{\partial r} \right]$$

$$= \frac{\partial^2 u}{\partial x^2}\cos^2\theta + \frac{\partial^2 u}{\partial y^2}\sin^2\theta + 2\frac{\partial^2 u}{\partial y\partial x}\cos\theta\sin\theta$$

Similarly $\dfrac{\partial u}{\partial \theta} = -\dfrac{\partial u}{\partial x}r\sin\theta + \dfrac{\partial u}{\partial y}r\cos\theta$ and

$$\frac{\partial^2 u}{\partial \theta^2} = \frac{\partial^2 u}{\partial x^2}r^2\sin^2\theta + \frac{\partial^2 u}{\partial y^2}r^2\cos^2\theta - 2\frac{\partial^2 u}{\partial y\partial x}r^2\sin\theta\cos\theta - \frac{\partial u}{\partial x}r\cos\theta - \frac{\partial u}{\partial y}r\sin\theta. \text{ So}$$

$$\frac{\partial^2 u}{\partial r^2} + \frac{1}{r}\frac{\partial u}{\partial r} + \frac{1}{r^2}\frac{\partial^2 u}{\partial \theta^2} + \frac{\partial^2 u}{\partial z^2}$$

$$= \frac{\partial^2 u}{\partial x^2}\cos^2\theta + \frac{\partial^2 u}{\partial y^2}\sin^2\theta + 2\frac{\partial^2 u}{\partial y\partial x}\cos\theta\sin\theta + \frac{\partial u}{\partial x}\frac{\cos\theta}{r} + \frac{\partial u}{\partial y}\frac{\sin\theta}{r}$$

$$+ \frac{\partial^2 u}{\partial x^2}\sin^2\theta + \frac{\partial^2 u}{\partial y^2}\cos^2\theta - 2\frac{\partial^2 u}{\partial y\partial x}\sin\theta\cos\theta - \frac{\partial u}{\partial x}\frac{\cos\theta}{r} - \frac{\partial u}{\partial y}\frac{\sin\theta}{r} + \frac{\partial^2 u}{\partial z^2}$$

$$= \frac{\partial^2 u}{\partial x^2} + \frac{\partial^2 u}{\partial y^2} + \frac{\partial^2 u}{\partial z^2}$$

(b) $x = \rho \sin \phi \cos \theta$, $y = \rho \sin \phi \sin \theta$, $z = \rho \cos \phi$. Then

$$\frac{\partial u}{\partial \rho} = \frac{\partial u}{\partial x}\frac{\partial x}{\partial \rho} + \frac{\partial u}{\partial y}\frac{\partial y}{\partial \rho} + \frac{\partial u}{\partial z}\frac{\partial z}{\partial \rho} = \frac{\partial u}{\partial x}\sin \phi \cos \theta + \frac{\partial u}{\partial y}\sin \phi \sin \theta + \frac{\partial u}{\partial z}\cos \phi, \text{ and}$$

$$\frac{\partial^2 u}{\partial \rho^2} = \sin \phi \cos \theta \left[\frac{\partial^2 u}{\partial x^2}\frac{\partial x}{\partial \rho} + \frac{\partial^2 u}{\partial y \partial x}\frac{\partial y}{\partial \rho} + \frac{\partial^2 u}{\partial z \partial x}\frac{\partial z}{\partial \rho}\right]$$

$$+ \sin \phi \sin \theta \left[\frac{\partial^2 u}{\partial y^2}\frac{\partial y}{\partial \rho} + \frac{\partial^2 u}{\partial x \partial y}\frac{\partial x}{\partial \rho} + \frac{\partial^2 u}{\partial z \partial y}\frac{\partial z}{\partial \rho}\right]$$

$$+ \cos \phi \left[\frac{\partial^2 u}{\partial z^2}\frac{\partial z}{\partial \rho} + \frac{\partial^2 u}{\partial x \partial z}\frac{\partial x}{\partial \rho} + \frac{\partial^2 u}{\partial y \partial z}\frac{\partial y}{\partial \rho}\right]$$

$$= 2 \frac{\partial^2 u}{\partial y \partial x}\sin^2 \phi \sin \theta \cos \theta + 2 \frac{\partial^2 u}{\partial z \partial x}\sin \phi \cos \phi \cos \theta + 2 \frac{\partial^2 u}{\partial y \partial z}\sin \phi \cos \phi \sin \theta$$

$$+ \frac{\partial^2 u}{\partial x^2}\sin^2 \phi \cos^2 \theta + \frac{\partial^2 u}{\partial y^2}\sin^2 \phi \sin^2 \theta + \frac{\partial^2 u}{\partial z^2}\cos^2 \phi$$

Similarly $\dfrac{\partial u}{\partial \phi} = \dfrac{\partial u}{\partial x}\rho \cos \phi \cos \theta + \dfrac{\partial u}{\partial y}\rho \cos \phi \sin \theta - \dfrac{\partial u}{\partial z}\rho \sin \phi$, and

$$\frac{\partial^2 u}{\partial \phi^2} = 2 \frac{\partial^2 u}{\partial y \partial x}\rho^2 \cos^2 \phi \sin \theta \cos \theta - 2 \frac{\partial^2 u}{\partial x \partial z}\rho^2 \sin \phi \cos \phi \cos \theta$$

$$- 2 \frac{\partial^2 u}{\partial y \partial z}\rho^2 \sin \phi \cos \phi \sin \theta + \frac{\partial^2 u}{\partial x^2}\rho^2 \cos^2 \phi \cos^2 \theta + \frac{\partial^2 u}{\partial y^2}\rho^2 \cos^2 \phi \sin^2 \theta$$

$$+ \frac{\partial^2 u}{\partial z^2}\rho^2 \sin^2 \phi - \frac{\partial u}{\partial x}\rho \sin \phi \cos \theta - \frac{\partial u}{\partial y}\rho \sin \phi \sin \theta - \frac{\partial u}{\partial z}\rho \cos \phi$$

And $\dfrac{\partial u}{\partial \theta} = -\dfrac{\partial u}{\partial x}\rho \sin \phi \sin \theta + \dfrac{\partial u}{\partial y}\rho \sin \phi \cos \theta$, while

$$\frac{\partial^2 u}{\partial \theta^2} = -2 \frac{\partial^2 u}{\partial y \partial x}\rho^2 \sin^2 \phi \cos \theta \sin \theta + \frac{\partial^2 u}{\partial x^2}\rho^2 \sin^2 \phi \sin^2 \theta$$

$$+ \frac{\partial^2 u}{\partial y^2}\rho^2 \sin^2 \phi \cos^2 \theta - \frac{\partial u}{\partial x}\rho \sin \phi \cos \theta - \frac{\partial u}{\partial y}\rho \sin \phi \sin \theta$$

Therefore

$$\frac{\partial^2 u}{\partial \rho^2} + \frac{2}{\rho}\frac{\partial u}{\partial \rho} + \frac{\cot \phi}{\rho^2}\frac{\partial u}{\partial \phi} + \frac{1}{\rho^2}\frac{\partial^2 u}{\partial \phi^2} + \frac{1}{\rho^2 \sin^2 \phi}\frac{\partial^2 u}{\partial \theta^2}$$

$$= \frac{\partial^2 u}{\partial x^2}\left[(\sin^2 \phi \cos^2 \theta) + (\cos^2 \phi \cos^2 \theta) + \sin^2 \theta\right]$$

$$+ \frac{\partial^2 u}{\partial y^2}\left[(\sin^2 \phi \sin^2 \theta) + (\cos^2 \phi \sin^2 \theta) + \cos^2 \theta\right] + \frac{\partial^2 u}{\partial z^2}\left[\cos^2 \phi + \sin^2 \phi\right]$$

$$+ \frac{\partial u}{\partial x}\left[\frac{2 \sin^2 \phi \cos \theta + \cos^2 \phi \cos \theta - \sin^2 \phi \cos \theta - \cos \theta}{\rho \sin \phi}\right]$$

$$+ \frac{\partial u}{\partial y}\left[\frac{2 \sin^2 \phi \sin \theta + \cos^2 \phi \sin \theta - \sin^2 \phi \sin \theta - \sin \theta}{\rho \sin \phi}\right]$$

But $2\sin^2\phi\cos\theta + \cos^2\phi\cos\theta - \sin^2\phi\cos\theta - \cos\theta = (\sin^2\phi + \cos^2\phi - 1)\cos\theta = 0$ and similarly the

coefficient of $\partial u/\partial y$ is 0. Also $\sin^2\phi\cos^2\theta + \cos^2\phi\cos^2\theta + \sin^2\theta = \cos^2\theta(\sin^2\phi + \cos^2\phi) + \sin^2\theta = 1$,

and similarly the coefficient of $\partial^2 u/\partial y^2$ is 1. So Laplace's Equation in spherical coordinates is as stated.

8. The tangent plane to the surface $xy^2 z^2 = 1$, at the point (x_0, y_0, z_0) is

$y_0^2 z_0^2(x - x_0) + 2x_0 y_0 z_0^2(y - y_0) + 2x_0 y_0^2 z_0(z - z_0) = 0 \implies$

$(y_0^2 z_0^2)x + (2x_0 y_0 z_0^2)y + (2x_0 y_0^2 z_0)z = 5x_0 y_0^2 z_0^2 = 5$. Using the formula derived in Example 9.5.8, we find that

the distance from $(0,0,0)$ to this tangent plane is $D(x_0, y_0, z_0) = \dfrac{|5x_0 y_0^2 z_0^2|}{\sqrt{(y_0^2 z_0^2)^2 + (2x_0 y_0 z_0^2)^2 + (2x_0 y_0^2 z_0)^2}}$. When

D is a maximum, D^2 is a maximum and $\nabla D^2 = \mathbf{0}$. Dropping the subscripts, let

$f(x, y, z) = D^2 = \dfrac{25(xyz)^2}{y^2 z^2 + 4x^2 z^2 + 4x^2 y^2}$. Now use the fact that for points on the surface $xy^2 z^2 = 1$ we have

$z^2 = \dfrac{1}{xy^2}$, to get $f(x, y) = D^2 = \dfrac{25x}{\dfrac{1}{x} + \dfrac{4x}{y^2} + 4x^2 y^2} = \dfrac{25x^2 y^2}{y^2 + 4x^2 + 4x^3 y^4}$. Now $\nabla D^2 = \mathbf{0} \implies f_x = 0$ and

$f_y = 0$. $f_x = 0 \implies \dfrac{50xy^2(y^2 + 4x^2 + 4x^3 y^4) - (8x + 12x^2 y^4)(25x^2 y^2)}{(y^2 + 4x^2 + 4x^3 y^4)^2} = 0 \implies$

$xy^2(y^2 + 4x^2 + 4x^3 y^4) - (4x + 6x^2 y^4)x^2 y^2 = 0 \implies xy^4 - 2x^4 y^6 = 0 \implies$

$xy^4(1 - 2x^3 y^2) = 0 \implies 1 = 2y^2 x^3$ (since $x = 0$, $y = 0$ both give a minimum distance of 0). Also $f_y = 0$

$\implies \dfrac{50x^2 y(y^2 + 4x^2 + 4x^3 y^4) - (2y + 16x^3 y^3)25x^2 y^2}{(y^2 + 4x^2 + 4x^3 y^4)^2} = 0 \implies 4x^4 y - 4x^5 y^5 = 0 \implies$

$x^4 y(1 - xy^4) = 0 \implies 1 = xy^4$. Now substituting $x = 1/y^4$ into $1 = 2y^2 x^3$, we get $1 = 2y^{-10} \implies$

$y = \pm 2^{1/10} \implies x = 2^{-2/5} \implies z^2 = \dfrac{1}{xy^2} = \dfrac{1}{(2^{-2/5})(2^{1/5})} = 2^{1/5} \implies z = \pm 2^{1/10}$.

Therefore the tangent planes that are farthest from the origin are at the four points $\left(2^{-2/5}, \pm 2^{1/10}, \pm 2^{1/10}\right)$. These

points all give a maximum since the minimum distance occurs when $x_0 = 0$ or $y_0 = 0$ in which case $D = 0$. The

equations are $\left(2^{1/5}2^{1/5}\right)x \pm \left[(2)\left(2^{-2/5}\right)\left(2^{1/10}\right)\left(2^{1/5}\right)\right]y \pm \left[(2)\left(2^{-2/5}\right)\left(2^{1/5}\right)\left(2^{1/10}\right)\right]z = 5 \implies$

$\left(2^{2/5}\right)x \pm \left(2^{9/10}\right)y \pm \left(2^{9/10}\right)z = 5$.

9. Since we are minimizing the area of the ellipse, and the circle lies above

the x-axis, the ellipse will intersect the circle for only one value of y. This

y-value must satisfy both the equation of the circle and the equation of the

ellipse. Now $\dfrac{x^2}{a^2} + \dfrac{y^2}{b^2} = 1 \implies x^2 = \dfrac{a^2}{b^2}(b^2 - y^2)$. Substituting into

the equation of the circle gives $\dfrac{a^2}{b^2}(b^2 - y^2) + y^2 - 2y = 0 \implies$

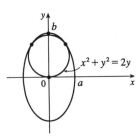

$\left(\dfrac{b^2 - a^2}{b^2}\right)y^2 - 2y + a^2 = 0$. In order for there to be only one solution to this quadratic equation, the discriminant must be 0, so $4 - 4a^2 \dfrac{b^2 - a^2}{b^2} = 0 \;\Rightarrow\; b^2 - a^2 b^2 + a^4 = 0$. The area of the ellipse is $A(a, b) = \pi a b$, and we

minimize this function subject to the constraint $g(a, b) = b^2 - a^2 b^2 + a^4 = 0$.

Now $\nabla A = \lambda \nabla g \;\Leftrightarrow\; \pi b = \lambda\left(4a^3 - 2ab^2\right), \pi a = \lambda\left(2b - 2ba^2\right) \;\Rightarrow\;$ (1) $\lambda = \dfrac{\pi b}{2a(2a^2 - b^2)}$,

(2) $\lambda = \dfrac{\pi a}{2b(1 - a^2)}$, (3) $b^2 - a^2 b^2 + a^4 = 0$. Comparing (1) and (2) gives $\dfrac{\pi b}{2a(2a^2 - b^2)} = \dfrac{\pi a}{2b(1 - a^2)} \;\Rightarrow\;$

$2\pi b^2 = 4\pi a^4 \;\Leftrightarrow\; a^2 = \frac{1}{\sqrt{2}} b$. Substitute this into (3) to get $b = \frac{3}{\sqrt{2}} \;\Rightarrow\; a = \sqrt{\frac{3}{2}}$.

12 **Multiple Integrals**

• • • • • • • • • • •

1. (a) $\sum_{i=1}^{2} \sum_{j=1}^{2} f\left(x_{ij}^{*}, y_{ij}^{*}\right) \Delta A = f\left(0, \frac{3}{2}\right) \Delta A + f(0, 2) \Delta A + f\left(1, \frac{3}{2}\right) \Delta A + f(1, 2) \Delta A$

$$= \left(-\frac{27}{4}\right)\frac{1}{2} + (-12)\frac{1}{2} + \left(1 - \frac{27}{4}\right)\frac{1}{2} + (1 - 12)\frac{1}{2} = -17.75$$

(b) $\frac{1}{2}\left[f\left(1, \frac{3}{2}\right) + f(1, 2) + f\left(2, \frac{3}{2}\right) + f(2, 2)\right] = \frac{1}{2}\left[-\frac{23}{4} + (-11) + \left(-\frac{19}{4}\right) + (-10)\right]$

$$= \frac{1}{2}\left(-\frac{63}{2}\right) = -15.75$$

(c) $\frac{1}{2}\left[f(0, 1) + f\left(0, \frac{3}{2}\right) + f(1, 1) + f\left(1, \frac{3}{2}\right)\right] = \frac{1}{2}\left[-3 - \frac{27}{4} - 2 - \frac{23}{4}\right] = -8.75$

(d) $\frac{1}{2}\left[f(1, 1) + f\left(1, \frac{3}{2}\right) + f(2, 1) + f\left(2, \frac{3}{2}\right)\right] = \frac{1}{2}\left[-2 - \frac{23}{4} - 1 - \frac{19}{4}\right] = -6.75$

2. $V \approx (1)\left[f\left(\frac{1}{2}, \frac{1}{2}\right) + f\left(\frac{1}{2}, \frac{3}{2}\right) + f\left(\frac{3}{2}, \frac{1}{2}\right) + f\left(\frac{3}{2}, \frac{3}{2}\right)\right] = \left[\frac{61}{4} + \frac{45}{4} + \frac{53}{4} + \frac{37}{4}\right] = 49$

3. (a) The subrectangles are shown in the figure.

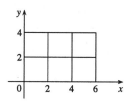

The surface is the graph of $f(x, y) = xy$ and $\Delta A = 4$, so we estimate

$$V \approx \sum_{i=1}^{3} \sum_{j=1}^{2} f(x_i, y_j) \Delta A$$

$$= f(2, 2) \Delta A + f(2, 4) \Delta A + f(4, 2) \Delta A + f(4, 4) \Delta A + f(6, 2) \Delta A + f(6, 4) \Delta A$$

$$= 4(4) + 8(4) + 8(4) + 16(4) + 12(4) + 24(4) = 288$$

(b) $V \approx \sum_{i=1}^{3} \sum_{j=1}^{2} f\left(\overline{x}_i, \overline{y}_j\right) \Delta A$

$$= f(1, 1) \Delta A + f(1, 3) \Delta A + f(3, 1) \Delta A + f(3, 3) \Delta A + f(5, 1) \Delta A + f(5, 3) \Delta A$$

$$= 1(4) + 3(4) + 3(4) + 9(4) + 5(4) + 15(4) = 144$$

4. The subrectangles are shown in the figure.

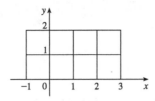

Since $\Delta A = 1$, we estimate

$$\iint_R (y^2 - 2x^2) \, dA \approx \sum_{i=1}^{4} \sum_{j=1}^{2} f(x_{ij}^*, y_{ij}^*) \, \Delta A$$

$$= f(-1, 1) \, \Delta A + f(-1, 2) \, \Delta A + f(0, 1) \, \Delta A + f(0, 2) \, \Delta A$$

$$+ f(1, 1) \, \Delta A + f(1, 2) \, \Delta A + f(2, 1) \, \Delta A + f(2, 2) \, \Delta A$$

$$= -1(1) + 2(1) + 1(1) + 4(1) - 1(1) + 2(1) - 7(1) - 4(1) = -4$$

5. (a) Each subrectangle and its midpoint are shown in the figure. The area of each
subrectangle is $\Delta A = 2$, so we evaluate f at each midpoint and estimate

$$\iint_R f(x, y) \, dA \approx \sum_{i=1}^{2} \sum_{j=1}^{2} f(\overline{x}_i, \overline{y}_j) \, \Delta A$$

$$= f(1.5, 1) \, \Delta A + f(1.5, 3) \, \Delta A$$

$$+ f(2.5, 1) \, \Delta A + f(2.5, 3) \, \Delta A$$

$$= 1(2) + (-8)(2) + 5(2) + (-1)(2) = -6$$

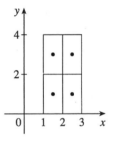

(b) The subrectangles are shown in the figure. In each subrectangle, the sample point
farthest from the origin is the upper right corner, and the area of each subrectangle
is $\Delta A = \frac{1}{2}$. Thus we estimate

$$\iint_R f(x, y) \, dA \approx \sum_{i=1}^{4} \sum_{j=1}^{4} f(x_i, y_j) \, \Delta A$$

$$= f(1.5, 1) \, \Delta A + f(1.5, 2) \, \Delta A + f(1.5, 3) \, \Delta A + f(1.5, 4) \, \Delta A$$

$$+ f(2, 1) \, \Delta A + f(2, 2) \, \Delta A + f(2, 3) \, \Delta A + f(2, 4) \, \Delta A$$

$$+ f(2.5, 1) \, \Delta A + f(2.5, 2) \, \Delta A + f(2.5, 3) \, \Delta A + f(2.5, 4) \, \Delta A$$

$$+ f(3, 1) \, \Delta A + f(3, 2) \, \Delta A + f(3, 3) \, \Delta A + f(3, 4) \, \Delta A$$

$$= 1\left(\tfrac{1}{2}\right) + (-4)\left(\tfrac{1}{2}\right) + (-8)\left(\tfrac{1}{2}\right) + (-6)\left(\tfrac{1}{2}\right) + 3\left(\tfrac{1}{2}\right) + 0\left(\tfrac{1}{2}\right) + (-5)\left(\tfrac{1}{2}\right) + (-8)\left(\tfrac{1}{2}\right)$$

$$+ 5\left(\tfrac{1}{2}\right) + 3\left(\tfrac{1}{2}\right) + (-1)\left(\tfrac{1}{2}\right) + (-4)\left(\tfrac{1}{2}\right) + 8\left(\tfrac{1}{2}\right) + 6\left(\tfrac{1}{2}\right) + 3\left(\tfrac{1}{2}\right) + 0\left(\tfrac{1}{2}\right)$$

$$= -3.5$$

6. To approximate the volume, let R be the planar region corresponding to the surface of the water in the pool, and place R on coordinate axes so that x and y correspond to the dimensions given. Then we define $f(x, y)$ to be the depth of the water at (x, y), so the volume of water in the pool is the volume of the solid that lies above the rectangle $R = [0, 20] \times [0, 30]$ and below the graph of $f(x, y)$. We can estimate this volume using the Midpoint Rule with $m = 2$ and $n = 3$, so $\Delta A = 100$.

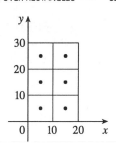

Each subrectangle with its midpoint is shown in the figure. Then

$$V \approx \sum_{i=1}^{2} \sum_{j=1}^{3} f(\overline{x}_i, \overline{y}_j) \, \Delta A$$

$$= \Delta A[f(5, 5) + f(5, 15) + f(5, 25) + f(15, 5) + f(15, 15) + f(15, 25)]$$

$$= 100(3 + 7 + 10 + 3 + 5 + 8) = 3600$$

Thus, we estimate that the pool contains 3600 cubic feet of water.

Alternatively, we can approximate the volume with a Riemann sum where $m = 4$, $n = 6$ and the sample points are taken to be, for example, the upper right corner of each subrectangle. Then $\Delta A = 25$ and

$$V \approx \sum_{i=1}^{4} \sum_{j=1}^{6} f(x_i, y_j) \, \Delta A$$

$$= 25[3 + 4 + 7 + 8 + 10 + 8 + 4 + 6 + 8 + 10 + 12 + 10 + 3 + 4$$

$$+ 5 + 6 + 8 + 7 + 2 + 2 + 2 + 3 + 4 + 4]$$

$$= 25(140) = 3500$$

So we estimate that the pool contains 3500 ft^3 of water.

7. The values of $f(x, y) = \sqrt{52 - x^2 - y^2}$ get smaller as we move farther from the origin, so on any of the subrectangles in the problem, the function will have its largest value at the lower left corner of the subrectangle and its smallest value at the upper right corner, and any other value will lie between these two. So using these subrectangles we have $U < V < L$. (Note that this is true no matter how R is divided into subrectangles.)

8. From the level curves we see that $f\left(\frac{1}{2}, \frac{1}{2}\right) \approx 11$. So, using the Midpoint Rule with only one subrectangle, we get $\iint_R f(x, y) \, dA \approx 1 \cdot f\left(\frac{1}{2}, \frac{1}{2}\right) \approx 11$. Dividing R into four squares of equal size, we get $\iint_R f(x, y) \, dA \approx \frac{1}{4} \left[f\left(\frac{1}{4}, \frac{1}{4}\right) + f\left(\frac{1}{4}, \frac{3}{4}\right) + f\left(\frac{3}{4}, \frac{1}{4}\right) + f\left(\frac{3}{4}, \frac{3}{4}\right) \right] \approx \frac{1}{4}(11 + 13 + 9.5 + 11) \approx 11$. Using sixteen squares we get the same result. So $\iint_R f(x, y) \, dA \approx 11$.

9. (a) With $m = n = 2$, we have $\Delta A = 4$. Using the contour map to estimate the value of f at the center of each subrectangle, we have

$$\iint_R f(x, y) \, dA \approx \sum_{i=1}^{2} \sum_{j=1}^{2} f(\overline{x}_i, \overline{y}_j) \, \Delta A = \Delta A[f(1, 1) + f(1, 3) + f(3, 1) + f(3, 3)]$$

$$\approx 4(27 + 4 + 14 + 17) = 248$$

(b) $f_{\text{ave}} = \frac{1}{A(R)} \iint_R f(x, y) \, dA \approx \frac{1}{16}(248) = 15.5$

10. As in Example 4, we place the origin at the southwest corner of the state. Then $R = [0, 388] \times [0, 276]$ (in miles) is the rectangle corresponding to Colorado and we define $f(x, y)$ to be the temperature at the location (x, y). The average temperature is given by

$$f_{ave} = \frac{1}{A(R)} \iint_R f(x, y) \, dA = \frac{1}{388 \cdot 276} \iint_R f(x, y) \, dA$$

We can use the Midpoint Rule with $m = n = 4$ to give a reasonable estimate of the value of the double integral.

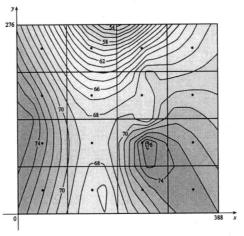

Thus, we divide R into 16 regions of equal size, as shown in the figure, with the center of each subrectangle indicated. The area of each subrectangle is $\Delta A = \frac{388}{4} \cdot \frac{276}{4} = 6693$, so using the contour map to estimate the function values at each midpoint, we have

$$\iint_R f(x, y) \, dA \approx \sum_{i=1}^{4} \sum_{j=1}^{4} f(\overline{x}_i, \overline{y}_j) \, \Delta A$$

$$\approx \Delta A[72.2 + 73.6 + 72.1 + 68.2 + 67.4 + 68.5 + 66.7 + 60.3$$

$$+ 72.0 + 74.9 + 68.4 + 63.7 + 73.2 + 72.3 + 70.3 + 67.7]$$

$$= 6693(1111.5)$$

Therefore, $f_{ave} \approx \dfrac{6693 \cdot 1111.5}{388 \cdot 276} \approx 69.5$, so the average temperature in Colorado on May 1, 1996, was approximately 69.5 °F.

Alternatively, we can use the Midpoint Rule with $m = n = 2$ which is easier computationally but will most likely be less accurate since we have fewer subrectangles. In this case, $\Delta A = \frac{388}{2} \cdot \frac{276}{2} = 26{,}772$ and we can use the same grid to estimate the function values at the midpoints of the four subrectangles. Then

$$\iint_R f(x, y) \, dA \approx \sum_{i=1}^{2} \sum_{j=1}^{2} f(\overline{x}_i, \overline{y}_j) \, \Delta A \approx 26{,}772[70.0 + 66.5 + 74.3 + 68.5]$$

$$= 26{,}772 \cdot 279.3$$

and $f_{ave} \approx \dfrac{26{,}772 \cdot 279.3}{388 \cdot 276} \approx 69.8$ °F.

11. $z = 3 > 0$, so we can interpret the integral as the volume of the solid S that lies below the plane $z = 3$ and above the rectangle $[-2, 2] \times [1, 6]$. S is a rectangular solid, thus $\iint_R 3 \, dA = 4 \cdot 5 \cdot 3 = 60$.

12. $z = 5 - x \geq 0$ for $0 \leq x \leq 5$, so we can interpret the integral as
the volume of the solid S that lies below the plane $z = 5 - x$ and
above the rectangle $[0, 5] \times [0, 3]$. S is a triangular cylinder whose
volume is $3(\text{area of triangle}) = 3\left(\frac{1}{2} \cdot 5 \cdot 5\right) = 37.5$. Thus,
$\iint_R (5 - x)\, dA = 37.5$.

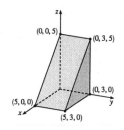

13. $z = f(x, y) = 4 - 2y \geq 0$ for $0 \leq y \leq 1$. Thus the integral
represents the volume of that part of the rectangular solid
$[0, 1] \times [0, 1] \times [0, 4]$ which lies below the plane $z = 4 - 2$. So

$$\iint_R (4 - y)\, dA = (1)(1)(2) + \tfrac{1}{2}(1)(1)(2) = 3$$

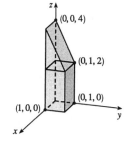

14. Here $z = \sqrt{9 - y^2}$, so $z^2 + y^2 = 9$, $z \geq 0$. Thus the integral
represents the volume of the top half of the part of the circular
cylinder $z^2 + y^2 = 9$ that lies above the rectangle $[0, 4] \times [0, 2]$.

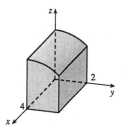

15. To calculate the estimates using a programmable calculator, we can use an algorithm
similar to that of Exercise 5.1.7. In Maple, we can define the function

$f(x, y) = e^{-x^2 - y^2}$ (calling it f), load the `student` package, and then use the
command

```
middlesum(middlesum(f,x=0..1,m),
                    y=0..1,m);
```

to get the estimate with $n = m^2$ squares of equal size. Mathematica has no special
Riemann sum command, but we can define f and then use nested `Sum` commands to
calculate the estimates.

n	estimate
1	0.6065
4	0.5694
16	0.5606
64	0.5585
256	0.5579
1024	0.5578

16.

n	estimate
1	0.9922
4	0.9262
16	0.8797

n	estimate
64	0.8660
256	0.8625
1024	0.8616

17. If we divide R into mn subrectangles, $\iint_R k\, dA \approx \sum_{i=1}^{m}\sum_{j=1}^{n} f\left(x_{ij}^*, y_{ij}^*\right) \Delta A$ for any choice of sample points

$\left(x_{ij}^*, y_{ij}^*\right)$. But $f\left(x_{ij}^*, y_{ij}^*\right) = k$ always and $\sum_{i=1}^{m}\sum_{j=1}^{n} \Delta A = $ area of $R = (b-a)(d-c)$. Thus, no matter how we

choose the sample points, $\sum_{i=1}^{m}\sum_{j=1}^{n} f\left(x_{ij}^*, y_{ij}^*\right) \Delta A = k \sum_{i=1}^{m}\sum_{j=1}^{n} \Delta A = k(b-a)(d-c)$ and so

$$\iint_R k\, dA = \lim_{m,n\to\infty} \sum_{i=1}^{m}\sum_{j=1}^{n} f\left(x_{ij}^*, y_{ij}^*\right) \Delta A = \lim_{m,n\to\infty} k \sum_{i=1}^{m}\sum_{j=1}^{n} \Delta A$$

$$= \lim_{m,n\to\infty} k(b-a)(d-c) = k(b-a)(d-c)$$

18. On R, $0 \leq x+y \leq 2 < \pi$ and $\sin\theta \geq 0$ for $0 \leq \theta \leq \pi$. Thus $f(x,y) = \sin(x+y) \geq 0$ for all $(x,y) \in R$. Since
$0 \leq \sin(x+y) \leq 1$, Property (9) gives $\iint_R 0\, dA \leq \iint_R \sin(x+y)\, dA \leq \iint_R 1\, dA$, so by Exercise 17 we have
$0 \leq \iint_R \sin(x+y)\, dA \leq 1$.

◈ 12.2 Iterated Integrals · · · · · · · · · · · · · · ·

1. $\int_0^3 \left(2x + 3x^2 y\right) dx = \left[x^2 + x^3 y\right]_{x=0}^{x=3} = (9 + 27y) - (0+0) = 9 + 27y$,

$\int_0^4 \left(2x + 3x^2 y\right) dy = \left[2xy + 3x^2 \dfrac{y^2}{2}\right]_{y=0}^{y=4} = \left(8x + 3x^2 \cdot \dfrac{16}{2}\right) - (0+0) = 8x + 24x^2$

2. $\displaystyle\int_0^3 \dfrac{y}{x+2}\, dx = y\ln|x+2|\ \Big|_{x=0}^{x=3} = y\ln 5 - y\ln 2 = y\ln\dfrac{5}{2}$,

$\displaystyle\int_0^4 \dfrac{y}{x+2}\, dy = \dfrac{1}{x+2}\left[\dfrac{y^2}{2}\right]_{y=0}^{y=4} = \dfrac{1}{x+2}\left(\dfrac{16}{2} - 0\right) = \dfrac{8}{x+2}$

3. $\int_1^3 \int_0^1 (1 + 4xy)\, dx\, dy = \int_1^3 \left[x + 2x^2 y\right]_{x=0}^{x=1} dy = \int_1^3 (1 + 2y)\, dy$

$\qquad\qquad = \left[y + y^2\right]_1^3 = (3+9) - (1+1) = 10$

4. $\int_2^4 \int_{-1}^1 \left(x^2 + y^2\right) dy\, dx = \int_2^4 \left[x^2 y + \tfrac{1}{3} y^3\right]_{y=-1}^{y=1} dx = \int_2^4 \left[\left(x^2 + \tfrac{1}{3}\right) - \left(-x^2 - \tfrac{1}{3}\right)\right] dx$

$\qquad\qquad = \int_2^4 \left(2x^2 + \tfrac{2}{3}\right) dx = \left[\tfrac{2}{3} x^3 + \tfrac{2}{3} x\right]_2^4 = \left(\tfrac{128}{3} + \tfrac{8}{3}\right) - \left(\tfrac{16}{3} + \tfrac{4}{3}\right) = \tfrac{116}{3}$

5. $\int_0^3 \int_0^1 \sqrt{x+y}\, dx\, dy = \int_0^3 \left[\tfrac{2}{3}(x+y)^{3/2}\right]_{x=0}^{x=1} dy = \tfrac{2}{3} \int_0^3 \left[(1+y)^{3/2} - y^{3/2}\right] dy$

$\qquad\qquad = \tfrac{2}{3}\left[\tfrac{2}{5}(1+y)^{5/2} - \tfrac{2}{5} y^{5/2}\right]_0^3 = \tfrac{4}{15}\left[32 - 3^{5/2} - 1\right] = \tfrac{4}{15}\left(31 - 9\sqrt{3}\right)$

6. $\int_1^4 \int_0^2 \left(x + \sqrt{y}\right) dx\, dy = \int_1^4 \left[\tfrac{1}{2} x^2 + x\sqrt{y}\right]_{x=0}^{x=2} dy = \int_1^4 \left(2 + 2\sqrt{y}\right) dy$

$\qquad\qquad = \left[2y + 2 \cdot \tfrac{2}{3} y^{3/2}\right]_1^4 = \left(8 + \tfrac{4}{3} \cdot 8\right) - \left(2 + \tfrac{4}{3}\right) = \tfrac{46}{3}$

7. $\displaystyle\int_1^4 \int_1^2 \left(\dfrac{x}{y} + \dfrac{y}{x}\right) dy\, dx = \int_1^4 \left[x\ln|y| + \dfrac{1}{x} \cdot \dfrac{1}{2} y^2\right]_{y=1}^{y=2} dx = \int_1^4 \left(x\ln 2 + \dfrac{3}{2x}\right) dx$

$\qquad\qquad = \left[\tfrac{1}{2} x^2 \ln 2 + \tfrac{3}{2} \ln|x|\right]_1^4 = 8\ln 2 + \tfrac{3}{2}\ln 4 - \tfrac{1}{2}\ln 2$

$\qquad\qquad = \tfrac{15}{2}\ln 2 + 3\ln 4^{1/2} = \tfrac{21}{2}\ln 2$

8. $\int_0^{\pi/2} \int_0^{\pi/2} \sin(x+y)\, dy\, dx = \int_0^{\pi/2} \left[-\cos(x+y) \right]_{y=0}^{y=\pi/2}\, dx = \int_0^{\pi/2} \left[\cos x - \cos\left(x + \frac{\pi}{2}\right) \right] dx$

$$= \left[\sin x - \sin\left(x + \frac{\pi}{2}\right) \right]_0^{\pi/2} = (1-0) - (0-1) = 2$$

9. $\int_0^{\ln 2} \int_0^{\ln 5} e^{2x-y}\, dx\, dy = \left(\int_0^{\ln 5} e^{2x}\, dx \right) \left(\int_0^{\ln 2} e^{-y}\, dy \right) = \left[\frac{1}{2} e^{2x} \right]_0^{\ln 5} \left[-e^{-y} \right]_0^{\ln 2}$

$$= \left(\frac{25}{2} - \frac{1}{2} \right)\left(-\frac{1}{2} + 1 \right) = 6$$

10. $\int_0^1 \int_0^1 \frac{xy}{\sqrt{x^2 + y^2 + 1}}\, dy\, dx = \int_0^1 \left[x \sqrt{x^2 + y^2 + 1} \right]_{y=0}^{y=1}\, dx = \int_0^1 x \left(\sqrt{x^2 + 2} - \sqrt{x^2 + 1} \right) dx$

$$= \frac{1}{3} \left[(x^2 + 2)^{3/2} - (x^2 + 1)^{3/2} \right]_0^1 = \frac{1}{3} \left[\left(3^{3/2} - 2^{3/2} \right) - \left(2^{3/2} - 1 \right) \right]$$

$$= \frac{1}{3} \left(3\sqrt{3} - 4\sqrt{2} + 1 \right)$$

11. $\iint_R \left(6x^2 y^3 - 5y^4 \right) dA = \int_0^3 \int_0^1 \left(6x^2 y^3 - 5y^4 \right) dy\, dx = \int_0^3 \left[\frac{3}{2} x^2 y^4 - y^5 \right]_{y=0}^{y=1}\, dx$

$$= \int_0^3 \left(\frac{3}{2} x^2 - 1 \right) dx = \left[\frac{1}{2} x^3 - x \right]_0^3 = \frac{27}{2} - 3 = \frac{21}{2}$$

12. $\iint_R xye^y\, dA = \int_0^2 \int_0^1 xye^y\, dy\, dx = \int_0^2 x\, dx \int_0^1 ye^y\, dy = \left[\frac{1}{2} x^2 \right]_0^2 \left[e^y (y-1) \right]_0^1$ (by integrating by parts)

$$= \frac{1}{2} (4-0)(0 + e^0) = 2$$

13. $\iint_R \frac{xy^2}{x^2 + 1}\, dA = \int_0^1 \int_{-3}^3 \frac{xy^2}{x^2 + 1}\, dy\, dx = \int_0^1 \frac{x}{x^2 + 1}\, dx \int_{-3}^3 y^2\, dy$

$$= \left[\frac{1}{2} \ln(x^2 + 1) \right]_0^1 \left[\frac{1}{3} y^3 \right]_{-3}^3 = \frac{1}{2} (\ln 2 - \ln 1) \cdot \frac{1}{3} (27 + 27) = 9 \ln 2$$

14. $\iint_R \frac{1 + x^2}{1 + y^2}\, dA = \int_0^1 \int_0^1 \frac{1 + x^2}{1 + y^2}\, dy\, dx = \int_0^1 \left(1 + x^2 \right) dx \int_0^1 \frac{1}{1 + y^2}\, dy$

$$= \left[x + \frac{1}{3} x^3 \right]_0^1 \left[\tan^{-1} y \right]_0^1 = \left(1 + \frac{1}{3} - 0 \right)\left(\frac{\pi}{4} - 0 \right) = \frac{\pi}{3}$$

15. $\int_0^{\pi/6} \int_0^{\pi/3} x \sin(x+y)\, dy\, dx$

$$= \int_0^{\pi/6} \left[-x \cos(x+y) \right]_{y=0}^{y=\pi/3}\, dx = \int_0^{\pi/6} \left[x \cos x - x \cos\left(x + \frac{\pi}{3}\right) \right] dx$$

$$= x \left[\sin x - \sin\left(x + \frac{\pi}{3}\right) \right]_0^{\pi/6} - \int_0^{\pi/6} \left[\sin x - \sin\left(x + \frac{\pi}{3}\right) \right] dx$$

(by integrating by parts separately for each term)

$$= \frac{\pi}{6} \left[\frac{1}{2} - 1 \right] - \left[-\cos x + \cos\left(x + \frac{\pi}{3}\right) \right]_0^{\pi/6} = -\frac{\pi}{12} - \left[-\frac{\sqrt{3}}{2} + 0 - \left(-1 + \frac{1}{2} \right) \right]$$

$$= \frac{\sqrt{3} - 1}{2} - \frac{\pi}{12}$$

16. $\int_0^1 \int_0^1 xe^{xy}\, dy\, dx = \int_0^1 \left[e^{xy} \right]_{y=0}^{y=1}\, dx = \int_0^1 (e^x - 1)\, dx = \left[e^x - x \right]_0^1 = e - 2$

17. $z = f(x, y) = 4 - x - 2y \geq 0$ for $0 \leq x \leq 1$ and $0 \leq y \leq 1$.
So the solid is the region in the first octant which lies below the
plane $z = 4 - x - 2y$ and above $[0, 1] \times [0, 1]$.

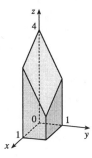

18. $z = 2 - x^2 - y^2 \geq 0$ for $0 \leq x \leq 1$ and $0 \leq y \leq 1$. So the solid
is the region in the first octant which lies below the circular
paraboloid $z = 2 - x^2 - y^2$ and above $[0, 1] \times [0, 1]$.

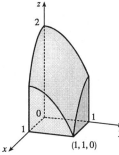

19. $V = \iint_R (2x + 5y + 1)\, dA = \int_1^4 \int_{-1}^0 (2x + 5y + 1)\, dx\, dy = \int_1^4 \left[x^2 + 5xy + x \right]_{x=-1}^{x=0} dy$

$\qquad = \int_1^4 5y\, dy = \frac{5}{2} y^2 \big]_1^4 = \frac{75}{2}$

20. $V = \iint_R (x^2 + y^2)\, dA = \int_{-3}^3 \int_{-2}^2 (x^2 + y^2)\, dx\, dy = \int_{-3}^3 \left[\frac{1}{3} x^3 + y^2 x \right]_{x=-2}^{x=2} dy$

$\qquad = \int_{-3}^3 \left[\frac{16}{3} + 4y^2 \right] dy = \left[\frac{16}{3} y + \frac{4}{3} y^3 \right]_{-3}^3 = 2(16 + 36) = 104$

21. $V = \int_{-2}^2 \int_{-1}^1 \left(1 - \frac{1}{4} x^2 - \frac{1}{9} y^2 \right) dx\, dy = 4 \int_0^2 \int_0^1 \left(1 - \frac{1}{4} x^2 - \frac{1}{9} y^2 \right) dx\, dy$

$\qquad = 4 \int_0^2 \left[x - \frac{1}{12} x^3 - \frac{1}{9} y^2 x \right]_{x=0}^{x=1} dy = 4 \int_0^2 \left(\frac{11}{12} - \frac{1}{9} y^2 \right) dy = 4 \left[\frac{11}{12} y - \frac{1}{27} y^3 \right]_0^2 = 4 \cdot \frac{83}{54} = \frac{166}{27}$

22. $V = \int_1^3 \int_{-1}^1 (y^2 - x^2)\, dx\, dy = 2 \int_1^3 \int_0^1 (y^2 - x^2)\, dx\, dy = 2 \int_1^3 \left[y^2 x - \frac{1}{3} x^3 \right]_{x=0}^{x=1} dy$

$\qquad = 2 \int_1^3 \left(y^2 - \frac{1}{3} \right) dy = \frac{2}{3} \left[y^3 - y \right]_1^3 = 16$

23. Here we need the volume of the solid lying under the surface $z = x\sqrt{x^2 + y}$ and above the square
$R = [0, 1] \times [0, 1]$ in the xy-plane.

$$V = \int_0^1 \int_0^1 x \sqrt{x^2 + y}\, dx\, dy = \int_0^1 \frac{1}{3} \left[(x^2 + y)^{3/2} \right]_{x=0}^{x=1} dy = \frac{1}{3} \int_0^1 \left[(1 + y)^{3/2} - y^{3/2} \right] dy$$

$$= \frac{1}{3} \cdot \frac{2}{5} \left[(1 + y)^{5/2} - y^{5/2} \right]_0^1 = \frac{4}{15} \left(2\sqrt{2} - 1 \right)$$

24. Here we need the volume of the solid lying under the surface $z = 1 + (x - 1)^2 + 4y^2$ and above the rectangle
$R = [0, 3] \times [0, 2]$ in the xy-plane.

$$V = \int_0^3 \int_0^2 \left[1 + (x - 1)^2 + 4y^2 \right] dy\, dx = \int_0^3 \left[y + (x - 1)^2 y + \frac{4}{3} y^3 \right]_{y=0}^{y=2} dx$$

$$= \int_0^3 \left[2 + 2(x - 1)^2 + \frac{32}{3} \right] dx = \left[\frac{38}{3} x + \frac{2}{3} (x - 1)^3 \right]_0^3 = 44$$

25. In the first octant, $z \geq 0 \quad \Rightarrow \quad y \leq 3$, so

$V = \int_0^3 \int_0^2 (9 - y^2)\, dx\, dy = \int_0^3 \left[9x - y^2 x \right]_{x=0}^{x=2} dy = \int_0^3 (18 - 2y^2)\, dy = \left[18y - \frac{2}{3} y^3 \right]_0^3 = 36$

26. (a) Here we need the volume of the solid lying under the surface $z = 6 - xy$ and above the rectangle $R = [-2, 2] \times [0, 3]$ in the xy-plane.

$$V = \int_{-2}^{2} \int_{0}^{3} (6 - xy) \, dy \, dx$$

$$= \int_{-2}^{2} \left[6y - \tfrac{1}{2}xy^2 \right]_{y=0}^{y=3} dx$$

$$= \int_{-2}^{2} \left(18 - \tfrac{9}{2}x \right) dx$$

$$= \left[18x - \tfrac{9}{4}x^2 \right]_{-2}^{2} = 72$$

(b) The solid occupies the region between the two surfaces shown.

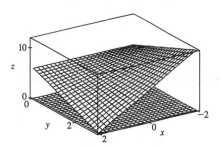

27. In Maple, we can calculate the integral by defining the integrand as f and then using the command `int(int(f,x=0..1),y=0..1);`. In Mathematica, we can use the command `Integrate[Integrate[f,{x,0,1}],{y,0,1}]`. We find that $\iint_R x^5 y^3 e^{xy} \, dA = 21e - 57 \approx 0.0839$. We can use `plot3d` (in Maple) or `Plot3d` (in Mathematica) to graph the function.

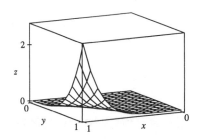

28. In Maple, we can calculate the integral by defining `f:=E^(-x^2)*cos(x^2+y^2);` and `g:=2-x^2-y^2;` and then [since $2 - x^2 - y^2 > e^{-x^2} \cos(x^2 + y^2)$ for $-1 \le x \le 1$, $-1 \le y \le 1$] using the command `evalf(int(int(g-f,x=-1..1),y=-1..1),5);`. In Mathematica, we can use the command `N[Integrate[Integrate[f,{x,0,1}],{y,0,1}],5]`.

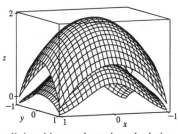

In each of these commands, the 5 indicates that we want only five significant digits; this speeds up the calculation considerably. We find that $\iint_R \left[(2 - x^2 - y^2) - \left(e^{-x^2} \cos(x^2 + y^2) \right) \right] dA \approx 3.0271$. We can use the `plot3d` command (in Maple) or `Plot3d` (in Mathematica) to graph both functions on the same screen.

29. R is the rectangle $[-1, 1] \times [0, 5]$. Thus, $A(R) = 2 \cdot 5 = 10$ and

$$f_{ave} = \frac{1}{A(R)} \iint_R f(x,y) dA = \tfrac{1}{10} \int_0^5 \int_{-1}^1 x^2 y \, dx \, dy = \tfrac{1}{10} \int_0^5 \left[\tfrac{1}{3} x^3 y \right]_{x=-1}^{x=1} dy = \tfrac{1}{10} \int_0^5 \tfrac{2}{3} y \, dy$$

$$= \tfrac{1}{10} \left[\tfrac{1}{3} y^2 \right]_0^5 = \tfrac{5}{6}$$

30. $A(R) = \tfrac{\pi}{2} \cdot 1 = \tfrac{\pi}{2}$, so

$$f_{ave} = \frac{1}{A(R)} \iint_R f(x,y) \, dA = \tfrac{1}{\pi/2} \int_0^{\pi/2} \int_0^1 x \sin xy \, dy \, dx = \tfrac{2}{\pi} \int_0^{\pi/2} \left[-\cos xy \right]_{y=0}^{y=1} dx$$

$$= \tfrac{2}{\pi} \int_0^{\pi/2} (1 - \cos x) \, dx = \tfrac{2}{\pi} [x - \sin x]_0^{\pi/2} = 1 - \tfrac{2}{\pi}$$

31. Let $f(x,y) = \dfrac{x-y}{(x+y)^3}$. Then a CAS gives $\int_0^1 \int_0^1 f(x,y)\, dy\, dx = \frac{1}{2}$ and $\int_0^1 \int_0^1 f(x,y)\, dx\, dy = -\frac{1}{2}$.

To explain the seeming violation of Fubini's Theorem, note that f has an infinite discontinuity at $(0,0)$ and thus does not satisfy the conditions of Fubini's Theorem. In fact, both iterated integrals involve improper integrals which diverge at their lower limits of integration.

32. (a) Loosely speaking, Fubini's Theorem says that the order of integration of a function of two variables does not affect the value of the double integral, while Clairaut's Theorem says that the order of differentiation of such a function does not affect the value of the second-order derivative. Also, both theorems require continuity (though Fubini's allows a finite number of smooth curves to contain discontinuities).

(b) To find g_{xy}, we first hold y constant and use the single-variable Fundamental Theorem of Calculus, Part 1:

$$g_x = \frac{d}{dx} g(x,y) = \frac{d}{dx} \int_a^x \left(\int_c^y f(s,t)\, dt \right) ds = \int_c^y f(x,t)\, dt. \text{ Now we use the Fundamental Theorem}$$

again: $g_{xy} = \dfrac{d}{dy} \displaystyle\int_c^y f(x,t)\, dt = f(x,y).$

To find g_{yx}, we first use Fubini's Theorem to find that $\int_a^x \int_c^y f(s,t)\, dt\, ds = \int_c^y \int_a^x f(s,t)\, dt\, ds$, and then use the Fundamental Theorem twice, as above, to get $g_{yx} = f(x,y)$. So $g_{xy} = g_{yx} = f(x,y)$.

 Double Integrals over General Regions • • • • • •

1. $\int_0^1 \int_0^{x^2} (x + 2y)\, dy\, dx = \int_0^1 \left[xy + y^2 \right]_{y=0}^{y=x^2} dx = \int_0^1 \left[x(x^2) + (x^2)^2 - 0 - 0 \right] dx$

$\qquad = \int_0^1 (x^3 + x^4)\, dx = \left[\frac{1}{4}x^4 + \frac{1}{5}x^5 \right]_0^1 = \frac{9}{20}$

2. $\int_1^2 \int_y^2 xy\, dx\, dy = \int_1^2 \left[\frac{1}{2}x^2 y \right]_{x=y}^{x=2} dy = \int_1^2 \frac{1}{2}y(4 - y^2)\, dy = \frac{1}{2} \int_1^2 (4y - y^3)\, dy$

$\qquad = \frac{1}{2} \left[2y^2 - \frac{1}{4}y^4 \right]_1^2 = \frac{1}{2}(8 - 4 - 2 + \frac{1}{4}) = \frac{9}{8}$

3. $\int_0^1 \int_y^{e^y} \sqrt{x}\, dx\, dy = \int_0^1 \left[\frac{2}{3}x^{3/2} \right]_{x=y}^{x=e^y} dy = \frac{2}{3} \int_0^1 \left(e^{3y/2} - y^{3/2} \right) dy = \frac{2}{3} \left[\frac{2}{3}e^{3y/2} - \frac{2}{5}y^{5/2} \right]_0^1$

$\qquad = \frac{2}{3} \left(\frac{2}{3}e^{3/2} - \frac{2}{5} - \frac{2}{3}e^0 + 0 \right) = \frac{4}{9}e^{3/2} - \frac{32}{45}$

4. $\int_0^1 \int_x^{2-x} (x^2 - y)\, dy\, dx = \int_0^1 \left[x^2 y - \frac{1}{2}y^2 \right]_{y=x}^{y=2-x} dx = \int_0^1 \left[x^2(2 - x) - \frac{1}{2}(2 - x)^2 - x^2(x) + \frac{1}{2}x^2 \right] dx$

$\qquad = \int_0^1 (-2x^3 + 2x^2 + 2x - 2)\, dx = \left[-\frac{1}{2}x^4 + \frac{2}{3}x^3 + x^2 - 2x \right]_0^1 = -\frac{5}{6}$

5. $\int_0^{\pi/2} \int_0^{\cos\theta} e^{\sin\theta}\, dr\, d\theta = \int_0^{\pi/2} \left[r e^{\sin\theta} \right]_{r=0}^{r=\cos\theta} d\theta = \int_0^{\pi/2} (\cos\theta)\, e^{\sin\theta}\, d\theta = e^{\sin\theta} \Big]_0^{\pi/2}$

$\qquad = e^{\sin(\pi/2)} - e^0 = e - 1$

6. $\int_0^1 \int_0^v \sqrt{1 - v^2}\, du\, dv = \int_0^1 \left[u\sqrt{1 - v^2} \right]_{u=0}^{u=v} dv = \int_0^1 v\sqrt{1 - v^2}\, dv = -\frac{1}{3}(1 - v^2)^{3/2} \Big]_0^1$

$\qquad = -\frac{1}{3}(0 - 1) = \frac{1}{3}$

7. $\iint_D x^3 y^2\, dA = \int_0^2 \int_{-x}^x x^3 y^2\, dy\, dx = \int_0^2 \left[\frac{1}{3}x^3 y^3 \right]_{y=-x}^{y=x} dx = \frac{1}{3} \int_0^2 2x^6\, dx$

$\qquad = \frac{2}{3} \left[\frac{1}{7}x^7 \right]_0^2 = \frac{2}{21}[2^7 - 0] = \frac{256}{21}$

8. $\displaystyle\iint_D \frac{4y}{x^3+2}\,dA = \int_1^2 \int_0^{2x} \frac{4y}{x^3+2}\,dy\,dx = \int_1^2 \left[\frac{2y^2}{x^3+2}\right]_{y=0}^{y=2x} dx = \int_1^2 \frac{8x^2}{x^3+2}\,dx$

$\qquad = \frac{8}{3}\ln\left|x^3+2\right|\,\Big]_1^2 = \frac{8}{3}(\ln 10 - \ln 3) = \frac{8}{3}\ln\frac{10}{3}$

9. $\displaystyle\int_0^1 \int_0^{\sqrt{x}} \frac{2y}{x^2+1}\,dy\,dx = \int_0^1 \left[\frac{y^2}{x^2+1}\right]_{y=0}^{y=\sqrt{x}} dx = \int_0^1 \frac{x}{x^2+1}\,dx$

$\qquad = \frac{1}{2}\ln\left|x^2+1\right|\,\Big]_0^1 = \frac{1}{2}(\ln 2 - \ln 1) = \frac{1}{2}\ln 2$

10. $\displaystyle\int_0^1 \int_0^y e^{y^2}\,dx\,dy = \int_0^1 \left[xe^{y^2}\right]_{x=0}^{x=y} dy = \int_0^1 ye^{y^2}\,dy = \frac{1}{2}e^{y^2}\Big]_0^1 = \frac{1}{2}(e-1)$

11. $\displaystyle\int_0^1 \int_0^{x^2} x\cos y\,dy\,dx = \int_0^1 [x\sin y]_{y=0}^{y=x^2}\,dx = \int_0^1 x\sin x^2\,dx = -\frac{1}{2}\cos x^2\big]_0^1 = \frac{1}{2}(1-\cos 1)$

12. $\displaystyle\int_0^1 \int_0^y x\sqrt{y^2-x^2}\,dx\,dy = \int_0^1 \left[-\frac{1}{3}\left(y^2-x^2\right)^{3/2}\right]_{x=0}^{x=y} dy = \frac{1}{3}\int_0^1 y^3\,dy = \frac{1}{3}\cdot\frac{1}{4}y^4\big]_0^1 = \frac{1}{12}$

13.

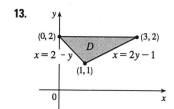

$\displaystyle\int_1^2 \int_{2-y}^{2y-1} y^3\,dx\,dy = \int_1^2 \left[xy^3\right]_{x=2-y}^{x=2y-1}\,dy = \int_1^2 [(2y-1)-(2-y)]\,y^3\,dy$

$\qquad = \int_1^2 \left(3y^4 - 3y^3\right)\,dy = \left[\frac{3}{5}y^5 - \frac{3}{4}y^4\right]_1^2$

$\qquad = \frac{96}{5} - 12 - \frac{3}{5} + \frac{3}{4} = \frac{147}{20}$

14.

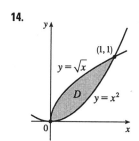

$\displaystyle\int_0^1 \int_{x^2}^{\sqrt{x}} (x+y)\,dy\,dx = \int_0^1 \left[xy + \frac{1}{2}y^2\right]_{y=x^2}^{y=\sqrt{x}}\,dx$

$\qquad = \int_0^1 \left(x^{3/2} + \frac{1}{2}x - x^3 - \frac{1}{2}x^4\right)\,dx$

$\qquad = \left[\frac{2}{5}x^{5/2} + \frac{1}{4}x^2 - \frac{1}{4}x^4 - \frac{1}{10}x^5\right]_0^1 = \frac{3}{10}$

15.

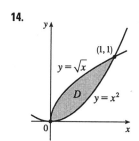

$\displaystyle\int_{-2}^2 \int_{-\sqrt{4-x^2}}^{\sqrt{4-x^2}} (2x-y)\,dy\,dx$

$\qquad = \int_{-2}^2 \left[2xy - \frac{1}{2}y^2\right]_{y=-\sqrt{4-x^2}}^{y=\sqrt{4-x^2}}\,dx$

$\qquad = \int_{-2}^2 \left[2x\sqrt{4-x^2} - \frac{1}{2}\left(4-x^2\right) + 2x\sqrt{4-x^2} + \frac{1}{2}\left(4-x^2\right)\right]\,dx$

$\qquad = \int_{-2}^2 4x\sqrt{4-x^2}\,dx = -\frac{4}{3}\left(4-x^2\right)^{3/2}\Big]_{-2}^2 = 0$

(Or, note that $4x\sqrt{4-x^2}$ is an odd function, so $\int_{-2}^2 4x\sqrt{4-x^2}\,dx = 0$.)

16.

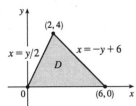

$\int_0^4 \int_{y/2}^{6-y} ye^x \, dx \, dy = \int_0^4 \left[ye^x \right]_{x=y/2}^{x=6-y} dy$

$\qquad = \int_0^4 \left(ye^{6-y} - ye^{y/2} \right) dy$

$\qquad = \left[y \left(-e^{6-y} - 2e^{y/2} \right) \right]_0^4 + \left[-e^{6-y} + 4e^{y/2} \right]_0^4$

(by integrating by parts separately for each term)

$\qquad = -12e^2 + 3e^2 + e^6 - 4$

$\qquad = e^6 - 9e^2 - 4$

17.

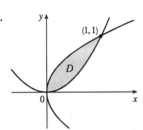

$V = \int_0^1 \int_{x^2}^{\sqrt{x}} \left(x^2 + y^2 \right) dy \, dx = \int_0^1 \left[\left(x^2 y + \frac{y^3}{3} \right) \right]_{y=x^2}^{y=\sqrt{x}} dx$

$\qquad = \int_0^1 \left(x^{5/2} - x^4 + \frac{1}{3}x^{3/2} - \frac{1}{3}x^6 \right) dx$

$\qquad = \left[\frac{2}{7}x^{7/2} - \frac{1}{5}x^5 + \frac{2}{15}x^{5/2} - \frac{1}{21}x^7 \right]_0^1$

$\qquad = \frac{18}{105} = \frac{6}{35}$

18.

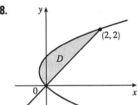

$V = \int_0^2 \int_{y^2-y}^{y} \left(3x^2 + y^2 \right) dx \, dy$

$\qquad = \int_0^2 \left[x^3 + y^2 x \right]_{x=y^2-y}^{x=y} dy$

$\qquad = \int_0^2 \left[2y^3 - \left(y^6 - 3y^5 + 4y^4 - 2y^3 \right) \right] dy$

$\qquad = \left[-\frac{y^7}{7} + \frac{y^6}{2} - \frac{4y^5}{5} + y^4 \right]_0^2 = \frac{144}{35}$

19.

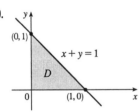

$V = \int_1^2 \int_1^{7-3y} xy \, dx \, dy$

$\qquad = \int_1^2 \left[\frac{1}{2}x^2 y \right]_{x=1}^{x=7-3y} dy$

$\qquad = \frac{1}{2} \int_1^2 \left(48y - 42y^2 + 9y^3 \right) dy$

$\qquad = \frac{1}{2} \left[24y^2 - 14y^3 + \frac{9}{4}y^4 \right]_1^2 = \frac{31}{8}$

20.

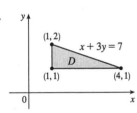

$V = \int_0^1 \int_0^{1-x} \left(x^2 + y^2 + 4 \right) dy \, dx = \int_0^1 \left[x^2 y + \frac{1}{3}y^3 + 4y \right]_{y=0}^{y=1-x} dx$

$\qquad = \int_0^1 \left[x^2 - x^3 + \frac{1}{3}(1-x)^3 + 4(1-x) \right] dx$

$\qquad = \left[\frac{1}{3}x^3 - \frac{1}{4}x^4 - \frac{1}{12}(1-x)^4 - 2(1-x^2) \right]_0^1 = \frac{13}{6}$

21.

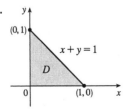

$V = \int_0^1 \int_0^{1-x} (1 - x - y) \, dy \, dx$

$\qquad = \int_0^1 \left[y - xy - \frac{y^2}{2} \right]_{y=0}^{y=1-x} dx$

$\qquad = \int_0^1 \left[(1-x)^2 - \frac{1}{2}(1-x)^2 \right] dx$

$\qquad = \int_0^1 \frac{1}{2}(1-x)^2 \, dx = \left[-\frac{1}{6}(1-x)^3 \right]_0^1 = \frac{1}{6}$

22.

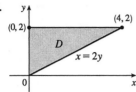

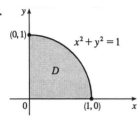

$V = \int_0^2 \int_0^{2y} \sqrt{4 - y^2}\, dx\, dy$

$= \int_0^2 \left[x\sqrt{4 - y^2} \right]_{x = 0}^{x = 2y} dy = \int_0^2 2y\sqrt{4 - y^2}\, dy$

$= \left[-\frac{2}{3}(4 - y^2)^{3/2} \right]_0^2 = 0 + \frac{16}{3} = \frac{16}{3}$

23.

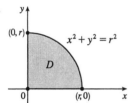

$V = \int_0^1 \int_0^{\sqrt{1 - x^2}} y\, dy\, dx = \int_0^1 \left[\frac{y^2}{2} \right]_{y = 0}^{y = \sqrt{1 - x^2}} dx$

$= \int_0^1 \frac{1 - x^2}{2}\, dx = \frac{1}{2}\left[x - \frac{1}{3}x^3 \right]_0^1 = \frac{1}{3}$

24.

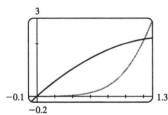

By symmetry, the desired volume V is 8 times the volume V_1 in the first octant. Now

$V_1 = \int_0^r \int_0^{\sqrt{r^2 - y^2}} \sqrt{r^2 - y^2}\, dx\, dy$

$= \int_0^r \left[x\sqrt{r^2 - y^2} \right]_{x = 0}^{x = \sqrt{r^2 - y^2}} dy$

$= \int_0^r (r^2 - y^2)\, dy = \left[r^2 y - \frac{1}{3}y^3 \right]_0^r = \frac{2}{3}r^3$

Thus $V = \frac{16}{3}r^3$.

25.

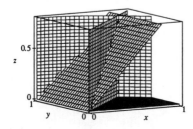

From the graph, it appears that the two curves intersect at $x = 0$ and at $x \approx 1.213$. Thus the desired integral is

$\iint_D x\, dA \approx \int_0^{1.213} \int_{x^4}^{3x - x^2} x\, dy\, dx$

$= \int_0^{1.213} [xy]_{y = x^4}^{y = 3x - x^2}\, dx$

$= \int_0^{1.213} \left(3x^2 - x^3 - x^5 \right) dx$

$= \left[x^3 - \frac{1}{4}x^4 - \frac{1}{6}x^6 \right]_0^{1.213} \approx 0.713$

26.

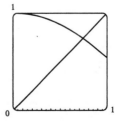

The desired solid is shown in the first graph. From the second graph, we estimate that $y = \cos x$ intersects $y = x$ at $x \approx 0.7391$. Therefore the volume of the solid is

$$V \approx \int_0^{0.7391} \int_x^{\cos x} z\, dy\, dx = \int_0^{0.7391} \int_x^{\cos x} x\, dy\, dx = \int_0^{0.7391} [xy]_{y=x}^{y=\cos x}\, dx$$

$$= \int_0^{0.7391} (x \cos x - x^2)\, dx = \left[\cos x + x \sin x - \tfrac{1}{3}x^3\right]_0^{0.7391} \approx 0.1024$$

Note: There is a different solid which can also be construed to satisfy the conditions stated in the exercise. This is the solid bounded by all of the given surfaces, as well as the plane $y = 0$. In case you calculated the volume of this solid and want to check your work, its volume is $V \approx \int_0^{0.7391} \int_0^x x\, dy\, dx + \int_{0.7391}^{\pi/2} \int_0^{\cos x} x\, dy\, dx \approx 0.4684$.

27. The two bounding curves $y = x^3 - x$ and $y = x^2 + x$ intersect at the origin and at $x = 2$, with $x^2 + x > x^3 - x$ on $(0, 2)$. Using a CAS, we find that the volume is

$$V = \int_0^2 \int_{x^3-x}^{x^2+x} z\, dy\, dx = \int_0^2 \int_{x^3-x}^{x^2+x} (x^3y^4 + xy^2)\, dy\, dx = \frac{13{,}984{,}735{,}616}{14{,}549{,}535}$$

28. For $|x| \le 1$ and $|y| \le 1$, $2x^2 + y^2 < 8 - x^2 - 2y^2$. Also, the cylinder is described by the inequalities $-1 \le x \le 1$, $-\sqrt{1-x^2} \le y \le \sqrt{1-x^2}$. So the volume is given by

$$V = \int_{-1}^1 \int_{-\sqrt{1-x^2}}^{\sqrt{1-x^2}} \left[(8 - x^2 - 2y^2) - (2x^2 + y^2)\right] dy\, dx = \frac{13\pi}{2} \quad \text{(using a CAS)}$$

29.

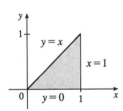

Because the region of integration is

$$D = \{(x,y) \mid 0 \le y \le x, 0 \le x \le 1\}$$
$$= \{(x,y) \mid y \le x \le 1, 0 \le y \le 1\}$$

we have

$$\int_0^1 \int_0^x f(x,y)\, dy\, dx = \iint_D f(x,y)\, dA$$
$$= \int_0^1 \int_y^1 f(x,y)\, dx\, dy$$

30.

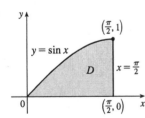

Because the region of integration is

$$D = \left\{(x,y) \mid 0 \le y \le \sin x, 0 \le x \le \tfrac{\pi}{2}\right\}$$
$$= \left\{(x,y) \mid \sin^{-1} y \le x \le \tfrac{\pi}{2}, 0 \le y \le 1\right\}$$

we have

$$\int_0^{\pi/2} \int_0^{\sin x} f(x,y)\, dy\, dx = \iint_D f(x,y)\, dA$$
$$= \int_0^1 \int_{\sin^{-1} y}^{\pi/2} f(x,y)\, dx\, dy$$

31.

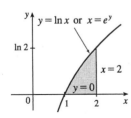

Because the region of integration is

$$D = \{(x,y) \mid 0 \le y \le \ln x, 1 \le x \le 2\}$$
$$= \{(x,y) \mid e^y \le x \le 2, 0 \le y \le \ln 2\}$$

we have

$$\int_1^2 \int_0^{\ln x} f(x,y)\, dy\, dx = \iint_D f(x,y)\, dA$$
$$= \int_0^{\ln 2} \int_{e^y}^2 f(x,y)\, dx\, dy$$

32.

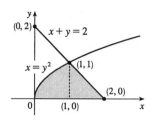

To reverse the order, we must break the region into two separate type I regions. Because the region of integration is

$$D = \{(x,y) \mid y^2 \le x \le 2 - y, 0 \le y \le 1\}$$
$$= \{(x,y) \mid 0 \le y \le \sqrt{x}, 0 \le x \le 1\}$$
$$\cup \{0 \le y \le 2 - x, 1 \le x \le 2\}$$

we have

$$\int_0^1 \int_{y^2}^{2-y} f(x,y)\, dx\, dy = \iint_D f(x,y)\, dA$$
$$= \int_0^1 \int_0^{\sqrt{x}} f(x,y)\, dy\, dx + \int_1^2 \int_0^{2-x} f(x,y)\, dy\, dx$$

33.

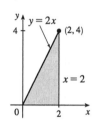

Because the region of integration is

$$D = \{(x,y) \mid y/2 \le x \le 2, 0 \le y \le 4\}$$
$$= \{(x,y) \mid 0 \le y \le 2x, 0 \le x \le 2\}$$

we have

$$\int_0^4 \int_{y/2}^2 f(x,y)\, dx\, dy = \iint_D f(x,y)\, dA$$
$$= \int_0^2 \int_0^{2x} f(x,y)\, dy\, dx$$

34.

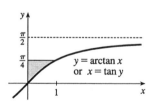

Because the region of integration is

$$D = \{(x,y) \mid \arctan x \le y \le \tfrac{\pi}{4}, 0 \le x \le 1\}$$
$$= \{(x,y) \mid 0 \le x \le \tan y, 0 \le y \le \tfrac{\pi}{4}\}$$

we have

$$\int_0^1 \int_{\arctan x}^{\pi/4} f(x,y)\, dy\, dx = \iint_D f(x,y)\, dA$$
$$= \int_0^{\pi/4} \int_0^{\tan y} f(x,y)\, dx\, dy$$

35.

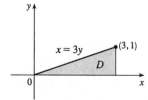

$$\int_0^1 \int_{3y}^3 e^{x^2}\, dx\, dy = \int_0^3 \int_0^{x/3} e^{x^2}\, dy\, dx$$
$$= \int_0^3 \left[e^{x^2} y \right]_{y=0}^{y=x/3}\, dx = \int_0^3 \left(\frac{x}{3}\right) e^{x^2}\, dx$$
$$= \frac{1}{6} e^{x^2} \Big]_0^3 = \frac{e^9 - 1}{6}$$

36.

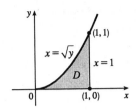

$$\int_0^1 \int_{\sqrt{y}}^1 \sqrt{x^3+1}\,dx\,dy = \int_0^1 \int_0^{x^2} \sqrt{x^3+1}\,dy\,dx$$
$$= \int_0^1 \left[\sqrt{x^3+1}\,y\right]_{y=0}^{y=x^2}\,dx$$
$$= \int_0^1 x^2\sqrt{x^3+1}\,dx$$
$$= \tfrac{2}{9}\left(x^3+1\right)^{3/2}\Big]_0^1$$
$$= \tfrac{2}{9}\left(2^{3/2}-1\right)$$

37.

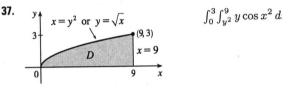

$$\int_0^3 \int_{y^2}^9 y\cos x^2\,dx\,dy = \int_0^9 \int_0^{\sqrt{x}} y\cos x^2\,dy\,dx$$
$$= \int_0^9 \cos x^2 \left[\frac{y^2}{2}\right]_{y=0}^{y=\sqrt{x}}\,dx$$
$$= \int_0^9 \tfrac{1}{2}x\cos x^2\,dx = \tfrac{1}{4}\sin x^2\Big]_0^9$$
$$= \tfrac{1}{4}\sin 81$$

38.

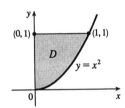

$$\int_0^1 \int_{x^2}^1 x^3 \sin\left(y^3\right)\,dy\,dx = \int_0^1 \int_0^{\sqrt{y}} x^3 \sin\left(y^3\right)\,dx\,dy$$
$$= \int_0^1 \left[\frac{x^4}{4}\sin\left(y^3\right)\right]_{x=0}^{x=\sqrt{y}}\,dy$$
$$= \int_0^1 \tfrac{1}{4}y^2 \sin\left(y^3\right)\,dy$$
$$= -\tfrac{1}{12}\cos\left(y^3\right)\Big]_0^1 = \tfrac{1}{12}(1-\cos 1)$$

39.

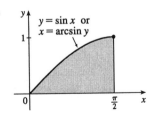

$$\int_0^1 \int_{\arcsin y}^{\pi/2} \cos x\sqrt{1+\cos^2 x}\,dx\,dy$$
$$= \int_0^{\pi/2} \int_0^{\sin x} \cos x\sqrt{1+\cos^2 x}\,dy\,dx$$
$$= \int_0^{\pi/2} \cos x\sqrt{1+\cos^2 x}\,[y]_{y=0}^{y=\sin x}\,dx$$
$$= \int_0^{\pi/2} \cos x\sqrt{1+\cos^2 x}\,\sin x\,dx$$
$$\left[\text{Let } u=\cos x,\; du=-\sin x\,dx,\; dx=du/(-\sin x)\right]$$
$$= \int_1^0 -u\sqrt{1+u^2}\,du = -\tfrac{1}{3}\left(1+u^2\right)^{3/2}\Big]_1^0$$
$$= \tfrac{1}{3}\left(\sqrt{8}-1\right) = \tfrac{1}{3}\left(2\sqrt{2}-1\right)$$

40.

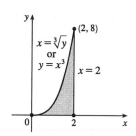

$$\int_0^8 \int_{\sqrt[3]{y}}^2 e^{x^4}\, dx\, dy = \int_0^2 \int_0^{x^3} e^{x^4}\, dy\, dx$$
$$= \int_0^2 e^{x^4} [y]_{y=0}^{y=x^3}\, dx$$
$$= \int_0^2 x^3 e^{x^4}\, dx$$
$$= \tfrac{1}{4} e^{x^4}\Big]_0^2 = \tfrac{1}{4}\left(e^{16}-1\right)$$

41. $D = \{(x,y) \mid 0 \le x \le 1,\ -x+1 \le y \le 1\} \cup \{(x,y) \mid -1 \le x \le 0,\ x+1 \le y \le 1\}$

$\cup \{(x,y) \mid 0 \le x \le 1,\ -1 \le y \le x-1\} \cup \{(x,y) \mid -1 \le x \le 0,\ -1 \le y \le -x-1\}$,

all type I.

$$\iint_D x^2\, dA = \int_0^1 \int_{1-x}^1 x^2\, dy\, dx + \int_{-1}^0 \int_{x+1}^1 x^2\, dy\, dx + \int_0^1 \int_{-1}^{x-1} x^2\, dy\, dx + \int_{-1}^0 \int_{-1}^{-x-1} x^2\, dy\, dx$$
$$= 4\int_0^1 \int_{1-x}^1 x^2\, dy\, dx \quad \text{[by symmetry of the regions and because } f(x,y) = x^2 \ge 0\text{]}$$
$$= 4\int_0^1 x^3\, dx = 4\left[\tfrac{1}{4}x^4\right]_0^1 = 1$$

42. $D = \left\{(x,y) \mid -1 \le x \le 0,\ -1 \le y \le 1+x^2\right\} \cup \left\{(x,y) \mid 0 \le x \le 1,\ \sqrt{x} \le y \le 1+x^2\right\}$

$\cup \left\{(x,y) \mid 0 \le x \le 1,\ -1 \le y \le -\sqrt{x}\right\}$, all type I.

$$\iint_D xy\, dA = \int_{-1}^0 \int_{-1}^{1+x^2} xy\, dy\, dx + \int_0^1 \int_{\sqrt{x}}^{1+x^2} xy\, dy\, dx + \int_0^1 \int_{-1}^{-\sqrt{x}} xy\, dy\, dx$$
$$= \int_{-1}^0 \left[\tfrac{1}{2}xy^2\right]_{y=-1}^{y=1+x^2}\, dx + \int_0^1 \left[\tfrac{1}{2}xy^2\right]_{y=\sqrt{x}}^{y=1+x^2}\, dx + \int_0^1 \left[\tfrac{1}{2}xy^2\right]_{y=-1}^{y=-\sqrt{x}}\, dx$$
$$= \int_{-1}^0 \left(x^3 + \tfrac{1}{2}x^5\right)\, dx + \int_0^1 \tfrac{1}{2}\left(x^5 + 2x^3 - x^2 + x\right)\, dx + \int_0^1 \tfrac{1}{2}\left(x^2 - x\right)\, dx$$
$$= \left[\tfrac{1}{4}x^4 + \tfrac{1}{12}x^6\right]_{-1}^0 + \tfrac{1}{2}\left[\tfrac{1}{6}x^6 + \tfrac{1}{2}x^4 - \tfrac{1}{3}x^3 + \tfrac{1}{2}x^2\right]_0^1 + \tfrac{1}{2}\left[\tfrac{1}{3}x^3 - \tfrac{1}{2}x^2\right]_0^1$$
$$= -\tfrac{1}{3} + \tfrac{5}{12} - \tfrac{1}{12} = 0$$

43. For $D = [0,1] \times [0,1]$, $0 \le \sqrt{x^3+y^3} \le \sqrt{2}$ and $A(D) = 1$, so $0 \le \iint_D \sqrt{x^3+y^3}\, dA \le \sqrt{2}$.

44. Since $D = \left\{(x,y) \mid x^2 + y^2 \le \tfrac{1}{4}\right\}$, $1 = e^0 \le e^{x^2+y^2} \le e^{1/4}$ and $A(D) = \tfrac{\pi}{4}$, so
$\tfrac{\pi}{4} \le \iint_D e^{x^2+y^2}\, dA \le \left(e^{1/4}\right)\tfrac{\pi}{4}$.

45. Since $m \le f(x,y) \le M$, $\iint_D m\, dA \le \iint_D f(x,y)\, dA \le \iint_D M\, dA$ by (8) $\Rightarrow$
$m\iint_D 1\, dA \le \iint_D f(x,y)\, dA \le M\iint_D 1\, dA$ by (7) $\Rightarrow$ $mA(D) \le \iint_D f(x,y)\, dA \le MA(D)$ by (10).

46.

$$\iint_D f(x,y)\, dA = \int_0^1 \int_0^{2y} f(x,y)\, dx\, dy + \int_1^3 \int_0^{3-y} f(x,y)\, dx\, dy$$
$$= \int_0^2 \int_{x/2}^{3-x} f(x,y)\, dy\, dx$$

47. $\iint_D \left(x^2 \tan x + y^3 + 4\right) dA = \iint_D x^2 \tan x\, dA + \iint_D y^3\, dA + \iint_D 4\, dA$. But $x^2 \tan x$ is an odd function of x and D is symmetric with respect to the y-axis, so $\iint_D x^2 \tan x\, dA = 0$. Similarly, y^3 is an odd function of y and D is symmetric with respect to the x-axis, so $\iint_D y^3\, dA = 0$. Thus

$$\iint_D \left(x^2 \tan x + y^3 + 4\right) dA = 4 \iint_D dA = 4(\text{area of } D) = 4 \cdot \pi \left(\sqrt{2}\right)^2 = 8\pi$$

48. First,

$$\iint_D (2 - 3x + 4y)\, dA = \iint_D 2\, dA - \iint_D 3x\, dA + \iint_D 4y\, dA$$

The region D, shown in the figure, is symmetric with respect to the y-axis and $3x$ is an odd function of x, so $\iint_D 3x\, dA = 0$. Similarly, $4y$ is an odd function of y and D is symmetric with respect to the x-axis, so $\iint_D 4y\, dA = 0$. Then

$$\iint_D (2 - 3x + 4y)\, dA = \iint_D 2\, dA = 2 \iint_D dA$$
$$= 2(\text{area of } D) = 2(50)$$
$$= 100$$

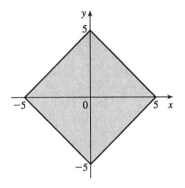

49. Since $\sqrt{1 - x^2 - y^2} \geq 0$, we can interpret $\iint_D \sqrt{1 - x^2 - y^2}\, dA$ as the volume of the solid that lies below the graph of $z = \sqrt{1 - x^2 - y^2}$ and above the region D in the xy-plane. $z = \sqrt{1 - x^2 - y^2}$ is equivalent to $x^2 + y^2 + z^2 = 1$, $z \geq 0$ which meets the xy-plane in the circle $x^2 + y^2 = 1$, the boundary of D. Thus, the solid is an upper hemisphere of radius 1 which has volume $\frac{1}{2} \left[\frac{4}{3}\pi (1)^3\right] = \frac{2}{3}\pi$.

50. To find the equations of the boundary curves, we require that the z-values of the two surfaces be the same. In Maple, we use the command `solve(4-x^2-y^2=1-x-y,y);` and in Mathematica, we use `Solve[4-x^2-y^2==1-x-y,y]`. We find that the curves have equations $y = \dfrac{1 \pm \sqrt{13 + 4x - 4x^2}}{2}$.

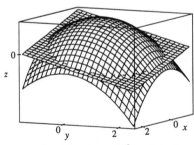

To find the two points of intersection of these curves, we use the CAS to solve $13 + 4x - 4x^2 = 0$, finding that $x = \frac{1 \pm \sqrt{14}}{2}$. So, using the CAS to evaluate the integral, the volume of intersection is

$$V = \int_{(1-\sqrt{14})/2}^{(1+\sqrt{14})/2} \int_{\left(1-\sqrt{13+4x-4x^2}\right)/2}^{\left(1+\sqrt{13+4x-4x^2}\right)/2} \left[(4 - x^2 - y^2) - (1 - x - y)\right] dy\, dx = \frac{49\pi}{8}.$$

12.4 Double Integrals in Polar Coordinates • • • • • • • •

1. The region R is more easily described by polar coordinates: $R = \{(r, \theta) \mid 0 \leq r \leq 2, 0 \leq \theta \leq 2\pi\}$.

Thus $\iint_R f(x, y)\, dA = \int_0^{2\pi} \int_0^2 f(r\cos\theta, r\sin\theta)\, r\, dr\, d\theta$.

2. The region R is more easily described by rectangular coordinates: $R = \{(r, \theta) \mid 0 \leq x \leq 2, 0 \leq y \leq 2 - x\}$.

Thus $\iint_R f(x, y)\, dA = \int_0^2 \int_0^{2-x} f(x, y)\, dy\, dx$.

3. The region R is more easily described by rectangular coordinates: $R = \{(x, y) \mid -2 \leq x \leq 2, x \leq y \leq 2\}$.

Thus $\iint_R f(x, y)\, dA = \int_{-2}^2 \int_x^2 f(x, y)\, dy\, dx$.

4. The region R is more easily described by polar coordinates: $R = \{(r, \theta) \mid 1 \leq r \leq 3, 0 \leq \theta \leq \frac{\pi}{2}\}$.

Thus $\iint_R f(x, y)\, dA = \int_0^{\pi/2} \int_1^3 f(r\cos\theta, r\sin\theta)\, r\, dr\, d\theta$.

5. The region R is more easily described by polar coordinates: $R = \{(r, \theta) \mid 2 \leq r \leq 5, 0 \leq \theta \leq 2\pi\}$.

Thus $\iint_R f(x, y)\, dA = \int_0^{2\pi} \int_2^5 f(r\cos\theta, r\sin\theta)\, r\, dr\, d\theta$.

6. The region R is more easily described by polar coordinates: $R = \{(r, \theta) \mid 0 \leq r \leq 2\sqrt{2}, \frac{\pi}{4} \leq \theta \leq \frac{5\pi}{4}\}$.

Thus $\iint_R f(x, y)\, dA = \int_{\pi/4}^{5\pi/4} \int_0^{2\sqrt{2}} f(r\cos\theta, r\sin\theta)\, r\, dr\, d\theta$.

7. The integral $\int_\pi^{2\pi} \int_4^7 r\, dr\, d\theta$ represents the area of the region

$R = \{(r, \theta) \mid 4 \leq r \leq 7, \pi \leq \theta \leq 2\pi\}$, the lower half of a ring.

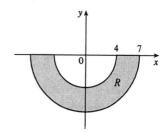

$$\int_\pi^{2\pi} \int_4^7 r\, dr\, d\theta = \left(\int_\pi^{2\pi} d\theta\right)\left(\int_4^7 r\, dr\right)$$

$$= [\theta]_\pi^{2\pi} \left[\frac{1}{2} r^2\right]_4^7 = \pi \cdot \frac{1}{2}(49 - 16) = \frac{33\pi}{2}$$

8. The integral $\int_0^{\pi/2} \int_0^{4\cos\theta} r\, dr\, d\theta$ represents the area of the region

$R = \{(r, \theta) \mid 0 \leq r \leq 4\cos\theta, 0 \leq \theta \leq \pi/2\}$. Since $r = 4\cos\theta \Leftrightarrow$

$r^2 = 4r\cos\theta \Leftrightarrow x^2 + y^2 = 4x \Leftrightarrow (x - 2)^2 + y^2 = 4$, R is the

portion in the first quadrant of a circle of radius 2 with center $(2, 0)$.

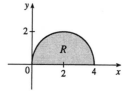

$$\int_0^{\pi/2} \int_0^{4\cos\theta} r\, dr\, d\theta = \int_0^{\pi/2} \left[\frac{1}{2} r^2\right]_{r=0}^{r=4\cos\theta} d\theta = \int_0^{\pi/2} 8\cos^2\theta\, d\theta$$

$$= \int_0^{\pi/2} 4(1 + \cos 2\theta)\, d\theta = 4\left[\theta + \frac{1}{2}\sin 2\theta\right]_0^{\pi/2} = 2\pi$$

9. The disk D can be described in polar coordinates as $D = \{(r, \theta) \mid 0 \leq r \leq 3, 0 \leq \theta \leq 2\pi\}$. Then

$$\iint_D xy\, dA = \int_0^{2\pi} \int_0^3 (r\cos\theta)(r\sin\theta)\, r\, dr\, d\theta = \left(\int_0^{2\pi} \sin\theta\cos\theta\, d\theta\right)\left(\int_0^3 r^3\, dr\right) = \left[\frac{1}{2}\sin^2\theta\right]_0^{2\pi} \left[\frac{1}{4} r^4\right]_0^3 = 0.$$

10. $\iint_R \sqrt{x^2 + y^2}\, dA = \int_0^\pi \int_1^3 \sqrt{r^2}\, r\, dr\, d\theta = \left(\int_0^\pi d\theta\right)\left(\int_1^3 r^2\, dr\right) = [\theta]_0^\pi \left[\frac{1}{3} r^3\right]_1^3 = \pi\left(\frac{27-1}{3}\right) = \frac{26}{3}\pi$

11. $\iint_D e^{-x^2 - y^2}\, dA = \int_{-\pi/2}^{\pi/2} \int_0^2 e^{-r^2}\, r\, dr\, d\theta = \left(\int_{-\pi/2}^{\pi/2} d\theta\right)\left(\int_0^2 re^{-r^2}\, dr\right)$

$$= [\theta]_{-\pi/2}^{\pi/2} \left[-\frac{1}{2} e^{-r^2}\right]_0^2 = \pi\left(-\frac{1}{2}\right)\left(e^{-4} - e^0\right) = \frac{\pi}{2}\left(1 - e^{-4}\right)$$

12. $\iint_R ye^x \, dA = \int_0^{\pi/2} \int_0^5 (r \sin\theta) e^{r\cos\theta} \, r \, dr \, d\theta = \int_0^5 \int_0^{\pi/2} r^2 \sin\theta \, e^{r\cos\theta} \, d\theta \, dr$. First we integrate

$\int_0^{\pi/2} r^2 \sin\theta \, e^{r\cos\theta} \, d\theta$: Let $u = r\cos\theta \Rightarrow du = -r\sin\theta \, d\theta$, and

$\int_0^{\pi/2} r^2 \sin\theta \, e^{r\cos\theta} \, d\theta = \int_{u=r}^{u=0} -r \, e^u \, du = -r[e^0 - e^r] = re^r - r$. Then

$\int_0^5 \int_0^{\pi/2} r^2 \sin\theta \, e^{r\cos\theta} \, d\theta \, dr = \int_0^5 (re^r - r) \, dr = \left[re^r - e^r - \frac{1}{2}r^2 \right]_0^5 = 4e^5 - \frac{23}{2}$, where we integrated by parts

in the first term.

13. R is the region shown in the figure, and can be described by

$R = \{(r,\theta) \mid -\pi/4 \le \theta \le \pi/4, 1 \le r \le 2\}$. Thus

$\iint_R \arctan(y/x) \, dA = \int_{-\pi/4}^{\pi/4} \int_1^2 \arctan(\tan\theta) \, r \, dr \, d\theta$ since

$y/x = \tan\theta$. Also, $\arctan(\tan\theta) = \theta$ for $-\frac{\pi}{4} \le \theta \le \frac{\pi}{4}$,

so the integral becomes

$\int_{-\pi/4}^{\pi/4} \int_1^2 \theta r \, dr \, d\theta = \left(\int_{-\pi/4}^{\pi/4} \theta \, d\theta \right) \left(\int_1^2 r \, dr \right) = \left[\frac{1}{2}\theta^2 \right]_{-\pi/4}^{\pi/4} \left[\frac{1}{2}r^2 \right]_1^2 = 0.$

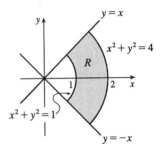

14.

$\iint_D x \, dA = \iint_{\substack{x^2+y^2 \le 4 \\ x \ge 0, y \ge 0}} x \, dA - \iint_{\substack{(x-1)^2+y^2 \le 1 \\ y \ge 0}} x \, dA$

$= \int_0^{\pi/2} \int_0^2 r^2 \cos\theta \, dr \, d\theta - \int_0^{\pi/2} \int_0^{2\cos\theta} r^2 \cos\theta \, dr \, d\theta$

$= \int_0^{\pi/2} \frac{1}{3}(8\cos\theta) \, d\theta - \int_0^{\pi/2} \frac{1}{3}(8\cos^4\theta) \, d\theta$

$= \frac{8}{3} - \frac{8}{12} \left[\cos^3\theta \sin\theta + \frac{3}{2}(\theta + \sin\theta\cos\theta) \right]_0^{\pi/2}$

$= \frac{8}{3} - \frac{2}{3} \left[0 + \frac{3}{2}\left(\frac{\pi}{2}\right) \right] = \frac{16 - 3\pi}{6}$

15. $V = \iint_{x^2+y^2 \le 9} (x^2 + y^2) \, dA = \int_0^{2\pi} \int_0^3 (r^2) r \, dr \, d\theta = \int_0^{2\pi} d\theta \int_0^3 r^3 \, dr = [\theta]_0^{2\pi} \left[\frac{1}{4}r^4 \right]_0^3 = 2\pi\left(\frac{81}{4}\right) = \frac{81\pi}{2}$

16. The sphere $x^2 + y^2 + z^2 = 16$ intersects the xy-plane in the circle $x^2 + y^2 = 16$, so

$V = 2 \iint_{4 \le x^2+y^2 \le 16} \sqrt{16 - x^2 - y^2} \, dA$ (by symmetry)

$= 2 \int_0^{2\pi} \int_2^4 \sqrt{16 - r^2} \, r \, dr \, d\theta = 2 \int_0^{2\pi} d\theta \int_2^4 r(16 - r^2)^{1/2} \, dr$

$= 2 \, [\theta]_0^{2\pi} \left[-\frac{1}{3}(16 - r^2)^{3/2} \right]_2^4 = -\frac{2}{3}(2\pi)\left(0 - 12^{3/2}\right) = \frac{4\pi}{3}\left(12\sqrt{12}\right) = 32\sqrt{3}\,\pi$

17. By symmetry,

$V = 2 \iint_{x^2+y^2 \le a^2} \sqrt{a^2 - x^2 - y^2} \, dA = 2 \int_0^{2\pi} \int_0^a \sqrt{a^2 - r^2} \, r \, dr \, d\theta = 2 \int_0^{2\pi} d\theta \int_0^a r\sqrt{a^2 - r^2} \, dr$

$= 2[\theta]_0^{2\pi} \left[-\frac{1}{3}(a^2 - r^2)^{3/2} \right]_0^a = 2(2\pi)\left(0 + \frac{1}{3}a^3\right) = \frac{4\pi}{3}a^3$

18. The paraboloid $z = 10 - 3x^2 - 3y^2$ intersects the plane $z = 4$ when $4 = 10 - 3x^2 - 3y^2$ or $x^2 + y^2 = 2$. So

$V = \iint_{x^2+y^2 \le 2} [(10 - 3x^2 - 3y^2) - 4] \, dA = \int_0^{2\pi} \int_0^{\sqrt{2}} (6 - 3r^2) r \, dr \, d\theta$

$= \int_0^{2\pi} d\theta \int_0^{\sqrt{2}} (6r - 3r^3) \, dr = [\theta]_0^{2\pi} \left[3r^2 - \frac{3}{4}r^4 \right]_0^{\sqrt{2}} = 6\pi$

19. The cone $z = \sqrt{x^2 + y^2}$ intersects the sphere $x^2 + y^2 + z^2 = 1$ when $x^2 + y^2 + \left(\sqrt{x^2 + y^2}\right)^2 = 1$

or $x^2 + y^2 = \frac{1}{2}$. So

$$V = \iint_{x^2 + y^2 \leq 1/2} \left(\sqrt{1 - x^2 - y^2} - \sqrt{x^2 + y^2}\right) dA = \int_0^{2\pi} \int_0^{1/\sqrt{2}} \left(\sqrt{1 - r^2} - r\right) r \, dr \, d\theta$$

$$= \int_0^{2\pi} d\theta \int_0^{1/\sqrt{2}} \left(r\sqrt{1 - r^2} - r^2\right) dr = [\theta]_0^{2\pi} \left[-\frac{1}{3}(1 - r^2)^{3/2} - \frac{1}{3}r^3\right]_0^{1/\sqrt{2}}$$

$$= 2\pi \left(-\frac{1}{3}\right)\left(\frac{1}{\sqrt{2}} - 1\right) = \frac{\pi}{3}\left(2 - \sqrt{2}\right)$$

20. The two paraboloids intersect when $3x^2 + 3y^2 = 4 - x^2 - y^2$ or $x^2 + y^2 = 1$. So

$$V = \iint_{x^2 + y^2 \leq 1} \left[(4 - x^2 - y^2) - 3\left(x^2 + y^2\right)\right] dA = \int_0^{2\pi} \int_0^1 4(1 - r^2) r \, dr \, d\theta$$

$$= \int_0^{2\pi} d\theta \int_0^1 (4r - 4r^3) \, dr = [\theta]_0^{2\pi} \left[2r^2 - r^4\right]_0^1 = 2\pi$$

21. The given solid is the region inside the cylinder $x^2 + y^2 = 4$ between the surfaces $z = \sqrt{64 - 4x^2 - 4y^2}$

and $z = -\sqrt{64 - 4x^2 - 4y^2}$. So

$$V = \iint_{x^2 + y^2 \leq 4} \left[\sqrt{64 - 4x^2 - 4y^2} - \left(-\sqrt{64 - 4x^2 - 4y^2}\right)\right] dA$$

$$= \iint_{x^2 + y^2 \leq 4} 2\sqrt{64 - 4x^2 - 4y^2} \, dA = 4 \int_0^{2\pi} \int_0^2 \sqrt{16 - r^2} \, r \, dr \, d\theta$$

$$= 4 \int_0^{2\pi} d\theta \int_0^2 r\sqrt{16 - r^2} \, dr = 4 [\theta]_0^{2\pi} \left[-\frac{1}{3}(16 - r^2)^{3/2}\right]_0^2$$

$$= 8\pi \left(-\frac{1}{3}\right)\left(12^{3/2} - 16^{2/3}\right) = \frac{8\pi}{3}\left(64 - 24\sqrt{3}\right)$$

22. (a) Here the region in the xy-plane is the annular region $r_1^2 \leq x^2 + y^2 \leq r_2^2$ and the desired volume is twice that
above the xy-plane. Hence

$$V = 2 \iint_{r_1^2 \leq x^2 + y^2 \leq r_2^2} \sqrt{r_2^2 - x^2 - y^2} \, dA = 2 \int_0^{2\pi} \int_{r_1}^{r_2} \sqrt{r_2^2 - r^2} \, r \, dr \, d\theta$$

$$= 2 \int_0^{2\pi} d\theta \int_{r_1}^{r_2} \sqrt{r_2^2 - r^2} \, r \, dr = \frac{4\pi}{3}\left[-(r_2^2 - r^2)^{3/2}\right]_{r_1}^{r_2} = \frac{4\pi}{3}(r_2^2 - r_1^2)^{3/2}$$

(b) A cross-sectional cut is shown in the figure. So $r_2^2 = \left(\frac{1}{2}h\right)^2 + r_1^2$

or $\frac{1}{4}h^2 = r_2^2 - r_1^2$. Thus the volume in terms of h is

$$V = \frac{4\pi}{3}\left(\frac{1}{4}h^2\right)^{3/2} = \frac{\pi}{6}h^3.$$

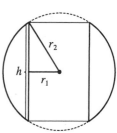

23. One loop is given by the region

$D = \{(r, \theta) \mid -\pi/6 \leq \theta \leq \pi/6, 0 \leq r \leq \cos 3\theta\}$, so the area is

$$\iint_D dA = \int_{-\pi/6}^{\pi/6} \int_0^{\cos 3\theta} r \, dr \, d\theta = \int_{-\pi/6}^{\pi/6} \left[\frac{1}{2}r^2\right]_{r=0}^{r=\cos 3\theta} d\theta$$

$$= \int_{-\pi/6}^{\pi/6} \frac{1}{2}\cos^2 3\theta \, d\theta = 2 \int_0^{\pi/6} \frac{1}{2}\left(\frac{1 + \cos 6\theta}{2}\right) d\theta$$

$$= \frac{1}{2}\left[\theta + \frac{1}{6}\sin 6\theta\right]_0^{\pi/6} = \frac{\pi}{12}$$

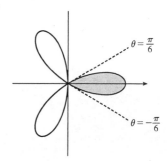

24. By symmetry,

$$A = 2 \int_{-\pi/2}^{\pi/2} \int_0^{1-\sin\theta} r \, dr \, d\theta = \int_{-\pi/2}^{\pi/2} \left[r^2 \right]_{r=0}^{r=1-\sin\theta} d\theta = \int_{-\pi/2}^{\pi/2} \left(1 - 2\sin\theta + \sin^2\theta \right) d\theta$$

$$= \int_{-\pi/2}^{\pi/2} \left[1 + \tfrac{1}{2}(1 - \cos 2\theta) \right] d\theta = \int_{-\pi/2}^{\pi/2} \left(\tfrac{3}{2} - \tfrac{1}{2}\cos 2\theta \right) d\theta$$

since $2\sin\theta$ is an odd function. But $\tfrac{3}{2} - \tfrac{1}{2}\cos 2\theta$ is an even function, so

$$A = \int_0^{\pi/2} (3 - \cos 2\theta) \, d\theta = \left[3\theta - \tfrac{1}{2}\sin 2\theta \right]_0^{\pi/2} = \tfrac{3\pi}{2}.$$

25.

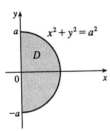

$$\int_0^1 \int_0^{\sqrt{1-x^2}} e^{x^2+y^2} \, dy \, dx = \int_0^{\pi/2} \int_0^1 e^{r^2} r \, dr \, d\theta = \int_0^{\pi/2} d\theta \int_0^1 r e^{r^2} \, dr$$

$$= \left[\theta \right]_0^{\pi/2} \left[\tfrac{1}{2} e^{r^2} \right]_0^1 = \tfrac{1}{4}\pi(e-1)$$

26.

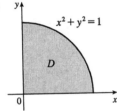

$$\int_{-\pi/2}^{\pi/2} \int_0^a \left(r^2 \right)^{3/2} r \, dr \, d\theta = \int_{-\pi/2}^{\pi/2} d\theta \int_0^a r^4 \, dr = \left[\theta \right]_{-\pi/2}^{\pi/2} \left[\tfrac{1}{5} r^5 \right]_0^a$$

$$= \tfrac{1}{5}\pi a^5$$

27.

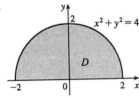

$$\int_0^\pi \int_0^2 (r\cos\theta)^2 (r\sin\theta)^2 r \, dr \, d\theta = \int_0^\pi (\sin\theta\cos\theta)^2 d\theta \int_0^2 r^5 \, dr$$

$$= \int_0^\pi \left(\tfrac{1}{2}\sin 2\theta \right)^2 d\theta \int_0^2 r^5 \, dr$$

$$= \tfrac{1}{4} \left[\tfrac{1}{2}\theta - \tfrac{1}{8}\sin 4\theta \right]_0^\pi \left[\tfrac{1}{6} r^6 \right]_0^2$$

$$= \tfrac{1}{4} \left(\tfrac{\pi}{2} \right) \left(\tfrac{64}{6} \right) = \tfrac{4\pi}{3}$$

28.

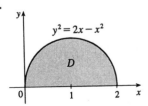

$$\int_0^{\pi/2} \int_0^{2\cos\theta} r^2 \, dr \, d\theta = \int_0^{\pi/2} \left[\tfrac{1}{3} r^3 \right]_{r=0}^{r=2\cos\theta} d\theta$$

$$= \int_0^{\pi/2} \left(\tfrac{8}{3}\cos^3\theta \right) d\theta$$

$$= \tfrac{8}{3} \left[\sin\theta - \tfrac{1}{3}\sin^3\theta \right]_0^{\pi/2} = \tfrac{16}{9}$$

29. The surface of the water in the pool is a circular disk D with radius 20 ft. If we place D on coordinate axes with the origin at the center of D and define $f(x, y)$ to be the depth of the water at (x, y), then the volume of water in the pool is the volume of the solid that lies above $D = \{(x, y) \mid x^2 + y^2 \le 400\}$ and below the graph of $f(x, y)$. We can associate north with the positive y-direction, so we are given that the depth is constant in the x-direction and the depth increases linearly in the y-direction from $f(0, -20) = 2$ to $f(0, 20) = 7$. The trace in the yz-plane is a line segment from $(0, -20, 2)$ to $(0, 20, 7)$. The slope of this line is $\frac{7-2}{20-(-20)} = \frac{1}{8}$, so an equation of the line is $z - 7 = \frac{1}{8}(y - 20)$ $\Rightarrow$ $z = \frac{1}{8}y + \frac{9}{2}$. Since $f(x, y)$ is independent of x, $f(x, y) = \frac{1}{8}y + \frac{9}{2}$. Thus the volume is given by $\iint_D f(x, y)\, dA$, which is most conveniently evaluated using polar coordinates. Then $D = \{(r, \theta) \mid 0 \le r \le 20,\, 0 \le \theta \le 2\pi\}$ and substituting $x = r\cos\theta$, $y = r\sin\theta$ the integral becomes

$$\int_0^{2\pi} \int_0^{20} \left(\tfrac{1}{8}r\sin\theta + \tfrac{9}{2}\right) r\, dr\, d\theta = \int_0^{2\pi} \left[\tfrac{1}{24}r^3 \sin\theta + \tfrac{9}{4}r^2\right]_{r=0}^{r=20} d\theta$$

$$= \int_0^{2\pi} \left(\tfrac{1000}{3}\sin\theta + 900\right) d\theta = \left[-\tfrac{1000}{3}\cos\theta + 900\theta\right]_0^{2\pi}$$

$$= 1800\pi$$

Thus the pool contains $1800\pi \approx 5655$ ft^3 of water.

30. (a) The total amount of water supplied each hour to the region within R feet of the sprinkler is

$$V = \int_0^{2\pi} \int_0^R e^{-r} r\, dr\, d\theta = \int_0^{2\pi} d\theta \int_0^R r e^{-r}\, dr = [\theta]_0^{2\pi} \left[-re^{-r} - e^{-r}\right]_0^R$$

$$= 2\pi\left[-Re^{-R} - e^{-R} + 0 + 1\right] = 2\pi\left(1 - Re^{-R} - e^{-R}\right) \text{ ft}^3$$

(b) The average amount of water per hour per square foot supplied to the region within R feet of the sprinkler is

$$\frac{V}{\text{area of region}} = \frac{V}{\pi R^2} = \frac{2\left(1 - Re^{-R} - e^{-R}\right)}{R^2} \text{ ft}^3 \text{ (per hour per square foot). See the definition of the average}$$

value of a function on page 844.

31. $\int_{1/\sqrt{2}}^{1} \int_{\sqrt{1-x^2}}^{x} xy\, dy\, dx + \int_1^{\sqrt{2}} \int_0^{x} xy\, dy\, dx + \int_{\sqrt{2}}^{2} \int_0^{\sqrt{4-x^2}} xy\, dy\, dx$

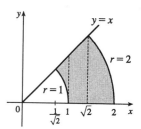

$$= \int_0^{\pi/4} \int_1^2 r^3 \cos\theta \sin\theta\, dr\, d\theta = \int_0^{\pi/4} \left[\frac{r^4}{4} \cos\theta \sin\theta\right]_{r=1}^{r=2} d\theta$$

$$= \frac{15}{4} \int_0^{\pi/4} \sin\theta \cos\theta\, d\theta \frac{15}{4} = \left[\frac{\sin^2 \theta}{2}\right]_0^{\pi/4} = \frac{15}{16}$$

32. (a) $\iint_{D_a} e^{-(x^2+y^2)} dA = \int_0^{2\pi} \int_0^a re^{-r^2}\, dr\, d\theta = 2\pi\left[-\frac{1}{2}e^{-r^2}\right]_0^a = \pi\left(1 - e^{-a^2}\right)$ for each a. Then

$\lim\limits_{a \to \infty} \pi\left(1 - e^{-a^2}\right) = \pi$ since $e^{-a^2} \to 0$ as $a \to \infty$. Hence $\int_{-\infty}^{\infty} \int_{-\infty}^{\infty} e^{-(x^2+y^2)} dA = \pi$.

(b) $\iint_{S_a} e^{-(x^2+y^2)} dA = \int_{-a}^{a} \int_{-a}^{a} e^{-x^2} e^{-y^2}\, dx\, dy = \left(\int_{-a}^{a} e^{-x^2}\, dx\right)\left(\int_{-a}^{a} e^{-y^2}\, dy\right)$ for each a. Then, from (a),

$\pi = \iint_{\mathbb{R}^2} - (x^2 + y^2)\, dA$, so

$$\pi = \lim_{a \to \infty} \iint_{S_a} e^{-(x^2+y^2)} dA = \lim_{a \to \infty} \left(\int_{-a}^{a} e^{-x^2}\, dx\right)\left(\int_{-a}^{a} e^{-y^2}\, dy\right) = \left(\int_{-\infty}^{\infty} e^{-x^2}\, dx\right)\left(\int_{-\infty}^{\infty} e^{-y^2}\, dy\right).$$

To evaluate $\lim\limits_{a \to \infty} \left(\int_{-a}^{a} e^{-x^2}\, dx\right)\left(\int_{-a}^{a} e^{-y^2}\, dy\right)$, we are using the fact that these integrals are bounded. This is true since on $[-1, 1]$, $0 < e^{-x^2} \le 1$ while on $(-\infty, -1)$, $0 < e^{-x^2} \le e^x$ and on $(1, \infty)$, $0 < e^{-x^2} < e^{-x}$. Hence $0 \le \int_{-\infty}^{\infty} e^{-x^2}\, dx \le \int_{-\infty}^{-1} e^x\, dx + \int_{-1}^{1} dx + \int_1^{\infty} e^{-x}\, dx = 2\left(e^{-1} + 1\right)$.

(c) Since $\left(\int_{-\infty}^{\infty} e^{-x^2}\, dx\right)\left(\int_{-\infty}^{\infty} e^{-y^2}\, dy\right) = \pi$ and y can be replaced by x, $\left(\int_{-\infty}^{\infty} e^{-x^2}\, dx\right)^2 = \pi$ implies that

$\int_{-\infty}^{\infty} e^{-x^2}\, dx = \pm\sqrt{\pi}$. But $e^{-x^2} \geq 0$ for all x, so $\int_{-\infty}^{\infty} e^{-x^2}\, dx = \sqrt{\pi}$.

(d) Letting $t = \sqrt{2}x$, $\int_{-\infty}^{\infty} e^{-x^2}\, dx = \int_{-\infty}^{\infty} \frac{1}{\sqrt{2}}\left(e^{-t^2/2}\right) dt$, so that $\sqrt{\pi} = \frac{1}{\sqrt{2}} \int_{-\infty}^{\infty} e^{-t^2/2}\, dt$ or

$\int_{-\infty}^{\infty} e^{-t^2/2}\, dt = \sqrt{2\pi}$.

33. (a) We integrate by parts with $u = x$ and $dv = xe^{-x^2}\, dx$. Then $du = dx$ and $v = -\frac{1}{2}e^{-x^2}$, so

$$\int_0^{\infty} x^2 e^{-x^2}\, dx = \lim_{t\to\infty} \int_0^t x^2 e^{-x^2}\, dx = \lim_{t\to\infty}\left(-\frac{1}{2}xe^{-x^2}\Big]_0^t + \int_0^t \frac{1}{2}e^{-x^2}\, dx\right)$$

$$= \lim_{t\to\infty}\left(-\frac{1}{2}te^{-t^2}\right) + \frac{1}{2}\int_0^{\infty} e^{-x^2}\, dx = 0 + \frac{1}{2}\int_0^{\infty} e^{-x^2}\, dx \quad \text{(by l'Hospital's Rule)}$$

$$= \frac{1}{4}\int_{-\infty}^{\infty} e^{-x^2}\, dx \text{ (since } e^{-x^2} \text{ is an even function)} = \frac{1}{4}\sqrt{\pi} \quad \text{[by Exercise 32(c)]}$$

(b) Let $u = \sqrt{x}$. Then $u^2 = x \;\Rightarrow\; dx = 2u\, du \;\Rightarrow$

$$\int_0^{\infty} \sqrt{x}e^{-x}\, dx = \lim_{t\to\infty}\int_0^t \sqrt{x}\,e^{-x}\, dx = \lim_{t\to\infty}\int_0^{\sqrt{t}} u e^{-u^2} 2u\, du = 2\int_0^{\infty} u^2 e^{-u^2}\, du$$

$$= 2\left(\frac{1}{4}\sqrt{\pi}\right) \text{ [by part(a)]} = \frac{1}{2}\sqrt{\pi}$$

12.5 Applications of Double Integrals · · · · · · · · · · ·

1. $Q = \iint_D \sigma(x,y)\, dA = \int_1^3 \int_0^2 (2xy + y^2)\, dy\, dx = \int_1^3 \left[xy^2 + \frac{1}{3}y^3\right]_{y=0}^{y=2} dx$

$= \int_1^3 \left(4x + \frac{8}{3}\right) dx = \left[2x^2 + \frac{8}{3}x\right]_1^3 = 16 + \frac{16}{3} = \frac{64}{3}$ C

2. $Q = \iint_D \sigma(x,y)\, dA = \iint_D (x + y + x^2 + y^2)\, dA = \int_0^{2\pi}\int_0^2 (r\cos\theta + r\sin\theta + r^2)\, r\, dr\, d\theta$

$= \int_0^{2\pi}\int_0^2 \left[r^2(\cos\theta + \sin\theta) + r^3\right] dr\, d\theta = \int_0^{2\pi}\left[\frac{1}{3}r^3(\cos\theta + \sin\theta) + \frac{1}{4}r^4\right]_{r=0}^{r=2} d\theta$

$= \int_0^{2\pi}\left[\frac{8}{3}(\cos\theta + \sin\theta) + 4\right] d\theta = \left[\frac{8}{3}(\sin\theta - \cos\theta) + 4\theta\right]_0^{2\pi} = 8\pi$ C

3. $m = \iint_D \rho(x,y)\, dA = \int_0^2 \int_{-1}^1 xy^2\, dy\, dx = \int_0^2 x\, dx \int_{-1}^1 y^2\, dy = \left[\frac{1}{2}x^2\right]_0^2 \left[\frac{1}{3}y^3\right]_{-1}^1 = 2\cdot\frac{2}{3} = \frac{4}{3}$,

$\bar{x} = \frac{1}{m}\iint_D x\rho(x,y)\, dA = \frac{3}{4}\int_0^2 \int_{-1}^1 x^2 y^2\, dy\, dx = \frac{3}{4}\int_0^2 x^2\, dx \int_{-1}^1 y^2\, dy = \frac{3}{4}\left[\frac{1}{3}x^3\right]_0^2 \left[\frac{1}{3}y^3\right]_{-1}^1 = \frac{3}{4}\cdot\frac{8}{3}\cdot\frac{2}{3} = \frac{4}{3}$,

$\bar{y} = \frac{1}{m}\iint_D y\rho(x,y)\, dA = \frac{3}{4}\int_0^2 \int_{-1}^1 xy^3\, dy\, dx = \frac{3}{4}\int_0^2 x\, dx \int_{-1}^1 y^3\, dy = \frac{3}{4}\left[\frac{1}{2}x^2\right]_0^2 \left[\frac{1}{4}y^4\right]_{-1}^1 = \frac{3}{4}\cdot 2\cdot 0 = 0$.

Hence, $(\bar{x}, \bar{y}) = \left(\frac{4}{3}, 0\right)$.

4. $m = \iint_D \rho(x,y)\, dA = \int_0^a \int_0^b cxy\, dy\, dx = c\int_0^a x\, dx \int_0^b y\, dy = c\left[\frac{1}{2}x^2\right]_0^a \left[\frac{1}{2}y^2\right]_0^b = \frac{1}{4}a^2 b^2 c$,

$M_y = \iint_D x\rho(x,y)\, dA = \int_0^a \int_0^b cx^2 y\, dy\, dx = c\int_0^a x^2\, dx \int_0^b y\, dy = c\left[\frac{1}{3}x^3\right]_0^a \left[\frac{1}{2}y^2\right]_0^b = \frac{1}{6}a^3 b^2 c$, and

$M_x = \iint_D y\rho(x,y)\, dA = \int_0^a \int_0^b cxy^2\, dy\, dx = c\int_0^a x\, dx \int_0^b y^2\, dy = c\left[\frac{1}{2}x^2\right]_0^a \left[\frac{1}{3}y^3\right]_0^b = \frac{1}{6}a^2 b^3 c$.

Hence, $(\bar{x}, \bar{y}) = \left(\dfrac{M_y}{m}, \dfrac{M_x}{m}\right) = \left(\dfrac{2}{3}a, \dfrac{2}{3}b\right)$.

5. $m = \int_0^2 \int_{x/2}^{3-x} (x + y)\, dy\, dx = \int_0^2 \left[xy + \frac{1}{2}y^2\right]_{y=x/2}^{y=3-x} dx = \int_0^2 \left[x(3 - \frac{3}{2}x) + \frac{1}{2}(3 - x)^2 - \frac{1}{8}x^2\right] dx$

$= \int_0^2 \left(-\frac{9}{8}x^2 + \frac{9}{2}\right) dx = \left[-\frac{9}{8}\left(\frac{1}{3}x^3\right) + \frac{9}{2}x\right]_0^2 = 6$,

$M_y = \int_0^2 \int_{x/2}^{3-x} (x^2 + xy)\, dy\, dx = \int_0^2 \left[x^2 y + \frac{1}{2}xy^2\right]_{y=x/2}^{y=3-x} dx = \int_0^2 \left(\frac{9}{2}x - \frac{9}{8}x^3\right) dx = \frac{9}{2}$, and

$M_x = \int_0^2 \int_{x/2}^{3-y} (xy + y^2)\, dy\, dx = \int_0^2 \left[\frac{1}{2}xy^2 + \frac{1}{3}y^3\right]_{y=x/2}^{y=3-x} dx = \int_0^2 \left(9 - \frac{9}{2}x\right) dx = 9.$

Hence $m = 6$, $(\overline{x}, \overline{y}) = \left(\dfrac{M_y}{m}, \dfrac{M_x}{m}\right) = \left(\dfrac{3}{4}, \dfrac{3}{2}\right).$

6. $m = \int_{-3}^3 \int_0^{9-x^2} y\, dy\, dx = \int_{-3}^3 \frac{1}{2}(81 - 18x^2 + x^4)\, dx = 243 - 162 + \frac{243}{5} = \frac{648}{5} = 3^4 \cdot \frac{8}{5}$. $M_y = 0$ since ρ is independent of x and the region is symmetric about the y-axis, and

$$M_x = \int_{-3}^3 \int_0^{9-x^2} y^2\, dy\, dx = \int_{-3}^3 \frac{1}{3}(9 - x^2)^3\, dx = 2\int_0^3 (243 - 81x^2 + 9x^4 - \frac{1}{3}x^6)\, dx$$

$$= 2\left[3^6 - 3^6 + \frac{1}{5}3^7 - \frac{1}{21}3^7\right] = 2\left[3^6 \cdot \frac{21-5}{35}\right] = 3^6 \cdot \frac{32}{35}$$

Hence $m = \frac{648}{5}$, $(\overline{x}, \overline{y}) = \left(0, \frac{36}{7}\right)$.

7.

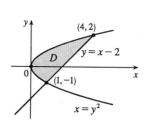

$m = \int_{-1}^2 \int_{y^2}^{y+2} 3\, dx\, dy = \int_{-1}^2 (3y + 6 - 3y^2)\, dy = \frac{27}{2}$,

$M_y = \int_{-1}^2 \int_{y^2}^{y+2} 3x\, dx\, dy = \int_{-1}^2 \frac{3}{2}\left[(y+2)^2 - y^4\right] dy$

$\qquad = \left[\frac{1}{2}(y+2)^3 - \frac{3}{10}y^5\right]_{-1}^2 = \frac{108}{5}$

and

$M_x = \int_{-1}^2 \int_{y^2}^{y+2} 3y\, dx\, dy = \int_{-1}^2 (3y^2 + 6y - 3y^3)\, dy$

$\qquad = \left[y^3 + 3y^2 - \frac{3}{4}y^4\right]_{-1}^2 = \frac{27}{4}$

Hence $m = \frac{27}{2}$, $(\overline{x}, \overline{y}) = \left(\frac{8}{5}, \frac{1}{2}\right)$.

8. $m = \int_0^{\pi/2} \int_0^{\cos x} x\, dy\, dx = \int_0^{\pi/2} x \cos x\, dx = [x \sin x + \cos x]_0^{\pi/2} = \frac{\pi}{2} - 1,$

$M_y = \int_0^{\pi/2} \int_0^{\cos x} x^2\, dy\, dx = \int_0^{\pi/2} x^2 \cos x\, dx = [x^2 \sin x + 2x \cos x - 2\sin x]_0^{\pi/2} = \frac{\pi^2}{4} - 2$, and

$M_x = \int_0^{\pi/2} \int_0^{\cos x} xy\, dy\, dx = \int_0^{\pi/2} \frac{1}{2}x \cos^2 x\, dx = \frac{1}{2}\left[\frac{1}{4}x^2 + \frac{1}{4}x \sin 2x + \frac{1}{8}\cos 2x\right]_0^{\pi/2} = \frac{\pi^2}{32} - \frac{1}{8}$. Hence

$m = \frac{\pi-2}{2}$, $(\overline{x}, \overline{y}) = \left(\frac{\pi^2-8}{2(\pi-2)}, \frac{\pi+2}{16}\right)$.

9. $\rho(x,y) = ky = kr \sin \theta$, $m = \int_0^{\pi/2} \int_0^1 kr^2 \sin \theta\, dr\, d\theta = \frac{1}{3}k \int_0^{\pi/2} \sin \theta\, d\theta = \frac{1}{3}k[-\cos\theta]_0^{\pi/2} = \frac{1}{3}k$,

$M_y = \int_0^{\pi/2} \int_0^1 kr^3 \sin \theta \cos \theta\, dr\, d\theta = \frac{1}{4}k \int_0^{\pi/2} \sin \theta \cos \theta\, d\theta = \frac{1}{8}k[-\cos 2\theta]_0^{\pi/2} = \frac{1}{8}k$,

$M_x = \int_0^{\pi/2} \int_0^1 kr^3 \sin^2 \theta\, dr\, d\theta = \frac{1}{4}k \int_0^{\pi/2} \sin^2 \theta\, d\theta = \frac{1}{8}k[\theta + \sin 2\theta]_0^{\pi/2} = \frac{\pi}{16}k$. Hence $(\overline{x}, \overline{y}) = \left(\frac{3}{8}, \frac{3\pi}{16}\right)$.

10. $\rho(x,y) = k(x^2 + y^2) = kr^2$, $m = \int_0^{\pi/2} \int_0^1 kr^3\, dr\, d\theta = \frac{\pi}{8}k$,

$M_y = \int_0^{\pi/2} \int_0^1 kr^4 \cos \theta\, dr\, d\theta = \frac{1}{5}k \int_0^{\pi/2} \cos \theta\, d\theta = \frac{1}{5}k[\sin\theta]_0^{\pi/2} = \frac{1}{5}k$,

$M_x = \int_0^{\pi/2} \int_0^1 kr^4 \sin \theta\, dr\, d\theta = \frac{1}{5}k \int_0^{\pi/2} \sin \theta\, d\theta = \frac{1}{5}k[-\cos\theta]_0^{\pi/2} = \frac{1}{5}k$. Hence $(\overline{x}, \overline{y}) = \left(\frac{8}{5\pi}, \frac{8}{5\pi}\right)$.

11. Placing the vertex opposite the hypotenuse at $(0,0)$, $\rho(x,y) = k(x^2 + y^2)$. Then

$$m = \int_0^a \int_0^{a-x} k(x^2 + y^2)\, dy\, dx = k\int_0^a \left[ax^2 - x^3 + \frac{1}{3}(a-x)^3\right] dx$$

$$= k\left[\frac{1}{3}ax^3 - \frac{1}{4}x^4 - \frac{1}{12}(a-x)^4\right]_0^a = \frac{1}{6}ka^4$$

By symmetry,

$$M_y = M_x = \int_0^a \int_0^{a-x} ky(x^2 + y^2)\, dy\, dx = k\int_0^a \left[\frac{1}{2}(a-x)^2 x^2 + \frac{1}{4}(a-x)^4\right] dx$$

$$= k\left[\frac{1}{6}a^2 x^3 - \frac{1}{4}ax^4 + \frac{1}{10}x^5 - \frac{1}{20}(a-x)^5\right]_0^a = \frac{1}{15}ka^5$$

Hence $(\overline{x}, \overline{y}) = \left(\frac{2}{5}a, \frac{2}{5}a\right)$.

12.

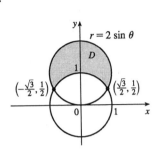

$$\rho(x, y) = k/\sqrt{x^2 + y^2} = k/r,$$

$$m = \int_{\pi/6}^{5\pi/6} \int_{1}^{2 \sin \theta} \frac{k}{r} \, r \, dr \, d\theta = k \int_{\pi/6}^{5\pi/6} [(2 \sin \theta) - 1] \, d\theta$$

$$= k[-2 \cos \theta - \theta]_{\pi/6}^{5\pi/6} = 2k\left(\sqrt{3} - \tfrac{\pi}{3}\right)$$

By symmetry of D and $f(x) = x$, $M_y = 0$, and

$$M_x = \int_{\pi/6}^{5\pi/6} \int_{1}^{2 \sin \theta} kr \sin \theta \, dr \, d\theta = \tfrac{1}{2}k \int_{\pi/6}^{5\pi/6} \left(4 \sin^3 \theta - \sin \theta\right) d\theta$$

$$= \tfrac{1}{2}k\left[-3 \cos \theta + \tfrac{4}{3} \cos^3 \theta\right]_{\pi/6}^{5\pi/6} = \sqrt{3}\,k$$

Hence $(\overline{x}, \overline{y}) = \left(0, \frac{3\sqrt{3}}{2(3\sqrt{3} - \pi)}\right)$.

13. $I_x = \iint_D y^2 \rho(x, y) \, dA = \int_0^2 \int_{-1}^1 y^2 (xy^2) \, dy \, dx = \int_0^2 x \, dx \int_{-1}^1 y^4 \, dy = \left[\tfrac{1}{2}x^2\right]_0^2 \left[\tfrac{1}{5}y^5\right]_{-1}^1 = 2 \cdot \tfrac{2}{5} = \tfrac{4}{5},$

$I_y = \iint_D x^2 \rho(x, y) \, dA = \int_0^2 \int_{-1}^1 x^2 (xy^2) \, dy \, dx = \int_0^2 x^3 \, dx \int_{-1}^1 y^2 \, dy = \left[\tfrac{1}{4}x^4\right]_0^2 \left[\tfrac{1}{3}y^3\right]_{-1}^1 = 4 \cdot \tfrac{2}{3} = \tfrac{8}{3}$, and

$I_0 = I_x + I_y = \tfrac{4}{5} + \tfrac{8}{3} = \tfrac{52}{15}$.

14. $I_x = \int_0^{\pi/2} \int_0^1 (r^2 \sin^2 \theta)(kr^2) \, r \, dr \, d\theta = \tfrac{1}{6}k \int_0^{\pi/2} \sin^2 \theta \, d\theta = \tfrac{1}{6}k\left[\tfrac{1}{4}(2\theta - \sin 2\theta)\right]_0^{\pi/2} = \tfrac{\pi}{24}k,$

$I_y = \int_0^{\pi/2} \int_0^1 (r^2 \cos^2 \theta)(kr^2) \, r \, dr \, d\theta = \tfrac{1}{6}k \int_0^{\pi/6} \cos^2 \theta \, d\theta = \tfrac{1}{6}k\left[\tfrac{1}{4}(2\theta + \sin 2\theta)\right]_0^{\pi/2} = \tfrac{\pi}{24}k$, and

$I_0 = I_x + I_y = \tfrac{\pi}{12}k$.

15. $I_x = \int_{-1}^2 \int_{y^2}^{y+2} 3y^2 \, dx \, dy = \int_{-1}^2 (3y^3 + 6y^2 - 3y^4) \, dy = \left[\tfrac{3}{4}y^4 + 2y^3 - \tfrac{3}{5}y^5\right]_{-1}^2 = \tfrac{189}{20},$

$I_y = \int_{-1}^2 \int_{y^2}^{y+2} 3x^2 \, dx \, dy = \int_{-1}^2 \left[(y + 2)^3 - y^6\right] dy = \left[\tfrac{1}{4}(y + 2)^4 - \tfrac{1}{7}y^7\right]_{-1}^2 = \tfrac{1269}{28}$, and

$I_0 = I_x + I_y = \tfrac{1917}{35}$.

16. If we find the moments of inertia about the x- and y-axes, we can determine in which direction rotation will be more difficult. (See the explanation following Example 4.) The moment of inertia about the x-axis is given by

$$I_x = \iint_D y^2 \rho(x, y) dA = \int_0^2 \int_0^2 y^2 (1 + 0.1x) \, dy \, dx = \int_0^2 (1 + 0.1x) \left[\tfrac{1}{3}y^3\right]_{y=0}^{y=2} dx$$

$$= \tfrac{8}{3} \int_0^2 (1 + 0.1x) \, dx = \tfrac{8}{3}\left[x + 0.1 \cdot \tfrac{1}{2}x^2\right]_0^2 = \tfrac{8}{3}(2.2) \approx 5.87$$

Similarly, the moment of inertia about the y-axis is given by

$$I_y = \iint_D x^2 \rho(x, y) \, dA = \int_0^2 \int_0^2 x^2 (1 + 0.1x) \, dy \, dx = \int_0^2 x^2 (1 + 0.1x) \, [y]_{y=0}^{y=2} \, dx$$

$$= 2 \int_0^2 (x^2 + 0.1x^3) \, dx = 2\left[\tfrac{1}{3}x^3 + 0.1 \cdot \tfrac{1}{4}x^4\right]_0^2 = 2\left(\tfrac{8}{3} + 0.4\right) \approx 6.13$$

Since $I_y > I_x$, more force is required to rotate the fan blade about the y-axis.

17. Using a CAS, we find $m = \iint_D \rho(x, y) \, dA = \int_0^\pi \int_0^{\sin x} xy \, dy \, dx = \dfrac{\pi^2}{8}$. Then

$$\overline{x} = \frac{1}{m} \iint_D x\rho(x, y) \, dA = \frac{8}{\pi^2} \int_0^\pi \int_0^{\sin x} x^2 y \, dy \, dx = \frac{2\pi}{3} - \frac{1}{\pi} \text{ and}$$

$$\overline{y} = \frac{1}{m} \iint_D y\rho(x, y) \, dA = \frac{8}{\pi^2} \int_0^\pi \int_0^{\sin x} xy^2 \, dy \, dx = \frac{16}{9\pi}, \text{ so } (\overline{x}, \overline{y}) = \left(\frac{2\pi}{3} - \frac{1}{\pi}, \frac{16}{9\pi}\right).$$

The moments of inertia are $I_x = \iint_D y^2 \rho(x, y) \, dA = \int_0^\pi \int_0^{\sin x} xy^3 \, dy \, dx = \dfrac{3\pi^2}{64},$

$$I_y = \iint_D x^2 \rho(x, y) \, dA = \int_0^\pi \int_0^{\sin x} x^3 y \, dy \, dx = \frac{\pi^2}{16}(\pi^2 - 3), \text{ and } I_0 = I_x + I_y = \frac{\pi^2}{64}(4\pi^2 - 9).$$

18. Using a CAS, we find $m = \iint_D \sqrt{x^2 + y^2}\, dA = \int_0^{2\pi} \int_0^{1+\cos\theta} r^2\, dr\, d\theta = \frac{5}{3}\pi$,

$\bar{x} = \frac{1}{m} \iint_D x\sqrt{x^2 + y^2}\, dA = \frac{3}{5\pi} \int_0^{2\pi} \int_0^{1+\cos\theta} r^3 \cos\theta\, dr\, d\theta = \frac{21}{20}$ and

$\bar{y} = \frac{1}{m} \iint_D y\sqrt{x^2 + y^2}\, dA = \frac{3}{5\pi} \int_0^{2\pi} \int_0^{1+\cos\theta} r^3 \sin\theta\, dr\, d\theta = 0$, so $(\bar{x}, \bar{y}) = \left(\frac{21}{20}, 0\right)$. The moments of

inertia are $I_x = \iint_D y^2 \sqrt{x^2 + y^2}\, dA = \int_0^{2\pi} \int_0^{1+\cos\theta} r^4 \sin^2\theta\, dr\, d\theta = \frac{33}{40}\pi$,

$I_y = \iint_D x^2 \sqrt{x^2 + y^2}\, dA = \int_0^{2\pi} \int_0^{1+\cos\theta} r^4 \cos^2\theta\, dr\, d\theta = \frac{93}{40}\pi$, and $I_0 = I_x + I_y = \frac{63}{20}\pi$.

19. (a) $f(x, y)$ is a joint density function, so we know $\iint_{\mathbb{R}^2} f(x, y)\, dA = 1$. Since $f(x, y) = 0$ outside the rectangle $[0, 1] \times [0, 2]$, we can say

$$\iint_{\mathbb{R}^2} f(x, y)\, dA = \int_{-\infty}^{\infty} \int_{-\infty}^{\infty} f(x, y)\, dy\, dx = \int_0^1 \int_0^2 Cx(1 + y)\, dy\, dx$$

$$= C \int_0^1 x\left[y + \frac{1}{2}y^2\right]_{y=0}^{y=2} dx = C \int_0^1 4x\, dx = C\left[2x^2\right]_0^1 = 2C$$

Then $2C = 1 \Rightarrow C = \frac{1}{2}$.

(b) $P(X \le 1, Y \le 1) = \int_{-\infty}^1 \int_{-\infty}^1 f(x, y)\, dy\, dx = \int_0^1 \int_0^1 \frac{1}{2}x(1 + y)\, dy\, dx$

$$= \int_0^1 \frac{1}{2}x\left[y + \frac{1}{2}y^2\right]_{y=0}^{y=1} dx = \int_0^1 \frac{1}{2}x\left(\frac{3}{2}\right) dx = \frac{3}{4}\left[\frac{1}{2}x^2\right]_0^1 = \frac{3}{8} \text{ or } 0.375$$

(c) $P(X + Y \le 1) = P((X, Y) \in D)$ where D is the triangular region
shown in the figure. Thus

$$P(X + Y \le 1) = \iint_D f(x, y)\, dA = \int_0^1 \int_0^{1-x} \frac{1}{2}x(1 + y)\, dy\, dx$$

$$= \int_0^1 \frac{1}{2}x\left[y + \frac{1}{2}y^2\right]_{y=0}^{y=1-x} dx = \int_0^1 \frac{1}{2}x\left(\frac{1}{2}x^2 - 2x + \frac{3}{2}\right) dx$$

$$= \frac{1}{4} \int_0^1 (x^3 - 4x^2 + 3x)\, dx = \frac{1}{4}\left[\frac{x^4}{4} - 4\frac{x^3}{3} + 3\frac{x^2}{2}\right]_0^1$$

$$= \frac{5}{48} \approx 0.1042$$

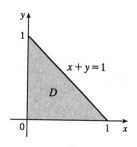

20. (a) $f(x, y) \ge 0$, so f is a joint density function if $\iint_{\mathbb{R}^2} f(x, y)\, dA = 1$. Here, $f(x, y) = 0$ outside the square

$[0, 1] \times [0, 1]$, so $\iint_{\mathbb{R}^2} f(x, y)\, dA = \int_0^1 \int_0^1 4xy\, dy\, dx = \int_0^1 \left[2xy^2\right]_{y=0}^{y=1} dx = \int_0^1 2x\, dx = x^2\Big]_0^1 = 1$.

Thus, $f(x, y)$ is a joint density function.

(b) (i) No restriction is placed on Y, so

$$P\left(X \ge \frac{1}{2}\right) = \int_{1/2}^{\infty} \int_{-\infty}^{\infty} f(x, y)\, dy\, dx = \int_{1/2}^1 \int_0^1 4xy\, dy\, dx$$

$$= \int_{1/2}^1 \left[2xy^2\right]_{y=0}^{y=1} dx = \int_{1/2}^1 2x\, dx = x^2\Big]_{1/2}^1 = \frac{3}{4}$$

(ii) $P\left(X \ge \frac{1}{2}, Y \le \frac{1}{2}\right) = \int_{1/2}^{\infty} \int_{-\infty}^{1/2} f(x, y)\, dy\, dx = \int_{1/2}^1 \int_0^{1/2} 4xy\, dy\, dx$

$$= \int_{1/2}^1 \left[2xy^2\right]_{y=0}^{y=1/2} dx = \int_{1/2}^1 \frac{1}{2}x\, dx = \frac{1}{2} \cdot \frac{1}{2}x^2\Big]_{1/2}^1 = \frac{3}{16}$$

(c) The expected value of X is given by

$$\mu_1 = \iint_{\mathbb{R}^2} x\, f(x, y)\, dA = \int_0^1 \int_0^1 x(4xy)\, dy\, dx = \int_0^1 2x^2\left[y^2\right]_{y=0}^{y=1} dx = 2 \int_0^1 x^2\, dx = 2\left[\frac{1}{3}x^3\right]_0^1 = \frac{2}{3}$$

The expected value of Y is

$$\mu_2 = \iint_{\mathbb{R}^2} y\, f(x, y)\, dA = \int_0^1 \int_0^1 y(4xy)\, dy\, dx = \int_0^1 4x\left[\frac{1}{3}y^3\right]_{y=0}^{y=1} dx = \frac{4}{3} \int_0^1 x\, dx = \frac{4}{3}\left[\frac{1}{2}x^2\right]_0^1 = \frac{2}{3}$$

21. **(a)** $f(x,y) \geq 0$, so f is a joint density function if $\iint_{\mathbb{R}^2} f(x,y)\,dA = 1$. Here, $f(x,y) = 0$ outside the first quadrant, so

$$\iint_{\mathbb{R}^2} f(x,y)\,dA = \int_0^\infty \int_0^\infty 0.1 e^{-(0.5x+0.2y)}\,dy\,dx = 0.1 \int_0^\infty \int_0^\infty e^{-0.5x} e^{-0.2y}\,dy\,dx$$

$$= 0.1 \int_0^\infty e^{-0.5x}\,dx \int_0^\infty e^{-0.2y}\,dy = 0.1 \lim_{t\to\infty} \int_0^t e^{-0.5x}\,dx \lim_{t\to\infty} \int_0^t e^{-0.2y}\,dy$$

$$= 0.1 \lim_{t\to\infty} \left[-2e^{-0.5x}\right]_0^t \lim_{t\to\infty} \left[-5e^{-0.2y}\right]_0^t$$

$$= 0.1 \lim_{t\to\infty} \left[-2\left(e^{-0.5t}-1\right)\right] \lim_{t\to\infty} \left[-5\left(e^{-0.2t}-1\right)\right]$$

$$= (0.1)\cdot(-2)(0-1)\cdot(-5)(0-1) = 1$$

Thus $f(x,y)$ is a joint density function.

(b) **(i)** No restriction is placed on X, so

$$P\,(Y \geq 1) = \int_{-\infty}^\infty \int_1^\infty f(x,y)\,dy\,dx = \int_0^\infty \int_1^\infty 0.1 e^{-(0.5x+0.2y)}\,dy\,dx$$

$$= 0.1 \int_0^\infty e^{-0.5x}\,dx \int_1^\infty e^{-0.2y}\,dy = 0.1 \lim_{t\to\infty} \int_0^t e^{-0.5x}\,dx \lim_{t\to\infty} \int_1^t e^{-0.2y}\,dy$$

$$= 0.1 \lim_{t\to\infty} \left[-2e^{-0.5x}\right]_0^t \lim_{t\to\infty} \left[-5e^{-0.2y}\right]_1^t$$

$$= 0.1 \lim_{t\to\infty} \left[-2\left(e^{-0.5t}-1\right)\right] \lim_{t\to\infty} \left[-5\left(e^{-0.2t}-e^{-0.2}\right)\right]$$

$$= (0.1)\cdot(-2)(0-1)\cdot(-5)\left(0-e^{-0.2}\right) = e^{-0.2} \approx 0.8187$$

(ii) $P\,(X \leq 2, Y \leq 4) = \int_{-\infty}^2 \int_{-\infty}^4 f(x,y)\,dy\,dx = \int_0^2 \int_0^4 0.1 e^{-(0.5x+0.2y)}\,dy\,dx$

$$= 0.1 \int_0^2 e^{-0.5x}\,dx \int_0^4 e^{-0.2y}\,dy = 0.1\left[-2e^{-0.5x}\right]_0^2 \left[-5e^{-0.2y}\right]_0^4$$

$$= (0.1)\cdot(-2)\left(e^{-1}-1\right)\cdot(-5)\left(e^{-0.8}-1\right)$$

$$= \left(e^{-1}-1\right)\left(e^{-0.8}-1\right) = 1 + e^{-1.8} - e^{-0.8} - e^{-1} \approx 0.3481$$

(c) The expected value of X is given by

$$\mu_1 = \iint_{\mathbb{R}^2} x\,f(x,y)\,dA = \int_0^\infty \int_0^\infty x\left[0.1 e^{-(0.5x+0.2y)}\right]\,dy\,dx$$

$$= 0.1 \int_0^\infty x e^{-0.5x}\,dx \int_0^\infty e^{-0.2y}\,dy = 0.1 \lim_{t\to\infty} \int_0^t x e^{-0.5x}\,dx \lim_{t\to\infty} \int_0^t e^{-0.2y}\,dy$$

To evaluate the first integral, we integrate by parts with $u = x$ and $dv = e^{-0.5x}\,dx$ (or we can use Formula 96 in the Table of Integrals):

$\int x e^{-0.5x}\,dx = -2x e^{-0.5x} - \int -2e^{-0.5x}\,dx = -2x e^{-0.5x} - 4e^{-0.5x} = -2\,(x+2)\,e^{-0.5x}$. Thus

$$\mu_1 = 0.1 \lim_{t\to\infty} \left[-2(x+2)e^{-0.5x}\right]_0^t \lim_{t\to\infty} \left[-5e^{-0.2y}\right]_0^t$$

$$= 0.1 \lim_{t\to\infty} (-2)\left[(t+2)e^{-0.5t}-2\right] \lim_{t\to\infty} (-5)\left[e^{-0.2t}-1\right]$$

$$= 0.1(-2)\left(\lim_{t\to\infty} \frac{t+2}{e^{0.5t}} - 2\right)(-5)(-1) = 2 \quad \text{(by l'Hospital's Rule)}$$

The expected value of Y is given by

$$\mu_2 = \iint_{\mathbb{R}^2} y\,f(x,y)\,dA = \int_0^\infty \int_0^\infty y\left[0.1 e^{-(0.5+0.2y)}\right]\,dy\,dx$$

$$= 0.1 \int_0^\infty e^{-0.5x}\,dx \int_0^\infty y e^{-0.2y}\,dy = 0.1 \lim_{t\to\infty} \int_0^t e^{-0.5x}\,dx \lim_{t\to\infty} \int_0^t y e^{-0.2y}\,dy$$

To evaluate the second integral, we integrate by parts with $u = y$ and $dv = e^{-0.2y} \, dy$ (or again we can use Formula 96 in the Table of Integrals) which gives

$\int y e^{-0.2y} \, dy = -5ye^{-0.2y} + \int 5e^{-0.2y} \, dy = -5(y+5)e^{-0.2y}$. Then

$$\mu_2 = 0.1 \lim_{t \to \infty} \left[-2e^{-0.5x}\right]_0^t \lim_{t \to \infty} \left[-5(y+5)e^{-0.2y}\right]_0^t$$

$$= 0.1 \lim_{t \to \infty} \left[-2\left(e^{-0.5t} - 1\right)\right] \lim_{t \to \infty} \left(-5\left[(t+5)e^{-0.2t} - 5\right]\right)$$

$$= 0.1(-2)(-1) \cdot (-5)\left(\lim_{t \to \infty} \frac{t+5}{e^{0.2t}} - 5\right) = 5 \quad \text{(by l'Hospital's Rule)}$$

22. (a) Each lamp has exponential density function

$$f(t) = \begin{cases} 0 & \text{if } t < 0 \\ \frac{1}{1000}e^{-t/1000} & \text{if } t \geq 0 \end{cases}$$

If X and Y are the lifetimes of the individual bulbs, then X and Y are independent, so the joint density function is the product of the individual density functions:

$$f(x,y) = \begin{cases} 10^{-6}e^{-(x+y)/1000} & \text{if } x \geq 0, y \geq 0 \\ 0 & \text{otherwise} \end{cases}$$

The probability that both of the bulbs fail within 1000 hours is

$$P(X \leq 1000, Y \leq 1000) = \int_{-\infty}^{1000} \int_{-\infty}^{1000} f(x,y) \, dy \, dx$$

$$= \int_0^{1000} \int_0^{1000} 10^{-6}e^{-(x+y)/1000} \, dy \, dx$$

$$= 10^{-6} \int_0^{1000} e^{-x/1000} \, dx \int_0^{1000} e^{-y/1000} \, dy$$

$$= 10^{-6} \left[-1000e^{-x/1000}\right]_0^{1000} \left[-1000e^{-y/1000}\right]_0^{1000}$$

$$= \left(e^{-1} - 1\right)^2 \approx 0.3996$$

(b) Now we are asked for the probability that the combined lifetimes of both bulbs is 1000 hours or less. Thus we want to find $P(X + Y \leq 1000)$, or equivalently $P((X,Y) \in D)$ where D is the triangular region shown in the figure. Then

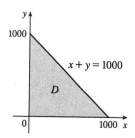

$$P(X + Y \leq 1000) = \iint_D f(x,y) \, dA = \int_0^{1000} \int_0^{1000-x} 10^{-6}e^{-(x+y)/1000} \, dy \, dx$$

$$= 10^{-6} \int_0^{1000} \left[-1000e^{-(x+y)/1000}\right]_{y=0}^{y=1000-x} dx = -10^{-3} \int_0^{1000} \left(e^{-1} - e^{-x/1000}\right) dx$$

$$= -10^{-3} \left[e^{-1}x + 1000e^{-x/1000}\right]_0^{1000} = 1 - 2e^{-1} \approx 0.2642$$

23. (a) The random variables X and Y are normally distributed with $\mu_1 = 45$, $\mu_2 = 20$, $\sigma_1 = 0.5$, and $\sigma_2 = 0.1$. The

individual density functions for X and Y, then, are $f_1(x) = \dfrac{1}{0.5\sqrt{2\pi}} e^{-(x-45)^2/0.5}$ and

$f_2(y) = \dfrac{1}{0.1\sqrt{2\pi}} e^{-(y-20)^2/0.02}$. Since X and Y are independent, the joint density function is the product

$$f(x,y) = f_1(x)f_2(y) = \frac{1}{0.5\sqrt{2\pi}} e^{-(x-45)^2/0.5} \frac{1}{0.1\sqrt{2\pi}} e^{-(y-20)^2/0.02}$$

$$= \frac{10}{\pi} e^{-2(x-45)^2 - 50(y-20)^2}$$

Then
$$P(40 \le X \le 50, 20 \le Y \le 25) = \int_{40}^{50} \int_{20}^{25} f(x,y)\, dy\, dx$$

$$= \frac{10}{\pi} \int_{40}^{50} \int_{20}^{25} e^{-2(x-45)^2 - 50(y-20)^2}\, dy\, dx$$

Using a CAS or calculator to evaluate the integral, we get $P(40 \le X \le 50, 20 \le Y \le 25) \approx 0.500$.

(b) $P\left(4(X-45)^2 + 100(Y-20)^2 \le 2\right) = \iint_D \frac{10}{\pi} e^{-2(x-45)^2 - 50(y-20)^2}\, dA$, where D is the region enclosed

by the ellipse $4(x-45)^2 + 100(y-20)^2 = 2$. Solving for y gives $y = 20 \pm \frac{1}{10}\sqrt{2 - 4(x-45)^2}$, the upper

and lower halves of the ellipse, and these two halves meet where $y = 20$ [since the ellipse is

centered at $(45, 20)$] $\Rightarrow$ $4(x-45)^2 = 2$ $\Rightarrow$ $x = 45 \pm \frac{1}{\sqrt{2}}$. Thus

$\iint_D \frac{10}{\pi} e^{-2(x-45)^2 - 50(y-20)^2}\, dA = \frac{10}{\pi} \int_{45-1/\sqrt{2}}^{45+1/\sqrt{2}} \int_{20-\frac{1}{10}\sqrt{2-4(x-45)^2}}^{20+\frac{1}{10}\sqrt{2-4(x-45)^2}} e^{-2(x-45)^2 - 50(y-20)^2}\, dy\, dx$. Using

a CAS or calculator to evaluate the integral, we get $P\left(4(X-45)^2 + 100(Y-20)^2 \le 2\right) \approx 0.632$.

24. Because X and Y are independent, the joint density function for Xavier's and Yolanda's arrival times is the product
of the individual density functions:

$$f(x,y) = f_1(x)f_2(y) = \begin{cases} \frac{1}{50} e^{-x} y & \text{if } x \ge 0, 0 \le y \le 10 \\ 0 & \text{otherwise} \end{cases}$$

Since Xavier won't wait for Yolanda, they won't meet unless $X \ge Y$. Additionally, Yolanda will wait up to half an
hour but no longer, so they won't meet unless $X - Y \le 30$. Thus the probability that they meet is $P((X,Y) \in D)$
where D is the parallelogram shown in the figure.

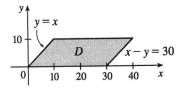

The integral is simpler to evaluate if we consider D as a type II region, so

$$P((X,Y) \in D) = \iint_D f(x,y)\, dx\, dy = \int_0^{10} \int_y^{y+30} \frac{1}{50} e^{-x} y\, dx\, dy = \frac{1}{50} \int_0^{10} y\left[-e^{-x}\right]_{x=y}^{x=y+30} dy$$

$$= \frac{1}{50} \int_0^{10} y\left(-e^{-(y+30)} + e^{-y}\right) dy = \frac{1}{50}\left(1 - e^{-30}\right) \int_0^{10} y e^{-y}\, dy$$

By integration by parts (or Formula 96 in the Table of Integrals), this is

$\frac{1}{50}\left(1 - e^{-30}\right)\left[-(y+1)e^{-y}\right]_0^{10} = \frac{1}{50}\left(1 - e^{-30}\right)\left(1 - 11e^{-10}\right) \approx 0.020$. Thus there is only about a 2% chance

they will meet. Such is student life!

25. (a) If $f(P, A)$ is the probability that an individual at A will be infected by an individual at P, and $k\,dA$ is the number of infected individuals in an element of area dA, then $f(P, A)k\,dA$ is the number of infections that should result from exposure of the individual at A to infected people in the element of area dA. Integration over D gives the number of infections of the person at A due to all the infected people in D. In rectangular coordinates (with the origin at the city's center), the exposure of a person at A is

$$E = \iint_D kf(P, A)\,dA = k\iint_D \frac{20 - d(P, A)}{20}\,dA$$

$$= k\iint_D \left[1 - \frac{\sqrt{(x - x_0)^2 + (y - y_0)^2}}{20}\right] dx\,dy$$

(b) If $A = (0, 0)$, then

$$E = k\iint_D \left[1 - \frac{1}{20}\sqrt{x^2 + y^2}\right] dx\,dy = k\int_0^{2\pi}\int_0^{10}\left(1 - \frac{r}{20}\right)r\,dr\,d\theta$$

$$= 2\pi k\left[\frac{r^2}{2} - \frac{r^3}{60}\right]_0^{10} = 2\pi k\left(50 - \tfrac{50}{3}\right) = \tfrac{200}{3}\pi k \approx 209k$$

For A at the edge of the city, it is convenient to use a polar coordinate system centered at A. Then the polar equation for the circular boundary of the city becomes $r = 20\cos\theta$ instead of $r = 10$, and the distance from A to a point P in the city is again r (see the figure). So

$$E = k\int_{-\pi/2}^{\pi/2}\int_0^{20\cos\theta}\left(1 - \frac{r}{20}\right)r\,dr\,d\theta$$

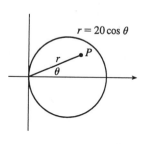

$$= k\int_{-\pi/2}^{\pi/2}\left[\frac{r^2}{2} - \frac{r^3}{60}\right]_{r=0}^{r=20\cos\theta} d\theta$$

$$= k\int_{-\pi/2}^{\pi/2}\left(200\cos^2\theta - \tfrac{400}{3}\cos^3\theta\right) d\theta$$

$$= 200k\int_{-\pi/2}^{\pi/2}\left[\tfrac{1}{2} + \tfrac{1}{2}\cos 2\theta - \tfrac{2}{3}\left(1 - \sin^2\theta\right)\cos\theta\right] d\theta$$

$$= 200k\left[\tfrac{1}{2}\theta + \tfrac{1}{4}\sin 2\theta - \tfrac{2}{3}\sin\theta + \tfrac{2}{3}\cdot\tfrac{1}{3}\sin^3\theta\right]_{-\pi/2}^{\pi/2}$$

$$= 200k\left[\tfrac{\pi}{4} + 0 - \tfrac{2}{3} + \tfrac{2}{9} + \tfrac{\pi}{4} + 0 - \tfrac{2}{3} + \tfrac{2}{9}\right]$$

$$= 200k\left(\tfrac{\pi}{2} - \tfrac{8}{9}\right) \approx 136k$$

Therefore the risk of infection is much lower at the edge of the city than in the middle, so it is better to live at the edge.

12.6 Surface Area • • • • • • • • • • • • • •

1. Here $z = f(x, y) = 2 + 3x + 4y$ and D is the rectangle $[0, 5] \times [1, 4]$, so by Formula 6 the area of the surface is

$$A(S) = \iint_D \sqrt{1 + \left(\frac{\partial z}{\partial x}\right)^2 + \left(\frac{\partial z}{\partial y}\right)^2} \, dA = \iint_D \sqrt{1 + 3^2 + 4^2} \, dA = \sqrt{26} \iint_D dA = \sqrt{26} \, A(D)$$

$$= \sqrt{26} \, (5)(3) = 15\sqrt{26}$$

2. $z = f(x, y) = 10 - 2x - 5y$ and D is the disk $x^2 + y^2 \le 9$, so by Formula 6

$$A(S) = \iint_D \sqrt{1 + (-2)^2 + (-5)^2} \, dA = \sqrt{30} \iint_D dA = \sqrt{30} \, A(D)$$

$$= \sqrt{30} \, (\pi \cdot 3^2) = 9\sqrt{30} \, \pi$$

3. $z = f(x, y) = 6 - 3x - 2y$ which intersects the xy-plane in the line $3x + 2y = 6$, so D is the triangular region given by $\{(x, y) \mid 0 \le x \le 2, 0 \le y \le 3 - \frac{3}{2}x\}$. Thus

$$A(S) = \iint_D \sqrt{1 + (-3)^2 + (-2)^2} \, dA = \sqrt{14} \iint_D dA = \sqrt{14} \, A(D$$

$$= \sqrt{14} \left(\frac{1}{2} \cdot 2 \cdot 3\right) = 3\sqrt{14}$$

4. $\mathbf{r}_u = \langle 0, 1, -5 \rangle$, $\mathbf{r}_v = \langle 1, -2, 1 \rangle$, and $\mathbf{r}_u \times \mathbf{r}_v = \langle -9, -5, -1 \rangle$. Then by Definition 4,

$$A(S) = \iint_D |\mathbf{r}_u \times \mathbf{r}_v| \, dA = \int_0^1 \int_0^1 |\langle -9, -5, -1 \rangle| \, du \, dv = \sqrt{107} \int_0^1 du \int_0^1 dv = \sqrt{107}$$

5. $z = f(x, y) = y^2 - x^2$ with $1 \le x^2 + y^2 \le 4$. Then

$$A(S) = \iint_D \sqrt{1 + 4x^2 + 4y^2} \, dA = \int_0^{2\pi} \int_1^2 \sqrt{1 + 4r^2} \, r \, dr \, d\theta = \int_0^{2\pi} d\theta \int_1^2 r\sqrt{1 + 4r^2} \, dr$$

$$= [\theta]_0^{2\pi} \left[\frac{1}{12}(1 + 4r^2)^{3/2}\right]_1^2 = \frac{\pi}{6}\left(17\sqrt{17} - 5\sqrt{5}\right)$$

6. $z = f(x, y) = x + y^2$ with $0 \le x \le y$, $0 \le y \le 1$. Thus, by Formula 6,

$$A(S) = \iint_D \sqrt{1 + 1 + 4y^2} \, dA = \int_0^1 \int_0^y \sqrt{2 + 4y^2} \, dx \, dy = \int_0^1 \left[x\sqrt{2 + 4y^2}\right]_{x=0}^{x=y} dy$$

$$= \int_0^1 y\sqrt{2 + 4y^2} \, dy = 2\left(\frac{1}{24}\right)(2 + 4y^2)^{3/2} \Big|_0^1 = \frac{1}{12}\left(6\sqrt{6} - 2\sqrt{2}\right)$$

$$= \frac{3}{\sqrt{6}} - \frac{1}{3\sqrt{2}}$$

7. $\mathbf{r}_u = \langle v, 1, 1 \rangle$, $\mathbf{r}_v = \langle u, 1, -1 \rangle$ and $\mathbf{r}_u \times \mathbf{r}_v = \langle -2, u + v, v - u \rangle$. Then

$$A(S) = \iint_{u^2 + v^2 \le 1} \sqrt{4 + 2u^2 + 2v^2} \, dA = \int_0^{2\pi} \int_0^1 r\sqrt{4 + 2r^2} \, dr \, d\theta = \int_0^{2\pi} d\theta \int_0^1 r\sqrt{4 + 2r^2} \, dr$$

$$= 2\pi \left[\frac{1}{6}(4 + 2r^2)^{3/2}\right]_0^1 = \frac{\pi}{3}\left(6\sqrt{6} - 8\right) = \pi\left(2\sqrt{6} - \frac{8}{3}\right)$$

8. $\mathbf{r}_u = \langle \cos v, \sin v, 0 \rangle$, $\mathbf{r}_v = \langle -u \sin v, u \cos v, 1 \rangle$, and $\mathbf{r}_u \times \mathbf{r}_v = \langle \sin v, -\cos v, u \rangle$. Then

$$A(S) = \int_0^\pi \int_0^1 \sqrt{1 + u^2} \, du \, dv = \int_0^\pi dv \int_0^1 \sqrt{1 + u^2} \, du$$

$$= \pi\left[\frac{u}{2}\sqrt{u^2 + 1} + \frac{1}{2}\ln\left|u + \sqrt{u^2 + 1}\right|\right]_0^1 = \frac{\pi}{2}\left[\sqrt{2} + \ln\left(1 + \sqrt{2}\right)\right]$$

9. A parametric representation of the surface is $x = x$, $y = 4x + z^2$, $z = z$ with $0 \leq x \leq 1$, $0 \leq z \leq 1$. Hence $\mathbf{r}_x \times \mathbf{r}_z = (\mathbf{i} + 4\mathbf{j}) \times (2z\,\mathbf{j} + \mathbf{k}) = 4\,\mathbf{i} - \mathbf{j} + 2z\,\mathbf{k}$.

Note: In general, if $y = f(x, z)$ then $\mathbf{r}_x \times \mathbf{r}_z = \dfrac{\partial f}{\partial x}\mathbf{i} - \mathbf{j} + \dfrac{\partial f}{\partial z}\mathbf{k}$ and

$$A(S) = \iint_D \sqrt{1 + \left(\frac{\partial f}{\partial x}\right)^2 + \left(\frac{\partial f}{\partial z}\right)^2}\, dA. \text{ Then}$$

$$A(S) = \int_0^1 \int_0^1 \sqrt{17 + 4z^2}\, dx\, dz = \int_0^1 \sqrt{17 + 4z^2}\, dz$$

$$= \tfrac{1}{2}\left(z\sqrt{17 + 4z^2} + \tfrac{17}{2}\ln\left|2z + \sqrt{4z^2 + 17}\right|\right)\Big]_0^1 = \tfrac{\sqrt{21}}{2} + \tfrac{17}{4}\left[\ln\left(2 + \sqrt{21}\right) - \ln\sqrt{17}\right]$$

10. A parametric representation of the surface is $x = y^2 + z^2$, $y = y$, $z = z$ with $0 \leq y^2 + z^2 \leq 9$. Hence $\mathbf{r}_y \times \mathbf{r}_z = (2y\,\mathbf{i} + \mathbf{j}) \times (2z\,\mathbf{i} + \mathbf{k}) = \mathbf{i} - 2y\,\mathbf{j} - 2z\,\mathbf{k}$.

Note: In general, if $x = f(y, z)$ then $\mathbf{r}_y \times \mathbf{r}_z = \mathbf{i} - \dfrac{\partial f}{\partial y}\mathbf{j} - \dfrac{\partial f}{\partial z}\mathbf{k}$, and

$$A(S) = \iint_D \sqrt{1 + \left(\frac{\partial f}{\partial y}\right)^2 + \left(\frac{\partial f}{\partial z}\right)^2}\, dA. \text{ Then}$$

$$A(S) = \iint_{0 \leq y^2 + z^2 \leq 9} \sqrt{1 + 4y^2 + 4z^2}\, dA = \int_0^{2\pi}\int_0^3 \sqrt{1 + 4r^2}\, r\, dr\, d\theta$$

$$= \int_0^{2\pi} d\theta \int_0^3 r\sqrt{1 + 4r^2}\, dr = 2\pi\left[\tfrac{1}{12}(1 + 4r^2)^{3/2}\right]_0^3 = \tfrac{\pi}{6}\left(37\sqrt{37} - 1\right)$$

11. $z = f(x, y) = xy$ with $0 \leq x^2 + y^2 \leq 1$, so $f_x = y$, $f_y = x$ $\Rightarrow$

$$A(S) = \iint_D \sqrt{1 + y^2 + x^2}\, dA = \int_0^{2\pi}\int_0^1 \sqrt{r^2 + 1}\, r\, dr\, d\theta = \int_0^{2\pi}\left[\tfrac{1}{3}(r^2 + 1)^{3/2}\right]_{r=0}^{r=1} d\theta$$

$$= \int_0^{2\pi} \tfrac{1}{3}\left(2\sqrt{2} - 1\right) d\theta = \tfrac{2\pi}{3}\left(2\sqrt{2} - 1\right)$$

12. $z = f(x, y) = \tfrac{2}{3}\left(x^{3/2} + y^{3/2}\right)$ and $D = \{(x, y) \mid 0 \leq x \leq 1, 0 \leq y \leq 1\}$. Then $f_x = x^{1/2}$, $f_y = y^{1/2}$ and

$$A(S) = \iint_D \sqrt{1 + \left(\sqrt{x}\right)^2 + \left(\sqrt{y}\right)^2}\, dA = \int_0^1\int_0^1 \sqrt{x + y + 1}\, dy\, dx$$

$$= \int_0^1 \left[\tfrac{2}{3}(x + y + 1)^{3/2}\right]_{y=0}^{y=1} dx = \tfrac{2}{3}\int_0^1 \left[(x + 2)^{3/2} - (x + 1)^{3/2}\right] dx$$

$$= \tfrac{2}{3}\left[\tfrac{2}{5}(x + 2)^{5/2} - \tfrac{2}{5}(x + 1)^{5/2}\right]_0^1 = \tfrac{4}{15}\left(3^{5/2} - 2^{5/2} - 2^{5/2} + 1\right)$$

$$\cdot = \tfrac{4}{15}\left(3^{5/2} - 2^{7/2} + 1\right)$$

13. (a) The midpoints of the four squares are $\left(\frac{1}{4}, \frac{1}{4}\right)$, $\left(\frac{1}{4}, \frac{3}{4}\right)$, $\left(\frac{3}{4}, \frac{1}{4}\right)$, and $\left(\frac{3}{4}, \frac{3}{4}\right)$. Since $z = x^2 + y^2$, the Midpoint Rule gives

$$A(S) = \iint_D \sqrt{1 + \left(\frac{\partial z}{\partial x}\right)^2 + \left(\frac{\partial z}{\partial y}\right)^2} \, dA = \iint_D \sqrt{1 + (2x)^2 + (2y)^2} \, dA$$

$$\approx \tfrac{1}{4}\left(\sqrt{1 + \left[2\left(\tfrac{1}{4}\right)\right]^2 + \left[2\left(\tfrac{1}{4}\right)\right]^2} + \sqrt{1 + \left[2\left(\tfrac{1}{4}\right)\right]^2 + \left[2\left(\tfrac{3}{4}\right)\right]^2}\right.$$

$$\left. + \sqrt{1 + \left[2\left(\tfrac{3}{4}\right)\right]^2 + \left[2\left(\tfrac{1}{4}\right)\right]^2} + \sqrt{1 + \left[2\left(\tfrac{3}{4}\right)\right]^2 + \left[2\left(\tfrac{3}{4}\right)\right]^2}\right)$$

$$= \tfrac{1}{4}\left(\sqrt{\tfrac{3}{2}} + 2\sqrt{\tfrac{7}{2}} + \sqrt{\tfrac{11}{2}}\right) \approx 1.8279$$

(b) A CAS estimates the integral to be

$A(S) = \iint_D \sqrt{1 + (2x)^2 + (2y)^2} \, dA = \int_0^1 \int_0^1 \sqrt{1 + 4x^2 + 4y^2} \, dy \, dx \approx 1.8616$. This agrees with the Midpoint estimate only in the first decimal place.

14. (a) With $m = n = 2$ we have four squares with midpoints $\left(\frac{1}{2}, \frac{1}{2}\right)$, $\left(\frac{1}{2}, \frac{3}{2}\right)$, $\left(\frac{3}{2}, \frac{1}{2}\right)$, and $\left(\frac{3}{2}, \frac{3}{2}\right)$. Since $z = xy + x^2 + y^2$, the Midpoint Rule gives

$$A(S) = \iint_D \sqrt{1 + \left(\frac{\partial z}{\partial x}\right)^2 + \left(\frac{\partial z}{\partial y}\right)^2} \, dA = \iint_D \sqrt{1 + (y + 2x)^2 + (x + 2y)^2} \, dA$$

$$\approx 1\left(\sqrt{1 + \left(\tfrac{3}{2}\right)^2 + \left(\tfrac{3}{2}\right)^2} + \sqrt{1 + \left(\tfrac{5}{2}\right)^2 + \left(\tfrac{7}{2}\right)^2} + \sqrt{1 + \left(\tfrac{7}{2}\right)^2 + \left(\tfrac{5}{2}\right)^2} + \sqrt{1 + \left(\tfrac{9}{2}\right)^2 + \left(\tfrac{9}{2}\right)^2}\right)$$

$$= \frac{\sqrt{22}}{2} + \frac{\sqrt{78}}{2} + \frac{\sqrt{78}}{2} + \frac{\sqrt{166}}{2} \approx 17.619$$

(b) Using a CAS, we have

$A(S) = \iint_D \sqrt{1 + (y + 2x)^2 + (x + 2y)^2} \, dA = \int_0^2 \int_0^2 \sqrt{1 + (y + 2x)^2 + (x + 2y)^2} \, dy \, dx \approx 17.7165$.
This is within about 0.1 of the Midpoint Rule estimate.

15. $\mathbf{r}(u, v) = \langle \cos^3 u \cos^3 v, \sin^3 u \cos^3 v, \sin^3 v \rangle$, so $\mathbf{r}_u = \langle -3 \cos^2 u \sin u \cos^3 v, 3 \sin^2 u \cos u \cos^3 v, 0 \rangle$,

$\mathbf{r}_v = \langle -3 \cos^3 u \cos^2 v \sin v, -3 \sin^3 u \cos^2 v \sin v, 3 \sin^2 v \cos v \rangle$, and

$\mathbf{r}_u \times \mathbf{r}_v = \langle 9 \cos u \sin^2 u \cos^4 v \sin^2 v, 9 \cos^2 u \sin u \cos^4 v \sin^2 v, 9 \cos^2 u \sin^2 u \cos^5 v \sin v \rangle$. Then

$$|\mathbf{r}_u \times \mathbf{r}_v| = 9 \sqrt{\cos^2 u \sin^4 u \cos^8 v \sin^4 v + \cos^4 u \sin^2 u \cos^8 v \sin^4 v + \cos^4 u \sin^4 u \cos^{10} v \sin^2 v}$$

$$= 9 \sqrt{\cos^2 u \sin^2 u \cos^8 v \sin^2 v \left(\sin^2 v + \cos^2 u \sin^2 u \cos^2 v\right)}$$

$$= 9 \cos^4 v \, |\cos u \sin u \sin v| \sqrt{\sin^2 v + \cos^2 u \sin^2 u \cos^2 v}$$

Using a CAS, we have

$A(S) = \int_0^\pi \int_0^{2\pi} 9 \cos^4 v \, |\cos u \sin u \sin v| \sqrt{\sin^2 v + \cos^2 u \sin^2 u \cos^2 v} \, dv \, du \approx 4.4506$.

16. Let $f(x, y) = \dfrac{1 + x^2}{1 + y^2}$. Then $f_x = \dfrac{2x}{1 + y^2}$,

$$f_y = (1 + x^2)\left[-\frac{2y}{(1 + y^2)^2}\right] = -\frac{2y(1 + x^2)}{(1 + y^2)^2}.$$

We use a CAS to estimate

$\int_{-1}^{1} \int_{-(1-|x|)}^{1-|x|} \sqrt{1 + f_x^2 + f_y^2}\, dy\, dx \approx 2.6959$. In order to

graph only the part of the surface above the square, we use

$-(1 - |x|) \le y \le 1 - |x|$ as the y-range in our plot

command.

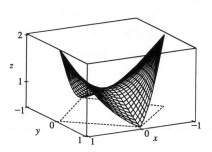

17. $z = 1 + 2x + 3y + 4y^2$, so

$$A(S) = \iint_D \sqrt{1 + \left(\frac{\partial z}{\partial x}\right)^2 + \left(\frac{\partial z}{\partial y}\right)^2}\, dA = \int_1^4 \int_0^1 \sqrt{1 + 4 + (3 + 8y)^2}\, dy\, dx$$

$$= \int_1^4 \int_0^1 \sqrt{14 + 48y + 64y^2}\, dy\, dx.$$

Using a CAS, we have

$\int_1^4 \int_0^1 \sqrt{14 + 48y + 64y^2}\, dy\, dx = \frac{45}{8}\sqrt{14} + \frac{15}{16}\ln\left(11\sqrt{5} + 3\sqrt{14}\sqrt{5}\right) - \frac{15}{16}\ln\left(3\sqrt{5} + \sqrt{14}\sqrt{5}\right)$ or

$\frac{45}{8}\sqrt{14} + \frac{15}{16}\ln\dfrac{11\sqrt{5} + 3\sqrt{70}}{3\sqrt{5} + \sqrt{70}}$.

18. (a) $\mathbf{r}_u = a\cos v\,\mathbf{i} + b\sin v\,\mathbf{j} + 2u\,\mathbf{k}$, $\mathbf{r}_v = -au\sin v\,\mathbf{i} + bu\cos v\,\mathbf{j} + 0\,\mathbf{k}$, and

$\mathbf{r}_u \times \mathbf{r}_v = -2bu^2\cos v\,\mathbf{i} - 2au^2\sin v\,\mathbf{j} + abu\,\mathbf{k}$.

$A(S) = \int_0^{2\pi} \int_0^2 |\mathbf{r}_u \times \mathbf{r}_v|\, du\, dv = \int_0^{2\pi} \int_0^2 \sqrt{4b^2u^4\cos^2 v + 4a^2u^4\sin^2 v + a^2b^2u^2}\, du\, dv$

(b) $x^2 = a^2u^2\cos^2 v$, $y^2 = b^2u^2\sin^2 v$, $z = u^2$ $\Rightarrow$ $x^2/a^2 + y^2/b^2 = u^2 = z$ which is an elliptic paraboloid.

To find D, notice that $0 \le u \le 2$ $\Rightarrow$ $0 \le z \le 4$ $\Rightarrow$ $0 \le x^2/a^2 + y^2/b^2 \le 4$. Therefore, using Formula 6,

we have $A(S) = \int_{-2a}^{2a} \int_{-b\sqrt{4 - (x^2/a^2)}}^{b\sqrt{4 - (x^2/a^2)}} \sqrt{1 + (2x/a^2)^2 + (2y/b^2)^2}\, dy\, dx$.

(c)

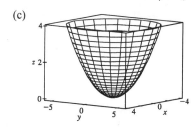

(d) We substitute $a = 2$, $b = 3$ in the integral in part (a) to get

$A(S) = \int_0^{2\pi} \int_0^2 2u\sqrt{9u^2\cos^2 v + 4u^2\sin^2 v + 9}\, du\, dv$. We use a

CAS to estimate the integral accurate to four decimal places. To

speed up the calculation, we can set `Digits:=7;` (in Maple) or use

the approximation command `N` (in Mathematica). We find that

$A(S) \approx 115.6596$.

19. (a) $x = a\sin u\cos v$, $y = b\sin u\sin v$, $z = c\cos u$ $\Rightarrow$

(b)

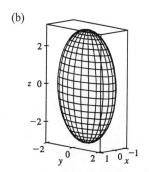

$$\frac{x^2}{a^2} + \frac{y^2}{b^2} + \frac{z^2}{c^2} = (\sin u\cos v)^2 + (\sin u\sin v)^2 + (\cos u)^2$$

$$= \sin^2 u + \cos^2 u = 1$$

and since the ranges of u and v are sufficient to generate the

entire graph, the parametric equations represent an ellipsoid.

(c) From the parametric equations (with $a = 1$, $b = 2$, and $c = 3$), we calculate

$\mathbf{r}_u = \cos u \cos v\,\mathbf{i} + 2\cos u \sin v\,\mathbf{j} - 3\sin u\,\mathbf{k}$ and

$\mathbf{r}_v = -\sin u \sin v\,\mathbf{i} + 2\sin u \cos v\,\mathbf{j}$. So $\mathbf{r}_u \times \mathbf{r}_v = 6\sin^2 u \cos v\,\mathbf{i} + 3\sin^2 u \sin v\,\mathbf{j} + 2\sin u \cos u\,\mathbf{k}$, and the

surface area is given by

$$A(S) = \int_0^{2\pi}\int_0^{\pi} |\mathbf{r}_u \times \mathbf{r}_v|\, du\, dv$$

$$= \int_0^{2\pi}\int_0^{\pi} \sqrt{36\sin^4 u \cos^2 v + 9\sin^4 u \sin^2 v + 4\cos^2 u \sin^2 u}\, du\, dv$$

20. (a) $x = a\cosh u \cos v$, $y = b\cosh u \sin v$, $z = c\sinh u$ $\Rightarrow$

(b)

$$\frac{x^2}{a^2} + \frac{y^2}{b^2} - \frac{z^2}{c^2} = \cosh^2 u \cos^2 v + \cosh^2 u \sin^2 v - \sinh^2 u$$

$$= \cosh^2 u - \sinh^2 u = 1$$

and the parametric equations represent a hyperboloid of one sheet.

(c) $\mathbf{r}_u = \sinh u \cos v\,\mathbf{i} + 2\sinh u \sin v\,\mathbf{j} + 3\cosh u\,\mathbf{k}$ and

$\mathbf{r}_v = -\cosh u \sin v\,\mathbf{i} + 2\cosh u \cos v\,\mathbf{j}$, so

$\mathbf{r}_u \times \mathbf{r}_v = -6\cosh^2 u \cos v\,\mathbf{i} - 3\cosh^2 u \sin v\,\mathbf{j} + 2\cosh u \sinh u\,\mathbf{k}$. We integrate between

$u = \sinh^{-1}(-1) = -\ln\left(1 + \sqrt{2}\right)$ and $u = \sinh^{-1} 1 = \ln\left(1 + \sqrt{2}\right)$, since then z varies between -3 and 3,

as desired. So the surface area is

$$A(S) = \int_0^{2\pi}\int_{-\ln\left(1+\sqrt{2}\right)}^{\ln\left(1+\sqrt{2}\right)} |\mathbf{r}_u \times \mathbf{r}_v|\, du\, dv$$

$$= \int_0^{2\pi}\int_{-\ln\left(1+\sqrt{2}\right)}^{\ln\left(1+\sqrt{2}\right)} \sqrt{36\cosh^4 u \cos^2 v + 9\cosh^4 u \sin^2 v + 4\cosh^2 u \sinh^2 u}\, du\, dv$$

21. To find the region D: $z = x^2 + y^2$ implies $z + z^2 = 4z$ or $z^2 - 3z = 0$. Thus $z = 0$ or $z = 3$ are the planes where

the surfaces intersect. But $x^2 + y^2 + z^2 = 4z$ implies $x^2 + y^2 + (z - 2)^2 = 4$, so $z = 3$ intersects the upper

hemisphere. Thus $(z - 2)^2 = 4 - x^2 - y^2$ or $z = 2 + \sqrt{4 - x^2 - y^2}$. Therefore D is the region inside the circle

$x^2 + y^2 + (3 - 2)^2 = 4$, that is, $D = \{(x, y) \mid x^2 + y^2 \le 3\}$.

$$A(S) = \iint_D \sqrt{1 + \left[(-x)(4 - x^2 - y^2)^{-1/2}\right]^2 + \left[(-y)(4 - x^2 - y^2)^{-1/2}\right]^2}\, dA$$

$$= \int_0^{2\pi}\int_0^{\sqrt{3}} \sqrt{1 + \frac{r^2}{4 - r^2}}\, r\, dr\, d\theta = \int_0^{2\pi}\int_0^{\sqrt{3}} \frac{2r\, dr}{\sqrt{4 - r^2}}\, d\theta = \int_0^{2\pi}\left[-2(4 - r^2)^{1/2}\right]_{r=0}^{r=\sqrt{3}}\, d\theta$$

$$= \int_0^{2\pi}(-2 + 4)\, d\theta = 2\theta\big]_0^{2\pi} = 4\pi$$

22. We first find the area of the face of the surface that intersects the positive y-axis. A parametric representation of the

surface is $x = x$, $y = \sqrt{1 - z^2}$, $z = z$ with $x^2 + z^2 \le 1$. Then $\mathbf{r}(x, z) = \left\langle x, \sqrt{1 - z^2}, z\right\rangle$ $\Rightarrow$ $\mathbf{r}_x = \langle 1, 0, 0\rangle$,

$\mathbf{r}_z = \left\langle 0, -z/\sqrt{1 - z^2}, 1\right\rangle$ and $\mathbf{r}_x \times \mathbf{r}_z = \left\langle 0, -1, -z/\sqrt{1 - z^2}\right\rangle$ $\Rightarrow$ $|\mathbf{r}_x \times \mathbf{r}_z| = \sqrt{1 + \frac{z^2}{1 - z^2}} = \frac{1}{\sqrt{1 - z^2}}$.

$$A(S) = \iint_{x^2 + z^2 \le 1} |\mathbf{r}_x \times \mathbf{r}_z|\, dA = \int_{-1}^{1}\int_{-\sqrt{1-z^2}}^{\sqrt{1-z^2}} \frac{1}{\sqrt{1 - z^2}}\, dx\, dz$$

$$= 4\int_0^1\int_0^{\sqrt{1-z^2}} \frac{1}{\sqrt{1 - z^2}}\, dx\, dz \quad \text{(by the symmetry of the surface)}$$

This integral is improper (when $z = 1$), so

$$A(S) = \lim_{t \to 1^-} 4 \int_0^t \int_0^{\sqrt{1-z^2}} \frac{1}{\sqrt{1-z^2}}\, dx\, dz = \lim_{t \to 1^-} 4 \int_0^t \frac{\sqrt{1-z^2}}{\sqrt{1-z^2}}\, dz$$

$$= \lim_{t \to 1^-} 4 \int_0^t dz = \lim_{t \to 1^-} 4t = 4$$

Since the complete surface consists of four congruent faces, the total surface area is $4(4) = 16$.

Alternate Solution: The face of the surface that intersects the positive y-axis can also be parametrized as
$\mathbf{r}(x, \theta) = \langle x, \cos\theta, \sin\theta \rangle$ for $-\frac{\pi}{2} \le \theta \le \frac{\pi}{2}$ and $x^2 + z^2 \le 1$ $\Leftrightarrow$ $x^2 + \sin^2\theta \le 1$ $\Leftrightarrow$
$-\sqrt{1 - \sin^2\theta} \le x \le \sqrt{1 - \sin^2\theta}$ $\Leftrightarrow$ $-\cos\theta \le x \le \cos\theta$. Then $\mathbf{r}_x = \langle 1, 0, 0 \rangle$,
$\mathbf{r}_\theta = \langle 0, -\sin\theta, \cos\theta \rangle$ and $\mathbf{r}_x \times \mathbf{r}_\theta = \langle 0, -\cos\theta, -\sin\theta \rangle$ $\Rightarrow$ $|\mathbf{r}_x \times \mathbf{r}_\theta| = 1$, so
$A(S) = \int_{-\pi/2}^{\pi/2} \int_{-\cos\theta}^{\cos\theta} 1\, dx\, d\theta = \int_{-\pi/2}^{\pi/2} 2\cos\theta\, d\theta = 2\sin\theta]_{-\pi/2}^{\pi/2} = 4$. Again, the area of the complete surface is
$4(4) = 16$.

23. If we revolve the curve $y = f(x)$, $a \le x \le b$ about the x-axis, where $f(x) \ge 0$, then from Equations 10.5.3 we
know we can parametrize the surface using $x = x$, $y = f(x)\cos\theta$, and $z = f(x)\sin\theta$, where $a \le x \le b$ and
$0 \le \theta \le 2\pi$. Thus we can say the surface is represented by $\mathbf{r}(x, \theta) = x\,\mathbf{i} + f(x)\cos\theta\,\mathbf{j} + f(x)\sin\theta\,\mathbf{k}$, with
$a \le x \le b$ and $0 \le \theta \le 2\pi$. Then by (4), the surface area is given by $A(S) = \iint_D |\mathbf{r}_x \times \mathbf{r}_\theta|\, dA$ where D is the
rectangular parameter region $[a, b] \times [0, 2\pi]$. Here, $\mathbf{r}_x(x, \theta) = \mathbf{i} + f'(x)\cos\theta\,\mathbf{j} + f'(x)\sin\theta\,\mathbf{k}$ and
$\mathbf{r}_\theta(x) = -f(x)\sin\theta\,\mathbf{j} + f(x)\cos\theta\,\mathbf{k}$. So

$$\mathbf{r}_x \times \mathbf{r}_\theta = \begin{vmatrix} \mathbf{i} & \mathbf{j} & \mathbf{k} \\ 1 & f'(x)\cos\theta & f'(x)\sin\theta \\ 0 & -f(x)\sin\theta & f(x)\cos\theta \end{vmatrix}$$

$$= \left[f(x)f'(x)\cos^2\theta + f(x)f'(x)\sin^2\theta \right]\mathbf{i} - f(x)\cos\theta\,\mathbf{j} - f(x)\sin\theta\,\mathbf{k}$$

$$= f(x)f'(x)\mathbf{i} - f(x)\cos\theta\,\mathbf{j} - f(x)\sin\theta\,\mathbf{k} \text{ and}$$

$$|\mathbf{r}_x \times \mathbf{r}_\theta| = \sqrt{[f(x)f'(x)]^2 + [f(x)]^2\cos^2\theta + [f(x)]^2\sin^2\theta}$$

$$= \sqrt{[f(x)]^2 ([f'(x)]^2 + 1)} = f(x)\sqrt{1 + [f'(x)]^2} \text{ [since } f(x) \ge 0 \text{]. Thus}$$

$$A(S) = \iint_D |\mathbf{r}_x \times \mathbf{r}_\theta|\, dA = \int_a^b \int_0^{2\pi} f(x)\sqrt{1 + [f'(x)]^2}\, d\theta\, dx$$

$$= \int_a^b f(x)\sqrt{1 + [f'(x)]^2}\, [\theta]_0^{2\pi}\, dx = 2\pi \int_a^b f(x)\sqrt{1 + [f'(x)]^2}\, dx$$

24. $y = x^3$ $\Rightarrow$ $y' = 3x^2$. So

$$S = \int_0^2 2\pi y \sqrt{1 + (y')^2}\, dx = 2\pi \int_0^2 x^3 \sqrt{1 + 9x^4}\, dx \quad \text{(Let } u = 1 + 9x^4 \text{, so } du = 36x^3\, dx\text{)}$$

$$= \frac{2\pi}{36} \int_1^{145} \sqrt{u}\, du = \frac{\pi}{18} \left[\frac{2}{3} u^{3/2} \right]_1^{145} = \frac{\pi}{27} \left(145\sqrt{145} - 1 \right)$$

25. $y = \sqrt{x}$ $\Rightarrow$ $1 + \left(\dfrac{dy}{dx}\right)^2 = 1 + \left(\dfrac{1}{2\sqrt{x}}\right)^2 = 1 + \dfrac{1}{4x}$. So

$$S = \int_4^9 2\pi y \sqrt{1 + \left(\frac{dy}{dx}\right)^2}\, dx = \int_4^9 2\pi \sqrt{x}\sqrt{1 + \frac{1}{4x}}\, dx = 2\pi \int_4^9 \left(x + \tfrac{1}{4}\right) dx$$

$$= 2\pi \left[\tfrac{2}{3}\left(x + \tfrac{1}{4}\right)^{3/2}\right]_4^9 = \tfrac{4\pi}{3}\left[\tfrac{1}{8}(4x + 1)^{3/2}\right]_4^9 = \tfrac{\pi}{6}\left(37\sqrt{37} - 17\sqrt{17}\right)$$

26. $x = b\cos\theta + a\cos\alpha\cos\theta$, $y = b\sin\theta + a\cos\alpha\sin\theta$, $z = a\sin\alpha$, so
$\mathbf{r}_\alpha = \langle -a\sin\alpha\cos\theta, -a\sin\alpha\sin\theta, a\cos\alpha \rangle$, $\mathbf{r}_\theta = \langle -(b + a\cos\alpha)\sin\theta, (b + a\cos\alpha)\cos\theta, 0 \rangle$ and

$$\mathbf{r}_\alpha \times \mathbf{r}_\theta = \left(-ab\cos\alpha\cos\theta - a^2\cos\alpha\cos^2\theta\right)\mathbf{i} + \left(-ab\sin\alpha\cos\theta - a^2\sin\alpha\cos^2\theta\right)\mathbf{j}$$
$$+ \left(-ab\cos^2\alpha\sin\theta - a^2\cos^2\alpha\sin\theta\cos\theta - ab\sin^2\alpha\sin\theta - a^2\sin^2\alpha\sin\theta\cos\theta\right)\mathbf{k}$$
$$= -a(b + a\cos\alpha)[(\cos\theta\cos\alpha)\mathbf{i} + (\sin\theta\cos\alpha)\mathbf{j} + (\sin\alpha)\mathbf{k}]$$

Then $|\mathbf{r}_\alpha \times \mathbf{r}_\theta| = a(b + a\cos\alpha)\sqrt{\cos^2\theta\cos^2\alpha + \sin^2\theta\cos^2\alpha + \sin^2\alpha} = a(b + a\cos\alpha)$.
Note: $b > a$, $-1 \le \cos\alpha \le 1$ so $|b + a\cos\alpha| = b + a\cos\alpha$. Hence
$A(S) = \int_0^{2\pi}\int_0^{2\pi} a(b + a\cos\alpha)\, d\alpha\, d\theta = 2\pi\left[ab\alpha + a^2\sin\alpha\right]_0^{2\pi} = 4\pi^2 ab$.

12.7 Triple Integrals · · · · · · · · · · · ·

1. $\iiint_B xyz^2\, dV = \int_0^1 \int_{-1}^2 \int_0^3 xyz^2\, dz\, dx\, dy = \int_0^1 \int_{-1}^2 xy\left[\tfrac{1}{3}z^3\right]_{z=0}^{z=3}\, dx\, dy = \int_0^1 \int_{-1}^2 9xy\, dx\, dy$

$= \int_0^1 \left[\tfrac{9}{2}x^2 y\right]_{x=-1}^{x=2}\, dy = \int_0^1 \tfrac{27}{2}y\, dy = \tfrac{27}{4}y^2\big]_0^1 = \tfrac{27}{4}$

2. There are six different possible orders of integration.

$$\iiint_E (xz - y^3)\, dV = \int_{-1}^1 \int_0^2 \int_0^1 (xz - y^3)\, dz\, dy\, dx = \int_{-1}^1 \int_0^2 \left[\tfrac{1}{2}xz^2 - y^3 z\right]_{z=0}^{z=1}\, dy\, dx$$

$$= \int_{-1}^1 \int_0^2 \left(\tfrac{1}{2}x - y^3\right) dy\, dx = \int_{-1}^1 \left[\tfrac{1}{2}xy - \tfrac{1}{4}y^4\right]_{y=0}^{y=2}\, dx$$

$$= \int_{-1}^1 (x - 4)\, dx = \left[\tfrac{1}{2}x^2 - 4x\right]_{-1}^1 = -8$$

$$\iiint_E (xz - y^3)\, dV = \int_0^2 \int_{-1}^1 \int_0^1 (xz - y^3)\, dz\, dx\, dy = \int_0^2 \int_{-1}^1 \left[\tfrac{1}{2}xz^2 - y^3 z\right]_{z=0}^{z=1}\, dx\, dy$$

$$= \int_0^2 \int_{-1}^1 \left(\tfrac{1}{2}x - y^3\right) dx\, dy = \int_0^2 \left[\tfrac{1}{4}x^2 - xy^3\right]_{x=-1}^{x=1}\, dy$$

$$= \int_0^2 -2y^3\, dy = -\tfrac{1}{2}y^4\big]_0^2 = -8$$

$$\iiint_E (xz - y^3)\, dV = \int_{-1}^{1} \int_0^1 \int_0^2 (xz - y^3)\, dy\, dz\, dx = \int_{-1}^1 \int_0^1 \left[xyz - \tfrac{1}{4}y^4 \right]_{y=0}^{y=2} dz\, dx$$

$$= \int_{-1}^1 \int_0^1 (2xz - 4)\, dz\, dx = \int_{-1}^1 \left[xz^2 - 4z \right]_{z=0}^{z=1} dx$$

$$= \int_{-1}^1 (x - 4)\, dx = \left[\tfrac{1}{2}x^2 - 4x \right]_{-1}^1 = -8$$

$$\iiint_E (xz - y^3)\, dV = \int_0^1 \int_{-1}^1 \int_0^2 (xz - y^3)\, dy\, dx\, dz = \int_0^1 \int_{-1}^1 \left[xyz - \tfrac{1}{4}y^4 \right]_{y=0}^{y=2} dx\, dz$$

$$= \int_0^1 \int_{-1}^1 (2xz - 4)\, dx\, dz = \int_0^1 \left[x^2 z - 4x \right]_{x=-1}^{x=1} dz$$

$$= \int_0^1 -8\, dz = -8z\big]_0^1 = -8$$

$$\iiint_E (xz - y^3)\, dV = \int_0^2 \int_0^1 \int_{-1}^1 (xz - y^3)\, dx\, dz\, dy = \int_0^2 \int_0^1 \left[\tfrac{1}{2}x^2 z - xy^3 \right]_{x=-1}^{x=1} dz\, dy$$

$$= \int_0^2 \int_0^1 -2y^3\, dz\, dy = \int_0^2 \left[-2y^3 z \right]_{z=0}^{z=1} dy = \int_0^2 -2y^3\, dy = -\tfrac{1}{2}y^4 \Big]_0^2 = -8$$

$$\iiint_E (xz - y^3)\, dV = \int_0^1 \int_0^2 \int_{-1}^1 (xz - y^3)\, dx\, dy\, dz = \int_0^1 \int_0^2 \left[\tfrac{1}{2}x^2 z - xy^3 \right]_{x=-1}^{x=1} dy\, dz$$

$$= \int_0^1 \int_0^2 -2y^3\, dy\, dz = \int_0^1 \left[-\tfrac{1}{2}y^4 \right]_{y=0}^{y=2} dz = \int_0^1 -8\, dz = -8z\big]_0^1 = -8$$

3. $\int_0^1 \int_0^z \int_0^{x+z} 6xz\, dy\, dx\, dz = \int_0^1 \int_0^z [6xyz]_{y=0}^{y=x+z}\, dx\, dz = \int_0^1 \int_0^z 6xz(x+z)\, dx\, dz$

$$= \int_0^1 \left[2x^3 z + 3x^2 z^2 \right]_{x=0}^{x=z} dz = \int_0^1 (2z^4 + 3z^4)\, dz = \int_0^1 5z^4\, dz = z^5 \big]_0^1 = 1$$

4. $\int_0^1 \int_x^{2x} \int_0^y 2xyz\, dz\, dy\, dx = \int_0^1 \int_x^{2x} \left[xyz^2 \right]_{z=0}^{z=y} dy\, dx = \int_0^1 \int_x^{2x} xy^3\, dy\, dx$

$$= \int_0^1 \left[\tfrac{1}{4}xy^4 \right]_{y=x}^{y=2x} dx = \int_0^1 \tfrac{15}{4}x^5\, dx = \tfrac{5}{8}x^6 \Big]_0^1 = \tfrac{5}{8}$$

5. $\int_0^3 \int_0^1 \int_0^{\sqrt{1-z^2}} ze^y\, dx\, dz\, dy = \int_0^3 \int_0^1 [xze^y]_{x=0}^{x=\sqrt{1-z^2}}\, dz\, dy = \int_0^3 \int_0^1 ze^y \sqrt{1-z^2}\, dz\, dy$

$$= \int_0^3 \left[-\tfrac{1}{3}(1-z^2)^{3/2}\, e^y \right]_{z=0}^{z=1} dy = \int_0^3 \tfrac{1}{3}e^y\, dy = \tfrac{1}{3}e^y \Big]_0^3 = \tfrac{1}{3}(e^3 - 1)$$

6. $\int_0^1 \int_0^z \int_0^y ze^{-y^2}\, dx\, dy\, dz = \int_0^1 \int_0^z \left[xze^{-y^2} \right]_{x=0}^{x=y} dy\, dz = \int_0^1 \int_0^z yze^{-y^2}\, dy\, dz = \int_0^1 \left[-\tfrac{1}{2}ze^{-y^2} \right]_{y=0}^{y=z} dz$

$$= \int_0^1 -\tfrac{1}{2}z\left(e^{-z^2} - 1 \right) dz = \tfrac{1}{2}\int_0^1 \left(z - ze^{-z^2} \right) dz$$

$$= \tfrac{1}{2}\left[\tfrac{1}{2}z^2 + \tfrac{1}{2}e^{-z^2} \right]_0^1 = \tfrac{1}{4}(1 + e^{-1} - 0 - 1) = \tfrac{1}{4e}$$

7. $\iiint_E 2x\, dV = \int_0^2 \int_0^{\sqrt{4-y^2}} \int_0^y 2x\, dz\, dx\, dy = \int_0^2 \int_0^{\sqrt{4-y^2}} [2xz]_{z=0}^{z=y}\, dx\, dy = \int_0^2 \int_0^{\sqrt{4-y^2}} 2xy\, dx\, dy$

$$= \int_0^2 \left[x^2 y \right]_{x=0}^{x=\sqrt{4-y^2}} dy = \int_0^2 (4 - y^2)\, y\, dy = \left[2y^2 - \tfrac{1}{4}y^4 \right]_0^2 = 4$$

8. $\iiint_E yz\cos(x^5)\,dV = \int_0^1\int_0^x\int_x^{2x} yz\cos(x^5)\,dz\,dy\,dx = \int_0^1\int_0^x \left[\frac{1}{2}yz^2\cos(x^5)\right]_{z=x}^{z=2x}\,dy\,dx$

$= \frac{1}{2}\int_0^1\int_0^x 3x^2y\cos(x^5)\,dy\,dx = \frac{1}{2}\int_0^1 \left[\frac{3}{2}x^2y^2\cos(x^5)\right]_{y=0}^{y=x}\,dx$

$= \frac{3}{4}\int_0^1 x^4\cos(x^5)\,dx = \frac{3}{4}\left[\frac{1}{5}\sin(x^5)\right]_0^1 = \frac{3}{20}(\sin 1 - \sin 0) = \frac{3}{20}\sin 1$

9. Here $E = \{(x,y,z) \mid 0 \le x \le 1, 0 \le y \le \sqrt{x}, 0 \le z \le 1 + x + y\}$, so

$\iiint_E 6xy\,dV = \int_0^1\int_0^{\sqrt{x}}\int_0^{1+x+y} 6xy\,dz\,dy\,dx = \int_0^1\int_0^{\sqrt{x}} [6xyz]_{z=0}^{z=1+x+y}\,dy\,dx$

$= \int_0^1\int_0^{\sqrt{x}} 6xy(1+x+y)\,dy\,dx = \int_0^1 \left[3xy^2 + 3x^2y^2 + 2xy^3\right]_{y=0}^{y=\sqrt{x}}\,dx$

$= \int_0^1 \left(3x^2 + 3x^3 + 2x^{5/2}\right)\,dx = \left[x^3 + \frac{3}{4}x^4 + \frac{4}{7}x^{7/2}\right]_0^1 = \frac{65}{28}$

10.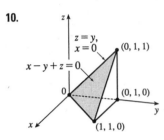

$\int_0^1\int_0^y\int_0^{y-z} xz\,dx\,dz\,dy = \int_0^1\int_0^y \frac{1}{2}(y-z)^2 z\,dz\,dy$

$= \frac{1}{2}\int_0^1 \left[\frac{1}{2}y^2z^2 - \frac{2}{3}yz^3 + \frac{1}{4}z^4\right]_{z=0}^{z=y}\,dy$

$= \frac{1}{24}\int_0^1 y^4\,dy = \frac{1}{24}\left[\frac{1}{5}y^5\right]_0^1 = \frac{1}{120}$

11.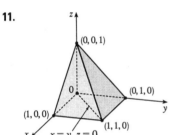

By symmetry $\iiint_E z\,dV = 2\iiint_{E'} z\,dV$ where E' is the part of E to the left [as viewed from $(10, 10, 0)$] of the plane $x = y$. So

$\iiint_E z\,dV = \int_0^1\int_y^1\int_0^{1-x} 2z\,dz\,dx\,dy = \int_0^1\int_y^1 (1-x)^2\,dx\,dy$

$= \int_0^1 \left[-\frac{1}{3}(1-x)^3\right]_{x=y}^{x=1}\,dy = \int_0^1 \frac{1}{3}(1-y)^3\,dy$

$= \frac{1}{12}(1-y)^4\Big]_0^1 = \frac{1}{12}$

12.

E is the solid above the region shown in the xy-plane and below the plane $z = x$. Thus,

$\iiint_E (x+2y)\,dV = \int_0^1\int_{x^2}^x\int_0^x (x+2y)\,dz\,dy\,dx$

$= \int_0^1\int_{x^2}^x (x^2 + 2yx)\,dy\,dx = \int_0^1 \left[x^2y + xy^2\right]_{y=x^2}^{y=x}\,dx$

$= \int_0^1 (2x^3 - x^4 - x^5)\,dx = \left[\frac{1}{2}x^4 - \frac{1}{5}x^5 - \frac{1}{6}x^6\right]_0^1 = \frac{2}{15}$

13.

The projection E on the yz-plane is the disk $y^2 + z^2 \le 1$. Using polar coordinates $y = r\cos\theta$ and $z = r\sin\theta$, we get

$\iiint_E x\,dV = \iint_D \left[\int_{4y^2+4z^2}^4 x\,dx\right]\,dA$

$= \frac{1}{2}\iint_D \left[4^2 - (4y^2 + 4z^2)^2\right]\,dA = 8\int_0^{2\pi}\int_0^1 (1 - r^4)\,r\,dr\,d\theta$

$= 8\int_0^{2\pi}d\theta\int_0^1 (r - r^5)\,dr = 8(2\pi)\left[\frac{1}{2}r^2 - \frac{1}{6}r^6\right]_0^1 = \frac{16\pi}{3}$

14.

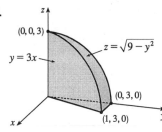

$$\int_0^1 \int_{3x}^3 \int_0^{\sqrt{9-y^2}} z \, dz \, dy \, dx = \int_0^1 \int_{3x}^3 \tfrac{1}{2}(9 - y^2) \, dy \, dx$$

$$= \int_0^1 \left[\tfrac{9}{2} y - \tfrac{1}{6} y^3 \right]_{y=3x}^{y=3} dx$$

$$= \int_0^1 \left[9 - \tfrac{27}{2} x + \tfrac{9}{2} x^3 \right] dx$$

$$= \left[9x - \tfrac{27}{4} x^2 + \tfrac{9}{8} x^4 \right]_0^1 = \tfrac{27}{8}$$

15. The plane $2x + y + z = 4$ intersects the xy-plane when

$2x + y + 0 = 4 \quad \Rightarrow \quad y = 4 - 2x$, so

$E = \{(x, y, z) \mid 0 \le x \le 2, 0 \le y \le 4 - 2x, 0 \le z \le 4 - 2x - y\}$

and

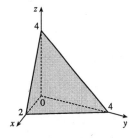

$$V = \int_0^2 \int_0^{4-2x} \int_0^{4-2x-y} dz \, dy \, dx = \int_0^2 \int_0^{4-2x} (4 - 2x - y) \, dy \, dx = \int_0^2 \left[4y - 2xy - \tfrac{1}{2} y^2 \right]_{y=0}^{y=4-2x} dx$$

$$= \int_0^2 \left[4(4 - 2x) - 2x(4 - 2x) - \tfrac{1}{2}(4 - 2x)^2 \right] dx = \int_0^2 (2x^2 - 8x + 8) \, dx = \left[\tfrac{2}{3} x^3 - 4x^2 + 8x \right]_0^2 = \tfrac{16}{3}$$

16.

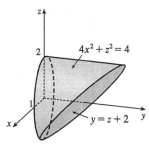

$$V = \int_{-1}^1 \int_{-\sqrt{4-4x^2}}^{\sqrt{4-4x^2}} \int_0^{z+2} dy \, dz \, dx$$

$$= 2 \int_0^1 \int_{-\sqrt{4-4x^2}}^{\sqrt{4-4x^2}} \int_0^{z+2} dy \, dz \, dx \quad \text{(by symmetry)}$$

$$= 2 \int_0^1 \int_{-\sqrt{4-4x^2}}^{\sqrt{4-4x^2}} (z + 2) \, dz \, dx$$

$$= 2 \int_0^1 \left[\tfrac{1}{2} z^2 + 2z \right]_{z=-2\sqrt{1-x^2}}^{z=2\sqrt{1-x^2}} dx = 2 \int_0^1 8 \sqrt{1 - x^2} \, dx$$

$$= 16 \left[\tfrac{1}{2} x \sqrt{1 - x^2} + \tfrac{1}{2} \sin^{-1} x \right]_0^1 = 8 \tfrac{\pi}{2} = 4\pi$$

17.

$$V = \int_0^1 \int_{-\sqrt{x}}^{\sqrt{x}} \int_0^{1-x} dz \, dy \, dx = \int_0^1 \int_{-\sqrt{x}}^{\sqrt{x}} (1 - x) \, dy \, dx$$

$$= \int_0^1 2 \sqrt{x} (1 - x) \, dx = \int_0^1 2 \left(\sqrt{x} - x^{3/2} \right) dx$$

$$= 2 \left[\tfrac{2}{3} x^{3/2} - \tfrac{2}{5} x^{5/2} \right]_0^1 = 2 \left(\tfrac{2}{3} - \tfrac{2}{5} \right) = \tfrac{8}{15}$$

18. The paraboloids $z = x^2 + y^2$ and $z = 18 - x^2 - y^2$ intersect when $x^2 + y^2 = 18 - x^2 - y^2$ $\Rightarrow$ $2x^2 + 2y^2 = 18$ $\Rightarrow$ $x^2 + y^2 = 9$. Thus, $E = \{(x, y, z) \mid x^2 + y^2 \leq 9, x^2 + y^2 \leq z \leq 18 - x^2 - y^2\}$. Let $D = \{(x, y) \mid x^2 + y^2 \leq 9\}$. Then

$$V = \iiint_E dV = \iint_D \left(\int_{x^2+y^2}^{18-x^2-y^2} dz \right) dA = \iint_D (18 - 2x^2 - 2y^2) \, dA$$

$$= \int_0^{2\pi} \int_0^3 (18 - 2r^2) \, r \, dr \, d\theta = \int_0^{2\pi} \left[9r^2 - \tfrac{1}{2}r^4 \right]_{r=0}^{r=3} d\theta = \int_0^{2\pi} \tfrac{81}{2} \, d\theta = 81\pi$$

19. (a) The wedge can be described as the region

$$D = \{(x, y, z) \mid y^2 + z^2 \leq 1, 0 \leq x \leq 1, 0 \leq y \leq x\}$$

$$= \left\{(x, y, z) \mid 0 \leq x \leq 1, 0 \leq y \leq x, 0 \leq z \leq \sqrt{1 - y^2}\right\}$$

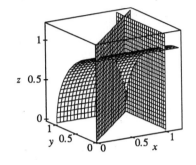

So the integral expressing the volume of the wedge is

$$\iiint_D dV = \int_0^1 \int_0^x \int_0^{\sqrt{1-y^2}} dz \, dy \, dx.$$

(b) A CAS gives $\int_0^1 \int_0^x \int_0^{\sqrt{1-y^2}} dz \, dy \, dx = \frac{\pi}{4} - \frac{1}{3}$.

(Or use Formulas 30 and 87 from the Table of Integrals.)

20. (a) Note that $\Delta V = \left(\tfrac{1}{2}\right)^3 = \tfrac{1}{8}$, so the Midpoint Rule gives

$$\iiint_B f(x, y, z) \, dV \approx \tfrac{1}{8} \left[f\left(\tfrac{1}{4}, \tfrac{1}{4}, \tfrac{1}{4}\right) + f\left(\tfrac{1}{4}, \tfrac{1}{4}, \tfrac{3}{4}\right) + f\left(\tfrac{1}{4}, \tfrac{3}{4}, \tfrac{1}{4}\right) + f\left(\tfrac{3}{4}, \tfrac{1}{4}, \tfrac{1}{4}\right) \right.$$

$$\left. + f\left(\tfrac{1}{4}, \tfrac{3}{4}, \tfrac{3}{4}\right) + f\left(\tfrac{3}{4}, \tfrac{1}{4}, \tfrac{3}{4}\right) + f\left(\tfrac{3}{4}, \tfrac{3}{4}, \tfrac{1}{4}\right) + f\left(\tfrac{3}{4}, \tfrac{3}{4}, \tfrac{3}{4}\right) \right]$$

$$= \tfrac{1}{8} \left[e^{-3(1/4)^2} + 3e^{-2(1/4)^2-(3/4)^2} + 3e^{-(1/4)^2-2(3/4)^2} + e^{-3(3/4)^2} \right] \approx 0.42968$$

(b) A CAS estimates the integral to be $\iiint_B e^{-x^2-y^2-z^2} \, dV \approx 0.42$. The estimate in part (a) is correct to one decimal place, and is larger than the actual value of the integral.

21. Here $f(x, y, z) = \dfrac{1}{\ln(1 + x + y + z)}$ and $\Delta V = 2 \cdot 4 \cdot 2 = 16$, so the Midpoint Rule gives

$$\iiint_B f(x, y, z) \, dV \approx \sum_{i=1}^l \sum_{j=1}^m \sum_{k=1}^n f(\overline{x}_i, \overline{y}_j, \overline{z}_k) \, \Delta V$$

$$= 16 \, [f(1, 2, 1) + f(1, 2, 3) + f(1, 6, 1) + f(1, 6, 3)$$

$$+ f(3, 2, 1) + f(3, 2, 3) + f(3, 6, 1) + f(3, 6, 3)]$$

$$= 16 \left[\frac{1}{\ln 5} + \frac{1}{\ln 7} + \frac{1}{\ln 9} + \frac{1}{\ln 11} + \frac{1}{\ln 7} + \frac{1}{\ln 9} + \frac{1}{\ln 11} + \frac{1}{\ln 13} \right] \approx 60.533$$

22. Here $f(x, y, z) = \sin(xy^2z^3)$ and $\Delta V = 2 \cdot 1 \cdot \frac{1}{2} = 1$, so the Midpoint Rule gives

$$\iiint_B f(x, y, z) \, dV \approx \sum_{i=1}^l \sum_{j=1}^m \sum_{k=1}^n f(\overline{x}_i, \overline{y}_j, \overline{z}_k) \, \Delta V$$

$$= 1 \, \left[f\left(1, \tfrac{1}{2}, \tfrac{1}{4}\right) + f\left(1, \tfrac{1}{2}, \tfrac{3}{4}\right) + f\left(1, \tfrac{3}{2}, \tfrac{1}{4}\right) + f\left(1, \tfrac{3}{2}, \tfrac{3}{4}\right) \right.$$

$$\left. + f\left(3, \tfrac{1}{2}, \tfrac{1}{4}\right) + f\left(3, \tfrac{1}{2}, \tfrac{3}{4}\right) + f\left(3, \tfrac{3}{2}, \tfrac{1}{4}\right) + f\left(3, \tfrac{3}{2}, \tfrac{3}{4}\right) \right]$$

$$= \sin \tfrac{1}{256} + \sin \tfrac{27}{256} + \sin \tfrac{9}{256} + \sin \tfrac{243}{256} + \sin \tfrac{3}{256} + \sin \tfrac{81}{256} + \sin \tfrac{27}{256} + \sin \tfrac{729}{256} \approx 1.675$$

23. $E = \{(x, y, z) \mid 0 \leq x \leq 1, 0 \leq z \leq 1 - x, 0 \leq y \leq 2 - 2z\}$,

the solid bounded by the three coordinate planes and the planes
$z = 1 - x$, $y = 2 - 2z$.

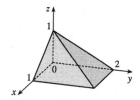

24. $E = \{(x, y, z) \mid 0 \leq y \leq 2, 0 \leq z \leq 2 - y, 0 \leq x \leq 4 - y^2\}$,

the solid bounded by the three coordinate planes, the plane $z = 2 - y$,
and the cylindrical surface $x = 4 - y^2$.

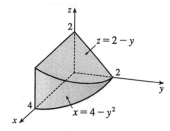

25.

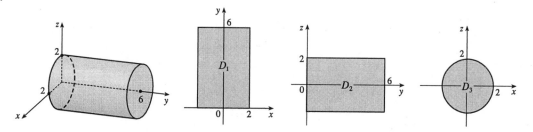

If D_1, D_2, D_3 are the projections of E on the xy-, yz-, and xz-planes, then

$$D_1 = \{(x, y) \mid -2 \leq x \leq 2, 0 \leq y \leq 6\}$$

$$D_2 = \{(y, z) \mid -2 \leq z \leq 2, 0 \leq y \leq 6\}$$

$$D_3 = \{(x, z) \mid x^2 + z^2 \leq 4\}$$

Therefore

$$E = \left\{ (x, y, z) \mid -\sqrt{4 - x^2} \leq z \leq \sqrt{4 - x^2}, \ -2 \leq x \leq 2, 0 \leq y \leq 6 \right\}$$

$$= \left\{ (x, y, z) \mid -\sqrt{4 - z^2} \leq x \leq \sqrt{4 - z^2}, \ -2 \leq z \leq 2, 0 \leq y \leq 6 \right\}$$

$$\iiint_E f(x, y, z) \, dV = \int_{-2}^{2} \int_{0}^{6} \int_{-\sqrt{4-x^2}}^{\sqrt{4-x^2}} f(x, y, z) \, dz \, dy \, dx = \int_{0}^{6} \int_{-2}^{2} \int_{-\sqrt{4-x^2}}^{\sqrt{4-x^2}} f(x, y, z) \, dz \, dx \, dy$$

$$= \int_{0}^{6} \int_{-2}^{2} \int_{-\sqrt{4-z^2}}^{\sqrt{4-z^2}} f(x, y, z) \, dx \, dz \, dy = \int_{-2}^{2} \int_{0}^{6} \int_{-\sqrt{4-z^2}}^{\sqrt{4-z^2}} f(x, y, z) \, dx \, dy \, dz$$

$$= \int_{-2}^{2} \int_{-\sqrt{4-x^2}}^{\sqrt{4-x^2}} \int_{0}^{6} f(x, y, z) \, dy \, dz \, dx = \int_{-2}^{2} \int_{-\sqrt{4-z^2}}^{\sqrt{4-z^2}} \int_{0}^{6} f(x, y, z) \, dy \, dx \, dz$$

26.

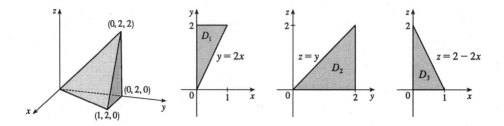

If D_1, D_2, and D_3 are the projections of E on the xy-, yz-, and xz-planes, then

$$D_1 = \{(x, y) \mid 0 \leq x \leq 1, 2x \leq y \leq 2\} = \{(x, y) \mid 0 \leq y \leq 2, 0 \leq x \leq y/2\},$$
$$D_2 = \{(y, z) \mid 0 \leq y \leq 2, 0 \leq z \leq y\} = \{(y, z) \mid 0 \leq z \leq 2, z \leq y \leq 2\}, \text{ and}$$
$$D_3 = \{(x, z) \mid 0 \leq x \leq 1, 0 \leq z \leq 2 - 2x\} = \{(x, z) \mid 0 \leq z \leq 2, 0 \leq x \leq (2 - z)/2\}$$

Therefore

$$
\begin{aligned}
E &= \{(x, y, z) \mid 0 \leq x \leq 1, 2x \leq y \leq 2, 0 \leq z \leq y - 2x\} \\
&= \{(x, y, z) \mid 0 \leq y \leq 2, 0 \leq x \leq y/2, 0 \leq z \leq y - 2x\} \\
&= \{(x, y, z) \mid 0 \leq y \leq 2, 0 \leq z \leq y, 0 \leq x \leq (y - z)/2\} \\
&= \{(x, y, z) \mid 0 \leq z \leq 2, z \leq y \leq 2, 0 \leq x \leq (y - z)/2\} \\
&= \{(x, y, z) \mid 0 \leq x \leq 1, 0 \leq z \leq 2 - 2x, z + 2x \leq y \leq 2\} \\
&= \{(x, y, z) \mid 0 \leq z \leq 2, 0 \leq x \leq (2 - z)/2, z + 2x \leq y \leq 2\}
\end{aligned}
$$

Then

$$
\begin{aligned}
\iiint_E f(x, y, z)\, dV &= \int_0^1 \int_{2x}^2 \int_0^{y-2x} f(x, y, z)\, dz\, dy\, dx \\
&= \int_0^2 \int_0^{y/2} \int_0^{y-2x} f(x, y, z)\, dz\, dx\, dy \\
&= \int_0^2 \int_0^y \int_0^{(y-z)/2} f(x, y, z)\, dx\, dz\, dy \\
&= \int_0^2 \int_z^2 \int_0^{(y-z)/2} f(x, y, z)\, dx\, dy\, dz \\
&= \int_0^1 \int_0^{2-2x} \int_{z+2x}^2 f(x, y, z)\, dy\, dz\, dx \\
&= \int_0^2 \int_0^{(2-z)/2} \int_{z+2x}^2 f(x, y, z)\, dy\, dx\, dz
\end{aligned}
$$

27.

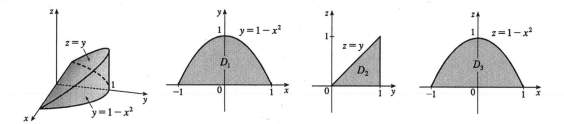

If D_1, D_2, and D_3 are the projections of E on the xy-, yz-, and xz-planes, then

$$D_1 = \left\{(x, y) \mid -1 \le x \le 1, 0 \le y \le 1 - x^2\right\} = \left\{(x, y) \mid 0 \le y \le 1, -\sqrt{1-y} \le x \le \sqrt{1-y}\right\},$$

$$D_2 = \left\{(y, z) \mid 0 \le y \le 1, 0 \le z \le y\right\} = \left\{(y, z) \mid 0 \le z \le 1, z \le y \le 1\right\}, \text{ and}$$

$$D_3 = \left\{(x, z) \mid -1 \le x \le 1, 0 \le z \le 1 - x^2\right\} = \left\{(x, z) \mid 0 \le z \le 1, -\sqrt{1-z} \le x \le \sqrt{1-z}\right\}.$$

Therefore

$$E = \left\{(x, y, z) \mid -1 \le x \le 1, 0 \le y \le 1 - x^2, 0 \le z \le y\right\}$$

$$= \left\{(x, y, z) \mid 0 \le y \le 1, -\sqrt{1-y} \le x \le \sqrt{1-y}, 0 \le z \le y\right\}$$

$$= \left\{(x, y, z) \mid 0 \le y \le 1, 0 \le z \le y, -\sqrt{1-y} \le x \le \sqrt{1-y}\right\}$$

$$= \left\{(x, y, z) \mid 0 \le z \le 1, z \le y \le 1, -\sqrt{1-y} \le x \le \sqrt{1-y}\right\}$$

$$= \left\{(x, y, z) \mid -1 \le x \le 1, 0 \le z \le 1 - x^2, z \le y \le 1 - x^2\right\}$$

$$= \left\{(x, y, z) \mid 0 \le z \le 1, -\sqrt{1-z} \le x \le \sqrt{1-z}, z \le y \le 1 - x^2\right\}$$

Then

$$\iiint_E f(x, y, z)\, dV = \int_{-1}^{1} \int_0^{1-x^2} \int_0^y f(x, y, z)\, dz\, dy\, dx = \int_0^1 \int_{-\sqrt{1-y}}^{\sqrt{1-y}} \int_0^y f(x, y, z)\, dz\, dx\, dy$$

$$= \int_0^1 \int_0^y \int_{-\sqrt{1-y}}^{\sqrt{1-y}} f(x, y, z)\, dx\, dz\, dy = \int_0^1 \int_z^1 \int_{-\sqrt{1-y}}^{\sqrt{1-y}} f(x, y, z)\, dx\, dy\, dz$$

$$= \int_{-1}^1 \int_0^{1-x^2} \int_z^{1-x^2} f(x, y, z)\, dy\, dz\, dx = \int_0^1 \int_{-\sqrt{1-z}}^{\sqrt{1-z}} \int_z^{1-x^2} f(x, y, z)\, dy\, dx\, dz$$

28.

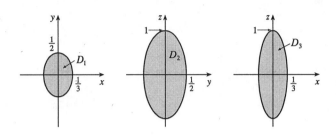

If D_1, D_2 and D_3 are the projections of E on the xy-, yz-, and xz-planes, then $D_1 = \{(x, y) \mid 9x^2 + 4y^2 \leq 1\}$, $D_2 = \{(y, z) \mid 4y^2 + z^2 \leq 1\}$, $D_3 = \{(x, z) \mid 9x^2 + z^2 \leq 1\}$. Therefore

$$\iiint_E f(x, y, z)\, dV = \int_{-1/3}^{1/3} \int_{-\sqrt{1-9x^2}/2}^{\sqrt{1-9x^2}/2} \int_{-\sqrt{1-9x^2-4y^2}}^{\sqrt{1-9x^2-4y^2}} f(x, y, z)\, dz\, dy\, dx$$

$$= \int_{-1/2}^{1/2} \int_{-\sqrt{1-4y^2}/3}^{\sqrt{1-4y^2}/3} \int_{-\sqrt{1-9x^2-4y^2}}^{\sqrt{1-9x^2-4y^2}} f(x, y, z)\, dz\, dx\, dy$$

$$= \int_{-1/2}^{1/2} \int_{-\sqrt{1-4y^2}}^{\sqrt{1-4y^2}} \int_{-\sqrt{1-4y^2-z^2}/3}^{\sqrt{1-4y^2-z^2}/3} f(x, y, z)\, dx\, dz\, dy$$

$$= \int_{-1}^{1} \int_{-\sqrt{1-z^2}/2}^{\sqrt{1-z^2}/2} \int_{-\sqrt{1-4y^2-z^2}/3}^{\sqrt{1-4y^2-z^2}/3} f(x, y, z)\, dx\, dy\, dz$$

$$= \int_{-1/3}^{1/3} \int_{-\sqrt{1-9x^2}}^{\sqrt{1-9x^2}} \int_{-\sqrt{1-9x^2-z^2}/2}^{\sqrt{1-9x^2-z^2}/2} f(x, y, z)\, dy\, dz\, dx$$

$$= \int_{-1}^{1} \int_{-\sqrt{1-z^2}/3}^{\sqrt{1-z^2}/3} \int_{-\sqrt{1-9x^2-z^2}/2}^{\sqrt{1-9x^2-z^2}/2} f(x, y, z)\, dy\, dx\, dz$$

29.

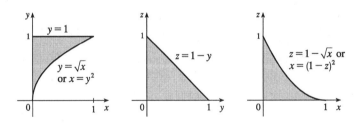

The diagrams show the projections of E on the xy-, yz-, and xz-planes. Therefore

$$\int_0^1 \int_{\sqrt{x}}^1 \int_0^{1-y} f(x, y, z)\, dz\, dy\, dx = \int_0^1 \int_0^{y^2} \int_0^{1-y} f(x, y, z)\, dz\, dx\, dy$$

$$= \int_0^1 \int_0^{1-z} \int_0^{y^2} f(x, y, z)\, dx\, dy\, dz$$

$$= \int_0^1 \int_0^{1-y} \int_0^{y^2} f(x, y, z)\, dx\, dz\, dy$$

$$= \int_0^1 \int_0^{1-\sqrt{x}} \int_{\sqrt{x}}^{1-z} f(x, y, z)\, dy\, dz\, dx$$

$$= \int_0^1 \int_0^{(1-z)^2} \int_{\sqrt{x}}^{1-z} f(x, y, z)\, dy\, dx\, dz$$

30.

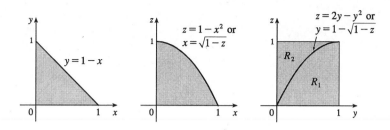

The projections of E onto the xy- and xz-planes are as in the first two diagrams and so

$$\int_0^1 \int_0^{1-x^2} \int_0^{1-x} f(x,y,z)\, dy\, dz\, dx = \int_0^1 \int_0^{\sqrt{1-z}} \int_0^{1-x} f(x,y,z)\, dy\, dx\, dz$$
$$= \int_0^1 \int_0^{1-y} \int_0^{1-x^2} f(x,y,z)\, dz\, dx\, dy = \int_0^1 \int_0^{1-x} \int_0^{1-x^2} f(x,y,z)\, dz\, dy\, dx$$

Now the surface $z = 1 - x^2$ intersects the plane $y = 1 - x$ in a curve whose projection in the yz-plane is $z = 1 - (1-y)^2$ or $z = 2y - y^2$. So we must split up the projection of E on the yz-plane into two regions as in the third diagram. For (y,z) in R_1, $0 \le x \le 1 - y$ and for (y,z) in R_2, $0 \le x \le \sqrt{1-z}$, and so the given integral is also equal to

$$\int_0^1 \int_0^{1-\sqrt{1-z}} \int_0^{\sqrt{1-z}} f(x,y,z)\, dx\, dy\, dz + \int_0^1 \int_{1-\sqrt{1-z}}^1 \int_0^{1-y} f(x,y,z)\, dx\, dy\, dz$$
$$= \int_0^1 \int_0^{2y-y^2} \int_0^{1-y} f(x,y,z)\, dx\, dz\, dy + \int_0^1 \int_{2y-y^2}^1 \int_0^{\sqrt{1-z}} f(x,y,z)\, dx\, dz\, dy.$$

31.

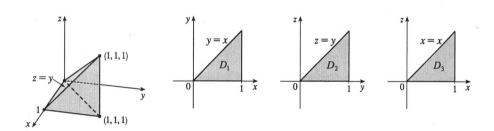

$$\int_0^1 \int_y^1 \int_0^y f(x,y,z)\, dz\, dx\, dy = \iiint_E f(x,y,z)\, dV \text{ where } E = \{(x,y,z) \mid 0 \le z \le y, y \le x \le 1, 0 \le y \le 1\}.$$

If D_1, D_2, and D_3 are the projections of E on the xy-, yz- and xz-planes then

$D_1 = \{(x,y) \mid 0 \le y \le 1, y \le x \le 1\} = \{(x,y) \mid 0 \le x \le 1, 0 \le y \le x\}$,

$D_2 = \{(y,z) \mid 0 \le y \le 1, 0 \le z \le y\} = \{(y,z) \mid 0 \le z \le 1, z \le y \le 1\}$, and

$D_3 = \{(x,z) \mid 0 \le x \le 1, 0 \le z \le x\} = \{(x,z) \mid 0 \le z \le 1, z \le x \le 1\}$.

Thus we also have

$E = \{(x,y,z) \mid 0 \le x \le 1, 0 \le y \le x, 0 \le z \le y\} = \{(x,y,z) \mid 0 \le y \le 1, 0 \le z \le y, y \le x \le 1\}$

$= \{(x,y,z) \mid 0 \le z \le 1, z \le y \le 1, y \le x \le 1\} = \{(x,y,z) \mid 0 \le x \le 1, 0 \le z \le x, z \le y \le x\}$

$= \{(x,y,z) \mid 0 \le z \le 1, z \le x \le 1, z \le y \le x\}.$

Then

$$\int_0^1 \int_y^1 \int_0^y f(x,y,z)\,dz\,dx\,dy = \int_0^1 \int_0^x \int_0^y f(x,y,z)\,dz\,dy\,dx = \int_0^1 \int_0^y \int_y^1 f(x,y,z)\,dx\,dz\,dy$$

$$= \int_0^1 \int_z^1 \int_y^1 f(x,y,z)\,dx\,dy\,dz = \int_0^1 \int_0^x \int_z^x f(x,y,z)\,dy\,dz\,dx$$

$$= \int_0^1 \int_z^1 \int_z^x f(x,y,z)\,dy\,dx\,dz$$

32.

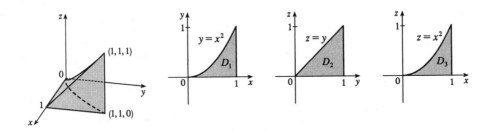

$\int_0^1 \int_0^{x^2} \int_0^y f(x,y,z)\,dz\,dy\,dx = \iiint_E f(x,y,z)\,dV$ where

$E = \{(x,y,z) \mid 0 \le x \le 1, 0 \le y \le x^2, 0 \le z \le y\}$. If D_1, D_2, D_3 are the projections of E on the xy-, yz-,

and xz-planes, then $D_1 = \{(x,y) \mid 0 \le x \le 1, 0 \le y \le x^2\} = \{(x,y) \mid 0 \le y \le 1, \sqrt{y} \le x \le 1\}$,

$D_2 = \{(y,z) \mid 0 \le y \le 1, 0 \le z \le y\} = \{(y,z) \mid 0 \le z \le 1, z \le y \le 1\}$,

$D_3 = \{(x,z) \mid 0 \le x \le 1, 0 \le z \le x^2\} = \{(x,z) \mid 0 \le z \le 1, \sqrt{z} \le x \le 1\}$. Thus we also have

$$E = \{(x,y,z) \mid 0 \le y \le 1, \sqrt{y} \le x \le 1, 0 \le z \le y\}$$

$$= \{(x,y,z) \mid 0 \le y \le 1, 0 \le z \le y, \sqrt{y} \le x \le 1\}$$

$$= \{(x,y,z) \mid 0 \le z \le 1, z \le y \le 1, \sqrt{y} \le x \le 1\}$$

$$= \{(x,y,z) \mid 0 \le x \le 1, 0 \le z \le x^2, z \le y \le x^2\}$$

$$= \{(x,y,z) \mid 0 \le z \le 1, \sqrt{z} \le x \le 1, z \le y \le x^2\}$$

Then

$$\int_0^1 \int_0^{x^2} \int_0^y f(x,y,z)\,dz\,dy\,dx = \int_0^1 \int_{\sqrt{y}}^1 \int_0^y f(x,y,z)\,dz\,dx\,dy$$

$$= \int_0^1 \int_0^y \int_{\sqrt{y}}^1 f(x,y,z)\,dx\,dz\,dy$$

$$= \int_0^1 \int_z^1 \int_{\sqrt{y}}^1 f(x,y,z)\,dx\,dy\,dz$$

$$= \int_0^1 \int_0^{x^2} \int_z^{x^2} f(x,y,z)\,dy\,dz\,dx$$

$$= \int_0^1 \int_{\sqrt{z}}^1 \int_z^{x^2} f(x,y,z)\,dy\,dx\,dz$$

33. $m = \iiint_E \rho(x,y,z)\, dV = \int_0^1 \int_0^{\sqrt{x}} \int_0^{1+x+y} 2\, dz\, dy\, dx$

$= \int_0^1 \int_0^{\sqrt{x}} 2(1+x+y)\, dy\, dx = \int_0^1 \left[2y + 2xy + y^2\right]_{y=0}^{y=\sqrt{x}} dx$

$= \int_0^1 \left(2\sqrt{x} + 2x^{3/2} + x\right) dx = \left[\frac{4}{3}x^{3/2} + \frac{4}{5}x^{5/2} + \frac{1}{2}x^2\right]_0^1 = \frac{79}{30}$

$M_{yz} = \iiint_E x\rho(x,y,z)\, dV = \int_0^1 \int_0^{\sqrt{x}} \int_0^{1+x+y} 2x\, dz\, dy\, dx$

$= \int_0^1 \int_0^{\sqrt{x}} 2x(1+x+y)\, dy\, dx = \int_0^1 \left[2xy + 2x^2 y + xy^2\right]_{y=0}^{y=\sqrt{x}} dx$

$= \int_0^1 \left(2x^{3/2} + 2x^{5/2} + x^2\right) dx = \left[\frac{4}{5}x^{5/2} + \frac{4}{7}x^{7/2} + \frac{1}{3}x^3\right]_0^1 = \frac{179}{105}$

$M_{xz} = \iiint_E y\rho(x,y,z)\, dV = \int_0^1 \int_0^{\sqrt{x}} \int_0^{1+x+y} 2y\, dz\, dy\, dx$

$= \int_0^1 \int_0^{\sqrt{x}} 2y(1+x+y)\, dy\, dx = \int_0^1 \left[y^2 + xy^2 + \frac{2}{3}y^3\right]_{y=0}^{y=\sqrt{x}} dx$

$= \int_0^1 \left(x + x^2 + \frac{2}{3}x^{3/2}\right) dx = \left[\frac{1}{2}x^2 + \frac{1}{3}x^3 + \frac{4}{15}x^{5/2}\right]_0^1 = \frac{11}{10}$

$M_{xy} = \iiint_E z\rho(x,y,z)\, dV = \int_0^1 \int_0^{\sqrt{x}} \int_0^{1+x+y} 2z\, dz\, dy\, dx$

$= \int_0^1 \int_0^{\sqrt{x}} \left[z^2\right]_{z=0}^{z=1+x+y} dy\, dx = \int_0^1 \int_0^{\sqrt{x}} (1+x+y)^2\, dy\, dx$

$= \int_0^1 \int_0^{\sqrt{x}} \left(1 + 2x + 2y + 2xy + x^2 + y^2\right) dy\, dx$

$= \int_0^1 \left[y + 2xy + y^2 + xy^2 + x^2 y + \frac{1}{3}y^3\right]_{y=0}^{y=\sqrt{x}} dx = \int_0^1 \left(\sqrt{x} + \frac{7}{3}x^{3/2} + x + x^2 + x^{5/2}\right) dx$

$= \left[\frac{2}{3}x^{3/2} + \frac{14}{15}x^{5/2} + \frac{1}{2}x^2 + \frac{1}{3}x^3 + \frac{2}{7}x^{7/2}\right]_0^1 = \frac{571}{210}$

Thus the mass is $\frac{79}{30}$ and the center of mass is $(\bar{x}, \bar{y}, \bar{z}) = \left(\dfrac{M_{yz}}{m}, \dfrac{M_{xz}}{m}, \dfrac{M_{xy}}{m}\right) = \left(\dfrac{358}{553}, \dfrac{33}{79}, \dfrac{571}{553}\right).$

34. $m = \int_{-1}^1 \int_0^{1-y^2} \int_0^{1-z} 4\, dx\, dz\, dy = 4\int_{-1}^1 \int_0^{1-y^2}(1-z)\, dz\, dy = 4\int_{-1}^1 \left[z - \frac{1}{2}z^2\right]_{z=0}^{z=1-y^2} dy$

$= 2\int_{-1}^1 \left(1 - y^4\right) dy = \frac{16}{5},$

$M_{yz} = \int_{-1}^1 \int_0^{1-y^2} \int_0^{1-z} 4x\, dx\, dz\, dy = 2\int_{-1}^1 \int_0^{1-y^2}(1-z)^2\, dz\, dy = 2\int_{-1}^1 \left[-\frac{1}{3}(1-z)^3\right]_{z=0}^{z=1-y^2} dy$

$= \frac{2}{3}\int_{-1}^1 \left(1 - y^6\right) dy = \left(\frac{4}{3}\right)\left(\frac{6}{7}\right) = \frac{24}{21}$

$M_{xz} = \int_{-1}^1 \int_0^{1-y^2} \int_0^{1-z} 4y\, dx\, dz\, dy = \int_{-1}^1 \int_0^{1-y^2} 4y(1-z)\, dz\, dy$

$= \int_{-1}^1 \left[4y(1-y^2) - 2y(1-y^2)^2\right] dy = \int_{-1}^1 (2y - 2y^5)\, dy = 0 \quad \text{(the integrand is odd)}$

$M_{xy} = \int_{-1}^1 \int_0^{1-y^2} \int_0^{1-z} 4z\, dx\, dz\, dy = \int_{-1}^1 \int_0^{1-y^2} (4z - 4z^2)\, dz\, dy$

$= 2\int_{-1}^1 \left[(1-y^2)^2 - \frac{2}{3}(1-y^2)^3\right] dy = 2\int_{-1}^1 \left[\frac{1}{3} - y^4 + \frac{2}{3}y^6\right] dy$

$= \left[\frac{4}{3}y - \frac{4}{5}y^5 + \frac{8}{21}y^7\right]_0^1 = \frac{96}{105} = \frac{32}{35}$

Thus, $(\bar{x}, \bar{y}, \bar{z}) = \left(\frac{5}{14}, 0, \frac{2}{7}\right)$

35. $m = \int_0^a \int_0^a \int_0^a \left(x^2 + y^2 + z^2\right) dx\,dy\,dz = \int_0^a \int_0^a \left[\frac{1}{3}x^3 + xy^2 + xz^2\right]_{x=0}^{x=a} dy\,dz$

$\qquad = \int_0^a \int_0^a \left(\frac{1}{3}a^3 + ay^2 + az^2\right) dy\,dz = \int_0^a \left[\frac{1}{3}a^3 y + \frac{1}{3}ay^3 + ayz^2\right]_{y=0}^{y=a} dz$

$\qquad = \int_0^a \left(\frac{2}{3}a^4 + a^2 z^2\right) dz = \left[\frac{2}{3}a^4 z + \frac{1}{3}a^2 z^3\right]_0^a = \frac{2}{3}a^5 + \frac{1}{3}a^5 = a^5$

$M_{yz} = \int_0^a \int_0^a \int_0^a \left[x^3 + x\left(y^2 + z^2\right)\right] dx\,dy\,dz = \int_0^a \int_0^a \left[\frac{1}{4}a^4 + \frac{1}{2}a^2\left(y^2 + z^2\right)\right] dy\,dz$

$\qquad = \int_0^a \left(\frac{1}{4}a^5 + \frac{1}{6}a^5 + \frac{1}{2}a^3 z^2\right) dz = \frac{1}{4}a^6 + \frac{1}{3}a^6 = \frac{7}{12}a^6$

$\qquad = M_{xz} = M_{xy}$ by symmetry of E and $\rho\left(x, y, z\right)$

Hence $(\overline{x}, \overline{y}, \overline{z}) = \left(\frac{7}{12}a, \frac{7}{12}a, \frac{7}{12}a\right)$.

36. $m = \int_0^1 \int_0^{1-x} \int_0^{1-x-y} y\,dz\,dy\,dx = \int_0^1 \int_0^{1-x} \left[(1-x)y - y^2\right] dy\,dx$

$\qquad = \int_0^1 \left[\frac{1}{2}(1-x)^3 - \frac{1}{3}(1-x)^3\right] dx = \frac{1}{6}\int_0^1 (1-x)^3\,dx = \frac{1}{24}$

$M_{yz} = \int_0^1 \int_0^{1-x} \int_0^{1-x-y} xy\,dz\,dy\,dx = \int_0^1 \int_0^{1-x} \left[\left(x - x^2\right)y - xy^2\right] dy\,dx$

$\qquad = \int_0^1 \left[\frac{1}{2}x(1-x)^3 - \frac{1}{3}x(1-x)^3\right] dx = \frac{1}{6}\int_0^1 \left(x - 3x^2 + 3x^3 - x^4\right) dx$

$\qquad = \frac{1}{6}\left(\frac{1}{2} - 1 + \frac{3}{4} - \frac{1}{5}\right) = \frac{1}{120}$

$M_{xz} = \int_0^1 \int_0^{1-x} \int_0^{1-x-y} y^2\,dz\,dy\,dx = \int_0^1 \int_0^{1-x} \left[(1-x)y^2 - y^3\right] dy\,dx$

$\qquad = \int_0^1 \left[\frac{1}{3}(1-x)^4 - \frac{1}{4}(1-x)^4\right] dx = \frac{1}{12}\left[-\frac{1}{5}(1-x)^5\right]_0^1 = \frac{1}{60}$

$M_{xy} = \int_0^1 \int_0^{1-x} \int_0^{1-x-y} yz\,dz\,dy\,dx = \int_0^1 \int_0^{1-x} \left[\frac{1}{2}y(1-x)^2\right] dy\,dx$

$\qquad = \frac{1}{2}\int_0^1 \int_0^{1-x} \left[(1-x)^2 y - 2(1-x)y^2 + y^3\right] dy\,dx$

$\qquad = \frac{1}{2}\int_0^1 \left[\frac{1}{2}(1-x)^4 - \frac{2}{3}(1-x)^4 + \frac{1}{4}(1-x)^4\right] dx$

$\qquad = \frac{1}{24}\int_0^1 (1-x)^4\,dx = -\frac{1}{24}\left[\frac{1}{5}(1-x)^5\right]_0^1 = \frac{1}{120}$

Hence $(\overline{x}, \overline{y}, \overline{z}) = \left(\frac{1}{5}, \frac{2}{5}, \frac{1}{5}\right)$.

37. (a) $m = \int_{-1}^1 \int_{-\sqrt{1-y^2}}^{\sqrt{1-y^2}} \int_{4y^2+4z^2}^4 \left(x^2 + y^2 + z^2\right) dx\,dz\,dy$

(b) $(\overline{x}, \overline{y}, \overline{z})$ where $\overline{x} = m^{-1} \int_{-1}^1 \int_{-\sqrt{1-y^2}}^{\sqrt{1-y^2}} \int_{4y^2+4z^2}^4 x\left(x^2 + y^2 + z^2\right) dx\,dz\,dy$,

$\qquad \overline{y} = m^{-1} \int_{-1}^1 \int_{-\sqrt{1-y^2}}^{\sqrt{1-y^2}} \int_{4y^2+4z^2}^4 y\left(x^2 + y^2 + z^2\right) dx\,dz\,dy$, and

$\qquad \overline{z} = m^{-1} \int_{-1}^1 \int_{-\sqrt{1-y^2}}^{\sqrt{1-y^2}} \int_{4y^2+4z^2}^4 z\left(x^2 + y^2 + z^2\right) dx\,dz\,dy$

(c) $I_z = \int_{-1}^1 \int_{-\sqrt{1-y^2}}^{\sqrt{1-y^2}} \int_{4y^2+4z^2}^4 \left(x^2 + y^2\right)\left(x^2 + y^2 + z^2\right) dx\,dz\,dy$

38. (a) $m = \int_{-1}^{1} \int_{-\sqrt{1-y^2}}^{\sqrt{1-y^2}} \int_{0}^{\sqrt{1-x^2-y^2}} \sqrt{x^2 + y^2 + z^2}\, dz\, dx\, dy$

(b) $(\overline{x}, \overline{y}, \overline{z})$ where $\overline{x} = m^{-1} \int_{-1}^{1} \int_{-\sqrt{1-y^2}}^{\sqrt{1-y^2}} \int_{0}^{\sqrt{1-x^2-y^2}} x\, \sqrt{x^2 + y^2 + z^2}\, dz\, dx\, dy,$

$\overline{y} = m^{-1} \int_{-1}^{1} \int_{-\sqrt{1-y^2}}^{\sqrt{1-y^2}} \int_{0}^{\sqrt{1-x^2-y^2}} y\, \sqrt{x^2 + y^2 + z^2}\, dz\, dx\, dy,$

$\overline{z} = m^{-1} \int_{-1}^{1} \int_{-\sqrt{1-y^2}}^{\sqrt{1-y^2}} \int_{0}^{\sqrt{1-x^2-y^2}} z\, \sqrt{x^2 + y^2 + z^2}\, dz\, dx\, dy$

(c) $I_z = \int_{-1}^{1} \int_{-\sqrt{1-y^2}}^{\sqrt{1-y^2}} \int_{0}^{\sqrt{1-x^2-y^2}} (x^2 + y^2)(1 + x + y + z)\, dz\, dx\, dy$

39. (a) $m = \int_{0}^{1} \int_{0}^{\sqrt{1-x^2}} \int_{0}^{y} (1 + x + y + z)\, dz\, dy\, dx = \frac{3\pi}{32} + \frac{11}{24}$

(b) $(\overline{x}, \overline{y}, \overline{z}) = \left(m^{-1} \int_{0}^{1} \int_{0}^{\sqrt{1-x^2}} \int_{0}^{y} x(1 + x + y + z)\, dz\, dy\, dx, \right.$

$m^{-1} \int_{0}^{1} \int_{0}^{\sqrt{1-x^2}} \int_{0}^{y} y(1 + x + y + z)\, dz\, dy\, dx,$

$\left. m^{-1} \int_{0}^{1} \int_{0}^{\sqrt{1-x^2}} \int_{0}^{y} z(1 + x + y + z)\, dz\, dy\, dx \right)$

$= \left(\dfrac{28}{9\pi + 44}, \dfrac{30\pi + 128}{45\pi + 220}, \dfrac{45\pi + 208}{135\pi + 660} \right)$

(c) $I_z = \int_{0}^{1} \int_{0}^{\sqrt{1-x^2}} \int_{0}^{y} (x^2 + y^2)(1 + x + y + z)\, dz\, dy\, dx = \dfrac{68 + 15\pi}{240}$

40. (a) $m = \int_{0}^{1} \int_{3x}^{3} \int_{0}^{\sqrt{9-y^2}} (x^2 + y^2)\, dz\, dy\, dx = \frac{56}{5} = 11.2$

(b) $(\overline{x}, \overline{y}, \overline{z})$ where $\overline{x} = m^{-1} \int_{0}^{1} \int_{3x}^{3} \int_{0}^{\sqrt{9-y^2}} x(x^2 + y^2)\, dz\, dy\, dx \approx 0.375,$

$\overline{y} = m^{-1} \int_{0}^{1} \int_{3x}^{3} \int_{0}^{\sqrt{9-y^2}} y(x^2 + y^2)\, dz\, dy\, dx = \frac{45\pi}{64} \approx 2.209,$

$\overline{z} = m^{-1} \int_{0}^{1} \int_{3x}^{3} \int_{0}^{\sqrt{9-y^2}} z(x^2 + y^2)\, dz\, dy\, dx = \frac{15}{16} = 0.9375.$

(c) $I_z = \int_{0}^{1} \int_{3x}^{3} \int_{0}^{\sqrt{9-y^2}} (x^2 + y^2)^2\, dz\, dy\, dx = \frac{10{,}464}{175} \approx 59.79$

41. $I_x = \int_{0}^{L} \int_{0}^{L} \int_{0}^{L} k(y^2 + z^2)\, dz\, dy\, dx = k \int_{0}^{L} \int_{0}^{L} (Ly^2 + \frac{1}{3}L^3)\, dy\, dx = k \int_{0}^{L} \frac{2}{3}L^4\, dx = \frac{2}{3}kL^5.$

By symmetry, $I_x = I_y = I_z = \frac{2}{3}kL^5.$

42. Let k be the density. Then

$$I_x = \int_{-c/2}^{c/2} \int_{-b/2}^{b/2} \int_{-a/2}^{a/2} k(y^2 + z^2)\, dx\, dy\, dz = ka \int_{-c/2}^{c/2} \int_{-b/2}^{b/2} (y^2 + z^2)\, dy\, dz$$

$$= ak \int_{-c/2}^{c/2} \left[\frac{1}{3}y^3 + z^2 y \right]_{y=-b/2}^{y=b/2}\, dz = ak \int_{-c/2}^{c/2} \left(\frac{1}{12}b^3 + bz^2 \right)\, dz = ak \left[\frac{1}{12}b^3 z + \frac{1}{3}bz^3 \right]_{-c/2}^{c/2}$$

$$= ak \left(\frac{1}{12}b^3 c + \frac{1}{12}bc^3 \right) = \frac{1}{12}kabc(b^2 + c^2)$$

By symmetry, $I_y = \frac{1}{12}kabc(a^2 + c^2)$ and $I_z = \frac{1}{12}kabc(a^2 + b^2).$

43. (a) $f(x, y, z)$ is a joint density function, so we know $\iiint_{\mathbb{R}^3} f(x, y, z)\, dV = 1$. Here we have

$$\iiint_{\mathbb{R}^3} f(x, y, z)\, dV = \int_{-\infty}^{\infty}\int_{-\infty}^{\infty}\int_{-\infty}^{\infty} f(x, y, z)\, dz\, dy\, dx = \int_0^2\int_0^2\int_0^2 Cxyz\, dz\, dy\, dx$$

$$= C\int_0^2 x\, dx \int_0^2 y\, dy \int_0^2 z\, dz = C\left[\frac{x^2}{2}\right]_0^2 \left[\frac{y^2}{2}\right]_0^2 \left[\frac{z^2}{2}\right]_0^2$$

$$= 8C$$

Then we must have $8C = 1 \;\Rightarrow\; C = \frac{1}{8}$.

(b) $P\,(X \le 1, Y \le 1, Z \le 1) = \int_{-\infty}^1\int_{-\infty}^1\int_{-\infty}^1 f(x, y, z)\, dz\, dy\, dx$

$$= \int_0^1\int_0^1\int_0^1 \tfrac{1}{8}xyz\, dz\, dy\, dx = \tfrac{1}{8}\int_0^1 x\, dx \int_0^1 y\, dy \int_0^1 z\, dz$$

$$= \frac{1}{8}\left[\frac{x^2}{2}\right]_0^1 \left[\frac{y^2}{2}\right]_0^1 \left[\frac{z^2}{2}\right]_0^1 = \tfrac{1}{8}\left(\tfrac{1}{2}\right)^3 = \tfrac{1}{64}$$

(c) $P(X + Y + Z \le 1) = P((X, Y, Z) \in E)$ where E is the solid region in the first octant bounded by the coordinate planes and the plane $x + y + z = 1$. The plane $x + y + z = 1$ meets the xy-plane in the line $x + y = 1$, so we have

$$P(X + Y + Z \le 1) = \iiint_E f(x, y, z)\, dV = \int_0^1\int_0^{1-x}\int_0^{1-x-y} \tfrac{1}{8}xyz\, dz\, dy\, dx$$

$$= \tfrac{1}{8}\int_0^1\int_0^{1-x} xy\left[\tfrac{1}{2}z^2\right]_{z=0}^{z=1-x-y}\, dy\, dx$$

$$= \tfrac{1}{16}\int_0^1\int_0^{1-x} xy(1 - x - y)^2\, dy\, dx$$

$$= \tfrac{1}{16}\int_0^1\int_0^{1-x} \left[(x^3 - 2x^2 + x)y + (2x^2 - 2x)y^2 + xy^3\right] dy\, dx$$

$$= \tfrac{1}{16}\int_0^1 \left[(x^3 - 2x^2 + x)\tfrac{1}{2}y^2 + (2x^2 - 2x)\tfrac{1}{3}y^3 + x\left(\tfrac{1}{4}y^4\right)\right]_{y=0}^{y=1-x}\, dx$$

$$= \tfrac{1}{192}\int_0^1 (x - 4x^2 + 6x^3 - 4x^4 + x^5)\, dx = \tfrac{1}{192}\left(\tfrac{1}{30}\right) = \tfrac{1}{5760}$$

44. (a) $f\,(x, y, z)$ is a joint density function, so we know $\iiint_{\mathbb{R}^3} f(x, y, z)\, dV = 1$. Here we have

$$\iiint_{\mathbb{R}^3} f(x, y, z)\, dV = \int_{-\infty}^{\infty}\int_{-\infty}^{\infty}\int_{-\infty}^{\infty} f(x, y, z)\, dz\, dy\, dx$$

$$= \int_0^{\infty}\int_0^{\infty}\int_0^{\infty} Ce^{-(0.5x + 0.2y + 0.1z)}\, dz\, dy\, dx$$

$$= C\int_0^{\infty} e^{-0.5x}\, dx \int_0^{\infty} e^{-0.2y}\, dy \int_0^{\infty} e^{-0.1z}\, dz$$

$$= C \lim_{t\to\infty}\int_0^t e^{-0.5x}\, dx \lim_{t\to\infty}\int_0^t e^{-0.2y}\, dy \lim_{t\to\infty}\int_0^t e^{-0.1z}\, dz$$

$$= C \lim_{t\to\infty}\left[-2e^{-0.5x}\right]_0^t \lim_{t\to\infty}\left[-5e^{-0.2y}\right]_0^t \lim_{t\to\infty}\left[-10e^{-0.1z}\right]_0^t$$

$$= C \lim_{t\to\infty}\left[-2\left(e^{-0.5t} - 1\right)\right] \lim_{t\to\infty}\left[-5\left(e^{-0.2t} - 1\right)\right] \lim_{t\to\infty}\left[-10\left(e^{-0.1t} - 1\right)\right]$$

$$= C \cdot (-2)(0 - 1) \cdot (-5)(0 - 1) \cdot (-10)(0 - 1) = 100C$$

So we must have $100C = 1 \;\Rightarrow\; C = \frac{1}{100}$.

(b) We have no restriction on Z, so

$$P(X \le 1, Y \le 1) = \int_{-\infty}^{1} \int_{-\infty}^{1} \int_{-\infty}^{\infty} f(x, y, z)\, dz\, dy\, dx = \int_{0}^{1} \int_{0}^{1} \int_{0}^{\infty} \frac{1}{100} e^{-(0.5x + 0.2y + 0.1z)}\, dz\, dy\, dx$$

$$= \frac{1}{100} \int_{0}^{1} e^{-0.5x}\, dx \int_{0}^{1} e^{-0.2y}\, dy \int_{0}^{\infty} e^{-0.1z}\, dz$$

$$= \frac{1}{100} \left[-2e^{-0.5x} \right]_{0}^{1} \left[-5e^{-0.2y} \right]_{0}^{1} \lim_{t \to \infty} \left[-10e^{-0.1z} \right]_{0}^{t} \quad \text{[by part (a)]}$$

$$= \frac{1}{100} \left(2 - 2e^{-0.5} \right) \left(5 - 5e^{-0.2} \right) (10) = \left(1 - e^{-0.5} \right) \left(1 - e^{-0.2} \right) \approx 0.07132$$

(c) $P(X \le 1, Y \le 1, Z \le 1) = \int_{-\infty}^{1} \int_{-\infty}^{1} \int_{-\infty}^{1} f(x, y, z)\, dz\, dy\, dx$

$$= \int_{0}^{1} \int_{0}^{1} \int_{0}^{1} \frac{1}{100} e^{-(0.5x + 0.2y + 0.1z)}\, dz\, dy\, dx$$

$$= \frac{1}{100} \int_{0}^{1} e^{-0.5x}\, dx \int_{0}^{1} e^{-0.2y}\, dy \int_{0}^{1} e^{-0.1z}\, dz$$

$$= \frac{1}{100} \left[-2e^{-0.5x} \right]_{0}^{1} \left[-5e^{-0.2y} \right]_{0}^{1} \left[-10e^{-0.1z} \right]_{0}^{1}$$

$$= \left(1 - e^{-0.5} \right) \left(1 - e^{-0.2} \right) \left(1 - e^{-0.1} \right) \approx 0.006787$$

45. $V(E) = L^3$,

$$f_{ave} = \frac{1}{L^3} \int_{0}^{L} \int_{0}^{L} \int_{0}^{L} xyz\, dx\, dy\, dz = \frac{1}{L^3} \int_{0}^{L} x\, dx \int_{0}^{L} y\, dy \int_{0}^{L} z\, dz$$

$$= \frac{1}{L^3} \left[\frac{x^2}{2} \right]_{0}^{L} \left[\frac{y^2}{2} \right]_{0}^{L} \left[\frac{z^2}{2} \right]_{0}^{L} = \frac{1}{L^3} \frac{L^2}{2} \frac{L^2}{2} \frac{L^2}{2} = \frac{L^3}{8}$$

46. $V(E) = \frac{(1)(1)(1)}{6} = \frac{1}{6}$. The equation of the plane through the last three vertices is $x + y + z = 1$, so

$$f_{ave} = \frac{1}{1/6} \int_{0}^{1} \int_{0}^{1-x} \int_{0}^{1-x-y} (x + y + z)\, dz\, dy\, dx$$

$$= 6 \int_{0}^{1} \int_{0}^{1-x} \left[(x + y)(1 - x - y) + \frac{1}{2}(1 - x - y)^2 \right] dy\, dx$$

$$= 3 \int_{0}^{1} \int_{0}^{1-x} \left(1 - 2xy - x^2 - y^2 \right) dy\, dx = 3 \int_{0}^{1} \int_{0}^{1-x} \left[1 - (x + y)^2 \right] dy\, dx$$

$$= 3 \int_{0}^{1} \left[y - \frac{1}{3}(x + y)^3 \right]_{y=0}^{y=1-x} dx = 3 \int_{0}^{1} \left(1 - x - \frac{1}{3} + \frac{1}{3}x^3 \right) dx = \int_{0}^{1} \left(x^3 - 3x + 2 \right) dx$$

$$= \frac{1}{4} - \frac{3}{2} + 2 = \frac{3}{4}$$

47. The triple integral will attain its maximum when the integrand $1 - x^2 - 2y^2 - 3z^2$ is positive in the region E and negative everywhere else. For if E contains some region F where the integrand is negative, the integral could be increased by excluding F from E, and if E fails to contain some part G of the region where the integrand is positive, the integral could be increased by including G in E. So we require that $x^2 + 2y^2 + 3z^2 \le 1$. This describes the region bounded by the ellipsoid $x^2 + 2y^2 + 3z^2 = 1$.

| **Discovery** | **Volumes of Hyperspheres** |
| **Project** | |

In this project we use V_n to denote the n-dimensional volume of an n-dimensional hypersphere.

1. The interior of the circle is the set of points $\left\{ (x,y) \mid -r \le y \le r, \ -\sqrt{r^2 - y^2} \le x \le \sqrt{r^2 - y^2} \right\}$. So, substituting $y = r \sin \theta$ and then using Formula 64 to evaluate the integral, we get

$$V_2 = \int_{-r}^{r} \int_{-\sqrt{r^2-y^2}}^{\sqrt{r^2-y^2}} dx \, dy = \int_{-r}^{r} 2\sqrt{r^2 - y^2} \, dy = \int_{-\pi/2}^{\pi/2} 2r \sqrt{1 - \sin^2 \theta} \ (r \cos \theta \, d\theta)$$

$$= 2r^2 \int_{-\pi/2}^{\pi/2} \cos^2 \theta \, d\theta = 2r^2 \left[\tfrac{1}{2}\theta + \tfrac{1}{4}\sin 2\theta \right]_{-\pi/2}^{\pi/2} = 2r^2 \left(\tfrac{\pi}{2} \right)$$

$$= \pi r^2$$

2. The region of integration is
$$\left\{ (x,y,z) \mid -r \le z \le r, \ -\sqrt{r^2 - z^2} \le y \le \sqrt{r^2 - z^2}, \ -\sqrt{r^2 - z^2 - y^2} \le x \le \sqrt{r^2 - z^2 - y^2} \right\}.$$
Substituting $y = \sqrt{r^2 - z^2} \sin \theta$ and using Formula 64 to integrate $\cos^2 \theta$, we get

$$V_3 = \int_{-r}^{r} \int_{-\sqrt{r^2-z^2}}^{\sqrt{r^2-z^2}} \int_{-\sqrt{r^2-z^2-y^2}}^{\sqrt{r^2-z^2-y^2}} dx \, dy \, dz = \int_{-r}^{r} \int_{-\sqrt{r^2-z^2}}^{\sqrt{r^2-z^2}} 2\sqrt{r^2 - z^2 - y^2} \, dy \, dz$$

$$= \int_{-r}^{r} \int_{-\pi/2}^{\pi/2} 2\sqrt{r^2 - z^2} \sqrt{1 - \sin^2 \theta} \left(\sqrt{r^2 - z^2} \cos \theta \, d\theta \right) dz$$

$$= 2 \left[\int_{-r}^{r} (r^2 - z^2) \, dz \right] \left[\int_{-\pi/2}^{\pi/2} \cos^2 \theta \, d\theta \right] = 2 \left(\frac{4r^3}{3} \right) \left(\frac{\pi}{2} \right)$$

$$= \frac{4\pi r^3}{3}$$

3. Here we substitute $y = \sqrt{r^2 - w^2 - z^2} \sin \theta$ and, later, $w = r \sin \phi$. Because $\int_{-\pi/2}^{\pi/2} \cos^p \theta \, d\theta$ seems to occur frequently in these calculations, it is useful to find a general formula for that integral. From Exercises 35 and 36 in Section 5.6, we have

$$\int_{0}^{\pi/2} \sin^{2k} x \, dx = \frac{1 \cdot 3 \cdot 5 \cdots (2k-1)}{2 \cdot 4 \cdot 6 \cdots 2k} \frac{\pi}{2} \qquad \text{and} \qquad \int_{0}^{\pi/2} \sin^{2k+1} x \, dx = \frac{2 \cdot 4 \cdot 6 \cdots 2k}{1 \cdot 3 \cdot 5 \cdots (2k+1)}$$

and from the symmetry of the sine and cosine functions, we can conclude that

$$\int_{-\pi/2}^{\pi/2} \cos^{2k} x \, dx = 2 \int_{0}^{\pi/2} \sin^{2k} x \, dx = \frac{1 \cdot 3 \cdot 5 \cdots (2k-1)\pi}{2 \cdot 4 \cdot 6 \cdots 2k} \qquad (1)$$

$$\int_{-\pi/2}^{\pi/2} \cos^{2k+1} x \, dx = 2 \int_{0}^{\pi/2} \sin^{2k+1} x \, dx = \frac{2 \cdot 2 \cdot 4 \cdot 6 \cdots 2k}{1 \cdot 3 \cdot 5 \cdots (2k+1)} \qquad (2)$$

Thus

$$V_4 = \int_{-r}^{r} \int_{-\sqrt{r^2 - w^2}}^{\sqrt{r^2 - w^2}} \int_{-\sqrt{r^2 - w^2 - z^2}}^{\sqrt{r^2 - w^2 - z^2}} \int_{-\sqrt{r^2 - w^2 - z^2 - y^2}}^{\sqrt{r^2 - w^2 - z^2 - y^2}} dx \, dy \, dz \, dw$$

$$= 2 \int_{-r}^{r} \int_{-\sqrt{r^2 - w^2}}^{\sqrt{r^2 - w^2}} \int_{-\sqrt{r^2 - w^2 - z^2}}^{\sqrt{r^2 - w^2 - z^2}} \sqrt{r^2 - w^2 - z^2 - y^2} \, dy \, dz \, dw$$

$$= 2 \int_{-r}^{r} \int_{-\sqrt{r^2 - w^2}}^{\sqrt{r^2 - w^2}} \int_{-\pi/2}^{\pi/2} \left(r^2 - w^2 - z^2\right) \cos^2 \theta \, d\theta \, dz \, dw$$

$$= 2 \left[\int_{-r}^{r} \int_{-\sqrt{r^2 - w^2}}^{\sqrt{r^2 - w^2}} \left(r^2 - w^2 - z^2\right) dz \, dw \right] \left[\int_{-\pi/2}^{\pi/2} \cos^2 \theta \, d\theta \right]$$

$$= 2 \left(\tfrac{\pi}{2}\right) \left[\int_{-r}^{r} \tfrac{4}{3} \left(r^2 - w^2\right)^{3/2} dw \right] = \pi \left(\tfrac{4}{3}\right) \int_{-\pi/2}^{\pi/2} r^4 \cos^4 \phi \, d\phi = \frac{4\pi}{3} r^4 \cdot \frac{1 \cdot 3 \cdot \pi}{2 \cdot 4} = \frac{\pi^2 r^4}{2}$$

4. By using the substitutions $x_i = \sqrt{r^2 - x_n^2 - x_{n-1}^2 - \cdots - x_{i+1}^2} \cos \theta_i$ and then applying Formulas 1 and 2 from Problem 3, we can write

$$V_4 = \int_{-r}^{r} \int_{-\sqrt{r^2 - x_n^2}}^{\sqrt{r^2 - x_n^2}} \cdots \int_{-\sqrt{r^2 - x_n^2 - x_{n-1}^2 - \cdots - x_3^2}}^{\sqrt{r^2 - x_n^2 - x_{n-1}^2 - \cdots - x_3^2}} \int_{-\sqrt{r^2 - x_n^2 - x_{n-1}^2 - \cdots - x_3^2 - x_2^2}}^{\sqrt{r^2 - x_n^2 - x_{n-1}^2 - \cdots - x_3^2 - x_2^2}} dx_1 \, dx_2 \cdots dx_{n-1} \, dx_n$$

$$= 2 \left[\int_{-\pi/2}^{\pi/2} \cos^2 \theta_2 \, d\theta_2 \right] \left[\int_{-\pi/2}^{\pi/2} \cos^3 \theta_3 \, d\theta_3 \right] \cdots \left[\int_{-\pi/2}^{\pi/2} \cos^{n-1} \theta_{n-1} \, d\theta_{n-1} \right] \left[\int_{-\pi/2}^{\pi/2} \cos^n \theta_n \, d\theta_n \right] r^n$$

$$= \begin{cases} \left[2 \cdot \dfrac{\pi}{2} \right] \left[\dfrac{2 \cdot 2}{1 \cdot 3} \cdot \dfrac{1 \cdot 3\pi}{2 \cdot 4} \right] \left[\dfrac{2 \cdot 2 \cdot 4}{1 \cdot 3 \cdot 5} \cdot \dfrac{1 \cdot 3 \cdot 5\pi}{2 \cdot 4 \cdot 6} \right] \cdots \left[\dfrac{2 \cdots (n-2)}{1 \cdots (n-1)} \cdot \dfrac{1 \cdots (n-1)\pi}{2 \cdots n} \right] r^n & n \text{ even} \\[20pt] 2 \left[\dfrac{\pi}{2} \cdot \dfrac{2 \cdot 2}{1 \cdot 3} \right] \left[\dfrac{1 \cdot 3\pi}{2 \cdot 4} \cdot \dfrac{2 \cdot 2 \cdot 4}{1 \cdot 3 \cdot 5} \right] \cdots \left[\dfrac{1 \cdots (n-2)\pi}{2 \cdots (n-1)} \cdot \dfrac{2 \cdots (n-1)}{1 \cdots n} \right] r^n & n \text{ odd} \end{cases}$$

By canceling within each set of brackets, we find that

$$V_4 = \begin{cases} \dfrac{2\pi}{2} \cdot \dfrac{2\pi}{4} \cdot \dfrac{2\pi}{6} \cdots\cdots \dfrac{2\pi}{n} r^n = \dfrac{(2\pi)^{n/2}}{2 \cdot 4 \cdot 6 \cdots\cdots n} r^n = \dfrac{\pi^{n/2}}{\left(\tfrac{1}{2}n\right)!} r^n & n \text{ even} \\[20pt] 2 \cdot \dfrac{2\pi}{3} \cdot \dfrac{2\pi}{5} \cdot \dfrac{2\pi}{7} \cdots\cdots \dfrac{2\pi}{n} r^n = \dfrac{2(2\pi)^{(n-1)/2}}{3 \cdot 5 \cdot 7 \cdots\cdots n} r^n = \dfrac{2^n \left[\tfrac{1}{2}(n-1)\right]! \, \pi^{(n-1)/2}}{n!} r^n & n \text{ odd} \end{cases}$$

<table>
<tr><td></td></tr>
</table>

12.8 **Triple Integrals in Cylindrical and Spherical Coordinates** • •

1. The region of integration is given in cylindrical coordinates by

$E = \{(r, \theta, z) \mid 0 \le \theta \le 2\pi, \, 0 \le r \le 4, \, r \le z \le 4\}$. This represents the solid region bounded below by the cone $z = r$ and above by the horizontal plane $z = 4$.

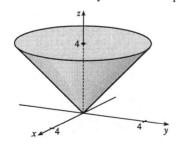

$$\int_0^4 \int_0^{2\pi} \int_r^4 r \, dz \, d\theta \, dr = \int_0^4 \int_0^{2\pi} \left[rz\right]_{z=r}^{z=4} d\theta \, dr$$

$$= \int_0^4 \int_0^{2\pi} r(4 - r) \, d\theta \, dr$$

$$= \int_0^4 \left(4r - r^2\right) dr \int_0^{2\pi} d\theta$$

$$= \left[2r^2 - \tfrac{1}{3}r^3\right]_0^4 [\theta]_0^{2\pi}$$

$$= \left(32 - \tfrac{64}{3}\right)(2\pi) = \frac{64\pi}{3}$$

2. The region of integration is given in cylindrical coordinates by
$E = \{(r, \theta, z) \mid 0 \le \theta \le \pi/2, 0 \le r \le 2, 0 \le z \le 9 - r^2\}$. This represents the solid region in the first octant enclosed by the circular cylinder $r = 2$, bounded above by $z = 9 - r^2$, a circular paraboloid, and bounded below by the xy-plane.

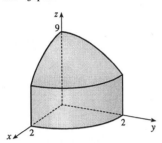

$$\int_0^{\pi/2} \int_0^2 \int_0^{9-r^2} r\, dz\, dr\, d\theta = \int_0^{\pi/2} \int_0^2 [rz]_{z=0}^{z=9-r^2}\, dr\, d\theta$$
$$= \int_0^{\pi/2} \int_0^2 r(9 - r^2)\, dr\, d\theta$$
$$= \int_0^{\pi/2} d\theta \int_0^2 (9r - r^3)\, dr$$
$$= [\theta]_0^{\pi/2} \left[\tfrac{9}{2}r^2 - \tfrac{1}{4}r^4 \right]_0^2$$
$$= \tfrac{\pi}{2}(18 - 4) = 7\pi$$

3. The region of integration is given in spherical coordinates by
$E = \{(\rho, \theta, \phi) \mid 0 \le \rho \le 3, 0 \le \theta \le \pi/2, 0 \le \phi \le \pi/6\}$. This represents the solid region in the first octant bounded above by the sphere $\rho = 3$ and below by the cone $\phi = \pi/6$.

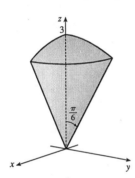

$$\int_0^{\pi/6} \int_0^{\pi/2} \int_0^3 \rho^2 \sin\phi\, d\rho\, d\theta\, d\phi = \int_0^{\pi/6} \sin\phi\, d\phi \int_0^{\pi/2} d\theta \int_0^3 \rho^2\, d\rho$$
$$= [-\cos\phi]_0^{\pi/6} [\theta]_0^{\pi/2} \left[\tfrac{1}{3}\rho^3 \right]_0^3$$
$$= \left(1 - \tfrac{\sqrt{3}}{2} \right) \left(\tfrac{\pi}{2} \right)(9)$$
$$= \tfrac{9\pi}{4} \left(2 - \sqrt{3} \right)$$

4. The region of integration is given in spherical coordinates by
$E = \{(\rho, \theta, \phi) \mid 1 \le \rho \le 2, 0 \le \theta \le 2\pi, \pi/2 \le \phi \le \pi\}$. This represents the solid region between the spheres $\rho = 1$ and $\rho = 2$ and below the xy-plane.

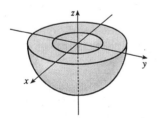

$$\int_0^{2\pi} \int_{\pi/2}^{\pi} \int_1^2 \rho^2 \sin\phi\, d\rho\, d\phi\, d\theta = \int_0^{2\pi} d\theta \int_{\pi/2}^{\pi} \sin\phi\, d\phi \int_1^2 \rho^2\, d\rho$$
$$= [\theta]_0^{2\pi} [-\cos\phi]_{\pi/2}^{\pi} \left[\tfrac{1}{3}\rho^3 \right]_1^2$$
$$= 2\pi\,(1) \left(\tfrac{7}{3} \right) = \tfrac{14\pi}{3}$$

5. The solid E is most conveniently described if we use cylindrical coordinates:
$E = \{(r, \theta, z) \mid 0 \le \theta \le \tfrac{\pi}{2}, 0 \le r \le 3, 0 \le z \le 2\}$. Then
$\iiint_E f(x, y, z)\, dV = \int_0^{\pi/2} \int_0^3 \int_0^2 f(r\cos\theta, r\sin\theta, z)\, r\, dz\, dr\, d\theta$.

6. The solid E is most conveniently described if we use spherical coordinates:
$E = \{(\rho, \theta, \phi) \mid 1 \le \rho \le 2, \tfrac{\pi}{2} \le \theta \le 2\pi, 0 \le \phi \le \tfrac{\pi}{2}\}$. Then
$\iiint_E f(x, y, z)\, dV = \int_0^{\pi/2} \int_{\pi/2}^{2\pi} \int_1^2 f(\rho\sin\phi\cos\theta, \rho\sin\phi\sin\theta, \rho\cos\phi)\, \rho^2 \sin\phi\, d\rho\, d\theta\, d\phi$.

7. In cylindrical coordinates, E is given by $\{(r, \theta, z) \mid 0 \le \theta \le 2\pi, 0 \le r \le 4, -5 \le z \le 4\}$. So

$$\iiint_E \sqrt{x^2 + y^2}\, dV = \int_0^{2\pi} \int_0^4 \int_{-5}^4 \sqrt{r^2}\, r \, dz \, dr \, d\theta = \int_0^{2\pi} d\theta \int_0^4 r^2 \, dr \int_{-5}^4 dz$$

$$= [\theta]_0^{2\pi} \left[\tfrac{1}{3}r^3\right]_0^4 [z]_{-5}^4 = (2\pi)\left(\tfrac{64}{3}\right)(9) = 384\pi$$

8. The paraboloid $z = 1 - x^2 - y^2$ intersects the xy-plane in the circle $x^2 + y^2 = r^2 = 1$ or $r = 1$, so in cylindrical coordinates, E is given by $\left\{(r, \theta, z) \mid 0 \le \theta \le \tfrac{\pi}{2}, 0 \le r \le 1, 0 \le z \le 1 - r^2\right\}$. Thus

$$\iiint_E (x^3 + xy^2)\, dV = \int_0^{\pi/2} \int_0^1 \int_0^{1-r^2} (r^3 \cos^3 \theta + r^3 \cos \theta \sin^2 \theta)\, r \, dz \, dr \, d\theta$$

$$= \int_0^{\pi/2} \int_0^1 \int_0^{1-r^2} r^4 \cos \theta \, dz \, dr \, d\theta = \int_0^{\pi/2} \int_0^1 r^4 \cos \theta\, [z]_{z=0}^{z=1-r^2} \, dr \, d\theta$$

$$= \int_0^{\pi/2} \int_0^1 r^4 (1 - r^2) \cos \theta \, dr \, d\theta = \int_0^{\pi/2} \cos \theta \left[\frac{1}{5}r^5 - \frac{1}{7}r^7\right]_{r=0}^{r=1} d\theta$$

$$= \int_0^{\pi/2} \frac{2}{35} \cos \theta \, d\theta = \frac{2}{35} [\sin \theta]_0^{\pi/2} = \frac{2}{35}$$

9. In cylindrical coordinates E is bounded by the cylinders $r = 1$ and $r = 2$, the plane $z = x + 2 = r \cos \theta + 2$, and the xy-plane, so E is given by $\{(r, \theta, z) \mid 0 \le \theta \le 2\pi, 1 \le r \le 2, 0 \le z \le r \cos \theta + 2\}$. Thus

$$\iiint_E y\, dV = \int_0^{2\pi} \int_1^2 \int_0^{2+r\cos\theta} (r \sin \theta)\, r \, dz \, dr \, d\theta = \int_0^{2\pi} \int_1^2 r^2 \sin \theta\, [z]_{z=0}^{z=2+r\cos\theta} \, dr \, d\theta$$

$$= \int_0^{2\pi} \int_1^2 (2r^2 + r^3 \cos \theta) \sin \theta \, dr \, d\theta = \int_0^{2\pi} \left[\tfrac{2}{3}r^3 + \tfrac{1}{4}r^4 \cos \theta\right]_{r=1}^{r=2} \sin \theta \, d\theta$$

$$= \int_0^{2\pi} \left(\tfrac{14}{3} + \tfrac{15}{4} \cos \theta\right) \sin \theta \, d\theta = \left[-\tfrac{14}{3} \cos \theta - \tfrac{15}{8} \cos^2 \theta\right]_0^{2\pi} = 0$$

10. In cylindrical coordinates, E is bounded by the cylinder $r = 1$ and the planes $z = 0$, $z = y = r \sin \theta$ with $y \ge 0$ $\Rightarrow$ $0 \le \theta \le \pi$, so E is given by $\{(r, \theta, z) \mid 0 \le \theta \le \pi, 0 \le r \le 1, 0 \le z \le r \sin \theta\}$. Thus

$$\iiint_E xz\, dV = \int_0^\pi \int_0^1 \int_0^{r\sin\theta} r^2 z \cos \theta \, dz \, dr \, d\theta = \int_0^\pi \int_0^1 \left[\tfrac{1}{2}z^2\right]_{z=0}^{z=r\sin\theta} r^2 \cos \theta \, dr \, d\theta$$

$$= \tfrac{1}{2} \int_0^\pi \int_0^1 r^4 \sin^2 \theta \cos \theta \, dr \, d\theta = \tfrac{1}{2} \int_0^\pi \left[\tfrac{1}{5}r^5\right]_{r=0}^{r=1} \sin^2 \theta \cos \theta \, d\theta$$

$$= \tfrac{1}{10} \int_0^\pi (\sin^2 \theta \cos \theta)\, d\theta = \tfrac{1}{30} \sin^3 \theta\big]_0^\pi = 0$$

11. In cylindrical coordinates, E is bounded by the cylinder $r = 1$, the plane $z = 0$, and the cone $z = 2r$. So $E = \{(r, \theta, z) \mid 0 \le \theta \le 2\pi, 0 \le r \le 1, 0 \le z \le 2r\}$ and

$$\iiint_E x^2\, dV = \int_0^{2\pi} \int_0^1 \int_0^{2r} r^2 \cos^2 \theta\, r \, dz \, dr \, d\theta = \int_0^{2\pi} \int_0^1 \left[r^3 \cos^2 \theta\, z\right]_{z=0}^{z=2r} dr \, d\theta$$

$$= \int_0^{2\pi} \int_0^1 2r^4 \cos^2 \theta \, dr \, d\theta = \int_0^{2\pi} \left[\tfrac{2}{5}r^5 \cos^2 \theta\right]_{r=0}^{r=1} d\theta = \tfrac{2}{5} \int_0^{2\pi} \cos^2 \theta \, d\theta$$

$$= \frac{2}{5} \int_0^{2\pi} \frac{1 + \cos 2\theta}{2} \, d\theta = \frac{1}{5}\left[\theta + \frac{1}{2} \sin 2\theta\right]_0^{2\pi} = \frac{2\pi}{5}$$

12. (a) $V = \int_{-\pi/2}^{\pi/2} \int_0^{a\cos\theta} \int_{-\sqrt{a^2-r^2}}^{\sqrt{a^2-r^2}} r\, dz\, dr\, d\theta$

(b)

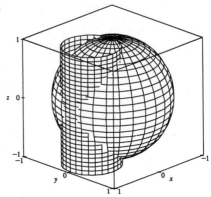

$= 4 \int_0^{\pi/2} \int_0^{a\cos\theta} \int_0^{\sqrt{a^2-r^2}} r\, dz\, dr\, d\theta$

$= 4 \int_0^{\pi/2} \int_0^{a\cos\theta} r\sqrt{a^2-r^2}\, dr\, d\theta$

$= -\tfrac{4}{3} \int_0^{\pi/2} \left[(a^2-r^2)^{3/2} \right]_{r=0}^{r=a\cos\theta} d\theta$

$= -\tfrac{4}{3} \int_0^{\pi/2} \left[(a^2 - a^2\cos^2\theta)^{3/2} - a^3 \right] d\theta$

$= -\tfrac{4}{3} \int_0^{\pi/2} \left[(a^2\sin^2\theta)^{3/2} - a^3 \right] d\theta$

$= -\tfrac{4}{3} \int_0^{\pi/2} (a^3\sin^3\theta - a^3)\, d\theta$

$= -\frac{4a^3}{3} \int_0^{\pi/2} \left[\sin\theta\,(1-\cos^2\theta) - 1 \right] d\theta$

$V = -\frac{4a^3}{3} \left[-\cos\theta + \tfrac{1}{3}\cos^3\theta - \theta \right]_0^{\pi/2} = -\frac{4a^3}{3}\left(-\tfrac{\pi}{2} + \tfrac{2}{3} \right) = \tfrac{2}{9}a^3(3\pi - 4)$

To plot the cylinder and the sphere on the same screen in Maple, we can use the sequence of commands

```
sphere:=plot3d(1,theta=0..2*Pi,phi=0..Pi,coords=spherical):
cylinder:=plot3d([cos(theta),theta,z],
theta=0..2*Pi,z=-1..1,coords=cylindrical):
with(plots):  display3d({sphere,cylinder});
```

In Mathematica, we can use

```
sphere=SphericalPlot3d[1,{theta,0,2Pi},{phi,0,Pi}]
cylinder=ParametricPlot3d[{Sin[theta],Cos[theta],z},
{theta,0,2Pi},{z,-1,1}]
Show[{sphere,cylinder}]
```

13. The paraboloid $z = 4x^2 + 4y^2$ intersects the plane $z = a$ when $a = 4x^2 + 4y^2$ or $x^2 + y^2 = \tfrac{1}{4}a$. So, in cylindrical coordinates, $E = \left\{ (r,\theta,z) \mid 0 \le r \le \tfrac{1}{2}\sqrt{a},\, 0 \le \theta \le 2\pi,\, 4r^2 \le z \le a \right\}$. Thus

$$m = \int_0^{2\pi} \int_0^{\sqrt{a}/2} \int_{4r^2}^{a} Kr\, dz\, dr\, d\theta = K \int_0^{2\pi} \int_0^{\sqrt{a}/2} (ar - 4r^3)\, dr\, d\theta$$

$$= K \int_0^{2\pi} \left[\tfrac{1}{2}ar^2 - r^4 \right]_{r=0}^{r=\sqrt{a}/2} d\theta = K \int_0^{2\pi} \tfrac{1}{16}a^2\, d\theta = \tfrac{1}{8}a^2\pi K$$

Since the region is homogeneous and symmetric, $M_{yz} = M_{xz} = 0$ and

$$M_{xy} = \int_0^{2\pi} \int_0^{\sqrt{a}/2} \int_{4r^2}^{a} Krz\, dz\, dr\, d\theta = K \int_0^{2\pi} \int_0^{\sqrt{a}/2} \left(\tfrac{1}{2}a^2 r - 8r^5 \right) dr\, d\theta$$

$$= K \int_0^{2\pi} \left[\tfrac{1}{4}a^2 r^2 - \tfrac{4}{3}r^6 \right]_{r=0}^{r=\sqrt{a}/2} d\theta = K \int_0^{2\pi} \tfrac{1}{24}a^3\, d\theta = \tfrac{1}{12}a^3\pi K$$

Hence $(\overline{x}, \overline{y}, \overline{z}) = \left(0, 0, \tfrac{2}{3}a \right)$.

14. (a) The paraboloids intersect when $x^2 + y^2 = 36 - 3x^2 - 3y^2 \;\Rightarrow\; x^2 + y^2 = 9$, so the region of integration is $D = \left\{ (x,y) \mid x^2 + y^2 \le 9 \right\}$. Then, in cylindrical coordinates, $E = \left\{ (r,\theta,z) \mid r^2 \le z \le 36 - 3r^2,\, 0 \le r \le 3,\, 0 \le \theta \le 2\pi \right\}$ and

$$V = \int_0^{2\pi} \int_0^3 \int_{r^2}^{36-3r^2} r\, dz\, dr\, d\theta = \int_0^{2\pi} \int_0^3 (36r - 4r^3)\, dr\, d\theta$$

$$= \int_0^{2\pi} \left[18r^2 - r^4 \right]_{r=0}^{r=3} d\theta = \int_0^{2\pi} 81\, d\theta = 162\pi$$

(b) $M_{yz} = \int_0^{2\pi} \int_0^3 \int_{r^2}^{36-3r^2} r^2 \cos\theta \, dz \, dr \, d\theta = 0 = M_{xz}$ by the symmetry of the region, and

$$M_{xy} = \int_0^{2\pi} \int_0^3 \int_{r^2}^{36-3r^2} rz \, dz \, dr \, d\theta = \int_0^{2\pi} \int_0^3 \left[\tfrac{1}{2}r(36-3r^2)^2 - \tfrac{1}{2}r^5\right] dr \, d\theta$$

$$= \int_0^{2\pi} \left[-\tfrac{1}{36}(36-3r^2)^3 - \tfrac{1}{12}r^6\right]_{r=0}^{r=3} d\theta = \int_0^{2\pi}(-3^4 + 36^2) \, d\theta = 2430\pi$$

Hence $(\overline{x}, \overline{y}, \overline{z}) = (0, 0, 15)$.

15. In spherical coordinates, B is represented by $\{(\rho, \theta, \phi) \,|\, 0 \le \rho \le 1, 0 \le \theta \le 2\pi, 0 \le \phi \le \pi\}$. Thus

$$\iiint_B (x^2 + y^2 + z^2) \, dV = \int_0^\pi \int_0^{2\pi} \int_0^1 (\rho^2) \, \rho^2 \sin\phi \, d\rho \, d\theta \, d\phi = \int_0^\pi \sin\phi \, d\phi \int_0^{2\pi} d\theta \int_0^1 \rho^4 \, d\rho$$

$$= [-\cos\phi]_0^\pi \, [\theta]_0^{2\pi} \, [\tfrac{1}{5}\rho^5]_0^1 = (2)(2\pi)(\tfrac{1}{5}) = \tfrac{4\pi}{5}$$

16. In spherical coordinates, H is represented by $\{(\rho, \theta, \phi) \,|\, 0 \le \rho \le 1, 0 \le \theta \le 2\pi, 0 \le \phi \le \tfrac{\pi}{2}\}$. Thus

$$\iiint_H (x^2 + y^2) \, dV = \int_0^{2\pi} \int_0^{\pi/2} \int_0^1 (\rho^2 \sin^2\phi) \, \rho^2 \sin\phi \, d\rho \, d\phi \, d\theta = \int_0^{2\pi} d\theta \int_0^{\pi/2} \sin^3\phi \, d\phi \int_0^1 \rho^4 \, d\rho$$

$$= [\theta]_0^{2\pi} \left[-\cos\phi + \tfrac{1}{3}\cos^3\phi\right]_0^{\pi/2} [\tfrac{1}{5}\rho^5]_0^1 = \tfrac{4\pi}{15}$$

17. In spherical coordinates, E is represented by $\{(\rho, \theta, \phi) \,|\, 1 \le \rho \le 2, 0 \le \theta \le \tfrac{\pi}{2}, 0 \le \phi \le \tfrac{\pi}{2}\}$. Thus

$$\iiint_E z \, dV = \int_0^{\pi/2} \int_0^{\pi/2} \int_1^2 (\rho\cos\phi) \, \rho^2 \sin\phi \, d\rho \, d\theta \, d\phi$$

$$= \int_0^{\pi/2} \cos\phi \sin\phi \, d\phi \int_0^{\pi/2} d\theta \int_1^2 \rho^3 \, d\rho = \left[\tfrac{1}{2}\sin^2\phi\right]_0^{\pi/2} [\theta]_0^{\pi/2} \left[\tfrac{1}{4}\rho^4\right]_1^2$$

$$= (\tfrac{1}{2})(\tfrac{\pi}{2})(\tfrac{15}{4}) = \tfrac{15\pi}{16}$$

18. $\iiint_E xe^{(x^2+y^2+z^2)^2} \, dV = \int_0^{\pi/2} \int_0^{\pi/2} \int_1^2 (\rho\sin\phi\cos\theta) \, e^{\rho^4} \, (\rho^2 \sin\phi) \, d\rho \, d\phi \, d\theta$

$$= \int_0^{\pi/2} \cos\theta \, d\theta \int_0^{\pi/2} \sin^2\phi \, d\phi \int_1^2 \rho^3 e^{\rho^4} \, d\rho$$

$$= [\sin\theta]_0^{\pi/2} \left[\tfrac{1}{2}\phi - \tfrac{1}{4}\sin 2\phi\right]_0^{\pi/2} \left[\tfrac{1}{4}e^{\rho^4}\right]_1^2$$

$$= (1)(\tfrac{\pi}{4})\left[\tfrac{1}{4}(e^{16} - e)\right] = \tfrac{1}{16}\pi \, (e^{16} - e)$$

19. $\iiint_E \sqrt{x^2 + y^2 + z^2} \, dV = \int_0^{2\pi} \int_0^{\pi/6} \int_0^2 (\rho)\rho^2 \sin\phi \, d\rho \, d\phi \, d\theta$

$$= \int_0^{2\pi} d\theta \int_0^{\pi/6} \sin\phi \, d\phi \int_0^2 \rho^3 \, d\rho = [\theta]_0^{2\pi} [-\cos\phi]_0^{\pi/6} \left[\tfrac{1}{4}\rho^4\right]_0^2$$

$$= (2\pi)\left(1 - \tfrac{\sqrt{3}}{2}\right)(4) = 8\pi\left(1 - \tfrac{\sqrt{3}}{2}\right) = 4\pi\,(2 - \sqrt{3})$$

20. In spherical coordinates, the sphere $x^2 + y^2 + z^2 = 4$ is equivalent to $\rho = 2$ and the cone $z = \sqrt{x^2 + y^2}$ is represented by $\phi = \tfrac{\pi}{4}$. Thus, the solid is given by $\{(\rho, \theta, \phi) \,|\, 0 \le \rho \le 2, 0 \le \theta \le 2\pi, \tfrac{\pi}{4} \le \phi \le \tfrac{\pi}{2}\}$ and

$$V = \int_{\pi/4}^{\pi/2} \int_0^{2\pi} \int_0^2 \rho^2 \sin\phi \, d\rho \, d\theta \, d\phi = \int_{\pi/4}^{\pi/2} \sin\phi \, d\phi \int_0^{2\pi} d\theta \int_0^2 \rho^2 \, d\rho$$

$$= [-\cos\phi]_{\pi/4}^{\pi/2} \, [\theta]_0^{2\pi} \, [\tfrac{1}{3}\rho^3]_0^2 = \left(\tfrac{\sqrt{2}}{2}\right)(2\pi)(\tfrac{8}{3}) = \tfrac{8\sqrt{2}\pi}{3}$$

21. (a) Since $\rho = 4\cos\phi$ implies $\rho^2 = 4\rho\cos\phi$, the equation is that of a sphere of radius 2 with center at $(0, 0, 2)$.

Thus

$$V = \int_0^{2\pi}\int_0^{\pi/3}\int_0^{4\cos\phi}\rho^2\sin\phi\,d\rho\,d\phi\,d\theta = \int_0^{2\pi}\int_0^{\pi/3}\left[\tfrac{1}{3}\rho^3\right]_{\rho=0}^{\rho=4\cos\phi}\sin\phi\,d\phi\,d\theta$$

$$= \int_0^{2\pi}\int_0^{\pi/3}\left(\tfrac{64}{3}\cos^3\phi\right)\sin\phi\,d\phi\,d\theta = \int_0^{2\pi}\left[-\tfrac{16}{3}\cos^4\phi\right]_{\phi=0}^{\phi=\pi/3}d\theta$$

$$= \int_0^{2\pi}-\tfrac{16}{3}\left(\tfrac{1}{16}-1\right)d\theta = 5\theta\big]_0^{2\pi} = 10\pi$$

(b) By the symmetry of the problem $M_{yz} = M_{xz} = 0$. Then

$$M_{xy} = \int_0^{2\pi}\int_0^{\pi/3}\int_0^{4\cos\phi}\rho^3\cos\phi\sin\phi\,d\rho\,d\phi\,d\theta = \int_0^{2\pi}\int_0^{\pi/3}\cos\phi\sin\phi\left(64\cos^4\phi\right)d\phi\,d\theta$$

$$= \int_0^{2\pi}64\left[-\tfrac{1}{6}\cos^6\phi\right]_{\phi=0}^{\phi=\pi/3}d\theta = \int_0^{2\pi}\tfrac{21}{2}d\theta = 21\pi$$

Hence $(\overline{x}, \overline{y}, \overline{z}) = (0, 0, 2.1)$.

22. (a) Placing the center of the base at $(0, 0, 0)$, $\rho(x, y, z) = K\sqrt{x^2 + y^2 + z^2}$ is the density function. So

$$m = \int_0^{2\pi}\int_0^{\pi/2}\int_0^a K\rho^3\sin\phi\,d\rho\,d\phi\,d\theta = K\int_0^{2\pi}d\theta\int_0^{\pi/2}\sin\phi\,d\phi\int_0^a\rho^3\,d\rho$$

$$= K[\theta]_0^{2\pi}\left[-\cos\phi\right]_0^{\pi/2}\left[\tfrac{1}{4}\rho^4\right]_0^a = K(2\pi)(1)\left(\tfrac{1}{4}a^4\right) = \tfrac{1}{2}\pi Ka^4$$

(b) By the symmetry of the problem $M_{yz} = M_{xz} = 0$. Then

$$M_{xy} = \int_0^{2\pi}\int_0^{\pi/2}\int_0^a K\rho^4\sin\phi\cos\phi\,d\rho\,d\phi\,d\theta = K\int_0^{2\pi}d\theta\int_0^{\pi/2}\sin\phi\cos\phi\,d\phi\int_0^a\rho^4\,d\rho$$

$$= K[\theta]_0^{2\pi}\left[\tfrac{1}{2}\sin^2\phi\right]_0^{\pi/2}\left[\tfrac{1}{5}\rho^5\right]_0^a = K(2\pi)\left(\tfrac{1}{2}\right)\left(\tfrac{1}{5}a^5\right) = \tfrac{1}{5}\pi Ka^5$$

Hence $(\overline{x}, \overline{y}, \overline{z}) = \left(0, 0, \tfrac{2}{5}a\right)$.

(c) $I_z = \int_0^{2\pi}\int_0^{\pi/2}\int_0^a\left(K\rho^3\sin\phi\right)\left(\rho^2\sin^2\phi\right)d\rho\,d\phi\,d\theta = K\int_0^{2\pi}d\theta\int_0^{\pi/2}\sin^3\phi\,d\phi\int_0^a\rho^5\,d\rho$

$$= K[\theta]_0^{2\pi}\left[-\cos\phi + \tfrac{1}{3}\cos^3\phi\right]_0^{\pi/2}\left[\tfrac{1}{6}\rho^6\right]_0^a = K(2\pi)\left(\tfrac{2}{3}\right)\left(\tfrac{1}{6}a^6\right) = \tfrac{2}{9}\pi Ka^6$$

23. (a) The density function is $\rho(x, y, z) = K$, a constant, and by the symmetry of the problem $M_{xz} = M_{yz} = 0$.

Then $M_{xy} = \int_0^{2\pi}\int_0^{\pi/2}\int_0^a K\rho^3\sin\phi\cos\phi\,d\rho\,d\phi\,d\theta = \tfrac{1}{2}\pi Ka^4\int_0^{\pi/2}\sin\phi\cos\phi\,d\phi = \tfrac{1}{8}\pi Ka^4$. But the mass is

$K(\text{volume of the hemisphere}) = \tfrac{2}{3}\pi Ka^3$, so the centroid is $\left(0, 0, \tfrac{3}{8}a\right)$.

(b) Place the center of the base at $(0, 0, 0)$; the density function is $\rho(x, y, z) = K$. By symmetry, the moments of inertia about any two such diameters will be equal, so we just need to find I_x:

$$I_x = \int_0^{2\pi}\int_0^{\pi/2}\int_0^a\left(K\rho^2\sin\phi\right)\rho^2\left(\sin^2\phi\sin^2\theta + \cos^2\phi\right)d\rho\,d\phi\,d\theta$$

$$= K\int_0^{2\pi}\int_0^{\pi/2}\left(\sin^3\phi\sin^2\theta + \sin\phi\cos^2\phi\right)\left(\tfrac{1}{5}a^5\right)d\phi\,d\theta$$

$$= \tfrac{1}{5}Ka^5\int_0^{2\pi}\left[\sin^2\theta\left(-\cos\phi + \tfrac{1}{3}\cos^3\phi\right) + \left(-\tfrac{1}{3}\cos^3\phi\right)\right]_{\phi=0}^{\phi=\pi/2}d\theta$$

$$= \tfrac{1}{5}Ka^5\int_0^{2\pi}\left[\tfrac{2}{3}\sin^2\theta + \tfrac{1}{3}\right]d\theta = \tfrac{1}{5}Ka^5\left[\tfrac{2}{3}\left(\tfrac{1}{2}\theta - \tfrac{1}{4}\sin 2\theta\right) + \tfrac{1}{3}\theta\right]_0^{2\pi}$$

$$= \tfrac{1}{5}Ka^5\left[\tfrac{2}{3}(\pi - 0) + \tfrac{1}{3}(2\pi - 0)\right] = \tfrac{4}{15}Ka^5\pi$$

24. Place the center of the base at $(0, 0, 0)$, then the density is $\rho(x, y, z) = Kz$, K a constant. Then

$$m = \int_0^{2\pi}\int_0^{\pi/2}\int_0^a(K\rho\cos\phi)\rho^2\sin\phi\,d\rho\,d\phi\,d\theta = 2\pi K\int_0^{\pi/2}\cos\phi\sin\phi\cdot\tfrac{1}{4}a^4\,d\phi$$

$$= \tfrac{1}{2}\pi Ka^4\left[-\tfrac{1}{4}\cos 2\phi\right]_0^{\pi/2} = \tfrac{\pi}{4}Ka^4$$

By the symmetry of the problem $M_{xz} = M_{yz} = 0$, and

$$M_{xy} = \int_0^{2\pi} \int_0^{\pi/2} \int_0^a K\rho^4 \cos^2\phi \sin\phi \, d\rho \, d\phi \, d\theta = \tfrac{2}{5}\pi K a^5 \int_0^{\pi/2} \cos^2\phi \sin\phi \, d\phi$$

$$= \tfrac{2}{5}\pi K a^5 \left[-\tfrac{1}{3}\cos^3\theta\right]_0^{\pi/2} = \tfrac{2}{15}\pi K a^5$$

Hence $(\overline{x}, \overline{y}, \overline{z}) = \left(0, 0, \tfrac{8}{15}a\right)$.

25. In spherical coordinates $z = \sqrt{x^2 + y^2}$ becomes $\cos\phi = \sin\phi$ or $\phi = \tfrac{\pi}{4}$. Then

$$V = \int_0^{2\pi}\int_0^{\pi/4}\int_0^1 \rho^2 \sin\phi \, d\rho \, d\phi \, d\theta = \int_0^{2\pi} d\theta \int_0^{\pi/4} \sin\phi \, d\phi \int_0^1 \rho^2 \, d\rho = \tfrac{1}{3}\pi\left(2 - \sqrt{2}\right),$$

$$M_{xy} = \int_0^{2\pi}\int_0^{\pi/4}\int_0^1 \rho^3 \sin\phi \cos\phi \, d\rho \, d\phi \, d\theta = 2\pi\left[-\tfrac{1}{4}\cos 2\phi\right]_0^{\pi/4}\left(\tfrac{1}{4}\right) = \tfrac{\pi}{8} \text{ and by symmetry } M_{yz} = M_{xz} = 0.$$

Hence $(\overline{x}, \overline{y}, \overline{z}) = \left(0, 0, \tfrac{3}{8(2-\sqrt{2})}\right)$.

26. Place the center of the sphere at $(0, 0, 0)$, let the diameter of intersection be along the z-axis, one of the planes be the xz-plane and the other be the plane whose angle with the xz-plane is $\theta = \tfrac{\pi}{6}$. Then in spherical coordinates the volume is given by $V = \int_0^{\pi/6}\int_0^\pi\int_0^a \rho^2 \sin\phi \, d\rho \, d\phi \, d\theta = \int_0^{\pi/6} d\theta \int_0^\pi \sin\phi \, d\phi \int_0^a \rho^2 \, d\rho = \tfrac{\pi}{6}(2)\left(\tfrac{1}{3}a^3\right) = \tfrac{1}{9}\pi a^3$.

27. In cylindrical coordinates the paraboloid is given by $z = r^2$ and the plane by $z = 2r\sin\theta$ and they intersect in the circle $r = 2\sin\theta$. Then $\iiint_E z \, dV = \int_0^\pi \int_0^{2\sin\theta} \int_{r^2}^{2r\sin\theta} rz \, dz \, dr \, d\theta = \tfrac{5\pi}{6}$ (using a CAS).

28. (a) The region enclosed by the torus is $\{(\rho, \theta, \phi) \mid 0 \le \theta \le 2\pi, 0 \le \phi \le \pi, 0 \le \rho \le \sin\phi\}$, so its volume is

$$V = \int_0^{2\pi}\int_0^\pi\int_0^{\sin\phi} \rho^2 \sin\phi \, d\rho \, d\phi \, d\theta = 2\pi \int_0^\pi \tfrac{1}{3}\sin^4\phi \, d\phi = \tfrac{2}{3}\pi\left[\tfrac{3}{8}\phi - \tfrac{1}{4}\sin 2\phi + \tfrac{1}{16}\sin 4\phi\right]_0^\pi = \tfrac{1}{4}\pi^2$$

(b) In Maple, we can plot the torus using the `plots[sphereplot]` command, or with the `coords=spherical` option in a regular `plot` command. In Mathematica, use `ParametricPlot3d`.

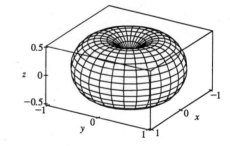

29. The region E of integration is the region above the paraboloid $z = x^2 + y^2$, or $z = r^2$, and below the paraboloid $z = 2 - x^2 - y^2$, or $z = 2 - r^2$. Also, we have $-1 \le x \le 1$ with $-\sqrt{1 - x^2} \le y \le \sqrt{1 - x^2}$ which describes the unit circle in the xy-plane. Thus,

$$\int_{-1}^1 \int_{-\sqrt{1-x^2}}^{\sqrt{1-x^2}} \int_{x^2+y^2}^{2-x^2-y^2} \left(x^2 + y^2\right)^{3/2} dz \, dy \, dx = \int_0^{2\pi}\int_0^1\int_{r^2}^{2-r^2} \left(r^2\right)^{3/2} r \, dz \, dr \, d\theta$$

$$= \int_0^{2\pi}\int_0^1 \left[r^4 z\right]_{z=r^2}^{z=2-r^2} dr \, d\theta = \int_0^{2\pi}\int_0^1 \left(2r^4 - r^6 - r^6\right) dr \, d\theta = \int_0^{2\pi}\left(\tfrac{2}{5} - \tfrac{2}{7}\right) d\theta = \tfrac{8\pi}{35}$$

30. The region of integration E is the region above the cone $z = \sqrt{x^2 + y^2}$ and below the sphere $x^2 + y^2 + z^2 = 18$ in the first octant. Because E is in the first octant we have $0 \le \theta \le \tfrac{\pi}{2}$. The cone has equation $\phi = \tfrac{\pi}{4}$ (as in Example 4) and so $0 \le \phi \le \tfrac{\pi}{4}$. Also $0 \le \rho \le \sqrt{18} = 3\sqrt{2}$. So the integral becomes

$$\int_0^{\pi/2}\int_0^{\pi/4}\int_0^{3\sqrt{2}} \rho^4 \sin\phi \, d\rho \, d\phi \, d\theta = \int_0^{\pi/2} d\theta \int_0^{\pi/4} \sin\phi \, d\phi \int_0^{3\sqrt{2}} \rho^4 \, d\rho$$

$$= \left[\theta\right]_0^{\pi/2}\left[-\cos\phi\right]_0^{\pi/4}\left[\tfrac{1}{5}\rho^5\right]_0^{3\sqrt{2}}$$

$$= \left(\tfrac{\pi}{2}\right)\left(1 - \tfrac{\sqrt{2}}{2}\right)\left(\tfrac{972\sqrt{2}}{5}\right) = 486\pi\left(\tfrac{\sqrt{2}-1}{5}\right)$$

31. If E is the solid enclosed by the surface $\rho = 1 + \frac{1}{5} \sin 6\theta \sin 5\phi$, it can be described in spherical coordinates as
$E = \{(\rho, \theta, \phi) \mid 0 \le \rho \le 1 + \frac{1}{5} \sin 6\theta \sin 5\phi, 0 \le \theta \le 2\pi, 0 \le \phi \le \pi\}$. Its volume is given by
$V((E)) = \iiint_E dV = \int_0^\pi \int_0^{2\pi} \int_0^{1 + (\sin 6\theta \sin 5\phi)/5} \rho^2 \sin \phi \, d\rho \, d\theta \, d\phi = \frac{136\pi}{99}$ (using a CAS).

32. The given integral is equal to
$\lim\limits_{R \to \infty} \int_0^{2\pi} \int_0^\pi \int_0^R \rho e^{-\rho^2} \rho^2 \sin \phi \, d\rho \, d\phi \, d\theta = \lim\limits_{R \to \infty} \left(\int_0^{2\pi} d\theta \right) \left(\int_0^\pi \sin \phi \, d\phi \right) \left(\int_0^R \rho^3 e^{-\rho^2} \, d\rho \right)$. Now use integration
by parts with $u = \rho^2$, $dv = \rho e^{-\rho^2} \, d\rho$ to get

$$\lim\limits_{R \to \infty} 2\pi(2) \left(\rho^2 \left(-\tfrac{1}{2}\right) e^{-\rho^2} \Big|_0^R - \int_0^R 2\rho \left(-\tfrac{1}{2}\right) e^{-\rho^2} \, d\rho \right) = \lim\limits_{R \to \infty} 4\pi \left(-\tfrac{1}{2} R^2 e^{-R^2} + \left[-\tfrac{1}{2} e^{-\rho^2} \right]_0^R \right)$$

$$= 4\pi \lim\limits_{R \to \infty} \left[-\tfrac{1}{2} R^2 e^{-R^2} - \tfrac{1}{2} e^{-R^2} + \tfrac{1}{2} \right] = 4\pi \left(\tfrac{1}{2} \right) = 2\pi$$

(Note that $R^2 e^{-R^2} \to 0$ as $R \to \infty$ by l'Hospital's Rule.)

33. (a) The mountain comprises a solid conical region C. The work done in lifting a small volume of material ΔV with
density $g(P)$ to a height $h(P)$ above sea level is $h(P)g(P) \, \Delta V$. Summing over the whole mountain we get
$W = \iiint_C h(P)g(P) \, \Delta V$.

(b) Here C is a solid right circular cone with radius $R = 62{,}000$ ft, height $H = 12{,}400$ ft, and density
$g(P) = 200$ lb/ft^3 at all points P in C. We use cylindrical coordinates:

$$W = \int_0^{2\pi} \int_0^H \int_0^{R(1-z/H)} z \cdot 200r \, dr \, dz \, d\theta$$

$$= 2\pi \int_0^H 200z \left[\tfrac{1}{2} r^2 \right]_{r=0}^{r=R(1-z/H)} dz$$

$$= 400\pi \int_0^H z \frac{R^2}{2} \left(1 - \frac{z}{H} \right)^2 dz$$

$$= 200\pi R^2 \int_0^H \left(z - \frac{2z^2}{H} + \frac{z^3}{H^2} \right) dz$$

$$= 200\pi R^2 \left[\frac{z^2}{2} - \frac{2z^3}{3H} + \frac{z^4}{4H^2} \right]_0^H$$

$$= 200\pi R^2 \left(\frac{H^2}{2} - \frac{2H^2}{3} + \frac{H^2}{4} \right) = \frac{50}{3} \pi R^2 H^2$$

$$= \frac{50}{3} \pi (62{,}000)^2 (12{,}400)^2 \approx 3.1 \times 10^{19} \text{ ft-lb}$$

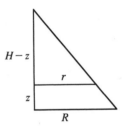

$$\frac{r}{R} = \frac{H - z}{H} = 1 - \frac{z}{H}$$

Applied Project	**Roller Derby**

1. $mgh = \frac{1}{2}mv^2 + \frac{1}{2}I\omega^2 = \frac{1}{2}\left(m + I/r^2\right)v^2$, so $v^2 = \dfrac{2mgh}{m + I/r^2} = \dfrac{2gh}{1 + I^*}$.

2. The vertical component of the speed is $v\sin\alpha$, so

$$\frac{dy}{dt} = \sqrt{\frac{2gy}{1 + I^*}}\sin\alpha = \sqrt{\frac{2g}{1 + I^*}}\sin\alpha\,\sqrt{y}.$$

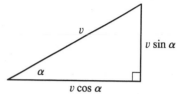

3. Solving the separable differential equation, we get $\dfrac{dy}{\sqrt{y}} = \sqrt{\dfrac{2g}{1 + I^*}}\sin\alpha\,dt \;\Rightarrow$

$2\sqrt{y} = \sqrt{\dfrac{2g}{1 + I^*}}\,(\sin\alpha)t + C$. But $y = 0$ when $t = 0$, so $C = 0$ and we have $2\sqrt{y} = \sqrt{\dfrac{2g}{1 + I^*}}\,(\sin\alpha)t$.

Solving for t when $y = h$ gives $T = \dfrac{2\sqrt{h}}{\sin\alpha}\sqrt{\dfrac{1 + I^*}{2g}} = \sqrt{\dfrac{2h(1 + I^*)}{g\sin^2\alpha}}$.

4. Assume that the length of each cylinder is ℓ. Then the density of the solid cylinder is $\dfrac{m}{\pi r^2\ell}$, and from

Formulas 12.7.16, its moment of inertia (using cylindrical coordinates) is

$$I_z = \iiint \frac{m}{\pi r^2\ell}\left(x^2 + y^2\right)dV = \int_0^\ell\int_0^{2\pi}\int_0^r \frac{m}{\pi r^2\ell}R^2 R\,dR\,d\theta\,dz = \frac{m}{\pi r^2\ell}2\pi\ell\left[\tfrac{1}{4}R^4\right]_0^r = \frac{mr^2}{2}$$

and so $I^* = \dfrac{I_z}{mr^2} = \dfrac{1}{2}$.

For the hollow cylinder, we consider its entire mass to lie a distance r from the axis of rotation, so $x^2 + y^2 = r^2$ is a constant. We express the density in terms of mass per unit area as $\rho = \dfrac{m}{2\pi r\ell}$, and then the moment of inertia is calculated as a double integral:

$$I_z = \iint \left(x^2 + y^2\right)\frac{m}{2\pi r\ell}\,dA = \frac{mr^2}{2\pi r\ell}\iint dA = mr^2$$

so $I^* = \dfrac{I_z}{mr^2} = 1$.

5. The volume of such a ball is $\frac{4}{3}\pi\left(r^3 - a^3\right) = \frac{4}{3}\pi r^3\left(1 - b^3\right)$, and so its density is $\dfrac{m}{\frac{4}{3}\pi r^3\left(1 - b^3\right)}$.

Using Formula 12.8.4, we get

$$I_z = \iiint \left(x^2 + y^2\right)\frac{m}{\frac{4}{3}\pi r^3(1 - b^3)}\,dV = \frac{m}{\frac{4}{3}\pi r^3(1 - b^3)}\int_a^r\int_0^{2\pi}\int_0^\pi \left(\rho^2\sin^2\phi\right)\left(\rho^2\sin\phi\right)d\phi\,d\theta\,d\rho$$

$$= \frac{m}{\frac{4}{3}\pi r^3(1 - b^3)}\cdot 2\pi\left[-\frac{(2 + \sin^2\phi)\cos\phi}{3}\right]_0^\pi\left[\frac{\rho^5}{5}\right]_a^r \quad \text{(from the Table of Integrals)}$$

$$= \frac{m}{\frac{4}{3}\pi r^3(1 - b^3)}\cdot 2\pi\cdot\frac{4}{3}\cdot\frac{r^5 - a^5}{5} = \frac{2mr^5\left(1 - b^5\right)}{5r^3(1 - b^3)} = \frac{2\left(1 - b^5\right)mr^2}{5(1 - b^3)}$$

Therefore $I^* = \dfrac{2\left(1 - b^5\right)}{5\left(1 - b^3\right)}$.

Since a represents the inner radius, $a \to 0$ corresponds to a solid ball, and $a \to r$ corresponds to a hollow ball.

6. For a solid ball, $a \to 0 \Rightarrow b \to 0$, so $I^* = \lim\limits_{b \to 0} \dfrac{2(1 - b^5)}{5(1 - b^3)} = \dfrac{2}{5}$. For a hollow ball, $a \to r \Rightarrow b \to 1$, so

$$I^* = \lim_{b \to 1} \frac{2(1 - b^5)}{5(1 - b^3)} = \frac{2}{5} \lim_{b \to 1} \frac{-5b^4}{-3b^2} = \frac{2}{5}\left(\frac{5}{3}\right) = \frac{2}{3} \text{ (by l'Hospital's Rule)}.$$

Note: We could instead have calculated $I^* = \lim\limits_{b \to 1} \dfrac{2(1 - b)(1 + b + b^2 + b^3 + b^4)}{5(1 - b)(1 + b + b^2)} = \dfrac{2 \cdot 5}{5 \cdot 3} = \dfrac{2}{3}$.

Thus the objects finish in the following order: solid ball $(I^* = \frac{2}{5})$, solid cylinder $(I^* = \frac{1}{2})$, hollow ball $(I^* = \frac{2}{3})$,

hollow cylinder $(I^* = 1)$.

<table>
<tr><td>

**Discovery
Project**

</td><td>

The Intersection of Three Cylinders

</td></tr>
</table>

1. The three cylinders in the illustration in the text can be
visualized as representing the surfaces $x^2 + y^2 = 1$,
$x^2 + z^2 = 1$, and $y^2 + z^2 = 1$. Then we sketch the solid
of intersection with the coordinate axes and equations
indicated. To be more precise, we start by finding the
bounding curves of the solid (shown in the first graph
below) enclosed by the two cylinders $x^2 + z^2 = 1$ and
$y^2 + z^2 = 1$: $x = \pm y = \pm\sqrt{1 - z^2}$ are the symmetric

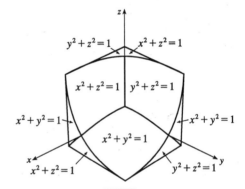

equations, and these can be expressed parametrically as $x = s$, $y = \pm s$, $z = \pm\sqrt{1 - s^2}$, $-1 \le s \le 1$. Now the
cylinder $x^2 + y^2 = 1$ intersects these curves at the eight points $\left(\pm\frac{1}{\sqrt{2}}, \pm\frac{1}{\sqrt{2}}, \pm\frac{1}{\sqrt{2}}\right)$. The resulting solid has twelve
curved faces bounded by "edges" which are arcs of circles, as shown in the third diagram. Each cylinder defines
four of the twelve faces.

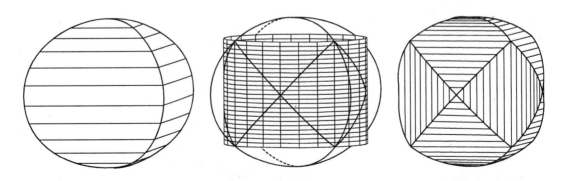

2. To find the volume, we split the solid into sixteen congruent pieces, one of which lies in the part of the first octant with $0 \le \theta \le \frac{\pi}{4}$. (Naturally, we use cylindrical coordinates!) This piece is described by

$$\{(r, \theta, z) \mid 0 \le r \le 1, 0 \le \theta \le \tfrac{\pi}{4}, 0 \le z \le \sqrt{1 - x^2}\},$$

and so, substituting $x = r \cos\theta$, the volume of the entire solid is

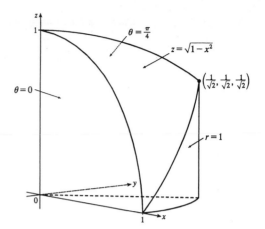

$$V = 16 \int_0^{\pi/4} \int_0^1 \int_0^{\sqrt{1-x^2}} r \, dz \, dr \, d\theta$$

$$= 16 \int_0^{\pi/4} \int_0^1 r \sqrt{1 - r^2 \cos^2\theta} \, dr \, d\theta$$

$$= 16 - 8\sqrt{2} \approx 4.6863$$

3. To graph the edges of the solid, we use parametrized curves similar to those found in Problem 1 for the intersection of two cylinders. We must restrict the parameter intervals so that each arc extends exactly to the desired vertex. One possible set of parametric equations (with all sign choices allowed) is

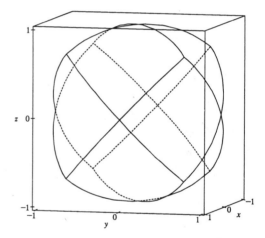

$$x = r, \, y = \pm r, \, z = \pm\sqrt{1 - r^2}, \, -\tfrac{1}{\sqrt{2}} \le r \le \tfrac{1}{\sqrt{2}};$$

$$x = \pm s, \, y = \pm\sqrt{1 - s^2}, \, z = s, \, -\tfrac{1}{\sqrt{2}} \le s \le \tfrac{1}{\sqrt{2}};$$

$$x = \pm\sqrt{1 - t^2}, \, y = t, \, z = \pm t, \, -\tfrac{1}{\sqrt{2}} \le t \le \tfrac{1}{\sqrt{2}}.$$

4. Let the three cylinders be $x^2 + y^2 = a^2$, $x^2 + z^2 = 1$, and $y^2 + z^2 = 1$.
If $a < 1$, then the four faces defined by the cylinder $x^2 + y^2 = 1$ in Problem 1 collapse into a single face, as in the first graph. If $1 < a < \sqrt{2}$, then each pair of vertically opposed faces, defined by one of the other two cylinders, collapse into a single face, as in the second graph. If $a \ge \sqrt{2}$, then the vertical cylinder encloses the solid of intersection of the other two cylinders completely, so the solid of intersection coincides with the solid of intersection of the two cylinders $x^2 + z^2 = 1$ and $y^2 + z^2 = 1$, as illustrated in Problem 1.
If we were to vary b or c instead of a, we would get solids with the same shape, but differently oriented.

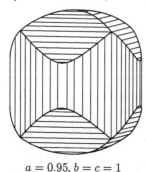

$$a = 0.95, b = c = 1$$

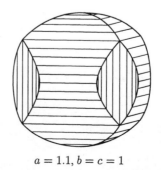

$$a = 1.1, b = c = 1$$

5. If $a < 1$, the solid looks similar to the first graph in Problem 4. As in Problem 2, we split the solid into sixteen congruent pieces, one of which can be described as the solid above the polar region $\{(r, \theta) \mid 0 \le r \le a, 0 \le \theta \le \frac{\pi}{4}\}$ in the xy-plane and below the surface $z = \sqrt{1 - x^2} = \sqrt{1 - r^2 \cos^2 \theta}$. Thus, the total volume is

$$V = 16 \int_0^{\pi/4} \int_0^a \sqrt{1 - r^2 \cos^2 \theta}\, r\, dr\, d\theta$$

If $a > 1$ and $a < \sqrt{2}$, we have a solid similar to the second graph in Problem 4. Its intersection with the xy-plane is graphed below. Again we split the solid into sixteen congruent pieces, one of which is the solid above the region shown in the second figure and below the surface $z = \sqrt{1 - x^2} = \sqrt{1 - r^2 \cos^2 \theta}$.

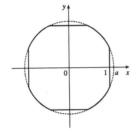
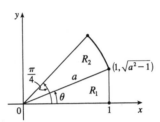

We split the region of integration where the outside boundary changes from the vertical line $x = 1$ to the circle $x^2 + y^2 = a^2$ or $r = 1$. R_1 is a right triangle, so $\cos \theta = \frac{1}{a}$. Thus, the boundary between R_1 and R_2 is $\theta = \cos^{-1} \frac{1}{a}$ in polar coordinates, or $y = \sqrt{a^2 - 1}\, x$ in rectangular coordinates. Using rectangular coordinates for the region R_1 and polar coordinates for R_2, we find the total volume of the solid to be

$$V = 16 \left[\int_0^1 \int_0^{\sqrt{a^2-1}\,x} \sqrt{1 - x^2}\, dy\, dx + \int_{\cos^{-1}(1/a)}^{\pi/4} \int_0^a \sqrt{1 - r^2 \cos^2 \theta}\, r\, dr\, d\theta \right]$$

If $a \ge \sqrt{2}$, the cylinder $x^2 + y^2 = 1$ completely encloses the intersection of the other two cylinders, so the solid of intersection of the three cylinders coincides with the intersection of $x^2 + z^2 = 1$ and $y^2 + z^2 = 1$ as illustrated in Exercise 12.6.22. Its volume is

$$V = 16 \int_0^1 \int_0^x \sqrt{1 - x^2}\, dy\, dx$$

12.9 Change of Variables in Multiple Integrals • • • • • •

1. $x = u + 4v,\ y = 3u - 2v$.

The Jacobian is $\dfrac{\partial(x, y)}{\partial(u, v)} = \begin{vmatrix} \partial x/\partial u & \partial x/\partial v \\ \partial y/\partial u & \partial y/\partial v \end{vmatrix} = \begin{vmatrix} 1 & 4 \\ 3 & -2 \end{vmatrix} = 1(-2) - 4(3) = -14.$

2. $\dfrac{\partial(x, y)}{\partial(u, v)} = \begin{vmatrix} \partial x/\partial u & \partial x/\partial v \\ \partial y/\partial u & \partial y/\partial v \end{vmatrix} = \begin{vmatrix} 2u & -2v \\ 2u & 2v \end{vmatrix} = 4uv - (-4uv) = 8uv$

3. $\dfrac{\partial(x, y)}{\partial(u, v)} = \begin{vmatrix} \dfrac{\partial x}{\partial u} & \dfrac{\partial x}{\partial v} \\ \dfrac{\partial y}{\partial u} & \dfrac{\partial y}{\partial v} \end{vmatrix} = \begin{vmatrix} \dfrac{v}{(u+v)^2} & -\dfrac{u}{(u+v)^2} \\ -\dfrac{v}{(u-v)^2} & \dfrac{u}{(u-v)^2} \end{vmatrix} = \dfrac{uv}{(u+v)^2(u-v)^2} - \dfrac{uv}{(u+v)^2(u-v)^2} = 0$

4. $\dfrac{\partial (x,y)}{\partial (\alpha,\beta)} = \begin{vmatrix} \partial x/\partial\alpha & \partial x/\partial\beta \\ \partial y/\partial\alpha & \partial y/\partial\beta \end{vmatrix} = \begin{vmatrix} \sin\beta & \alpha\cos\beta \\ \cos\beta & -\alpha\sin\beta \end{vmatrix} = -\alpha\sin^2\beta - \alpha\cos^2\beta = -\alpha$

5. $\dfrac{\partial (x,y,z)}{\partial (u,v,w)} = \begin{vmatrix} \partial x/\partial u & \partial x/\partial v & \partial x/\partial w \\ \partial y/\partial u & \partial y/\partial v & \partial y/\partial w \\ \partial z/\partial u & \partial z/\partial v & \partial z/\partial w \end{vmatrix} = \begin{vmatrix} v & u & 0 \\ 0 & w & v \\ w & 0 & u \end{vmatrix}$

$= v\begin{vmatrix} w & v \\ 0 & u \end{vmatrix} - u\begin{vmatrix} 0 & v \\ w & u \end{vmatrix} + 0\begin{vmatrix} 0 & w \\ w & 0 \end{vmatrix} = v(uw - 0) - u(0 - vw) = 2uvw$

6. $\dfrac{\partial (x,y,z)}{\partial (u,v,w)} = \begin{vmatrix} e^{u-v} & -e^{u-v} & 0 \\ e^{u+v} & e^{u+v} & 0 \\ e^{u+v+w} & e^{u+v+w} & e^{u+v+w} \end{vmatrix} = e^{u+v+w}\begin{vmatrix} e^{u-v} & -e^{u-v} \\ e^{u+v} & e^{u+v} \end{vmatrix}$

$= e^{u+v+w}\left(e^{u-v}e^{u+v} + e^{u-v}e^{u+v}\right) = e^{u+v+w}\left(2e^{2u}\right) = 2e^{3u+v+w}$

7. The transformation maps the boundary of S to the boundary of the image R, so we first look at side S_1 in the uv-plane. S_1 is described by $v = 0$ $(0 \le u \le 3)$, so $x = 2u + 3v = 2u$ and $y = u - v = u$. Eliminating u, we have $x = 2y$, $0 \le x \le 6$. S_2 is the line segment $u = 3$, $0 \le v \le 2$, so $x = 6 + 3v$ and $y = 3 - v$. Then $v = 3 - y \;\Rightarrow\; x = 6 + 3(3 - y) = 15 - 3y$, $6 \le x \le 12$. S_3 is the line segment $v = 2$, $0 \le u \le 3$, so $x = 2u + 6$ and $y = u - 2$, giving $u = y + 2 \;\Rightarrow\; x = 2y + 10$, $6 \le x \le 12$. Finally, S_4 is the segment $u = 0$, $0 \le v \le 2$, so $x = 3v$ and $y = -v \;\Rightarrow\; x = -3y$, $0 \le x \le 6$. The image of set S is the region R shown in the xy-plane, a parallelogram bounded by these four segments.

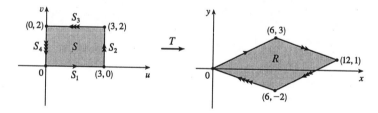

8. S_1 is the line segment $v = 0$, $0 \le u \le 1$, so $x = v = 0$ and $y = u(1 + v^2) = u$. Since $0 \le u \le 1$, the image is the line segment $x = 0$, $0 \le y \le 1$. S_2 is the segment $u = 1$, $0 \le v \le 1$, so $x = v$ and $y = u(1 + v^2) = 1 + x^2$. Thus the image is the portion of the parabola $y = 1 + x^2$ for $0 \le x \le 1$. S_3 is the segment $v = 1$, $0 \le u \le 1$, so $x = 1$ and $y = 2u$. The image is the segment $x = 1$, $0 \le y \le 2$. S_4 is described by $u = 0$, $0 \le v \le 1$, so $0 \le x = v \le 1$ and $y = u(1 + v^2) = 0$. The image is the line segment $y = 0$, $0 \le x \le 1$. Thus, the image of S is the region R bounded by the parabola $y = 1 + x^2$, the x-axis, and the lines $x = 0$, $x = 1$.

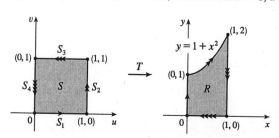

9. S_1 is the line segment $u = v$, $0 \le u \le 1$, so $y = v = u$ and $x = u^2 = y^2$. Since $0 \le u \le 1$, the image is the portion of the parabola $x = y^2$, $0 \le y \le 1$. S_2 is the segment $v = 1$, $0 \le u \le 1$, thus $y = v = 1$ and $x = u^2$, so $0 \le x \le 1$. The image is the line segment $y = 1$, $0 \le x \le 1$. S_3 is the segment $u = 0$, $0 \le v \le 1$, so $x = u^2 = 0$ and $y = v$ $\Rightarrow$ $0 \le y \le 1$. The image is the segment $x = 0$, $0 \le y \le 1$. Thus, the image of S is the region R in the first quadrant bounded by the parabola $x = y^2$, the y-axis, and the line $y = 1$.

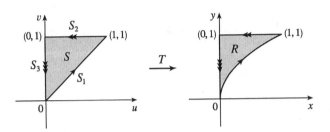

10. Substituting $u = \dfrac{x}{a}$, $v = \dfrac{y}{b}$ into $u^2 + v^2 \le 1$ gives $\dfrac{x^2}{a^2} + \dfrac{y^2}{b^2} \le 1$, so the image of $u^2 + v^2 \le 1$ is the elliptical

region $\dfrac{x^2}{a^2} + \dfrac{y^2}{b^2} \le 1$.

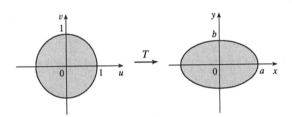

11. $\dfrac{\partial (x, y)}{\partial (u, v)} = \begin{vmatrix} 1/3 & 1/3 \\ -2/3 & 1/3 \end{vmatrix} = \frac{1}{3}$ and $3x + 4y = (u + v) + \frac{4}{3}(v - 2u) = \frac{1}{3}(7v - 5u)$. To find the region S in the uv-plane that corresponds to R we first find the corresponding boundary under the given tranformation: The line $y = x$ is the image of $\frac{1}{3}(v - 2u) = \frac{1}{3}(u + v)$ or $u = 0$, $y = x - 2$ $\Rightarrow$ $\frac{1}{3}(v - 2u) = \frac{1}{3}(u + v) - 2$ or $u = 2$, $y = -2x$ $\Rightarrow$ $\frac{1}{3}(v - 2u) = -\frac{2}{3}(u + v)$ or $v = 0$, and $y = 3 - 2x$ $\Rightarrow$ $\frac{1}{3}(v - 2u) = 3 - \frac{2}{3}(u + v)$ or $v = 3$. Thus S is the rectangle $[0, 2] \times [0, 3]$ in the uv-plane and

$$\iint_R (3x + 4y) \, dA = \iint_S \frac{1}{3} (7v - 5u) \left| \frac{\partial (x, y)}{\partial (u, v)} \right| du \, dv = \int_0^3 \int_0^2 \frac{1}{3} (7v - 5u) \left(\frac{1}{3} \right) du \, dv$$

$$= \frac{1}{9} \int_0^3 (14v - 10) \, dv = \frac{1}{9}(33) = \frac{11}{3}$$

12. $\dfrac{\partial (x, y)}{\partial (u, v)} = \begin{vmatrix} 2 & 3 \\ 3 & -2 \end{vmatrix} = -13$, $x + y = 5u + v$ and since $u = \dfrac{2x + 3y}{13}$ and $v = \dfrac{3x - 2y}{13}$, R is the image

of the square with vertices $(0, 0)$, $(1, 0)$, $(1, 1)$, $(0, 1)$. Thus

$\iint_R (x + y) \, dA = \int_0^1 \int_0^1 (5u + v) |{-13}| \, du \, dv = 13 \int_0^1 \left(\frac{5}{2} + v \right) dv = 13(3) = 39$.

13. $\dfrac{\partial (x, y)}{\partial (u, v)} = \begin{vmatrix} 2 & 0 \\ 0 & 3 \end{vmatrix} = 6$, $x^2 = 4u^2$ and the planar ellipse $9x^2 + 4y^2 \le 36$ is the image of the disk $u^2 + v^2 \le 1$.

Thus

$$\iint_R x^2 \, dA = \iint_{u^2+v^2\le 1} (4u^2)(6) \, du \, dv = \int_0^{2\pi}\int_0^1 (24r^2 \cos^2 \theta) \, r \, dr \, d\theta$$

$$= 24 \int_0^{2\pi} \cos^2 \theta \, d\theta \int_0^1 r^3 \, dr = 24\left[\tfrac{1}{2}x + \tfrac{1}{4}\sin 2x\right]_0^{2\pi} \left[\tfrac{1}{4}r^4\right]_0^1$$

$$= 24(\pi)\left(\tfrac{1}{4}\right) = 6\pi$$

14. $\dfrac{\partial (x, y)}{\partial (u, v)} = \begin{vmatrix} \sqrt{2} & -\sqrt{2/3} \\ \sqrt{2} & \sqrt{2/3} \end{vmatrix} = \tfrac{4}{\sqrt{3}}$, $x^2 - xy + y^2 = 2u^2 + 2v^2$ and the planar ellipse

$x^2 - xy + y^2 \le 2$ is the image of the disk $u^2 + v^2 \le 1$. Thus

$$\iint_R (x^2 - xy + y^2) \, dA = \iint_{u^2+v^2\le 1} (2u^2 + 2v^2)\left(\tfrac{4}{\sqrt{3}} du \, dv\right) = \int_0^{2\pi}\int_0^1 \tfrac{8}{\sqrt{3}}r^3 \, dr \, d\theta = \tfrac{4\pi}{\sqrt{3}}.$$

15. $\dfrac{\partial (x, y)}{\partial (u, v)} = \begin{vmatrix} 1/v & -u/v^2 \\ 0 & 1 \end{vmatrix} = \dfrac{1}{v}$, $xy = u$, $y = x$ is the image of the parabola $v^2 = u$, $y = 3x$ is the image of the

parabola $v^2 = 3u$, and the hyperbolas $xy = 1$, $xy = 3$ are the images of the lines $u = 1$ and $u = 3$ respectively.
Thus

$$\iint_R xy \, dA = \int_1^3 \int_{\sqrt{u}}^{\sqrt{3u}} u\left(\tfrac{1}{v}\right) dv \, du = \int_1^3 u\left(\ln\sqrt{3u} - \ln\sqrt{u}\right) du$$

$$= \int_1^3 u \ln\sqrt{3} \, du = 4\ln\sqrt{3} = 2\ln 3$$

16. Here $y = \dfrac{v}{u}$, $x = \dfrac{u^2}{v}$ so $\dfrac{\partial (x, y)}{\partial (u, v)} = \begin{vmatrix} 2u/v & -u^2/v^2 \\ -v/u^2 & 1/u \end{vmatrix} = \dfrac{1}{v}$

and R is the image of the square with vertices $(1, 1)$, $(2, 1)$, $(2, 2)$,

and $(1, 2)$. So

$$\iint_R y^2 \, dA = \int_1^2 \int_1^2 \dfrac{v^2}{u^2}\left(\tfrac{1}{v}\right) du \, dv = \int_1^2 \dfrac{v}{2} \, dv = \dfrac{3}{4}.$$

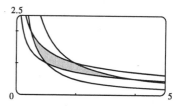

17. (a) $\dfrac{\partial (x, y, z)}{\partial (u, v, w)} = \begin{vmatrix} a & 0 & 0 \\ 0 & b & 0 \\ 0 & 0 & c \end{vmatrix} = abc$ and since $u = \dfrac{x}{a}$, $v = \dfrac{y}{b}$, $w = \dfrac{z}{c}$ the solid enclosed by

the ellipsoid is the image of the ball $u^2 + v^2 + w^2 \le 1$.

So $\iiint_E dV = \iiint_{u^2+v^2+w^2 \le 1} abc \, du \, dv \, dw = (abc)(\text{volume of the ball}) = \tfrac{4}{3}\pi abc$.

(b) If we approximate the surface of Earth by the ellipsoid $\dfrac{x^2}{6378^2} + \dfrac{y^2}{6378^2} + \dfrac{z^2}{6356^2} = 1$, then we can estimate

the volume of Earth by finding the volume of the solid E enclosed by the ellipsoid. From part (a), this is

$\iiint_E dV = \tfrac{4}{3}\pi(6378)(6378)(6356) \approx 1.083 \times 10^{12} \text{ km}^3$.

18. $\dfrac{\partial(x,y,z)}{\partial(u,v,w)} = \begin{vmatrix} a & 0 & 0 \\ 0 & b & 0 \\ 0 & 0 & c \end{vmatrix} = abc$ and the solid enclosed by the ellipsoid is the image of the ball $u^2 + v^2 + w^2 \leq 1$.

Now $x^2 y = (a^2 u^2)(bv)$, so

$$\iiint_E x^2 y \, dV = \iiint_{u^2+v^2+w^2 \leq 1} (a^2 b u^2 v)(abc) \, du \, dv \, dw$$

$$= \int_0^{2\pi} \int_0^\pi \int_0^1 (a^3 b^2 c)(\rho^2 \sin^2\phi \cos^2\theta)(\rho \sin\phi \sin\theta) \, \rho^2 \sin\phi \, d\rho \, d\phi \, d\theta$$

$$= a^3 b^2 c \int_0^{2\pi} \int_0^\pi \int_0^1 (\rho^5 \sin^4\phi \cos^2\theta \sin\theta) \, d\rho \, d\phi \, d\theta$$

$$= a^3 b^2 c \int_0^{2\pi} \cos^2\theta \sin\theta \, d\theta \int_0^\pi \sin^4\phi \, d\phi \int_0^1 \rho^5 d\rho$$

$$= 0 \quad \text{since } \int_0^{2\pi} \cos^2\theta \sin\theta \, d\theta = 0.$$

19. Letting $u = 2x - y$ and $v = 3x + y$, we have $x = \frac{1}{5}(u+v)$, $y = \frac{1}{5}(2v - 3u)$. Then

$$\frac{\partial(x,y)}{\partial(u,v)} = \begin{vmatrix} 1/5 & 1/5 \\ -3/5 & 2/5 \end{vmatrix} = \frac{1}{5} \text{ and}$$

$$\iint_R xy \, dA = \int_{-2}^1 \int_{-3}^1 \frac{(u+v)(2v-3u)}{25}\left(\frac{1}{5}\right) du \, dv = \frac{1}{125} \int_{-2}^1 \int_{-3}^1 (2v^2 - uv - 3u^2) \, du \, dv$$

$$= \frac{1}{125} \int_{-2}^1 (8v^2 + 4v - 28) \, dv = -\frac{66}{125}$$

20. Let $u = x - y$, $v = x + 2y$, so $y = \frac{1}{3}(v - u)$ and $x = \frac{1}{3}(2u + v)$. Then $\dfrac{\partial(x,y)}{\partial(u,v)} = \begin{vmatrix} 2/3 & 1/3 \\ -1/3 & 1/3 \end{vmatrix} = \frac{1}{3}$ and

$$\iint_R \frac{x+2y}{\cos(x-y)} \, dA = \frac{1}{3} \int_0^1 \int_0^2 \frac{v}{\cos u} \, dv \, du = \frac{2}{3} \int_0^1 \sec u \, du = \frac{2}{3}[\ln|\sec u + \tan u|]_0^1$$

$$= \frac{2}{3}[\ln(\sec 1 + \tan 1) - \ln 1] = \frac{2}{3}\ln(\sec 1 + \tan 1)$$

21. Letting $u = y - x$, $v = y + x$, we have $y = \frac{1}{2}(u + v)$, $x = \frac{1}{2}(v - u)$. Then $\dfrac{\partial(x,y)}{\partial(u,v)} = \begin{vmatrix} -1/2 & 1/2 \\ 1/2 & 1/2 \end{vmatrix} = -\frac{1}{2}$ and

R is the image of the trapezoidal region with vertices $(-1, 1)$, $(-2, 2)$, $(2, 2)$, and $(1, 1)$. Thus

$$\iint_R \cos\frac{y-x}{y+x} \, dA = \int_1^2 \int_{-v}^v \cos\frac{u}{v}\left|-\frac{1}{2}\right| du \, dv = \frac{1}{2} \int_1^2 \left[v\sin\frac{u}{v}\right]_{u=-v}^{u=v} dv$$

$$= \frac{1}{2} \int_1^2 2v \sin(1) \, dv = \frac{3}{2}\sin 1$$

22. Letting $u = 3x$, $v = 2y$, we have $9x^2 + 4y^2 = u^2 + v^2$, $x = \frac{1}{3}u$, and $y = \frac{1}{2}v$. Then $\dfrac{\partial(x,y)}{\partial(u,v)} = \frac{1}{6}$ and R is the

image of the quarter-disk D given by $u^2 + v^2 \leq 1$, $u \geq 0$, $v \geq 0$. Thus

$$\iint_R \sin(9x^2 + 4y^2) \, dA = \iint_D \frac{1}{6}\sin(u^2 + v^2) \, du \, dv = \int_0^{\pi/2} \int_0^1 \frac{1}{6}\sin(r^2) \, r \, dr \, d\theta$$

$$= \frac{\pi}{12}\left[-\frac{1}{2}\cos r^2\right]_0^1 = \frac{\pi}{24}(1 - \cos 1)$$

23. Let $u = x + y$ and $v = -x + y$. Then $u + v = 2y \Rightarrow y = \frac{1}{2}(u+v)$ and

$$u - v = 2x \Rightarrow x = \frac{1}{2}(u-v). \quad \frac{\partial(x,y)}{\partial(u,v)} = \begin{vmatrix} 1/2 & -1/2 \\ 1/2 & 1/2 \end{vmatrix} = \frac{1}{2}.$$

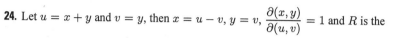

Now $|u| = |x + y| \leq |x| + |y| \leq 1 \Rightarrow -1 \leq u \leq 1$, and

$|v| = |-x + y| \leq |x| + |y| \leq 1 \Rightarrow -1 \leq v \leq 1$.

R is the image of the square region with vertices $(1, 1)$, $(1, -1)$, $(-1, -1)$, and

$(-1, 1)$. So $\iint_R e^{x+y} \, dA = \frac{1}{2} \int_{-1}^{1} \int_{-1}^{1} e^u \, du \, dv = \frac{1}{2} [e^u]_{-1}^{1} [v]_{-1}^{1} = e - e^{-1}$.

24. Let $u = x + y$ and $v = y$, then $x = u - v$, $y = v$, $\dfrac{\partial(x,y)}{\partial(u,v)} = 1$ and R is the

image under T of the triangular region with vertices $(0, 0)$, $(1, 0)$ and $(1, 1)$. Thus

$\iint_R f(x + y) \, dA = \int_0^1 \int_0^u (1) f(u) \, dv \, du = \int_0^1 f(u) [v]_{v=0}^{v=u} \, du = \int_0^1 u f(u) \, du$ as desired.

 Review

• CONCEPT CHECK •
---

1. (a) A double Riemann sum of f is $\sum_{i=1}^{m} \sum_{j=1}^{n} f(x_{ij}^*, y_{ij}^*) \, \Delta A$, where ΔA is the area of each subrectangle and

(x_{ij}^*, y_{ij}^*) is a sample point in each subrectangle. If $f(x, y) \geq 0$, this sum represents an approximation to the volume of the solid that lies above the rectangle R and below the graph of f.

(b) $\iint_R f(x, y) \, dA = \lim_{m,n\to\infty} \sum_{i=1}^{m} \sum_{j=1}^{n} f(x_{ij}^*, y_{ij}^*) \, \Delta A$

(c) If $f(x, y) \geq 0$, $\iint_R f(x, y) \, dA$ represents the volume of the solid that lies above the rectangle R and below the surface $z = f(x, y)$. If f takes on both positive and negative values, $\iint_R f(x, y) \, dA$ is the difference of the volume above R but below the surface $z = f(x, y)$ and the volume below R but above the surface $z = f(x, y)$.

(d) We usually evaluate $\iint_R f(x, y) \, dA$ as an iterated integral according to Fubini's Theorem (see Theorem 12.2.4).

(e) The Midpoint Rule for Double Integrals says that we approximate the double integral $\iint_R f(x, y) \, dA$ by the double Riemann sum $\sum_{i=1}^{m} \sum_{j=1}^{n} f(\overline{x}_i, \overline{y}_j) \, \Delta A$ where the sample points $(\overline{x}_i, \overline{y}_j)$ are the centers of the subrectangles.

(f) $f_{\text{ave}} = \dfrac{1}{A(R)} \iint_R f(x, y) \, dA$ where $A(R)$ is the area of R.

2. (a) See (1) and (2) and the accompanying discussion in Section 12.3.

(b) See (3) and the preceding discussion in Section 12.3.

(c) See (5) and the preceding discussion in Section 12.3.

(d) See (6)–(11) in Section 12.3.

3. We may want to change from rectangular to polar coordinates in a double integral if the region R of integration is more easily described in polar coordinates. To accomplish this, we use

$\iint_R f(x, y) \, dA = \int_\alpha^\beta \int_a^b f(r\cos\theta, r\sin\theta) \, r \, dr \, d\theta$ where R is given by $0 \leq a \leq r \leq b$, $\alpha \leq \theta \leq \beta$.

4. (a) $m = \iint_D \rho(x, y) \, dA$

(b) $M_x = \iint_D y\rho(x, y) \, dA$, $M_y = \iint_D x\rho(x, y) \, dA$

(c) The center of mass is $(\bar{x}, \bar{y})$ where $\bar{x} = \dfrac{M_y}{m}$ and $\bar{y} = \dfrac{M_x}{m}$.

(d) $I_x = \iint_D y^2 \rho(x, y) \, dA$, $I_y = \iint_D x^2 \rho(x, y) \, dA$, $I_0 = \iint_D (x^2 + y^2)\rho(x, y) \, dA$

5. (a) $P(a \le X \le b, c \le Y \le d) = \int_a^b \int_c^d f(x, y) \, dy \, dx$

(b) $f(x, y) \ge 0$ and $\iint_{\mathbb{R}^2} f(x, y) \, dA = 1$.

(c) The expected value of X is $\mu_1 = \iint_{\mathbb{R}^2} xf(x, y) \, dA$; the expected value of Y is $\mu_2 = \iint_{\mathbb{R}^2} yf(x, y) \, dA$.

6. (a) $A(S) = \iint_D |\mathbf{r}_u \times \mathbf{r}_v| \, dA$

(b) $A(S) = \iint_D \sqrt{1 + \left(\dfrac{\partial z}{\partial x}\right)^2 + \left(\dfrac{\partial z}{\partial y}\right)^2} \, dA$

(c) $A(S) = 2\pi \int_a^b f(x)\sqrt{1 + [f'(x)]^2} \, dx$

7. (a) $\iiint_B f(x, y, z) \, dV = \lim_{l,m,n \to \infty} \sum_{i=1}^l \sum_{j=1}^m \sum_{k=1}^n f(x_{ijk}^*, y_{ijk}^*, z_{ijk}^*) \, \Delta V$

(b) We usually evaluate $\iiint_B f(x, y, z) \, dV$ as an iterated integral according to Fubini's Theorem for Triple Integrals (see Theorem 12.7.4).

(c) See the paragraph following Example 12.7.1.

(d) See (5) and (6) and the accompanying discussion in Section 12.7.

(e) See (10) and the accompanying discussion in Section 12.7.

(f) See (11) and the preceding discussion in Section 12.7.

8. (a) $m = \iiint_E \rho(x, y, z) \, dV$

(b) $M_{yz} = \iiint_E x\rho(x, y, z) \, dV$, $M_{xz} = \iiint_E y\rho(x, y, z) \, dV$, $M_{xy} = \iiint_E z\rho(x, y, z) \, dV$.

(c) The center of mass is $(\bar{x}, \bar{y}, \bar{z})$ where $\bar{x} = \dfrac{M_{yz}}{m}$, $\bar{y} = \dfrac{M_{xz}}{m}$, and $\bar{z} = \dfrac{M_{xy}}{m}$.

(d) $I_x = \iiint_E (y^2 + z^2)\rho(x, y, z) \, dV$, $I_y = \iiint_E (x^2 + z^2)\rho(x, y, z) \, dV$,
$I_z = \iiint_E (x^2 + y^2)\rho(x, y, z) \, dV$.

9. (a) See Formula 12.8.2 and the accompanying discussion.

(b) See Formula 12.8.4 and the accompanying discussion.

(c) We may want to change from rectangular to cylindrical or spherical coordinates in a triple integral if the region E of integration is more easily described in cylindrical or spherical coordinates or if the triple integral is easier to evaluate using cylindrical or spherical coordinates.

10. (a) $\dfrac{\partial(x, y)}{\partial(u, v)} = \begin{vmatrix} \partial x/\partial u & \partial x/\partial v \\ \partial y/\partial u & \partial y/\partial v \end{vmatrix} = \dfrac{\partial x}{\partial u}\dfrac{\partial y}{\partial v} - \dfrac{\partial x}{\partial v}\dfrac{\partial y}{\partial u}$.

(b) See (9) and the accompanying discussion in Section 12.9.

(c) See (13) and the accompanying discussion in Section 12.9.

─────────────── ▲ **TRUE–FALSE QUIZ** ▲ ───────────────

1. This is true by Fubini's Theorem.

2. $\int_{-1}^{1} \int_{0}^{1} e^{x^2+y^2} \sin y \, dx \, dy = \left(\int_{0}^{1} e^{x^2} \, dx \right) \left(\int_{-1}^{1} e^{y^2} \sin y \, dy \right) = \left(\int_{0}^{1} e^{x^2} \, dx \right)(0) = 0$, since $e^{y^2} \sin y$ is an odd function. Therefore the statement is true.

3. True:

$\iint_D \sqrt{4 - x^2 - y^2} \, dA = $ the volume under the surface $x^2 + y^2 + z^2 = 4$ and above the xy-plane

$= \frac{1}{2}$ (the volume of the sphere $x^2 + y^2 + z^2 = 4$) $= \frac{1}{2} \cdot \frac{4}{3}\pi(2)^3 = \frac{16}{3}\pi$

4. This statement is true because in the given region, $(x^2 + \sqrt{y}) \sin(x^2 y^2) \le (1 + 2)(1) = 3$, so

$\int_1^4 \int_0^1 (x^2 + \sqrt{y}) \sin(x^2 y^2) \, dx \, dy \le \int_1^4 \int_0^1 3 \, dA = 3A(D) = 3(3) = 9$.

5. The volume enclosed by the cone $z = \sqrt{x^2 + y^2}$ and the plane $z = 2$ is, in cylindrical coordinates,

$V = \int_0^{2\pi} \int_0^2 \int_r^2 r \, dz \, dr \, d\theta \ne \int_0^{2\pi} \int_0^2 \int_r^2 dz \, dr \, d\theta$, so the assertion is false.

6. True. The moment of inertia about the z-axis of a solid E with constant density k is

$I_z = \iiint_E (x^2 + y^2) \rho(x, y, z) \, dV = \iiint_E (kr^2) r \, dz \, dr \, d\theta = \iiint_E kr^3 \, dz \, dr \, d\theta$.

─────────────── ◆ **EXERCISES** ◆ ───────────────

1. As shown in the contour map, we divide R into 9 equally sized subsquares, each with area $\Delta A = 1$. Then we approximate $\iint_R f(x, y) \, dA$ by a Riemann sum with $m = n = 3$ and the sample points the upper right corners of each square, so

$$\iint_R f(x, y) \, dA \approx \sum_{i=1}^{3} \sum_{j=1}^{3} f(x_i, y_j) \, \Delta A$$

$$= \Delta A \, [f(1, 1) + f(1, 2) + f(1, 3) + f(2, 1) + f(2, 2)$$

$$+ f(2, 3) + f(3, 1) + f(3, 2) + f(3, 3)]$$

Using the contour lines to estimate the function values, we have

$$\iint_R f(x, y) \, dA \approx 1[2.7 + 4.7 + 8.0 + 4.7 + 6.7 + 10.0 + 6.7 + 8.6 + 11.9] \approx 64.0$$

2. As in Exercise 1, we have $m = n = 3$ and $\Delta A = 1$. Using the contour map to estimate the value of f at the center of each subsquare, we have

$$\iint_R f(x, y) \, dA \approx \sum_{i=1}^{3} \sum_{j=1}^{3} f(\overline{x}_i, \overline{y}_j) \, \Delta A$$

$$= \Delta A \, [f(0.5, 0.5) + (0.5, 1.5) + (0.5, 2.5) + (1.5, 0.5) + f(1.5, 1.5)$$

$$+ f(1.5, 2.5) + (2.5, 0.5) + f(2.5, 1.5) + f(2.5, 2.5)]$$

$$\approx 1[1.2 + 2.5 + 5.0 + 3.2 + 4.5 + 7.1 + 5.2 + 6.5 + 9.0] = 44.2$$

3. $\int_1^2 \int_0^2 (y + 2xe^y) \, dx \, dy = \int_1^2 [xy + x^2 e^y]_{x=0}^{x=2} \, dy = \int_1^2 (2y + 4e^y) \, dy = [y^2 + 4e^y]_1^2$

$= 4 + 4e^2 - 1 - 4e = 4e^2 - 4e + 3$

4. $\int_0^1 \int_0^1 ye^{xy} \, dx \, dy = \int_0^1 [e^{xy}]_{x=0}^{x=1} \, dy = \int_0^1 (e^y - 1) \, dy = [e^y - y]_0^1 = e - 2$

5. $\int_0^1 \int_0^x \cos(x^2) \, dy \, dx = \int_0^1 [\cos(x^2) \, y]_{y=0}^{y=x} \, dx = \int_0^1 x \cos(x^2) \, dx = \frac{1}{2} \sin(x^2)]_0^1 = \frac{1}{2} \sin 1$

6. $\int_0^1 \int_x^{e^x} 3xy^2 \, dy \, dx = \int_0^1 \left[xy^3 \right]_{y=x}^{y=e^x} dx = \int_0^1 \left(xe^{3x} - x^4 \right) dx$

$\qquad = \frac{1}{3}xe^{3x} \Big]_0^1 - \int_0^1 \frac{1}{3}e^{3x} \, dx - \left[\frac{1}{5}x^5 \right]_0^1$ (integrating by parts in the first term)

$\qquad = \frac{1}{3}e^3 - \left[\frac{1}{9}e^{3x} \right]_0^1 - \frac{1}{5} = \frac{2}{9}e^3 - \frac{4}{45}$

7. $\int_0^\pi \int_0^1 \int_0^{\sqrt{1-y^2}} y \sin x \, dz \, dy \, dx = \int_0^\pi \int_0^1 \left[(y \sin x) \, z \right]_{z=0}^{z=\sqrt{1-y^2}} dy \, dx = \int_0^\pi \int_0^1 y \sqrt{1-y^2} \sin x \, dy \, dx$

$\qquad = \int_0^\pi \left[-\frac{1}{3} \left(1 - y^2 \right)^{3/2} \sin x \right]_{y=0}^{y=1} dx = \int_0^\pi \frac{1}{3} \sin x \, dx = -\frac{1}{3} \cos x \Big]_0^\pi = \frac{2}{3}$

8. $\int_0^1 \int_{\sqrt{y}}^1 \int_0^y xy \, dz \, dx \, dy = \int_0^1 \int_{\sqrt{y}}^1 xy^2 \, dx \, dy = \int_0^1 \left[\frac{1}{2}x^2 y^2 \right]_{x=\sqrt{y}}^{x=1} dy = \int_0^1 \left(\frac{1}{2}y^2 - \frac{1}{2}y^3 \right) dy$

$\qquad = \left[\frac{1}{6}y^3 - \frac{1}{8}y^4 \right]_0^1 = \frac{1}{6} - \frac{1}{8} = \frac{1}{24}$

9. The region R is more easily described by polar coordinates: $R = \{(r, \theta) \mid 2 \le r \le 4, 0 \le \theta \le \pi\}$. Thus
$\iint_R f(x, y) \, dA = \int_0^\pi \int_2^4 f(r \cos \theta, r \sin \theta) \, r \, dr \, d\theta$.

10. The region R is a type II region that can be described as the region enclosed by the lines $y = 4 - x$, $y = 4 + x$, and the x-axis. So using rectangular coordinates, we can say $R = \{(x, y) \mid y - 4 \le x \le 4 - y, 0 \le y \le 4\}$ and
$\iint_R f(x, y) \, dA = \int_0^4 \int_{y-4}^{4-y} f(x, y) \, dx \, dy$.

11.

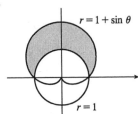

The region whose area is given by $\int_0^\pi \int_1^{1+\sin \theta} r \, dr \, d\theta$ is

$\{(r, \theta) \mid 0 \le \theta \le \pi, 1 \le r \le 1 + \sin \theta\}$, which is the region outside the

circle $r = 1$ and inside the cardioid $r = 1 + \sin \theta$.

12. The solid is $\{(\rho, \theta, \phi) \mid 1 \le \rho \le 3, 0 \le \theta \le 2\pi, 0 \le \phi \le \frac{\pi}{6}\}$, which lies inside the sphere $\rho = 3$, outside the sphere $\rho = 1$, and within the cone $\phi = \frac{\pi}{6}$.

$$\int_0^{2\pi} \int_0^{\pi/6} \int_1^3 \rho^2 \sin \phi \, d\rho \, d\phi \, d\theta = \int_0^{2\pi} d\theta \int_0^{\pi/6} \sin \phi \, d\phi \int_1^3 \rho^2 \, d\rho$$

$$= \left[\theta \right]_0^{2\pi} \left[-\cos \phi \right]_0^{\pi/6} \left[\frac{1}{3}\rho^3 \right]_1^3$$

$$= (2\pi) \left(1 - \frac{\sqrt{3}}{2} \right) \left(\frac{26}{3} \right) = \frac{26\pi}{3} \left(2 - \sqrt{3} \right)$$

13.

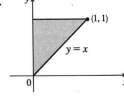

$\int_0^1 \int_x^1 e^{x/y} \, dy \, dx = \int_0^1 \int_0^y e^{x/y} \, dx \, dy$

$\qquad = \int_0^1 \left[y e^{x/y} \right]_{x=0}^{x=y} dy$

$\qquad = \int_0^1 (ey - y) \, dy = \left[\frac{e}{2}y^2 - \frac{1}{2}y^2 \right]_0^1$

$\qquad = \frac{1}{2}(e - 1)$

14.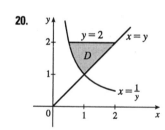

$x = y^2$ (1, 1)

$$\int_0^1 \int_{y^2}^1 y \sin(x^2)\, dx\, dy = \int_0^1 \int_0^{\sqrt{x}} y \sin(x^2)\, dy\, dx$$

$$= \int_0^1 \tfrac{1}{2} x \sin(x^2)\, dx$$

$$= \left[-\tfrac{1}{4} \cos(x^2) \right]_0^1 = \tfrac{1}{4}(1 - \cos 1)$$

15. $\displaystyle \int_2^4 \int_0^1 \frac{1}{(x-y)^2}\, dx\, dy = \int_2^4 \left[-(x-y)^{-1} \right]_{x=0}^{x=1} dy = \int_2^4 \left(-\frac{1}{y} - \frac{1}{1-y} \right) dy$

$$= \left[-\ln y + \ln|1-y| \right]_2^4 = -\ln 4 + \ln 3 + \ln 2 = \ln \tfrac{3}{2}$$

16. $\displaystyle \int_{-1}^1 \int_{x^2-1}^{x+1} x^3\, dy\, dx = \int_{-1}^1 \left(2x^3 + x^4 - x^5 \right) dx = \left[\tfrac{1}{2} x^4 + \tfrac{1}{5} x^5 - \tfrac{1}{6} x^6 \right]_{-1}^1 = \tfrac{2}{5}$

17. The curves $y^2 = x^3$ and $y = x$ intersect when $x^3 = x$, that is when $x = 0$ and $x = 1$ (note that $x \neq -1$ since $x^3 = y^2 \;\Rightarrow\; x \geq 0$.) So $\int_0^1 \int_{x^{3/2}}^x xy\, dy\, dx = \int_0^1 \left[\tfrac{1}{2} x^3 - \tfrac{1}{2} x^4 \right] dx = \left[\tfrac{1}{8} x^4 - \tfrac{1}{10} x^5 \right]_0^1 = \tfrac{1}{40}$.

18. $\displaystyle \int_0^1 \int_0^{x^2} x e^y\, dy\, dx = \int_0^1 x \left(e^{x^2} - 1 \right) dx = \tfrac{1}{2} \left(e^{x^2} - x^2 \right) \Big]_0^1 = \frac{e-2}{2}$

19. $\displaystyle \int_0^1 \int_0^{1-y^2} (xy + 2x + 3y)\, dx\, dy = \int_0^1 \left[\tfrac{1}{2} x^2 y + x^2 + 3xy \right]_{x=0}^{x=1-y^2} dy$

$$= \int_0^1 \left[\tfrac{1}{2} y (1-y^2)^2 + (1-y^2)^2 + 3y(1-y^2) \right] dy$$

$$= \tfrac{1}{2} y^5 + y^4 - 4y^3 - 2y^2 + \tfrac{7}{2} y + 1 = \tfrac{1}{5} + \tfrac{1}{12} - \tfrac{2}{3} + \tfrac{7}{4} = \tfrac{41}{30}$$

20.

$y = 2$ $x = y$

2

D

1

$x = \dfrac{1}{y}$

0   1   2

$$\iint_D y\, dA = \int_1^2 \int_{1/y}^y y\, dx\, dy = \int_1^2 y \left(y - \frac{1}{y} \right) dy$$

$$= \int_1^2 (y^2 - 1)\, dy = \left[\tfrac{1}{3} y^3 - y \right]_1^2$$

$$= \left(\tfrac{8}{3} - 2 \right) - \left(\tfrac{1}{3} - 1 \right) = \tfrac{4}{3}$$

21.

3   $\left(\tfrac{3}{2}, \tfrac{\sqrt{27}}{2} \right)$

$y = \sqrt{3}x$ $x^2 + y^2 = 9$

D

0   3

$$\iint_D (x^2 + y^2)^{3/2}\, dA = \int_0^{\pi/3} \int_0^3 (r^2)^{3/2} r\, dr\, d\theta$$

$$= \int_0^{\pi/3} d\theta \int_0^3 r^4\, dr = [\theta]_0^{\pi/3} \left[\tfrac{1}{5} r^5 \right]_0^3$$

$$= \frac{\pi}{3} \frac{3^5}{5} = \frac{81\pi}{5}$$

22. The circle bounding the disk is given by $x^2 + (y-1)^2 = 1$ or $x^2 + y^2 = 2y$ and in polar coordinates $r = 2 \sin\theta$. Thus $\iint_D \sqrt{x^2 + y^2}\, dA = \int_0^\pi \int_0^{2\sin\theta} r^2\, dr\, d\theta = \int_0^\pi \tfrac{8}{3} \sin^3\theta\, d\theta = \tfrac{8}{3} \left[-\cos\theta + \tfrac{1}{3} \cos^3\theta \right]_0^\pi = \tfrac{32}{9}$.

23. $\displaystyle \iiint_E x^2 z\, dV = \int_0^2 \int_0^{2x} \int_0^x x^2 z\, dz\, dy\, dx = \int_0^2 \int_0^{2x} \tfrac{1}{2} x^4\, dy\, dx = \int_0^2 x^5\, dx = \tfrac{1}{6} \cdot 2^6 = \tfrac{32}{3}$

24. $\displaystyle \iiint_T y\, dV = \int_0^1 \int_0^{2-2x} \int_0^{2-2x-y} y\, dz\, dy\, dx = \int_0^1 \int_0^{2-2x} \left[(2-2x)y - y^2 \right] dy\, dx$

$$= \int_0^1 \left[\tfrac{1}{2} (2-2x)^3 - \tfrac{1}{3} (2-2x)^3 \right] dx = \int_0^1 \tfrac{1}{6} (2-2x)^3\, dx = -\tfrac{1}{48} (2-2x)^4 \Big]_0^1 = \tfrac{1}{3}$$

25. $\iiint_E y^2 z^2 \, dV = \int_{-1}^1 \int_{-\sqrt{1-y^2}}^{\sqrt{1-y^2}} \int_0^{1-y^2-z^2} y^2 z^2 \, dx \, dz \, dy = \int_{-1}^1 \int_{-\sqrt{1-y^2}}^{\sqrt{1-y^2}} y^2 z^2 \left(1 - y^2 - z^2\right) dz \, dy$

$$= \int_0^{2\pi} \int_0^1 \left(r^2 \cos^2 \theta\right)\left(r^2 \sin^2 \theta\right)\left(1 - r^2\right) r \, dr \, d\theta = \int_0^{2\pi} \int_0^1 \tfrac{1}{4} \sin^2 2\theta \left(r^5 - r^7\right) dr \, d\theta$$

$$= \int_0^{2\pi} \tfrac{1}{8}(1 - \cos 4\theta)\left[\tfrac{1}{6}r^6 - \tfrac{1}{8}r^8\right]_{r=0}^{r=1} d\theta = \tfrac{1}{192}\left[\theta - \tfrac{1}{4}\sin 4\theta\right]_0^{2\pi} = \tfrac{2\pi}{192} = \tfrac{\pi}{96}$$

26. $\iiint_E z \, dV = \int_0^1 \int_0^{\sqrt{1-y^2}} \int_0^{2-y} z \, dx \, dz \, dy = \int_0^1 \int_0^{\sqrt{1-y^2}} (2-y) z \, dz \, dy = \int_0^1 \tfrac{1}{2}(2-y)\left(1 - y^2\right) dy$

$$= \int_0^1 \tfrac{1}{2}\left(2 - y - y^2 + y^3\right) dy = \tfrac{11}{24}$$

27. $\iiint_E yz \, dV = \int_{-2}^2 \int_0^{\sqrt{4-x^2}} \int_0^y yz \, dz \, dy \, dx = \int_{-2}^2 \int_0^{\sqrt{4-x^2}} \tfrac{1}{2} y^3 \, dy \, dx = \int_0^\pi \int_0^2 \tfrac{1}{2} r^3 \left(\sin^3 \theta\right) r \, dr \, d\theta$

$$= \tfrac{16}{5} \int_0^\pi \sin^3 \theta \, d\theta = \tfrac{16}{5}\left[-\cos\theta + \tfrac{1}{3}\cos^3 \theta\right]_0^\pi = \tfrac{64}{15}$$

28. $\iiint_H z^3 \sqrt{x^2 + y^2 + z^2} \, dV = \int_0^{2\pi} \int_0^{\pi/2} \int_0^1 \left(\rho^3 \cos^3 \phi\right)\rho\left(\rho^2 \sin \phi\right) d\rho \, d\phi \, d\theta$

$$= \int_0^{2\pi} d\theta \int_0^{\pi/2} \cos^3 \phi \sin \phi \, d\phi \int_0^1 \rho^6 \, d\rho = 2\pi \left[-\tfrac{1}{4}\cos^4 \phi\right]_0^{\pi/2}\left(\tfrac{1}{7}\right) = \tfrac{\pi}{14}$$

29. $V = \int_0^2 \int_1^4 \left(x^2 + 4y^2\right) dy \, dx = \int_0^2 \left[x^2 y + \tfrac{4}{3} y^3\right]_{y=1}^{y=4} dx = \int_0^2 \left(3x^2 + 84\right) dx = 176$

30.

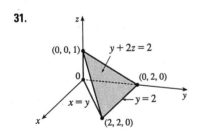

$V = \int_0^1 \int_{y+1}^{4-2y} \int_0^{x^2 y} dz \, dx \, dy = \int_0^1 \int_{y+1}^{4-2y} x^2 y \, dx \, dy$

$\quad = \int_0^1 \tfrac{1}{3}\left[(4-2y)^3 y - (y+1)^3 y\right] dy$

$\quad = \int_0^1 3\left(-y^4 + 5y^3 - 11y^2 + 7y\right) dy$

$\quad = 3\left(-\tfrac{1}{5} + \tfrac{5}{4} - \tfrac{11}{3} + \tfrac{7}{2}\right) = \tfrac{53}{20}$

31.

$V = \int_0^2 \int_0^y \int_0^{(2-y)/2} dz \, dx \, dy$

$\quad = \int_0^2 \int_0^y \left(1 - \tfrac{1}{2}y\right) dx \, dy$

$\quad = \int_0^2 \left(y - \tfrac{1}{2}y^2\right) dy = \tfrac{2}{3}$

32. $V = \int_0^{2\pi} \int_0^2 \int_0^{3-r\sin\theta} r \, dz \, dr \, d\theta = \int_0^{2\pi} \int_0^2 \left(3r - r^2 \sin\theta\right) dr \, d\theta = \int_0^{2\pi} \left[6 - \tfrac{8}{3}\sin\theta\right] d\theta$

$$= 6\theta\big]_0^{2\pi} + 0 = 12\pi$$

33. Using the wedge above the plane $z = 0$ and below the plane $z = mx$ and noting that we have the same volume for
$m < 0$ as for $m > 0$ (so use $m > 0$), we have

$$V = 2 \int_0^{a/3} \int_0^{\sqrt{a^2 - 9y^2}} mx \, dx \, dy = 2 \int_0^{a/3} \tfrac{1}{2} m\left(a^2 - 9y^2\right) dy = m\left[a^2 y - 3y^3\right]_0^{a/3}$$

$$= m\left(\tfrac{1}{3}a^3 - \tfrac{1}{9}a^3\right) = \tfrac{2}{9}ma^3$$

34. The paraboloid and the half-cone intersect when $x^2 + y^2 = \sqrt{x^2 + y^2}$, that is when $x^2 + y^2 = 1$ or 0. So

$$V = \iint_{x^2+y^2\le 1} \int_{x^2+y^2}^{\sqrt{x^2+y^2}} dz \, dA = \int_0^{2\pi} \int_0^1 \int_{r^2}^{r} r \, dz \, dr \, d\theta = \int_0^{2\pi} \int_0^1 (r^2 - r^3) \, dr \, d\theta$$

$$= \int_0^{2\pi} \left(\tfrac{1}{3} - \tfrac{1}{4}\right) d\theta = \tfrac{1}{12}(2\pi) = \tfrac{\pi}{6}$$

35. (a) $m = \int_0^1 \int_0^{1-y^2} y \, dx \, dy = \int_0^1 (y - y^3) \, dy = \tfrac{1}{2} - \tfrac{1}{4} = \tfrac{1}{4}$

(b) $M_y = \int_0^1 \int_0^{1-y^2} xy \, dx \, dy = \int_0^1 \tfrac{1}{2}y(1-y^2)^2 \, dy = -\tfrac{1}{12}(1-y^2)^3\Big]_0^1 = \tfrac{1}{12}$,

$M_x = \int_0^1 \int_0^{1-y^2} y^2 \, dx \, dy = \int_0^1 (y^2 - y^4) \, dy = \tfrac{2}{15}$. Hence $(\overline{x}, \overline{y}) = \left(\tfrac{1}{3}, \tfrac{8}{15}\right)$.

(c) $I_x = \int_0^1 \int_0^{1-y^2} y^3 \, dx \, dy = \int_0^1 (y^3 - y^5) \, dy = \tfrac{1}{12}$,

$I_y = \int_0^1 \int_0^{1-y^2} yx^2 \, dx \, dy = \int_0^1 \tfrac{1}{3}y(1-y^2)^3 \, dy = -\tfrac{1}{24}(1-y^2)^4\Big]_0^1 = \tfrac{1}{24}$.

36. (a) $m = \tfrac{1}{4}\pi K a^2$ where K is constant,

$M_y = \iint_{x^2+y^2\le a^2} Kx \, dA = K \int_0^{\pi/2} \int_0^a r^2 \cos\theta \, dr \, d\theta = \tfrac{1}{3}Ka^3 \int_0^{\pi/2} \cos\theta \, d\theta = \tfrac{1}{3}a^3 K$, and

$M_x = K \int_0^{\pi/2} \int_0^a r^2 \sin\theta \, dr \, d\theta = \tfrac{1}{3}a^3 K$ (by symmetry $M_y = M_x$). Hence the centroid is

$(\overline{x}, \overline{y}) = \left(\tfrac{4}{3\pi}a, \tfrac{4}{3\pi}a\right)$.

(b) $m = \int_0^{\pi/2} \int_0^a r^4 \cos\theta \sin^2\theta \, dr \, d\theta = \left[\tfrac{1}{3}\sin^3\theta\right]_0^{\pi/2}\left(\tfrac{1}{5}a^5\right) = \tfrac{1}{15}a^5$,

$M_y = \int_0^{\pi/2} \int_0^a r^5 \cos^2\theta \sin^2\theta \, dr \, d\theta = \tfrac{1}{8}\left[\theta - \tfrac{1}{4}\sin 4\theta\right]_0^{\pi/2}\left(\tfrac{1}{6}a^6\right) = \tfrac{1}{96}\pi a^6$, and

$M_x = \int_0^{\pi/2} \int_0^a r^5 \cos\theta \sin^3\theta \, dr \, d\theta = \left[\tfrac{1}{4}\sin^4\theta\right]_0^{\pi/2}\left(\tfrac{1}{6}a^6\right) = \tfrac{1}{24}a^6$. Hence $(\overline{x}, \overline{y}) = \left(\tfrac{5}{32}\pi a, \tfrac{5}{8}a\right)$.

37. (a) The equation of the cone with the suggested orientation is $(h - z) = \tfrac{h}{a}\sqrt{x^2 + y^2}, 0 \le z \le h$. Then

$V = \tfrac{1}{3}\pi a^2 h$ is the volume of one frustum of a cone; by symmetry $M_{yz} = M_{xz} = 0$; and

$$M_{xy} = \iint_{x^2+y^2\le a^2} \int_0^{h-(h/a)\sqrt{x^2+y^2}} z \, dz \, dA = \int_0^{2\pi} \int_0^a \int_0^{(h/a)(a-r)} rz \, dz \, dr \, d\theta$$

$$= \pi \int_0^a r\frac{h^2}{a^2}(a-r)^2 \, dr = \frac{\pi h^2}{a^2} \int_0^a (a^2 r - 2ar^2 + r^3) \, dr = \frac{\pi h^2}{a^2}\left(\frac{a^4}{2} - \frac{2a^4}{3} + \frac{a^4}{4}\right) = \frac{\pi h^2 a^2}{12}$$

Hence the centroid is $(\overline{x}, \overline{y}, \overline{z}) = \left(0, 0, \tfrac{1}{4}h\right)$.

(b) $I_z = \int_0^{2\pi} \int_0^a \int_0^{(h/a)(a-r)} r^3 \, dz \, dr \, d\theta = 2\pi \int_0^a \frac{h}{a}(ar^3 - r^4) \, dr = \frac{2\pi h}{a}\left(\frac{a^5}{4} - \frac{a^5}{5}\right) = \frac{\pi a^4 h}{10}$

38. (a) By Definition 12.6.4, the area of S is given by

$$A(S) = \int_0^3 \int_{-3}^3 \sqrt{(2u^2)^2 + (4uv)^2 + (2v^2)^2} \, dv \, du = 2\int_0^3 \int_{-3}^3 \sqrt{u^4 + 4u^2 v^2 + v^4} \, dv \, du.$$

(b) Using a CAS, we have $2\int_0^3 \int_{-3}^3 \sqrt{u^4 + 4u^2 v^2 + v^4} \, dv \, du \approx 247.8$. (Ask your CAS to evaluate the integral numerically rather than symbolically.)

39. Let D represent the given triangle; then D can be described as the area enclosed by the x- and y-axes and the line $y = 2 - 2x$, or equivalently $D = \{(x, y) \mid 0 \le x \le 1, 0 \le y \le 2 - 2x\}$. We want to find the surface area of the part of the graph of $z = x^2 + y$ that lies over D, so using Equation 12.6.6 we have

$$A(S) = \iint_D \sqrt{1 + \left(\frac{\partial z}{\partial x}\right)^2 + \left(\frac{\partial z}{\partial y}\right)^2} \, dA = \iint_D \sqrt{1 + (2x)^2 + (1)^2} \, dA$$

$$= \int_0^1 \int_0^{2-2x} \sqrt{2 + 4x^2} \, dy \, dx = \int_0^1 \sqrt{2 + 4x^2} \, [y]_0^{2-2x} \, dx = \int_0^1 (2 - 2x) \sqrt{2 + 4x^2} \, dx$$

$$= \int_0^1 2\sqrt{2 + 4x^2} \, dx - \int_0^1 2x \sqrt{2 + 4x^2} \, dx$$

Using Formula 21 in the Table of Integrals with $a = \sqrt{2}$, $u = 2x$, and $du = 2 \, dx$, we have
$\int 2\sqrt{2 + 4x^2} \, dx = x\sqrt{2 + 4x^2} + \ln(2x + \sqrt{2 + 4x^2})$. If we substitute $u = 2 + 4x^2$ in the second integral, then
$du = 8x \, dx$ and $\int 2x\sqrt{2 + 4x^2} \, dx = \frac{1}{4} \int \sqrt{u} \, du = \frac{1}{4} \cdot \frac{2}{3} u^{3/2} = \frac{1}{6}(2 + 4x^2)^{3/2}$. Thus

$$A(S) = \left[x\sqrt{2 + 4x^2} + \ln\left(2x + \sqrt{2 + 4x^2}\right) - \frac{1}{6}(2 + 4x^2)^{3/2}\right]_0^1$$

$$= \sqrt{6} + \ln\left(2 + \sqrt{6}\right) - \frac{1}{6}(6)^{3/2} - \ln\sqrt{2} + \frac{\sqrt{2}}{3}$$

$$= \ln\frac{2+\sqrt{6}}{\sqrt{2}} + \frac{\sqrt{2}}{3} = \ln\left(\sqrt{2} + \sqrt{3}\right) + \frac{\sqrt{2}}{3} \approx 1.6176$$

40. Using Formula 12.6.6 with $\partial z / \partial x = \sin y$,
$\partial z / \partial y = x \cos y$, we get

$$S = \int_{-\pi}^{\pi} \int_{-3}^{3} \sqrt{\sin^2 y + x^2 \cos^2 y + 1} \, dx \, dy$$

$$\approx 62.9714$$

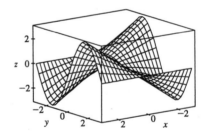

41.

(0, 2)

$(\sqrt{2}, \sqrt{2})$

D

(2, 0)

$$\int_0^{\sqrt{2}} \int_y^{\sqrt{4-y^2}} \frac{1}{1 + x^2 + y^2} \, dx \, dy = \int_0^{\pi/4} \int_0^2 \frac{1}{1 + r^2} r \, dr \, d\theta$$

$$= \int_0^{\pi/4} d\theta \int_0^2 \frac{r}{1 + r^2} \, dr$$

$$= [\theta]_0^{\pi/4} \left[\frac{1}{2} \ln|1 + r^2|\right]_0^2$$

$$= \frac{\pi}{4}\left(\frac{1}{2} \ln 5\right) = \frac{\pi}{8} \ln 5$$

42. $\int_0^1 \int_0^{\sqrt{1-x^2}} \int_0^{\sqrt{1-x^2-y^2}} (x^2 + y^2 + z^2)^2 \, dz \, dy \, dx = \int_0^{\pi/2} \int_0^{\pi/2} \int_0^1 (\rho^2)^2 \rho^2 \sin\phi \, d\rho \, d\theta \, d\phi$

$= \int_0^{\pi/2} \sin\phi \, d\phi \int_0^{\pi/2} d\theta \int_0^1 \rho^6 \, d\rho = [-\cos\phi]_0^{\pi/2} [\theta]_0^{\pi/2} \left[\frac{1}{7}\rho^7\right]_0^1 = 1 \cdot \frac{\pi}{2} \cdot \frac{1}{7} = \frac{\pi}{14}$

43. From the graph, it appears that $1 - x^2 = e^x$ at $x \approx -0.71$ and at $x = 0$, with $1 - x^2 > e^x$ on $(-0.71, 0)$. So the desired integral is

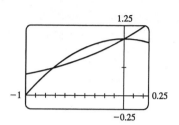

$$\iint_D y^2 \, dA \approx \int_{-0.71}^{0} \int_{e^x}^{1-x^2} y^2 \, dy \, dx$$

$$= \tfrac{1}{3} \int_{-0.71}^{0} \left[(1-x^2)^3 - e^{3x} \right] dx$$

$$= \tfrac{1}{3} \left[x - x^3 + \tfrac{3}{5}x^5 - \tfrac{1}{7}x^7 - \tfrac{1}{3}e^{3x} \right]_{-0.71}^{0} \approx 0.0512$$

44. Let the tetrahedron be called T. The front face of T is given by the plane $x + \tfrac{1}{2}y + \tfrac{1}{3}z = 1$, or $z = 3 - 3x - \tfrac{3}{2}y$, which intersects the xy-plane in the line $y = 2 - 2x$. So the total mass is

$$m = \iiint_T \rho(x, y, z) \, dV = \int_0^1 \int_0^{2-2x} \int_0^{3-3x-3y/2} (x^2 + y^2 + z^2) \, dz \, dy \, dx = \tfrac{7}{5}. \text{ The center of mass is}$$

$$(\overline{x}, \overline{y}, \overline{z}) = \left(m^{-1} \iiint_T x\rho(x, y, z) \, dV, m^{-1} \iiint_T y\rho(x, y, z) \, dV, m^{-1} \iiint_T z\rho(x, y, z) \, dV \right)$$

$$= \left(\tfrac{4}{21}, \tfrac{11}{21}, \tfrac{8}{7} \right)$$

45. (a) $f(x, y)$ is a joint density function, so we know that $\iint_{\mathbb{R}^2} f(x, y) \, dA = 1$. Since $f(x, y) = 0$ outside the rectangle $[0, 3] \times [0, 2]$, we can say

$$\iint_{\mathbb{R}^2} f(x, y) \, dA = \int_{-\infty}^{\infty} \int_{-\infty}^{\infty} f(x, y) \, dy \, dx = \int_0^3 \int_0^2 C(x + y) \, dy \, dx$$

$$= C \int_0^3 \left[xy + \tfrac{1}{2}y^2 \right]_{y=0}^{y=2} dx = C \int_0^3 (2x + 2) \, dx = C \left[x^2 + 2x \right]_0^3 = 15C$$

Then $15C = 1 \ \Rightarrow \ C = \tfrac{1}{15}$.

(b) $P(X \leq 2, Y \geq 1) = \int_{-\infty}^{2} \int_{1}^{\infty} f(x, y) \, dy \, dx = \int_0^2 \int_1^2 \tfrac{1}{15}(x, y) \, dy \, dx = \tfrac{1}{15} \int_0^2 \left[xy + \tfrac{1}{2}y^2 \right]_{y=1}^{y=2} dx$

$= \tfrac{1}{15} \int_0^2 \left(x + \tfrac{3}{2} \right) dx = \tfrac{1}{15} \left[\tfrac{1}{2}x^2 + \tfrac{3}{2}x \right]_0^2 = \tfrac{1}{3}$

(c) $P(X + Y \leq 1) = P((X, Y) \in D)$ where D is the triangular region shown in the figure. Thus

$$P(X + Y \leq 1) = \iint_D f(x, y) \, dA = \int_0^1 \int_0^{1-x} \tfrac{1}{15}(x + y) \, dy \, dx$$

$$= \tfrac{1}{15} \int_0^1 \left[xy + \tfrac{1}{2}y^2 \right]_{y=0}^{y=1-x} dx$$

$$= \tfrac{1}{15} \int_0^1 \left[x(1 - x) + \tfrac{1}{2}(1 - x)^2 \right] dx$$

$$= \tfrac{1}{30} \int_0^1 (1 - x^2) \, dx = \tfrac{1}{30} \left[x - \tfrac{1}{3}x^3 \right]_0^1 = \tfrac{1}{45}$$

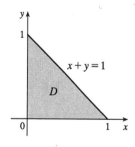

46. Each lamp has exponential density function

$$f(t) = \begin{cases} 0 & \text{if } t < 0 \\ \tfrac{1}{800}e^{-t/800} & \text{if } t \geq 0 \end{cases}$$

If X, Y, and Z are the lifetimes of the individual bulbs, then X, Y, and Z are independent, so the joint density function is the product of the individual density functions:

$$f(x, y, z) = \begin{cases} \tfrac{1}{800^3}e^{-(x+y+z)/800} & \text{if } x \geq 0, y \geq 0, z \geq 0 \\ 0 & \text{otherwise} \end{cases}$$

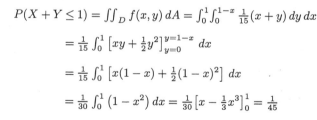

The probability that all three bulbs fail within a total of 1000 hours is $P(X + Y + Z \leq 1000)$, or equivalently $P((X, Y, Z) \in E)$ where E is the solid region in the first octant bounded by the coordinate planes and the plane $x + y + z = 1000$. The plane $x + y + z = 1000$ meets the xy-plane in the line $x + y = 1000$, so we have

$$P(X + Y + Z \leq 1000) = \iiint_E f(x, y, z)\, dV$$

$$= \int_0^{1000} \int_0^{1000-x} \int_0^{1000-x-y} \frac{1}{800^3} e^{-(x+y+z)/800}\, dz\, dy\, dx$$

$$= \frac{1}{800^3} \int_0^{1000} \int_0^{1000-x} -800 \left[e^{-(x+y+z)/800} \right]_{z=0}^{z=1000-x-y}\, dy\, dx$$

$$= \frac{-1}{800^2} \int_0^{1000} \int_0^{1000-x} \left[e^{-5/4} - e^{-(x+y)/800} \right]\, dy\, dx$$

$$= \frac{-1}{800^2} \int_0^{1000} \left[e^{-5/4} y + 800 e^{-(x+y)/800} \right]_{y=0}^{y=1000-x}\, dx$$

$$= \frac{-1}{800^2} \int_0^{1000} \left[e^{-5/4}(1800 - x) - 800 e^{-x/800} \right]\, dx$$

$$= \frac{-1}{800^2} \left[-\tfrac{1}{2} e^{-5/4}(1800 - x)^2 + 800^2 e^{-x/800} \right]_0^{1000}$$

$$= \frac{-1}{800^2} \left[-\tfrac{1}{2} e^{-5/4}(800)^2 + 800^2 e^{-5/4} + \tfrac{1}{2} e^{-5/4}(1800)^2 - 800^2 \right]$$

$$= 1 - \tfrac{97}{32} e^{-5/4} \approx 0.1315$$

47.

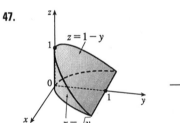 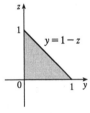

$$\int_{-1}^{1} \int_{x^2}^{1} \int_0^{1-y} f(x, y, z)\, dz\, dy\, dx = \int_0^1 \int_0^{1-z} \int_{-\sqrt{y}}^{\sqrt{y}} f(x, y, z)\, dx\, dy\, dz$$

48.

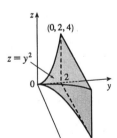 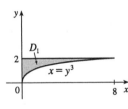 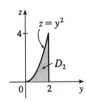 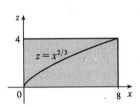

$$\int_0^2 \int_0^{y^3} \int_0^{y^2} f(x, y, z)\, dz\, dx\, dy = \iiint_E f(x, y, z)\, dV \text{ where}$$

$E = \{(x, y, z) \mid 0 \leq y \leq 2, 0 \leq x \leq y^3, 0 \leq z \leq y^2\}$. If D_1, D_2, and D_3 are the projections of E on the xy-, yz-, and xz-planes, then $D_1 = \{(x, y) \mid 0 \leq y \leq 2, 0 \leq x \leq y^3\} = \{(x, y) \mid 0 \leq x \leq 8, \sqrt[3]{x} \leq y \leq 2\}$,
$D_2 = \{(y, z) \mid 0 \leq z \leq 4, \sqrt{z} \leq y \leq 2\} = \{(y, z) \mid 0 \leq y \leq 2, 0 \leq z \leq y^2\}$,
$D_3 = \{(x, z) \mid 0 \leq x \leq 8, 0 \leq z \leq 4\}$.

Therefore we have

$$\int_0^2 \int_0^{y^3} \int_0^{y^2} f(x,y,z)\, dz\, dx\, dy = \int_0^8 \int_{\sqrt[3]{x}}^2 \int_0^{y^2} f(x,y,z)\, dz\, dy\, dx$$

$$= \int_0^4 \int_{\sqrt{z}}^2 \int_0^{y^3} f(x,y,z)\, dx\, dy\, dz = \int_0^2 \int_0^{y^2} \int_0^{y^3} f(x,y,z)\, dx\, dz\, dy$$

$$= \int_0^8 \int_0^{x^{2/3}} \int_{\sqrt[3]{x}}^2 f(x,y,z)\, dy\, dz\, dx + \int_0^8 \int_{x^{2/3}}^4 \int_{\sqrt{z}}^2 f(x,y,z)\, dy\, dz\, dx$$

$$= \int_0^4 \int_0^{z^{3/2}} \int_{\sqrt{z}}^2 f(x,y,z)\, dy\, dx\, dz + \int_0^4 \int_{z^{3/2}}^8 \int_{\sqrt[3]{x}}^2 f(x,y,z)\, dy\, dx\, dz$$

49. Since $u = x - y$ and $v = x + y$, $x = \frac{1}{2}(u+v)$ and $y = \frac{1}{2}(v-u)$.

Thus $\dfrac{\partial(x,y)}{\partial(u,v)} = \begin{vmatrix} 1/2 & 1/2 \\ -1/2 & 1/2 \end{vmatrix} = \dfrac{1}{2}$ and $\displaystyle\iint_R \frac{x-y}{x+y}\, dA = \int_2^4 \int_{-2}^0 \frac{u}{v}\left(\frac{1}{2}\right) du\, dv = -\int_2^4 \frac{dv}{v} = -\ln 2.$

50. $\dfrac{\partial(x,y,z)}{\partial(u,v,w)} = \begin{vmatrix} 2u & 0 & 0 \\ 0 & 2v & 0 \\ 0 & 0 & 2w \end{vmatrix} = 8uvw$, so

$$V = \iiint_E dV = \int_0^1 \int_0^{1-u} \int_0^{1-u-v} 8uvw\, dw\, dv\, du = \int_0^1 \int_0^{1-u} 4uv(1-u-v)^2\, du$$

$$= \int_0^1 \int_0^{1-u} \left[4u(1-u)^2 v - 8u(1-u)v^2 + 4uv^3\right] dv\, du$$

$$= \int_0^1 \left[2u(1-u)^4 - \tfrac{8}{3}u(1-u)^4 + u(1-u)^4\right] du = \int_0^1 \tfrac{1}{3}u(1-u)^4 du$$

$$= \int_0^1 \tfrac{1}{3}\left[(1-u)^4 - (1-u)^5\right] du = \tfrac{1}{3}\left[-\tfrac{1}{5}(1-u)^5 + \tfrac{1}{6}(1-u)^6\right]_0^1 = \tfrac{1}{3}\left(-\tfrac{1}{6} + \tfrac{1}{5}\right) = \tfrac{1}{90}$$

51. Let $u = y - x$ and $v = y + x$ so $x = y - u = (v-x) - u \;\Rightarrow\; x = \frac{1}{2}(v-u)$ and

$y = v - \frac{1}{2}(v-u) = \frac{1}{2}(v+u)$. $\left|\dfrac{\partial(x,y)}{\partial(u,v)}\right| = \left|\dfrac{\partial x}{\partial u}\dfrac{\partial y}{\partial v} - \dfrac{\partial x}{\partial v}\dfrac{\partial y}{\partial u}\right| = \left|-\tfrac{1}{2}\left(\tfrac{1}{2}\right) - \tfrac{1}{2}\left(\tfrac{1}{2}\right)\right| = \left|-\tfrac{1}{2}\right| = \tfrac{1}{2}$. R is the

image under this transformation of the square with vertices $(u,v) = (0,0)$, $(-2,0)$, $(0,2)$, and $(-2,2)$. So

$$\iint_R xy\, dA = \int_0^2 \int_{-2}^0 \frac{v^2 - u^2}{4}\left(\frac{1}{2}\right) du\, dv = \tfrac{1}{8}\int_0^2 \left[v^2 u - \tfrac{1}{3}u^3\right]_{u=-2}^{u=0} dv = \tfrac{1}{8}\int_0^2 \left(2v^2 - \tfrac{8}{3}\right) dv$$

$$= \tfrac{1}{8}\left[\tfrac{2}{3}v^3 - \tfrac{8}{3}v\right]_0^2 = 0$$

This result could have been anticipated by symmetry, since the integrand is an odd function of y and R is symmetric about the x-axis.

52. (a) $\displaystyle\iint_D \frac{1}{(x^2 + y^2)^{n/2}}\, dA = \int_0^{2\pi} \int_r^R \frac{1}{(t^2)^{n/2}} t\, dt\, d\theta = 2\pi \int_r^R t^{1-n}\, dt$

$$= \begin{cases} \dfrac{2\pi}{2-n} t^{2-n} \Big]_r^R = \dfrac{2\pi}{2-n}\left(R^{2-n} - r^{2-n}\right) & \text{if } n \neq 2 \\[2mm] 2\pi \ln(R/r) & \text{if } n = 2 \end{cases}$$

(b) The integral in part (a) has a limit as $r \to 0^+$ for all values of n such that $2 - n > 0 \iff n < 2$.

(c) $\displaystyle\iiint_E \frac{1}{(x^2 + y^2 + z^2)^{n/2}} \, dV = \int_r^R \int_0^\pi \int_0^{2\pi} \frac{1}{(\rho^2)^{n/2}} \rho^2 \sin\phi \, d\theta \, d\phi \, d\rho$

$$= 2\pi \int_r^R \int_0^\pi \rho^{2-n} \sin\phi \, d\phi \, d\rho$$

$$= \begin{cases} \dfrac{4\pi}{3-n} \rho^{3-n} \Big]_r^R = \dfrac{4\pi}{3-n} \left(R^{3-n} - r^{3-n} \right) & \text{if } n \neq 3 \\[4mm] 4\pi \ln(R/r) & \text{if } n = 3 \end{cases}$$

(d) As $r \to 0^+$, the above integral has a limit, provided that $3 - n > 0 \iff n < 3$.

Focus on Problem Solving

1.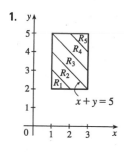

Let $R = \bigcup_{i=1}^5 R_i$, where

$R_i = \{(x,y) \mid x+y \geq i+2, x+y < i+3, 1 \leq x \leq 3, 2 \leq y \leq 5\}$.

$\iint_R [\![x+y]\!]\, dA = \sum_{i=1}^5 \iint_{R_i} [\![x+y]\!]\, dA = \sum_{i=1}^5 [\![x+y]\!] \iint_{R_i} dA$, since

$[\![x+y]\!] = \text{constant} = i+2$ for $(x,y) \in R_i$. Therefore

$$\iint_R [\![x+y]\!]\, dA = \sum_{i=1}^5 (i+2)\,[A(R_i)]$$

$$= 3A(R_1) + 4A(R_2) + 5A(R_3) + 6A(R_4) + 7A(R_5)$$

$$= 3\left(\tfrac{1}{2}\right) + 4\left(\tfrac{3}{2}\right) + 5(2) + 6\left(\tfrac{3}{2}\right) + 7\left(\tfrac{1}{2}\right) = 30$$

2.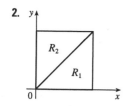

Let $R = \{(x,y) \mid 0 \leq x, y \leq 1\}$. For $x, y \in R$, $\max\{x^2, y^2\} = x^2$ if $x \geq y$, and $\max\{x^2, y^2\} = y^2$ if $x \leq y$. Therefore we divide R into two regions: $R = R_1 \cup R_2$, where $R_1 = \{(x,y) \mid 0 \leq x \leq 1, 0 \leq y \leq x\}$ and $R_2 = \{(x,y) \mid 0 \leq y \leq 1, 0 \leq x \leq y\}$. Now $\max\{x^2, y^2\} = x^2$ for $(x,y) \in R_1$, and $\max\{x^2, y^2\} = y^2$ for $(x,y) \in R_2$ $\Rightarrow$

$$\int_0^1 \int_0^1 e^{\max\{x^2,y^2\}}\, dy\, dx = \iint_R e^{\max\{x^2,y^2\}}\, dA = \iint_{R_1} e^{\max\{x^2,y^2\}}\, dA + \iint_{R_2} e^{\max\{x^2,y^2\}}\, dA$$

$$= \int_0^1 \int_0^x e^{x^2}\, dy\, dx + \int_0^1 \int_0^y e^{y^2}\, dx\, dy = \int_0^1 x e^{x^2}\, dx + \int_0^1 y e^{y^2}\, dy$$

$$= e^{x^2}\Big]_0^1 = e - 1$$

3. $f_{\text{ave}} = \dfrac{1}{b-a} \displaystyle\int_a^b f(x)\, dx = \dfrac{1}{1-0} \int_0^1 \left[\int_x^1 \cos(t^2)\, dt \right] dx$

$\qquad = \int_0^1 \int_x^1 \cos(t^2)\, dt\, dx$

$\qquad = \int_0^1 \int_0^t \cos(t^2)\, dx\, dt \quad$ (changing the order of integration)

$\qquad = \int_0^1 t\cos(t^2)\, dt = \tfrac{1}{2}\sin(t^2)\Big]_0^1 = \tfrac{1}{2}\sin 1$

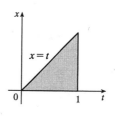

4. Let $u = \mathbf{a} \cdot \mathbf{r}$, $v = \mathbf{b} \cdot \mathbf{r}$, $w = \mathbf{c} \cdot \mathbf{r}$, where $\mathbf{a} = \langle a_1, a_2, a_3 \rangle$, $\mathbf{b} = \langle b_1, b_2, b_3 \rangle$, $\mathbf{c} = \langle c_1, c_2, c_3 \rangle$. Under this change of variables, E corresponds to the rectangular box $0 \leq u \leq \alpha$, $0 \leq v \leq \beta$, $0 \leq w \leq \gamma$. So, by Formula 12.9.13,

$\int_0^\gamma \int_0^\beta \int_0^\alpha uvw \, du \, dv \, dw = \iiint_E (\mathbf{a} \cdot \mathbf{r})(\mathbf{b} \cdot \mathbf{r})(\mathbf{c} \cdot \mathbf{r}) \left| \dfrac{\partial(u, v, w)}{\partial(x, y, z)} \right| dV$. But

$$\left| \dfrac{\partial(u, v, w)}{\partial(x, y, z)} \right| = \begin{vmatrix} a_1 & a_2 & a_3 \\ b_1 & b_2 & b_3 \\ c_1 & c_2 & c_3 \end{vmatrix} = |\mathbf{a} \cdot \mathbf{b} \times \mathbf{c}| \quad \Rightarrow$$

$$\iiint_E (\mathbf{a} \cdot \mathbf{r})(\mathbf{b} \cdot \mathbf{r})(\mathbf{c} \cdot \mathbf{r}) \, dV = \dfrac{1}{|\mathbf{a} \cdot \mathbf{b} \times \mathbf{c}|} \int_0^\gamma \int_0^\beta \int_0^\alpha uvw \, du \, dv \, dw$$

$$= \dfrac{1}{|\mathbf{a} \cdot \mathbf{b} \times \mathbf{c}|} \left(\dfrac{\alpha^2}{2} \right) \left(\dfrac{\beta^2}{2} \right) \left(\dfrac{\gamma^2}{2} \right) = \dfrac{(\alpha\beta\gamma)^2}{8 |\mathbf{a} \cdot \mathbf{b} \times \mathbf{c}|}$$

5. Since $|xy| < 1$, except at $(1, 1)$, the formula for the sum of a geometric series gives $\dfrac{1}{1 - xy} = \sum_{n=0}^\infty (xy)^n$, so

$$\int_0^1 \int_0^1 \dfrac{1}{1 - xy} \, dx \, dy = \int_0^1 \int_0^1 \sum_{n=0}^\infty (xy)^n \, dx \, dy = \sum_{n=0}^\infty \int_0^1 \int_0^1 (xy)^n \, dx \, dy = \sum_{n=0}^\infty \left[\int_0^1 x^n \, dx \right] \left[\int_0^1 y^n \, dy \right]$$

$$= \sum_{n=0}^\infty \dfrac{1}{n+1} \cdot \dfrac{1}{n+1} = \sum_{n=0}^\infty \dfrac{1}{(n+1)^2} = \dfrac{1}{1^2} + \dfrac{1}{2^2} + \dfrac{1}{3^2} + \cdots = \sum_{n=1}^\infty \dfrac{1}{n^2}$$

6. Let $x = \dfrac{u - v}{\sqrt{2}}$ and $y = \dfrac{u + v}{\sqrt{2}}$. We know the region of integration in the xy-plane, so to find its image in the

uv-plane we get u and v in terms of x and y, and then use the methods of Section 12.9.

$x + y = \dfrac{u - v}{\sqrt{2}} + \dfrac{u + v}{\sqrt{2}} = \sqrt{2}u$, so $u = \dfrac{x + y}{\sqrt{2}}$, and similarly $v = \dfrac{y - x}{\sqrt{2}}$. S_1 is given by $y = 0, 0 \le x \le 1$, so

from the equations derived above, the image of S_1 is S_1': $u = \frac{1}{\sqrt{2}}x$, $v = -\frac{1}{\sqrt{2}}x$, $0 \le x \le 1$, that is, $v = -u$,

$0 \le u \le \frac{1}{\sqrt{2}}$. Similarly, the image of S_2 is S_2': $v = u - \sqrt{2}$, $\frac{1}{\sqrt{2}} \le u \le \sqrt{2}$, the image of S_3 is S_3': $v = \sqrt{2} - u$,

$\frac{1}{\sqrt{2}} \le u \le \sqrt{2}$, and the image of S_4 is S_4': $v - u$, $0 \le u \le \frac{1}{\sqrt{2}}$.

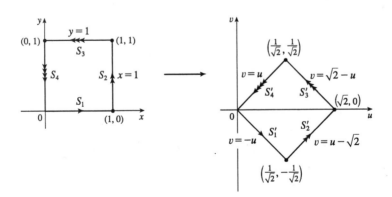

The Jacobian of the transformation is $\dfrac{\partial(x, y)}{\partial(u, v)} = \begin{vmatrix} \partial x/\partial u & \partial x/\partial v \\ \partial y/\partial u & \partial y/\partial v \end{vmatrix} = \begin{vmatrix} \frac{1}{\sqrt{2}} & -\frac{1}{\sqrt{2}} \\ \frac{1}{\sqrt{2}} & \frac{1}{\sqrt{2}} \end{vmatrix} = 1$. From the diagram, we

see that we must evaluate two integrals: one over the region $\left\{ (u, v) \mid 0 \le u \le \frac{1}{\sqrt{2}}, -u \le v \le u \right\}$ and the other over $\left\{ (u, v) \mid \frac{1}{\sqrt{2}} \le u \le \sqrt{2}, \; -\sqrt{2} + u \le v \le \sqrt{2} - u \right\}$. So

$$\int_0^1 \int_0^1 \frac{dx\,dy}{1 - xy} = \int_0^{\sqrt{2}/2} \int_{-u}^{u} \frac{dv\,du}{1 - \left[\frac{1}{\sqrt{2}}(u + v) \right]\left[\frac{1}{\sqrt{2}}(u - v) \right]}$$

$$+ \int_{\sqrt{2}/2}^{\sqrt{2}} \int_{-\sqrt{2}+u}^{\sqrt{2}-u} \frac{dv\,du}{1 - \left[\frac{1}{\sqrt{2}}(u + v) \right]\left[\frac{1}{\sqrt{2}}(u - v) \right]}$$

$$= \int_0^{\sqrt{2}/2} \int_{-u}^{u} \frac{2\,dv\,du}{2 - u^2 + v^2} + \int_{\sqrt{2}/2}^{\sqrt{2}} \int_{-\sqrt{2}+u}^{\sqrt{2}-u} \frac{2\,dv\,du}{2 - u^2 + v^2}$$

$$= 2\left[\int_0^{\sqrt{2}/2} \frac{1}{\sqrt{2 - u^2}} \left[\arctan \frac{v}{\sqrt{2 - u^2}} \right]_{-u}^{u} du + \int_{\sqrt{2}/2}^{\sqrt{2}} \frac{1}{\sqrt{2 - u^2}} \left[\arctan \frac{v}{\sqrt{2 - u^2}} \right]_{-\sqrt{2}+u}^{\sqrt{2}-u} du \right]$$

$$= 4\left[\int_0^{\sqrt{2}/2} \frac{1}{\sqrt{2 - u^2}} \arctan \frac{u}{\sqrt{2 - u^2}}\,du + \int_{\sqrt{2}/2}^{\sqrt{2}} \frac{1}{\sqrt{2 - u^2}} \arctan \frac{\sqrt{2} - u}{\sqrt{2 - u^2}}\,du \right]$$

Now let $u = \sqrt{2} \sin\theta$, so $du = \sqrt{2} \cos\theta\,d\theta$ and the limits change to 0 and $\frac{\pi}{6}$ (in the first integral) and $\frac{\pi}{6}$ and $\frac{\pi}{2}$ (in the second integral). Continuing:

$$\int_0^1 \int_0^1 \frac{dx\,dy}{1 - xy} = 4\left[\int_0^{\pi/6} \frac{1}{\sqrt{2 - 2\sin^2\theta}} \arctan\left(\frac{\sqrt{2}\sin\theta}{\sqrt{2 - 2\sin^2\theta}} \right)\left(\sqrt{2}\cos\theta\,d\theta \right) \right.$$

$$\left. + \int_{\pi/6}^{\pi/2} \frac{1}{\sqrt{2 - 2\sin^2\theta}} \arctan\left(\frac{\sqrt{2} - \sqrt{2}\sin\theta}{\sqrt{2 - 2\sin^2\theta}} \right)\left(\sqrt{2}\cos\theta\,d\theta \right) \right]$$

$$= 4\left[\int_0^{\pi/6} \frac{\sqrt{2}\cos\theta}{\sqrt{2}\cos\theta} \arctan\left(\frac{\sqrt{2}\sin\theta}{\sqrt{2}\cos\theta} \right)d\theta + \int_{\pi/6}^{\pi/2} \frac{\sqrt{2}\cos\theta}{\sqrt{2}\cos\theta} \arctan\left(\frac{\sqrt{2}(1 - \sin\theta)}{\sqrt{2}\cos\theta} \right)d\theta \right]$$

$$= 4\left[\int_0^{\pi/6} \arctan(\tan\theta)\,d\theta + \int_{\pi/6}^{\pi/2} \arctan\left(\frac{1 - \sin\theta}{\cos\theta} \right)d\theta \right]$$

But (following the hint)

$$\frac{1 - \sin\theta}{\cos\theta} = \frac{1 - \cos\left(\frac{\pi}{2} - \theta \right)}{\sin\left(\frac{\pi}{2} - \theta \right)} = \frac{1 - \left[1 - 2\sin^2\left(\frac{1}{2}\left(\frac{\pi}{2} - \theta \right) \right) \right]}{2\sin\left(\frac{1}{2}\left(\frac{\pi}{2} - \theta \right) \right)\cos\left(\frac{1}{2}\left(\frac{\pi}{2} - \theta \right) \right)} \qquad \text{(half-angle formulas)}$$

$$= \frac{2\sin^2\left(\frac{1}{2}\left(\frac{\pi}{2} - \theta \right) \right)}{2\sin\left(\frac{1}{2}\left(\frac{\pi}{2} - \theta \right) \right)\cos\left(\frac{1}{2}\left(\frac{\pi}{2} - \theta \right) \right)} = \tan\left(\frac{1}{2}\left(\frac{\pi}{2} - \theta \right) \right)$$

Continuing:

$$\int_0^1 \int_0^1 \frac{dx\,dy}{1 - xy} = 4\left[\int_0^{\pi/6} \arctan(\tan\theta)\,d\theta + \int_{\pi/6}^{\pi/2} \arctan\left(\tan\left(\frac{1}{2}\left(\frac{\pi}{2} - \theta \right) \right) \right)d\theta \right]$$

$$= 4\left[\int_0^{\pi/6} \theta\,d\theta + \int_{\pi/6}^{\pi/2} \left[\frac{1}{2}\left(\frac{\pi}{2} - \theta \right) \right]d\theta \right]$$

$$= 4\left(\left[\frac{\theta^2}{2} \right]_0^{\pi/6} + \left[\frac{\pi\theta}{4} - \frac{\theta^2}{4} \right]_{\pi/6}^{\pi/2} \right) = 4\left(\frac{3\pi^2}{72} \right) = \frac{\pi^2}{6}$$

7. (a) Since $|xyz| < 1$ except at $(1, 1, 1)$, the formula for the sum of a geometric series gives $\dfrac{1}{1 - xyz} = \displaystyle\sum_{n=0}^{\infty} (xyz)^n$,

so

$$\int_0^1\!\!\int_0^1\!\!\int_0^1 \frac{1}{1-xyz}\,dx\,dy\,dz = \int_0^1\!\!\int_0^1\!\!\int_0^1 \sum_{n=0}^{\infty}(xyz)^n\,dx\,dy\,dz = \sum_{n=0}^{\infty}\int_0^1\!\!\int_0^1\!\!\int_0^1 (xyz)^n\,dx\,dy\,dz$$

$$= \sum_{n=0}^{\infty}\left[\int_0^1 x^n\,dx\right]\left[\int_0^1 y^n\,dy\right]\left[\int_0^1 z^n\,dz\right]$$

$$= \sum_{n=0}^{\infty} \frac{1}{n+1}\cdot\frac{1}{n+1}\cdot\frac{1}{n+1}$$

$$= \sum_{n=0}^{\infty} \frac{1}{(n+1)^3} = \frac{1}{1^3} + \frac{1}{2^3} + \frac{1}{3^3} + \cdots = \sum_{n=1}^{\infty} \frac{1}{n^3}.$$

(b) Since $|-xyz| < 1$, except at $(1, 1, 1)$, the formula for the sum of a geometric series gives

$$\frac{1}{1 + xyz} = \sum_{n=0}^{\infty}(-xyz)^n, \text{ so}$$

$$\int_0^1\!\!\int_0^1\!\!\int_0^1 \frac{1}{1+xyz}\,dx\,dy\,dz = \int_0^1\!\!\int_0^1\!\!\int_0^1 \sum_{n=0}^{\infty}(-xyz)^n\,dx\,dy\,dz$$

$$= \sum_{n=0}^{\infty}\int_0^1\!\!\int_0^1\!\!\int_0^1 (-xyz)^n\,dx\,dy\,dz$$

$$= \sum_{n=0}^{\infty}(-1)^n\left[\int_0^1 x^n\,dx\right]\left[\int_0^1 y^n\,dy\right]\left[\int_0^1 z^n\,dz\right]$$

$$= \sum_{n=0}^{\infty}(-1)^n \frac{1}{n+1}\cdot\frac{1}{n+1}\cdot\frac{1}{n+1}$$

$$= \sum_{n=0}^{\infty} \frac{(-1)^n}{(n+1)^3} = \frac{1}{1^3} - \frac{1}{2^3} + \frac{1}{3^3} - \cdots = \sum_{n=1}^{\infty} \frac{(-1)^{n-1}}{n^3}.$$

To evaluate this sum, we first write out a few terms: $s = 1 - \dfrac{1}{2^3} + \dfrac{1}{3^3} - \dfrac{1}{4^3} + \dfrac{1}{5^3} - \dfrac{1}{6^3} \approx 0.8998$. Notice that

$a_7 = \dfrac{1}{7^3} < 0.003$. By the Alternating Series Estimation Theorem from Section 8.4, we have

$|s - s_6| \le a_7 < 0.003$. This error of 0.003 will not affect the second decimal place, so we have $s \approx 0.90$.

8. $\displaystyle\int_0^{\infty} \frac{\arctan \pi x - \arctan x}{x}\,dx = \int_0^{\infty}\left[\frac{\arctan yx}{x}\right]_{y=1}^{y=\pi}\,dx = \int_0^{\infty}\!\!\int_1^{\pi} \frac{1}{1+y^2x^2}\,dy\,dx$

$$= \int_1^{\pi}\!\!\int_0^{\infty} \frac{1}{1+y^2x^2}\,dx\,dy = \int_1^{\pi} \lim_{t\to\infty}\left[\frac{\arctan yx}{y}\right]_{x=0}^{x=t}\,dy$$

$$= \int_1^{\pi} \frac{\pi}{2y}\,dy = \tfrac{\pi}{2}[\ln y]_1^{\pi} = \tfrac{\pi}{2}\ln \pi$$

9. $\int_0^x \int_0^y \int_0^z f(t)\, dt\, dz\, dy = \iiint_E f(t)\, dV$, where

$E = \{(t, z, y) \mid 0 \le t \le z, 0 \le z \le y, 0 \le y \le x\}$.

If we let D be the projection of E on the yt-plane then

$D = \{(y, t) \mid 0 \le t \le x, t \le y \le x\}$. And we see from the diagram

that $E = \{(t, z, y) \mid t \le z \le y, t \le y \le x, 0 \le t \le x\}$. So

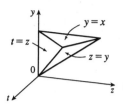

$$\int_0^x \int_0^y \int_0^z f(t)\, dt\, dz\, dy = \int_0^x \int_t^x \int_t^y f(t)\, dz\, dy\, dt = \int_0^x \left[\int_t^x (y - t) f(t)\, dy \right] dt$$

$$= \int_0^x \left[\left(\tfrac{1}{2} y^2 - ty \right) f(t) \right]_{y=t}^{y=x} dt = \int_0^x \left[\tfrac{1}{2} x^2 - tx - \tfrac{1}{2} t^2 + t^2 \right] f(t)\, dt$$

$$= \int_0^x \left[\tfrac{1}{2} x^2 - tx + \tfrac{1}{2} t^2 \right] f(t)\, dt = \int_0^x \left(\tfrac{1}{2} x^2 - 2tx + t^2 \right) f(t)\, dt$$

$$= \tfrac{1}{2} \int_0^x (x - t)^2 f(t)\, dt$$

10. (a) Consider a polar division of the disk, similar to that in Figure 12.4.4, where

$0 = \theta_0 < \theta_1 < \theta_2 < \cdots < \theta_n = 2\pi, 0 = r_1 < r_2 < \cdots < r_m = R$, and where the polar subrectangle R_{ij}, as

well as $r_i^*, \theta_j^*, \Delta r$ and $\Delta \theta$ are the same as in that figure. Thus $\Delta A_i = r_i^* \Delta r \Delta \theta$. The mass of R_{ij} is $\rho\, \Delta A_i$,

and its distance from m is $s_{ij} \approx \sqrt{(r_i^*)^2 + d^2}$. According to Newton's Law of Gravitation, the force of

attraction experienced by m due to this polar subrectangle is in the direction from m towards R_{ij} and has

magnitude $\dfrac{Gm\rho\, \Delta A_i}{s_{ij}^2}$. The symmetry of the lamina with respect to the x- and y-axes and the position of m are

such that all horizontal components of the gravitational force cancel, so that the total force is simply in the

z-direction. Thus, we need only be concerned with the components of this vertical force; that is,

$\dfrac{Gm\rho\, \Delta A_i}{s_{ij}^2} \sin \alpha$, where α is the angle between the origin, r_i^* and the mass m. Thus $\sin \alpha = \dfrac{d}{s_{ij}}$ and the

previous result becomes $\dfrac{Gm\rho d\, \Delta A_i}{s_{ij}^3}$. The total attractive force is just the Riemann sum

$$\sum_{i=1}^m \sum_{j=1}^n \frac{Gm\rho d\, \Delta A_i}{s_{ij}^3} = \sum_{i=1}^m \sum_{j=1}^n \frac{Gm\rho d (r_i^*)\, \Delta r\, \Delta \theta}{[(r_i^*)^2 + d^2]^{3/2}} \text{ which becomes } \int_0^R \int_0^{2\pi} \frac{Gm\rho d}{(r^2 + d^2)^{3/2}} r\, d\theta\, dr \text{ as}$$

$m \to \infty$ and $n \to \infty$. Therefore,

$$F = 2\pi Gm\rho d \int_0^R \frac{r}{(r^2 + d^2)^{3/2}}\, dr = 2\pi Gm\rho d \left[-\frac{1}{\sqrt{r^2 + d^2}} \right]_0^R = 2\pi Gm\rho d \left(\frac{1}{d} - \frac{1}{\sqrt{R^2 + d^2}} \right)$$

(b) This is just the result of part (a) in the limit as $R \to \infty$. In this case $\dfrac{1}{\sqrt{R^2 + d^2}} \to 0$, and we are left with

$$F = 2\pi Gm\rho d \left(\frac{1}{d} - 0 \right) = 2\pi Gm\rho.$$

Vector Calculus

 Vector Fields • • • • • • • • • • • • • • • •

1. $\mathbf{F}(x, y) = \frac{1}{2}(\mathbf{i} + \mathbf{j})$

All vectors in this field are identical, with length $\frac{1}{\sqrt{2}}$ and direction parallel to the line $y = x$.

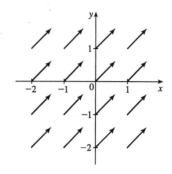

2. $\mathbf{F}(x, y) = \mathbf{i} + x\mathbf{j}$

The length of the vector $\mathbf{i} + x\mathbf{j}$ is $\sqrt{1 + x^2}$. Vectors are tangent to parabolas opening about the y-axis.

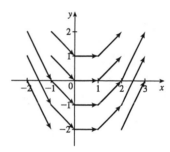

3. $\mathbf{F}(x, y) = x\mathbf{i} + y\mathbf{j}$

The length of the vector $x\mathbf{i} + y\mathbf{j}$ is the distance from $(0, 0)$ to (x, y). Each vector points away from the origin.

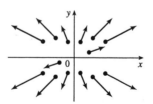

4. $\mathbf{F}(x, y) = x\mathbf{i} - y\mathbf{j}$

The length of the vector $x\mathbf{i} - y\mathbf{j}$ is the distance from $(0, 0)$ to (x, y). For each (x, y), $\mathbf{F}(x, y)$ terminates on the x-axis at the point $(2x, 0)$.

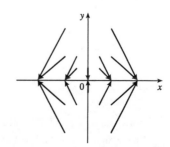

5. $\mathbf{F}(x, y) = \dfrac{y\,\mathbf{i} + x\,\mathbf{j}}{\sqrt{x^2 + y^2}}$

The length of the vector $\dfrac{y\,\mathbf{i} + x\,\mathbf{j}}{\sqrt{x^2 + y^2}}$ is 1.

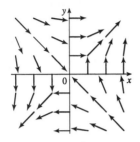

6. $\mathbf{F}(x, y) = \dfrac{y\,\mathbf{i} - x\,\mathbf{j}}{\sqrt{x^2 + y^2}}$

All the vectors $\mathbf{F}(x, y)$ are unit vectors tangent to circles centered at the origin with radius $\sqrt{x^2 + y^2}$.

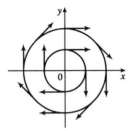

7. $\mathbf{F}(x, y, z) = \mathbf{j}$

All vectors in this field are parallel to the y-axis and have length 1.

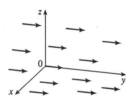

8. $\mathbf{F}(x, y, z) = z\,\mathbf{j}$

At each point (x, y, z), $\mathbf{F}(x, y, z)$ is a vector of length $|z|$. For $z > 0$, all point in the direction of the positive y-axis while for $z < 0$, all are in the direction of the negative y-axis.

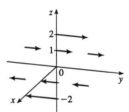

9. $\mathbf{F}(x, y, z) = y\,\mathbf{j}$

The length of $\mathbf{F}(x, y, z)$ is $|y|$. No vectors emanate from the xz-plane since $y = 0$ there. In each plane $y = b$, all the vectors are identical.

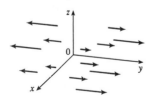

10. $\mathbf{F}(x, y, z) = \mathbf{j} - \mathbf{i}$

All vectors in this field have length $\sqrt{2}$ and point in the same direction, parallel to the xy-plane.

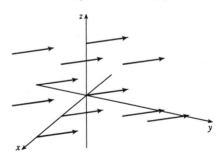

11. $\mathbf{F}(x, y) = \langle y, x \rangle$ corresponds to graph III, since in the first quadrant all the vectors have positive x- and y-components, in the second quadrant all vectors have positive x-components and negative y-components, in the third quadrant all vectors have negative x- and y-components, and in the fourth quadrant all vectors have negative x-components and positive y-components.

12. $\mathbf{F}(x, y) = \langle 2x - 3y, 2x + 3y \rangle$ corresponds to graph IV, since as we move to the right (so x increases and y is constant), both the x- and the y-components of the vectors get larger, and as we move upward (so y increases and x is constant), the x-components decrease, while the y-components increase.

13. $\mathbf{F}(x, y) = \langle \sin x, \sin y \rangle$ corresponds to graph II, since the vector field is the same on each square of the form $[2n\pi, 2(n+1)\pi] \times [2m\pi, 2(m+1)\pi]$, m, n any integers.

14. $\mathbf{F}(x, y) = \langle \ln(1 + x^2 + y^2), x \rangle$ corresponds to graph I, since $\ln(1 + x^2 + y^2)$ is always positive, so all vectors point to the right.

15. $\mathbf{F}(x, y, z) = \mathbf{i} + 2\mathbf{j} + 3\mathbf{k}$ corresponds to graph IV, since all vectors have identical length and direction.

16. $\mathbf{F}(x, y, z) = \mathbf{i} + 2\mathbf{j} + z\mathbf{k}$ corresponds to graph I, since the horizontal vector components remain constant, but the vectors above the xy-plane point generally upward while the vectors below the xy-plane point generally downward.

17. $\mathbf{F}(x, y, z) = x\mathbf{i} + y\mathbf{j} + 3\mathbf{k}$ corresponds to graph III; the projection of each vector onto the xy-plane is $x\mathbf{i} + y\mathbf{j}$, which points away from the origin, and the vectors point generally upward because their z-components are all 3.

18. $\mathbf{F}(x, y, z) = x\mathbf{i} + y\mathbf{j} + z\mathbf{k}$ corresponds to graph II; each vector $\mathbf{F}(x, y, z)$ has the same length and direction as the position vector of the point (x, y, z), and therefore the vectors all point directly away from the origin.

19.

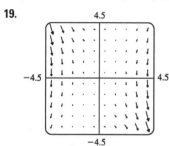

The vector field seems to have very short vectors near the line $y = 2x$.

For $\mathbf{F}(x, y) = \langle 0, 0 \rangle$ we must have $y^2 - 2xy = 0$ and $3xy - 6x^2 = 0$. The first equation holds if $y = 0$ or $y = 2x$, and the second holds if $x = 0$ or $y = 2x$. So both equations hold [and thus $\mathbf{F}(x, y) = \mathbf{0}$] along the line $y = 2x$.

20.

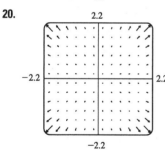

From the graph, it appears that all of the vectors in the field lie on lines through the origin, and that the vectors have very small magnitudes near the circle $|\mathbf{x}| = 2$ and near the origin. Note that $\mathbf{F}(\mathbf{x}) = \mathbf{0}$ $\Leftrightarrow$ $r(r - 2) = 0$ $\Leftrightarrow$ $r = 0$ or 2, so as we suspected, $\mathbf{F}(\mathbf{x}) = \mathbf{0}$ for $|\mathbf{x}| = 2$ and for $|\mathbf{x}| = 0$. Note that where $r^2 - r < 0$, the vectors point towards the origin, and where $r^2 - r > 0$, they point away from the origin.

21. $\nabla f(x, y) = f_x(x, y)\mathbf{i} + f_y(x, y)\mathbf{j} = \dfrac{1}{x + 2y}\mathbf{i} + \dfrac{2}{x + 2y}\mathbf{j}$

22. $\nabla f(x, y) = f_x(x, y)\mathbf{i} + f_y(x, y)\mathbf{j} = \left[x^\alpha(-\beta e^{-\beta x}) + \alpha x^{\alpha - 1} e^{-\beta x} \right]\mathbf{i} + 0\mathbf{j} = (\alpha - \beta x)x^{\alpha - 1}e^{-\beta x}\mathbf{i}$

23. $\nabla f(x, y, z) = f_x(x, y, z)\mathbf{i} + f_y(x, y, z)\mathbf{j} + f_z(x, y, z)\mathbf{k}$

$$= \dfrac{x}{\sqrt{x^2 + y^2 + z^2}}\mathbf{i} + \dfrac{y}{\sqrt{x^2 + y^2 + z^2}}\mathbf{j} + \dfrac{z}{\sqrt{x^2 + y^2 + z^2}}\mathbf{k}$$

24. $\nabla f(x, y, z) = f_x(x, y, z)\mathbf{i} + f_y(x, y, z)\mathbf{j} + f_z(x, y, z)\mathbf{k}$

$$= \left(\cos\dfrac{y}{z} \right)\mathbf{i} - x\left(\sin\dfrac{y}{z} \right)\left(\dfrac{1}{z} \right)\mathbf{j} - x\left(\sin\dfrac{y}{z} \right)\left(-\dfrac{y}{z^2} \right)\mathbf{k}$$

$$= \left(\cos\dfrac{y}{z} \right)\mathbf{i} - \dfrac{x}{z}\left(\sin\dfrac{y}{z} \right)\mathbf{j} + \dfrac{xy}{z^2}\left(\sin\dfrac{y}{z} \right)\mathbf{k}$$

25. $f(x,y) = xy - 2x \Rightarrow$
$\nabla f(x,y) = (y-2)\,\mathbf{i} + x\,\mathbf{j}.$
The length of $\nabla f(x,y)$ is $\sqrt{(y-2)^2 + x^2}$ and
$\nabla f(x,y)$ terminates on the line $y = x + 2$ at
the point $(x+y-2, x+y)$.

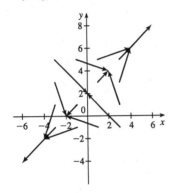

26. $f(x,y) = \frac{1}{4}(x+y)^2 \Rightarrow$
$\nabla f(x,y) = \frac{1}{2}(x+y)\,\mathbf{i} + \frac{1}{2}(x+y)\,\mathbf{j}.$
The length of $\nabla f(x,y)$ is
$\sqrt{\frac{1}{2}(x+y)^2} = \frac{1}{\sqrt{2}}|x+y|$. The vectors are
perpendicular to the line $y = -x$ and point
away from the line, with length that increases as
the distance from the line $y = -x$ increases.

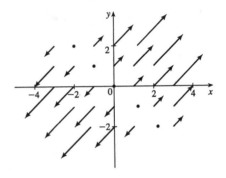

27. We graph ∇f along with a contour map of f.

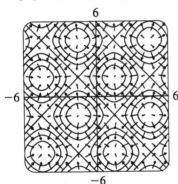

The graph shows that the gradient vectors are
perpendicular to the level curves. Also, the gradient
vectors point in the direction in which f is increasing
and are longer where the level curves are closer
together.

28. We graph ∇f along with a contour map of f.

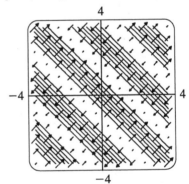

The graph shows that the gradient vectors are
perpendicular to the level curves. Also, the gradient
vectors point in the direction in which f is increasing
and are longer where the level curves are closer
together.

29. $f(x,y) = xy \Rightarrow \nabla f(x,y) = y\,\mathbf{i} + x\,\mathbf{j}.$ In the first quadrant, both components of each vector are positive, while
in the third quadrant both components are negative. However, in the second quadrant each vector's x-component is
positive while its y-component is negative (and vice versa in the fourth quadrant). Thus, ∇f is graph IV.

30. $f(x,y) = x^2 - y^2 \Rightarrow \nabla f(x,y) = 2x\,\mathbf{i} - 2y\,\mathbf{j}.$ In the first quadrant, the x-component of each vector is positive
while the y-component is negative. The other three quadrants are similar, where the x-component of each vector has

the same sign as the x-value of its initial point, and the y-component has sign opposite that of the y-value of the initial point. Thus, ∇f is graph III.

31. $f(x, y) = x^2 + y^2 \Rightarrow \nabla f(x, y) = 2x\,\mathbf{i} + 2y\,\mathbf{j}$. Thus, each vector $\nabla f(x, y)$ has the same direction and twice the length of the position vector of the point (x, y), so the vectors all point directly away from the origin and their lengths increase as we move away from the origin. Hence, ∇f is graph II.

32. $f(x, y) = \sqrt{x^2 + y^2} \Rightarrow \nabla f(x, y) = \dfrac{x}{\sqrt{x^2 + y^2}}\,\mathbf{i} + \dfrac{y}{\sqrt{x^2 + y^2}}\,\mathbf{j}$. Then

$|\nabla f(x, y)| = \dfrac{1}{\sqrt{x^2 + y^2}}\sqrt{x^2 + y^2} = 1$, so all vectors are unit vectors. In addition, each vector $\nabla f(x, y)$ has the

same direction as the position vector of the point (x, y), so the vectors all point directly away from the origin. Hence, ∇f is graph I.

33. (a) We sketch the vector field $\mathbf{F}(x, y) = x\,\mathbf{i} - y\,\mathbf{j}$ along with several approximate flow lines. The flow lines appear to be hyperbolas with shape similar to the graph of $y = \pm 1/x$, so we might guess that the flow lines have equations

$y = C/x$.

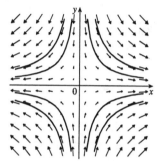

(b) If $x = x(t)$ and $y = y(t)$ are parametric equations of a flow line, then the velocity vector of the flow line at the point (x, y) is $x'(t)\,\mathbf{i} + y'(t)\,\mathbf{j}$. Since the velocity vectors coincide with the vectors in the vector field, we have

$x'(t)\,\mathbf{i} + y'(t)\,\mathbf{j} = x\,\mathbf{i} - y\,\mathbf{j} \Rightarrow dx/dt = x, \; dy/dt = -y$. To solve these differential equations, we know

$dx/dt = x \Rightarrow dx/x = dt \Rightarrow \ln|x| = t + C \Rightarrow x = \pm e^{t+C} = Ae^t$ for some constant A, and

$dy/dt = -y \Rightarrow dy/y = -dt \Rightarrow \ln|y| = -t + K \Rightarrow y = \pm e^{-t+K} = Be^{-t}$ for some constant B.

Therefore $xy = Ae^t Be^{-t} = AB = $ constant. If the flow line passes through $(1, 1)$ then

$(1)(1) = $ constant $= 1 \Rightarrow xy = 1 \Rightarrow y = 1/x, \; x > 0$.

34. (a) We sketch the vector field $\mathbf{F}(x, y) = \mathbf{i} + x\,\mathbf{j}$ along with several approximate flow lines. The flow lines appear to be parabolas.

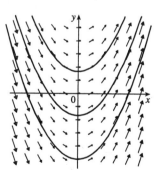

(b) If $x = x(t)$ and $y = y(t)$ are parametric equations of a flow line, then the velocity vector of the flow line at the point (x, y) is $x'(t)\,\mathbf{i} + y'(t)\,\mathbf{j}$. Since the velocity vectors coincide with the vectors in the vector field, we have

$x'(t)\,\mathbf{i} + y'(t)\,\mathbf{j} = \mathbf{i} + x\,\mathbf{j} \Rightarrow \dfrac{dx}{dt} = 1, \dfrac{dy}{dt} = x$. Thus $\dfrac{dy}{dx} = \dfrac{dy/dt}{dx/dt} = \dfrac{x}{1} = x$.

(c) From part (b), $dy/dx = x$. Integrating, we have $y = \frac{1}{2}x^2 + c$. Since the particle starts at the origin, we know $(0, 0)$ is on the curve, so $0 = 0 + c \Rightarrow c = 0$ and the path the particle follows is $y = \frac{1}{2}x^2$.

13.2 Line Integrals • • • • • • • • • • • • • • •

1. $x = t^2$ and $y = t$, $0 \le t \le 2$, so by Formula 3

$$\int_C y\, ds = \int_0^2 t \sqrt{\left(\frac{dx}{dt}\right)^2 + \left(\frac{dy}{dt}\right)^2}\, dt = \int_0^2 t \sqrt{(2t)^2 + (1)^2}\, dt$$

$$= \int_0^2 t\sqrt{4t^2 + 1}\, dt = \tfrac{1}{12}\left(4t^2 + 1\right)^{3/2}\Big]_0^2 = \tfrac{1}{12}\left(17\sqrt{17} - 1\right)$$

2. $\int_C \frac{y}{x}\, ds = \int_{1/2}^1 \frac{t^3}{t^4}\sqrt{(4t^3)^2 + (3t^2)^2}\, dt = \int_{1/2}^1 \frac{1}{t}\sqrt{16t^6 + 9t^4}\, dt = \int_{1/2}^1 t\sqrt{16t^2 + 9}\, dt$

$$= \tfrac{1}{48}\left(16t^2 + 9\right)^{3/2}\Big]_{1/2}^1 = \tfrac{1}{48}\left(25^{3/2} - 13^{3/2}\right) = \tfrac{1}{48}\left(125 - 13\sqrt{13}\right)$$

3. Parametric equatons for C are $x = 4\cos t$, $y = 4\sin t$, $-\frac{\pi}{2} \le t \le \frac{\pi}{2}$. Then

$$\int_C xy^4\, ds = \int_{-\pi/2}^{\pi/2}(4\cos t)(4\sin t)^4\sqrt{(-4\sin t)^2 + (4\cos t)^2}\, dt$$

$$= \int_{-\pi/2}^{\pi/2} 4^5 \cos t \sin^4 t \sqrt{16\left(\sin^2 t + \cos^2 t\right)}\, dt$$

$$= 4^5\int_{-\pi/2}^{\pi/2}\left(\sin^4 t \cos t\right)(4)\, dt = (4)^6\left[\tfrac{1}{5}\sin^5 t\right]_{-\pi/2}^{\pi/2} = \tfrac{2 \cdot 4^6}{5} = 1638.4$$

4. Choosing y as the parameter, we have $x = y^4$, $y = y$, $-1 \le y \le 1$. Then

$\int_C \sin x\, dx = \int_{-1}^1 \left(\sin y^4\right)\left(4y^3\right) dy = -\cos y^4\big]_{-1}^1 = 0.$

5.

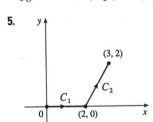

$C = C_1 + C_2$

On C_1: $x = x$, $y = 0$ $\Rightarrow$ $dy = 0\, dx$, $0 \le x \le 2$.

On C_2: $x = x$, $y = 2x - 4$ $\Rightarrow$ $dy = 2\, dx$, $2 \le x \le 3$.

Then

$\int_C xy\, dx + (x - y)\, dy = \int_{C_1} xy\, dx + (x - y)\, dy + \int_{C_2} xy\, dx + (x - y)\, dy$

$= \int_0^2 (0 + 0)\, dx + \int_2^3 \left[(2x^2 - 4x) + (-x + 4)(2)\right] dx$

$= \int_2^3 \left(2x^2 - 6x + 8\right) dx = \tfrac{17}{3}$

6.

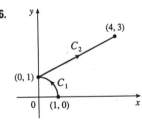

On C_1: $x = \cos t$ $\Rightarrow$ $dx = -\sin t\, dt$, $y = \sin t$ $\Rightarrow$

$y = \cos t\, dt$, $0 \le t \le \frac{\pi}{2}$.

On C_2: $x = 4t$ $\Rightarrow$ $dx = 4\, dt$, $y = 2t + 1$ $\Rightarrow$

$dy = 2\, dt$, $0 \le t \le 1$.

Then $\int_C x\sqrt{y}\, dx + 2y\sqrt{x}\, dy$

$= \int_{C_1} x\sqrt{y}\, dx + 2y\sqrt{x}\, dy + \int_{C_2} x\sqrt{y}\, dx + 2y\sqrt{x}\, dy$

$= \int_0^{\pi/2}\left[-\cos t(\sin t)^{3/2} + 2\sin t(\cos t)^{3/2}\right] dt + \int_0^1 \left[16t\sqrt{2t + 1} + 8(2t + 1)\sqrt{t}\right] dt$

$= \left[-\tfrac{2}{5}(\sin t)^{5/2} - \tfrac{4}{5}(\cos t)^{5/2}\right]_0^{\pi/2} + \left[\tfrac{16}{3}t(2t + 1)^{3/2} - \tfrac{16}{15}(2t + 1)^{5/2} + 8\left(\tfrac{4}{5}t^{5/2} + \tfrac{2}{3}t^{3/2}\right)\right]_0^1$

$= \tfrac{2}{5} + \tfrac{16}{3}\cdot 3\sqrt{3} - \tfrac{16}{15}\cdot 3^2\cdot\sqrt{3} + \tfrac{16}{15} + 8\left(\tfrac{4}{5} + \tfrac{2}{3}\right) = \tfrac{32\sqrt{3} + 66}{5}$

7. $x = 4\sin t$, $y = 4\cos t$, $z = 3t$, $0 \le t \le \frac{\pi}{2}$. Then by Formula 9,

$$\int_C xy^3\,ds = \int_0^{\pi/2} (4\sin t)(4\cos t)^3 \sqrt{\left(\frac{dx}{dt}\right)^2 + \left(\frac{dy}{dt}\right)^2 + \left(\frac{dz}{dt}\right)^2}\,dt$$

$$= \int_0^{\pi/2} 4^4 \cos^3 t \sin t \sqrt{(4\cos t)^2 + (-4\sin t)^2 + (3)^2}\,dt$$

$$= \int_0^{\pi/2} 256\cos^3 t \sin t \sqrt{16(\cos^2 t + \sin^2 t) + 9}\,dt$$

$$= 1280 \int_0^{\pi/2} \cos^3 t \sin t\,dt = -320\cos^4 t\Big]_0^{\pi/2} = 320$$

8. Parametric equations for C are $x = 4t$, $y = 6 - 5t$, $z = -1 + 6t$, $0 \le t \le 1$. Then

$$\int_C x^2 z\,ds = \int_0^1 (4t)^2(6t - 1)\sqrt{4^2 + (-5)^2 + 6^2}\,dt = \sqrt{77}\int_0^1 (96t^3 - 16t^2)\,dt$$

$$= \sqrt{77}\left[96\cdot\frac{t^4}{4} - 16\cdot\frac{t^3}{3}\right]_0^1 = \tfrac{56}{3}\sqrt{77}$$

9. Parametric equations for C are $x = t$, $y = 2t$, $z = 3t$, $0 \le t \le 1$. Then

$$\int_C xe^{yz}\,ds = \int_0^1 te^{(2t)(3t)}\sqrt{1^2 + 2^2 + 3^2}\,dt = \sqrt{14}\int_0^1 te^{6t^2}\,dt$$

$$= \sqrt{14}\left[\tfrac{1}{12}e^{6t^2}\right]_0^1 = \tfrac{\sqrt{14}}{12}(e^6 - 1)$$

10. $\int_C yz\,dy + xy\,dz = \int_0^1 (t)(t^2)\,dt + \int_0^1 \sqrt{t}\,(t)\,2t\,dt = \int_0^1 \left(t^3 + 2t^{5/2}\right)dt = \left[\tfrac{1}{4}t^4 + \tfrac{4}{7}t^{7/2}\right]_0^1 = \tfrac{23}{28}$

11. On C_1: $x = 0 \Rightarrow dx = 0\,dt$, $y = t \Rightarrow dy = dt$, $z = t \Rightarrow$
$dz = dt$, $0 \le t \le 1$.

On C_2: $x = t \Rightarrow dx = dt$, $y = t + 1 \Rightarrow dy = dt$, $z = 2t + 1 \Rightarrow$
$dz = 2\,dt$, $0 \le t \le 1$.

On C_3: $x = 1 \Rightarrow dx = 0\,dt$, $y = 2 \Rightarrow dy = 0\,dt$, $z = t + 3 \Rightarrow$
$dz = dt$, $0 \le t \le 1$.

Then

$\int_C z^2\,dx - z\,dy + 2y\,dz$

$$= \int_0^1 (0 - t + 2t)dt + \int_0^1 \left[(2t + 1)^2 - (2t + 1) + 2(2t + 1)(2)\right]dt + \int_0^1 (0 + 0 + 4)\,dt$$

$$= \tfrac{1}{2} + \left[\tfrac{4}{3}t^3 + 3t^2 + 4t\right]_0^1 + 4 = \tfrac{77}{6}$$

12. C_1: $(0, 0, 0)$ to $(2, 0, 0)$: $x = 2t$, $y = z = 0$, $0 \le t \le 1$.

C_2: $(2, 0, 0)$ to $(1, 3, -1)$: $x = -t + 2$, $y = 3t$, $z = -t$, $0 \le t \le 1$.

C_3: $(1, 3, -1)$ to $(1, 3, 0)$: $x = 1$, $y = 3$, $z = t - 1$, $0 \le t \le 1$.

Then

$$\int_C yz\,dx + xz\,dy + xy\,dz = 0 + \int_0^1 \left[(3t^2) + 3(t^2 - 2t) - 3(2t - t^2)\right]dt + \int_0^1 3\,dt$$

$$= \left[3t^3 - 6t^2\right]_0^1 + 3 = 0.$$

13. (a) Along the line $x = -3$, the vectors of $\mathbf{F}$ have positive y-components, so since the path goes upward, the integrand $\mathbf{F} \cdot \mathbf{T}$ is always positive. Therefore $\int_{C_1} \mathbf{F} \cdot d\mathbf{r} = \int_{C_1} \mathbf{F} \cdot \mathbf{T} \, ds$ is positive.

(b) All of the (nonzero) field vectors along the circle with radius 3 are pointed in the clockwise direction, that is, opposite the direction to the path. So $\mathbf{F} \cdot \mathbf{T}$ is negative, and therefore $\int_{C_2} \mathbf{F} \cdot d\mathbf{r} = \int_{C_2} \mathbf{F} \cdot \mathbf{T} \, ds$ is negative.

14. Vectors starting on C_1 point in roughly the same direction as C_1, so the tangential component $\mathbf{F} \cdot \mathbf{T}$ is positive. Then $\int_{C_1} \mathbf{F} \cdot d\mathbf{r} = \int_{C_1} \mathbf{F} \cdot \mathbf{T} \, ds$ is positive. On the other hand, no vectors starting on C_2 point in the same direction as C_2, while some vectors point in roughly the opposite direction, so we would expect $\int_{C_2} \mathbf{F} \cdot d\mathbf{r} = \int_{C_2} \mathbf{F} \cdot \mathbf{T} \, ds$ to be negative.

15. $\mathbf{r}(t) = t^2 \, \mathbf{i} - t^3 \mathbf{j}$, so $\mathbf{F}(\mathbf{r}(t)) = (t^2)^2 (-t^3)^3 \, \mathbf{i} - (-t^3) \sqrt{t^2} \, \mathbf{j} = -t^{13} \, \mathbf{i} + t^4 \, \mathbf{j}$ and $\mathbf{r}'(t) = 2t \, \mathbf{i} - 3t^2 \, \mathbf{j}$. Thus

$$\int_C \mathbf{F} \cdot d\mathbf{r} = \int_0^1 \mathbf{F}(\mathbf{r}(t)) \cdot \mathbf{r}'(t) \, dt = \int_0^1 \left(-2t^{14} - 3t^6\right) dt = \left[-\tfrac{2}{15} t^{15} - \tfrac{3}{7} t^7\right]_0^1 = -\tfrac{59}{105}$$

16. $\mathbf{F}(\mathbf{r}(t)) = (t^2)(t^3) \, \mathbf{i} + (t)(t^3) \, \mathbf{j} + (t)(t^2) \, \mathbf{k} = t^5 \, \mathbf{i} + t^4 \, \mathbf{j} + t^3 \, \mathbf{k}$, $\mathbf{r}'(t) = \mathbf{i} + 2t \, \mathbf{j} + 3t^2 \, \mathbf{k}$.

$$\int_C \mathbf{F} \cdot d\mathbf{r} = \int_0^2 \mathbf{F}(\mathbf{r}(t)) \cdot \mathbf{r}'(t) \, dt = \int_0^2 \left(t^5 + 2t^5 + 3t^5\right) dt = t^6 \Big]_0^2 = 64$$

17. $\int_C \mathbf{F} \cdot d\mathbf{r} = \int_0^1 \left\langle \sin t^3, \cos\left(-t^2\right), t^4 \right\rangle \cdot \left\langle 3t^2, -2t, 1 \right\rangle dt$

$$= \int_0^1 \left(3t^2 \sin t^3 - 2t \cos t^2 + t^4\right) dt = \left[-\cos t^3 - \sin t^2 + \tfrac{1}{5} t^5\right]_0^1 = \tfrac{6}{5} - \cos 1 - \sin 1$$

18. $\int_C \mathbf{F} \cdot d\mathbf{r} = \int_0^{\pi/2} \left\langle \sin^2 t, \sin t \cos t, t^4 \right\rangle \cdot \left\langle \cos t, -\sin t, 2t \right\rangle dt$

$$= \int_0^{\pi/2} \left(\sin^2 t \cos t - \sin^2 t \cos t + 2t^5\right) dt = \left[\tfrac{1}{3} t^6\right]_0^{\pi/2} = \frac{\pi^6}{192}$$

19. We graph $\mathbf{F}(x, y) = (x - y) \, \mathbf{i} + xy \, \mathbf{j}$ and the curve C. We see that most of the vectors starting on C point in roughly the same direction as C, so for these portions of C the tangential component $\mathbf{F} \cdot \mathbf{T}$ is positive. Although some vectors in the third quadrant which start on C point in roughly the opposite direction, and hence give negative tangential components, it seems reasonable that the effect of these portions of C is outweighed by the positive tangential components. Thus, we would expect $\int_C \mathbf{F} \cdot d\mathbf{r} = \int_C \mathbf{F} \cdot \mathbf{T} \, ds$ to be positive.

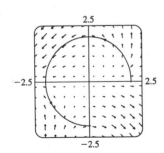

To verify, we evaluate $\int_C \mathbf{F} \cdot d\mathbf{r}$. The curve C can be represented by $\mathbf{r}(t) = 2 \cos t \, \mathbf{i} + 2 \sin t \, \mathbf{j}$, $0 \le t \le \frac{3\pi}{2}$, so

$\mathbf{F}(\mathbf{r}(t)) = (2 \cos t - 2 \sin t) \, \mathbf{i} + 4 \cos t \sin t \, \mathbf{j}$ and

$\mathbf{r}'(t) = -2 \sin t \, \mathbf{i} + 2 \cos t \, \mathbf{j}$. Then

$\int_C \mathbf{F} \cdot d\mathbf{r} = \int_0^{3\pi/2} \mathbf{F}(\mathbf{r}(t)) \cdot \mathbf{r}'(t) \, dt$

$\qquad = \int_0^{3\pi/2} \left[-2 \sin t (2 \cos t - 2 \sin t) + 2 \cos t (4 \cos t \sin t)\right] dt$

$\qquad = 4 \int_0^{3\pi/2} \left(\sin^2 t - \sin t \cos t + 2 \sin t \cos^2 t\right) dt$

$\qquad = 3\pi + \tfrac{2}{3}$ (using a CAS)

20. We graph $\mathbf{F}(x, y) = \dfrac{x}{\sqrt{x^2 + y^2}}\mathbf{i} + \dfrac{y}{\sqrt{x^2 + y^2}}\mathbf{j}$ and the curve C. In

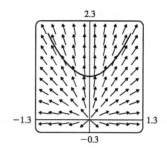

the first quadrant, each vector starting on C points in roughly the same direction as C, so the tangential component $\mathbf{F} \cdot \mathbf{T}$ is positive. In the second quadrant, each vector starting on C points in roughly the direction opposite to C, so $\mathbf{F} \cdot \mathbf{T}$ is negative. Here, it appears that the tangential components in the first and second quadrants counteract each other, so it seems reasonable to guess that $\int_C \mathbf{F} \cdot d\mathbf{r} = \int_C \mathbf{F} \cdot \mathbf{T}\, ds$ is zero. To verify, we evaluate $\int_C \mathbf{F} \cdot d\mathbf{r}$. The curve C can be represented by

$\mathbf{r}(t) = t\,\mathbf{i} + (1 + t^2)\,\mathbf{j}$, $-1 \le t \le 1$, so

$\mathbf{F}(\mathbf{r}(t)) = \dfrac{t}{\sqrt{t^2 + (1 + t^2)^2}}\mathbf{i} + \dfrac{1 + t^2}{\sqrt{t^2 + (1 + t^2)^2}}\mathbf{j}$ and $\mathbf{r}'(t) = \mathbf{i} + 2t\,\mathbf{j}$. Then

$$\int_C \mathbf{F} \cdot d\mathbf{r} = \int_{-1}^{1} \mathbf{F}(\mathbf{r}(t)) \cdot \mathbf{r}'(t)\, dt$$

$$= \int_{-1}^{1} \left(\frac{t}{\sqrt{t^2 + (1 + t^2)^2}} + \frac{2t(1 + t^2)}{\sqrt{t^2 + (1 + t^2)^2}} \right) dt$$

$$= \int_{-1}^{1} \frac{t(3 + 2t^2)}{\sqrt{t^4 + 3t^2 + 1}}\, dt = 0 \quad \text{(since the integrand is an odd function)}$$

21. (a) $\int_C \mathbf{F} \cdot d\mathbf{r} = \int_0^1 \left\langle e^{t^2 - 1}, t^5 \right\rangle \cdot \left\langle 2t, 3t^2 \right\rangle dt = \int_0^1 \left(2te^{t^2 - 1} + 3t^7 \right) dt = \left[e^{t^2 - 1} + \frac{3}{8}t^8 \right]_0^1 = \frac{11}{8} - 1/e$

(b) $\mathbf{r}(0) = 0$, $\mathbf{F}(\mathbf{r}(0)) = \left\langle e^{-1}, 0 \right\rangle$; $\mathbf{r}\!\left(\frac{1}{\sqrt{2}}\right) = \left\langle \frac{1}{2}, \frac{1}{2\sqrt{2}} \right\rangle$, $\mathbf{F}\!\left(\mathbf{r}\!\left(\frac{1}{\sqrt{2}}\right)\right) = \left\langle e^{-1/2}, \frac{1}{4\sqrt{2}} \right\rangle$;

$\mathbf{r}(1) = \langle 1, 1 \rangle$, $\mathbf{F}(\mathbf{r}(1)) = \langle 1, 1 \rangle$.

In order to generate the graph with Maple, we use the PLOT command (not to be confused with the plot command) to define each of the vectors. For example,

```
v1:=PLOT(CURVES([[0,0],[evalf(1/exp(1)),0]]));
```

generates the vector from the vector field at the point $(0, 0)$ (but without an arrowhead) and gives it the name v1. To show everything on the same screen, we use the display command.

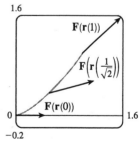

In Mathematica, we use ListPlot (with the PlotJoined -> True option) to generate the vectors, and then Show to show everything on the same screen.

22. (a) $\int_C \mathbf{F} \cdot d\mathbf{r} = \int_{-1}^{1} \langle 2t, t^2, 3t \rangle \cdot \langle 2, 3, -2t \rangle \, dt = \int_{-1}^{1} \left(4t + 3t^2 - 6t^2 \right) dt = \left[2t^2 - t^3 \right]_{-1}^{1} = -2.$

(b) Now $\mathbf{F}(\mathbf{r}(t)) = \langle 2t, t^2, 3t \rangle$, so $\mathbf{F}(\mathbf{r}(-1)) = \langle -2, 1, -3 \rangle$, $\mathbf{F}\left(\mathbf{r}\left(-\frac{1}{2}\right)\right) = \langle -1, \frac{1}{4}, -\frac{3}{2} \rangle$, $\mathbf{F}\left(\mathbf{r}\left(\frac{1}{2}\right)\right) = \langle 1, \frac{1}{4}, \frac{3}{2} \rangle$, and $\mathbf{F}(\mathbf{r}(1)) = \langle 2, 1, 3 \rangle$.

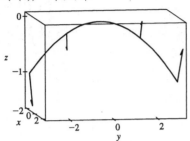 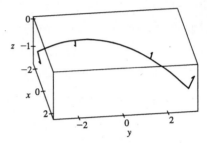

23. The part of the astroid that lies in the quadrant is parametrized by $x = \cos^3 t$,

$y = \sin^3 t, 0 \le t \le \frac{\pi}{2}$. Now $\dfrac{dx}{dt} = 3\cos^2 t \, (-\sin t)$ and $\dfrac{dy}{dt} = 3\sin^2 t \cos t$, so

$$\sqrt{\left(\frac{dx}{dt}\right)^2 + \left(\frac{dy}{dt}\right)^2} = \sqrt{9\cos^4 t \sin^2 t + 9\sin^4 t \cos^2 t} = 3\cos t \sin t \sqrt{\cos^2 t + \sin^2 t} = 3\cos t \sin t.$$

Therefore $\int_C x^3 y^5 \, ds = \int_0^{\pi/2} \cos^9 t \sin^{15} t \, (3\cos t \sin t) \, dt = \frac{945}{16,777,216}\pi.$

24. (a) We parametrize the circle C as $\mathbf{r}(t) = 2\cos t\,\mathbf{i} + 2\sin t\,\mathbf{j}, 0 \le t \le 2\pi$. So $\mathbf{F}(\mathbf{r}(t)) = \langle 4\cos^2 t, 4\cos t \sin t \rangle$,

$\mathbf{r}'(t) = \langle -2\sin t, 2\cos t \rangle$, and $W = \int_C \mathbf{F} \cdot d\mathbf{r} = \int_0^{2\pi} \left(-8\cos^2 t \sin t + 8\cos^2 t \sin t \right) dt = 0.$

(b)

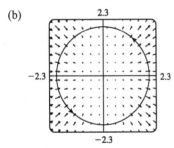

From the graph, we see that all of the vectors in the field are perpendicular to the path. This indicates that the field does no work on the particle, since the field never pulls the particle in the direction in which it is going. In other words, at any point along C, $\mathbf{F} \cdot \mathbf{T} = 0$, and so certainly $\int_C \mathbf{F} \cdot d\mathbf{r} = 0$.

25. We use the parametrization $x = 2\cos t, y = 2\sin t, -\frac{\pi}{2} \le t \le \frac{\pi}{2}$.

Then $ds = \sqrt{\left(\dfrac{dx}{dt}\right)^2 + \left(\dfrac{dy}{dt}\right)^2} \, dt = \sqrt{(-2\sin t)^2 + (2\cos t)^2} \, dt = 2\,dt$, so

$m = \int_C k \, ds = 2k \int_{-\pi/2}^{\pi/2} dt = 2k(\pi)$, $\bar{x} = \frac{1}{2\pi k} \int_C xk \, ds = \frac{1}{2\pi} \int_{-\pi/2}^{\pi/2} (2\cos t) 2 \, dt = \frac{1}{2\pi}[4\sin t]_{-\pi/2}^{\pi/2} = \frac{4}{\pi}$,

$\bar{y} = \frac{1}{2\pi k} \int_C yk \, ds = \frac{1}{2\pi} \int_{-\pi/2}^{\pi/2} (2\sin t) 2 \, dt = 0$. Hence $(\bar{x}, \bar{y}) = \left(\frac{4}{\pi}, 0 \right)$.

26. We use the parametrization $x = r\cos t, y = r\sin t, 0 \le t \le \frac{\pi}{2}$.

Then $ds = \sqrt{\left(\dfrac{dx}{dt}\right)^2 + \left(\dfrac{dy}{dt}\right)^2} \, dt = \sqrt{(-r\sin t)^2 + (r\cos t)^2} \, dt = r\,dt$, so

$m = \int_C (x + y) \, ds = \int_0^{\pi/2} (r\cos t + r\sin t) r \, dt = r^2 [\sin t - \cos t]_0^{\pi/2} = 2r^2$,

$\bar{x} = \frac{1}{2r^2} \int_C x(x + y) \, ds = \frac{1}{2r^2} \int_0^{\pi/2} \left(r^2 \cos^2 t + r^2 \cos t \sin t \right) r \, dt = \frac{r}{2} \left[\frac{t}{2} + \frac{\sin 2t}{4} - \frac{\cos 2t}{4} \right]_0^{\pi/2}$

$= \frac{r(\pi + 2)}{8}$, and

$$\bar{y} = \frac{1}{2r^2} \int_C y(x+y)\,ds = \frac{1}{2r^2} \int_0^{\pi/2} \left(r^2 \sin t \cos t + r^2 \sin^2 t\right) r\,dt$$

$$= \frac{r}{2}\left[-\frac{\cos 2t}{4} + \frac{t}{2} - \frac{\sin 2t}{4}\right]_0^{\pi/2} = \frac{r(\pi+2)}{8}.$$

Therefore $(\bar{x}, \bar{y}) = \left(\dfrac{r(\pi+2)}{8}, \dfrac{r(\pi+2)}{8}\right)$.

27. (a) $\bar{x} = \dfrac{1}{m}\displaystyle\int_C x\rho(x,y,z)\,ds$, $\bar{y} = \dfrac{1}{m}\displaystyle\int_C y\rho(x,y,z)\,ds$, $\bar{z} = \dfrac{1}{m}\displaystyle\int_C z\rho(x,y,z)\,ds$ where $m = \displaystyle\int_C \rho(x,y,z)\,ds$.

(b) $m = \int_C k\,ds = k\int_0^{2\pi} \sqrt{4\sin^2 t + 4\cos^2 t + 9}\,dt = k\sqrt{13}\int_0^{2\pi} dt = 2\pi k\sqrt{13}$,

$$\bar{x} = \frac{1}{2\pi k\sqrt{13}}\int_0^{2\pi} k2\sqrt{13}\,\sin t\,dt = 0, \bar{y} = \frac{1}{2\pi k\sqrt{13}}\int_0^{2\pi} k2\sqrt{13}\,\cos t\,dt = 0,$$

$$\bar{z} = \frac{1}{2\pi k\sqrt{13}}\int_0^{2\pi}\left(k\sqrt{13}\right)(3t)\,dt = \frac{3}{2\pi}\left(2\pi^2\right) = 3\pi.$$ Hence $(\bar{x}, \bar{y}, \bar{z}) = (0, 0, 3\pi)$.

28. $m = \int_C \left(x^2+y^2+z^2\right) ds = \int_0^{2\pi}\left(t^2+1\right)\sqrt{(1)^2 + (-\sin t)^2 + (\cos t)^2}\,dt = \int_0^{2\pi}\left(t^2+1\right)\sqrt{2}\,dt$

$$= \sqrt{2}\left(\tfrac{8}{3}\pi^3 + 2\pi\right),$$

$$\bar{x} = \frac{1}{\sqrt{2}\left(\tfrac{8}{3}\pi^3 + 2\pi\right)}\int_0^{2\pi}\sqrt{2}\left(t^3 + t\right)dt = \frac{4\pi^4 + 2\pi^2}{\tfrac{8}{3}\pi^3 + 2\pi} = \frac{3\pi\left(2\pi^2 + 1\right)}{4\pi^2 + 3},$$

$$\bar{y} = \frac{3}{2\sqrt{2}\pi(4\pi^2 + 3)}\int_0^{2\pi}\left(\sqrt{2}\cos t\right)\left(t^2+1\right)dt = 0, \text{ and}$$

$$\bar{z} = \frac{3}{2\sqrt{2}\pi(4\pi^2 + 3)}\int_0^{2\pi}\left(\sqrt{2}\sin t\right)\left(t^2+1\right)dt = 0. \text{ Hence } (\bar{x}, \bar{y}, \bar{z}) = \left(\frac{3\pi\left(2\pi^2 + 1\right)}{4\pi^2 + 3}, 0, 0\right).$$

29. From Example 3, $\rho(x,y) = k(1-y)$, $x = \cos t$, $y = \sin t$, and $ds = dt$, $0 \le t \le \pi$ $\Rightarrow$

$$I_x = \int_C y^2\rho(x,y)\,ds = \int_0^\pi \sin^2 t\,[k(1-\sin t)]\,dt = k\int_0^\pi \left(\sin^2 t - \sin^3 t\right)dt$$

$$= \tfrac{1}{2}k\int_0^\pi (1-\cos 2t)\,dt - k\int_0^\pi \left(1 - \cos^2 t\right)\sin t\,dt \qquad \begin{array}{l}(\text{Let } u = \cos t,\ du = -\sin t\,dt \\ \text{in the second integral})\end{array}$$

$$= k\left[\tfrac{\pi}{2} + \int_1^{-1}\left(1 - u^2\right)du\right] = k\left(\tfrac{\pi}{2} - \tfrac{4}{3}\right)$$

$$I_y = \int_C x^2\rho(x,y)\,ds = k\int_0^\pi \cos^2 t\,(1 - \sin t)\,dt = \tfrac{k}{2}\int_0^\pi (1 + \cos 2t)\,dt - k\int_0^\pi \cos^2 t\,\sin t\,dt$$

$$= k\left(\tfrac{\pi}{2} - \tfrac{2}{3}\right), \text{ using the same substitution as above.}$$

30. The wire is given as $x = 2\sin t$, $y = 2\cos t$, $z = 3t$, $0 \le t \le 2\pi$ with $\rho(x,y,z) = k$. Then

$ds = \sqrt{(2\cos t)^2 + (-2\sin t)^2 + 3^2} = \sqrt{4\left(\cos^2 t + \sin^2 t\right) + 9} = \sqrt{13}$ and

$$I_x = \int_C \left(y^2 + z^2\right)\rho(x,y,z)\,ds = \int_0^{2\pi}\left(4\cos^2 t + 9t^2\right)(k)\sqrt{13}\,dt = \sqrt{13}\,k\left[4\left(\tfrac{1}{2}t + \tfrac{1}{4}\sin 2t\right) + 3t^3\right]_0^{2\pi}$$

$$= \sqrt{13}\,k\left(4\pi + 24\pi^3\right) = 4\sqrt{13}\,\pi k\left(1 + 6\pi^2\right)$$

$$I_y = \int_C \left(x^2 + z^2\right)\rho(x,y,z)\,ds = \int_0^{2\pi}\left(4\sin^2 t + 9t^2\right)(k)\sqrt{13}\,dt = \sqrt{13}\,k\left[4\left(\tfrac{1}{2}t - \tfrac{1}{4}\sin 2t\right) + 3t^3\right]_0^{2\pi}$$

$$= \sqrt{13}\,k\left(4\pi + 24\pi^3\right) = 4\sqrt{13}\,\pi k\left(1 + 6\pi^2\right)$$

$$I_z = \int_C \left(x^2 + y^2\right)\rho(x,y,z)\,ds = \int_0^{2\pi}\left(4\sin^2 t + 4\cos^2 t\right)(k)\sqrt{13}\,dt = 4\sqrt{13}\,k\int_0^{2\pi} dt = 8\pi\sqrt{13}\,k$$

31. $W = \int_C \mathbf{F} \cdot d\mathbf{r} = \int_0^{2\pi} \langle t - \sin t, 3 - \cos t \rangle \cdot \langle 1 - \cos t, \sin t \rangle \, dt$

$\qquad = \int_0^{2\pi} (t - t \cos t - \sin t + \sin t \cos t + 3 \sin t - \sin t \cos t) \, dt$

$\qquad = \int_0^{2\pi} (t - t \cos t + 2 \sin t) \, dt = \left[\frac{1}{2} t^2 - (t \sin t + \cos t) - 2 \cos t \right]_0^{2\pi}$ $\quad$ (by integrating by parts in the second term)

$\qquad = 2\pi^2$

32. $x = x, \; y = x^2, \; -1 \le x \le 2,$

$\qquad W = \int_{-1}^2 \langle x \sin x^2, x^2 \rangle \cdot \langle 1, 2x \rangle \, dx = \int_{-1}^2 \left(x \sin x^2 + 2x^3 \right) dx = \left[-\frac{1}{2} \cos x^2 + \frac{1}{2} x^4 \right]_{-1}^2$

$\qquad = \frac{1}{2}(15 + \cos 1 - \cos 4)$

33. $W = \int_C \mathbf{F} \cdot d\mathbf{r} = \int_0^1 \langle t^6, -t^5, -t^7 \rangle \cdot \langle 2t, -3t^2, 4t^3 \rangle \, dt = \int_0^1 \left(5t^7 - 4t^{10} \right) dt = \frac{5}{8} - \frac{4}{11} = \frac{23}{88}$

34. $\mathbf{r}(t) = 2\mathbf{i} + t\mathbf{j} + 5t\mathbf{k}, \; 0 \le t \le 1.$ Therefore

$$W = \int_C \mathbf{F} \cdot d\mathbf{r} = \int_0^1 \frac{K \langle 2, t, 5t \rangle}{(4 + 26t^2)^{3/2}} \cdot \langle 0, 1, 5 \rangle \, dt = K \int_0^1 \frac{26t}{(4 + 26t^2)^{3/2}} \, dt$$

$$= K \left[-(4 + 26t^2)^{-1/2} \right]_0^1 = K \left(\frac{1}{2} - \frac{1}{\sqrt{30}} \right)$$

35. Let $\mathbf{F} = 185 \, \mathbf{k}$. To parametrize the staircase, let

$\qquad x = 20 \cos t, \; y = 20 \sin t, \; z = \frac{90}{6\pi} t = \frac{15}{\pi} t, \; 0 \le t \le 6\pi \quad \Rightarrow$

$\qquad W = \int_C \mathbf{F} \cdot d\mathbf{r} = \int_0^{6\pi} \langle 0, 0, 185 \rangle \cdot \langle -20 \sin t, 20 \cos t, \frac{15}{\pi} \rangle \, dt = (185) \frac{15}{\pi} \int_0^{6\pi} dt = (185)(90)$

$\qquad \approx 1.67 \times 10^4$ ft-lb

36. This time m is a function of t: $m = 185 - \frac{9}{6\pi} t = 185 - \frac{3}{2\pi} t$. So let $\mathbf{F} = \left(185 - \frac{3}{2\pi} t \right) \mathbf{k}$. To parametrize the staircase, let $x = 20 \cos t, \; y = 20 \sin t, \; z = \frac{90}{6\pi} t = \frac{15}{\pi} t, \; 0 \le t \le 6\pi$. Therefore

$\qquad W = \int_C \mathbf{F} \cdot d\mathbf{r} = \int_0^{6\pi} \langle 0, 0, 185 - \frac{3}{2\pi} t \rangle \cdot \langle -20 \sin t, 20 \cos t, \frac{15}{\pi} \rangle \, dt = \frac{15}{\pi} \int_0^{6\pi} \left(185 - \frac{3}{2\pi} t \right) dt$

$\qquad = \frac{15}{\pi} \left[185t - \frac{3}{4\pi} t^2 \right]_0^{6\pi} = 90 \left(185 - \frac{9}{2} \right) \approx 1.62 \times 10^4$ ft-lb

37. The work done in moving the object is $\int_C \mathbf{F} \cdot d\mathbf{r} = \int_C \mathbf{F} \cdot \mathbf{T} \, ds$. We can approximate this integral by dividing C into 7 segments of equal length $\Delta s = 2$ and approximating $\mathbf{F} \cdot \mathbf{T}$, that is, the tangential component of force, at a point (x_i^*, y_i^*) on each segment. Since C is composed of straight line segments, $\mathbf{F} \cdot \mathbf{T}$ is the scalar projection of each force vector onto C. If we choose (x_i^*, y_i^*) to be the point on the segment closest to the origin, then the work done is

$$\int_C \mathbf{F} \cdot \mathbf{T} \, ds \approx \sum_{i=1}^7 \left[\mathbf{F}(x_i^*, y_i^*) \cdot \mathbf{T}(x_i^*, y_i^*) \right] \Delta s$$

$$= [2 + 2 + 2 + 2 + 1 + 1 + 1](2) = 22$$

Thus, we estimate the work done to be approximately 22 J.

38. Use the orientation pictured in the figure. Then since $\mathbf{B}$ is tangent to any circle that lies in the plane perpendicular to the wire, $\mathbf{B} = |\mathbf{B}| \, \mathbf{T}$ where $\mathbf{T}$ is the unit tangent to the circle C: $x = r \cos \theta, \; y = r \sin \theta$. Thus $\mathbf{B} = |\mathbf{B}| \langle -\sin \theta, \cos \theta \rangle$. Then $\int_C \mathbf{B} \cdot d\mathbf{r} = \int_0^{2\pi} |\mathbf{B}| \langle -\sin \theta, \cos \theta \rangle \cdot \langle -r \sin \theta, r \cos \theta \rangle \, d\theta = \int_0^{2\pi} |\mathbf{B}| \, r \, d\theta = 2\pi r \, |\mathbf{B}|$. (Note that $|\mathbf{B}|$ here is the magnitude of the field at a distance r from the wire's center.) But by Ampere's Law $\int_C \mathbf{B} \cdot d\mathbf{r} = \mu_0 I$. Hence $|\mathbf{B}| = \mu_0 I / (2\pi r)$.

The Fundamental Theorem for Line Integrals • • • • •

1. C appears to be a smooth curve, and since ∇f is continuous, we know f is differentiable. Then Theorem 2 says that the value of $\int_C \nabla f \cdot d\mathbf{r}$ is simply the difference of the values of f at the terminal and initial points of C. From the graph, this is $50 - 10 = 40$.

2. C is represented by the vector function $\mathbf{r}(t) = (t^2 + 1)\mathbf{i} + (t^3 + t)\mathbf{j}$, $0 \le t \le 1$, so $\mathbf{r}'(t) = 2t\mathbf{i} + (3t^2 + 1)\mathbf{j}$. Since $3t^2 + 1 \ne 0$, we have $\mathbf{r}'(t) \ne \mathbf{0}$, thus C is a smooth curve. ∇f is continuous, and hence f is differentiable, so by Theorem 2 we have $\int_C \nabla f \cdot d\mathbf{r} = f(\mathbf{r}(1)) - f(\mathbf{r}(0)) = f(2, 2) - f(1, 0) = 9 - 3 = 6$.

3. $\partial(6x + 5y)/\partial y = 5 = \partial(5x + 4y)/\partial x$ and the domain of $\mathbf{F}$ is $\mathbb{R}^2$ which is open and simply-connected, so by Theorem 6 $\mathbf{F}$ is conservative. Thus, there exists a function f such that $\nabla f = \mathbf{F}$, that is, $f_x(x, y) = 6x + 5y$ and $f_y(x, y) = 5x + 4y$. But $f_x(x, y) = 6x + 5y$ implies $f(x, y) = 3x^2 + 5xy + g(y)$ and differentiating both sides of this equation with respect to y gives $f_y(x, y) = 5x + g'(y)$. Thus $5x + 4y = 5x + g'(y)$ so $g'(y) = 4y$ and $g(y) = 2y^2 + K$ where K is a constant. Hence $f(x, y) = 3x^2 + 5xy + 2y^2 + K$ is a potential function for $\mathbf{F}$.

4. $\partial(x^3 + 4xy)/\partial y = 4x$, $\partial(4xy - y^3)/\partial x = 4y$. Since these are not equal, $\mathbf{F}$ is not conservative.

5. $\partial(xe^y)/\partial y = xe^y$, $\partial(ye^x)/\partial x = ye^x$. Since these are not equal, $\mathbf{F}$ is not conservative.

6. $\partial(e^y)/\partial y = e^y = \partial(xe^y)/\partial x$ and the domain of $\mathbf{F}$ is $\mathbb{R}^2$. Hence $\mathbf{F}$ is conservative so there exists a function f such that $\nabla f = \mathbf{F}$. Then $f_x(x, y) = e^y$ implies $f(x, y) = xe^y + g(y)$ and $f_y(x, y) = xe^y + g'(y)$. But $f_y(x, y) = xe^y$ so $g'(y) = 0 \implies g(y) = K$. Then $f(x, y) = xe^y + K$ is a potential function for $\mathbf{F}$.

7. $\partial(2x \cos y - y \cos x)/\partial y = -2x \sin y - \cos x = \partial(-x^2 \sin y - \sin x)/\partial x$ and the domain of $\mathbf{F}$ is $\mathbb{R}^2$. Hence $\mathbf{F}$ is conservative so there exists a function f such that $\nabla f = \mathbf{F}$. Then $f_x(x, y) = 2x \cos y - y \cos x$ implies $f(x, y) = x^2 \cos y - y \sin x + g(y)$ and $f_y(x, y) = -x^2 \sin y - \sin x + g'(y)$. But $f_y(x, y) = -x^2 \sin y - \sin x$ so $g'(y) = 0 \implies g(y) = K$. Then $f(x, y) = x^2 \cos y - y \sin x + K$ is a potential function for $\mathbf{F}$.

8. $\partial(1 + 2xy + \ln x)/\partial y = 2x = \partial(x^2)/\partial x$ and the domain of $\mathbf{F}$ is $\{(x, y) \mid x > 0\}$ which is open and simply-connected. Hence $\mathbf{F}$ is conservative, so there exists a function f such that $\nabla f = \mathbf{F}$. Then $f_x(x, y) = 1 + 2xy + \ln x$ implies $f(x, y) = x + x^2 y + x \ln x - x + g(y)$ and $f_y(x, y) = x^2 + g'(y)$. But $f_y(x, y) = x^2$ so $g'(y) = 0 \implies g(y) = K$. Then $f(x, y) = x^2 y + x \ln x + K$ is a potential function for $\mathbf{F}$.

9. $\partial(ye^x + \sin y)/\partial y = e^x + \cos y = \partial(e^x + x \cos y)/\partial x$ and the domain of $\mathbf{F}$ is $\mathbb{R}^2$. Hence $\mathbf{F}$ is conservative so there exists a function f such that $\nabla f = \mathbf{F}$. Then $f_x(x, y) = ye^x + \sin y$ implies $f(x, y) = ye^x + x \sin y + g(y)$ and $f_y(x, y) = e^x + x \cos y + g'(y)$. But $f_y(x, y) = e^x + x \cos y$ so $g(y) = K$ and $f(x, y) = ye^x + x \sin y + K$ is a potential function for $\mathbf{F}$.

10. $\partial(ye^{xy} + 4x^3 y)/\partial y = e^{xy}(yx + 1) + 4x^3 = \partial(xe^{xy} + x^4)/\partial x$ and the domain of $\mathbf{F}$ is $\mathbb{R}^2$. Thus $\mathbf{F}$ is conservative so there exists a function f such that $\nabla f = \mathbf{F}$. Then $f_x(x, y) = ye^{xy} + 4x^3 y$ implies $f(x, y) = e^{xy} + x^4 y + g(y)$ and $f_y(x, y) = xe^{yx} + x^4 + g'(y)$. But $f_y(x, y) = xe^{xy} + x^4$ so $g(y) = K$ and $f(x, y) = e^{xy} + x^4 y + K$ is a potential function for $\mathbf{F}$.

11. (a) $\mathbf{F}$ has continuous first-order partial derivatives and $\dfrac{\partial}{\partial y} 2xy = 2x = \dfrac{\partial}{\partial x}(x^2)$ on $\mathbb{R}^2$, which is open and simply-connected. Thus, $\mathbf{F}$ is conservative by Theorem 6. Then we know that the line integral of $\mathbf{F}$ is independent of path; in particular, the value of $\int_C \mathbf{F} \cdot d\mathbf{r}$ depends only on the endpoints of C. Since all three curves have the same initial and terminal points, $\int_C \mathbf{F} \cdot d\mathbf{r}$ will have the same value for each curve.

(b) We first find a potential function f, so that $\nabla f = \mathbf{F}$. We know $f_x(x, y) = 2xy$ and $f_y(x, y) = x^2$. Integrating $f_x(x, y)$ with respect to x, we have $f(x, y) = x^2 y + g(y)$. Differentiating both sides with respect to y gives $f_y(x, y) = x^2 + g'(y)$, so we must have $x^2 + g'(y) = x^2 \implies g'(y) = 0 \implies g(y) = K$, a constant. Thus $f(x, y) = x^2 y + K$. All three curves start at $(1, 2)$ and end at $(3, 2)$, so by Theorem 2, $\int_C \mathbf{F} \cdot d\mathbf{r} = f(3, 2) - f(1, 2) = 18 - 2 = 16$ for each curve.

12. (a) $f_x(x, y) = y$ implies $f(x, y) = xy + g(y)$ and $f_y(x, y) = x + g'(y)$. But $f_y(x, y) = x + 2y$ so
$g'(y) = 2y \implies g(y) = y^2 + K$. We can take $K = 0$, so $f(x, y) = xy + y^2$.

(b) $\int_C \mathbf{F} \cdot d\mathbf{r} = f(2, 1) - f(0, 1) = 3 - 1 = 2$.

13. (a) $f_x(x, y) = x^3 y^4$ implies $f(x, y) = \frac{1}{4} x^4 y^4 + g(y)$ and $f_y(x, y) = x^4 y^3 + g'(y)$. But $f_y(x, y) = x^4 y^3$ so
$g'(y) = 0 \implies g(y) = K$, a constant. We can take $K = 0$, so $f(x, y) = \frac{1}{4} x^4 y^4$.

(b) The initial point of C is $\mathbf{r}(0) = (0, 1)$ and the terminal point is $\mathbf{r}(1) = (1, 2)$, so
$\int_C \mathbf{F} \cdot d\mathbf{r} = f(1, 2) - f(0, 1) = 4 - 0 = 4$.

14. (a) $f_x(x, y) = e^{2y}$ implies $f(x, y) = xe^{2y} + g(y)$ and $f_y(x, y) = 2xe^{2y} + g'(y)$. But $f_y(x, y) = 1 + 2xe^{2y}$ so
$g'(y) = 1$ and $g(y) = y$ (setting $K = 0$). Thus $f(x, y) = xe^{2y} + y$.

(b) Since $\mathbf{r}(0) = \langle 0, 1 \rangle$ and $\mathbf{r}(1) = \langle e, 2 \rangle$, $\int_C \mathbf{F} \cdot d\mathbf{r} = f(e, 2) - f(0, 1) = (e)e^4 + 2 - 1 = e^5 + 1$.

15. (a) $f_x(x, y, z) = yz$ implies $f(x, y, z) = xyz + g(y, z)$ and so $f_y(x, y, z) = xz + g_y(y, z)$. But $f_y(x, y, z) = xz$
so $g_y(y, z) = 0 \implies g(y, z) = h(z)$. Thus $f(x, y, z) = xyz + h(z)$ and $f_z(x, y, z) = xy + h'(z)$. But
$f_z(x, y, z) = xy + 2z$, so $h'(z) = 2z \implies h(z) = z^2 + K$. Hence $f(x, y, z) = xyz + z^2$ (taking $K = 0$).

(b) $\int_C \mathbf{F} \cdot d\mathbf{r} = f(4, 6, 3) - f(1, 0, -2) = 81 - 4 = 77$.

16. (a) $f_x(x, y, z) = 2xz + y^2$ implies $f(x, y, z) = x^2 z + xy^2 + g(y, z)$ and so $f_y(x, y, z) = 2xy + g_y(y, z)$. But
$f_y(x, y, z) = 2xy$ so $g_y(y, z) = 0 \implies g(y, z) = h(z)$. Thus $f(x, y, z) = x^2 z + xy^2 + h(z)$ and
$f_z(x, y, z) = x^2 + h'(z)$. But $f_z(x, y, z) = x^2 + 3z^2$, so $h'(z) = 3z^2 \implies h(z) = z^3 + K$. Hence
$f(x, y, z) = x^2 z + xy^2 + z^3$ (taking $K = 0$).

(b) $t = 0$ corresponds to the point $(0, 1, -1)$ and $t = 1$ corresponds to $(1, 2, 1)$, so
$\int_C \mathbf{F} \cdot d\mathbf{r} = f(1, 2, 1) - f(0, 1, -1) = 6 - (-1) = 7$.

17. (a) $f_x(x, y, z) = y^2 \cos z$ implies $f(x, y, z) = xy^2 \cos z + g(y, z)$ and so $f_y(x, y, z) = 2xy \cos z + g_y(y, z)$. But
$f_y(x, y, z) = 2xy \cos z$ so $g_y(y, z) = 0 \implies g(y, z) = h(z)$. Thus $f(x, y, z) = xy^2 \cos z + h(z)$ and
$f_z(x, y, z) = -xy^2 \sin z + h'(z)$. But $f_z(x, y, z) = -xy^2 \sin z$, so $h'(z) = 0 \implies h(z) = K$. Hence
$f(x, y, z) = xy^2 \cos z$ (taking $K = 0$).

(b) $\mathbf{r}(0) = \langle 0, 0, 0 \rangle$, $\mathbf{r}(\pi) = \langle \pi^2, 0, \pi \rangle$ so $\int_C \mathbf{F} \cdot d\mathbf{r} = f(\pi^2, 0, \pi) - f(0, 0, 0) = 0 - 0 = 0$.

18. (a) $f_x(x, y, z) = e^y$ implies $f(x, y, z) = xe^y + g(y, z)$ and so $f_y(x, y, z) = xe^y + g_y(y, z)$. But
$f_y(x, y, z) = xe^y$ so $g_y(y, z) = 0 \implies g(y, z) = h(z)$. Thus $f(x, y, z) = xe^y + h(z)$ and
$f_z(x, y, z) = 0 + h'(z)$. But $f_z(x, y, z) = (z + 1)e^z$, so $h'(z) = (z + 1)e^z \implies h(z) = ze^z + K$ (using
integration by parts). Hence $f(x, y, z) = xe^y + ze^z$ (taking $K = 0$).

(b) $\mathbf{r}(0) = \langle 0, 0, 0 \rangle$, $\mathbf{r}(1) = \langle 1, 1, 1 \rangle$ so $\int_C \mathbf{F} \cdot d\mathbf{r} = f(1, 1, 1) - f(0, 0, 0) = 2e - 0 = 2e$.

19. Here $\mathbf{F}(x, y) = (2x \sin y) \mathbf{i} + (x^2 \cos y - 3y^2) \mathbf{j}$. Then $f(x, y) = x^2 \sin y - y^3$ is a potential function for $\mathbf{F}$, that
is, $\nabla f = \mathbf{F}$ so $\mathbf{F}$ is conservative and thus its line integral is independent of path. Hence
$\int_C 2x \sin y \, dx + (x^2 \cos y - 3y^2) \, dy = \int_C \mathbf{F} \cdot d\mathbf{r} = f(5, 1) - f(-1, 0) = 25 \sin 1 - 1$.

20. Here $\mathbf{F}(x, y) = (2y^2 - 12x^3y^3)\,\mathbf{i} + (4xy - 9x^4y^2)\,\mathbf{j}$. Then $f(x, y) = 2xy^2 - 3x^4y^3$ is a potential function for
$\mathbf{F}$, that is, $\nabla f = \mathbf{F}$. Hence $\mathbf{F}$ is conservative and its line integral is independent of path.
$\int_C (2y^2 - 12x^3y^3)\,dx + (4xy - 9x^4y^2)\,dy = \int_C \mathbf{F} \cdot d\mathbf{r} = f(3, 2) - f(1, 1) = -1920 - (-1) = -1919.$

21. $\mathbf{F}(x, y) = x^2y^3\,\mathbf{i} + x^3y^2\,\mathbf{j}$, $W = \int_C \mathbf{F} \cdot d\mathbf{r}$. Since $\partial(x^2y^3)/\partial y = 3x^2y^2 = \partial(x^3y^2)/\partial x$, there exists a function
f such that $\nabla f = \mathbf{F}$. In fact, $f_x = x^2y^3 \;\Rightarrow\; f(x, y) = \frac{1}{3}x^3y^3 + g(y) \;\Rightarrow\; f_y = x^3y^2 + g'(y) \;\Rightarrow$
$g'(y) = 0$, so we can take $f(x, y) = \frac{1}{3}x^3y^3$. Thus $W = \int_C \mathbf{F} \cdot d\mathbf{r} = f(2, 1) - f(0, 0) = \frac{1}{3}(2^3)(1^3) - 0 = \frac{8}{3}$.

22. $\mathbf{F}(x, y) = \dfrac{y^2}{x^2}\,\mathbf{i} - \dfrac{2y}{x}\,\mathbf{j}$, $W = \int_C \mathbf{F} \cdot d\mathbf{r}$. Since $\dfrac{\partial}{\partial y}\left(\dfrac{y^2}{x^2}\right) = \dfrac{2y}{x^2} = \dfrac{\partial}{\partial x}\left(-\dfrac{2y}{x}\right)$, there exists a function f such that
$\nabla f = \mathbf{F}$. In fact, $f_x = y^2/x^2 \;\Rightarrow\; f(x, y) = -y^2/x + g(y) \;\Rightarrow\; f_y = -2y/x + g'(y) \;\Rightarrow$
$g'(y) = 0$, so we can take $f(x, y) = -y^2/x$ as a potential function for $\mathbf{F}$. Thus
$W = \int_C \mathbf{F} \cdot d\mathbf{r} = f(4, -2) - f(1, 1) = -\left[(-2)^2/4\right] + (1/1) = 0.$

23. We know that if the vector field (call it $\mathbf{F}$) is conservative, then around any closed path C, $\int_C \mathbf{F} \cdot d\mathbf{r} = 0$. But take
C to be some circle centered at the origin, oriented counterclockwise. All of the field vectors along C oppose
motion along C, so the integral around C will be negative. Therefore the field is not conservative.

24.

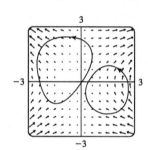

From the graph, it appears that $\mathbf{F}$ is conservative, since around all closed
paths, the number and size of the field vectors pointing in directions
similar to that of the path seem to be roughly the same as the number and
size of the vectors pointing in the opposite direction. To check, we

calculate $\dfrac{\partial}{\partial y}(2xy + \sin y) = 2x + \cos y,$

$\dfrac{\partial}{\partial x}(x^2 + x\cos y) = 2x + \cos y.$ Thus $\mathbf{F}$ is conservative, by Theorem 6.

25.

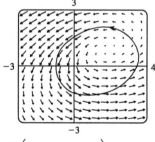

From the graph, it appears that $\mathbf{F}$ is not conservative. For example, any

closed curve containing the point $(2, 1)$ seems to have many field vectors

pointing counterclockwise along it, and none pointing clockwise. So along

this path the integral $\int \mathbf{F} \cdot d\mathbf{r} \neq 0$. To confirm our guess, we calculate

$\dfrac{\partial}{\partial y}\left(\dfrac{x - 2y}{\sqrt{1 + x^2 + y^2}}\right) = (x - 2y)\left[\dfrac{-y}{(1 + x^2 + y^2)^{3/2}}\right] - \dfrac{2}{\sqrt{1 + x^2 + y^2}} = \dfrac{-2 - 2x^2 - xy}{(1 + x^2 + y^2)^{3/2}},$

$\dfrac{\partial}{\partial x}\left(\dfrac{x - 2}{\sqrt{1 + x^2 + y^2}}\right) = (x - 2)\left[\dfrac{-x}{(1 + x^2 + y^2)^{3/2}}\right] + \dfrac{1}{\sqrt{1 + x^2 + y^2}} = \dfrac{1 + y^2 + 2x}{(1 + x^2 + y^2)^{3/2}}.$ These are not

equal, so the field is not conservative, by Theorem 5.

26. $\nabla f(x, y) = \cos(x - 2y)\mathbf{i} - 2\cos(x - 2y)\mathbf{j}$

(a) We use Theorem 2: $\int_{C_1} \mathbf{F} \cdot d\mathbf{r} = \int_{C_1} \nabla f \cdot d\mathbf{r} = f(\mathbf{r}(b)) - f(\mathbf{r}(a))$ where C_1 starts at $t = a$ and ends at $t = b$.
So because $f(0, 0) = \sin 0 = 0$ and $f(\pi, \pi) = \sin(\pi - 2\pi) = 0$, one possible curve C_1 is the straight line from
$(0, 0)$ to (π, π); that is, $\mathbf{r}(t) = \pi t\,\mathbf{i} + \pi t\,\mathbf{j}$, $0 \leq t \leq 1$.

(b) From (a), $\int_{C_2} \mathbf{F} \cdot d\mathbf{r} = f(\mathbf{r}(b)) - f(\mathbf{r}(a))$. So because $f(0,0) = \sin 0 = 0$ and $f\left(\frac{\pi}{2},0\right) = 1$, one possible curve C_2 is $\mathbf{r}(t) = \frac{\pi}{2}t\,\mathbf{i}, 0 \leq t \leq 1$, the straight line from $(0,0)$ to $\left(\frac{\pi}{2},0\right)$.

27. Since $\mathbf{F}$ is conservative, there exists a function f such that $\mathbf{F} = \nabla f$, that is, $P = f_x, Q = f_y$, and $R = f_z$. Since P, Q and R have continuous first order partial derivatives, Clairaut's Theorem says that
$\partial P/\partial y = f_{xy} = f_{yx} = \partial Q/\partial x, \partial P/\partial z = f_{xz} = f_{zx} = \partial R/\partial x$, and $\partial Q/\partial z = f_{yz} = f_{zy} = \partial R/\partial y$.

28. Here $\mathbf{F}(x,y,z) = y\,\mathbf{i} + x\,\mathbf{j} + xyz\,\mathbf{k}$. Then using the notation of Exercise 27, $\partial P/\partial z = 0$ while $\partial R/\partial x = yz$. Since these aren't equal, $\mathbf{F}$ is not conservative. Thus by Theorem 4, the line integral of $\mathbf{F}$ is not independent of path.

29. $D = \{(x,y) \mid x > 0, y > 0\}$ = the first quadrant (excluding the axes).

(a) D is open because around every point in D we can put a disk that lies in D.

(b) D is connected because the straight line segment joining any two points in D lies in D.

(c) D is simply-connected because it's connected and has no holes.

30. $D = \{(x,y) \mid x \neq 0\}$ consists of all points in the xy-plane except for those on the y-axis.

(a) D is open.

(b) Points on opposite sides of the y-axis cannot be joined by a path that lies in D, so D is not connected.

(c) D is not simply-connected because it is not connected.

31. $D = \{(x,y) \mid 1 < x^2 + y^2 < 4\}$ = the annular region between the circles with center $(0,0)$ and radii 1 and 2.

(a) D is open.

(b) D is connected.

(c) D is not simply-connected. For example, $x^2 + y^2 = (1.5)^2$ is simple and closed and lies within D but encloses points that are not in D. (Or we can say, D has a hole, so is not simply-connected.)

32. $D = \{(x,y) \mid x^2 + y^2 \leq 1 \text{ or } 4 \leq x^2 + y^2 \leq 9\}$ = the points on or inside the circle $x^2 + y^2 = 1$, together with the points on or between the circles $x^2 + y^2 = 4$ and $x^2 + y^2 = 9$.

(a) D is not open because, for instance, no disk with center $(0,2)$ lies entirely within D.

(b) D is not connected because, for example, $(0,0)$ and $(0,2.5)$ lie in D but cannot be joined by a path that lies entirely in D.

(c) D is not simply-connected because, for example, $x^2 + y^2 = 9$ is a simple closed curve in D but encloses points that are not in D.

33. (a) $P = -\dfrac{y}{x^2 + y^2}, \dfrac{\partial P}{\partial y} = \dfrac{y^2 - x^2}{(x^2 + y^2)^2}$ and $Q = \dfrac{x}{x^2 + y^2}, \dfrac{\partial Q}{\partial x} = \dfrac{y^2 - x^2}{(x^2 + y^2)^2}$. Thus $\dfrac{\partial P}{\partial y} = \dfrac{\partial Q}{\partial x}$.

(b) $C_1: x = \cos t, y = \sin t, 0 \leq t \leq \pi, C_2: x = \cos t, y = \sin t, t = 2\pi$ to $t = \pi$. Then
$$\int_{C_1} \mathbf{F} \cdot d\mathbf{r} = \int_0^\pi \frac{(-\sin t)(-\sin t) + (\cos t)(\cos t)}{\cos^2 t + \sin^2 t}\,dt = \int_0^\pi dt = \pi \text{ and } \int_{C_2} \mathbf{F} \cdot d\mathbf{r} = \int_{2\pi}^\pi dt = -\pi.$$
Since these aren't equal, the line integral of $\mathbf{F}$ isn't independent of path. (Or notice

that $\int_{C_3} \mathbf{F} \cdot d\mathbf{r} = \int_0^{2\pi} dt = 2\pi$ where C_3 is the circle $x^2 + y^2 = 1$, and apply the contrapositive of Theorem 3.)
This doesn't contradict Theorem 6, since the domain of $\mathbf{F}$, which is $\mathbb{R}^2$ except the origin, isn't
simply-connected.

34. (a) Here $\mathbf{F}(\mathbf{r}) = c\mathbf{r}/|\mathbf{r}|^3$ and $\mathbf{r} = x\,\mathbf{i} + y\,\mathbf{j} + z\,\mathbf{k}$. Then $f(\mathbf{r}) = -c/|\mathbf{r}|$ is a potential function for $\mathbf{F}$, that is,
$\nabla f = \mathbf{F}$. (See the discussion of gradient fields in Section 13.1.) Hence $\mathbf{F}$ is conservative and its line integral is
independent of path.
Let $P_1 = (x_1, y_1, z_1)$ and $P_2 = (x_2, y_2, z_2)$.
$$W = \int_C \mathbf{F} \cdot d\mathbf{r} = f(P_2) - f(P_1) = -\frac{c}{(x_2^2 + y_2^2 + z_2^2)^{1/2}} + \frac{c}{(x_1^2 + y_1^2 + z_1^2)^{1/2}} = c\left(\frac{1}{d_1} - \frac{1}{d_2}\right).$$

(b) In this case, $c = -(mMG) \Rightarrow$
$$W = -mMG\left(\frac{1}{1.52 \times 10^8} - \frac{1}{1.47 \times 10^8}\right)$$
$$= -\left(5.97 \times 10^{24}\right)\left(1.99 \times 10^{30}\right)\left(6.67 \times 10^{-11}\right)\left(-2.2377 \times 10^{-10}\right) \approx 1.77 \times 10^{35} \text{ J}$$

(c) In this case, $c = \epsilon q Q \Rightarrow$
$$W = \epsilon q Q\left(\frac{1}{10^{-12}} - \frac{1}{5 \times 10^{-13}}\right) = \left(8.985 \times 10^{10}\right)(1)\left(-1.6 \times 10^{-19}\right)\left(-10^{12}\right) \approx 1.4 \times 10^4 \text{ J}.$$

13.4 Green's Theorem • • • • • • • • • • • • • •

1. (a)

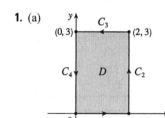

$C_1: x = t \Rightarrow dx = dt, y = 0 \Rightarrow dy = 0\,dt, 0 \le t \le 2.$
$C_2: x = 2 \Rightarrow dx = 0\,dt, y = t \Rightarrow dy = dt, 0 \le t \le 3.$
$C_3: x = 2 - t \Rightarrow dx = -dt, y = 3 \Rightarrow dy = 0\,dt, 0 \le t \le 2$
$C_4: x = 0 \Rightarrow dx = 0\,dt, y = 3 - t \Rightarrow dy = -dt, 0 \le t \le 3.$

Thus $\oint_C xy^2\,dx + x^3\,dy = \oint_{C_1 + C_2 + C_3 + C_4} xy^2\,dx + x^3\,dy$
$$= \int_0^2 0\,dt + \int_0^3 8\,dt + \int_0^2 -9(2 - t)\,dt + \int_0^3 0\,dt$$
$$= 0 + 24 - 18 + 0 = 6$$

(b) $\oint_C xy^2\,dx + x^3\,dy = \iint_D \left[\frac{\partial}{\partial x}\left(x^3\right) - \frac{\partial}{\partial y}\left(xy^2\right)\right]dA = \int_0^2 \int_0^3 \left(3x^2 - 2xy\right)dy\,dx$
$$= \int_0^2 \left(9x^2 - 9x\right)dx = 24 - 18 = 6$$

2. (a) $x = \cos t, y = \sin t, 0 \le t \le 2\pi$. Then
$$\oint_C y\,dx - x\,dy = \int_0^{2\pi} [\sin t\,(-\sin t) - \cos t\,(\cos t)]\,dt = -\int_0^{2\pi} dt = -2\pi.$$

(b) $\oint_C y\,dx - x\,dy = \iint_D \left[\frac{\partial}{\partial x}(-x) - \frac{\partial}{\partial y}(y)\right]dA = -2\iint_D dA = -2A(D) = -2\pi(1)^2 = -2\pi$

3. (a)

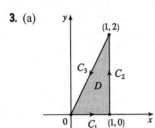

$C_1: x = t \implies dx = dt, y = 0 \implies dy = 0\,dt, 0 \le t \le 1.$

$C_2: x = 1 \implies dx = 0\,dt, y = t \implies dy = dt, 0 \le t \le 2.$

$C_3: x = 1 - t \implies dx = -dt, y = 2 - 2t \implies dy = -2\,dt, 0 \le t \le 1.$

Thus $\oint_C xy\,dx + x^2 y^3\,dy = \oint_{C_1 + C_2 + C_3} xy\,dx + x^2 y^3\,dy$

$$= \int_0^1 0\,dt + \int_0^2 t^3\,dt + \int_0^1 \left[-(1-t)(2-2t) - 2(1-t)^2(2-2t)^3\right] dt$$

$$= 0 + \left[\tfrac{1}{4}t^4\right]_0^2 + \left[\tfrac{2}{3}(1-t)^3 + \tfrac{8}{3}(1-t)^6\right]_0^1 = 4 - \tfrac{10}{3} = \tfrac{2}{3}$$

(b) $\oint_C xy\,dx + x^2 y^3\,dy = \iint_D \left[\frac{\partial}{\partial x}(x^2 y^3) - \frac{\partial}{\partial y}(xy)\right] dA = \int_0^1 \int_0^{2x} (2xy^3 - x)\,dy\,dx$

$$= \int_0^1 \left[\tfrac{1}{2}xy^4 - xy\right]_{y=0}^{y=2x} dx = \int_0^1 (8x^5 - 2x^2)\,dx = \tfrac{4}{3} - \tfrac{2}{3} = \tfrac{2}{3}$$

4. (a)

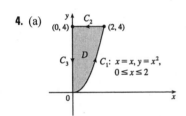

$C_1: x = x, y = x^2,$
$\quad 0 \le x \le 2$

$\oint_C (x^2 + y^2)\,dx + 2xy\,dy = \oint_{C_1 + C_2 + C_3} (x^2 + y^2)\,dx + 2xy\,dy$

$$= \int_0^2 \left[(x^2 + x^4) + (2x^3)(2x)\right] dx$$

$$\quad + \int_2^0 (x^2 + 16)\,dx + \int_4^0 0\,dy$$

$$= \tfrac{8}{3} + 32 - \tfrac{8}{3} - 32 = 0$$

(b) $\oint_C (x^2 + y^2)\,dx + 2xy\,dy = \iint_D \left[\frac{\partial}{\partial x}(2xy) - \frac{\partial}{\partial y}(x^2 + y^2)\right] dA$

$$= \iint_D (2y - 2y)\,dA = \iint_D (0)\,dA = 0$$

5. We can parametrize C as $x = \cos\theta, y = \sin\theta, 0 \le \theta \le 2\pi$. Then the line integral is

$\oint_C P\,dx + Q\,dy = \int_0^{2\pi} \cos^4\theta \sin^5\theta\,(-\sin\theta)\,d\theta + \int_0^{2\pi} (-\cos^7\theta \sin^6\theta)\cos\theta\,d\theta = -\frac{29\pi}{1024}$, according to a CAS.

The double integral is $\iint_D \left(\frac{\partial Q}{\partial x} - \frac{\partial P}{\partial y}\right) dA = \int_{-1}^1 \int_{-\sqrt{1-x^2}}^{\sqrt{1-x^2}} (-7x^6 y^6 - 5x^4 y^4)\,dy\,dx = -\frac{29\pi}{1024}$, verifying

Green's Theorem in this case.

6. Since $y = x^2$ along the first part of C and $y = x$ along the second part, the line integral is

$$\oint_C P\,dx + Q\,dy = \int_0^1 \left[x^4 \sin x + x^2 \sin(x^2)(2x)\right] dx + \int_1^0 (x^2 \sin x + x^2 \sin x)\,dx$$

$$= -16\cos 1 - 23\sin 1 + 28$$

according to a CAS. The double integral is

$$\iint_R \left(\frac{\partial Q}{\partial x} - \frac{\partial P}{\partial y}\right) dA = \int_0^1 \int_{x^2}^x (2x \sin y - 2y \sin x)\,dy\,dx = -16\cos 1 - 23\sin 1 + 28.$$

7. The region D enclosed by C is $[0, 1] \times [0, 1]$, so

$$\int_C e^y\,dx + 2xe^y\,dy = \iint_D \left[\frac{\partial}{\partial x}(2xe^y) - \frac{\partial}{\partial y}(e^y)\right] dA = \int_0^1 \int_0^1 (2e^y - e^y)\,dy\,dx$$

$$= \int_0^1 dx \int_0^1 e^y\,dy = (1)(e^1 - e^0) = e - 1$$

8. The region D enclosed by C is given by $\{(x,y) \mid 0 \le x \le 1, 3x \le y \le 3\}$, so

$$\int_C x^2 y^2\,dx + 4xy^3\,dy = \iint_D \left[\frac{\partial}{\partial x}\left(4xy^3\right) - \frac{\partial}{\partial y}\left(x^2 y^2\right)\right] dA = \int_0^1 \int_{3x}^3 \left(4y^3 - 2x^2 y\right) dy\,dx$$

$$= \int_0^1 \left[y^4 - x^2 y^2\right]_{y=3x}^{y=3}\,dx = \int_0^1 \left(81 - 9x^2 - 72x^4\right) dx = 81 - 3 - \tfrac{72}{5} = \tfrac{318}{5}$$

9. $\int_C \left(y + e^{\sqrt{x}}\right) dx + \left(2x + \cos y^2\right) dy = \iint_D \left[\frac{\partial}{\partial x}\left(2x + \cos y^2\right) - \frac{\partial}{\partial y}\left(y + e^{\sqrt{x}}\right)\right] dA$

$$= \int_0^1 \int_{y^2}^{\sqrt{y}} (2-1)\,dx\,dy = \int_0^1 \left(y^{1/2} - y^2\right) dy = \tfrac{1}{3}$$

10. $\iint_D \left[\frac{\partial}{\partial x}\left(3x + \sin y\right) - \frac{\partial}{\partial y}\left(y^2 - \tan^{-1} x\right)\right] dA = \int_{-2}^2 \int_{x^2}^4 (3 - 2y)\,dy\,dx$

$$= \int_{-2}^2 \left(-4 - 3x^2 + x^4\right) dx = -\tfrac{96}{5}$$

11. $\int_C y^3\,dx - x^3\,dy = \iint_D \left[\frac{\partial}{\partial x}\left(-x^3\right) - \frac{\partial}{\partial y}\left(y^3\right)\right] dA = \iint_D \left(-3x^2 - 3y^2\right) dA = \int_0^{2\pi} \int_0^2 \left(-3r^2\right) r\,dr\,d\theta$

$$= -3 \int_0^{2\pi} d\theta \int_0^2 r^3\,dr = -3\,(2\pi)\,(4) = -24\pi$$

12. $\int_C \sin y\,dx + x \cos y\,dy = \iint_D \left[\frac{\partial}{\partial x}\left(x \cos y\right) - \frac{\partial}{\partial y}\left(\sin y\right)\right] dA = \iint_D \left(\cos y - \cos y\right) dA = \iint_D 0\,dA = 0$

13. The region D enclosed by C is given by $\{(x,y) \mid -2 \le x \le 2, -\sqrt{4 - x^2} \le y \le \sqrt{4 - x^2}\}$ or, in polar coordinates, $\{(r,\theta) \mid 0 \le \theta \le \pi, 0 \le r \le 2\}$. Thus,

$$\int_C xy\,dx + 2x^2\,dy = \iint_D \left[\frac{\partial}{\partial x}\left(2x^2\right) - \frac{\partial}{\partial y}\left(xy\right)\right] dA = \iint_D (4x - x)\,dA = \int_0^\pi \int_0^2 (3r\cos\theta)\,r\,dr\,d\theta$$

$$= 3 \int_0^\pi \cos\theta\,d\theta \int_0^2 r^2\,dr = 3[\sin\theta]_0^\pi \left[\tfrac{1}{3}r^3\right]_0^2 = 3(0)\left(\tfrac{8}{3}\right) = 0$$

14. $\int_C \left(x^3 - y^3\right) dx + \left(x^3 + y^3\right) dy = \iint_{1 \le x^2 + y^2 \le 9} \left[\frac{\partial}{\partial x}\left(x^3 + y^3\right) - \frac{\partial}{\partial y}\left(x^3 - y^3\right)\right] dA$

$$= \iint_{1 \le x^2 + y^2 \le 9} \left(3x^2 + 3y^2\right) dA$$

$$= 3 \int_{-\pi}^\pi \int_1^3 r^3\,dr\,d\theta = 6\pi\left(\tfrac{81}{4} - \tfrac{1}{4}\right) = 120\pi$$

15. The region D enclosed by C is given, in polar coordinates, by $\{(r,\theta) \mid 0 \le \theta \le \tfrac{\pi}{4}, 0 \le r \le 2\}$. Thus

$$\int_C \mathbf{F} \cdot d\mathbf{r} = \int_C \left(y^2 - x^2 y\right) dx + xy^2\,dy = \iint_D \left(y^2 - 2y + x^2\right) dA$$

$$= \int_0^{\pi/4} \int_0^2 \left(r^2 - 2r\sin\theta\right) r\,dr\,d\theta = \int_0^{\pi/4} \left[4 - \tfrac{16}{3}\sin\theta\right] d\theta$$

$$= \left[4\theta + \tfrac{16}{3}\cos\theta\right]_0^{\pi/4} = \pi + \tfrac{8}{3}\left(\sqrt{2} - 2\right)$$

16. $\int_C \mathbf{F} \cdot d\mathbf{r} = \int_C y^6\,dx + xy^5\,dy = \iint_D \left[\frac{\partial}{\partial x}\left(xy^5\right) - \frac{\partial}{\partial y}\left(y^6\right)\right] dA = \iint_D -5y^5\,dA = 0$ since $-5y^5$ is an odd function of y and D is symmetric with respect to the y-axis.

17. By Green's Theorem, $W = \int_C \mathbf{F} \cdot d\mathbf{r} = \int_C x(x + y)\,dx + xy^2\,dy = \iint_D \left(y^2 - x\right) dy\,dx$ where C is the path described in the question and D is the triangle bounded by C. So

$$W = \int_0^1 \int_0^{1-x} \left(y^2 - x\right) dy\,dx = \int_0^1 \left[\tfrac{1}{3}y^3 - xy\right]_{y=0}^{y=1-x}\,dx = \int_0^1 \left(\tfrac{1}{3}(1 - x)^3 - x(1 - x)\right) dx$$

$$= \left[-\tfrac{1}{12}(1 - x)^4 - \tfrac{1}{2}x^2 + \tfrac{1}{3}x^3\right]_0^1 = \left(-\tfrac{1}{2} + \tfrac{1}{3}\right) - \left(-\tfrac{1}{12}\right) = -\tfrac{1}{12}$$

18. By Green's Theorem, $W = \int_C \mathbf{F} \cdot d\mathbf{r} = \int_C x\,dx + \left(x^3 + 3xy^2\right) dy = \iint_D \left(3x^2 + 3y^2 - 0\right) dA$, where D is the semicircular region bounded by C. Converting to polar coordinates, we have

$$W = 3 \int_0^2 \int_0^\pi r^2 \cdot r\,d\theta\,dr = 3\pi\left[\tfrac{1}{4}r^4\right]_0^2 = 12\pi.$$

19. $A = \oint_C x\,dy = \int_0^{2\pi} \left(\cos^3 t\right)\left(3\sin^2 t\cos t\right)dt = 3\int_0^{2\pi}\left(\cos^4 t\sin^2 t\right)dt$

$= 3\left[-\frac{1}{6}\left(\sin t\cos^5 t\right) + \frac{1}{6}\left[\frac{1}{4}\left(\sin t\cos^3 t\right) + \frac{3}{8}\left(\cos t\sin t\right) + \frac{3}{8}t\right]\right]_0^{2\pi} = 3\left(\frac{1}{6}\right)\left(\frac{6}{8}\pi\right) = \frac{3}{8}\pi$

Or: $3\int_0^{2\pi}\left(\cos^4 t\sin^2 t\right)dt = 3\int_0^{2\pi}\frac{1}{8}\left[\frac{1}{2}(1-\cos 4t) + \sin^2 2t\cos 2t\right]dt = \frac{3}{8}\pi$

20. $A = \oint_C x\,dy = \int_0^{2\pi}\left(\cos t\right)\left(3\sin^2 t\cos t\right)dt = 3\int_0^{2\pi}\frac{1}{8}\left(1-\cos 4t\right)dt = \frac{3}{4}\pi$

21. (a) Using Equation 13.2.8, we write parametric equations of the line segment as $x = (1-t)x_1 + tx_2$,
$y = (1-t)y_1 + ty_2, 0 \le t \le 1$. Then $dx = (x_2 - x_1)\,dt$ and $dy = (y_2 - y_1)\,dt$, so

$\int_C x\,dy - y\,dx = \int_0^1 [(1-t)x_1 + tx_2](y_2 - y_1)\,dt + [(1-t)y_1 + ty_2](x_2 - x_1)\,dt$

$= \int_0^1 \left(x_1(y_2 - y_1) - y_1(x_2 - x_1) + t[(y_2 - y_1)(x_2 - x_1) - (x_2 - x_1)(y_2 - y_1)]\right)dt$

$= \int_0^1 (x_1 y_2 - x_2 y_1)\,dt = x_1 y_2 - x_2 y_1$

(b) We apply Green's Theorem to the path $C = C_1 \cup C_2 \cup \cdots \cup C_n$, where C_i is the line segment that joins
(x_i, y_i) to (x_{i+1}, y_{i+1}) for $i = 1, 2, \ldots, n-1$, and C_n is the line segment that joins (x_n, y_n) to (x_1, y_1). From
(5), $\frac{1}{2}\int_C x\,dy - y\,dx = \iint_D dA$, where D is the polygon bounded by C. Therefore

area of polygon $= A(D) = \iint_D dA = \frac{1}{2}\int_C x\,dy - y\,dx$

$= \frac{1}{2}\left(\int_{C_1} x\,dy - y\,dx + \int_{C_2} x\,dy - y\,dx + \cdots + \int_{C_{n-1}} x\,dy - y\,dx + \int_{C_n} x\,dy - y\,dx\right)$

To evaluate these integrals we use the formula from (a) to get

$A(D) = \frac{1}{2}[(x_1 y_2 - x_2 y_1) + (x_2 y_3 - x_3 y_2) + \cdots + (x_{n-1}y_n - x_n y_{n-1}) + (x_n y_1 - x_1 y_n)]$.

(c) $A = \frac{1}{2}[(0\cdot 1 - 2\cdot 0) + (2\cdot 3 - 1\cdot 1) + (1\cdot 2 - 0\cdot 3) + (0\cdot 1 - (-1)\cdot 2) + (-1\cdot 0 - 0\cdot 1)]$
$= \frac{1}{2}(0 + 5 + 2 + 2) = \frac{9}{2}$

22. By Green's Theorem, $\frac{1}{2A}\oint_C x^2\,dy = \frac{1}{2A}\iint_D 2x\,dA = \frac{1}{A}\iint_D x\,dA = \bar{x}$ and
$-\frac{1}{2A}\oint_C y^2\,dx = -\frac{1}{2A}\iint_D(-2y)\,dA = \frac{1}{A}\iint_D y\,dA = \bar{y}$.

23. Here $A = \frac{1}{2}(1)(1) = \frac{1}{2}$ and $C = C_1 + C_2 + C_3$, where $C_1: x = x, y = 0, 0 \le x \le 1$;
$C_2: x = x, y = 1 - x, x = 1$ to $x = 0$; and $C_3: x = 0, y = 1$ to $y = 0$. Then
$\bar{x} = \frac{1}{2A}\int_C x^2\,dy = \int_{C_1} x^2\,dy + \int_{C_2} x^2\,dy + \int_{C_3} x^2\,dy = 0 + \int_1^0 (x^2)(-dx) + 0 = \frac{1}{3}$. Similarly,
$\bar{y} = -\frac{1}{2A}\int_C y^2\,dx = \int_{C_1} y^2\,dx + \int_{C_2} y^2\,dx + \int_{C_3} y^2\,dx = 0 + \int_1^0 (1-x)^2(-dx) + 0 = \frac{1}{3}$.
Therefore $(\bar{x}, \bar{y}) = \left(\frac{1}{3}, \frac{1}{3}\right)$.

24. $A = \frac{\pi a^2}{2}$ so $\bar{x} = \frac{1}{\pi a^2}\oint_C x^2\,dy$ and $\bar{y} = -\frac{1}{\pi a^2}\oint_C y^2\,dx$. Orienting the
semicircular region as in the figure,
$\bar{x} = \frac{1}{\pi a^2}\oint_{C_1 + C_2} x^2\,dy = \frac{1}{\pi a^2}\left[0 + \int_0^\pi (a^2\cos^2 t)(a\cos t)\,dt\right] = 0$
and

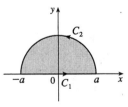

$\bar{y} = -\frac{1}{\pi a^2}\left[\int_{-a}^a 0\,dx + \int_0^\pi (a^2\sin^2 t)(-a\sin t)\,dt\right]$

$= \frac{a}{\pi}\int_0^\pi \sin^3 t\,dt = \frac{a}{\pi}\left[-\cos t + \frac{1}{3}(\cos^3 t)\right]_0^\pi = \frac{4a}{3\pi}$

Thus $(\bar{x}, \bar{y}) = \left(0, \frac{4a}{3\pi}\right)$.

25. By Green's Theorem, $-\frac{1}{3}\rho \oint_C y^3 \, dx = -\frac{1}{3}\rho \iint_D (-3y^2) \, dA = \iint_D y^2 \rho \, dA = I_x$ and
$\frac{1}{3}\rho \oint_C x^3 \, dy = \frac{1}{3}\rho \iint_D (3x^2) \, dA = \iint_D x^2 \rho \, dA = I_y$.

26. By symmetry the moments of inertia about any two diameters are equal. Centering the disk at the origin, the moment of inertia about a diameter equals

$$I_y = \tfrac{1}{3}\rho \oint_C x^3 \, dy = \tfrac{1}{3}\rho \int_0^{2\pi} (a^4 \cos^4 t) \, dt = \tfrac{1}{3}a^4\rho \int_0^{2\pi} \left[\tfrac{3}{8} + \tfrac{1}{2}\cos 2t + \tfrac{1}{8}\cos 4t\right] dt$$

$$= \tfrac{1}{3}a^4\rho \cdot \tfrac{3(2\pi)}{8} = \tfrac{1}{4}\pi a^4\rho$$

27. Since C is a simple closed path which doesn't pass through or enclose the origin, there exists an open region that doesn't contain the origin but does contain D. Thus $P = -y/(x^2 + y^2)$ and $Q = x/(x^2 + y^2)$ have continuous partial derivatives on this open region containing D and we can apply Green's Theorem. But by Exercise 13.3.33(a), $\partial P/\partial y = \partial Q/\partial x$, so $\oint_C \mathbf{F} \cdot d\mathbf{r} = \iint_D 0 \, dA = 0$.

28. We express D as a type II region: $D = \{(x, y) \mid f_1(y) \le x \le f_2(y), c \le y \le d\}$ where f_1 and f_2 are continuous functions. Then $\iint_D \dfrac{\partial Q}{\partial x} \, dA = \int_c^d \int_{f_1(y)}^{f_2(y)} \dfrac{\partial Q}{\partial x} \, dx \, dy = \int_c^d [Q(f_2(y), y) - Q(f_1(y), y)] \, dy$ by

the Fundamental Theorem of Calculus. But referring to the figure,

$\oint_C Q \, dy = \oint_{C_1 + C_2 + C_3 + C_4} Q \, dy$. Then $\int_{C_1} Q \, dy = \int_d^c Q(f_1(y), y) \, dy$,

$\int_{C_2} Q \, dy = \int_{C_4} Q \, dy = 0$, and $\int_{C_3} Q \, dy = \int_c^d Q(f_2(y), y) \, dy$. Hence

$\oint_C Q \, dy = \int_c^d [Q(f_2(y), y) - Q(f_1(y), y)] \, dy = \iint_D (\partial Q/\partial x) \, dA$.

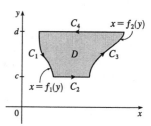

29. Using the first part of (5), we have that $\iint_R dx \, dy = A(R) = \int_{\partial R} x \, dy$. But $x = g(u, v)$, and $dy = \dfrac{\partial h}{\partial u} \, du + \dfrac{\partial h}{\partial v} \, dv$, and we orient ∂S by taking the positive direction to be that which corresponds, under the mapping, to the positive direction along ∂R, so

$$\int_{\partial R} x \, dy = \int_{\partial S} g(u, v) \left(\frac{\partial h}{\partial u} \, du + \frac{\partial h}{\partial v} \, dv\right) = \int_{\partial S} g(u, v) \frac{\partial h}{\partial u} \, du + g(u, v) \frac{\partial h}{\partial v} \, dv$$

$$= \pm \iint_S \left[\frac{\partial}{\partial u}\left(g(u, v) \frac{\partial h}{\partial v}\right) - \frac{\partial}{\partial v}\left(g(u, v) \frac{\partial h}{\partial u}\right)\right] dA \quad \text{(using Green's Theorem in the } uv\text{-plane)}$$

$$= \pm \iint_S \left(\frac{\partial g}{\partial u} \frac{\partial h}{\partial v} + g(u, v) \frac{\partial^2 h}{\partial u \partial v} - \frac{\partial g}{\partial v} \frac{\partial h}{\partial u} - g(u, v) \frac{\partial^2 h}{\partial v \partial u}\right) dA \quad \text{(using the Chain Rule)}$$

$$= \pm \iint_S \left(\frac{\partial x}{\partial u} \frac{\partial y}{\partial v} - \frac{\partial x}{\partial v} \frac{\partial y}{\partial u}\right) dA \text{ (by the equality of mixed partials) } = \pm \iint_S \frac{\partial(x, y)}{\partial(u, v)} \, du \, dv$$

The sign is chosen to be positive if the orientation that we gave to ∂S corresponds to the usual positive orientation, and it is negative otherwise. In either case, since $A(R)$ is positive, the sign chosen must be the same as the sign of $\dfrac{\partial(x, y)}{\partial(u, v)}$. Therefore $A(R) = \iint_R dx \, dy = \iint_S \left|\dfrac{\partial(x, y)}{\partial(u, v)}\right| du \, dv$.

◀13.5▶ Curl and Divergence • • • • • • • • • • • •

1. (a) curl $\mathbf{F} = \nabla \times \mathbf{F} = \begin{vmatrix} \mathbf{i} & \mathbf{j} & \mathbf{k} \\ \partial/\partial x & \partial/\partial y & \partial/\partial z \\ xy & yz & zx \end{vmatrix}$

$= \left[\dfrac{\partial}{\partial y}(zx) - \dfrac{\partial}{\partial z}(yz) \right] \mathbf{i} - \left[\dfrac{\partial}{\partial x}(zx) - \dfrac{\partial}{\partial z}(xy) \right] \mathbf{j} + \left[\dfrac{\partial}{\partial x}(yz) - \dfrac{\partial}{\partial y}(xy) \right] \mathbf{k}$

$= (0 - y)\mathbf{i} - (z - 0)\mathbf{j} + (0 - x)\mathbf{k} = -y\mathbf{i} - z\mathbf{j} - x\mathbf{k}$

(b) div $\mathbf{F} = \nabla \cdot \mathbf{F} = \dfrac{\partial}{\partial x}(xy) + \dfrac{\partial}{\partial y}(yz) + \dfrac{\partial}{\partial z}(zx) = y + z + x = x + y + z$

2. (a) curl $\mathbf{F} = \nabla \times \mathbf{F} = \begin{vmatrix} \mathbf{i} & \mathbf{j} & \mathbf{k} \\ \partial/\partial x & \partial/\partial y & \partial/\partial z \\ x - 2z & x + y + z & x - 2y \end{vmatrix} = (-2 - 1)\mathbf{i} - (1 + 2)\mathbf{j} + (1 - 0)\mathbf{k} = -3\mathbf{i} - 3\mathbf{j} + \mathbf{k}$

(b) div $\mathbf{F} = \nabla \cdot \mathbf{F} = \dfrac{\partial}{\partial x}(x - 2z) + \dfrac{\partial}{\partial y}(x + y + z) + \dfrac{\partial}{\partial z}(x - 2y) = 1 + 1 + 0 = 2$

3. (a) curl $\mathbf{F} = \nabla \times \mathbf{F} = \begin{vmatrix} \mathbf{i} & \mathbf{j} & \mathbf{k} \\ \partial/\partial x & \partial/\partial y & \partial/\partial z \\ xyz & 0 & -x^2 y \end{vmatrix} = (-x^2 - 0)\mathbf{i} - (-2xy - xy)\mathbf{j} + (0 - xz)\mathbf{k}$

$= -x^2\mathbf{i} + 3xy\mathbf{j} - xz\mathbf{k}$

(b) div $\mathbf{F} = \nabla \cdot \mathbf{F} = \dfrac{\partial}{\partial x}(xyz) + \dfrac{\partial}{\partial y}(0) + \dfrac{\partial}{\partial z}(-x^2 y) = yz + 0 + 0 = yz$

4. (a) curl $\mathbf{F} = \nabla \times \mathbf{F} = \begin{vmatrix} \mathbf{i} & \mathbf{j} & \mathbf{k} \\ \partial/\partial x & \partial/\partial y & \partial/\partial z \\ 0 & xe^y & ye^z \end{vmatrix} = (e^z - 0)\mathbf{i} - (0 - 0)\mathbf{j} + (e^y - 0)\mathbf{k} = e^z\mathbf{i} + e^y\mathbf{k}$

(b) div $\mathbf{F} = \nabla \cdot \mathbf{F} = \dfrac{\partial}{\partial x}(0) + \dfrac{\partial}{\partial y}(xe^y) + \dfrac{\partial}{\partial z}(ye^z) = xe^y + ye^z$

5. (a) curl $\mathbf{F} = \nabla \times \mathbf{F} = \begin{vmatrix} \mathbf{i} & \mathbf{j} & \mathbf{k} \\ \partial/\partial x & \partial/\partial y & \partial/\partial z \\ e^x \sin y & e^x \cos y & z \end{vmatrix} = (0 - 0)\mathbf{i} - (0 - 0)\mathbf{j} + (e^x \cos y - e^x \cos y)\mathbf{k} = \mathbf{0}$

(b) div $\mathbf{F} = \nabla \cdot \mathbf{F} = \dfrac{\partial}{\partial x}(e^x \sin y) + \dfrac{\partial}{\partial y}(e^x \cos y) + \dfrac{\partial}{\partial z}(z) = e^x \sin y - e^x \sin y + 1 = 1$

6. (a) curl $\mathbf{F} = \nabla \times \mathbf{F} = \begin{vmatrix} \mathbf{i} & \mathbf{j} & \mathbf{k} \\ \partial/\partial x & \partial/\partial y & \partial/\partial z \\ \dfrac{x}{x^2 + y^2 + z^2} & \dfrac{y}{x^2 + y^2 + z^2} & \dfrac{z}{x^2 + y^2 + z^2} \end{vmatrix}$

$= \dfrac{1}{(x^2 + y^2 + z^2)^2}\left[(-2yz + 2yz)\mathbf{i} - (-2xz + 2xz)\mathbf{j} + (-2xy + 2xy)\mathbf{k} \right] = \mathbf{0}$

(b) div $\mathbf{F} = \nabla \cdot \mathbf{F} = \dfrac{\partial}{\partial x}\left(\dfrac{x}{x^2+y^2+z^2}\right) + \dfrac{\partial}{\partial y}\left(\dfrac{y}{x^2+y^2+z^2}\right) + \dfrac{\partial}{\partial z}\left(\dfrac{z}{x^2+y^2+z^2}\right)$

$= \dfrac{x^2+y^2+z^2-2x^2}{(x^2+y^2+z^2)^2} + \dfrac{x^2+y^2+z^2-2y^2}{(x^2+y^2+z^2)^2} + \dfrac{x^2+y^2+z^2-2z^2}{(x^2+y^2+z^2)^2}$

$= \dfrac{x^2+y^2+z^2}{(x^2+y^2+z^2)^2} = \dfrac{1}{x^2+y^2+z^2}$

7. If the vector field is $\mathbf{F} = P\,\mathbf{i} + Q\,\mathbf{j} + R\,\mathbf{k}$, then we know $R = 0$. In addition, the x-component of each vector of $\mathbf{F}$

is 0, so $P = 0$, hence $\dfrac{\partial P}{\partial x} = \dfrac{\partial P}{\partial y} = \dfrac{\partial P}{\partial z} = \dfrac{\partial R}{\partial x} = \dfrac{\partial R}{\partial y} = \dfrac{\partial R}{\partial z} = 0$. Q decreases as y increases, so $\dfrac{\partial Q}{\partial y} < 0$, but

Q doesn't change in the x- or z-directions, so $\dfrac{\partial Q}{\partial x} = \dfrac{\partial Q}{\partial z} = 0$.

(a) div $\mathbf{F} = \dfrac{\partial P}{\partial x} + \dfrac{\partial Q}{\partial y} + \dfrac{\partial R}{\partial z} = 0 + \dfrac{\partial Q}{\partial y} + 0 < 0$

(b) curl $\mathbf{F} = \left(\dfrac{\partial R}{\partial y} - \dfrac{\partial Q}{\partial z}\right)\mathbf{i} + \left(\dfrac{\partial P}{\partial z} - \dfrac{\partial R}{\partial x}\right)\mathbf{j} + \left(\dfrac{\partial Q}{\partial x} - \dfrac{\partial P}{\partial y}\right)\mathbf{k} = (0-0)\,\mathbf{i} + (0-0)\,\mathbf{j} + (0-0)\,\mathbf{k} = \mathbf{0}$

8. If the vector field is $\mathbf{F} = P\,\mathbf{i} + Q\,\mathbf{j} + R\,\mathbf{k}$, then we know $R = 0$. In addition, P and Q don't vary in the z-direction,

so $\dfrac{\partial R}{\partial x} = \dfrac{\partial R}{\partial y} = \dfrac{\partial R}{\partial z} = \dfrac{\partial P}{\partial z} = \dfrac{\partial Q}{\partial z} = 0$. As x increases, the x-component of each vector of $\mathbf{F}$ increases while the

y-component remains constant, so $\dfrac{\partial P}{\partial x} > 0$ and $\dfrac{\partial Q}{\partial x} = 0$. Similarly, as y increases, the y-component of each vector

increases while the x-component remains constant, so $\dfrac{\partial Q}{\partial y} > 0$ and $\dfrac{\partial P}{\partial y} = 0$.

(a) div $\mathbf{F} = \dfrac{\partial P}{\partial x} + \dfrac{\partial Q}{\partial y} + \dfrac{\partial R}{\partial z} = \dfrac{\partial P}{\partial x} + \dfrac{\partial Q}{\partial y} + 0 > 0$

(b) curl $\mathbf{F} = \left(\dfrac{\partial R}{\partial y} - \dfrac{\partial Q}{\partial z}\right)\mathbf{i} + \left(\dfrac{\partial P}{\partial z} - \dfrac{\partial R}{\partial x}\right)\mathbf{j} + \left(\dfrac{\partial Q}{\partial x} - \dfrac{\partial P}{\partial y}\right)\mathbf{k}$

$= (0-0)\,\mathbf{i} + (0-0)\,\mathbf{j} + (0-0)\,\mathbf{k} = \mathbf{0}$

9. If the vector field is $\mathbf{F} = P\,\mathbf{i} + Q\,\mathbf{j} + R\,\mathbf{k}$, then we know $R = 0$. In addition, the y-component of each vector of $\mathbf{F}$

is 0, so $Q = 0$, hence $\dfrac{\partial Q}{\partial x} = \dfrac{\partial Q}{\partial y} = \dfrac{\partial Q}{\partial z} = \dfrac{\partial R}{\partial x} = \dfrac{\partial R}{\partial y} = \dfrac{\partial R}{\partial z} = 0$. P increases as y increases, so $\dfrac{\partial P}{\partial y} > 0$, but P

doesn't change in the x- or z-directions, so $\dfrac{\partial P}{\partial x} = \dfrac{\partial P}{\partial z} = 0$.

(a) div $\mathbf{F} = \dfrac{\partial P}{\partial x} + \dfrac{\partial Q}{\partial y} + \dfrac{\partial R}{\partial z} = 0 + 0 + 0 = 0$

(b) curl $\mathbf{F} = \left(\dfrac{\partial R}{\partial y} - \dfrac{\partial Q}{\partial z}\right)\mathbf{i} + \left(\dfrac{\partial P}{\partial z} - \dfrac{\partial R}{\partial x}\right)\mathbf{j} + \left(\dfrac{\partial Q}{\partial x} - \dfrac{\partial P}{\partial y}\right)\mathbf{k}$

$= (0-0)\,\mathbf{i} + (0-0)\,\mathbf{j} + \left(0 - \dfrac{\partial P}{\partial y}\right)\mathbf{k} = -\dfrac{\partial P}{\partial y}\mathbf{k}$

Since $\dfrac{\partial P}{\partial y} > 0$, $-\dfrac{\partial P}{\partial y}\mathbf{k}$ is a vector pointing in the negative z-direction.

10. (a) curl $f = \nabla \times f$ is meaningless because f is a scalar field.

(b) grad f is a vector field.

(c) div $\mathbf{F}$ is a scalar field.

(d) curl (grad f) is a vector field.

(e) grad $\mathbf{F}$ is meaningless because $\mathbf{F}$ is not a scalar field.

(f) grad (div $\mathbf{F}$) is a vector field.

(g) div(grad f) is a scalar field.

(h) grad (div f) is meaningless because f is a scalar field.

(i) curl (curl $\mathbf{F}$) is a vector field.

(j) div(div $\mathbf{F}$) is meaningless because div $\mathbf{F}$ is a scalar field.

(k) (grad f) × (div $\mathbf{F}$) is meaningless because div $\mathbf{F}$ is a scalar field.

(l) div(curl (grad f)) is a scalar field.

11. curl $\mathbf{F} = \nabla \times \mathbf{F} = \begin{vmatrix} \mathbf{i} & \mathbf{j} & \mathbf{k} \\ \partial/\partial x & \partial/\partial y & \partial/\partial z \\ yz & xz & xy \end{vmatrix} = (x - x)\,\mathbf{i} - (y - y)\,\mathbf{j} + (z - z)\,\mathbf{k} = \mathbf{0}$ and $\mathbf{F}$ is defined on all of $\mathbb{R}^3$

with component functions which have continuous partial derivatives, so by Theorem 4, $\mathbf{F}$ is conservative. Thus, there exists a function f such that $\mathbf{F} = \nabla f$. Then $f_x(x, y, z) = yz$ implies $f(x, y, z) = xyz + g(y, z)$ and $f_y(x, y, z) = xz + g_y(y, z)$. But $f_y(x, y, z) = xz$, so $g(y, z) = h(z)$ and $f(x, y, z) = xyz + h(z)$. Thus $f_z(x, y, z) = xy + h'(z)$ but $f_z(x, y, z) = xy$ so $h(z) = K$, a constant. Hence a potential function for $\mathbf{F}$ is $f(x, y, z) = xyz + K$.

12. curl $\mathbf{F} = \nabla \times \mathbf{F} = \begin{vmatrix} \mathbf{i} & \mathbf{j} & \mathbf{k} \\ \partial/\partial x & \partial/\partial y & \partial/\partial z \\ x & y & z \end{vmatrix} = (0 - 0)\,\mathbf{i} - (0 - 0)\,\mathbf{j} + (0 - 0)\,\mathbf{k} = \mathbf{0}$, $\mathbf{F}$ is defined on all of $\mathbb{R}^3$, and

the partial derivatives of the component functions are continuous, so $\mathbf{F}$ is conservative. Thus there exists a function f such that $\nabla f = \mathbf{F}$. Then $f_x(x, y, z) = x$ implies $f(x, y, z) = \frac{1}{2}x^2 + g(y, z)$ and $f_y(x, y, z) = g_y(y, z)$. But $f_y(x, y, z) = y$, so $g(y, z) = \frac{1}{2}y^2 + h(z)$ and $f(x, y, z) = \frac{1}{2}x^2 + \frac{1}{2}y^2 + h(z)$. Thus $f_z(x, y, z) = h'(z)$ but $f_z(x, y, z) = z$ so $h(z) = \frac{1}{2}z^2 + K$ and $f(x, y, z) = \frac{1}{2}x^2 + \frac{1}{2}y^2 + \frac{1}{2}z^2 + K$.

13. curl $\mathbf{F} = \nabla \times \mathbf{F} = \begin{vmatrix} \mathbf{i} & \mathbf{j} & \mathbf{k} \\ \partial/\partial x & \partial/\partial y & \partial/\partial z \\ 2xy & x^2 + 2yz & y^2 \end{vmatrix} = (2y - 2y)\,\mathbf{i} - (0 - 0)\,\mathbf{j} + (2x - 2x)\,\mathbf{k} = \mathbf{0}$, $\mathbf{F}$ is defined on all

of $\mathbb{R}^3$, and the partial derivatives of the component functions are continuous, so $\mathbf{F}$ is conservative. Thus there exists a function f such that $\nabla f = \mathbf{F}$. Then $f_x(x, y, z) = 2xy$ implies $f(x, y, z) = x^2y + g(y, z)$ and $f_y(x, y, z) = x^2 + g_y(y, z)$. But $f_y(x, y, z) = x^2 + 2yz$, so $g(y, z) = y^2z + h(z)$ and $f(x, y, z) = x^2y + y^2z + h(z)$. Thus $f_z(x, y, z) = y^2 + h'(z)$ but $f_z(x, y, z) = y^2$ so $h(z) = K$ and $f(x, y, z) = x^2y + y^2z + K$.

14. curl $\mathbf{F} = \nabla \times \mathbf{F} = \begin{vmatrix} \mathbf{i} & \mathbf{j} & \mathbf{k} \\ \partial/\partial x & \partial/\partial y & \partial/\partial z \\ xy^2z^3 & 2x^2yz^3 & 3x^2y^2z^2 \end{vmatrix}$

$= (6x^2yz^2 - 6x^2yz^2)\,\mathbf{i} - (6xy^2z^2 - 3xy^2z^2)\,\mathbf{j} + (4xyz^3 - 2xyz^3)\,\mathbf{k} \neq \mathbf{0}$,

so $\mathbf{F}$ isn't conservative.

15. $\operatorname{curl} \mathbf{F} = \nabla \times \mathbf{F} = \begin{vmatrix} \mathbf{i} & \mathbf{j} & \mathbf{k} \\ \partial/\partial x & \partial/\partial y & \partial/\partial z \\ e^x & e^z & e^y \end{vmatrix} = (e^y - e^z)\,\mathbf{i} - (0 - 0)\,\mathbf{j} + (0 - 0)\,\mathbf{k} \neq \mathbf{0}$, so $\mathbf{F}$ isn't conservative.

16. $\operatorname{curl} \mathbf{F} = \nabla \times \mathbf{F} = \begin{vmatrix} \mathbf{i} & \mathbf{j} & \mathbf{k} \\ \partial/\partial x & \partial/\partial y & \partial/\partial z \\ yze^{xz} & e^{xz} & xye^{xz} \end{vmatrix}$

$\qquad = (xe^{xz} - xe^{xz})\,\mathbf{i} - [(xyze^{xz} + ye^{xz}) - (xyze^{xz} + ye^{xz})]\,\mathbf{j} + (ze^{xz} - ze^{xz})\,\mathbf{k} = \mathbf{0}$,

$\mathbf{F}$ is defined on all of $\mathbb{R}^3$, and the partial derivatives of the component functions are continuous, so $\mathbf{F}$ is conservative. Thus there exists a function f such that $\nabla f = \mathbf{F}$. Then $f_x(x, y, z) = yze^{xz}$ implies $f(x, y, z) = ye^{xz} + g(y, z)$ and $f_y(x, y, z) = e^{xz} + g_y(y, z)$. But $f_y(x, y, z) = e^{xz}$, so $g(y, z) = h(z)$ and $f(x, y, z) = ye^{xz} + h(z)$. Thus $f_z(x, y, z) = xye^{xz} + h'(z)$ but $f_z(x, y, z) = xye^{xz}$ so $h(z) = K$ and $f(x, y, z) = ye^{xz} + K$.

17. No. Assume there is such a $\mathbf{G}$. Then $\operatorname{div}(\operatorname{curl} \mathbf{G}) = y^2 + z^2 + x^2 \neq 0$, which contradicts Theorem 11.

18. No. Assume there is such a $\mathbf{G}$. Then $\operatorname{div}(\operatorname{curl} \mathbf{G}) = xz \neq 0$ which contradicts Theorem 11.

19. $\operatorname{curl} \mathbf{F} = \begin{vmatrix} \mathbf{i} & \mathbf{j} & \mathbf{k} \\ \partial/\partial x & \partial/\partial y & \partial/\partial z \\ f(x) & g(y) & h(z) \end{vmatrix} = (0 - 0)\,\mathbf{i} + (0 - 0)\,\mathbf{j} + (0 - 0)\,\mathbf{k} = \mathbf{0}$.

Hence $\mathbf{F} = f(x)\,\mathbf{i} + g(y)\,\mathbf{j} + h(z)\,\mathbf{k}$ is irrotational.

20. $\operatorname{div} \mathbf{F} = \dfrac{\partial(f(y, z))}{\partial x} + \dfrac{\partial(g(x, z))}{\partial y} + \dfrac{\partial(h(x, y))}{\partial z} = 0$ so $\mathbf{F}$ is incompressible.

For Exercises 21–27, let $\mathbf{F}(x, y, z) = P_1\,\mathbf{i} + Q_1\,\mathbf{j} + R_1\,\mathbf{k}$ and $\mathbf{G}(x, y, z) = P_2\,\mathbf{i} + Q_2\,\mathbf{j} + R_2\,\mathbf{k}$.

21. $\operatorname{div}(\mathbf{F} + \mathbf{G}) = \dfrac{\partial(P_1 + P_2)}{\partial x} + \dfrac{\partial(Q_1 + Q_2)}{\partial y} + \dfrac{\partial(R_1 + R_2)}{\partial z}$

$\qquad = \left(\dfrac{\partial P_1}{\partial x} + \dfrac{\partial Q_1}{\partial y} + \dfrac{\partial R_1}{\partial z} \right) + \left(\dfrac{\partial P_2}{\partial x} + \dfrac{\partial Q_2}{\partial y} + \dfrac{\partial R_3}{\partial z} \right) = \operatorname{div} \mathbf{F} + \operatorname{div} \mathbf{G}$

22. $\operatorname{curl} \mathbf{F} + \operatorname{curl} \mathbf{G} = \left[\left(\dfrac{\partial R_1}{\partial y} - \dfrac{\partial Q_1}{\partial z} \right)\mathbf{i} + \left(\dfrac{\partial P_1}{\partial z} - \dfrac{\partial R_1}{\partial x} \right)\mathbf{j} + \left(\dfrac{\partial Q_1}{\partial x} - \dfrac{\partial P_1}{\partial y} \right)\mathbf{k} \right]$

$\qquad + \left[\left(\dfrac{\partial R_2}{\partial y} - \dfrac{\partial Q_2}{\partial z} \right)\mathbf{i} + \left(\dfrac{\partial P_2}{\partial z} - \dfrac{\partial R_2}{\partial x} \right)\mathbf{j} + \left(\dfrac{\partial Q_2}{\partial x} - \dfrac{\partial P_2}{\partial y} \right)\mathbf{k} \right]$

$\qquad = \left[\dfrac{\partial(R_1 + R_2)}{\partial y} - \dfrac{\partial(Q_1 + Q_2)}{\partial z} \right]\mathbf{i} + \left[\dfrac{\partial(P_1 + P_2)}{\partial z} - \dfrac{\partial(R_1 + R_2)}{\partial x} \right]\mathbf{j}$

$\qquad + \left[\dfrac{\partial(Q_1 + Q_2)}{\partial x} - \dfrac{\partial(P_1 + P_2)}{\partial y} \right]\mathbf{k} = \operatorname{curl}(\mathbf{F} + \mathbf{G})$

23. $\text{div}\,(f\mathbf{F}) = \dfrac{\partial(fP_1)}{\partial x} + \dfrac{\partial(fQ_1)}{\partial y} + \dfrac{\partial(fR_1)}{\partial z}$

$\qquad = \left(f\dfrac{\partial P_1}{\partial x} + P_1\dfrac{\partial f}{\partial x} \right) + \left(f\dfrac{\partial Q_1}{\partial y} + Q_1\dfrac{\partial f}{\partial y} \right) + \left(f\dfrac{\partial R_1}{\partial z} + R_1\dfrac{\partial f}{\partial z} \right)$

$\qquad = f\left(\dfrac{\partial P_1}{\partial x} + \dfrac{\partial Q_1}{\partial y} + \dfrac{\partial R_1}{\partial z} \right) + \langle P_1, Q_1, R_1 \rangle \cdot \left\langle \dfrac{\partial f}{\partial x}, \dfrac{\partial f}{\partial y}, \dfrac{\partial f}{\partial z} \right\rangle = f\,\text{div}\,\mathbf{F} + \mathbf{F} \cdot \nabla f$

24. $\text{curl}\,(f\mathbf{F}) = \left[\dfrac{\partial(fR_1)}{\partial y} - \dfrac{\partial(fQ_1)}{\partial z} \right]\mathbf{i} + \left[\dfrac{\partial(fP_1)}{\partial z} - \dfrac{\partial(fR_1)}{\partial x} \right]\mathbf{j} + \left[\dfrac{\partial(fQ_1)}{\partial x} - \dfrac{\partial(fP_1)}{\partial y} \right]\mathbf{k}$

$\qquad = \left[f\dfrac{\partial R_1}{\partial y} + R_1\dfrac{\partial f}{\partial y} - f\dfrac{\partial Q_1}{\partial z} - Q_1\dfrac{\partial f}{\partial z} \right]\mathbf{i} + \left[f\dfrac{\partial P_1}{\partial z} + P_1\dfrac{\partial f}{\partial z} - f\dfrac{\partial R_1}{\partial x} - R_1\dfrac{\partial f}{\partial x} \right]\mathbf{j}$

$\qquad\qquad + \left[f\dfrac{\partial Q_1}{\partial x} + Q_1\dfrac{\partial f}{\partial x} - f\dfrac{\partial P_1}{\partial y} - P_1\dfrac{\partial f}{\partial y} \right]\mathbf{k}$

$\qquad = f\left[\dfrac{\partial R_1}{\partial y} - \dfrac{\partial Q_1}{\partial z} \right]\mathbf{i} + f\left[\dfrac{\partial P_1}{\partial z} - \dfrac{\partial R_1}{\partial x} \right]\mathbf{j} + f\left[\dfrac{\partial Q_1}{\partial x} - \dfrac{\partial P_1}{\partial y} \right]\mathbf{k}$

$\qquad\qquad + \left[R_1\dfrac{\partial f}{\partial y} - Q_1\dfrac{\partial f}{\partial z} \right]\mathbf{i} + \left[P_1\dfrac{\partial f}{\partial z} - R_1\dfrac{\partial f}{\partial x} \right]\mathbf{j} + \left[Q_1\dfrac{\partial f}{\partial x} - P_1\dfrac{\partial f}{\partial y} \right]\mathbf{k}$

$\qquad = f\,\text{curl}\,\mathbf{F} + (\nabla f) \times \mathbf{F}$

25. $\text{div}(\mathbf{F} \times \mathbf{G}) = \nabla \cdot (\mathbf{F} \times \mathbf{G}) = \begin{vmatrix} \partial/\partial x & \partial/\partial y & \partial/\partial z \\ P_1 & Q_1 & R_1 \\ P_2 & Q_2 & R_2 \end{vmatrix} = \dfrac{\partial}{\partial x}\begin{vmatrix} Q_1 & R_1 \\ Q_2 & R_2 \end{vmatrix} - \dfrac{\partial}{\partial y}\begin{vmatrix} P_1 & R_1 \\ P_2 & R_2 \end{vmatrix} + \dfrac{\partial}{\partial z}\begin{vmatrix} P_1 & Q_1 \\ P_2 & Q_2 \end{vmatrix}$

$\qquad = \left[Q_1\dfrac{\partial R_2}{\partial x} + R_2\dfrac{\partial Q_1}{\partial x} - Q_2\dfrac{\partial R_1}{\partial x} - R_1\dfrac{\partial Q_2}{\partial x} \right]$

$\qquad\qquad - \left[P_1\dfrac{\partial R_2}{\partial y} + R_2\dfrac{\partial P_1}{\partial y} - P_2\dfrac{\partial R_1}{\partial y} - R_1\dfrac{\partial P_2}{\partial y} \right]$

$\qquad\qquad + \left[P_1\dfrac{\partial Q_2}{\partial z} + Q_2\dfrac{\partial P_1}{\partial z} - P_2\dfrac{\partial Q_1}{\partial z} - Q_1\dfrac{\partial P_2}{\partial z} \right]$

$\qquad = \left[P_2\left(\dfrac{\partial R_1}{\partial y} - \dfrac{\partial Q_1}{\partial z} \right) + Q_2\left(\dfrac{\partial P_1}{\partial z} - \dfrac{\partial R_1}{\partial x} \right) + R_2\left(\dfrac{\partial Q_1}{\partial x} - \dfrac{\partial P_1}{\partial y} \right) \right]$

$\qquad\qquad - \left[P_1\left(\dfrac{\partial R_2}{\partial y} - \dfrac{\partial Q_2}{\partial z} \right) + Q_1\left(\dfrac{\partial P_2}{\partial z} - \dfrac{\partial R_2}{\partial x} \right) + R_1\left(\dfrac{\partial Q_2}{\partial x} - \dfrac{\partial P_2}{\partial y} \right) \right]$

$\qquad = \mathbf{G} \cdot \text{curl}\,\mathbf{F} - \mathbf{F} \cdot \text{curl}\,\mathbf{G}$

26. $\text{div}(\nabla f \times \nabla g) = \nabla g \cdot \text{curl}\,(\nabla f) - \nabla f \cdot \text{curl}\,(\nabla g)$ (by Exercise 25) $= 0$ (by Theorem 3)

27. $\operatorname{curl}\operatorname{curl}\mathbf{F} = \nabla \times (\nabla \times \mathbf{F}) = \begin{vmatrix} \mathbf{i} & \mathbf{j} & \mathbf{k} \\ \partial/\partial x & \partial/\partial y & \partial/\partial z \\ \partial R_1/\partial y - \partial Q_1/\partial z & \partial P_1/\partial z - \partial R_1/\partial x & \partial Q_1/\partial x - \partial P_1/\partial y \end{vmatrix}$

$$= \left(\frac{\partial^2 Q_1}{\partial y \partial x} - \frac{\partial^2 P_1}{\partial y^2} - \frac{\partial^2 P_1}{\partial z^2} + \frac{\partial^2 R_1}{\partial z \partial x} \right) \mathbf{i} + \left(\frac{\partial^2 R_1}{\partial z \partial y} - \frac{\partial^2 Q_1}{\partial z^2} - \frac{\partial^2 Q_1}{\partial x^2} + \frac{\partial^2 P_1}{\partial x \partial y} \right) \mathbf{j}$$

$$+ \left(\frac{\partial^2 P_1}{\partial x \partial z} - \frac{\partial^2 R_1}{\partial x^2} - \frac{\partial^2 R_1}{\partial y^2} + \frac{\partial^2 Q_1}{\partial y \partial z} \right) \mathbf{k}$$

Now let's consider grad div $\mathbf{F} - \nabla^2 \mathbf{F}$ and compare with the above.
(Note that $\nabla^2 \mathbf{F}$ is defined on page 956.)

$$\operatorname{grad}\operatorname{div}\mathbf{F} - \nabla^2 \mathbf{F} = \left[\left(\frac{\partial^2 P_1}{\partial x^2} + \frac{\partial^2 Q_1}{\partial x \partial y} + \frac{\partial^2 R_1}{\partial x \partial z} \right) \mathbf{i} + \left(\frac{\partial^2 P_1}{\partial y \partial x} + \frac{\partial^2 Q_1}{\partial y^2} + \frac{\partial^2 R_1}{\partial y \partial z} \right) \mathbf{j} \right.$$

$$\left. + \left(\frac{\partial^2 P_1}{\partial z \partial x} + \frac{\partial^2 Q_1}{\partial z \partial y} + \frac{\partial^2 R_1}{\partial z^2} \right) \mathbf{k} \right]$$

$$- \left[\left(\frac{\partial^2 P_1}{\partial x^2} + \frac{\partial^2 P_1}{\partial y^2} + \frac{\partial^2 P_1}{\partial z^2} \right) \mathbf{i} + \left(\frac{\partial^2 Q_1}{\partial x^2} + \frac{\partial^2 Q_1}{\partial y^2} + \frac{\partial^2 Q_1}{\partial z^2} \right) \mathbf{j} \right.$$

$$\left. + \left(\frac{\partial^2 R_1}{\partial x^2} + \frac{\partial^2 R_1}{\partial y^2} + \frac{\partial^2 R_1}{\partial z^2} \right) \mathbf{k} \right]$$

$$= \left(\frac{\partial^2 Q_1}{\partial x \partial y} + \frac{\partial^2 R_1}{\partial x \partial z} - \frac{\partial^2 P_1}{\partial y^2} - \frac{\partial^2 P_1}{\partial z^2} \right) \mathbf{i} + \left(\frac{\partial^2 P_1}{\partial y \partial x} + \frac{\partial^2 R_1}{\partial y \partial z} - \frac{\partial^2 Q_1}{\partial x^2} - \frac{\partial^2 Q_1}{\partial z^2} \right) \mathbf{j}$$

$$+ \left(\frac{\partial^2 P_1}{\partial z \partial x} + \frac{\partial^2 Q_1}{\partial z \partial y} - \frac{\partial^2 R_1}{\partial x^2} - \frac{\partial^2 R_2}{\partial y^2} \right) \mathbf{k}$$

Then applying Clairaut's Theorem to reverse the order of differentiation in the second partial derivatives as needed and comparing, we have $\operatorname{curl}\operatorname{curl}\mathbf{F} = \operatorname{grad}\operatorname{div}\mathbf{F} - \nabla^2 \mathbf{F}$ as desired.

28. (a) $\nabla \cdot \mathbf{r} = \left(\frac{\partial}{\partial x} \mathbf{i} + \frac{\partial}{\partial y} \mathbf{j} + \frac{\partial}{\partial z} \mathbf{k} \right) \cdot (x\,\mathbf{i} + y\,\mathbf{j} + z\,\mathbf{k}) = 1 + 1 + 1 = 3$

(b) $\nabla \cdot (r\mathbf{r}) = \nabla \cdot \sqrt{x^2 + y^2 + z^2}\,(x\,\mathbf{i} + y\,\mathbf{j} + z\,\mathbf{k})$

$$= \left(\frac{x^2}{\sqrt{x^2 + y^2 + z^2}} + \sqrt{x^2 + y^2 + z^2} \right) + \left(\frac{y^2}{\sqrt{x^2 + y^2 + z^2}} + \sqrt{x^2 + y^2 + z^2} \right)$$

$$+ \left(\frac{z^2}{\sqrt{x^2 + y^2 + z^2}} + \sqrt{x^2 + y^2 + z^2} \right)$$

$$= \frac{1}{\sqrt{x^2 + y^2 + z^2}} \left(4x^2 + 4y^2 + 4z^2 \right) = 4\sqrt{x^2 + y^2 + z^2} = 4r$$

Another method:
By Exercise 23, $\nabla \cdot (r\mathbf{r}) = \operatorname{div}(r\mathbf{r}) = r \operatorname{div}\mathbf{r} + \mathbf{r} \cdot \nabla r = 3r + \mathbf{r} \cdot \dfrac{\mathbf{r}}{r}$ [see Exercise 29(a) below] $= 4r$.

(c) $\nabla^2 r^3 = \nabla^2 \left(x^2 + y^2 + z^2\right)^{3/2}$

$$= \frac{\partial}{\partial x}\left[\frac{3}{2}\left(x^2 + y^2 + z^2\right)^{1/2}(2x)\right] + \frac{\partial}{\partial y}\left[\frac{3}{2}\left(x^2 + y^2 + z^2\right)^{1/2}(2y)\right]$$

$$+ \frac{\partial}{\partial z}\left[\frac{3}{2}\left(x^2 + y^2 + z^2\right)^{1/2}(2z)\right]$$

$$= 3\left[\frac{1}{2}\left(x^2 + y^2 + z^2\right)^{-1/2}(2x)(x) + \left(x^2 + y^2 + z^2\right)^{1/2}\right]$$

$$+ 3\left[\frac{1}{2}\left(x^2 + y^2 + z^2\right)^{-1/2}(2y)(y) + \left(x^2 + y^2 + z^2\right)^{1/2}\right]$$

$$+ 3\left[\frac{1}{2}\left(x^2 + y^2 + z^2\right)^{-1/2}(2z)(z) + \left(x^2 + y^2 + z^2\right)^{1/2}\right]$$

$$= 3\left(x^2 + y^2 + z^2\right)^{-1/2}\left(4x^2 + 4y^2 + 4z^2\right) = 12\left(x^2 + y^2 + z^2\right)^{1/2}$$

$$= 12r$$

Another method: $\dfrac{\partial}{\partial x}\left(x^2 + y^2 + z^2\right)^{3/2} = 3x\sqrt{x^2 + y^2 + z^2} \;\Rightarrow\; \nabla r^3 = 3r(x\,\mathbf{i} + y\,\mathbf{j} + z\,\mathbf{k}) = 3r\,\mathbf{r}$, so $\nabla^2 r^3 = \nabla \cdot \nabla r^3 = \nabla \cdot (3r\,\mathbf{r}) = 3(4r) = 12r$ by part (b).

29. (a) $\nabla r = \nabla\sqrt{x^2 + y^2 + z^2} = \dfrac{x}{\sqrt{x^2 + y^2 + z^2}}\,\mathbf{i} + \dfrac{y}{\sqrt{x^2 + y^2 + z^2}}\,\mathbf{j} + \dfrac{z}{\sqrt{x^2 + y^2 + z^2}}\,\mathbf{k}$

$$= \frac{x\,\mathbf{i} + y\,\mathbf{j} + z\,\mathbf{k}}{\sqrt{x^2 + y^2 + z^2}} = \frac{\mathbf{r}}{r}$$

(b) $\nabla \times \mathbf{r} = \begin{vmatrix} \mathbf{i} & \mathbf{j} & \mathbf{k} \\ \dfrac{\partial}{\partial x} & \dfrac{\partial}{\partial y} & \dfrac{\partial}{\partial z} \\ x & y & z \end{vmatrix}$

$$= \left[\frac{\partial}{\partial y}(z) - \frac{\partial}{\partial z}(y)\right]\mathbf{i} + \left[\frac{\partial}{\partial z}(x) - \frac{\partial}{\partial x}(z)\right]\mathbf{j} + \left[\frac{\partial}{\partial x}(y) - \frac{\partial}{\partial y}(x)\right]\mathbf{k} = \mathbf{0}$$

(c) $\nabla\left(\dfrac{1}{r}\right) = \nabla\left(\dfrac{1}{\sqrt{x^2 + y^2 + z^2}}\right)$

$$= \frac{-\dfrac{1}{2\sqrt{x^2 + y^2 + z^2}}(2x)}{x^2 + y^2 + z^2}\,\mathbf{i} - \frac{\dfrac{1}{2\sqrt{x^2 + y^2 + z^2}}(2y)}{x^2 + y^2 + z^2}\,\mathbf{j} - \frac{\dfrac{1}{2\sqrt{x^2 + y^2 + z^2}}(2z)}{x^2 + y^2 + z^2}\,\mathbf{k}$$

$$= -\frac{x\,\mathbf{i} + y\,\mathbf{j} + z\,\mathbf{k}}{\left(x^2 + y^2 + z^2\right)^{3/2}} = -\frac{\mathbf{r}}{r^3}$$

(d) $\nabla \ln r = \nabla \ln(x^2 + y^2 + z^2)^{1/2} = \frac{1}{2}\nabla \ln(x^2 + y^2 + z^2)$

$$= \frac{x}{x^2+y^2+z^2}\,\mathbf{i} + \frac{y}{x^2+y^2+z^2}\,\mathbf{j} + \frac{z}{x^2+y^2+z^2}\,\mathbf{k} = \frac{x\,\mathbf{i}+y\,\mathbf{j}+z\,\mathbf{k}}{x^2+y^2+z^2} = \frac{\mathbf{r}}{r^2}$$

30. $\mathbf{r} = x\,\mathbf{i} + y\,\mathbf{j} + z\,\mathbf{k}$ $\Rightarrow$ $r = |\mathbf{r}| = \sqrt{x^2+y^2+z^2}$, so

$$\mathbf{F} = \frac{\mathbf{r}}{r^p} = \frac{x}{(x^2+y^2+z^2)^{p/2}}\,\mathbf{i} + \frac{y}{(x^2+y^2+z^2)^{p/2}}\,\mathbf{j} + \frac{z}{(x^2+y^2+z^2)^{p/2}}\,\mathbf{k}$$

Then $\dfrac{\partial}{\partial x}\dfrac{x}{(x^2+y^2+z^2)^{p/2}} = \dfrac{(x^2+y^2+z^2) - px^2}{(x^2+y^2+z^2)^{1+p/2}} = \dfrac{r^2 - px^2}{r^{p+2}}$. Similarly,

$\dfrac{\partial}{\partial y}\dfrac{y}{(x^2+y^2+z^2)^{p/2}} = \dfrac{r^2 - py^2}{r^{p+2}}$ and $\dfrac{\partial}{\partial z}\dfrac{z}{(x^2+y^2+z^2)^{p/2}} = \dfrac{r^2 - pz^2}{r^{p+2}}$. Thus

$$\operatorname{div}\mathbf{F} = \nabla \cdot \mathbf{F} = \frac{r^2 - px^2}{r^{p+2}} + \frac{r^2 - py^2}{r^{p+2}} + \frac{r^2 - pz^2}{r^{p+2}} = \frac{3r^2 - px^2 - py^2 - pz^2}{r^{p+2}}$$

$$= \frac{3r^2 - p(x^2+y^2+z^2)}{r^{p+2}} = \frac{3r^2 - pr^2}{r^{p+2}} = \frac{3-p}{r^p}$$

Consequently, if $p = 3$ we have $\operatorname{div}\mathbf{F} = 0$.

31. By (13), $\oint_C f\,(\nabla g) \cdot \mathbf{n}\,ds = \iint_D \operatorname{div}(f\nabla g)\,dA = \iint_D [f\operatorname{div}(\nabla g) + \nabla g \cdot \nabla f]\,dA$ by Exercise 23. But $\operatorname{div}(\nabla g) = \nabla^2 g$. Hence $\iint_D f\nabla^2 g\,dA = \oint_C f(\nabla g)\cdot \mathbf{n}\,ds - \iint_D \nabla g \cdot \nabla f\,dA$.

32. By Exercise 31, $\iint_D f\nabla^2 g\,dA = \oint_C f\,(\nabla g)\cdot \mathbf{n}\,ds - \iint_D \nabla g \cdot \nabla f\,dA$ and
$\iint_D g\nabla^2 f\,dA = \oint_C g\,(\nabla f)\cdot \mathbf{n}\,ds - \iint_D \nabla f \cdot \nabla g\,dA$. Hence

$$\iint_D \left(f\nabla^2 g - g\nabla^2 f\right)dA = \oint_C [f\,(\nabla g)\cdot \mathbf{n} - g\,(\nabla f)\cdot \mathbf{n}]\,ds + \iint_D (\nabla f \cdot \nabla g - \nabla g \cdot \nabla f)\,dA$$
$$= \oint_C [f\nabla g - g\nabla f]\cdot \mathbf{n}\,ds$$

33. (a) We know that $\omega = v/d$, and from the diagram $\sin\theta = d/r$ $\Rightarrow$ $v = d\omega = (\sin\theta)\,r\omega = |\mathbf{w} \times \mathbf{r}|$. But $\mathbf{v}$ is perpendicular to both $\mathbf{w}$ and $\mathbf{r}$, so that $\mathbf{v} = \mathbf{w} \times \mathbf{r}$.

(b) From (a), $\mathbf{v} = \mathbf{w} \times \mathbf{r} = \begin{vmatrix} \mathbf{i} & \mathbf{j} & \mathbf{k} \\ 0 & 0 & \omega \\ x & y & z \end{vmatrix} = (0\cdot z - \omega y)\,\mathbf{i} + (\omega x - 0\cdot z)\,\mathbf{j} + (0\cdot y - x\cdot 0)\,\mathbf{k} = -\omega y\,\mathbf{i} + \omega x\,\mathbf{j}$

(c) $\operatorname{curl}\mathbf{v} = \nabla \times \mathbf{v} = \begin{vmatrix} \mathbf{i} & \mathbf{j} & \mathbf{k} \\ \partial/\partial x & \partial/\partial y & \partial/\partial z \\ -\omega y & \omega x & 0 \end{vmatrix}$

$$= \left[\frac{\partial}{\partial y}(0) - \frac{\partial}{\partial z}(\omega x)\right]\mathbf{i} + \left[\frac{\partial}{\partial z}(-\omega y) - \frac{\partial}{\partial x}(0)\right]\mathbf{j} + \left[\frac{\partial}{\partial x}(\omega x) - \frac{\partial}{\partial y}(-\omega y)\right]\mathbf{k}$$

$$= [\omega - (-\omega)]\,\mathbf{k} = 2\omega\,\mathbf{k} = 2\mathbf{w}$$

34. Let $\mathbf{H} = \langle h_1, h_2, h_3 \rangle$ and $\mathbf{E} = \langle E_1, E_2, E_3 \rangle$.

(a) $\nabla \times (\nabla \times \mathbf{E}) = \nabla \times (\text{curl}\,\mathbf{E}) = \nabla \times \left(-\dfrac{1}{c} \dfrac{\partial \mathbf{H}}{\partial t} \right) = -\dfrac{1}{c} \begin{vmatrix} \mathbf{i} & \mathbf{j} & \mathbf{k} \\ \partial/\partial x & \partial/\partial y & \partial/\partial z \\ \partial h_1/\partial t & \partial h_2/\partial t & \partial h_3/\partial t \end{vmatrix}$

$$= -\dfrac{1}{c} \left[\left(\dfrac{\partial^2 h_3}{\partial y \partial t} - \dfrac{\partial^2 h_2}{\partial z \partial t} \right) \mathbf{i} + \left(\dfrac{\partial^2 h_1}{\partial z \partial t} - \dfrac{\partial^2 h_3}{\partial x \partial t} \right) \mathbf{j} + \left(\dfrac{\partial^2 h_2}{\partial x \partial t} - \dfrac{\partial^2 h_1}{\partial y \partial t} \right) \mathbf{k} \right]$$

$$= -\dfrac{1}{c} \dfrac{\partial}{\partial t} \left[\left(\dfrac{\partial h_3}{\partial y} - \dfrac{\partial h_2}{\partial z} \right) \mathbf{i} + \left(\dfrac{\partial h_1}{\partial z} - \dfrac{\partial h_3}{\partial x} \right) \mathbf{j} + \left(\dfrac{\partial h_2}{\partial x} - \dfrac{\partial h_1}{\partial y} \right) \mathbf{k} \right]$$

(assuming that the partial derivatives are continuous

so that the order of differentiation does not matter)

$$= -\dfrac{1}{c} \dfrac{\partial}{\partial t}\,\text{curl}\,\mathbf{H} = -\dfrac{1}{c} \dfrac{\partial}{\partial t} \left(\dfrac{1}{c} \dfrac{\partial \mathbf{E}}{\partial t} \right) = -\dfrac{1}{c^2} \dfrac{\partial^2 \mathbf{E}}{\partial t^2}$$

(b) $\nabla \times (\nabla \times \mathbf{H}) = \nabla \times (\text{curl}\,\mathbf{H}) = \nabla \times \left(\dfrac{1}{c} \dfrac{\partial \mathbf{E}}{\partial t} \right) = \dfrac{1}{c} \begin{vmatrix} \mathbf{i} & \mathbf{j} & \mathbf{k} \\ \partial/\partial x & \partial/\partial y & \partial/\partial z \\ \partial E_1/\partial t & \partial E_2/\partial t & \partial E_3/\partial t \end{vmatrix}$

$$= \dfrac{1}{c} \left[\left(\dfrac{\partial^2 E_3}{\partial y \partial t} - \dfrac{\partial^2 E_2}{\partial z \partial t} \right) \mathbf{i} + \left(\dfrac{\partial^2 E_1}{\partial z \partial t} - \dfrac{\partial^2 E_3}{\partial x \partial t} \right) \mathbf{j} + \left(\dfrac{\partial^2 E_2}{\partial x \partial t} - \dfrac{\partial^2 E_1}{\partial y \partial t} \right) \mathbf{k} \right]$$

$$= \dfrac{1}{c} \dfrac{\partial}{\partial t} \left[\left(\dfrac{\partial E_3}{\partial y} - \dfrac{\partial E_2}{\partial z} \right) \mathbf{i} + \left(\dfrac{\partial E_1}{\partial z} - \dfrac{\partial E_3}{\partial x} \right) \mathbf{j} + \left(\dfrac{\partial E_2}{\partial x} - \dfrac{\partial E_1}{\partial y} \right) \mathbf{k} \right]$$

(assuming that the partial derivatives are continuous

so that the order of differentiation does not matter)

$$= \dfrac{1}{c} \dfrac{\partial}{\partial t}\,\text{curl}\,\mathbf{E} = \dfrac{1}{c} \dfrac{\partial}{\partial t} \left(-\dfrac{1}{c} \dfrac{\partial \mathbf{H}}{\partial t} \right) = -\dfrac{1}{c^2} \dfrac{\partial^2 \mathbf{H}}{\partial t^2}$$

(c) Using Exercise 27, we have that $\text{curl\,curl}\,\mathbf{E} = \text{grad\,div}\,\mathbf{E} - \nabla^2 \mathbf{E} \;\Rightarrow$

$\nabla^2 \mathbf{E} = \text{grad\,div}\,\mathbf{E} - \text{curl\,curl}\,\mathbf{E} = \text{grad}\,0 + \dfrac{1}{c^2} \dfrac{\partial^2 \mathbf{E}}{\partial t^2}$ [from part (a)] $= \dfrac{1}{c^2} \dfrac{\partial^2 \mathbf{E}}{\partial t^2}$.

(d) As in part (c), $\nabla^2 \mathbf{H} = \text{grad\,div}\,\mathbf{H} - \text{curl\,curl}\,\mathbf{H} = \text{grad}\,0 + \dfrac{1}{c^2} \dfrac{\partial^2 \mathbf{H}}{\partial t^2}$ [using part (b)] $= \dfrac{1}{c^2} \dfrac{\partial^2 \mathbf{H}}{\partial t^2}$.

13.6 **Surface Integrals**   •   •   •   •   •   •   •   •   •   •   •   •   •

1. Each face of the cube has surface area $2^2 = 4$, and the points P_{ij}^* are the points where the cube intersects the coordinate axes. Here, $f(x, y, z) = \sqrt{x^2 + 2y^2 + 3z^2}$, so by Definition 1,

$$\iint_S f(x, y, z)\, dS \approx [f(1,0,0)](4) + [f(-1,0,0)](4) + [f(0,1,0)](4) + [f(0,-1,0)](4)$$
$$+ [f(0,0,1)](4) + [f(0,0,-1)](4)$$
$$= 4\left(1 + 1 + 2\sqrt{2} + 2\sqrt{3}\right) = 8\left(1 + \sqrt{2} + \sqrt{3}\right) \approx 33.170$$

2. Each quarter-cylinder has surface area $\frac{1}{4}[2\pi(1)(2)] = \pi$, and the top and bottom disks have surface area $\pi(1)^2 = \pi$. We can take $(0, 0, 1)$ as a sample point in the top disk, $(0, 0, -1)$ in the bottom disk, and $(\pm 1, 0, 0)$, $(0, \pm 1, 0)$ in the four quarter-cylinders. Then $\iint_S f(x, y, z)\, dS$ can be approximated by the Riemann sum

$f(1,0,0)(\pi) + f(-1,0,0)(\pi) + f(0,1,0)\,(\pi) + f(0,-1,0)(\pi) + f(0,0,1)(\pi) + f(0,0,-1)(\pi) =$
$(2 + 2 + 3 + 3 + 4 + 4)\pi = 18\pi \approx 56.5.$

3. We can use the xz- and yz-planes to divide H into four patches of equal size, each with surface area equal to $\frac{1}{8}$ the surface area of a sphere with radius $\sqrt{50}$, so $\Delta S = \frac{1}{8}(4)\pi\left(\sqrt{50}\right)^2 = 25\pi$. Then $(\pm 3, \pm 4, 5)$ are sample points in the four patches, and using a Riemann sum as in Definition 1, we have

$$\iint_H f(x, y, z)\, dS \approx f(3, 4, 5)\,\Delta S + f(3, -4, 5)\,\Delta S + f(-3, 4, 5)\,\Delta S + f(-3, -4, 5)\,\Delta S$$
$$= (7 + 8 + 9 + 12)(25\pi) = 900\pi \approx 2827$$

4. On the surface, $f(x, y, z) = g\left(\sqrt{x^2 + y^2 + z^2}\right) = g(2) = -5$. So since the area of a sphere is $4\pi r^2$,

$\iint_S f(x, y, z)\, dS = \iint_S g(2)\, dS = -5 \iint_S dS = -5\left[4\pi(2)^2\right] = -80\pi.$

5. $\mathbf{r}(u, v) = uv\,\mathbf{i} + (u + v)\,\mathbf{j} + (u - v)\,\mathbf{k}$, $u^2 + v^2 \le 1$ and $|\mathbf{r}_u \times \mathbf{r}_v| = \sqrt{4 + 2u^2 + 2v^2}$
(see Exercise 12.6.7). Then

$$\iint_S yx\, dS = \iint_{u^2 + v^2 \le 1} (u^2 - v^2)\sqrt{4 + 2u^2 + 2v^2}\, dA = \int_0^{2\pi} \int_0^1 r^2(\cos^2\theta - \sin^2\theta)\sqrt{4 + 2r^2}\, r\, dr\, d\theta$$
$$= \left[\int_0^{2\pi} (\cos^2\theta - \sin^2\theta)\, d\theta\right]\left[\int_0^1 r^3\sqrt{4 + 2r^2}\, dr\right] = 0$$

since the first integral is 0.

6. $\mathbf{r}_u = \cos v\,\mathbf{i} + \sin v\,\mathbf{j}$, $\mathbf{r}_v = -u\sin v\,\mathbf{i} + u\cos v\,\mathbf{j} + \mathbf{k}$ $\Rightarrow$ $\mathbf{r}_u \times \mathbf{r}_v = \sin v\,\mathbf{i} - \cos v\,\mathbf{j} + u\,\mathbf{k}$ $\Rightarrow$
$|\mathbf{r}_u \times \mathbf{r}_v| = \sqrt{1 + u^2}$, so $\iint_S \sqrt{1 + x^2 + y^2}\, dS = \int_0^\pi \int_0^1 \sqrt{1 + u^2}\,\sqrt{1 + u^2}\, du\, dv = \frac{4}{3}\pi.$

7. $z = 1 + 2x + 3y$ so $\dfrac{\partial z}{\partial x} = 2$ and $\dfrac{\partial z}{\partial y} = 3$. Then by Formula 4,

$$\iint_S x^2 yz\, dS = \iint_D x^2 yz\sqrt{\left(\frac{\partial z}{\partial x}\right)^2 + \left(\frac{\partial z}{\partial y}\right)^2 + 1}\, dA$$
$$= \int_0^3 \int_0^2 x^2 y(1 + 2x + 3y)\sqrt{4 + 9 + 1}\, dy\, dx$$
$$= \sqrt{14}\int_0^3 \int_0^2 (x^2 y + 2x^3 y + 3x^2 y^2)\, dy\, dx$$
$$= \sqrt{14}\int_0^3 \left[\tfrac{1}{2}x^2 y^2 + x^3 y^2 + x^2 y^3\right]_{y=0}^{y=2}\, dx$$
$$= \sqrt{14}\int_0^3 (10x^2 + 4x^3)\, dx = \sqrt{14}\left[\tfrac{10}{3}x^3 + x^4\right]_0^3 = 171\sqrt{14}$$

8. S is the region in the plane $2x + y + z = 2$ or $z = 2 - 2x - y$ over $D = \{(x, y) \mid 0 \le x \le 1, 0 \le y \le 2 - 2x\}$. Thus

$$\iint_S xy \, dS = \iint_D xy \sqrt{(-2)^2 + (-1)^2 + 1} \, dA$$
$$= \sqrt{6} \int_0^1 \int_0^{2-2x} xy \, dy \, dx = \sqrt{6} \int_0^1 \left[\tfrac{1}{2} xy^2 \right]_{y=0}^{y=2-2x} dx$$
$$= \tfrac{\sqrt{6}}{2} \int_0^1 \left(4x - 8x^2 + 4x^3 \right) dx = \tfrac{\sqrt{6}}{2} \left(2 - \tfrac{8}{3} + 1 \right) = \tfrac{\sqrt{6}}{6}$$

9. S is the part of the plane $z = 1 - x - y$ over the region $D = \{(x, y) \mid 0 \le x \le 1, 0 \le y \le 1 - x\}$. Thus

$$\iint_S yz \, dS = \iint_D y (1 - x - y) \sqrt{(-1)^2 + (-1)^2 + 1} \, dA$$
$$= \sqrt{3} \int_0^1 \int_0^{1-x} (y - xy - y^2) \, dy \, dx = \sqrt{3} \int_0^1 \left[\tfrac{1}{2} y^2 - \tfrac{1}{2} xy^2 - \tfrac{1}{3} y^3 \right]_{y=0}^{y=1-x} dx$$
$$= \sqrt{3} \int_0^1 \tfrac{1}{6} (1 - x)^3 dx = -\tfrac{\sqrt{3}}{24} (1 - x)^4 \Big|_0^1 = \tfrac{\sqrt{3}}{24}$$

10. $z = \tfrac{2}{3} \left(x^{3/2} + y^{3/2} \right)$ and

$$\iint_S y \, dS = \iint_D y \sqrt{(\sqrt{x})^2 + (\sqrt{y})^2 + 1} \, dA = \int_0^1 \int_0^1 y \sqrt{x + y + 1} \, dx \, dy$$
$$= \int_0^1 y \left[\tfrac{2}{3} (x + y + 1)^{3/2} \right]_{x=0}^{x=1} dy = \int_0^1 \tfrac{2}{3} y \left[(y + 2)^{3/2} - (y + 1)^{3/2} \right] dy$$

Substituting $u = y + 2$ in the first term and $t = y + 1$ in the second, we have

$$\iint_S y \, dS = \tfrac{2}{3} \int_2^3 (u - 2) u^{3/2} \, du - \tfrac{2}{3} \int_1^2 (t - 1) t^{3/2} \, dt$$
$$= \tfrac{2}{3} \left[\tfrac{2}{7} u^{7/2} - \tfrac{4}{5} u^{5/2} \right]_2^3 - \tfrac{2}{3} \left[\tfrac{2}{7} t^{7/2} - \tfrac{2}{5} t^{5/2} \right]_1^2$$
$$= \tfrac{2}{3} \left[\tfrac{2}{7} \left(3^{7/2} - 2^{7/2} \right) - \tfrac{4}{5} \left(3^{5/2} - 2^{5/2} \right) - \tfrac{2}{7} \left(2^{7/2} - 1 \right) + \tfrac{2}{5} \left(2^{5/2} - 1 \right) \right]$$
$$= \tfrac{2}{3} \left(\tfrac{18}{35} \sqrt{3} + \tfrac{8}{35} \sqrt{2} - \tfrac{4}{35} \right) = \tfrac{4}{105} \left(9 \sqrt{3} + 4 \sqrt{2} - 2 \right)$$

11. Using x and z as parameters, we have $\mathbf{r}(x, z) = x \mathbf{i} + (x^2 + 4z) \mathbf{j} + z \mathbf{k}$, $0 \le x \le 2$, $0 \le z \le 2$. Then
$\mathbf{r}_x \times \mathbf{r}_z = (\mathbf{i} + 2x \mathbf{j}) \times (4\mathbf{j} + \mathbf{k}) = 2x \mathbf{i} - \mathbf{j} + 4\mathbf{k}$ and $|\mathbf{r}_x \times \mathbf{r}_z| = \sqrt{4x^2 + 17}$. Thus

$$\iint_S x \, dS = \int_0^2 \int_0^2 x \sqrt{4x^2 + 17} \, dx \, dz = \int_0^2 dz \int_0^2 x \sqrt{4x^2 + 17} \, dx$$
$$= 2 \left[\tfrac{1}{12} (4x^2 + 17)^{3/2} \right]_0^2 = \frac{33 \sqrt{33} - 17 \sqrt{17}}{6}$$

12. $\mathbf{r}(y, z) = (4 - y^2 - z^2) \mathbf{i} + y \mathbf{j} + z \mathbf{k}$, $0 \le y^2 + z^2 \le 4$, so
$\mathbf{r}_y \times \mathbf{r}_z = (-2y \mathbf{i} + \mathbf{j}) \times (-2z \mathbf{i} + \mathbf{k}) = \mathbf{i} + 2y \mathbf{j} + 2z \mathbf{k}$ and $|\mathbf{r}_y \times \mathbf{r}_z| = \sqrt{4y^2 + 4z^2 + 1}$. Then

$$\iint_S (y^2 + z^2) \, dS = \iint_{y^2 + z^2 \le 4} (y^2 + z^2) \sqrt{4y^2 + 4z^2 + 1} \, dA = \int_0^{2\pi} \int_0^2 r^2 \sqrt{4r^2 + 1} \, r \, dr \, d\theta$$
$$= \int_0^{2\pi} d\theta \int_0^2 r^3 \sqrt{4r^2 + 1} \, dr$$

Substituting $u = 4r^2 + 1$, so $du = 8r\,dr$ and $r = \frac{1}{4}(u-1)$, gives

$$\iint_S (y^2 + z^2)\,dS = 2\pi \int_1^{17} \tfrac{1}{8}\tfrac{1}{4}(u-1)\sqrt{u}\,du = \tfrac{\pi}{16}\left[\tfrac{2}{5}u^{5/2} - \tfrac{2}{3}u^{3/2}\right]_1^{17}$$

$$= \tfrac{\pi}{16}\left[\tfrac{2}{5}\left(289\sqrt{17}-1\right) - \tfrac{2}{3}\left(17\sqrt{17}-1\right)\right]$$

$$= \tfrac{\pi}{16}\left(\tfrac{1564}{15}\sqrt{17} + \tfrac{4}{15}\right) = \tfrac{\pi}{60}\left(391\sqrt{17}+1\right)$$

13. S is the part of the plane $z = y + 3$ over the disk $D = \{(x,y) \mid x^2 + y^2 \le 1\}$. Thus

$$\iint_S yz\,dS = \iint_D y(y+3)\sqrt{(0)^2 + (1)^2 + 1}\,dA = \sqrt{2}\int_0^{2\pi}\int_0^1 r\sin\theta\,(r\sin\theta + 3)\,r\,dr\,d\theta$$

$$= \sqrt{2}\int_0^{2\pi}\left[\tfrac{1}{4}r^4\sin^2\theta + r^3\sin\theta\right]_{r=0}^{r=1}d\theta = \sqrt{2}\int_0^{2\pi}\left(\tfrac{1}{4}\sin^2\theta + \sin\theta\right)d\theta$$

$$= \sqrt{2}\left[\tfrac{1}{4}\left(\tfrac{1}{2}\theta - \tfrac{1}{4}\sin 2\theta\right) - \cos\theta\right]_0^{2\pi} = \tfrac{\pi}{2\sqrt{2}}$$

14. Here S consists of three surfaces: S_1, the lateral surface of the cylinder; S_2, the front formed by the plane $x + y = 2$; and the back, S_3, in the plane $y = 0$. On S_1: using cylindrical coordinates,
$\mathbf{r}(\theta, y) = \sin\theta\,\mathbf{i} + y\mathbf{j} + \cos\theta\,\mathbf{k}$, $0 \le \theta \le 2\pi$, $0 \le y \le 2 - \sin\theta$, $|\mathbf{r}_\theta \times \mathbf{r}_y| = 1$ and
$\iint_{S_1} xy\,dS = \int_0^{2\pi}\int_0^{2-\sin\theta}(\sin\theta)\,y\,dy\,d\theta = \int_0^{2\pi}\left[2\sin\theta - 2\sin^2\theta + \tfrac{1}{2}\sin^3\theta\right]d\theta = -2\pi$.
On S_2: $\mathbf{r}(x, z) = x\mathbf{i} + (2 - x)\mathbf{j} + z\mathbf{k}$ and $|\mathbf{r}_x \times \mathbf{r}_z| = |-\mathbf{i} - \mathbf{j}| = \sqrt{2}$, where $x^2 + z^2 \le 1$ and

$$\iint_{S_2} xy\,dS = \iint_{x^2 + z^2 \le 1} x(2 - x)\sqrt{2}\,dA = \int_0^{2\pi}\int_0^1 \sqrt{2}\left(2r\sin\theta - r^2\sin^2\theta\right)r\,dr\,d\theta$$

$$= \sqrt{2}\int_0^{2\pi}\left[\tfrac{2}{3}\sin\theta - \tfrac{1}{4}\sin^2\theta\right]d\theta = -\tfrac{\sqrt{2}}{4}\pi$$

On S_3: $y = 0$ so $\iint_{S_3} xy\,dS = 0$. Hence $\iint_S xy\,dS = -2\pi - \tfrac{\sqrt{2}}{4}\pi = -\tfrac{1}{4}\left(8 + \sqrt{2}\right)\pi$.

15. Using spherical coordinates and Example 12.6.1 we have
$\mathbf{r}(\phi, \theta) = 2\sin\phi\cos\theta\,\mathbf{i} + 2\sin\phi\sin\theta\,\mathbf{j} + 2\cos\phi\,\mathbf{k}$ and $|\mathbf{r}_\phi \times \mathbf{r}_\theta| = 4\sin\phi$. Then
$\iint_S (x^2z + y^2z)\,dS = \int_0^{2\pi}\int_0^{\pi/2}\left(4\sin^2\phi\right)(2\cos\phi)(4\sin\phi)\,d\phi\,d\theta = 16\pi\sin^4\phi\big]_0^{\pi/2} = 16\pi$.

16. Using spherical coordinates, $\mathbf{r}(\phi, \theta) = \sin\phi\cos\theta\,\mathbf{i} + \sin\phi\sin\theta\,\mathbf{j} + \cos\phi\,\mathbf{k}$, $0 \le \phi \le \tfrac{\pi}{4}$, $0 \le \theta \le 2\pi$, and
$|\mathbf{r}_\phi \times \mathbf{r}_\theta| = \sin\phi$ (see Example 12.6.1). Then $\iint_S xyz\,dS = \int_0^{2\pi}\int_0^{\pi/4}\left(\sin^3\phi\cos\phi\cos\theta\sin\theta\right)d\phi\,d\theta = 0$
since $\int_0^{2\pi}\cos\theta\sin\theta\,d\theta = 0$.

17. Using cylindrical coordinates, we have $\mathbf{r}(\theta, z) = 3\cos\theta\,\mathbf{i} + 3\sin\theta\,\mathbf{j} + z\mathbf{k}$, $0 \le \theta \le 2\pi$, $0 \le z \le 2$,
and $|\mathbf{r}_\theta \times \mathbf{r}_z| = 3$.
$\iint_S (x^2y + z^2)\,dS = \int_0^{2\pi}\int_0^2\left(27\cos^2\theta\sin\theta + z^2\right)3\,dz\,d\theta = \int_0^{2\pi}\left(162\cos^2\theta\sin\theta + 8\right)d\theta = 16\pi$

18. Let S_1 be the lateral surface, S_2 the top disk, and S_3 the bottom disk.
On S_1: $\mathbf{r}(\theta, z) = 3\cos\theta\,\mathbf{i} + 3\sin\theta\,\mathbf{j} + z\mathbf{k}$, $0 \le \theta \le 2\pi$, $0 \le z \le 2$, $|\mathbf{r}_\theta \times \mathbf{r}_z| = 3$,
$\iint_{S_1} (x^2 + y^2 + z^2)\,dS = \int_0^{2\pi}\int_0^2 (9 + z^2)\,3\,dz\,d\theta = 2\pi(54 + 8) = 124\pi$.
On S_2: $\mathbf{r}(\theta, r) = r\cos\theta\,\mathbf{i} + r\sin\theta\,\mathbf{j} + 2\mathbf{k}$, $0 \le r \le 3$, $0 \le \theta \le 2\pi$, $|\mathbf{r}_\theta \times \mathbf{r}_r| = r$,
$\iint_{S_2} (x^2 + y^2 + z^2)\,dS = \int_0^{2\pi}\int_0^3 (r^2 + 4)\,r\,dr\,d\theta = 2\pi\left(\tfrac{81}{4} + 18\right) = \tfrac{153}{2}\pi$.
On S_3: $\mathbf{r}(\theta, r) = r\cos\theta\,\mathbf{i} + r\sin\theta\,\mathbf{j}$, $0 \le r \le 3$, $0 \le \theta \le 2\pi$, $|\mathbf{r}_\theta \times \mathbf{r}_r| = r$,
$\iint_{S_3} (x^2 + y^2 + z^2)\,dS = \int_0^{2\pi}\int_0^3 (r^2 + 0)\,r\,dr\,d\theta = 2\pi\left(\tfrac{81}{4}\right) = \tfrac{81}{2}\pi$.
Hence $\iint_S (x^2 + y^2 + z^2)\,dS = 124\pi + \tfrac{153}{2}\pi + \tfrac{81}{2}\pi = 241\pi$.

19. $\mathbf{F}(x, y, z) = xy\,\mathbf{i} + yz\,\mathbf{j} + zx\,\mathbf{k}$, $z = g(x, y) = 4 - x^2 - y^2$, and D is the square $[0, 1] \times [0, 1]$, so by Equation 10

$$\iint_S \mathbf{F} \cdot d\mathbf{S} = \iint_D \left[-xy(-2x) - yz(-2y) + zx\right] dA$$

$$= \int_0^1 \int_0^1 \left[2x^2 y + 2y^2\left(4 - x^2 - y^2\right) + x\left(4 - x^2 - y^2\right)\right] dy\,dx$$

$$= \int_0^1 \left(\tfrac{1}{3}x^2 + \tfrac{11}{3}x - x^3 + \tfrac{34}{15}\right) dx = \tfrac{713}{180}$$

20. $\mathbf{r}_u = \cos v\,\mathbf{i} + \sin v\,\mathbf{j}$, $\mathbf{r}_v = -u \sin v\,\mathbf{i} + u \cos v\,\mathbf{j} + \mathbf{k}$ $\Rightarrow$ $\mathbf{r}_u \times \mathbf{r}_v = \sin v\,\mathbf{i} - \cos v\,\mathbf{j} + u\mathbf{k}$ and
$\mathbf{F}(\mathbf{r}(u, v)) = u \sin v\,\mathbf{i} + u \cos v\,\mathbf{j} + v^2\mathbf{k}$. Then

$$\iint_S \mathbf{F} \cdot d\mathbf{S} = \int_0^\pi \int_0^1 \left(u \sin^2 v - u \cos^2 v + uv^2\right) du\,dv = \int_0^\pi \int_0^1 \left(-u \cos 2v + uv^2\right) du\,dv$$

$$= \int_0^\pi \left[-\tfrac{1}{2}\cos 2v + \tfrac{1}{2}v^2\right] dv = \tfrac{1}{6}\pi^3.$$

21. $\mathbf{F}(x, y, z) = xze^y\,\mathbf{i} - xze^y\,\mathbf{j} + z\,\mathbf{k}$, $z = g(x, y) = 1 - x - y$, and $D = \{(x, y) \mid 0 \le x \le 1, 0 \le y \le 1 - x\}$.
Since S has downward orientation, we have

$$\iint_S \mathbf{F} \cdot d\mathbf{S} = -\iint_D \left[-xze^y(-1) - (-xze^y)(-1) + z\right] dA = -\int_0^1 \int_0^{1-x} (1 - x - y)\,dy\,dx$$

$$= -\int_0^1 \left(\tfrac{1}{2}x^2 - x + \tfrac{1}{2}\right) dx = -\tfrac{1}{6}$$

22. $\mathbf{F}(x, y, z) = x\mathbf{i} + y\mathbf{j} + z^4\mathbf{k}$, $z = g(x, y) = \sqrt{x^2 + y^2}$, and D is the disk $\{(x, y) \mid x^2 + y^2 \le 1\}$. Since S has
downward orientation, we have

$$\iint_S \mathbf{F} \cdot d\mathbf{S} = -\iint_D \left[-x\left(\frac{x}{\sqrt{x^2 + y^2}}\right) - y\left(\frac{y}{\sqrt{x^2 + y^2}}\right) + z^4\right] dA$$

$$= -\iint_D \left[\frac{-x^2 - y^2}{\sqrt{x^2 + y^2}} + \left(\sqrt{x^2 + y^2}\right)^4\right] dA = -\int_0^{2\pi} \int_0^1 \left(\frac{-r^2}{r} + r^4\right) r\,dr\,d\theta$$

$$= -\int_0^{2\pi} d\theta \int_0^1 \left(r^5 - r^2\right) dr = -2\pi\left(\tfrac{1}{6} - \tfrac{1}{3}\right) = \frac{\pi}{3}$$

23. $\mathbf{F}(\mathbf{r}(\phi, \theta)) = 3 \sin \phi \cos \theta\,\mathbf{i} + 3 \sin \phi \sin \theta\,\mathbf{j} + 3 \cos \phi\,\mathbf{k}$ and
$\mathbf{r}_\phi \times \mathbf{r}_\theta = 9 \sin^2 \phi \cos \theta\,\mathbf{i} + 9 \sin^2 \phi \sin \theta\,\mathbf{j} + 9 \sin \phi \cos \phi\,\mathbf{k}$. Then
$\mathbf{F}(\mathbf{r}(\phi, \theta)) \cdot (\mathbf{r}_\phi \times \mathbf{r}_\theta) = 27 \sin^3 \phi \cos^2 \theta + 27 \sin^3 \phi \sin^2 \theta + 27 \sin \phi \cos^2 \phi = 27 \sin \phi$ and
$\iint_S \mathbf{F} \cdot d\mathbf{S} = \int_0^{2\pi} \int_0^\pi 27 \sin \phi\,d\phi\,d\theta = (2\pi)(54) = 108\pi$.

24. $\mathbf{F}(\mathbf{r}(\phi, \theta)) = -4 \sin \phi \sin \theta\,\mathbf{i} + 4 \sin \phi \cos \theta\,\mathbf{j} + 12 \cos \phi\,\mathbf{k}$ and
$\mathbf{r}_\phi \times \mathbf{r}_\theta = 16 \sin^2 \phi \cos \theta\,\mathbf{i} + 16 \sin^2 \phi \sin \theta\,\mathbf{j} + 16 \sin \phi \cos \phi\,\mathbf{k}$. Then

$$\mathbf{F}(\mathbf{r}(\phi, \theta)) \cdot (\mathbf{r}_\phi \times \mathbf{r}_\theta) = -64 \sin^3 \phi \sin \theta \cos \theta + 64 \sin^3 \phi \sin \theta \cos \theta + 192 \sin \phi \cos^2 \phi$$

$$= 192 \sin \phi \cos^2 \phi$$

and $\iint_S \mathbf{F} \cdot d\mathbf{S} = \int_0^{2\pi} \int_0^{\pi/2} 192 \sin \phi \cos^2 \phi\,d\phi\,d\theta = 2\pi\left[-64 \cos^3 \phi\right]_0^{\pi/2} = 128\pi$.

25. Let S_1 be the paraboloid $y = x^2 + z^2$, $0 \le y \le 1$ and S_2 the disk $x^2 + z^2 \le 1$, $y = 1$. Since S is a closed
surface, we use the outward orientation. On S_1: $\mathbf{F}(\mathbf{r}(x, z)) = \left(x^2 + z^2\right)\mathbf{j} - z\mathbf{k}$ and $\mathbf{r}_x \times \mathbf{r}_z = 2x\,\mathbf{i} - \mathbf{j} + 2z\,\mathbf{k}$

(since the **j**-component must be negative on S_1). Then

$$\iint_{S_1} \mathbf{F} \cdot d\mathbf{S} = \iint_{x^2+z^2 \le 1} \left[-\left(x^2 + z^2\right) - 2z^2 \right] dA = -\int_0^{2\pi} \int_0^1 \left(r^2 + 2r^2 \cos^2 \theta\right) r \, dr \, d\theta$$

$$= -\int_0^{2\pi} \tfrac{1}{4} \left(1 + 2\cos^2 \theta\right) d\theta = -\left(\tfrac{\pi}{2} + \tfrac{\pi}{2}\right) = -\pi$$

On S_2: $\mathbf{F}\left(\mathbf{r}\left(x, z\right)\right) = \mathbf{j} - z\,\mathbf{k}$ and $\mathbf{r}_z \times \mathbf{r}_x = \mathbf{j}$. Then $\iint_{S_2} \mathbf{F} \cdot d\mathbf{S} = \iint_{x^2+z^2 \le 1} (1) \, dA = \pi$. Hence
$\iint_S \mathbf{F} \cdot d\mathbf{S} = -\pi + \pi = 0$.

26. Here S consists of three surfaces: S_1, the lateral surface of the cylinder; S_2, the front formed by the plane $x + y = 2$; and the back, S_3, in the plane $y = 0$.
On S_1: $\mathbf{F}\left(\mathbf{r}\left(\theta, y\right)\right) = \sin\theta\,\mathbf{i} + y\,\mathbf{j} + 5\,\mathbf{k}$ and $\mathbf{r}_\theta \times \mathbf{r}_y = \sin\theta\,\mathbf{i} + \cos\theta\,\mathbf{k}$ $\Rightarrow$

$$\iint_{S_1} \mathbf{F} \cdot d\mathbf{S} = \int_0^{2\pi} \int_0^{2-\sin\theta} \left(\sin^2\theta + 5\cos\theta\right) dy \, d\theta$$

$$= \int_0^{2\pi} \left(2\sin^2\theta + 10\cos\theta - \sin^3\theta - 5\sin\theta\cos\theta\right) d\theta = 2\pi$$

On S_2: $\mathbf{F}\left(\mathbf{r}\left(x, z\right)\right) = x\,\mathbf{i} + (2 - x)\,\mathbf{j} + 5\,\mathbf{k}$ and $\mathbf{r}_z \times \mathbf{r}_x = \mathbf{i} + \mathbf{j}$.
$\iint_{S_2} \mathbf{F} \cdot d\mathbf{S} = \iint_{x^2+z^2 \le 1} \left[x + (2 - x)\right] dA = 2\pi$.
On S_3: $\mathbf{F}\left(\mathbf{r}\left(x, z\right)\right) = x\,\mathbf{i} + 5\,\mathbf{k}$ and $\mathbf{r}_x \times \mathbf{r}_z = -\mathbf{j}$ so $\iint_{S_3} \mathbf{F} \cdot d\mathbf{S} = 0$. Hence $\iint_S \mathbf{F} \cdot d\mathbf{S} = 4\pi$.

27. Here S consists of the six faces of the cube as labeled in the figure. On S_1:

$\mathbf{F} = \mathbf{i} + 2y\mathbf{j} + 3z\mathbf{k}$, $\mathbf{r}_y \times \mathbf{r}_z = \mathbf{i}$ and $\iint_{S_1} \mathbf{F} \cdot d\mathbf{S} = \int_{-1}^{1} \int_{-1}^{1} dy \, dz = 4$;

S_2: $\mathbf{F} = x\mathbf{i} + 2\mathbf{j} + 3z\mathbf{k}$, $\mathbf{r}_z \times \mathbf{r}_x = \mathbf{j}$ and $\iint_{S_2} \mathbf{F} \cdot d\mathbf{S} = \int_{-1}^{1} \int_{-1}^{1} 2 \, dx \, dz = 8$;

S_3: $\mathbf{F} = x\mathbf{i} + 2y\mathbf{j} + 3\mathbf{k}$, $\mathbf{r}_x \times \mathbf{r}_y = \mathbf{k}$ and $\iint_{S_3} \mathbf{F} \cdot d\mathbf{S} = \int_{-1}^{1} \int_{-1}^{1} 3 \, dx \, dy = 12$;

S_4: $\mathbf{F} = -\mathbf{i} + 2y\mathbf{j} + 3z\mathbf{k}$, $\mathbf{r}_z \times \mathbf{r}_y = -\mathbf{i}$ and $\iint_{S_4} \mathbf{F} \cdot d\mathbf{S} = 4$;

S_5: $\mathbf{F} = x\mathbf{i} - 2\mathbf{j} + 3z\mathbf{k}$, $\mathbf{r}_x \times \mathbf{r}_z = -\mathbf{j}$ and $\iint_{S_5} \mathbf{F} \cdot d\mathbf{S} = 8$;

S_6: $\mathbf{F} = x\mathbf{i} + 2y\mathbf{j} - 3\mathbf{k}$, $\mathbf{r}_y \times \mathbf{r}_x = -\mathbf{k}$ and $\iint_{S_6} \mathbf{F} \cdot d\mathbf{S} = \int_{-1}^{1} \int_{-1}^{1} 3 \, dx \, dy = 12$.

Hence $\iint_S \mathbf{F} \cdot d\mathbf{S} = \sum_{i=1}^{6} \iint_{S_i} \mathbf{F} \cdot d\mathbf{S} = 48$.

28. **(a)** $z = xy$ $\Rightarrow$ $\partial z / \partial x = y$, $\partial z / \partial y = x$, so by Formula 4, a CAS gives
$\iint_S xyz \, dS = \int_0^1 \int_0^1 xy \, (xy) \sqrt{y^2 + x^2 + 1} \, dx \, dy \approx 0.1642$.

(b) As in part (a), we use a CAS to calculate
$\iint_S x^2 yz \, dS = \int_0^1 \int_0^1 x^2 y \, (xy) \sqrt{y^2 + x^2 + 1} \, dx \, dy$

$= \tfrac{1}{60}\sqrt{3} - \tfrac{1}{12}\ln\left(1 + \sqrt{3}\right) - \tfrac{1}{192}\ln\left(\sqrt{2} + 1\right) + \tfrac{317}{2880}\sqrt{2} + \tfrac{1}{24}\ln 2$.

29. We use Formula 4 with $z = 3 - 2x^2 - y^2$ $\Rightarrow$ $\partial z / \partial x = -4x$, $\partial z / \partial y = -2y$. The boundaries of the region

$3 - 2x^2 - y^2 \ge 0$ are $-\sqrt{\tfrac{3}{2}} \le x \le \sqrt{\tfrac{3}{2}}$ and $-\sqrt{3 - 2x^2} \le y \le \sqrt{3 - 2x^2}$, so we use a CAS (with precision

reduced to seven or fewer digits; otherwise the calculation takes a very long time) to calculate

$\iint_S x^2 y^2 z^2 \, dS = \int_{-\sqrt{3/2}}^{\sqrt{3/2}} \int_{-\sqrt{3-2x^2}}^{\sqrt{3-2x^2}} x^2 y^2 \left(3 - 2x^2 - y^2\right)^2 \sqrt{16x^2 + 4y^2 + 1} \, dy \, dx \approx 3.4895$.

30. The flux of **F** across S is given by $\iint_S \mathbf{F} \cdot d\mathbf{S} = \iint_S \mathbf{F} \cdot \mathbf{n}\, dS$. Now on S, $z = g(x, y) = 2\sqrt{1 - y^2}$, so $\partial g / \partial x = 0$ and $\partial g / \partial y = -2y(1 - y^2)^{-1/2}$. Therefore, by (10),

$$\iint_S \mathbf{F} \cdot d\mathbf{S} = \int_{-2}^{2} \int_{-1}^{1} \left(-x^2 y \left[-2y\left(1 - y^2\right)^{-1/2} \right] + \left[2\sqrt{1 - y^2} \right]^2 e^{x/5} \right) dy\, dx$$

$$= \tfrac{1}{3}\left(16\pi + 80e^{2/5} - 80e^{-2/5} \right)$$

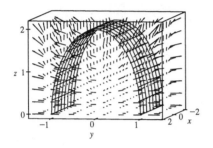 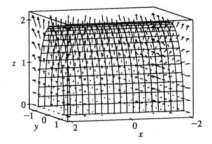

31. If S is given by $y = h(x, z)$, then S is also the level surface $f(x, y, z) = y - h(x, z) = 0$.

$\mathbf{n} = \dfrac{\nabla f(x, y, z)}{|\nabla f(x, y, z)|} = \dfrac{-h_x\,\mathbf{i} + \mathbf{j} - h_z\,\mathbf{k}}{\sqrt{h_x^2 + 1 + h_z^2}}$, and $-\mathbf{n}$ is the unit normal that points to the left. Now we proceed as in

the derivation of (10), using Formula 4 to evaluate

$$\iint_S \mathbf{F} \cdot d\mathbf{S} = \iint_S \mathbf{F} \cdot \mathbf{n}\, dS = \iint_D (P\mathbf{i} + Q\mathbf{j} + R\mathbf{k}) \, \frac{\dfrac{\partial h}{\partial x}\mathbf{i} - \mathbf{j} + \dfrac{\partial h}{\partial z}\mathbf{k}}{\sqrt{\left(\dfrac{\partial h}{\partial x}\right)^2 + 1 + \left(\dfrac{\partial h}{\partial z}\right)^2}} \sqrt{\left(\dfrac{\partial h}{\partial x}\right)^2 + 1 + \left(\dfrac{\partial h}{\partial z}\right)^2}\, dA$$

where D is the projection of $f(x, y, z)$ onto the xz-plane. Therefore

$$\iint_S \mathbf{F} \cdot d\mathbf{S} = \iint_D \left(P\frac{\partial h}{\partial x} - Q + R\frac{\partial h}{\partial z} \right) dA.$$

32. If S is given by $x = k(y, z)$, then S is also the level surface $f(x, y, z) = x - k(y, z) = 0$.

$\mathbf{n} = \dfrac{\nabla f(x, y, z)}{|\nabla f(x, y, z)|} = \dfrac{\mathbf{i} - k_y\mathbf{j} - k_z\mathbf{k}}{\sqrt{1 + k_y^2 + k_z^2}}$, and since the x-component is positive this is the unit normal that points

forward. Now we proceed as in the derivation of (10), using Formula 4 for

$$\iint_S \mathbf{F} \cdot d\mathbf{S} = \iint_S \mathbf{F} \cdot \mathbf{n}\, dS$$

$$= \iint_D (P\mathbf{i} + Q\mathbf{j} + R\mathbf{k}) \, \frac{\mathbf{i} - \dfrac{\partial k}{\partial y}\mathbf{j} - \dfrac{\partial k}{\partial z}\mathbf{k}}{\sqrt{1 + \left(\dfrac{\partial k}{\partial y}\right)^2 + \left(\dfrac{\partial k}{\partial z}\right)^2}} \sqrt{1 + \left(\dfrac{\partial k}{\partial y}\right)^2 + \left(\dfrac{\partial k}{\partial z}\right)^2}\, dA.$$

where D is the projection of $f(x, y, z)$ onto the yz-plane. Therefore

$$\iint_S \mathbf{F} \cdot d\mathbf{S} = \iint_D \left(P - Q\frac{\partial k}{\partial y} - R\frac{\partial k}{\partial z} \right) dA.$$

33. $m = \iint_S K\, dS = K \cdot 4\pi\left(\tfrac{1}{2}a^2\right) = 2\pi a^2 K$; by symmetry $M_{xz} = M_{yz} = 0$, and

$M_{xy} = \iint_S zK\, dS = K \int_0^{2\pi} \int_0^{\pi/2} (a\cos\phi)(a^2 \sin\phi)\, d\phi\, d\theta = 2\pi K a^3 \left[-\tfrac{1}{4}\cos 2\phi \right]_0^{\pi/2} = \pi K a^3$.

Hence $(\overline{x}, \overline{y}, \overline{z}) = \left(0, 0, \tfrac{1}{2}a\right)$.

34. S is given by $\mathbf{r}(x,y) = x\,\mathbf{i} + y\,\mathbf{j} + \sqrt{x^2 + y^2}\,\mathbf{k}$, $|\mathbf{r}_x \times \mathbf{r}_y| = \sqrt{1 + \dfrac{x^2 + y^2}{x^2 + y^2}} = \sqrt{2}$ so

$$m = \iint_S \left(10 - \sqrt{x^2 + y^2}\right) dS = \iint_{1 \leq x^2 + y^2 \leq 16} \left(10 - \sqrt{x^2 + y^2}\right) \sqrt{2}\, dA$$

$$= \int_0^{2\pi} \int_1^4 \sqrt{2}\,(10 - r)\,r\,dr\,d\theta = 2\pi\sqrt{2}\left[5r^2 - \tfrac{1}{3}r^3\right]_1^4 = 108\sqrt{2}\,\pi$$

35. (a) $I_z = \iint_S (x^2 + y^2)\,\rho(x,y,z)\,dS$

(b) $I_z = \iint_S (x^2 + y^2)\left(10 - \sqrt{x^2 + y^2}\right) dS = \iint_{1 \leq x^2 + y^2 \leq 16} (x^2 + y^2)\left(10 - \sqrt{x^2 + y^2}\right)\sqrt{2}\,dA$

$$= \int_0^{2\pi} \int_1^4 \sqrt{2}\,(10r^3 - r^4)\,dr\,d\theta = 2\sqrt{2}\,\pi\left(\tfrac{4329}{10}\right) = \tfrac{4329}{5}\sqrt{2}\,\pi$$

36. S is given by $\mathbf{r}(x,y) = x\,\mathbf{i} + y\,\mathbf{j} + \sqrt{x^2 + y^2}\,\mathbf{k}$ and $|\mathbf{r}_x \times \mathbf{r}_y| = \sqrt{2}$.

(a) $m = \iint_S k\,dS = k\iint_{0 \leq x^2 + y^2 \leq a^2} \sqrt{2}\,dS = \sqrt{2}\,a^2 k\pi$; by symmetry $M_{xz} = M_{yz} = 0$, and

$M_{xy} = \iint_S zk\,dS = k\int_0^{2\pi}\int_0^a \sqrt{2}\,r^2\,dr\,d\theta = \tfrac{2}{3}\sqrt{2}\,a^3 k\pi$. Hence $(\overline{x}, \overline{y}, \overline{z}) = \left(0, 0, \tfrac{2}{3}a\right)$.

(b) $I_z = \iint_S (x^2 + y^2)\,k\,dS = \int_0^{2\pi}\int_0^a \sqrt{2}\,kr^3\,dr\,d\theta = 2\pi\sqrt{2}\,k\left(\tfrac{1}{4}a^4\right) = \tfrac{\sqrt{2}}{2}\pi k a^4$.

37. $\rho(x,y,z) = 1200$, $\mathbf{V} = y\,\mathbf{i} + \mathbf{j} + z\,\mathbf{k}$, $\mathbf{F} = \rho\mathbf{V} = (1200)(y\,\mathbf{i} + \mathbf{j} + z\,\mathbf{k})$. S is given by
$\mathbf{r}(x,y) = x\,\mathbf{i} + y\,\mathbf{j} + \left[9 - \tfrac{1}{4}(x^2 + y^2)\right]\mathbf{k}$, $0 \leq x^2 + y^2 \leq 36$ and $\mathbf{r}_x \times \mathbf{r}_y = \tfrac{1}{2}x\,\mathbf{i} + \tfrac{1}{2}y\,\mathbf{j} + \mathbf{k}$. Thus the rate of
flow is given by

$$\iint_S \mathbf{F}\cdot d\mathbf{S} = \iint_{0 \leq x^2 + y^2 \leq 36} (1200)\left(\tfrac{1}{2}xy + \tfrac{1}{2}y + \left[9 - \tfrac{1}{4}(x^2 + y^2)\right]\right) dA$$

$$= 1200\int_0^6\int_0^{2\pi}\left[\tfrac{1}{2}r^2\sin\theta\cos\theta + \tfrac{1}{2}r\sin\theta + 9 - \tfrac{1}{4}r^2\right] r\,d\theta\,dr$$

$$= 1200\int_0^6 2\pi\left(9r - \tfrac{1}{4}r^3\right) dr = (1200)(2\pi)(81) = 194{,}400\pi$$

38. $\rho(x,y,z) = 1500$, $\mathbf{F} = \rho\mathbf{V} = (1500)(-y\,\mathbf{i} + x\,\mathbf{j} + 2z\,\mathbf{k})$. S is given by
$\mathbf{r}(\phi,\theta) = 5\sin\phi\cos\theta\,\mathbf{i} + 5\sin\phi\sin\theta\,\mathbf{j} + 5\cos\phi\,\mathbf{k}$, $0 \leq \phi \leq \pi$, $0 \leq \theta \leq 2\pi$, and
$\mathbf{r}_\phi \times \mathbf{r}_\theta = 25\sin^2\phi\cos\theta\,\mathbf{i} + 25\sin^2\phi\sin\theta\,\mathbf{j} + 25\sin\phi\cos\phi\,\mathbf{k}$. Thus the rate of outward flow is

$$\iint_S \mathbf{F}\cdot d\mathbf{S} = 1500\int_0^{2\pi}\int_0^\pi \left(-125\sin^3\phi\sin\theta\cos\theta + 125\sin^3\phi\sin\theta\cos\theta + 250\sin\phi\cos^2\phi\right) d\phi\,d\theta$$

$$= (3000\pi)(250)\left(-\tfrac{1}{3}\cos^3\phi\right)\Big]_0^\pi = 500{,}000\pi.$$

39. S consists of the hemisphere S_1 given by $z = \sqrt{a^2 - x^2 - y^2}$ and the disk S_2 given by
$0 \leq x^2 + y^2 \leq a^2$, $z = 0$. On S_1: $\mathbf{E} = a\sin\phi\cos\theta\,\mathbf{i} + a\sin\phi\sin\theta\,\mathbf{j} + 2a\cos\phi\,\mathbf{k}$,
$\mathbf{T}_\phi \times \mathbf{T}_\theta = a^2\sin^2\phi\cos\theta\,\mathbf{i} + a^2\sin^2\phi\sin\theta\,\mathbf{j} + a^2\sin\phi\cos\phi\,\mathbf{k}$. Thus

$$\iint_{S_1} \mathbf{E}\cdot d\mathbf{S} = \int_0^{2\pi}\int_0^{\pi/2}\left(a^3\sin^3\phi + 2a^3\sin\phi\cos^2\phi\right) d\phi\,d\theta$$

$$= \int_0^{2\pi}\int_0^{\pi/2}\left(a^3\sin\phi + a^3\sin\phi\cos^2\phi\right) d\phi\,d\theta = (2\pi)a^3\left(1 + \tfrac{1}{3}\right) = \tfrac{8}{3}\pi a^3$$

On S_2: $\mathbf{E} = x\,\mathbf{i} + y\,\mathbf{j}$, and $\mathbf{r}_y \times \mathbf{r}_x = -\mathbf{k}$ so $\iint_{S_2} \mathbf{E}\cdot d\mathbf{S} = 0$. Hence the total charge is
$q = \epsilon_0 \iint_S \mathbf{E}\cdot d\mathbf{S} = \tfrac{8}{3}\pi a^3\epsilon_0$.

40. Referring to the figure in Exercise 27, on

S_1: $\mathbf{E} = \mathbf{i} + y\mathbf{j} + z\mathbf{k}$, $\mathbf{r}_y \times \mathbf{r}_z = \mathbf{i}$ and $\iint_{S_1} \mathbf{E} \cdot d\mathbf{S} = \int_{-1}^{1} \int_{-1}^{1} dy\, dz = 4$;

S_2: $\mathbf{E} = x\mathbf{i} + \mathbf{j} + z\mathbf{k}$, $\mathbf{r}_z \times \mathbf{r}_x = \mathbf{j}$ and $\iint_{S_2} \mathbf{E} \cdot d\mathbf{S} = \int_{-1}^{1} \int_{-1}^{1} dx\, dz = 4$;

S_3: $\mathbf{E} = x\mathbf{i} + y\mathbf{j} + \mathbf{k}$, $\mathbf{r}_x \times \mathbf{r}_y = \mathbf{k}$ and $\iint_{S_3} \mathbf{E} \cdot d\mathbf{S} = \int_{-1}^{1} \int_{-1}^{1} dx\, dy = 4$;

S_4: $\mathbf{E} = -\mathbf{i} + y\mathbf{j} + z\mathbf{k}$, $\mathbf{r}_z \times \mathbf{r}_y = -\mathbf{i}$ and $\iint_{S_4} \mathbf{E} \cdot d\mathbf{S} = 4$.

Similarly $\iint_{S_5} \mathbf{E} \cdot d\mathbf{S} = \iint_{S_6} \mathbf{E} \cdot d\mathbf{S} = 4$. Hence $q = \epsilon_0 \iint_S \mathbf{E} \cdot d\mathbf{S} = \epsilon_0 \sum_{i=1}^{6} \iint_{S_i} \mathbf{E} \cdot d\mathbf{S} = 24\epsilon_0$.

41. $K\nabla u = 6.5(4y\mathbf{j} + 4z\mathbf{k})$. S is given by $\mathbf{r}(x, \theta) = x\mathbf{i} + \sqrt{6}\,\cos\theta\,\mathbf{j} + \sqrt{6}\,\sin\theta\,\mathbf{k}$ and since we want the inward heat flow, we use $\mathbf{r}_x \times \mathbf{r}_\theta = -\sqrt{6}\,\cos\theta\,\mathbf{j} - \sqrt{6}\,\sin\theta\,\mathbf{k}$. Then the rate of heat flow inward is given by

$\iint_S (-K\,\nabla u) \cdot d\mathbf{S} = \int_0^{2\pi} \int_0^4 -(6.5)(-24)\, dx\, d\theta = (2\pi)(156)(4) = 1248\pi$.

42. $u(x, y, z) = c/\sqrt{x^2 + y^2 + z^2}$,

$$\mathbf{F} = -K\nabla u = -K\left[-\frac{cx}{(x^2 + y^2 + z^2)^{3/2}}\mathbf{i} - \frac{cy}{(x^2 + y^2 + z^2)^{3/2}}\mathbf{j} - \frac{cz}{(x^2 + y^2 + z^2)^{3/2}}\mathbf{k}\right]$$

$$= \frac{cK}{(x^2 + y^2 + z^2)^{3/2}}(x\mathbf{i} + y\mathbf{j} + z\mathbf{k})$$

and the outward unit normal is $\mathbf{n} = \dfrac{1}{a}(x\mathbf{i} + y\mathbf{j} + z\mathbf{k})$.

Thus $\mathbf{F} \cdot \mathbf{n} = \dfrac{cK}{a\,(x^2 + y^2 + z^2)^{3/2}}(x^2 + y^2 + z^2)$, but on S, $x^2 + y^2 + z^2 = a^2$ so $\mathbf{F} \cdot \mathbf{n} = \dfrac{cK}{a^2}$. Hence the rate

of heat flow across S is $\displaystyle\iint_S \mathbf{F} \cdot d\mathbf{S} = \frac{cK}{a^2}\iint_S dS = \frac{cK}{a^2}\left(4\pi a^2\right) = 4\pi Kc$.

13.7 Stokes' Theorem • • • • • • • • • • • • •

1. Both H and P are oriented piecewise-smooth surfaces that are bounded by the simple, closed, smooth curve $x^2 + y^2 = 4$, $z = 0$ (which we can take to be oriented positively for both surfaces). Then H and P satisfy the hypotheses of Stokes' Theorem, so by (3) we know $\iint_H \text{curl}\,\mathbf{F} \cdot d\mathbf{S} = \int_C \mathbf{F} \cdot d\mathbf{r} = \iint_P \text{curl}\,\mathbf{F} \cdot d\mathbf{S}$ (where C is the boundary curve).

2. The plane $z = 5$ intersects the paraboloid $z = 9 - x^2 - y^2$ in the circle $x^2 + y^2 = 4$, $z = 5$. This boundary curve C is oriented in the counterclockwise direction, so the vector equation is $\mathbf{r}(t) = 2\cos t\,\mathbf{i} + 2\sin t\,\mathbf{j} + 5\,\mathbf{k}$, $0 \le t \le 2\pi$. Then $\mathbf{r}'(t) = -2\sin t\,\mathbf{i} + 2\cos t\,\mathbf{j}$, $\mathbf{F}(\mathbf{r}(t)) = 10\sin t\,\mathbf{i} + 10\cos t\,\mathbf{j} + 4\cos t\sin t\,\mathbf{k}$, and by Stokes' Theorem,

$$\iint_S \text{curl}\,\mathbf{F} \cdot d\mathbf{S} = \int_C \mathbf{F} \cdot d\mathbf{r} = \int_0^{2\pi} \mathbf{F}(\mathbf{r}(t)) \cdot \mathbf{r}'(t)\, dt = \int_0^{2\pi} \left(-20\sin^2 t + 20\cos^2 t\right) dt$$

$$= 20\int_0^{2\pi} \cos 2t\, dt = 0$$

3. The boundary curve C is the circle $x^2 + y^2 = 4$, $z = 0$ oriented in the counterclockwise direction. The vector equation is $\mathbf{r}(t) = 2\cos t\,\mathbf{i} + 2\sin t\,\mathbf{j}$, $0 \le t \le 2\pi$, so $\mathbf{r}'(t) = -2\sin t\,\mathbf{i} + 2\cos t\,\mathbf{j}$ and
$\mathbf{F}(\mathbf{r}(t)) = (2\cos t)^2 e^{(2\sin t)(0)}\,\mathbf{i} + (2\sin t)^2 e^{(2\cos t)(0)}\,\mathbf{j} + (0)^2 e^{(2\cos t)(2\sin t)}\,\mathbf{k} = 4\cos^2 t\,\mathbf{i} + 4\sin^2 t\,\mathbf{j}$. Then, by Stokes' Theorem,

$$\iint_S \operatorname{curl}\mathbf{F} \cdot d\mathbf{S} = \int_C \mathbf{F} \cdot d\mathbf{r} = \int_0^{2\pi} \mathbf{F}(\mathbf{r}(t)) \cdot \mathbf{r}'(t)\,dt = \int_0^{2\pi} \left(-8\cos^2 t\sin t + 8\sin^2 t\cos t\right)dt$$

$$= 8\left[\tfrac{1}{3}\cos^3 t + \tfrac{1}{3}\sin^3 t\right]_0^{2\pi} = 0$$

4. C is the circle $y^2 + z^2 = 4$, $x = \sqrt{5}$ with vector equation $\mathbf{r}(t) = \sqrt{5}\,\mathbf{i} + 2\cos t\,\mathbf{j} + 2\sin t\,\mathbf{k}$, $0 \le t \le 2\pi$.
Then $\mathbf{F}(\mathbf{r}(t)) = \left[\sqrt{5} + \tan^{-1}(4\cos t\sin t)\right]\mathbf{i} + 8\cos^2 t\sin t\,\mathbf{j} + 2\sin t\,\mathbf{k}$ and
$\mathbf{F}(\mathbf{r}(t)) \cdot \mathbf{r}'(t) = -16\cos^2 t\sin^2 t + 4\sin t\cos t = -2 + 2\cos 2t + 2\sin 2t$. Thus
$\iint_S \operatorname{curl}\mathbf{F} \cdot d\mathbf{S} = \oint_C \mathbf{F} \cdot d\mathbf{r} = 2\int_0^{2\pi}(-1 + \cos 2t + \sin 2t)\,dt = -4\pi$.

5. C is the square in the plane $z = -1$. By (3), $\iint_{S_1} \operatorname{curl}\mathbf{F} \cdot d\mathbf{S} = \oint_C \mathbf{F} \cdot d\mathbf{r} = \iint_{S_2} \operatorname{curl}\mathbf{F} \cdot d\mathbf{S}$ where
S_1 is the original cube without the bottom and S_2 is the bottom face of the cube.
$\operatorname{curl}\mathbf{F} = x^2 z\,\mathbf{i} + (xy - 2xyz)\,\mathbf{j} + (y - xz)\,\mathbf{k}$. For S_2, we choose $\mathbf{n} = \mathbf{k}$ so that C has the same orientation for both surfaces. Then $\operatorname{curl}\mathbf{F} \cdot \mathbf{n} = y - xz = x + y$ on S_2, where $z = -1$. Thus
$\iint_{S_2} \operatorname{curl}\mathbf{F} \cdot d\mathbf{S} = \int_{-1}^1 \int_{-1}^1 (x + y)\,dx\,dy = 0$ so $\iint_{S_1} \operatorname{curl}\mathbf{F} \cdot d\mathbf{S} = 0$.

6. Here S consists of the 4 sides of the pyramid but not the base in the xz-plane.
Call the base S_1. Then $\iint_S \operatorname{curl}\mathbf{F} \cdot d\mathbf{S} = \oint_C \mathbf{F} \cdot d\mathbf{r}$ where C is the boundary of the base. To avoid calculating four line integrals, apply Stokes' Theorem again. Then $\oint_C \mathbf{F} \cdot d\mathbf{r} = \iint_{S_1} \operatorname{curl}\mathbf{F} \cdot d\mathbf{S}$. But
$\operatorname{curl}\mathbf{F} = (2xy - e^z)\,\mathbf{i} - y^2\,\mathbf{j} - x\,\mathbf{k}$ and $\mathbf{n} = \mathbf{j}$, so $\operatorname{curl}\mathbf{F} \cdot \mathbf{n} = -y^2 = 0$ on
S_1, $\iint_{S_1} \operatorname{curl}\mathbf{F} \cdot d\mathbf{S} = 0$ and $\iint_S \operatorname{curl}\mathbf{F} \cdot d\mathbf{S} = 0$.

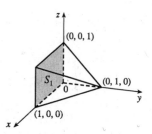

7. $\operatorname{curl}\mathbf{F} = -2z\,\mathbf{i} - 2x\,\mathbf{j} - 2y\,\mathbf{k}$ and we take the surface S to be the planar region enclosed by C, so S is the portion of the plane $x + y + z = 1$ over $D = \{(x, y) \mid 0 \le x \le 1, 0 \le y \le 1 - x\}$. Since C is oriented counterclockwise, we orient S upward. Using Equation 13.6.10, we have $z = g(x, y) = 1 - x - y$, $P = -2z$, $Q = -2x$, $R = -2y$, and

$$\int_C \mathbf{F} \cdot d\mathbf{r} = \iint_S \operatorname{curl}\mathbf{F} \cdot d\mathbf{S} = \iint_D [-(-2z)(-1) - (-2x)(-1) + (-2y)]\,dA$$

$$= \int_0^1 \int_0^{1-x}(-2)\,dy\,dx = -2\int_0^1(1 - x)\,dx = -1$$

8. $\operatorname{curl}\mathbf{F} = e^x\,\mathbf{k}$ and S is the portion of the plane $2x + y + 2z = 2$ over $D = \{(x, y) \mid 0 \le x \le 1, 0 \le y \le 2 - 2x\}$.
We orient S upward and use Equation 13.6.10 with $z = g(x, y) = 1 - x - \tfrac{1}{2}y$:

$$\int_C \mathbf{F} \cdot d\mathbf{r} = \iint_S \operatorname{curl}\mathbf{F} \cdot d\mathbf{S} = \iint_D (0 + 0 + e^x)\,dA = \int_0^1 \int_0^{2-2x} e^x\,dy\,dx$$

$$= \int_0^1 (2 - 2x)e^x\,dx = [(2 - 2x)e^x + 2e^x]_0^1 \quad \text{(by integrating by parts)}$$

$$= 2e - 4$$

9. The curve of intersection is an ellipse in the plane $z = x + 4$ with unit normal $\mathbf{n} = \tfrac{1}{\sqrt{2}}(-\mathbf{i} + \mathbf{k})$ and
$\operatorname{curl}\mathbf{F} = 5\,\mathbf{i} + 2\,\mathbf{j} + 4\,\mathbf{k}$ so $\operatorname{curl}\mathbf{F} \cdot \mathbf{n} = -\tfrac{1}{\sqrt{2}}$. Then
$\oint_C \mathbf{F} \cdot d\mathbf{r} = -\iint_S \tfrac{1}{\sqrt{2}}\,dS = -\tfrac{1}{\sqrt{2}}(\text{surface area of planar ellipse}) = -\tfrac{1}{\sqrt{2}}\pi(2)(2\sqrt{2}) = -4\pi$. (Recall that the area of an ellipse with semiaxes a and b is πab.)

10. S is the part of the surface $z = 1 - x^2 - y^2$ in the first octant. $\text{curl } \mathbf{F} = 2y\,\mathbf{i} - 2x\,\mathbf{j}$.

Using Equation 13.6.10 with $g(x,y) = 1 - x^2 - y^2$, $P = 2y$, $Q = -2x$, we have

$\int_C \mathbf{F} \cdot d\mathbf{r} = \iint_S \text{curl } \mathbf{F} \cdot d\mathbf{S} = \iint_D \left[-2y(-2x) + (2x)(-2y) \right] dA = \iint_D 0\, dA = 0.$

11. (a) The curve of intersection is an ellipse in the plane $x + y + z = 1$ with unit normal $\mathbf{n} = \frac{1}{\sqrt{3}}(\mathbf{i} + \mathbf{j} + \mathbf{k})$,

$\text{curl } \mathbf{F} = x^2\,\mathbf{j} + y^2\,\mathbf{k}$ and $\text{curl } \mathbf{F} \cdot \mathbf{n} = \frac{1}{\sqrt{3}}(x^2 + y^2)$. Then

$$\oint_C \mathbf{F} \cdot d\mathbf{r} = \iint_S \frac{1}{\sqrt{3}}(x^2 + y^2)\, dS = \iint_{x^2 + y^2 \le 9} (x^2 + y^2)\, dx\, dy$$

$$= \int_0^{2\pi} \int_0^3 r^3\, dr\, d\theta = 2\pi\left(\frac{81}{4}\right) = \frac{81\pi}{2}$$

(b)

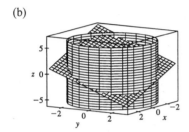

(c) One possible parametrization is $x = 3\cos t$, $y = 3\sin t$,

$z = 1 - 3\cos t - 3\sin t$, $0 \le t \le 2\pi$.

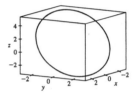

12. (a) S is the part of the surface $z = y^2 - x^2$ that lies above the unit disk D.

$\text{curl } \mathbf{F} = x\,\mathbf{i} - y\,\mathbf{j} + (x^2 - x^2)\,\mathbf{k} = x\,\mathbf{i} - y\,\mathbf{j}$. Using Equation 13.6.10 with $g(x,y) = y^2 - x^2$, $P = x$,

$Q = -y$, we have

$$\int_C \mathbf{F} \cdot d\mathbf{r} = \iint_S \text{curl } \mathbf{F} \cdot d\mathbf{S} = \iint_D \left[-x(-2x) - (-y)(2y) \right] dA = 2 \iint_D (x^2 + y^2)\, dA$$

$$= 2 \int_0^{2\pi} \int_0^1 r^2 r\, dr\, d\theta = 2(2\pi)\left[\frac{1}{4} r^4 \right]_0^1 = \pi$$

(b)

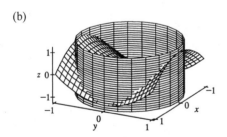

(c) One possible set of parametric equations is $x = \cos t$,

$y = \sin t$, $z = \sin^2 t - \cos^2 t$, $0 \le t \le 2\pi$.

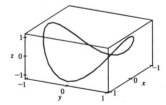

13. The boundary curve C is the circle $x^2 + y^2 = 1$, $z = 1$ oriented in the counterclockwise direction as viewed from

above. We can parametrize C by $\mathbf{r}(t) = \cos t\,\mathbf{i} + \sin t\,\mathbf{j} + \mathbf{k}$, $0 \le t \le 2\pi$, and then $\mathbf{r}'(t) = -\sin t\,\mathbf{i} + \cos t\,\mathbf{j}$. Thus

$\mathbf{F}(\mathbf{r}(t)) = \sin^2 t\,\mathbf{i} + \cos t\,\mathbf{j} + \mathbf{k}$, $\mathbf{F}(\mathbf{r}(t)) \cdot \mathbf{r}'(t) = \cos^2 t - \sin^3 t$, and

$$\oint_C \mathbf{F} \cdot d\mathbf{r} = \int_0^{2\pi} (\cos^2 t - \sin^3 t)\, dt = \int_0^{2\pi} \tfrac{1}{2}(1 + \cos 2t)\, dt - \int_0^{2\pi} (1 - \cos^2 t) \sin t\, dt$$

$$= \tfrac{1}{2}\left[t + \tfrac{1}{2}\sin 2t \right]_0^{2\pi} - \left[-\cos t + \tfrac{1}{3}\cos^3 t \right]_0^{2\pi} = \pi$$

Now $\text{curl } \mathbf{F} = (1 - 2y)\,\mathbf{k}$, and the projection D of S on the xy-plane is the disk $x^2 + y^2 \le 1$, so by

Equation 13.6.10 with $z = g(x, y) = x^2 + y^2$ we have

$$\iint_S \text{curl } \mathbf{F} \cdot d\mathbf{S} = \iint_D (1 - 2y) \, dA = \int_0^{2\pi} \int_0^1 (1 - 2r \sin \theta) r \, dr \, d\theta = \int_0^{2\pi} \left(\tfrac{1}{2} - \tfrac{2}{3} \sin \theta \right) d\theta = \pi$$

14. The plane intersects the coordinate axes at $x = 1$, $y = z = 2$ so the boundary curve C consists of the three line segments C_1: $\mathbf{r}_1(t) = (1 - t)\,\mathbf{i} + 2t\,\mathbf{j}$, $0 \le t \le 1$, C_2: $\mathbf{r}_2(t) = (2 - 2t)\,\mathbf{j} + 2t\,\mathbf{k}$, $0 \le t \le 1$, C_3: $\mathbf{r}_3(t) = t\,\mathbf{i} + (2 - 2t)\,\mathbf{k}$, $0 \le t \le 1$. Then

$$\oint_C \mathbf{F} \cdot d\mathbf{r} = \int_0^1 [(1 - t)\,\mathbf{i} + 2t\,\mathbf{j}] \cdot (-\mathbf{i} + 2\,\mathbf{j}) \, dt + \int_0^1 [(2 - 2t)\,\mathbf{j}] \cdot (-2\,\mathbf{j} + 2\,\mathbf{k}) \, dt + \int_0^1 (t\,\mathbf{i}) \cdot (\mathbf{i} - 2\,\mathbf{k}) \, dt$$

$$= \int_0^1 (5t - 1) \, dt + \int_0^1 (4t - 4) \, dt + \int_0^1 t \, dt = \tfrac{3}{2} - 2 + \tfrac{1}{2} = 0$$

Now curl $\mathbf{F} = xz\,\mathbf{i} - yz\,\mathbf{j}$, so by Equation 13.6.10 with $z = g(x, y) = 2 - 2x - y$ we have

$$\iint_S \text{curl } \mathbf{F} \cdot d\mathbf{S} = \iint_D [-x(2 - 2x - y)(-2) + y(2 - 2x - y)(-1)] \, dA$$

$$= \int_0^1 \int_0^{2-2x} \left(4x - 4x^2 - 2y + y^2 \right) dy \, dx$$

$$= \int_0^1 \left[4x(2 - 2x) - 4x^2(2 - 2x) - (2 - 2x)^2 + \tfrac{1}{3}(2 - 2x)^3 \right] dx$$

$$= \int_0^1 \left(\tfrac{16}{3}x^3 - 12x^2 + 8x - \tfrac{4}{3} \right) dx = \left[\tfrac{4}{3}x^4 - 4x^3 + 4x^2 - \tfrac{4}{3}x \right]_0^1 = 0$$

15. The boundary curve C is the circle $x^2 + z^2 = 1$, $y = 0$ oriented in the counterclockwise direction as viewed from the positive y-axis. Then C can be described by $\mathbf{r}(t) = \cos t\,\mathbf{i} - \sin t\,\mathbf{k}$, $0 \le t \le 2\pi$, and $\mathbf{r}'(t) = -\sin t\,\mathbf{i} - \cos t\,\mathbf{k}$. Thus $\mathbf{F}(\mathbf{r}(t)) = -\sin t\,\mathbf{j} + \cos t\,\mathbf{k}$, $\mathbf{F}(\mathbf{r}(t)) \cdot \mathbf{r}'(t) = -\cos^2 t$, and

$$\oint_C \mathbf{F} \cdot d\mathbf{r} = \int_0^{2\pi} -\cos^2 t \, dt = \left[-\tfrac{1}{2}t - \tfrac{1}{4} \sin 2t \right]_0^{2\pi} = -\pi$$

Now curl $\mathbf{F} = -\mathbf{i} - \mathbf{j} - \mathbf{k}$, and S can be parametrized (see Example 12.6.1) by $\mathbf{r}(\phi, \theta) = \sin \phi \cos \theta\,\mathbf{i} + \sin \phi \sin \theta\,\mathbf{j} + \cos \phi\,\mathbf{k}$, $0 \le \theta \le \pi$, $0 \le \phi \le \pi$. Then $\mathbf{r}_\phi \times \mathbf{r}_\theta = \sin^2 \phi \cos \theta\,\mathbf{i} + \sin^2 \phi \sin \theta\,\mathbf{j} + \sin \phi \cos \phi\,\mathbf{k}$ and

$$\iint_S \text{curl } \mathbf{F} \cdot d\mathbf{S} = \iint_{x^2+z^2 \le 1} \text{curl } \mathbf{F} \cdot (\mathbf{r}_\phi \times \mathbf{r}_\theta) \, dA$$

$$= \int_0^\pi \int_0^\pi \left(-\sin^2 \phi \cos \theta - \sin^2 \phi \sin \theta - \sin \phi \cos \phi \right) d\theta \, d\phi$$

$$= \int_0^\pi \left(-2 \sin^2 \phi - \pi \sin \phi \cos \phi \right) d\phi = \left[\tfrac{1}{2} \sin 2\phi - \phi - \tfrac{\pi}{2} \sin^2 \phi \right]_0^\pi = -\pi$$

16. The components of $\mathbf{F}$ are polynomials, which have continuous partial derivatives throughout $\mathbb{R}^3$, and both the curve C and the surface S meet the requirements of Stokes' Theorem. If there is a vector field $\mathbf{G}$ where $\mathbf{F} = \text{curl } \mathbf{G}$, then Stokes' Theorem says $\iint_S \mathbf{F} \cdot d\mathbf{S} = \iint_S \text{curl } \mathbf{G} \cdot d\mathbf{S}$ depends only on the values of $\mathbf{G}$ on C, and hence is independent of the choice of S. By Theorem 13.5.11, div curl $\mathbf{G} = 0$, so div $\mathbf{F} = 0$ ⟺ $(3ax^2 - 3z^2) + (x^2 + 3by^2) + (3cz^2) = 0$ ⟺ $(3a + 1)x^2 + 3by^2 + (3c - 3)z^2 = 0$ ⟺ $a = -\tfrac{1}{3}$, $b = 0$, $c = 1$.

17. $\operatorname{curl} \mathbf{F} = \begin{vmatrix} \mathbf{i} & \mathbf{j} & \mathbf{k} \\ \partial/\partial x & \partial/\partial y & \partial/\partial z \\ x^x + z^2 & y^y + x^2 & z^z + y^2 \end{vmatrix} = 2y\,\mathbf{i} + 2z\,\mathbf{j} + 2x\,\mathbf{k}$ and $W = \int_C \mathbf{F} \cdot d\mathbf{r} = \iint_S \operatorname{curl} \mathbf{F} \cdot d\mathbf{S}.$

To parametrize the surface, let $x = 2\cos\theta\sin\phi$, $y = 2\sin\theta\sin\phi$, $z = 2\cos\phi$, so that
$\mathbf{r}(\phi, \theta) = 2\sin\phi\cos\theta\,\mathbf{i} + 2\sin\phi\sin\theta\,\mathbf{j} + 2\cos\phi\,\mathbf{k}$, $0 \le \phi \le \frac{\pi}{2}$, $0 \le \theta \le \frac{\pi}{2}$, and
$\mathbf{r}_\phi \times \mathbf{r}_\theta = 4\sin^2\phi\cos\theta\,\mathbf{i} + 4\sin^2\phi\sin\theta\,\mathbf{j} + 4\sin\phi\cos\phi\,\mathbf{k}$. Then
$\operatorname{curl}\mathbf{F}(\mathbf{r}(\phi,\theta)) = 4\sin\phi\sin\theta\,\mathbf{i} + 4\cos\phi\,\mathbf{j} + 4\sin\phi\cos\theta\,\mathbf{k}$, and
$\operatorname{curl}\mathbf{F} \cdot (\mathbf{r}_\phi \times \mathbf{r}_\theta) = 16\sin^3\phi\sin\theta\cos\theta + 16\cos\phi\sin^2\phi\sin\theta + 16\sin^2\phi\cos\phi\cos\theta$. Therefore

$$\iint_S \operatorname{curl}\mathbf{F} \cdot d\mathbf{S} = \iint_D \operatorname{curl}\mathbf{F} \cdot (\mathbf{r}_\phi \times \mathbf{r}_\theta)\,dA$$

$$= 16\left[\int_0^{\pi/2}\sin\theta\cos\theta\,d\theta\right]\left[\int_0^{\pi/2}\sin^3\phi\,d\phi\right] + 16\left[\int_0^{\pi/2}\sin\theta\,d\theta\right]\left[\int_0^{\pi/2}\sin^2\phi\cos\phi\,d\phi\right]$$

$$+ 16\left[\int_0^{\pi/2}\cos\theta\,d\theta\right]\left[\int_0^{\pi/2}\sin^2\phi\cos\phi\,d\phi\right]$$

$$= 8\left[-\cos\phi + \tfrac{1}{3}\cos^3\phi\right]_0^{\pi/2} + 16(1)\left[\tfrac{1}{3}\sin^3\phi\right]_0^{\pi/2} + 16(1)\left[\tfrac{1}{3}\sin^3\phi\right]_0^{\pi/2}$$

$$= 8\left[0 + 1 + 0 - \tfrac{1}{3}\right] + 16\left(\tfrac{1}{3}\right) + 16\left(\tfrac{1}{3}\right) = \tfrac{16}{3} + \tfrac{16}{3} + \tfrac{16}{3} = 16$$

18. $\int_C (y + \sin x)\,dx + (z^2 + \cos y)\,dy + x^3\,dz = \int_C \mathbf{F} \cdot d\mathbf{r}$, where
$\mathbf{F}(x, y, z) = (y + \sin x)\,\mathbf{i} + (z^2 + \cos y)\,\mathbf{j} + x^3\,\mathbf{k} \ \Rightarrow \ \operatorname{curl}\mathbf{F} = -2z\,\mathbf{i} - 3x^2\,\mathbf{j} - \mathbf{k}$. Since
$\sin 2t = 2\sin t\cos t$, C lies on the surface $z = 2xy$. Let S be the part of this surface that is bounded by C. Then
the projection of S onto the xy-plane is the unit disk D $(x^2 + y^2 \le 1)$. C is traversed clockwise (when viewed
from above) so S is oriented downward. Using Equation 13.6.10 with $g(x, y) = 2xy$, $P = -2(2xy) = -4xy$,
$Q = -3x^2$, $R = -1$, we have

$$\int_C \mathbf{F} \cdot d\mathbf{r} = -\iint_S \operatorname{curl}\mathbf{F} \cdot d\mathbf{S} = -\iint_D \left[-(-4xy)(2y) - (-3x^2)(2x) - 1\right] dA$$

$$= -\iint_D (8xy^2 + 6x^3 - 1)\,dA = -\int_0^{2\pi}\int_0^1 (8r^3\cos\theta\sin^2\theta + 6r^3\cos^3\theta - 1)\,r\,dr\,d\theta$$

$$= -\int_0^{2\pi}\left(\tfrac{8}{5}\cos\theta\sin^2\theta + \tfrac{6}{5}\cos^3\theta - \tfrac{1}{2}\right) r\,dr\,d\theta$$

$$= -\left[\tfrac{8}{15}\sin^3\theta + \tfrac{6}{5}\left(\sin\theta - \tfrac{1}{3}\sin^3\theta\right) - \tfrac{1}{2}\theta\right]_0^{2\pi} = \pi$$

19. Assume S is centered at the origin with radius a and let H_1 and H_2 be the upper and lower hemispheres,
respectively, of S. Then $\iint_S \operatorname{curl}\mathbf{F} \cdot d\mathbf{S} = \iint_{H_1} \operatorname{curl}\mathbf{F} \cdot d\mathbf{S} + \iint_{H_2} \operatorname{curl}\mathbf{F} \cdot d\mathbf{S} = \oint_{C_1} \mathbf{F} \cdot d\mathbf{r} + \oint_{C_2} \mathbf{F} \cdot d\mathbf{r}$ by
Stokes' Theorem. But C_1 is the circle $x^2 + y^2 = a^2$ oriented in the counterclockwise direction while C_2 is the
same circle oriented in the clockwise direction. Hence $\oint_{C_2} \mathbf{F} \cdot d\mathbf{r} = -\oint_{C_1} \mathbf{F} \cdot d\mathbf{r}$ so $\iint_S \operatorname{curl}\mathbf{F} \cdot d\mathbf{S} = 0$ as
desired.

20. (a) By Exercise 13.5.24, $\operatorname{curl}(f\nabla g) = f\operatorname{curl}(\nabla g) + \nabla f \times \nabla g = \nabla f \times \nabla g$ since $\operatorname{curl}(\nabla g) = \mathbf{0}$. Hence by
Stokes' Theorem $\int_C (f\nabla g) \cdot d\mathbf{r} = \iint_S (\nabla f \times \nabla g) \cdot d\mathbf{S}$.

(b) As in (a), $\operatorname{curl}(f\nabla f) = \nabla f \times \nabla f = \mathbf{0}$, so by Stokes' Theorem, $\int_C (f\nabla f) \cdot d\mathbf{r} = \iint_S [\operatorname{curl}(f\nabla f)] \cdot d\mathbf{S} = 0$.

(c) As in (a),

$$\operatorname{curl}(f\nabla g + g\nabla f) = \operatorname{curl}(f\nabla g) + \operatorname{curl}(g\nabla f) \quad \text{(by Exercise 13.5.22)}$$

$$= (\nabla f \times \nabla g) + (\nabla g \times \nabla f) = \mathbf{0} \quad [\text{since } \mathbf{u} \times \mathbf{v} = -(\mathbf{v} \times \mathbf{u})]$$

Hence by Stokes' Theorem, $\int_C (f\nabla g + g\nabla f) \cdot d\mathbf{r} = \iint_S \operatorname{curl}(f\nabla g + g\nabla f) \cdot d\mathbf{S} = 0$.

13.8 The Divergence Theorem • • • • • • • • • • • •

1. The vectors that end near P_1 are longer than the vectors that start near P_1, so the net flow is inward near P_1 and div $\mathbf{F}(P_1)$ is negative. The vectors that end near P_2 are shorter than the vectors that start near P_2, so the net flow is outward near P_2 and div $\mathbf{F}(P_2)$ is positive.

2. (a) The vectors that end near P_1 are shorter than the vectors that start near P_1, so the net flow is outward and P_1 is a source. The vectors that end near P_2 are longer than the vectors that start near P_2, so the net flow is inward and P_2 is a sink.

(b) $\mathbf{F}(x, y) = \langle x, y^2 \rangle \Rightarrow \text{div } \mathbf{F} = \nabla \cdot \mathbf{F} = 1 + 2y$. The y-value at P_1 is positive, so div $\mathbf{F} = 1 + 2y$ is positive, thus P_1 is a source. At P_2, $y < -1$, so div $\mathbf{F} = 1 + 2y$ is negative, and P_2 is a sink.

3. div $\mathbf{F} = 3 + x + 2x = 3 + 3x$, so

$\iiint_E \text{div } \mathbf{F} \, dV = \int_0^1 \int_0^1 \int_0^1 (3x + 3) \, dx \, dy \, dz = \frac{9}{2}$ (notice the triple integral is three times the volume of the cube plus three times $\bar{x}$).

To compute $\iint_S \mathbf{F} \cdot d\mathbf{S}$, on S_1: $\mathbf{n} = \mathbf{i}$, $\mathbf{F} = 3\,\mathbf{i} + y\,\mathbf{j} + 2z\,\mathbf{k}$, and

$\iint_{S_1} \mathbf{F} \cdot d\mathbf{S} = \iint_{S_1} 3 \, dS = 3;$

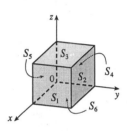

S_2: $\mathbf{F} = 3x\,\mathbf{i} + x\,\mathbf{j} + 2xz\,\mathbf{k}$, $\mathbf{n} = \mathbf{j}$ and $\iint_{S_2} \mathbf{F} \cdot d\mathbf{S} = \iint_{S_2} x \, dS = \frac{1}{2};$

S_3: $\mathbf{F} = 3x\,\mathbf{i} + xy\,\mathbf{j} + 2x\,\mathbf{k}$, $\mathbf{n} = \mathbf{k}$ and $\iint_{S_3} \mathbf{F} \cdot d\mathbf{S} = \iint_{S_3} 2x \, dS = 1;$

S_4: $\mathbf{F} = 0$, $\iint_{S_4} \mathbf{F} \cdot d\mathbf{S} = 0$; S_5: $\mathbf{F} = 3x\,\mathbf{i} + 2x\,\mathbf{k}$, $\mathbf{n} = -\mathbf{j}$ and $\iint_{S_5} \mathbf{F} \cdot d\mathbf{S} = \iint_{S_5} 0 \, dS = 0;$

S_6: $\mathbf{F} = 3x\,\mathbf{i} + xy\,\mathbf{j}$, $\mathbf{n} = -\mathbf{k}$ and $\iint_{S_6} \mathbf{F} \cdot d\mathbf{S} = \iint_{S_6} 0 \, dS = 0$. Thus $\iint_S \mathbf{F} \cdot d\mathbf{S} = \frac{9}{2}$.

4. div $\mathbf{F} = 8z$, so

$\iiint_E \text{div } \mathbf{F} \, dV = \int_0^{2\pi} \int_0^1 \int_{r^2}^1 8zr \, dz \, dr \, d\theta = 2\pi \int_0^1 (4r - 4r^5) \, dr = \frac{8}{3}\pi.$

On S_1: $\mathbf{F} = x\,\mathbf{i} + y\,\mathbf{j} + 3\,\mathbf{k}$, $\mathbf{n} = \mathbf{k}$ and $\iint_{S_1} \mathbf{F} \cdot d\mathbf{S} = \iint_{S_1} 3 \, dS = 3\pi.$

S_2: $\mathbf{F} = (x^3 + xy^2)\,\mathbf{i} + (y^3 + yx^2)\,\mathbf{j} + 3(x^2 + y^2)^2\,\mathbf{k}$,

$-(\mathbf{r}_x \times \mathbf{r}_y) = 2x\,\mathbf{i} + 2y\,\mathbf{j} - \mathbf{k}$ and

$$\iint_{S_2} \mathbf{F} \cdot d\mathbf{S} = \iint_{x^2 + y^2 \leq 1} (-x^4 - y^4 - 2x^2 y^2) \, dA$$

$$= -\int_0^{2\pi} \int_0^1 r^5 \, dr \, d\theta = -\frac{\pi}{3}$$

Hence $\iint_S \mathbf{F} \cdot d\mathbf{S} = 3\pi - \frac{\pi}{3} = \frac{8}{3}\pi.$

5. div $\mathbf{F} = x + y + z$, so

$$\iiint_E \text{div } \mathbf{F} \, dV = \int_0^{2\pi} \int_0^1 \int_0^1 (r\cos\theta + r\sin\theta + z)\, r \, dz \, dr \, d\theta = \int_0^{2\pi} \int_0^1 (r^2 \cos\theta + r^2 \sin\theta + \frac{1}{2}r) \, dr \, d\theta$$

$$= \int_0^{2\pi} (\frac{1}{3}\cos\theta + \frac{1}{3}\sin\theta + \frac{1}{4}) \, d\theta = \frac{1}{4}(2\pi) = \frac{\pi}{2}$$

Let S_1 be the top of the cylinder, S_2 the bottom, and S_3 the vertical edge. On S_1, $z = 1$, $\mathbf{n} = \mathbf{k}$, and $\mathbf{F} = xy\,\mathbf{i} + y\,\mathbf{j} + x\,\mathbf{k}$, so

$\iint_{S_1} \mathbf{F} \cdot d\mathbf{S} = \iint_{S_1} \mathbf{F} \cdot \mathbf{n} \, dS = \iint_{S_1} x \, dS = \int_0^{2\pi} \int_0^1 (r\cos\theta) \, r \, dr \, d\theta = [\sin\theta]_0^{2\pi} \left[\frac{1}{3}r^3\right]_0^1 = 0.$ On S_2, $z = 0$,

$\mathbf{n} = -\mathbf{k}$, and $\mathbf{F} = xy\,\mathbf{i}$ so $\iint_{S_2} \mathbf{F} \cdot d\mathbf{S} = \iint_{S_2} 0 \, dS = 0$. S_3 is given by $\mathbf{r}(\theta, z) = \cos\theta\,\mathbf{i} + \sin\theta\,\mathbf{j} + z\,\mathbf{k}$,

$0 \le \theta \le 2\pi$, $0 \le z \le 1$. Then $\mathbf{r}_\theta \times \mathbf{r}_z = \cos\theta\,\mathbf{i} + \sin\theta\,\mathbf{j}$ and

$$\iint_{S_3} \mathbf{F} \cdot d\mathbf{S} = \iint_D \mathbf{F} \cdot (\mathbf{r}_\theta \times \mathbf{r}_z) \, dA = \int_0^{2\pi} \int_0^1 \left(\cos^2\theta\sin\theta + z\sin^2\theta\right) dz \, d\theta$$

$$= \int_0^{2\pi} \left(\cos^2\theta\sin\theta + \frac{1}{2}\sin^2\theta\right) d\theta = \left[-\frac{1}{3}\cos^3\theta + \frac{1}{4}\left(\theta - \frac{1}{2}\sin 2\theta\right)\right]_0^{2\pi} = \frac{\pi}{2}$$

Thus $\iint_S \mathbf{F} \cdot d\mathbf{S} = 0 + 0 + \frac{\pi}{2} = \frac{\pi}{2}$.

6. div $\mathbf{F} = 1 + 1 + 1 = 3$, so $\iiint_E \text{div } \mathbf{F} \, dV = \iiint_E 3 \, dV = 3(\text{volume of ball}) = 3\left(\frac{4}{3}\pi\right) = 4\pi$. To find

$\iint_S \mathbf{F} \cdot d\mathbf{S}$ we use spherical coordinates. S is the unit sphere, represented by

$\mathbf{r}(\phi, \theta) = \sin\phi\cos\theta\,\mathbf{i} + \sin\phi\sin\theta\,\mathbf{j} + \cos\phi\,\mathbf{k}$, $0 \le \phi \le \pi$, $0 \le \theta \le 2\pi$. Then

$\mathbf{r}_\phi \times \mathbf{r}_\theta = \sin^2\phi\cos\theta\,\mathbf{i} + \sin^2\phi\sin\theta\,\mathbf{j} + \sin\phi\cos\phi\,\mathbf{k}$ (see Example 12.6.1) and

$\mathbf{F}(\mathbf{r}(\phi, \theta)) = \sin\phi\cos\theta\,\mathbf{i} + \sin\phi\sin\theta\,\mathbf{j} + \cos\phi\,\mathbf{k}$. Thus

$$\iint_S \mathbf{F} \cdot d\mathbf{S} = \iint_D \mathbf{F} \cdot (\mathbf{r}_\phi \times \mathbf{r}_\theta) \, dA = \int_0^{2\pi} \int_0^\pi \left(\sin^3\phi\cos^2\theta + \sin^3\phi\sin^2\theta + \sin\phi\cos^2\phi\right) d\phi \, d\theta$$

$$= \int_0^{2\pi} d\theta \int_0^\pi \sin\phi \, d\phi = (2\pi)(2) = 4\pi$$

7. div $\mathbf{F} = \frac{\partial}{\partial x}(e^x\sin y) + \frac{\partial}{\partial y}(e^x\cos y) + \frac{\partial}{\partial z}(yz^2) = e^x\sin y - e^x\sin y + 2yz = 2yz$, so by the Divergence Theorem,

$$\iint_S \mathbf{F} \cdot d\mathbf{S} = \iiint_E \text{div } \mathbf{F} \, dV = \int_0^1 \int_0^1 \int_0^2 2yz \, dz \, dy \, dx = 2\int_0^1 dx \int_0^1 y \, dy \int_0^1 z \, dz$$

$$= 2[x]_0^1 \left[\frac{1}{2}y^2\right]_0^1 \left[\frac{1}{2}z^2\right]_0^2 = 2$$

8. div $\mathbf{F} = \frac{\partial}{\partial x}(x^2z^3) + \frac{\partial}{\partial y}(2xyz^3) + \frac{\partial}{\partial z}(xz^4) = 2xz^3 + 2xz^3 + 4xz^3 = 8xz^3$, so by the Divergence Theorem,

$$\iint_S \mathbf{F} \cdot d\mathbf{S} = \iiint_E \text{div } \mathbf{F} \, dV = \int_{-1}^1 \int_{-2}^2 \int_{-3}^3 8xz^3 \, dz \, dy \, dx = 8\int_{-1}^1 x \, dx \int_{-2}^2 dy \int_{-3}^3 z^3 \, dz$$

$$= 8\left[\frac{1}{2}x^2\right]_{-1}^1 [y]_{-2}^2 \left[\frac{1}{4}z^4\right]_{-3}^3 = 0$$

9. div $\mathbf{F} = 3y^2 + 0 + 3z^2$, so using cylindrical coordinates with $y = r\cos\theta$, $z = r\sin\theta$, $x = x$ we have

$$\iint_S \mathbf{F} \cdot d\mathbf{S} = \iiint_E (3y^2 + 3z^2) \, dV = \int_0^{2\pi} \int_0^1 \int_{-1}^2 (3r^2\cos^2\theta + 3r^2\sin^2\theta) \, r \, dx \, dr \, d\theta$$

$$= 3\int_0^{2\pi} d\theta \int_0^1 r^3 \, dr \int_{-1}^2 dx = 3(2\pi)\left(\frac{1}{4}\right)(3) = \frac{9\pi}{2}$$

10. div $\mathbf{F} = 3x^2y - 2x^2y - x^2y = 0$, so $\iint_S \mathbf{F} \cdot d\mathbf{S} = \iiint_E 0 \, dV = 0$.

11. div $\mathbf{F} = y\sin z + 0 - y\sin z = 0$, so by the Divergence Theorem, $\iint_S \mathbf{F} \cdot d\mathbf{S} = \iiint_E 0 \, dV = 0$.

12. $\iint_S \mathbf{F} \cdot d\mathbf{S} = \iiint_E 3(x^2 + y^2) \, dV = \int_0^{2\pi} \int_0^2 \int_0^{4 - r^2} 3r^3 \, dz \, dr \, d\theta = 2\pi \int_0^2 (12r^3 - 3r^5) \, dr = 32\pi$

13. $\iint_S \mathbf{F} \cdot d\mathbf{S} = \iiint_E 3(x^2 + y^2 + z^2) \, dV = \int_0^{2\pi} \int_0^\pi \int_0^1 3\rho^4\sin\phi \, d\rho \, d\phi \, d\theta = 2\pi \int_0^\pi \frac{3}{5}\sin\phi \, d\phi = \frac{12}{5}\pi$

14. $\iint_S \mathbf{F} \cdot d\mathbf{S} = \iiint_E 3(x^2 + y^2 + 1) \, dV = \int_0^{2\pi} \int_0^{\pi/2} \int_1^2 3(\rho^2\sin^2\phi + 1) \, \rho^2\sin\phi \, d\rho \, d\phi \, d\theta$

$$= 2\pi \int_0^{\pi/2} \left[\frac{93}{5}\sin^3\phi + 7\sin\phi\right] d\phi = 2\pi\left[\frac{93}{5}\left(-\cos\phi + \frac{1}{3}\cos^3\phi\right) - 7\cos\phi\right]_0^{\pi/2} = \frac{194}{5}\pi$$

15. $\iint_S \mathbf{F} \cdot d\mathbf{S} = \iiint_E \sqrt{3 - x^2} \, dV = \int_{-1}^1 \int_{-1}^1 \int_0^{2 - x^4 - y^4} \sqrt{3 - x^2} \, dz \, dy \, dx = \frac{341}{60}\sqrt{2} + \frac{81}{20}\sin^{-1}\left(\frac{\sqrt{3}}{3}\right)$

16.

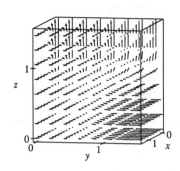 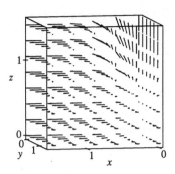

By the Divergence Theorem, the flux of **F** across the surface of the cube is

$$\iint_S \mathbf{F} \cdot d\mathbf{S} = \int_0^{\pi/2} \int_0^{\pi/2} \int_0^{\pi/2} \left[\cos x \cos^2 y + 3 \sin^2 y \cos y \cos^4 z + 5 \sin^4 z \cos z \cos^6 x\right] dz\, dy\, dx = \tfrac{19}{64}\pi^2$$

17. For S_1 we have $\mathbf{n} = -\mathbf{k}$, so $\mathbf{F} \cdot \mathbf{n} = \mathbf{F} \cdot (-\mathbf{k}) = -x^2 z - y^2 = -y^2$ (since $z = 0$ on S_1). So if D is the unit disk,

we get $\iint_{S_1} \mathbf{F} \cdot d\mathbf{S} = \iint_{S_1} \mathbf{F} \cdot \mathbf{n}\, dS = \iint_D (-y^2)\, dA = -\int_0^{2\pi} \int_0^1 r^2 \sin^2 \theta\, r\, dr\, d\theta = -\tfrac{1}{4}\pi$. Now

since S_2 is closed, we can use the Divergence Theorem. Since

$$\operatorname{div} \mathbf{F} = \frac{\partial}{\partial x}\left(z^2 x\right) + \frac{\partial}{\partial y}\left(\tfrac{1}{3}y^3 + \tan z\right) + \frac{\partial}{\partial z}\left(x^2 z + y^2\right) = z^2 + y^2 + x^2,$$ we use spherical coordinates to get

$$\iint_{S_2} \mathbf{F} \cdot d\mathbf{S} = \iiint_E \operatorname{div} \mathbf{F}\, dV = \int_0^{2\pi} \int_0^{\pi/2} \int_0^1 \rho^2 \cdot \rho^2 \sin\phi\, d\rho\, d\phi\, d\theta = \tfrac{2}{5}\pi.$$ Finally

$$\iint_S \mathbf{F} \cdot d\mathbf{S} = \iint_{S_2} \mathbf{F} \cdot d\mathbf{S} - \iint_{S_1} \mathbf{F} \cdot d\mathbf{S} = \tfrac{2}{5}\pi - \left(-\tfrac{1}{4}\pi\right) = \tfrac{13}{20}\pi.$$

18. As in the hint to Exercise 17, we create a closed surface $S_2 = S \cup S_1$, where S is the part of the paraboloid

$x^2 + y^2 + z = 2$ that lies above the plane $z = 1$, and S_1 is the disk $x^2 + y^2 = 1$ on the plane $z = 1$ oriented

downward, and we then apply the Divergence Theorem. Since the disk S_1 is oriented downward, its unit normal

vector is $\mathbf{n} = -\mathbf{k}$ and $\mathbf{F} \cdot (-\mathbf{k}) = -z = -1$ on S_1. So

$$\iint_{S_1} \mathbf{F} \cdot d\mathbf{S} = \iint_{S_1} \mathbf{F} \cdot \mathbf{n}\, dS = \iint_{S_1}(-1)\, dS = -A(S_1) = -\pi.$$ Let E be the region bounded by S_2. Then

$$\iint_{S_2} \mathbf{F} \cdot d\mathbf{S} = \iiint_E \operatorname{div} \mathbf{F}\, dV = \iiint_E 1\, dV = \int_0^1 \int_0^{2\pi} \int_1^{2-r^2} r\, dz\, d\theta\, dr = \int_0^1 \int_0^{2\pi} \left(r - r^3\right) d\theta\, dr$$

$$= (2\pi)\tfrac{1}{4} = \tfrac{\pi}{2}.$$

Thus the flux of **F** across S is $\iint_S \mathbf{F} \cdot d\mathbf{S} = \iint_{S_2} \mathbf{F} \cdot d\mathbf{S} - \iint_{S_1} \mathbf{F} \cdot d\mathbf{S} = \tfrac{\pi}{2} - (-\pi) = \tfrac{3\pi}{2}.$

19. Since $\dfrac{\mathbf{x}}{|\mathbf{x}|^3} = \dfrac{x\mathbf{i} + y\mathbf{j} + z\mathbf{k}}{(x^2 + y^2 + z^2)^{3/2}}$ and $\dfrac{\partial}{\partial x}\left(\dfrac{x}{(x^2 + y^2 + z^2)^{3/2}}\right) = \dfrac{(x^2 + y^2 + z^2) - 3x^2}{(x^2 + y^2 + z^2)^{5/2}}$ with similar

expressions for $\dfrac{\partial}{\partial y}\left(\dfrac{y}{(x^2 + y^2 + z^2)^{3/2}}\right)$ and $\dfrac{\partial}{\partial z}\left(\dfrac{z}{(x^2 + y^2 + z^2)^{3/2}}\right)$, we have

$$\operatorname{div}\left(\dfrac{\mathbf{x}}{|\mathbf{x}|^3}\right) = \dfrac{3(x^2 + y^2 + z^2) - 3(x^2 + y^2 + z^2)}{(x^2 + y^2 + z^2)^{5/2}} = 0,\text{ except at } (0, 0, 0) \text{ where it is undefined.}$$

20. We first need to find **F** so that $\iint_S \mathbf{F} \cdot \mathbf{n}\, dS = \iint_S \left(2x + 2y + z^2\right) dS$, so $\mathbf{F} \cdot \mathbf{n} = 2x + 2y + z^2$. But for S,

$$\mathbf{n} = \dfrac{x\mathbf{i} + y\mathbf{j} + z\mathbf{k}}{\sqrt{x^2 + y^2 + z^2}} = x\mathbf{i} + y\mathbf{j} + z\mathbf{k}.$$ Thus $\mathbf{F} = 2\mathbf{i} + 2\mathbf{j} + z\mathbf{k}$ and $\operatorname{div} \mathbf{F} = 1$. If

$B = \left\{(x, y, z)\mid x^2 + y^2 + z^2 \le 1\right\}$, then $\iint_S \left(2x + 2y + z^2\right) dS = \iiint_B dV = V(B) = \tfrac{4}{3}\pi(1)^3 = \tfrac{4}{3}\pi.$

21. $\iint_S \mathbf{a} \cdot \mathbf{n}\, dS = \iiint_E \operatorname{div} \mathbf{a}\, dV = 0$ since $\operatorname{div} \mathbf{a} = 0.$

22. $\tfrac{1}{3}\iint_S \mathbf{F} \cdot d\mathbf{S} = \tfrac{1}{3}\iiint_E \operatorname{div} \mathbf{F}\, dV = \tfrac{1}{3}\iiint_E 3\, dV = V(E)$

23. $\iint_S \operatorname{curl} \mathbf{F} \cdot d\mathbf{S} = \iiint_E \operatorname{div}(\operatorname{curl} \mathbf{F})\, dV = 0$ by Theorem 13.5.11.

24. $\iint_S D_{\mathbf{n}} f \, dS = \iint_S (\nabla f \cdot \mathbf{n}) \, dS = \iiint_E \operatorname{div}(\nabla f) \, dV = \iiint_E \nabla^2 f \, dV$

25. $\iint_S (f \nabla g) \cdot \mathbf{n} \, dS = \iiint_E \operatorname{div}(f \nabla g) \, dV = \iiint_E (f \nabla^2 g + \nabla g \cdot \nabla f) \, dV$ by Exercise 13.5.23.

26. $\iint_S (f \nabla g - g \nabla f) \cdot \mathbf{n} \, dS = \iiint_E \left[(f \nabla^2 g + \nabla g \cdot \nabla f) - (g \nabla^2 f + \nabla g \cdot \nabla f) \right] dV$ (by Exercise 25). But
$\nabla g \cdot \nabla f = \nabla f \cdot \nabla g$, so that $\iint_S (f \nabla g - g \nabla f) \cdot \mathbf{n} \, dS = \iiint_E (f \nabla^2 g - g \nabla^2 f) \, dV$.

27. If $\mathbf{c} = c_1 \mathbf{i} + c_2 \mathbf{j} + c_3 \mathbf{k}$ is an arbitrary constant vector, we define $\mathbf{F} = f \mathbf{c} = f c_1 \mathbf{i} + f c_2 \mathbf{j} + f c_3 \mathbf{k}$. Then

$\operatorname{div} \mathbf{F} = \operatorname{div} f \mathbf{c} = \dfrac{\partial f}{\partial x} c_1 + \dfrac{\partial f}{\partial y} c_2 + \dfrac{\partial f}{\partial z} c_3 = \nabla f \cdot \mathbf{c}$ and the Divergence Theorem says

$\iint_S \mathbf{F} \cdot d\mathbf{S} = \iiint_E \operatorname{div} \mathbf{F} \, dV \;\Rightarrow\; \iint_S \mathbf{F} \cdot \mathbf{n} \, dS = \iiint_E \nabla f \cdot \mathbf{c} \, dV$. In particular, if $\mathbf{c} = \mathbf{i}$ then

$\iint_S f \mathbf{i} \cdot \mathbf{n} \, dS = \iiint_E \nabla f \cdot \mathbf{i} \, dV \;\Rightarrow\; \iint_S f n_1 \, dS = \iiint_E \dfrac{\partial f}{\partial x} \, dV$ (where $\mathbf{n} = n_1 \mathbf{i} + n_2 \mathbf{j} + n_3 \mathbf{k}$).

Similarly, if $\mathbf{c} = \mathbf{j}$ we have $\iint_S f n_2 \, dS = \iiint_E \dfrac{\partial f}{\partial y} \, dV$, and $\mathbf{c} = \mathbf{k}$ gives $\iint_S f n_3 \, dS = \iiint_E \dfrac{\partial f}{\partial z} \, dV$. Then

$$\iint_S f \mathbf{n} \, dS = \left(\iint_S f n_1 \, dS \right) \mathbf{i} + \left(\iint_S f n_2 \, dS \right) \mathbf{j} + \left(\iint_S f n_3 \, dS \right) \mathbf{k}$$

$$= \left(\iiint_E \dfrac{\partial f}{\partial x} \, dV \right) \mathbf{i} + \left(\iiint_E \dfrac{\partial f}{\partial y} \, dV \right) \mathbf{j} + \left(\iiint_E \dfrac{\partial f}{\partial z} \, dV \right) \mathbf{k}$$

$$= \iiint_E \left(\dfrac{\partial f}{\partial x} \mathbf{i} + \dfrac{\partial f}{\partial y} \mathbf{j} + \dfrac{\partial f}{\partial z} \mathbf{k} \right) dV = \iiint_E \nabla f \, dV$$

as desired.

28. By Exercise 27, $\iint_S p \mathbf{n} \, dS = \iiint_E \nabla p \, dV$, so

$$\mathbf{F} = - \iint_S p \mathbf{n} \, dS = - \iiint_E \nabla p \, dV = - \iiint_E \nabla (\rho g z) \, dV = - \iiint_E (\rho g \, \mathbf{k}) \, dV$$

$$= -\rho g \left(\iiint_E dV \right) \mathbf{k} = -\rho g V(E) \, \mathbf{k}$$

But the weight of the displaced liquid is volume × density × $g = \rho g V(E)$, thus $\mathbf{F} = -W \mathbf{k}$ as desired.

13 Review

1. See Definitions 1 and 2 in Section 13.1. A vector field can represent, for example, the wind velocity at any location in space, the speed and direction of the ocean current at any location, or the force vectors of Earth's gravitational field at a location in space.

2. (a) A conservative vector field $\mathbf{F}$ is a vector field which is the gradient of some scalar function f.

   (b) The function f in part (a) is called a potential function for $\mathbf{F}$, that is, $\mathbf{F} = \nabla f$.

3. (a) See Definition 13.2.2.

   (b) We normally evaluate the line integral using Formula 13.2.3.

   (c) The mass is $m = \int_C \rho(x, y) \, ds$, and the center of mass is $(\overline{x}, \overline{y})$ where $\overline{x} = \frac{1}{m} \int_C x \rho(x, y) \, ds$, $\overline{y} = \frac{1}{m} \int_C y \rho(x, y) \, ds$.

   (d) See (5) and (6) in Section 13.2 for plane curves; we have similar definitions when C is a space curve (see the equation preceding (10) on page 930).

   (e) For plane curves, see Equations 13.2.7. We have similar results for space curves (see the equation preceding (10) on page 930).

4. (a) See Definition 13.2.13.

   (b) If $\mathbf{F}$ is a force field, $\int_C \mathbf{F} \cdot d\mathbf{r}$ represents the work done by $\mathbf{F}$ in moving a particle along the curve C.

   (c) $\int_C \mathbf{F} \cdot d\mathbf{r} = \int_C P \, dx + Q \, dy + R \, dz$

5. See Theorem 13.3.2.

6. (a) $\int_C \mathbf{F} \cdot d\mathbf{r}$ is independent of path if the line integral has the same value for any two curves that have the same initial and terminal points.

   (b) See Theorem 13.3.4.

7. See the statement of Green's Theorem on page 945.

8. See Equations 13.4.5.

9. (a) $\operatorname{curl} \mathbf{F} = \left(\dfrac{\partial R}{\partial y} - \dfrac{\partial Q}{\partial z} \right) \mathbf{i} + \left(\dfrac{\partial P}{\partial z} - \dfrac{\partial R}{\partial x} \right) \mathbf{j} + \left(\dfrac{\partial Q}{\partial x} - \dfrac{\partial P}{\partial y} \right) \mathbf{k} = \nabla \times \mathbf{F}$

   (b) $\operatorname{div} \mathbf{F} = \dfrac{\partial P}{\partial x} + \dfrac{\partial Q}{\partial y} + \dfrac{\partial R}{\partial z} = \nabla \cdot \mathbf{F}$

   (c) For curl $\mathbf{F}$, see the discussion accompanying Figure 1 on page 955 as well as Figure 6 and the accompanying discussion on page 975. For div $\mathbf{F}$, see the discussion following Example 5 on page 956 as well as the discussion preceding (8) on page 982.

10. See Theorem 13.3.6; see Theorem 13.5.4.

11. (a) See (1) in Section 13.6.

    (b) We normally evaluate the surface integral using Formula 13.6.2.

    (c) See Formula 13.6.4.

    (d) The mass is $m = \iint_S \rho(x, y, z) \, dS$ and the center of mass is $(\overline{x}, \overline{y}, \overline{z})$ where $\overline{x} = \frac{1}{m} \iint_S x \rho(x, y, z) \, dS$, $\overline{y} = \frac{1}{m} \iint_S y \rho(x, y, z) \, dS$, $\overline{z} = \frac{1}{m} \iint_S z \rho(x, y, z) \, dS$.

12. (a) See Figures 6 and 7 and the accompanying discussion in Section 13.6. A Möbius strip is a nonorientable surface; see Figures 4 and 5 and the accompanying discussion on page 964.

   (b) See Definition 13.6.8.

   (c) See Formula 13.6.9.

   (d) See Formula 13.6.10.

13. See the statement of Stokes' Theorem on page 971.

14. See the statement of the Divergence Theorem on page 978.

15. In each theorem, we have an integral of a "derivative" over a region on the left side, while the right side involves the values of the original function only on the boundary of the region.

───────────────────────── ▲ **TRUE–FALSE QUIZ** ▲ ─────────────────────────

1. False; div $\mathbf{F}$ is a scalar field.

2. True. (See Definition 13.5.1.)

3. True, by Theorem 13.5.3 and the fact that div $\mathbf{0} = 0$.

4. True, by Theorem 13.3.2.

5. False. See Exercise 13.3.33. (But the assertion is true if D is simply-connected; see Theorem 13.3.6.)

6. False. See the discussion accompanying Figure 8 on page 929.

7. True. Apply the Divergence Theorem and use the fact that div $\mathbf{F} = 0$.

8. False by Theorem 13.5.11, because if it were true, then div curl $\mathbf{F} = 3 \neq 0$.

───────────────────────── ◆ **EXERCISES** ◆ ─────────────────────────

1. (a) Vectors starting on C point in roughly the direction opposite to C, so the tangential component $\mathbf{F} \cdot \mathbf{T}$ is negative. Thus $\int_C \mathbf{F} \cdot d\mathbf{r} = \int_C \mathbf{F} \cdot \mathbf{T} \, ds$ is negative.

   (b) The vectors that end near P are shorter than the vectors that start near P, so the net flow is outward near P and div $\mathbf{F}(P)$ is positive.

2. We can parametrize C by $x = x$, $y = x^2$, $0 \le x \le 1$ so

$$\int_C x \, ds = \int_0^1 x \sqrt{1 + (2x)^2} \, dx = \tfrac{1}{12}(1 + 4x^2)^{3/2}\Big]_0^1 = \tfrac{1}{12}\left(5\sqrt{5} - 1\right).$$

3. $\int_C x^3 z \, ds = \int_0^{\pi/2} (2\sin t)^3 (2\cos t) \sqrt{(2\cos t)^2 + (1)^2 + (-2\sin t)^2} \, dt = \int_0^{\pi/2} (16\sin^3 t \cos t)\sqrt{5} \, dt$

$$= 4\sqrt{5}\sin^4 t\Big]_0^{\pi/2} = 4\sqrt{5}$$

4. $\int_C xy \, dx + y \, dy = \int_0^{\pi/2} (x\sin x + \sin x \cos x) \, dx = -x\cos x + \sin x - \tfrac{1}{4}\cos 2x\Big]_0^{\pi/2} = \tfrac{3}{2}$

5. $x = \cos t \Rightarrow dx = -\sin t \, dt$, $y = \sin t \Rightarrow dy = \cos t \, dt$, $0 \le t \le 2\pi$ and

$$\int_C x^3 y \, dx - x \, dy = \int_0^{2\pi} \left(-\cos^3 t \sin^2 t - \cos^2 t\right) dt = \int_0^{2\pi} \left(-\cos^3 t \sin^2 t - \cos^2 t\right) dt = -\pi$$

Or: Since C is a simple closed curve, apply Green's Theorem giving

$$\iint_{x^2 + y^2 \le 1} \left(-1 - x^3\right) dA = \int_0^1 \int_0^{2\pi} \left(-r - r^4 \cos^3 \theta\right) d\theta = -\pi.$$

6. $\int_C x \sin y \, dx + xyz \, dz = \int_0^1 \left(t \sin t^2 + 3t^8 \right) dt = -\frac{1}{2} \cos t^2 + \frac{1}{3} t^9 \Big]_0^1 = \frac{5}{6} - \frac{1}{2} \cos 1$

7.

$C_1 : x = t, y = t, z = 2t, 0 \le t \le 1;$

$C_2 : x = 1 + 2t, y = 1, z = 2 + 2t, 0 \le t \le 1.$

Then $\int_C y \, dx + z \, dy + x \, dz = \int_0^1 5t \, dt + \int_0^1 (4 + 4t) \, dt = \frac{17}{2}$.

8. $\mathbf{F}(\mathbf{r}(t)) = -t^7 \mathbf{i} + e^{-t^3} \mathbf{j}$, $\mathbf{F} \cdot \mathbf{r}'(t) = -2t^8 - 3t^2 e^{-t^3}$ and

$\int_C \mathbf{F} \cdot d\mathbf{r} = \int_0^1 \left(-2t^8 - 3t^2 e^{-t^3} \right) dt = -\frac{2}{9} t^9 + e^{-t^3} \Big]_0^1 = e^{-1} - \frac{11}{9}$.

9. $\mathbf{F}(\mathbf{r}(t)) = \left(2t + t^2 \right) \mathbf{i} + t^4 \mathbf{j} + 4t^4 \mathbf{k}$, $\mathbf{F} \cdot \mathbf{r}'(t) = 4t + 2t^2 + 2t^5 + 16t^7$ and

$\int_C \mathbf{F} \cdot d\mathbf{r} = \int_0^1 \left(4t + 2t^2 + 2t^5 + 16t^7 \right) dt = 5$.

10. (a) $C: x = 3 - 3t, y = \frac{\pi}{2} t, z = 3t, 0 \le t \le 1$. Then

$$W = \int_C \mathbf{F} \cdot d\mathbf{r} = \int_0^1 \left[3t \, \mathbf{i} + (3 - 3t) \, \mathbf{j} + \frac{\pi}{2} t \, \mathbf{k} \right] \cdot \left[-3 \, \mathbf{i} + \frac{\pi}{2} \, \mathbf{j} + 3 \, \mathbf{k} \right] dt = \int_0^1 \left[-9t + \frac{3\pi}{2} \right] dt$$
$$= \frac{1}{2} (3\pi - 9)$$

(b) $W = \int_C \mathbf{F} \cdot d\mathbf{r} = \int_0^{\pi/2} (3 \sin t \, \mathbf{i} + 3 \cos t \, \mathbf{j} + t \, \mathbf{k}) \cdot (-3 \sin t \, \mathbf{i} + \mathbf{j} + 3 \cos t \, \mathbf{k}) \, dt$

$= \int_0^{\pi/2} \left(-9 \sin^2 t + 3 \cos t + 3t \cos t \right) dt$

$= \left[-\frac{9}{2} (t - \sin t \cos t) + 3 \sin t + 3(t \sin t + \cos t) \right]_0^{\pi/2} = -\frac{9\pi}{4} + 3 + \frac{3\pi}{2} - 3 = -\frac{3\pi}{4}$

11. $\frac{\partial}{\partial y} \left[(1 + xy) \, e^{xy} \right] = 2x e^{xy} + x^2 y e^{xy} = \frac{\partial}{\partial x} \left[e^y + x^2 e^{xy} \right]$ and the domain of $\mathbf{F}$ is $\mathbb{R}^2$, so $\mathbf{F}$ is conservative. Thus there exists a function f such that $\mathbf{F} = \nabla f$. Then $f_y(x, y) = e^y + x^2 e^{xy}$ implies $f(x, y) = e^y + x e^{xy} + g(x)$ and then $f_x(x, y) = x y e^{xy} + e^{xy} + g'(x) = (1 + xy) e^{xy} + g'(x)$. But $f_x(x, y) = (1 + xy) e^{xy}$, so $g'(x) = 0 \Rightarrow g(x) = K$. Thus $f(x, y) = e^y + x e^{xy} + K$ is a potential function for $\mathbf{F}$.

12. $\mathbf{F}$ is defined on all of $\mathbb{R}^3$, its components have continuous partial derivatives, and curl $\mathbf{F} = (0 - 0) \, \mathbf{i} - (0 - 0) \, \mathbf{j} + (\cos y - \cos y) \, \mathbf{k} = \mathbf{0}$, so $\mathbf{F}$ is conservative by Theorem 13.5.4. Thus there exists a function f such that $\nabla f = \mathbf{F}$. Then $f_x(x, y, z) = \sin y$ implies $f(x, y, z) = x \sin y + g(y, z)$ and then $f_y(x, y, z) = x \cos y + g_y(y, z)$. But $f_y(x, y, z) = x \cos y$, so $g_y(y, z) = 0 \Rightarrow g(y, z) = h(z)$. Then $f(x, y, z) = x \sin y + h(z)$ implies $f_z(x, y, z) = h'(z)$. But $f_z(x, y, z) = -\sin z$, so $h(z) = \cos z + K$. Thus a potential function for $\mathbf{F}$ is $f(x, y, z) = x \sin y + \cos z + K$.

13. Since $\frac{\partial}{\partial y} \left(4x^3 y^2 - 2xy^3 \right) = 8x^3 y - 6xy^2 = \frac{\partial}{\partial x} \left(2x^4 y - 3x^2 y^2 + 4y^3 \right)$ and the domain of $\mathbf{F}$ is $\mathbb{R}^2$, $\mathbf{F}$ is conservative. Furthermore $f(x, y) = x^4 y^2 - x^2 y^3 + y^4$ is a potential function for $\mathbf{F}$. $t = 0$ corresponds to the point $(0, 1)$ and $t = 1$ corresponds to $(1, 1)$, so $\int_C \mathbf{F} \cdot d\mathbf{r} = f(1, 1) - f(0, 1) = 1 - 1 = 0$.

14. Here curl $\mathbf{F} = \mathbf{0}$, the domain of $\mathbf{F}$ is $\mathbb{R}^3$, and the components of $\mathbf{F}$ have continuous partial derivatives, so $\mathbf{F}$ is conservative. Furthermore $f(x, y, z) = x e^y + y e^z$ is a potential function for $\mathbf{F}$. Then $\int_C \mathbf{F} \cdot d\mathbf{r} = f(4, 0, 3) - f(0, 2, 0) = 4 - 2 = 2$.

15.

C_1: $\mathbf{r}(t) = t\,\mathbf{i} + t^2\,\mathbf{j},\ -1 \le t \le 1$; C_2: $\mathbf{r}(t) = -t\,\mathbf{i} + \mathbf{j},\ -1 \le t \le 1$. Then

$$\int_C xy^2\,dx - x^2 y\,dy = \int_{-1}^{1} (t^5 - 2t^5)\,dt + \int_{-1}^{1} t\,dt$$

$$= \left[-\frac{1}{6}t^6\right]_{-1}^{1} + \left[\frac{1}{2}t^2\right]_{-1}^{1} = 0$$

Using Green's Theorem, we have

$$\int_C xy^2\,dx - x^2 y\,dy = \iint_D \left[\frac{\partial}{\partial x}(-x^2 y) - \frac{\partial}{\partial y}(xy^2)\right] dA = \iint_D (-2xy - 2xy)\,dA$$

$$= \int_{-1}^{1}\int_{x^2}^{1} -4xy\,dy\,dx = \int_{-1}^{1} \left[-2xy^2\right]_{y=x^2}^{y=1} dx$$

$$= \int_{-1}^{1} (2x^5 - 2x)\,dx = \left[\tfrac{1}{3}x^6 - x^2\right]_{-1}^{1} = 0$$

16. $\int_C \sqrt{1+x^3}\,dx + 2xy\,dy = \iint_D \left[\frac{\partial}{\partial x}(2xy) - \frac{\partial}{\partial y}\left(\sqrt{1+x^3}\right)\right] dA = \int_0^1 \int_0^{3x} (2y - 0)\,dy\,dx$

$$= \int_0^1 9x^2\,dx = 3x^3\big]_0^1 = 3$$

17. $\int_C x^2 y\,dx - xy^2\,dy = \iint_{x^2+y^2 \le 4} \left[\frac{\partial}{\partial x}(-xy^2) - \frac{\partial}{\partial y}(x^2 y)\right] dA$

$$= \iint_{x^2+y^2 \le 4} (-y^2 - x^2)\,dA = -\int_0^{2\pi}\int_0^2 r^3\,dr\,d\theta = -8\pi$$

18. $\operatorname{curl}\mathbf{F} = (0 - e^{-y}\cos z)\,\mathbf{i} - (e^{-z}\cos x - 0)\,\mathbf{j} + (0 - e^{-x}\cos y)\,\mathbf{k} = -e^{-y}\cos z\,\mathbf{i} - e^{-z}\cos x\,\mathbf{j} - e^{-x}\cos y\,\mathbf{k}$,

$\operatorname{div}\mathbf{F} = -e^{-x}\sin y - e^{-y}\sin z - e^{-z}\sin x$

19. If we assume there is such a vector field $\mathbf{G}$, then $\operatorname{div}(\operatorname{curl}\mathbf{G}) = 2 + 3z - 2xz$. But $\operatorname{div}(\operatorname{curl}\mathbf{F}) = 0$ for all vector fields $\mathbf{F}$. Thus such a $\mathbf{G}$ cannot exist.

20. Let $\mathbf{F} = P_1\,\mathbf{i} + Q_1\,\mathbf{j} + R_1\,\mathbf{k}$ and $\mathbf{G} = P_2\,\mathbf{i} + Q_2\,\mathbf{j} + R_2\,\mathbf{k}$ be vector fields whose first partials exist and are continuous. Then

$\mathbf{F}\operatorname{div}\mathbf{G} - \mathbf{G}\operatorname{div}\mathbf{F}$

$$= \left[P_1\left(\frac{\partial P_2}{\partial x} + \frac{\partial Q_2}{\partial y} + \frac{\partial R_2}{\partial z}\right)\mathbf{i} + Q_1\left(\frac{\partial P_2}{\partial x} + \frac{\partial Q_2}{\partial y} + \frac{\partial R_2}{\partial z}\right)\mathbf{j} + R_1\left(\frac{\partial P_2}{\partial x} + \frac{\partial Q_2}{\partial y} + \frac{\partial R_2}{\partial z}\right)\mathbf{k}\right]$$

$$- \left[P_2\left(\frac{\partial P_1}{\partial x} + \frac{\partial Q_1}{\partial y} + \frac{\partial R_1}{\partial z}\right)\mathbf{i} + Q_2\left(\frac{\partial P_1}{\partial x} + \frac{\partial Q_1}{\partial y} + \frac{\partial R_1}{\partial z}\right)\mathbf{j} + R_2\left(\frac{\partial P_1}{\partial x} + \frac{\partial Q}{\partial y} + \frac{\partial R_1}{\partial z}\right)\mathbf{k}\right]$$

and

$$(\mathbf{G} \cdot \nabla)\mathbf{F} - (\mathbf{F} \cdot \nabla)\mathbf{G} = \left[\left(P_2\frac{\partial P_1}{\partial x} + Q_2\frac{\partial P_1}{\partial y} + R_2\frac{\partial P_1}{\partial z}\right)\mathbf{i} + \left(P_2\frac{\partial Q_1}{\partial x} + Q_2\frac{\partial Q_1}{\partial y} + R_2\frac{\partial Q_1}{\partial z}\right)\mathbf{j}\right.$$

$$\left. + \left(P_2\frac{\partial R_1}{\partial x} + Q_2\frac{\partial R_1}{\partial y} + R_2\frac{\partial R_1}{\partial z}\right)\mathbf{k}\right]$$

$$- \left[\left(P_1\frac{\partial P_2}{\partial x} + Q_1\frac{\partial P_2}{\partial y} + R_1\frac{\partial P_2}{\partial z}\right)\mathbf{i} + \left(P_1\frac{\partial Q_2}{\partial x} + Q_1\frac{\partial Q_2}{\partial y} + R_1\frac{\partial Q_2}{\partial z}\right)\mathbf{j}\right.$$

$$\left. + \left(P_1\frac{\partial R_2}{\partial x} + Q_1\frac{\partial R_2}{\partial y} + R_1\frac{\partial R_2}{\partial z}\right)\mathbf{k}\right]$$

Hence

$$\mathbf{F}\operatorname{div}\mathbf{G} - \mathbf{G}\operatorname{div}\mathbf{F} + (\mathbf{G}\cdot\nabla)\mathbf{F} - (\mathbf{F}\cdot\nabla)\mathbf{G}$$

$$= \left[\left(P_1\frac{\partial Q_2}{\partial y} + Q_2\frac{\partial P_1}{\partial x}\right) - \left(P_2\frac{\partial Q_1}{\partial y} + Q_1\frac{\partial P_2}{\partial y}\right)\right.$$

$$\left. - \left(P_2\frac{\partial R_1}{\partial z} + R_1\frac{\partial P_2}{\partial z}\right) + \left(P_1\frac{\partial R_2}{\partial z} + R_2\frac{\partial P_1}{\partial z}\right)\right]\mathbf{i}$$

$$+ \left[\left(Q_1\frac{\partial R_2}{\partial z} + R_2\frac{\partial Q_1}{\partial z}\right) - \left(Q_2\frac{\partial R_1}{\partial z} + R_1\frac{\partial Q_2}{\partial z}\right)\right.$$

$$\left. - \left(P_1\frac{\partial Q_2}{\partial x} + Q_2\frac{\partial P_1}{\partial x}\right) + \left(P_2\frac{\partial Q_1}{\partial x} + Q_1\frac{\partial P_2}{\partial x}\right)\right]\mathbf{j}$$

$$+ \left[\left(P_2\frac{\partial R_1}{\partial x} + R_1\frac{\partial P_2}{\partial x}\right) - \left(P_1\frac{\partial R_2}{\partial x} + R_2\frac{\partial P_1}{\partial x}\right)\right.$$

$$\left. - \left(Q_1\frac{\partial R_2}{\partial y} + R_2\frac{\partial Q_1}{\partial y}\right) + \left(Q_2\frac{\partial R_1}{\partial y} + R_1\frac{\partial Q_2}{\partial y}\right)\right]\mathbf{k}$$

$$= \left[\frac{\partial}{\partial y}(P_1Q_2 - P_2Q_1) - \frac{\partial}{\partial z}(P_2R_1 - P_1R_2)\right]\mathbf{i} + \left[\frac{\partial}{\partial z}(Q_1R_2 - Q_2R_1) - \frac{\partial}{\partial x}(P_1Q_2 - P_2Q_1)\right]\mathbf{j}$$

$$+ \left[\frac{\partial}{\partial x}(P_2R_1 - P_1R_2) - \frac{\partial}{\partial y}(Q_1R_2 - Q_2R_1)\right]\mathbf{k}$$

$$= \operatorname{curl}(\mathbf{F}\times\mathbf{G})$$

21. For any piecewise-smooth simple closed plane curve C bounding a region D, we can apply Green's Theorem to

$$\mathbf{F}(x, y) = f(x)\,\mathbf{i} + g(y)\,\mathbf{j} \text{ to get } \int_C f(x)\,dx + g(y)\,dy = \iint_D\left[\frac{\partial}{\partial x}g(y) - \frac{\partial}{\partial y}f(x)\right]dA = \iint_D 0\,dA = 0.$$

22. $\nabla^2(fg) = \dfrac{\partial^2(fg)}{\partial x^2} + \dfrac{\partial^2(fg)}{\partial y^2} + \dfrac{\partial^2(fg)}{\partial z^2}$

$$= \frac{\partial}{\partial x}\left(\frac{\partial f}{\partial x}g + f\frac{\partial g}{\partial x}\right) + \frac{\partial}{\partial y}\left(\frac{\partial f}{\partial y}g + f\frac{\partial g}{\partial y}\right) + \frac{\partial}{\partial z}\left(\frac{\partial f}{\partial z}g + f\frac{\partial g}{\partial z}\right) \quad \text{(Product Rule)}$$

$$= \frac{\partial^2 f}{\partial x^2}g + 2\frac{\partial f}{\partial x}\frac{\partial g}{\partial x} + f\frac{\partial^2 g}{\partial x^2} + \frac{\partial^2 f}{\partial y^2}g + 2\frac{\partial f}{\partial y}\frac{\partial g}{\partial y}$$

$$+ f\frac{\partial^2 g}{\partial y^2} + \frac{\partial^2 f}{\partial z^2}g + 2\frac{\partial f}{\partial z}\frac{\partial g}{\partial z} + f\frac{\partial^2 g}{\partial z^2} \quad \text{(Product Rule)}$$

$$= f\left(\frac{\partial^2 g}{\partial x^2} + \frac{\partial^2 g}{\partial y^2} + \frac{\partial^2 g}{\partial z^2}\right) + g\left(\frac{\partial^2 f}{\partial x^2} + \frac{\partial^2 f}{\partial y^2} + \frac{\partial^2 f}{\partial z^2}\right) + 2\left\langle\frac{\partial f}{\partial x}, \frac{\partial f}{\partial y}, \frac{\partial f}{\partial z}\right\rangle\cdot\left\langle\frac{\partial g}{\partial x}, \frac{\partial g}{\partial y}, \frac{\partial g}{\partial z}\right\rangle$$

$$= f\nabla^2 g + g\nabla^2 f + 2\nabla f\cdot\nabla g$$

[continued]

Another method: Using the rules in Exercises 11.6.33(b) and 13.5.23, we have

$$\nabla^2(fg) = \nabla \cdot \nabla(fg) = \nabla \cdot (g\nabla f + f\nabla g) = \nabla g \cdot \nabla f + g\nabla \cdot \nabla f + \nabla f \cdot \nabla g + f\nabla \cdot \nabla g$$
$$= g\nabla^2 f + f\nabla^2 g + 2\nabla f \cdot \nabla g$$

23. $\nabla^2 f = 0$ means that $\dfrac{\partial^2 f}{\partial x^2} + \dfrac{\partial^2 f}{\partial y^2} = 0$. Now if $\mathbf{F} = f_y\,\mathbf{i} - f_x\,\mathbf{j}$ and C is any closed path in D, then applying Green's Theorem, we get

$$\int_C \mathbf{F} \cdot d\mathbf{r} = \int_C f_y\,dx - f_x\,dy = \iint_D \left[\tfrac{\partial}{\partial x}(-f_x) - \tfrac{\partial}{\partial y}(f_y) \right] dA = -\iint_D (f_{xx} + f_{yy})\,dA$$
$$= -\iint_D 0\,dA = 0$$

Therefore the line integral is independent of path, by Theorem 13.3.3.

24. (a) $x^2 + y^2 = \cos^2 t + \sin^2 t = 1$, so C lies on the circular cylinder $x^2 + y^2 = 1$. But also $y = z$, so C lies on the plane $y = z$. Thus C is the intersection of the plane $y = z$ and the cylinder $x^2 + y^2 = 1$.

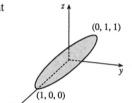

(b) Apply Stokes' Theorem, $\int_C \mathbf{F} \cdot d\mathbf{r} = \iint_S \operatorname{curl} \mathbf{F} \cdot d\mathbf{S}$:

$$\operatorname{curl} \mathbf{F} = \begin{vmatrix} \mathbf{i} & \mathbf{j} & \mathbf{k} \\ \partial/\partial x & \partial/\partial y & \partial/\partial z \\ 2xe^{2y} & 2x^2e^{2y} + 2y\cot z & -y^2\csc^2 z \end{vmatrix}$$

$$= \left\langle -2y\csc^2 z - (-2y\csc^2 z),\, 0,\, 4xe^{2y} - 4xe^{2y} \right\rangle = \mathbf{0}$$

Therefore $\int_C \mathbf{F} \cdot d\mathbf{r} = \iint_S \mathbf{0} \cdot d\mathbf{S} = 0$.

25. $z = f(x, y) = x^2 + y^2$ with $0 \le x^2 + y^2 \le 4$ so $\mathbf{r}_x \times \mathbf{r}_y = -2x\,\mathbf{i} - 2y\,\mathbf{j} + \mathbf{k}$ (using upward orientation). Then

$$\iint_S z\,dS = \iint_{x^2+y^2 \le 4} (x^2 + y^2)\sqrt{4x^2 + 4y^2 + 1}\,dA = \int_0^{2\pi}\int_0^2 r^3\sqrt{1 + 4r^2}\,dr\,d\theta$$
$$= \tfrac{1}{60}\pi\left(391\sqrt{17} + 1\right)$$

(Substitute $u = 1 + 4r^2$ and use tables.)

26. $z = f(x, y) = 4 + x + y$ with $0 \le x^2 + y^2 \le 4$ so $\mathbf{r}_x \times \mathbf{r}_y = -\mathbf{i} - \mathbf{j} + \mathbf{k}$. Then

$$\iint_S (x^2 z + y^2 z)\,dS = \iint_{x^2+y^2 \le 4} (x^2 + y^2)(4 + x + y)\sqrt{3}\,dA$$
$$= \int_0^2\int_0^{2\pi} \sqrt{3}\,r^3(4 + r\cos\theta + r\sin\theta)\,d\theta\,dr = \int_0^2 8\pi\sqrt{3}\,r^3\,dr = 32\pi\sqrt{3}$$

27. Since the sphere bounds a simple solid region, the Divergence Theorem applies and

$$\iint_S \mathbf{F} \cdot d\mathbf{S} = \iiint_E (z - 2)\,dV = \iiint_E z\,dV - 2\iiint_E dV = m\bar{z} - 2\left(\tfrac{4}{3}\pi 2^3\right) = -\tfrac{64}{3}\pi.$$

Alternate solution: $\mathbf{F}(\mathbf{r}(\phi, \theta)) = 4\sin\phi\cos\theta\cos\phi\,\mathbf{i} - 4\sin\phi\sin\theta\,\mathbf{j} + 6\sin\phi\cos\theta\,\mathbf{k}$,

$\mathbf{r}_\phi \times \mathbf{r}_\theta = 4\sin^2\phi\cos\theta\,\mathbf{i} + 4\sin^2\phi\sin\theta\,\mathbf{j} + 4\sin\phi\cos\phi\,\mathbf{k}$, and

$\mathbf{F} \cdot (\mathbf{r}_\phi \times \mathbf{r}_\theta) = 16\sin^3\phi\cos^2\theta\cos\phi - 16\sin^3\phi\sin^2\theta + 24\sin^2\phi\cos\phi\cos\theta$. Then

$$\iint_S \mathbf{F} \cdot d\mathbf{S} = \int_0^{2\pi}\int_0^\pi \left(16\sin^3\phi\cos\phi\cos^2\theta - 16\sin^3\phi\sin^2\theta + 24\sin^2\phi\cos\phi\cos\theta\right) d\phi\,d\theta$$
$$= \int_0^{2\pi} \tfrac{4}{3}\left(-16\sin^2\theta\right) d\theta = -\tfrac{64}{3}\pi$$

28. $z = f(x, y) = x^2 + y^2$, $\mathbf{r}_x \times \mathbf{r}_y = -2x\,\mathbf{i} - 2y\,\mathbf{j} + \mathbf{k}$ (because of upward orientation) and

$\mathbf{F}\left(\mathbf{r}(x, y)\right) \cdot (\mathbf{r}_x \times \mathbf{r}_y) = -2x^3 - 2xy^2 + x^2 + y^2$. Then

$$\iint_S \mathbf{F} \cdot d\mathbf{S} = \iint_{x^2 + y^2 \le 1} \left(-2x^3 - 2xy^2 + x^2 + y^2\right) dA$$

$$= \int_0^1 \int_0^{2\pi} \left(-2r^3 \cos^3 \theta - 2r^3 \cos \theta \sin^2 \theta + r^2\right) r \, dr \, d\theta = \int_0^1 r^3 (2\pi) \, dr = \tfrac{\pi}{2}$$

29. Since $\operatorname{curl} \mathbf{F} = \mathbf{0}$, $\iint_S (\operatorname{curl} \mathbf{F}) \cdot d\mathbf{S} = 0$. We parametrize C: $\mathbf{r}(t) = \cos t\,\mathbf{i} + \sin t\,\mathbf{j}$, $0 \le t \le 2\pi$ and

$\oint_C \mathbf{F} \cdot d\mathbf{r} = \int_0^{2\pi} \left(-\cos^2 t \sin t + \sin^2 t \cos t\right) dt = \tfrac{1}{3}\cos^3 t + \tfrac{1}{3}\sin^3 t\Big]_0^{2\pi} = 0$.

30. $\iint_S \operatorname{curl} \mathbf{F} \cdot d\mathbf{S} = \oint_C \mathbf{F} \cdot d\mathbf{r}$ where C: $\mathbf{r}(t) = 2\cos t\,\mathbf{i} + 2\sin t\,\mathbf{j} + \mathbf{k}$, $0 \le t \le 2\pi$, so

$\mathbf{r}'(t) = -2\sin t\,\mathbf{i} + 2\cos t\,\mathbf{j}$, $\mathbf{F}(\mathbf{r}(t)) = 8\cos^2 t \sin t\,\mathbf{i} + 2\sin t\,\mathbf{j} + e^{4\cos t \sin t}\,\mathbf{k}$, and

$\mathbf{F}(\mathbf{r}(t)) \cdot \mathbf{r}'(t) = -16\cos^2 t \sin^2 t + 4\sin t \cos t$. Thus

$\oint_C \mathbf{F} \cdot d\mathbf{r} = \int_0^{2\pi} \left(-16\cos^2 t \sin^2 t + 4\sin t \cos t\right) dt$

$\qquad = \left[-16\left(-\tfrac{1}{4}\sin t \cos^3 t + \tfrac{1}{16}\sin 2t + \tfrac{1}{8}t\right) + 2\sin^2 t\right]_0^{2\pi} = -4\pi$.

31. The surface is given by $x + y + z = 1$ or $z = 1 - x - y$, $0 \le x \le 1$, $0 \le y \le 1 - x$ and $\mathbf{r}_x \times \mathbf{r}_y = \mathbf{i} + \mathbf{j} + \mathbf{k}$.

Then

$$\oint_C \mathbf{F} \cdot d\mathbf{r} = \iint_S \operatorname{curl} \mathbf{F} \cdot d\mathbf{S} = \iint_D (-y\,\mathbf{i} - z\,\mathbf{j} - x\,\mathbf{k}) \cdot (\mathbf{i} + \mathbf{j} + \mathbf{k}) \, dA$$

$$= \iint_D (-1) \, dA = -(\text{area of } D) = -\tfrac{1}{2}$$

32. $\iint_S \mathbf{F} \cdot d\mathbf{S} = \iiint_E 3\left(x^2 + y^2 + z^2\right) dV = \int_0^{2\pi} \int_0^1 \int_0^2 \left(3r^2 + 3z^2\right) r \, dz \, dr \, d\theta = 2\pi \int_0^1 \left(6r^3 + 8r\right) dr = 11\pi$

33. $\iiint_E \operatorname{div} \mathbf{F} \, dV = \iiint_{x^2 + y^2 + z^2 \le 1} 3 \, dV = 3(\text{volume of sphere}) = 4\pi$. Then

$\mathbf{F}(\mathbf{r}(\phi, \theta)) \cdot (\mathbf{r}_\phi \times \mathbf{r}_\theta) = \sin^3 \phi \cos^2 \theta + \sin^3 \phi \sin^2 \theta + \sin \phi \cos^2 \phi = \sin \phi$ and

$\iint_S \mathbf{F} \cdot d\mathbf{S} = \int_0^{2\pi} \int_0^\pi \sin \phi \, d\phi \, d\theta = (2\pi)(2) = 4\pi$.

34. Here we must use Equation 13.8.6 since $\mathbf{F}$ is not defined at the origin. Let S_1 be the sphere of radius 1 with center at the origin and outer unit normal $\mathbf{n}_1$. Let S_2 be the surface of the ellipsoid with outer unit normal $\mathbf{n}_2$ and let E be the solid region between S_1 and S_2. Then the outward flux of $\mathbf{F}$ through the ellipsoid is given by

$\iint_{S_2} \mathbf{F} \cdot \mathbf{n}_2 \, dS = -\iint_{S_1} \mathbf{F} \cdot (-\mathbf{n}_1) \, dS + \iiint_E \operatorname{div} \mathbf{F} \, dV$. But $\mathbf{F} = \mathbf{r}/|\mathbf{r}|^3$, so

$\operatorname{div} \mathbf{F} = \nabla \cdot \left(|\mathbf{r}|^{-3}\,\mathbf{r}\right) = |\mathbf{r}|^{-3}\,(\nabla \cdot \mathbf{r}) + \mathbf{r} \cdot \left(\nabla |\mathbf{r}|^{-3}\right) = |\mathbf{r}|^{-3}\,(3) + \mathbf{r} \cdot \left(-3|\mathbf{r}|^{-4}\right)\left(\mathbf{r}|\mathbf{r}|^{-1}\right) = 0$. (Here we have

used Exercises 13.5.28(a) and 13.5.29(a).) And $\mathbf{F} \cdot \mathbf{n}_1 = \dfrac{\mathbf{r}}{|\mathbf{r}|^3} \cdot \dfrac{\mathbf{r}}{|\mathbf{r}|} = |\mathbf{r}|^{-2} = 1$ on S_1. Thus

$\iint_{S_2} \mathbf{F} \cdot \mathbf{n}_2 \, dS = \iint_{S_1} dS + \iiint_E 0 \, dV = (\text{surface area of the unit sphere}) = 4\pi(1)^2 = 4\pi$.

35. Because $\operatorname{curl} \mathbf{F} = \mathbf{0}$, $\mathbf{F}$ is conservative, and if $f(x, y, z) = x^3 yz - 3xy + z^2$, then $\nabla f = \mathbf{F}$. Hence

$\int_C \mathbf{F} \cdot d\mathbf{r} = \int_C \nabla f \cdot d\mathbf{r} = f(0, 3, 0) - f(0, 0, 2) = 0 - 4 = -4$.

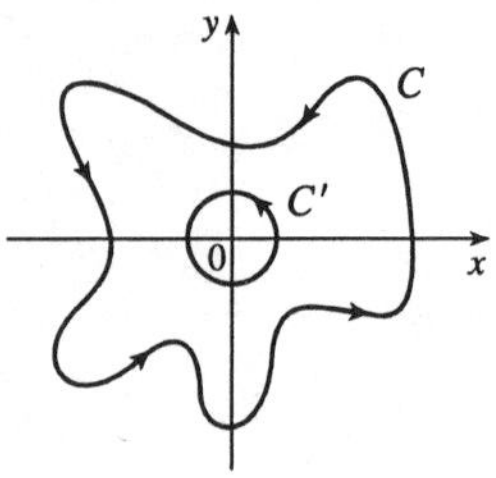

36. Let C' be the circle with center at the origin and radius a as in the figure. Let D be the region bounded by C and C'. Then D's positively oriented boundary is $C \cup (-C')$. Hence by Green's Theorem

$$\int_C \mathbf{F} \cdot d\mathbf{r} + \int_{-C'} \mathbf{F} \cdot d\mathbf{r} = \iint_D \left(\frac{\partial Q}{\partial x} - \frac{\partial P}{\partial y} \right) dA = 0, \text{ so}$$

$$\int_C \mathbf{F} \cdot d\mathbf{r} = -\int_{-C'} \mathbf{F} \cdot d\mathbf{r} = \int_{C'} \mathbf{F} \cdot d\mathbf{r} = \int_0^{2\pi} \mathbf{F}(\mathbf{r}(t)) \cdot \mathbf{r}'(t) \, dt$$

$$= \int_0^{2\pi} \left[\frac{2a^3 \cos^3 t + 2a^3 \cos t \sin^2 t - 2a \sin t}{a^2} (-a \sin t) \right.$$

$$\left. + \frac{2a^3 \sin^3 t + 2a^3 \cos^2 t \sin t + 2a \cos t}{a^2} (a \cos t) \right] dt$$

$$= \int_0^{2\pi} \frac{2a^2}{a^2} \, dt = 4\pi$$

37. By the Divergence Theorem, $\iint_S \mathbf{F} \cdot \mathbf{n} \, dS = \iiint_E \operatorname{div} \mathbf{F} \, dV = 3(\text{volume of } E) = 3(8 - 1) = 21$.

38. The stated conditions allow us to use the Divergence Theorem. Hence

$\iint_S \operatorname{curl} \mathbf{F} \cdot d\mathbf{S} = \iiint_E \operatorname{div}(\operatorname{curl} \mathbf{F}) \, dV = 0$ since $\operatorname{div}(\operatorname{curl} \mathbf{F}) = 0$.

1. Let S_1 be the portion of $\Omega(S)$ between $S(a)$ and S, and let ∂S_1 be its boundary. Also let S_L be the lateral surface of S_1 [that is, the surface of S_1 except S and $S(a)$]. Applying the Divergence Theorem we have

$$\iint_{\partial S_1} \frac{\mathbf{r} \cdot \mathbf{n}}{r^3} \, dS = \iiint_{S_1} \nabla \cdot \frac{\mathbf{r}}{r^3} \, dV. \text{ But}$$

$$\nabla \cdot \frac{\mathbf{r}}{r^3} = \left\langle \frac{\partial}{\partial x}, \frac{\partial}{\partial y}, \frac{\partial}{\partial z} \right\rangle \cdot \left\langle \frac{x}{(x^2 + y^2 + z^2)^{3/2}}, \frac{y}{(x^2 + y^2 + z^2)^{3/2}}, \frac{z}{(x^2 + y^2 + z^2)^{3/2}} \right\rangle$$

$$= \frac{(x^2 + y^2 + z^2 - 3x^2) + (x^2 + y^2 + z^2 - 3y^2) + (x^2 + y^2 + z^2 - 3z^2)}{(x^2 + y^2 + z^2)^{5/2}} = 0$$

$$\Rightarrow \iint_{\partial S_1} \frac{\mathbf{r} \cdot \mathbf{n}}{r^3} \, dS = \iiint_{S_1} 0 \, dV = 0. \text{ On the other hand, notice that for the surfaces of } \partial S_1 \text{ other than } S(a)$$

and $S, \mathbf{r} \cdot \mathbf{n} = 0 \Rightarrow$

$$0 = \iint_{\partial S_1} \frac{\mathbf{r} \cdot \mathbf{n}}{r^3} \, dS = \iint_S \frac{\mathbf{r} \cdot \mathbf{n}}{r^3} \, dS + \iint_{S(a)} \frac{\mathbf{r} \cdot \mathbf{n}}{r^3} \, dS + \iint_{S_L} \frac{\mathbf{r} \cdot \mathbf{n}}{r^3} \, dS$$

$$= \iint_S \frac{\mathbf{r} \cdot \mathbf{n}}{r^3} \, dS + \iint_{S(a)} \frac{\mathbf{r} \cdot \mathbf{n}}{r^3} \, dS$$

$$\Rightarrow \iint_S \frac{\mathbf{r} \cdot \mathbf{n}}{r^3} \, dS = - \iint_{S(a)} \frac{\mathbf{r} \cdot \mathbf{n}}{r^3} \, dS. \text{ Notice that on } S(a), r = a \Rightarrow \mathbf{n} = -\frac{\mathbf{r}}{r} = -\frac{\mathbf{r}}{a} \text{ and } \mathbf{r} \cdot \mathbf{r} = r^2 = a^2,$$

so that $-\iint_{S(a)} \frac{\mathbf{r} \cdot \mathbf{n}}{r^3} \, dS = \iint_{S(a)} \frac{\mathbf{r} \cdot \mathbf{r}}{a^4} \, dS = \iint_{S(a)} \frac{a^2}{a^4} \, dS = \frac{1}{a^2} \iint_{S(a)} dS = \frac{\text{area of } S(a)}{a^2} = |\Omega(S)|.$

Therefore $|\Omega(S)| = \iint_S \frac{\mathbf{r} \cdot \mathbf{n}}{r^3} \, dS.$

2. By Green's Theorem

$$\int_C (y^3 - y) \, dx - 2x^3 \, dy = \iint_D \left[\frac{\partial(-2x^3)}{\partial x} - \frac{\partial(y^3 - y)}{\partial y} \right] dA = \iint_D (1 - 6x^2 - 3y^2) \, dA$$

Notice that for $6x^2 + 3y^2 > 1$, the integrand is negative. The integral has maximum value if it is evaluated only in the region where the integrand is positive, which is within the ellipse $6x^2 + 3y^2 = 1$. So the simple closed curve that gives a maximum value for the line integral is the ellipse $6x^2 + 3y^2 = 1$.

3. The given line integral $\frac{1}{2}\int_C (bz - cy)\,dx + (cx - az)\,dy + (ay - bx)\,dz$ can be expressed as $\int_C \mathbf{F} \cdot d\mathbf{r}$ if we define

the vector field $\mathbf{F}$ by $\mathbf{F}(x, y, z) = P\mathbf{i} + Q\mathbf{j} + R\mathbf{k} = \frac{1}{2}(bz - cy)\mathbf{i} + \frac{1}{2}(cx - az)\mathbf{j} + \frac{1}{2}(ay - bx)\mathbf{k}$. Then define S

to be the planar interior of C, so S is an oriented, smooth surface. Stokes' Theorem says

$\int_C \mathbf{F} \cdot d\mathbf{r} = \iint_S \text{curl}\,\mathbf{F} \cdot d\mathbf{S} = \iint_S \text{curl}\,\mathbf{F} \cdot \mathbf{n}\,dS$. Now

$$\text{curl}\,\mathbf{F} = \left(\frac{\partial R}{\partial y} - \frac{\partial Q}{\partial z}\right)\mathbf{i} + \left(\frac{\partial P}{\partial z} - \frac{\partial R}{\partial x}\right)\mathbf{j} + \left(\frac{\partial Q}{\partial x} - \frac{\partial P}{\partial y}\right)\mathbf{k}$$

$$= \left(\tfrac{1}{2}a + \tfrac{1}{2}a\right)\mathbf{i} + \left(\tfrac{1}{2}b + \tfrac{1}{2}b\right)\mathbf{j} + \left(\tfrac{1}{2}c + \tfrac{1}{2}c\right)\mathbf{k} = a\mathbf{i} + b\mathbf{j} + c\mathbf{k} = \mathbf{n}$$

so $\text{curl}\,\mathbf{F} \cdot \mathbf{n} = \mathbf{n} \cdot \mathbf{n} = |\mathbf{n}|^2 = 1$, hence $\iint_S \text{curl}\,\mathbf{F} \cdot \mathbf{n}\,dS = \iint_S dS$ which is simply the surface area of S. Thus,

$\int_C \mathbf{F} \cdot d\mathbf{r} = \frac{1}{2}\int_C (bz - cy)\,dx + (cx - az)\,dy + (ay - bx)\,dz$ is the plane area enclosed by C.

4. (a) First we place the piston on coordinate axes so the top of the cylinder is at the origin and $x(t) \geq 0$ is the distance

from the top of the cylinder to the piston at time t. Let C_1 be the curve traced out by the piston during one

four-stroke cycle, so C_1 is given by $\mathbf{r}(t) = x(t)\mathbf{i}$, $a \leq t \leq b$. (Thus, the curve lies on the positive x-axis and

reverses direction several times.) The force on the piston is $AP(t)\mathbf{i}$, where A is the area of the top of the piston

and $P(t)$ is the pressure in the cylinder at time t. As in Section 13.2, the work done on the piston is

$\int_{C_1} \mathbf{F} \cdot d\mathbf{r} = \int_a^b AP(t)\mathbf{i} \cdot x'(t)\mathbf{i}\,dt = \int_a^b AP(t)\,x'(t)\,dt$. Here, the volume of the cylinder at time t is

$V(t) = Ax(t) \Rightarrow V'(t) = Ax'(t) \Rightarrow \int_a^b AP(t)\,x'(t)\,dt = \int_a^b P(t)\,V'(t)\,dt$. Since the curve C in the

PV-plane corresponds to the values of P and V at time t, $a \leq t \leq b$, we have

$W = \int_a^b AP(t)\,x'(t)\,dt = \int_a^b P(t)\,V'(t)\,dt = \int_C P\,dV$.

Another method: If we divide the time interval $[a, b]$ into n subintervals of equal length Δt, the amount of work

done on the piston in the ith time interval is approximately $AP(t_i)[x(t_i) - x(t_{i-1})]$. Thus we estimate the total

work done during one cycle to be $\sum_{i=1}^n AP(t_i)[x(t_i) - x(t_{i-1})]$. If we allow $n \to \infty$, we have

$$W = \lim_{n \to \infty} \sum_{i=1}^n AP(t_i)[x(t_i) - x(t_{i-1})] = \lim_{n \to \infty} \sum_{i=1}^n P(t_i)[Ax(t_i) - Ax(t_{i-1})]$$

$$= \lim_{n \to \infty} \sum_{i=1}^n P(t_i)[V(t_i) - V(t_{i-1})] = \int_C P\,dV$$

(b) Let C_L be the lower loop of the curve C and C_U the upper loop. Then $C = C_L \cup C_U$. C_L is positively

oriented, so from Formula 13.4.5 we know the area of the lower loop in the PV-plane is given by $-\oint_{C_L} P\,dV$.

C_U is negatively oriented, so the area of the upper loop is given by $-\left(-\oint_{C_U} P\,dV\right) = \oint_{C_U} P\,dV$. From

part (a), $W = \int_C P\,dV = \int_{C_L \cup C_U} P\,dV = \oint_{C_L} P\,dV + \oint_{C_U} P\,dV = \oint_{C_U} P\,dV - \left(-\oint_{C_L} P\,dV\right)$,

the difference of the areas enclosed by the two loops of C.

Appendixes

D   Precise Definitions of Limits   • • • • • • • • • • •

1. (*Note:* This is Exercise 21 in the full version of the text.)

Let $\varepsilon > 0$. We want to find $\delta > 0$ such that

$$\left| \frac{xy}{\sqrt{x^2 + y^2}} - 0 \right| < \varepsilon \qquad \text{whenever} \qquad 0 < \sqrt{x^2 + y^2} < \delta$$

that is,

$$\frac{|xy|}{\sqrt{x^2 + y^2}} < \varepsilon \qquad \text{whenever} \qquad 0 < \sqrt{x^2 + y^2} < \delta$$

But $|x| = \sqrt{x^2} \le \sqrt{x^2 + y^2}$ and $|y| = \sqrt{y^2} \le \sqrt{x^2 + y^2}$, so

$$\frac{|xy|}{\sqrt{x^2 + y^2}} \le \frac{\left(\sqrt{x^2 + y^2} \right)^2}{\sqrt{x^2 + y^2}} = \sqrt{x^2 + y^2}$$

Thus, if we choose $\delta = \varepsilon$ and let $0 < \sqrt{x^2 + y^2} < \delta$, then

$$\left| \frac{xy}{\sqrt{x^2 + y^2}} - 0 \right| \le \sqrt{x^2 + y^2} < \delta = \varepsilon$$

Hence, by Definition 1 (Definition 5 in the full version of the text),

$$\lim_{(x,y) \to (0,0)} \frac{xy}{\sqrt{x^2 + y^2}} = 0$$

H Polar Coordinates · · · · · · · · · · · · · ·

H.1 Curves in Polar Coordinates · · · · · · · · · · ·

1. (a) By adding 2π to $\frac{\pi}{2}$, we obtain the point $\left(1, \frac{5\pi}{2}\right)$. The direction opposite $\frac{\pi}{2}$ is $\frac{3\pi}{2}$, so $\left(-1, \frac{3\pi}{2}\right)$ is a point that satisfies the $r < 0$ requirement.

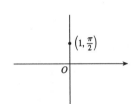

(b) $\left(-2, \frac{\pi}{4}\right)$

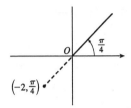

$\left(2, \frac{5\pi}{4}\right), \left(-2, \frac{9\pi}{4}\right)$

(c) $(3, 2)$

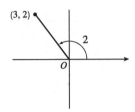

$(3, 2 + 2\pi), (-3, 2 + \pi)$

2. (a) $(3, 0)$

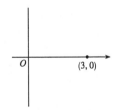

$(3, 2\pi), (-3, \pi)$

(b) $\left(2, -\frac{\pi}{7}\right)$

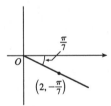

$\left(2, \frac{13\pi}{7}\right), \left(-2, \frac{6\pi}{7}\right)$

(c) $\left(-1, -\frac{\pi}{2}\right)$

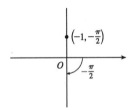

$\left(1, \frac{\pi}{2}\right), \left(-1, \frac{3\pi}{2}\right)$

3. (a)

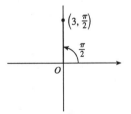

$x = 3 \cos \frac{\pi}{2} = 3(0) = 0$ and $y = 3 \sin \frac{\pi}{2} = 3(1) = 3$ give us the Cartesian coordinates $(0, 3)$.

(b)

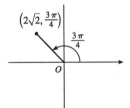

$x = 2\sqrt{2} \cos \frac{3\pi}{4}$
$= 2\sqrt{2} \left(-\frac{1}{\sqrt{2}}\right) = -2$ and
$y = 2\sqrt{2} \sin \frac{3\pi}{4} = 2\sqrt{2} \left(\frac{1}{\sqrt{2}}\right) = 2$
give us $(-2, 2)$.

(c)

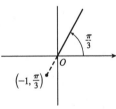

$x = -1 \cos \frac{\pi}{3} = -\frac{1}{2}$ and $y = -1 \sin \frac{\pi}{3} = -\frac{\sqrt{3}}{2}$ give us $\left(-\frac{1}{2}, -\frac{\sqrt{3}}{2}\right)$.

4. (a)

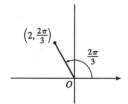

$x = 2\cos\frac{2\pi}{3} = -1,$

$y = 2\sin\frac{2\pi}{3} = \sqrt{3}$

(b)

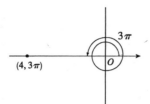

$x = 4\cos 3\pi = -4,$

$y = 4\sin 3\pi = 0$

(c)

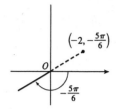

$x = -2\cos\left(-\frac{5\pi}{6}\right) = \sqrt{3},$

$y = -2\sin\left(-\frac{5\pi}{6}\right) = 1$

5. (a) $x = 1$ and $y = 1$ $\Rightarrow$ $r = \sqrt{1^2 + 1^2} = \sqrt{2}$ and $\theta = \tan^{-1}\left(\frac{1}{1}\right) = \frac{\pi}{4}$. Since $(1,1)$ is in the first quadrant, the polar coordinates are (i) $\left(\sqrt{2}, \frac{\pi}{4}\right)$ and (ii) $\left(-\sqrt{2}, \frac{5\pi}{4}\right)$.

(b) $x = 2\sqrt{3}$ and $y = -2$ $\Rightarrow$ $r = \sqrt{\left(2\sqrt{3}\right)^2 + (-2)^2} = \sqrt{12 + 4} = \sqrt{16} = 4$ and $\theta = \tan^{-1}\left(-\frac{2}{2\sqrt{3}}\right) = \tan^{-1}\left(-\frac{1}{\sqrt{3}}\right) = -\frac{\pi}{6}$. Since $\left(2\sqrt{3}, -2\right)$ is in the fourth quadrant and $0 \le \theta \le 2\pi$, the polar coordinates are (i) $\left(4, \frac{11\pi}{6}\right)$ and (ii) $\left(-4, \frac{5\pi}{6}\right)$.

6. (a) $(x, y) = \left(-1, -\sqrt{3}\right), r = \sqrt{1 + 3} = 2, \tan\theta = y/x = \sqrt{3}$ and (x, y) is in the third quadrant, so $\theta = \frac{4\pi}{3}$. The polar coordinates are (i) $\left(2, \frac{4\pi}{3}\right)$ and (ii) $\left(-2, \frac{\pi}{3}\right)$.

(b) $(x, y) = (-2, 3), r = \sqrt{4 + 9} = \sqrt{13}, \tan\theta = y/x = -\frac{3}{2}$ and (x, y) is in the second quadrant, so $\theta = \tan^{-1}\left(-\frac{3}{2}\right) + \pi$. The polar coordinates are (i) $\left(\sqrt{13}, \theta\right)$ and (ii) $\left(-\sqrt{13}, \theta + \pi\right)$.

7. $r > 1$

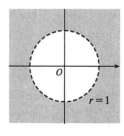

8. $0 \le \theta < \frac{\pi}{4}$

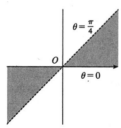

9. $0 \le r \le 2, \quad \frac{\pi}{2} \le \theta \le \pi$

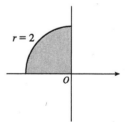

10. $1 \le r < 3, \quad -\frac{\pi}{4} \le \theta \le \frac{\pi}{4}$

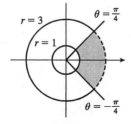

11. $2 < r < 3, \quad \frac{5\pi}{3} \le \theta \le \frac{7\pi}{3}$

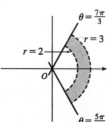

12. $-1 \le r \le 1, \quad \frac{\pi}{4} \le \theta \le \frac{3\pi}{4}$

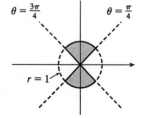

13. $r = 3 \sin \theta \implies r^2 = 3r \sin \theta \iff x^2 + y^2 = 3y \iff x^2 + y^2 - 3y = 0 \iff x^2 + y^2 - 3y + \frac{9}{4} = \frac{9}{4}$

$\iff x^2 + \left(y - \frac{3}{2}\right)^2 = \left(\frac{3}{2}\right)^2$, a circle of radius $\frac{3}{2}$ centered at $\left(0, \frac{3}{2}\right)$. The first two equations are actually equivalent

since $r^2 = 3r \sin \theta \implies r(r - 3 \sin \theta) = 0 \implies r = 0$ or $r = 3 \sin \theta$. But $r = 3 \sin \theta$ gives the point $r = 0$

(the pole) when $\theta = 0$. Thus, the single equation $r = 3 \sin \theta$ is equivalent to the compound condition $(r = 0$

or $r = 3 \sin \theta)$.

14. $r \cos \theta = 1 \iff x = 1$, a vertical line.

15. $r^2 = \sin 2\theta = 2 \sin \theta \cos \theta \iff r^2 \cdot r^2 = r^2 \cdot 2 \sin \theta \cos \theta \iff r^4 = 2r \sin \theta \, r \cos \theta \iff$

$\left(r^2\right)^2 = 2(r \sin \theta)(r \cos \theta) \iff \left(x^2 + y^2\right)^2 = 2yx$

16. $r = \dfrac{1}{1 + 2 \sin \theta} \implies r + 2r \sin \theta = 1 \iff r = 1 - 2r \sin \theta \iff \sqrt{x^2 + y^2} = 1 - 2y \implies$

$x^2 + y^2 = 1 - 4y + 4y^2 \iff 3y^2 - 4y - x^2 = -1 \iff 3\left(y^2 - \frac{4}{3}y + \frac{4}{9}\right) - x^2 = \frac{4}{3} - 1 \iff$

$3\left(y - \frac{2}{3}\right)^2 - x^2 = \frac{1}{3} \iff 9\left(y - \frac{2}{3}\right)^2 - 3x^2 = 1 \iff \dfrac{\left(y - \frac{2}{3}\right)^2}{\left(\frac{1}{3}\right)^2} - \dfrac{x^2}{\left(\frac{1}{\sqrt{3}}\right)^2} = 1$. This is a hyperbola opening

up and down and centered at $\left(0, \frac{2}{3}\right)$.

17. $y = 5 \iff r \sin \theta = 5$ (or $r = 5 \csc \theta$)

18. $y = 2x - 1 \iff r \sin \theta = 2r \cos \theta - 1 \iff r(2 \cos \theta - \sin \theta) = 1 \iff r = \dfrac{1}{2 \cos \theta - \sin \theta}$. (We can divide

by $2 \cos \theta - \sin \theta$ because it must be nonzero in order that its product with r equal 1.)

19. $x^2 + y^2 = 25 \iff r^2 = 25 \implies r = 5$

20. $x^2 = 4y \iff r^2 \cos^2 \theta = 4r \sin \theta \iff r \cos^2 \theta = 4 \sin \theta \iff r = 4 \tan \theta \sec \theta$

21. (a) The description leads immediately to the polar equation $\theta = \frac{\pi}{6}$, and the Cartesian equation

$y = \tan\left(\frac{\pi}{6}\right) x = \frac{1}{\sqrt{3}} x$ is slightly more difficult to derive.

(b) The easier description here is the Cartesian equation $x = 3$.

22. (a) Because its center is not at the origin, it is more easily described by its Cartesian equation,

$(x - 2)^2 + (y - 3)^2 = 5^2$.

(b) This circle is more easily given in polar coordinates: $r = 4$. The Cartesian equation is also simple:

$x^2 + y^2 = 16$.

23. As in Example 4, $r = 5$ represents the circle with center O and radius 5.

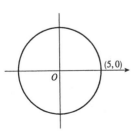

24. $\theta = \frac{3\pi}{4}$ is a line through the origin.

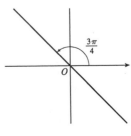

25. $r = \sin\theta \;\Leftrightarrow\; r^2 = r\sin\theta \;\Leftrightarrow\; x^2 + y^2 = y \;\Leftrightarrow$
$x^2 + \left(y - \frac{1}{2}\right)^2 = \left(\frac{1}{2}\right)^2$. The reasoning here is the same as in
Exercise 13. This is a circle of radius $\frac{1}{2}$ centered at $\left(0, \frac{1}{2}\right)$.

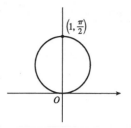

26. $r = 1 - 3\cos\theta$. This is a limaçon.

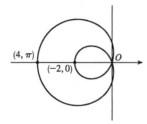

27. $r = \theta$, $\theta \geq 0$

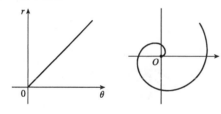

28. $r = \sqrt{\theta}$. This curve is a spiral.

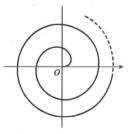

29. $r = 1 - 2\cos\theta$

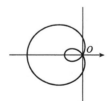

30. $r = 2 + \cos\theta$

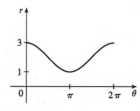
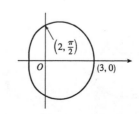

31. $r = 2\cos 4\theta$

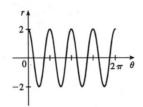
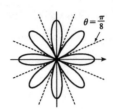

32. $r = \sin 5\theta$

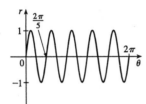
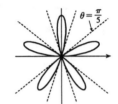

33. $r^2 = 4\cos 2\theta$

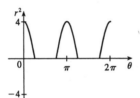
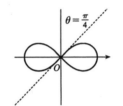

34. $r = 2\cos\left(\frac{3}{2}\theta\right)$

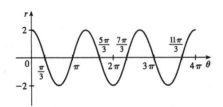

35. For $\theta = 0$, π, and 2π, r has its minimum value of about 0.5.
For $\theta = \frac{\pi}{2}$ and $\frac{3\pi}{2}$, r attains its maximum value of 2. We see that
the graph has a similar shape for $0 \le \theta \le \pi$ and $\pi \le \theta \le 2\pi$.

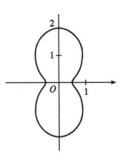

36.

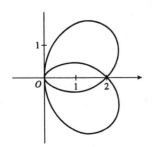

37. $x = (r)\cos\theta = (4 + 2\sec\theta)\cos\theta = 4\cos\theta + 2$. Now, $r \to \infty \;\Rightarrow\; (4 + 2\sec\theta) \to \infty \;\Rightarrow\; \theta \to \left(\frac{\pi}{2}\right)^-$ or

$\theta \to \left(\frac{3\pi}{2}\right)^+$ (since we need only consider $0 \le \theta < 2\pi$), so $\lim\limits_{r \to \infty} x = \lim\limits_{\theta \to \pi/2^-}(4\cos\theta + 2) = 2$. Also, $r \to -\infty$

$\Rightarrow\; (4 + 2\sec\theta) \to -\infty \;\Rightarrow\; \theta \to \left(\frac{\pi}{2}\right)^+$ or $\theta \to \left(\frac{3\pi}{2}\right)^-$, so $\lim\limits_{r \to -\infty} x = \lim\limits_{\theta \to \pi/2^+}(4\cos\theta + 2) = 2$. Therefore,

$\lim\limits_{r \to \pm\infty} x = 2 \;\Rightarrow\; x = 2$ is a vertical asymptote.

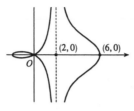

38. To show that $x = 1$ is an asymptote we must prove $\lim\limits_{r \to \pm\infty} x = 1$.

$x = (r)\cos\theta = (\sin\theta\,\tan\theta)\cos\theta = \sin^2\theta$. Now, $r \to \infty \;\Rightarrow\; \sin\theta\,\tan\theta \to \infty$

$\Rightarrow\; \theta \to \left(\frac{\pi}{2}\right)^-$, so $\lim\limits_{r \to \infty} x = \lim\limits_{\theta \to \pi/2^-}\sin^2\theta = 1$. Also, $r \to -\infty \;\Rightarrow$

$\sin\theta\,\tan\theta \to -\infty \;\Rightarrow\; \theta \to \left(\frac{\pi}{2}\right)^+$, so $\lim\limits_{r \to -\infty} x = \lim\limits_{\theta \to \pi/2^+}\sin^2\theta = 1$.

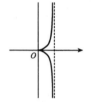

Therefore, $\lim\limits_{r \to \pm\infty} x = 1 \;\Rightarrow\; x = 1$ is a vertical asymptote. Also notice that $x = \sin^2\theta \ge 0$ for all θ, and

$x = \sin^2\theta \le 1$ for all θ. And $x \ne 1$, since the curve is not defined at odd multiples of $\frac{\pi}{2}$. Therefore, the curve lies entirely within the vertical strip $0 \le x < 1$.

39. (a) We see that the curve crosses itself at the origin, where $r = 0$ (in fact the inner loop corresponds to negative r-values,) so we solve the equation of the limaçon for $r = 0 \;\Leftrightarrow\; c\sin\theta = -1 \;\Leftrightarrow\; \sin\theta = -1/c$. Now if $|c| < 1$, then this equation has no solution and hence there is no inner loop. But if $c < -1$, then on the interval $(0, 2\pi)$ the equation has the two solutions $\theta = \sin^{-1}(-1/c)$ and $\theta = \pi - \sin^{-1}(-1/c)$, and if $c > 1$, the solutions are $\theta = \pi + \sin^{-1}(1/c)$ and $\theta = 2\pi - \sin^{-1}(1/c)$. In each case, $r < 0$ for θ between the two solutions, indicating a loop.

(b) For $0 < c < 1$, the dimple (if it exists) is characterized by the fact that y has a local maximum at $\theta = \frac{3\pi}{2}$. So we

determine for what c-values $\dfrac{d^2y}{d\theta^2}$ is negative at $\theta = \frac{3\pi}{2}$, since by the Second Derivative Test this indicates a

maximum: $y = r\sin\theta = \sin\theta + c\sin^2\theta \;\Rightarrow\; \dfrac{dy}{d\theta} = \cos\theta + 2c\sin\theta\cos\theta = \cos\theta + c\sin 2\theta \;\Rightarrow$

$\dfrac{d^2y}{d\theta^2} = -\sin\theta + 2c\cos 2\theta$. At $\theta = \frac{3\pi}{2}$, this is equal to $-(-1) + 2c(-1) = 1 - 2c$, which is negative only for

$c > \frac{1}{2}$. A similar argument shows that for $-1 < c < 0$, y only has a local minimum at $\theta = \frac{\pi}{2}$ (indicating a dimple) for $c < -\frac{1}{2}$.

40. (a) $r = \sin(\theta/2)$. This equation must correspond to one of II, III or VI, since these are the only graphs which are bounded. In fact it must be VI, since this is the only graph which is completed after a rotation of exactly 4π.

(b) $r = \sin(\theta/4)$. This equation must correspond to III, since this is the only graph which is completed after a rotation of exactly 8π.

(c) $r = \sec(3\theta)$. This must correspond to IV, since the graph is unbounded at $\theta = \frac{\pi}{6}, \frac{\pi}{2}, \frac{2\pi}{3}$, and so on.

(d) $r = \theta \sin \theta$. This must correspond to V. Note that $r = 0$ whenever θ is a multiple of π. This graph is unbounded, and each time θ moves through an interval of 2π, the same basic shape is repeated (because of the periodic $\sin \theta$ factor) but it gets larger each time (since θ increases each time we go around.)

(e) $r = 1 + 4 \cos 5\theta$. This corresponds to II, since it is bounded, has fivefold rotational symmetry, and takes only one takes only one rotation through 2π to be complete.

(f) $r = 1/\sqrt{\theta}$. This corresponds to I, since it is unbounded at $\theta = 0$, and r decreases as θ increases; in fact $r \to 0$ as $\theta \to \infty$.

41. Using Equation 3 with $r = 3 \cos \theta$ and $dr/d\theta = -3 \sin \theta$, we have

$$\frac{dy}{dx} = \frac{dy/d\theta}{dx/d\theta} = \frac{(dr/d\theta)(\sin \theta) + r \cos \theta}{(dr/d\theta)(\cos \theta) - r \sin \theta} = \frac{-3 \sin \theta \sin \theta + 3 \cos \theta \cos \theta}{-3 \sin \theta \cos \theta - 3 \cos \theta \sin \theta} = \frac{3(\cos^2 \theta - \sin^2 \theta)}{-3(2 \sin \theta \cos \theta)}$$

$$= -\frac{\cos 2\theta}{\sin 2\theta} = -\cot 2\theta = \frac{1}{\sqrt{3}} \text{ when } \theta = \frac{\pi}{3}$$

Another solution: $r = 3 \cos \theta \implies x = r \cos \theta = 3 \cos^2 \theta, y = r \sin \theta = 3 \sin \theta \cos \theta \implies$

$$\frac{dy}{dx} = \frac{dy/d\theta}{dx/d\theta} = \frac{-3 \sin^2 \theta + 3 \cos^2 \theta}{-6 \cos \theta \sin \theta} = \frac{\cos 2\theta}{-\sin 2\theta} = -\cot 2\theta = \frac{1}{\sqrt{3}} \text{ when } \theta = \frac{\pi}{3}$$

42. Using Equation 3 with $r = \cos \theta + \sin \theta$, we have

$$\frac{dy}{dx} = \frac{(dr/d\theta) \sin \theta + r \cos \theta}{(dr/d\theta) \cos \theta - r \sin \theta} = \frac{(-\sin \theta + \cos \theta) \sin \theta + (\cos \theta + \sin \theta) \cos \theta}{(-\sin \theta + \cos \theta) \cos \theta - (\cos \theta + \sin \theta) \sin \theta} = -1 \text{ when } \theta = \frac{\pi}{4}$$

Another solution: $r = \cos \theta + \sin \theta \implies$
$x = r \cos \theta = (\cos \theta + \sin \theta) \cos \theta, y = r \sin \theta = (\cos \theta + \sin \theta) \sin \theta \implies$

$$\frac{dy}{dx} = \frac{dy/d\theta}{dx/d\theta} = \frac{\sin \theta (-\sin \theta + \cos \theta) + (\cos \theta + \sin \theta) \cos \theta}{\cos \theta (-\sin \theta + \cos \theta) - (\cos \theta + \sin \theta) \sin \theta} = -1 \text{ when } \theta = \frac{\pi}{4}$$

43. $r = 1 + \cos \theta \implies x = r \cos \theta = \cos \theta + \cos^2 \theta, y = r \sin \theta = \sin \theta + \sin \theta \cos \theta \implies$

$$\frac{dy}{dx} = \frac{dy/d\theta}{dx/d\theta} = \frac{\cos \theta + \cos^2 \theta - \sin^2 \theta}{-\sin \theta - 2 \cos \theta \sin \theta} = \frac{\cos \theta + \cos 2\theta}{-\sin \theta - \sin 2\theta}$$

When $\theta = \frac{\pi}{6}, \frac{dy}{dx} = \frac{\frac{\sqrt{3}}{2} + \frac{1}{2}}{-\frac{1}{2} - \frac{\sqrt{3}}{2}} = \frac{\frac{\sqrt{3}}{2} + \frac{1}{2}}{-\left(\frac{1}{2} + \frac{\sqrt{3}}{2}\right)} = -1.$

44. $r = \ln \theta \implies x = r \cos \theta = \ln \theta \cos \theta, y = r \sin \theta = \ln \theta \sin \theta \implies$

$$\frac{dy}{dx} = \frac{dy/d\theta}{dx/d\theta} = \frac{\sin \theta (1/\theta) + \ln \theta \cos \theta}{\cos \theta (1/\theta) - \ln \theta \sin \theta} = \frac{\sin e + e \cos e}{\cos e - e \sin e} \text{ when } \theta = e$$

45. $r = 3\cos\theta \Rightarrow x = r\cos\theta = 3\cos\theta\cos\theta, y = r\sin\theta = 3\cos\theta\sin\theta \Rightarrow$
$dy/d\theta = -3\sin^2\theta + 3\cos^2\theta = 3\cos 2\theta = 0 \Rightarrow 2\theta = \frac{\pi}{2}$ or $\frac{3\pi}{2} \Leftrightarrow \theta = \frac{\pi}{4}$ or $\frac{3\pi}{4}$. So the tangent is
horizontal at $\left(\frac{3}{\sqrt{2}}, \frac{\pi}{4}\right)$ and $\left(-\frac{3}{\sqrt{2}}, \frac{3\pi}{4}\right)$ $\left[\text{same as } \left(\frac{3}{\sqrt{2}}, -\frac{\pi}{4}\right)\right]$. $dx/d\theta = -6\sin\theta\cos\theta = -3\sin 2\theta = 0 \Rightarrow$
$2\theta = 0$ or $\pi \Leftrightarrow \theta = 0$ or $\frac{\pi}{2}$. So the tangent is vertical at $(3, 0)$ and $\left(0, \frac{\pi}{2}\right)$.

46. $\dfrac{dy}{d\theta} = e^\theta\sin\theta + e^\theta\cos\theta = e^\theta(\sin\theta + \cos\theta) = 0 \Rightarrow \sin\theta = -\cos\theta \Rightarrow \tan\theta = -1 \Rightarrow$
$\theta = -\frac{1}{4}\pi + n\pi$ (n any integer) $\Rightarrow$ horizontal tangents at $\left(e^{\pi(n-1/4)}, \pi\left(n - \frac{1}{4}\right)\right)$.
$\dfrac{dx}{d\theta} = e^\theta\cos\theta - e^\theta\sin\theta = e^\theta(\cos\theta - \sin\theta) = 0 \Rightarrow \sin\theta = \cos\theta \Rightarrow \tan\theta = 1 \Rightarrow$
$\theta = \frac{1}{4}\pi + n\pi$ (n any integer) $\Rightarrow$ vertical tangents at $\left(e^{\pi(n+1/4)}, \pi\left(n + \frac{1}{4}\right)\right)$.

47. $r = 1 + \cos\theta \Rightarrow x = r\cos\theta = \cos\theta(1 + \cos\theta), y = r\sin\theta = \sin\theta(1 + \cos\theta) \Rightarrow$
$dy/d\theta = (1 + \cos\theta)\cos\theta - \sin^2\theta = 2\cos^2\theta + \cos\theta - 1 = (2\cos\theta - 1)(\cos\theta + 1) = 0 \Rightarrow \cos\theta = \frac{1}{2}$ or
$-1 \Rightarrow \theta = \frac{\pi}{3}, \pi,$ or $\frac{5\pi}{3} \Rightarrow$ horizontal tangent at $\left(\frac{3}{2}, \frac{\pi}{3}\right), (0, \pi),$ and $\left(\frac{3}{2}, \frac{5\pi}{3}\right)$.
$dx/d\theta = -(1 + \cos\theta)\sin\theta - \cos\theta\sin\theta = -\sin\theta(1 + 2\cos\theta) = 0 \Rightarrow \sin\theta = 0$ or $\cos\theta = -\frac{1}{2} \Rightarrow$
$\theta = 0, \pi, \frac{2\pi}{3},$ or $\frac{4\pi}{3} \Rightarrow$ vertical tangent at $(2, 0), \left(\frac{1}{2}, \frac{2\pi}{3}\right),$ and $\left(\frac{1}{2}, \frac{4\pi}{3}\right)$. Note that the tangent is horizontal, not
vertical when $\theta = \pi$, since $\displaystyle\lim_{\theta\to\pi}\dfrac{dy/d\theta}{dx/d\theta} = 0$.

48. By differentiating implicitly, $r^2 = \sin 2\theta \Rightarrow 2r(dr/d\theta) = 2\cos 2\theta \Rightarrow$
$dr/d\theta = (1/r)\cos 2\theta$, so

$$\frac{dy}{d\theta} = \frac{1}{r}\cos 2\theta\sin\theta + r\cos\theta = \frac{1}{r}\left(\cos 2\theta\sin\theta + r^2\cos\theta\right)$$

$$= \frac{1}{r}(\cos 2\theta\sin\theta + \sin 2\theta\cos\theta) = \frac{1}{r}\sin 3\theta$$

This is 0 when $\sin 3\theta = 0 \Rightarrow \theta = 0, \frac{\pi}{3}$ or $\frac{4\pi}{3}$ (restricting θ to the domain of the lemniscate), so there are
horizontal tangents at $\left(\sqrt[4]{\frac{3}{4}}, \frac{\pi}{3}\right), \left(\sqrt[4]{\frac{3}{4}}, \frac{4\pi}{3}\right)$ and $(0, 0)$. Similarly, $dx/d\theta = (1/r)\cos 3\theta = 0$ when $\theta = \frac{\pi}{6}$ or $\frac{7\pi}{6}$,
so there are vertical tangents at $\left(\sqrt[4]{\frac{3}{4}}, \frac{\pi}{6}\right)$ and $\left(\sqrt[4]{\frac{3}{4}}, \frac{7\pi}{6}\right)$ [and $(0, 0)$].

49. $r = a\sin\theta + b\cos\theta \Rightarrow r^2 = ar\sin\theta + br\cos\theta \Rightarrow x^2 + y^2 = ay + bx \Rightarrow$
$x^2 - bx + \left(\frac{1}{2}b\right)^2 + y^2 - ay + \left(\frac{1}{2}a\right)^2 = \left(\frac{1}{2}b\right)^2 + \left(\frac{1}{2}a\right)^2 \Rightarrow \left(x - \frac{1}{2}b\right)^2 + \left(y - \frac{1}{2}a\right)^2 = \frac{1}{4}\left(a^2 + b^2\right)$, and this
is a circle with center $\left(\frac{1}{2}b, \frac{1}{2}a\right)$ and radius $\frac{1}{2}\sqrt{a^2 + b^2}$.

50. These curves are circles which intersect at the origin and at $\left(\frac{1}{\sqrt{2}}a, \frac{\pi}{4}\right)$. At the origin, the first circle has a horizontal
tangent and the second a vertical one, so the tangents are perpendicular here. For the first circle ($r = a\sin\theta$),
$dy/d\theta = a\cos\theta\sin\theta + a\sin\theta\cos\theta = a\sin 2\theta = a$ at $\theta = \frac{\pi}{4}$ and $dx/d\theta = a\cos^2\theta - a\sin^2\theta = a\cos 2\theta = 0$ at
$\theta = \frac{\pi}{4}$, so the tangent here is vertical. Similarly, for the second circle ($r = a\cos\theta$), $dy/d\theta = a\cos 2\theta = 0$ and
$dx/d\theta = -a\sin 2\theta = -a$ at $\theta = \frac{\pi}{4}$, so the tangent is horizontal, and again the tangents are perpendicular.

Note for Exercises 51–54: Maple is able to plot polar curves using the `polarplot` command, or using the `coords=polar` option in a regular `plot` command. In Mathematica, use `PolarPlot`. In Derive, change to `Polar` under `Options State`. If your graphing device cannot plot polar equations, you must convert to parametric equations. For example, in Exercise 51,

$x = r \cos \theta = [1 + 2 \sin(\theta/2)] \cos \theta$, $y = r \sin \theta = [1 + 2 \sin(\theta/2)] \sin \theta$.

51. $r = 1 + 2 \sin(\theta/2)$. The parameter interval is $[0, 4\pi]$.

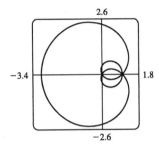

52. $r = \sqrt{1 - 0.8 \sin^2 \theta}$. The parameter interval is $[0, 2\pi]$.

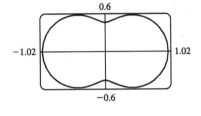

53. $r = e^{\sin \theta} - 2 \cos(4\theta)$. The parameter interval is $[0, 2\pi]$.

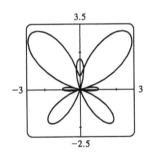

54. $r = \sin^2(4\theta) + \cos(4\theta)$. The parameter interval is $[0, 2\pi]$.

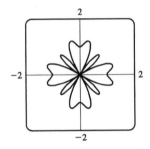

55.

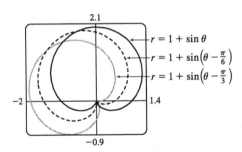

$r = 1 + \sin \theta$
$r = 1 + \sin\left(\theta - \frac{\pi}{6}\right)$
$r = 1 + \sin\left(\theta - \frac{\pi}{3}\right)$

It appears that the graph of $r = 1 + \sin\left(\theta - \frac{\pi}{6}\right)$ is the same shape as the graph of $r = 1 + \sin \theta$, but rotated counterclockwise about the origin by $\frac{\pi}{6}$. Similarly, the graph of $r = 1 + \sin\left(\theta - \frac{\pi}{3}\right)$ is rotated by $\frac{\pi}{3}$. In general, the graph of $r = f(\theta - \alpha)$ is the same shape as that of $r = f(\theta)$, but rotated counterclockwise through α about the origin. That is, for any point (r_0, θ_0) on the curve $r = f(\theta)$, the point $(r_0, \theta_0 + \alpha)$ is on the curve $r = f(\theta - \alpha)$, since $r_0 = f(\theta_0) = f((\theta_0 + \alpha) - \alpha)$.

56.

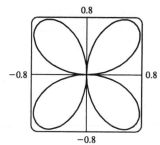

From the graph, the highest points seem to have $y \approx 0.77$. To find the exact value, we solve $dy/d\theta = 0$.
$y = r \sin \theta = \sin \theta \sin 2\theta \Rightarrow$

$$dy/d\theta = 2 \sin \theta \, \cos 2\theta + \cos \theta \, \sin 2\theta$$
$$= 2 \sin \theta \left(2 \cos^2 \theta - 1\right) + \cos \theta \left(2 \sin \theta \, \cos \theta\right)$$
$$= 2 \sin \theta \left(3 \cos^2 \theta - 1\right)$$

In the first quadrant, this is 0 when $\cos \theta = \frac{1}{\sqrt{3}} \Leftrightarrow \sin \theta = \sqrt{\frac{2}{3}} \Leftrightarrow$
$y = 2 \sin^2 \theta \cos \theta = 2 \cdot \frac{2}{3} \cdot \frac{1}{\sqrt{3}} = \frac{4\sqrt{3}}{9} \approx 0.77$.

57. (a) $r = \sin n\theta$. From the graphs, it seems that when n is even, the number of loops in the curve (called a rose) is $2n$, and when n is odd, the number of loops is simply n.

This is because in the case of n odd, every point on the graph is traversed twice, due to the fact that

$$r(\theta + \pi) = \sin[n(\theta + \pi)] = \sin n\theta \, \cos n\pi + \cos n\theta \, \sin n\pi = \begin{cases} \sin n\theta & \text{if } n \text{ is even} \\ -\sin n\theta & \text{if } n \text{ is odd} \end{cases}$$

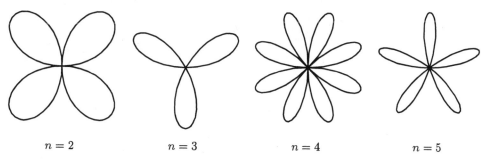

$n = 2$ $\qquad\qquad$ $n = 3$ $\qquad\qquad$ $n = 4$ $\qquad\qquad$ $n = 5$

(b) The graph of $r = |\sin n\theta|$ has $2n$ loops whether n is odd or even, since $r(\theta + \pi) = r(\theta)$.

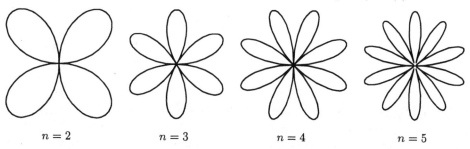

$n = 2$ $\qquad\qquad$ $n = 3$ $\qquad\qquad$ $n = 4$ $\qquad\qquad$ $n = 5$

58. $r = 1 + c \sin n\theta$. We vary n while keeping c constant at 2. As n changes, the curves change in the same way as those in Exercise 57: the number of loops increases. Note that if n is even, the smaller loops are outside the larger ones; if n is odd, they are inside.

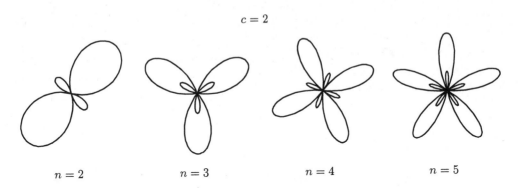

$c = 2$

$n = 2$ $n = 3$ $n = 4$ $n = 5$

Now we vary c while keeping $n = 3$. As c increases toward 0, the entire graph gets smaller (the graphs below are not to scale) and the smaller loops shrink in relation to the large ones. At $c = -1$, the small loops disappear entirely, and for $-1 < c < 1$, the graph is a simple, closed curve (at $c = 0$ it is a circle). As c continues to increase, the same changes are seen, but in reverse order, since $1 + (-c) \sin n\theta = 1 + c \sin n(\theta + \pi)$, so the graph for $c = c_0$ is the same as that for $c = -c_0$, with a rotation through π. As $c \to \infty$, the smaller loops get relatively closer in size to the large ones. Note that the distance between the outermost points of corresponding inner and outer loops is always 2. Maple's `animate` command (or Mathematica's `Animate`) is very useful for seeing the changes that occur as c varies.

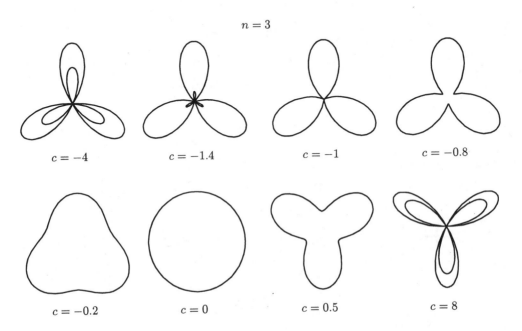

$n = 3$

$c = -4$ $c = -1.4$ $c = -1$ $c = -0.8$

$c = -0.2$ $c = 0$ $c = 0.5$ $c = 8$

59. $r = \dfrac{1 - a\cos\theta}{1 + a\cos\theta}$. We start with $a = 0$, since in this case the curve is simply the circle $r = 1$.

As a increases, the graph moves to the left, and its right side becomes flattened. As a increases through about 0.4, the right side seems to grow a dimple, which upon closer investigation (with narrower θ-ranges) seems to appear at $a \approx 0.42$ (the actual value is $\sqrt{2} - 1$). As $a \to 1$, this dimple becomes more pronounced, and the curve begins to stretch out horizontally, until at $a = 1$ the denominator vanishes at $\theta = \pi$, and the dimple becomes an actual cusp. For $a > 1$ we must choose our parameter interval carefully, since $r \to \infty$ as $1 + a\cos\theta \to 0 \iff$ $\theta \to \pm\cos^{-1}(-1/a)$. As a increases from 1, the curve splits into two parts. The left part has a loop, which grows larger as a increases, and the right part grows broader vertically, and its left tip develops a dimple when $a \approx 2.42$ (actually, $\sqrt{2} + 1$). As a increases, the dimple grows more and more pronounced. If $a < 0$, we get the same graph as we do for the corresponding positive a-value, but with a rotation through π about the pole, as happened when c was replaced with $-c$ in Exercise 58.

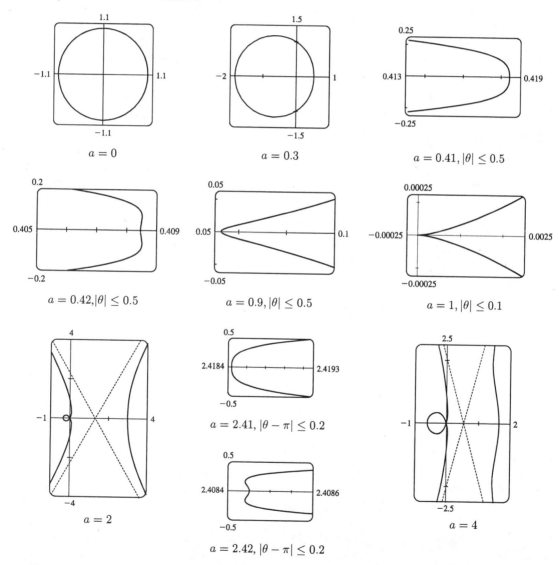

60. Most graphing devices cannot plot implicit polar equations, so we must first find an explicit expression (or expressions) for r in terms of θ, a, and c. We note that the given equation is a quadratic in r^2, so we use the quadratic formula and find that

$$r^2 = \frac{2c^2 \cos 2\theta \pm \sqrt{4c^4 \cos^2 2\theta - 4\left(c^4 - a^4\right)}}{2}$$

$$= c^2 \cos 2\theta \pm \sqrt{a^4 - c^4 \sin^2 2\theta}$$

so $r = \pm\sqrt{c^2 \cos 2\theta \pm \sqrt{a^4 - c^4 \sin^2 2\theta}}$. So for each graph, we must plot four curves to be sure of plotting all the points which satisfy the given equation. Note that all four functions have period π.

We start with the case $a = c = 1$, and the resulting curve resembles the symbol for infinity. If we let a decrease, the curve splits into two symmetric parts, and as a decreases further, the parts become smaller, further apart, and rounder. If instead we let a increase from 1, the two lobes of the curve join together, and as a increases further they continue to merge, until at $a \approx 1.4$, the graph no longer has dimples, and has an oval shape. As $a \to \infty$, the oval becomes larger and rounder, since the c^2 and c^4 terms lose their significance. Note that the shape of the graph seems to depend only on the ratio c/a, while the size of the graph varies as c and a jointly increase.

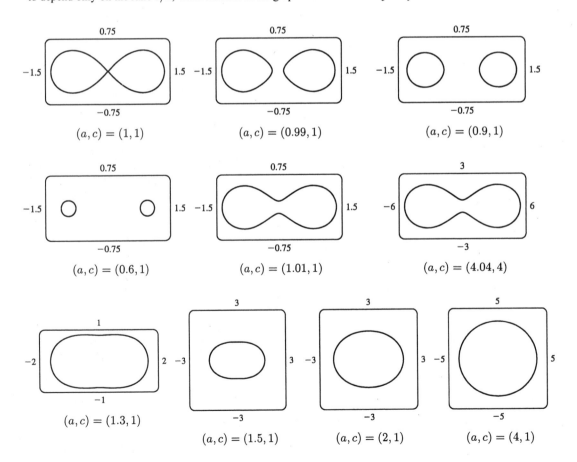

61.

$$\tan\psi = \tan(\phi - \theta) = \frac{\tan\phi - \tan\theta}{1 + \tan\phi\,\tan\theta} = \frac{\dfrac{dy}{dx} - \tan\theta}{1 + \dfrac{dy}{dx}\tan\theta} = \frac{\dfrac{dy/d\theta}{dx/d\theta} - \tan\theta}{1 + \dfrac{dy/d\theta}{dx/d\theta}\tan\theta}$$

$$= \frac{\dfrac{dy}{d\theta} - \dfrac{dx}{d\theta}\tan\theta}{\dfrac{dx}{d\theta} + \dfrac{dy}{d\theta}\tan\theta} = \frac{\left(\dfrac{dr}{d\theta}\sin\theta + r\cos\theta\right) - \tan\theta\left(\dfrac{dr}{d\theta}\cos\theta - r\sin\theta\right)}{\left(\dfrac{dr}{d\theta}\cos\theta - r\sin\theta\right) + \tan\theta\left(\dfrac{dr}{d\theta}\sin\theta + r\cos\theta\right)}$$

$$= \frac{r\cos\theta + r\cdot\dfrac{\sin^2\theta}{\cos\theta}}{\dfrac{dr}{d\theta}\cos\theta + \dfrac{dr}{d\theta}\cdot\dfrac{\sin^2\theta}{\cos\theta}} = \frac{r\cos^2\theta + r\sin^2\theta}{\dfrac{dr}{d\theta}\cos^2\theta + \dfrac{dr}{d\theta}\sin^2\theta} = \frac{r}{dr/d\theta}$$

62. (a) $r = e^\theta \;\Rightarrow\; dr/d\theta = e^\theta$, so by
Exercise 61, $\tan\psi = r/e^\theta = 1 \;\Rightarrow\;$
$\psi = \arctan 1 = \frac{\pi}{4}$.

(c) Let a be the tangent of the angle between
the tangent and radial lines, that is,
$a = \tan\psi$. Then, by Exercise 61,

$$a = \frac{r}{dr/d\theta} \;\Rightarrow\; \frac{dr}{d\theta} = \frac{1}{a}r \;\Rightarrow\;$$

$r = Ce^{\theta/a}$ (by Theorem 7.4.2).

(b) The Cartesian equation of the tangent line at $(1,0)$ is
$y = x - 1$, and that of the tangent line at $\left(0, e^{\pi/2}\right)$
is $y = e^{\pi/2} - x$.

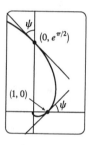

##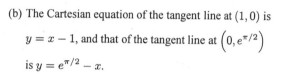
H.2   Areas and Lengths in Polar Coordinates • • • • • • • •

1. $r = \sqrt{\theta},\, 0 \le \theta \le \frac{\pi}{4}$. $A = \int_0^{\pi/4} \frac{1}{2}r^2\,d\theta = \int_0^{\pi/4} \frac{1}{2}\left(\sqrt{\theta}\right)^2 d\theta = \int_0^{\pi/4} \frac{1}{2}\theta\,d\theta = \left[\frac{1}{4}\theta^2\right]_0^{\pi/4} = \frac{1}{64}\pi^2$

2. $r = e^{\theta/2},\, \pi \le \theta \le 2\pi$. $A = \int_\pi^{2\pi} \frac{1}{2}\left(e^{\theta/2}\right)^2 d\theta = \int_\pi^{2\pi} \frac{1}{2}e^\theta\,d\theta = \frac{1}{2}\left[e^\theta\right]_\pi^{2\pi} = \frac{1}{2}\left(e^{2\pi} - e^\pi\right)$

3. $r = \sin\theta,\, \frac{\pi}{3} \le \theta \le \frac{2\pi}{3}$.

$$A = \int_{\pi/3}^{2\pi/3} \frac{1}{2}\sin^2\theta\,d\theta = \frac{1}{4}\int_{\pi/3}^{2\pi/3}(1 - \cos 2\theta)\,d\theta = \frac{1}{4}\left[\theta - \frac{1}{2}\sin 2\theta\right]_{\pi/3}^{2\pi/3}$$

$$= \frac{1}{4}\left[\frac{2\pi}{3} - \frac{1}{2}\sin\frac{4\pi}{3} - \frac{\pi}{3} + \frac{1}{2}\sin\frac{2\pi}{3}\right] = \frac{1}{4}\left[\frac{2\pi}{3} - \frac{1}{2}\left(-\frac{\sqrt{3}}{2}\right) - \frac{\pi}{3} + \frac{1}{2}\left(\frac{\sqrt{3}}{2}\right)\right] = \frac{1}{4}\left(\frac{\pi}{3} + \frac{\sqrt{3}}{2}\right) = \frac{\pi}{12} + \frac{\sqrt{3}}{8}$$

4. $r = \sqrt{\sin\theta},\, 0 \le \theta \le \pi$. $A = \int_0^\pi \frac{1}{2}\left(\sqrt{\sin\theta}\right)^2 d\theta = \int_0^\pi \frac{1}{2}\sin\theta\,d\theta = \left[-\frac{1}{2}\cos\theta\right]_0^\pi = \frac{1}{2} + \frac{1}{2} = 1$

5. $r = \theta,\, 0 \le \theta \le \pi$. $A = \int_0^\pi \frac{1}{2}\theta^2\,d\theta = \left[\frac{1}{6}\theta^3\right]_0^\pi = \frac{1}{6}\pi^3$

6. $r = 1 + \sin\theta,\, \frac{\pi}{2} \le \theta \le \pi$.

$$A = \int_{\pi/2}^\pi \frac{1}{2}(1 + \sin\theta)^2\,d\theta = \frac{1}{2}\int_{\pi/2}^\pi(1 + 2\sin\theta + \sin^2\theta)\,d\theta = \frac{1}{2}\int_{\pi/2}^\pi\left[1 + 2\sin\theta + \frac{1}{2}(1 - \cos 2\theta)\right]d\theta$$

$$= \frac{1}{2}\left[\theta - 2\cos\theta + \frac{1}{2}\theta - \frac{1}{4}\sin 2\theta\right]_{\pi/2}^\pi = \frac{1}{2}\left[\pi + 2 + \frac{\pi}{2} - 0 - \left(\frac{\pi}{2} - 0 + \frac{\pi}{4} - 0\right)\right] = \frac{1}{2}\left(\frac{3\pi}{4} + 2\right) = \frac{3\pi}{8} + 1$$

7. $r = 4 + 3\sin\theta$, $-\frac{\pi}{2} \le \theta \le \frac{\pi}{2}$.

$$A = \int_{-\pi/2}^{\pi/2} \frac{1}{2}(4 + 3\sin\theta)^2 d\theta = \frac{1}{2}\int_{-\pi/2}^{\pi/2}(16 + 24\sin\theta + 9\sin^2\theta)\,d\theta$$

$$= \frac{1}{2}\int_{-\pi/2}^{\pi/2}(16 + 9\sin^2\theta)\,d\theta \quad \text{[by Theorem 5.5.6(b)]}$$

$$= \frac{1}{2} \cdot 2\int_{0}^{\pi/2}\left[16 + 9 \cdot \frac{1}{2}(1 - \cos 2\theta)\right]d\theta \quad \text{[by Theorem 5.5.6(a)]}$$

$$= \int_{0}^{\pi/2}\left(\frac{41}{2} - \frac{9}{2}\cos 2\theta\right)d\theta = \left[\frac{41}{2}\theta - \frac{9}{4}\sin 2\theta\right]_{0}^{\pi/2} = \left(\frac{41\pi}{4} - 0\right) - (0 - 0) = \frac{41\pi}{4}$$

8. $r = \sin 4\theta$, $0 \le \theta \le \frac{\pi}{4}$. $A = \int_{0}^{\pi/4}\frac{1}{2}\sin^2 4\theta\,d\theta = \int_{0}^{\pi/4}\frac{1}{4}(1 - \cos 8\theta)\,d\theta = \left[\frac{1}{4}\theta - \frac{1}{32}\sin 8\theta\right]_{0}^{\pi/4} = \frac{\pi}{16}$

9. The curve goes through the pole when $\theta = \pi/4$, so we'll find the area for
$0 \le \theta \le \pi/4$ and multiply it by 4.

$$A = 4\int_{0}^{\pi/4}\frac{1}{2}r^2\,d\theta = 2\int_{0}^{\pi/4}(4\cos 2\theta)\,d\theta$$

$$= 8\int_{0}^{\pi/4}\cos 2\theta\,d\theta = 4\left[\sin 2\theta\right]_{0}^{\pi/4} = 4$$

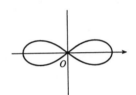

10. $A = \int_{0}^{2\pi}\frac{1}{2}r^2\,d\theta = \int_{0}^{2\pi}\frac{1}{2}\left[3(1 + \cos\theta)\right]^2 d\theta$

$$= \frac{9}{2}\int_{0}^{2\pi}(1 + 2\cos\theta + \cos^2\theta)\,d\theta$$

$$= \frac{9}{2}\int_{0}^{2\pi}\left[1 + 2\cos\theta + \frac{1}{2}(1 + \cos 2\theta)\right]d\theta$$

$$= \frac{9}{2}\left[\frac{3}{2}\theta + 2\sin\theta + \frac{1}{4}\sin 2\theta\right]_{0}^{2\pi} = \frac{27}{2}\pi$$

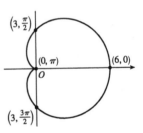

11. The curve is symmetric about the vertical line $\theta = \pi/2$, so we'll find the area of the right side and double it.

$$A = 2\int_{-\pi/2}^{\pi/2}\frac{1}{2}(4 - \sin\theta)^2\,d\theta = \int_{-\pi/2}^{\pi/2}(16 - 8\sin\theta + \sin^2\theta)\,d\theta$$

$$= \int_{-\pi/2}^{\pi/2}(16 + \sin^2\theta)\,d\theta \quad \text{[by Theorem 5.5.6(b)]}$$

$$= 2\int_{0}^{\pi/2}(16 + \sin^2\theta)\,d\theta \quad \text{[by Theorem 5.5.6(a)]}$$

$$= 2\int_{0}^{\pi/2}\left[16 + \frac{1}{2}(1 - \cos 2\theta)\right]d\theta = 2\left[\frac{33}{2}\theta - \frac{1}{4}\sin 2\theta\right]_{0}^{\pi/2}$$

$$= \frac{33\pi}{2}$$

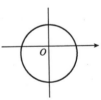

12. $A = 3\int_{0}^{\pi/3}\frac{1}{2}r^2\,d\theta = \frac{3}{2}\int_{0}^{\pi/3}\sin^2 3\theta\,d\theta$

$$= \frac{3}{2}\int_{0}^{\pi/3}\frac{1}{2}(1 - \cos 6\theta)\,d\theta = \frac{3}{4}\left[\theta - \frac{1}{6}\sin 6\theta\right]_{0}^{\pi/3}$$

$$= \frac{3}{4}\left(\frac{\pi}{3}\right) = \frac{\pi}{4}$$

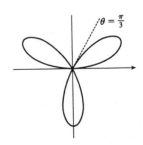

13. By symmetry, the total area is twice the area enclosed above the polar axis, so

$$A = 2\int_0^\pi \tfrac{1}{2}r^2\,d\theta = \int_0^\pi (2 + \cos 6\theta)^2\,d\theta = \int_0^\pi (4 + 4\cos 6\theta + \cos^2 6\theta)\,d\theta$$

$$= \int_0^\pi \left[4 + 4\cos 6\theta + \tfrac{1}{2}(1 + \cos 12\theta)\right]d\theta$$

$$= \left[4\theta + 4\left(\tfrac{1}{6}\sin 6\theta\right) + \left(\tfrac{1}{24}\sin 12\theta + \tfrac{1}{2}\theta\right)\right]_0^\pi = 4\pi + \tfrac{\pi}{2} = \tfrac{9\pi}{2}$$

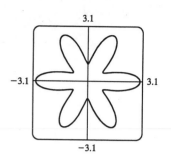

14. Note that the entire curve $r = 2\sin\theta \cos^2\theta$ is generated by $\theta \in [0, \pi]$. The radius is positive on this interval, so the area enclosed is

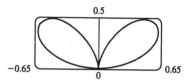

$$A = \int_0^\pi \tfrac{1}{2}r^2\,d\theta = \int_0^\pi \tfrac{1}{2}\left(2\sin\theta \cos^2\theta\right)^2 d\theta = 2\int_0^\pi \sin^2\theta \cos^4\theta\,d\theta$$

$$= 2\int_0^\pi (\sin\theta \cos\theta)^2 \cos^2\theta\,d\theta = 2\int_0^\pi \left(\tfrac{1}{2}\sin 2\theta\right)^2 \cos^2\theta\,d\theta$$

$$= \tfrac{1}{4}\int_0^\pi \sin^2 2\theta\,(\cos 2\theta + 1)\,d\theta = \tfrac{1}{4}\left[\int_0^\pi \sin^2 2\theta \cos 2\theta\,d\theta + \int_0^\pi \sin^2 2\theta\,d\theta\right]$$

$$= \tfrac{1}{4}\left[\tfrac{1}{2}\theta - \tfrac{1}{4}\sin 4\theta\right]_0^\pi \quad \text{[the first integral vanishes]} \quad = \tfrac{\pi}{8}$$

15. The shaded loop is traced out from $\theta = 0$ to $\theta = \pi/2$.

$$A = \int_0^{\pi/2} \tfrac{1}{2}r^2\,d\theta = \tfrac{1}{2}\int_0^{\pi/2} \sin^2 2\theta\,d\theta$$

$$= \tfrac{1}{2}\int_0^{\pi/2} \tfrac{1}{2}(1 - \cos 4\theta)\,d\theta = \tfrac{1}{4}\left[\theta - \tfrac{1}{4}\sin 4\theta\right]_0^{\pi/2}$$

$$= \tfrac{1}{4}\left(\tfrac{\pi}{2}\right) = \tfrac{\pi}{8}$$

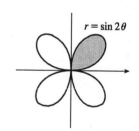

$r = \sin 2\theta$

16. $A = \int_0^{\pi/3} \tfrac{1}{2}(4\sin 3\theta)^2\,d\theta = 8\int_0^{\pi/3} \sin^2 3\theta\,d\theta$

$$= 4\int_0^{\pi/3} (1 - \cos 6\theta)\,d\theta = 4\left[\theta - \tfrac{1}{6}\sin 6\theta\right]_0^{\pi/3} = \tfrac{4\pi}{3}$$

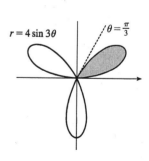

$r = 4\sin 3\theta$

$\theta = \tfrac{\pi}{3}$

17.

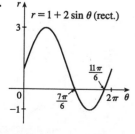

$r = 1 + 2\sin\theta$ (rect.)

$\left(3, \tfrac{\pi}{2}\right)$

$r = 1 + 2\sin\theta$

$\left(-1, \tfrac{3\pi}{2}\right)$

$\theta = \tfrac{7\pi}{6}$

$\theta = \tfrac{11\pi}{6}$

This is a limaçon, with inner loop traced out between $\theta = \tfrac{7\pi}{6}$ and $\tfrac{11\pi}{6}$ [found by solving $r = 0$].

$A = 2 \int_{7\pi/6}^{3\pi/2} \frac{1}{2}(1 + 2\sin\theta)^2 \, d\theta = \int_{7\pi/6}^{3\pi/2} (1 + 4\sin\theta + 4\sin^2\theta) \, d\theta = \int_{7\pi/6}^{3\pi/2} \left[1 + 4\sin\theta + 4 \cdot \frac{1}{2}(1 - \cos 2\theta)\right] d\theta$

$= [\theta - 4\cos\theta + 2\theta - \sin 2\theta]_{7\pi/6}^{3\pi/2} = \left(\frac{9\pi}{2}\right) - \left(\frac{7\pi}{2} + 2\sqrt{3} - \frac{\sqrt{3}}{2}\right) = \pi - \frac{3\sqrt{3}}{2}$

18. $2 + 3\cos\theta = 0 \;\Rightarrow\; \cos\theta = -\frac{2}{3} \;\Rightarrow\; \theta = \cos^{-1}\left(-\frac{2}{3}\right) \; [= \alpha] \text{ or } 2\pi - \cos^{-1}\left(-\frac{2}{3}\right) \;\Rightarrow$

$A = 2 \int_\alpha^\pi \frac{1}{2}(2 + 3\cos\theta)^2 \, d\theta = \int_\alpha^\pi (4 + 12\cos\theta + 9\cos^2\theta) \, d\theta = \int_\alpha^\pi \left(\frac{17}{2} + 12\cos\theta + \frac{9}{2}\cos 2\theta\right) d\theta$

$= \left[\frac{17}{2}\theta + 12\sin\theta + \frac{9}{4}\sin 2\theta\right]_\alpha^\pi = \frac{17}{2}(\pi - \alpha) - 12\sin\alpha - \frac{9}{2}\sin\alpha\cos\alpha$

$= \frac{17}{2}\left[\pi - \cos^{-1}\left(-\frac{2}{3}\right)\right] - 12\left(\frac{\sqrt{5}}{3}\right) - \frac{9}{2}\left(\frac{\sqrt{5}}{3}\right)\left(-\frac{2}{3}\right) = \frac{17}{2}\cos^{-1}\left(\frac{2}{3}\right) - 3\sqrt{5}$

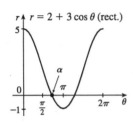

$r \blacktriangle\; r = 2 + 3\cos\theta \text{ (rect.)}$

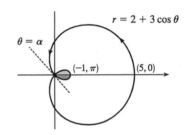

$r = 2 + 3\cos\theta$

19. $4\sin\theta = 2 \;\Leftrightarrow\; \sin\theta = \frac{1}{2} \;\Leftrightarrow\; \theta = \frac{\pi}{6} \text{ or } \frac{5\pi}{6} \text{ (for } 0 \le \theta \le 2\pi\text{). We'll}$
subtract the unshaded area from the shaded area for $\pi/6 \le \theta \le \pi/2$ and double
that value.

$A = 2 \int_{\pi/6}^{\pi/2} \frac{1}{2}(4\sin\theta)^2 \, d\theta - 2\int_{\pi/6}^{\pi/2} \frac{1}{2}(2)^2 \, d\theta = 2 \int_{\pi/6}^{\pi/2} \frac{1}{2}\left[(4\sin\theta)^2 - 2^2\right] d\theta$

$= \int_{\pi/6}^{\pi/2} \left(16\sin^2\theta - 4\right) d\theta = \int_{\pi/6}^{\pi/2} [8(1 - \cos 2\theta) - 4] \, d\theta$

$= \int_{\pi/6}^{\pi/2} (4 - 8\cos 2\theta) \, d\theta = [4\theta - 4\sin 2\theta]_{\pi/6}^{\pi/2}$

$= (2\pi - 0) - \left(\frac{2\pi}{3} - 4 \cdot \frac{\sqrt{3}}{2}\right) = \frac{4}{3}\pi + 2\sqrt{3}$

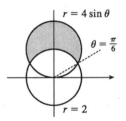

$r = 4\sin\theta$

$\theta = \frac{\pi}{6}$

$r = 2$

20. $3\cos\theta = 2 - \cos\theta \;\Rightarrow\; \cos\theta = \frac{1}{2} \;\Rightarrow\; \theta = \pm\frac{\pi}{3} \;\Rightarrow$

$A = 2 \int_0^{\pi/3} \frac{1}{2}\left[(3\cos\theta)^2 - (2 - \cos\theta)^2\right] d\theta$

$= \int_0^{\pi/3} \left(8\cos^2\theta + 4\cos\theta - 4\right) d\theta = \int_0^{\pi/3} \left[4(2\cos^2\theta - 1) + 4\cos\theta\right] d\theta$

$= \int_0^{\pi/3} (4\cos 2\theta + 4\cos\theta) \, d\theta = [2\sin 2\theta + 4\sin\theta]_0^{\pi/3}$

$= 2 \cdot \frac{\sqrt{3}}{2} + 4 \cdot \frac{\sqrt{3}}{2} = 3\sqrt{3}$

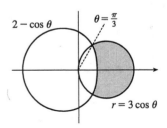

$2 - \cos\theta$

$\theta = \frac{\pi}{3}$

$r = 3\cos\theta$

21. $3\cos\theta = 1 + \cos\theta \iff \cos\theta = \frac{1}{2} \implies \theta = \frac{\pi}{3}$ or $-\frac{\pi}{3}$.

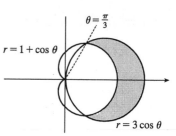

$r = 1 + \cos\theta$

$\theta = \frac{\pi}{3}$

$r = 3\cos\theta$

$$A = 2\int_0^{\pi/3} \frac{1}{2}\left[(3\cos\theta)^2 - (1+\cos\theta)^2\right] d\theta$$

$$= \int_0^{\pi/3}\left(8\cos^2\theta - 2\cos\theta - 1\right) d\theta$$

$$= \int_0^{\pi/3}\left[4(1+\cos 2\theta) - 2\cos\theta - 1\right] d\theta$$

$$= \int_0^{\pi/3}\left(3 + 4\cos 2\theta - 2\cos\theta\right) d\theta = \left[3\theta + 2\sin 2\theta - 2\sin\theta\right]_0^{\pi/3}$$

$$= \pi + \sqrt{3} - \sqrt{3} = \pi$$

22. Note that $r = 1 + \cos\theta$ goes through the pole when $\theta = \pi$, but $r = 3\cos\theta$ goes through the pole when $\theta = \pi/2$.

$$A = 2\int_{\pi/3}^{\pi} \frac{1}{2}(1+\cos\theta)^2 d\theta - 2\int_{\pi/3}^{\pi/2} \frac{1}{2}(3\cos\theta)^2 d\theta$$

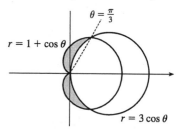

$r = 1 + \cos\theta$

$\theta = \frac{\pi}{3}$

$r = 3\cos\theta$

$$= \int_{\pi/3}^{\pi}\left[1 + 2\cos\theta + \frac{1}{2}(1+\cos 2\theta)\right] d\theta - \frac{9}{2}\int_{\pi/3}^{\pi/2}(1+\cos 2\theta) d\theta$$

$$= \left[\theta + 2\sin\theta + \frac{1}{2}\left(\theta + \frac{1}{2}\sin 2\theta\right)\right]_{\pi/3}^{\pi} - \frac{9}{2}\left[\theta + \frac{1}{2}\sin 2\theta\right]_{\pi/3}^{\pi/2}$$

$$= \left(\pi - \frac{9}{8}\sqrt{3}\right) - \frac{9}{2}\left(\frac{\pi}{6} - \frac{1}{4}\sqrt{3}\right) = \frac{\pi}{4}$$

23. $A = 2\int_0^{\pi/4} \frac{1}{2}\sin^2\theta \, d\theta = \int_0^{\pi/4} \frac{1}{2}(1 - \cos 2\theta) \, d\theta$

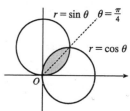

$r = \sin\theta \quad \theta = \frac{\pi}{4}$

$r = \cos\theta$

$$= \frac{1}{2}\left[\theta - \frac{1}{2}\sin 2\theta\right]_0^{\pi/4} = \frac{1}{2}\left[\left(\frac{\pi}{4} - \frac{1}{2}\cdot 1\right) - (0 - 0)\right]$$

$$= \frac{1}{8}\pi - \frac{1}{4}$$

24. $r = \sin 2\theta$ takes on both positive and negative values.

$\sin\theta = \pm\sin 2\theta = \pm 2\sin\theta\cos\theta \implies \sin\theta(1 \pm 2\cos\theta) = 0$. From the figure we can see that the intersections occur where $\cos\theta = \pm\frac{1}{2}$, or $\theta = \frac{\pi}{3}$ and $\frac{2\pi}{3}$.

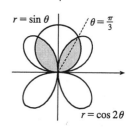

$r = \sin\theta \qquad \theta = \frac{\pi}{3}$

$r = \cos 2\theta$

$$A = 2\left[\int_0^{\pi/3} \frac{1}{2}\sin^2\theta \, d\theta + \int_{\pi/3}^{\pi/2} \frac{1}{2}\sin^2 2\theta \, d\theta\right]$$

$$= \int_0^{\pi/3} \frac{1}{2}(1 - \cos 2\theta) \, d\theta + \int_{\pi/3}^{\pi/2} \frac{1}{2}(1 - \cos 4\theta) \, d\theta$$

$$= \frac{1}{2}\left[\theta - \frac{1}{2}\sin 2\theta\right]_0^{\pi/3} + \frac{1}{2}\left[\theta - \frac{1}{4}\sin 4\theta\right]_{\pi/3}^{\pi/2} = \frac{4\pi - 3\sqrt{3}}{16}$$

25. $\sin 2\theta = \cos 2\theta \implies \dfrac{\sin 2\theta}{\cos 2\theta} = 1 \implies \tan 2\theta = 1 \implies 2\theta = \frac{\pi}{4} \implies$

$\theta = \frac{\pi}{8} \implies$

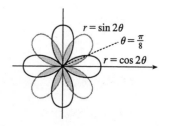

$r = \sin 2\theta$

$\theta = \frac{\pi}{8}$

$r = \cos 2\theta$

$$A = 8 \cdot 2\int_0^{\pi/8} \frac{1}{2}\sin^2 2\theta \, d\theta = 8\int_0^{\pi/8} \frac{1}{2}(1 - \cos 4\theta) \, d\theta$$

$$= 4\left[\theta - \frac{1}{4}\sin 4\theta\right]_0^{\pi/8} = 4\left(\frac{\pi}{8} - \frac{1}{4}\cdot 1\right) = \frac{1}{2}\pi - 1$$

26. $2 \sin 2\theta = 1^2 \Rightarrow \sin 2\theta = \frac{1}{2} \Rightarrow 2\theta = \frac{\pi}{6}$ or $\frac{5\pi}{6} \Rightarrow \theta = \frac{\pi}{12}$ or $\frac{5\pi}{12}$.

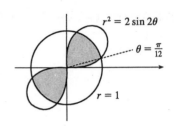

$$A = 4 \left[\int_0^{\pi/12} \frac{1}{2} \cdot 2 \sin 2\theta \, d\theta + \int_{\pi/12}^{\pi/4} \frac{1}{2}(1^2) \, d\theta \right]$$

$$= [-2 \cos 2\theta]_0^{\pi/12} + [2\theta]_{\pi/12}^{\pi/4} = -2\left(\frac{\sqrt{3}}{2} - 1\right) + 2\left(\frac{1}{4}\pi - \frac{1}{12}\pi\right)$$

$$= 2 - \sqrt{3} + \frac{\pi}{3}$$

27. The darker shaded region (from $\theta = 0$ to $\theta = 2\pi/3$) represents $\frac{1}{2}$ of the desired area plus $\frac{1}{2}$ of the area of the inner loop. From this area, we'll subtract $\frac{1}{2}$ of the area of the inner loop (the lighter shaded region from $\theta = 2\pi/3$ to $\theta = \pi$), and then double that difference to obtain the desired area.

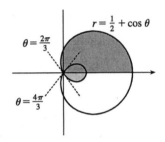

$$A = 2 \left[\int_0^{2\pi/3} \frac{1}{2} \left(\frac{1}{2} + \cos\theta\right)^2 d\theta - \int_{2\pi/3}^{\pi} \frac{1}{2}\left(\frac{1}{2} + \cos\theta\right)^2 d\theta \right]$$

$$= \int_0^{2\pi/3} \left(\frac{1}{4} + \cos\theta + \cos^2\theta\right) d\theta - \int_{2\pi/3}^{\pi} \left(\frac{1}{4} + \cos\theta + \cos^2\theta\right) d\theta$$

$$= \int_0^{2\pi/3} \left[\frac{1}{4} + \cos\theta + \frac{1}{2}(1 + \cos 2\theta)\right] d\theta$$
$$\qquad - \int_{2\pi/3}^{\pi} \left[\frac{1}{4} + \cos\theta + \frac{1}{2}(1 + \cos 2\theta)\right] d\theta$$

$$= \left[\frac{\theta}{4} + \sin\theta + \frac{\theta}{2} + \frac{\sin 2\theta}{4}\right]_0^{2\pi/3} - \left[\frac{\theta}{4} + \sin\theta + \frac{\theta}{2} + \frac{\sin 2\theta}{4}\right]_{2\pi/3}^{\pi}$$

$$= \left(\frac{\pi}{6} + \frac{\sqrt{3}}{2} + \frac{\pi}{3} - \frac{\sqrt{3}}{8}\right) - \left(\frac{\pi}{4} + \frac{\pi}{2}\right) + \left(\frac{\pi}{6} + \frac{\sqrt{3}}{2} + \frac{\pi}{3} - \frac{\sqrt{3}}{8}\right)$$

$$= \frac{\pi}{4} + \frac{3}{4}\sqrt{3} = \frac{1}{4}\left(\pi + 3\sqrt{3}\right)$$

28. The points of intersection occur where $\sqrt{1 - 0.8 \sin^2\theta} = \sin\theta \Leftrightarrow 1.8 \sin^2\theta = 1 \Leftrightarrow$
$\theta = \arcsin\sqrt{\frac{5}{9}} \ [= \alpha$, so $\cos\alpha = \frac{2}{3}]$. So the area is

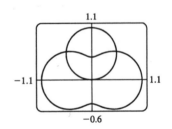

$$A = 2 \int_0^{\alpha} \frac{1}{2} \sin^2\theta \, d\theta + 2 \int_{\alpha}^{\pi/2} \frac{1}{2}\left(\sqrt{1 - 0.8 \sin^2\theta}\right)^2 d\theta$$

$$= \left[\frac{1}{2}\theta - \frac{1}{4}\sin 2\theta\right]_0^{\alpha} + \left[\theta - 0.8\left(\frac{1}{2}\theta - \frac{1}{4}\sin 2\theta\right)\right]_{\alpha}^{\pi/2}$$

$$= \frac{1}{2}\alpha - \frac{1}{4}(2 \sin\alpha \cos\alpha) + 0.6 \cdot \frac{\pi}{2} - [0.6\alpha + 0.2(2 \sin\alpha \cos\alpha)]$$

$$= \frac{1}{2} \arcsin\frac{\sqrt{5}}{3} - \frac{1}{2}\frac{\sqrt{5}}{3}\frac{2}{3} + 0.3\pi - 0.6 \arcsin\frac{\sqrt{5}}{3} - 0.4 \cdot \frac{\sqrt{5}}{3}\frac{2}{3}$$

$$= \frac{3}{10}\pi - \frac{1}{10} \arcsin\frac{\sqrt{5}}{3} - \frac{1}{5}\sqrt{5} \approx 0.411$$

29. The curves intersect at the pole since $\left(0, \frac{\pi}{2}\right)$ satisfies $r = \cos\theta$ and
$(0,0)$ satisfies $r = 1 - \cos\theta$. Now $\cos\theta = 1 - \cos\theta \Rightarrow$
$2 \cos\theta = 1 \Rightarrow \cos\theta = \frac{1}{2} \Rightarrow \theta = \frac{\pi}{3}$ or $\frac{5\pi}{3} \Rightarrow$
the other intersection points are $\left(\frac{1}{2}, \frac{\pi}{3}\right)$ and $\left(\frac{1}{2}, \frac{5\pi}{3}\right)$.

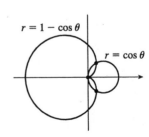

30. Clearly the pole lies on both curves. $\sin 3\theta = \cos 3\theta \Rightarrow$
$\tan 3\theta = 1 \Rightarrow 3\theta = \frac{\pi}{4} + n\pi$ (n any integer) $\Rightarrow$
$\theta = \frac{\pi}{12} + \frac{\pi}{3}n \Rightarrow \theta = \frac{\pi}{12}, \frac{5\pi}{12},$ or $\frac{3\pi}{4}$, so the three remaining
intersection points are $\left(\frac{1}{\sqrt{2}}, \frac{\pi}{12}\right)$, $\left(-\frac{1}{\sqrt{2}}, \frac{5\pi}{12}\right)$, and $\left(\frac{1}{\sqrt{2}}, \frac{3\pi}{4}\right)$.

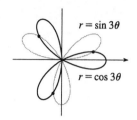

31. The pole is a point of intersection. $\sin \theta = \sin 2\theta = 2 \sin \theta \cos \theta$
$\Leftrightarrow \sin \theta (1 - 2 \cos \theta) = 0 \Leftrightarrow \sin \theta = 0$ or $\cos \theta = \frac{1}{2} \Rightarrow$
$\theta = 0, \pi, \frac{\pi}{3}, -\frac{\pi}{3} \Rightarrow \left(\frac{\sqrt{3}}{2}, \frac{\pi}{3}\right)$ and $\left(\frac{\sqrt{3}}{2}, \frac{2\pi}{3}\right)$ (by symmetry) are
the other intersection points.

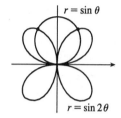

32. Clearly the pole is a point of intersection. $\sin 2\theta = \cos 2\theta \Rightarrow$
$\tan 2\theta = 1 \Rightarrow 2\theta = \frac{\pi}{4} + 2n\pi$ (since $\sin 2\theta$ and $\cos 2\theta$ must be
positive in the equations) $\Rightarrow \theta = \frac{\pi}{8} + n\pi \Rightarrow \theta = \frac{\pi}{8}$ or $\frac{9\pi}{8}$.
So the curves also intersect at $\left(\frac{1}{\sqrt[4]{2}}, \frac{\pi}{8}\right)$ and $\left(\frac{1}{\sqrt[4]{2}}, \frac{9\pi}{8}\right)$.

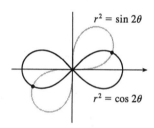

33.

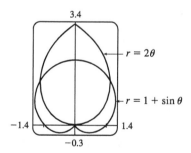

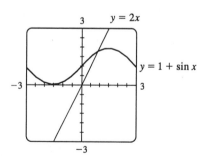

From the first graph, we see that the pole is one point of intersection. By zooming in or using the cursor, we find the
θ-values of the intersection points to be $\alpha \approx 0.88786 \approx 0.89$ and $\pi - \alpha \approx 2.25$. (The first of these values may be
more easily estimated by plotting $y = 1 + \sin x$ and $y = 2x$ in rectangular coordinates; see the second graph.)
By symmetry, the total area contained is twice the area contained in the first quadrant, that is,

$$A = 2 \int_0^\alpha \tfrac{1}{2}(2\theta)^2 \, d\theta + 2 \int_\alpha^{\pi/2} \tfrac{1}{2}(1 + \sin \theta)^2 \, d\theta = \int_0^\alpha 4\theta^2 \, d\theta + \int_\alpha^{\pi/2} \left[1 + 2\sin \theta + \tfrac{1}{2}(1 - \cos 2\theta)\right] d\theta$$

$$= \left[\tfrac{4}{3}\theta^3\right]_0^\alpha + \left[\theta - 2\cos \theta + \left(\tfrac{1}{2}\theta - \tfrac{1}{4}\sin 2\theta\right)\right]_\alpha^{\pi/2}$$

$$= \tfrac{4}{3}\alpha^3 + \left[\left(\tfrac{\pi}{2} + \tfrac{\pi}{4}\right) - \left(\alpha - 2\cos \alpha + \tfrac{1}{2}\alpha - \tfrac{1}{4}\sin 2\alpha\right)\right] \approx 3.4645$$

34.

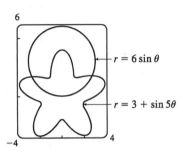
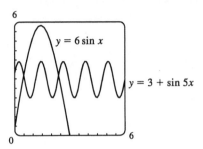

From the first graph, it appears that the θ-values of the points of intersection are $\alpha \approx 0.57504 \approx 0.58$ and $\pi - \alpha \approx 2.57$. (These values may be more easily estimated by plotting $y = 3 + \sin 5x$ and $y = 6 \sin x$ in rectangular coordinates; see the second graph.) By symmetry, the total area enclosed in both curves is

$$A = 2 \int_0^\alpha \tfrac{1}{2}(6 \sin \theta)^2 \, d\theta + 2 \int_\alpha^{\pi/2} \tfrac{1}{2}(3 + \sin 5\theta)^2 \, d\theta = \int_0^\alpha 36 \sin^2 \theta \, d\theta + \int_\alpha^{\pi/2} \left(9 + 6 \sin 5\theta + \sin^2 5\theta\right) d\theta$$

$$= \int_0^\alpha 36 \cdot \tfrac{1}{2}(1 - \cos 2\theta) \, d\theta + \int_\alpha^{\pi/2} \left[9 + 6 \sin 5\theta + \tfrac{1}{2}(1 - \cos 10\theta)\right] d\theta$$

$$= \left[36\left(\tfrac{1}{2}\theta - \tfrac{1}{4}\sin 2\theta\right)\right]_0^\alpha + \left[9\theta - \tfrac{6}{5}\cos 5\theta + \left(\tfrac{1}{2}\theta - \tfrac{1}{20}\sin 10\theta\right)\right]_\alpha^{\pi/2} \approx 10.41$$

35. $L = \int_a^b \sqrt{r^2 + (dr/d\theta)^2} \, d\theta = \int_0^{3\pi/4} \sqrt{(5 \cos \theta)^2 + (-5 \sin \theta)^2} \, d\theta = \int_0^{3\pi/4} \sqrt{25 \cos^2 \theta + 25 \sin^2 \theta} \, d\theta$

$= 5 \int_0^{3\pi/4} \sqrt{\cos^2 \theta + \sin^2 \theta} \, d\theta = 5 \int_0^{3\pi/4} d\theta = 5[\theta]_0^{3\pi/4} = 5\left(\tfrac{3\pi}{4}\right) = \tfrac{15}{4}\pi$

36. $L = \int_a^b \sqrt{r^2 + (dr/d\theta)^2} \, d\theta = \int_0^{2\pi} \sqrt{(e^{2\theta})^2 + (2e^{2\theta})^2} \, d\theta = \int_0^{2\pi} \sqrt{e^{4\theta} + 4e^{4\theta}} \, d\theta = \int_0^{2\pi} \sqrt{5e^{4\theta}} \, d\theta$

$= \sqrt{5} \int_0^{2\pi} e^{2\theta} \, d\theta = \tfrac{\sqrt{5}}{2}\left[e^{2\theta}\right]_0^{2\pi} = \tfrac{\sqrt{5}}{2}\left(e^{4\pi} - 1\right)$

37. $L = \int_a^b \sqrt{r^2 + (dr/d\theta)^2} \, d\theta = \int_0^{2\pi} \sqrt{(\theta^2)^2 + (2\theta)^2} \, d\theta = \int_0^{2\pi} \sqrt{\theta^4 + 4\theta^2} \, d\theta$

$= \int_0^{2\pi} \sqrt{\theta^2 (\theta^2 + 4)} \, d\theta = \int_0^{2\pi} \theta \sqrt{\theta^2 + 4} \, d\theta$

Now let $u = \theta^2 + 4$, so that $du = 2\theta \, d\theta$ $\left[\theta \, d\theta = \tfrac{1}{2} du\right]$ and

$$\int_0^{2\pi} \theta \sqrt{\theta^2 + 4} \, d\theta = \int_4^{4\pi^2 + 4} \tfrac{1}{2} \sqrt{u} \, du = \tfrac{1}{2} \cdot \tfrac{2}{3}\left[u^{3/2}\right]_4^{4(\pi^2 + 1)} = \tfrac{1}{3}\left[4^{3/2}\left(\pi^2 + 1\right)^{3/2} - 4^{3/2}\right]$$

$$= \tfrac{8}{3}\left[\left(\pi^2 + 1\right)^{3/2} - 1\right]$$

38. $L = \int_a^b \sqrt{r^2 + (dr/d\theta)^2} \, d\theta = \int_0^{2\pi} \sqrt{\theta^2 + 1} \, d\theta \overset{21}{=} \left[\tfrac{\theta}{2}\sqrt{\theta^2 + 1} + \tfrac{1}{2}\ln\left(\theta + \sqrt{\theta^2 + 1}\right)\right]_0^{2\pi}$

$= \pi\sqrt{4\pi^2 + 1} + \tfrac{1}{2}\ln\left(2\pi + \sqrt{4\pi^2 + 1}\right)$

39. From Figure 4 in Example 1 with $r = \cos 2\theta$ and $r' = -2 \sin 2\theta$,

$$L = \int_{-\pi/4}^{\pi/4} \sqrt{r^2 + (r')^2} \, d\theta = 2 \int_0^{\pi/4} \sqrt{\cos^2 2\theta + 4 \sin^2 2\theta} \, d\theta \approx 2(1.211056) \approx 2.4221$$

40. We first determine the values of θ for which $r = 4 + 2\sec\theta$ goes

through the pole. $4 + 2\sec\theta = 0 \;\Rightarrow\; \sec\theta = -2 \;\Rightarrow$

$\cos\theta = -\frac{1}{2} \;\Rightarrow\; \theta = \frac{2\pi}{3}, \frac{4\pi}{3}$.

$L = \int_{2\pi/3}^{4\pi/3} \sqrt{r^2 + (r')^2}\, d\theta$

$= \int_{2\pi/3}^{4\pi/3} \sqrt{(4 + 2\sec\theta)^2 + (2\sec\theta\tan\theta)^2}\, d\theta \approx 5.8128$

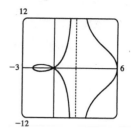

Discovery Project | Conic Sections in Polar Coordinates

1. We see from Figure 1 that $|PF| = r$ and $|Pl| = d - r\cos\theta$. Thus, the condition $|PF|/|Pl| = e$, or $|PF| = e|Pl|$, becomes $r = e(d - r\cos\theta)$.

2. If we square both sides of $r = e(d - r\cos\theta)$ and convert to rectangular coordinates, we get

$x^2 + y^2 = e^2(d - x)^2 = e^2(d^2 - 2dx + x^2)$ or $(1 - e^2)x^2 + 2de^2x + y^2 = e^2 d^2$. After completing the square,

we have $\left(x + \dfrac{e^2 d}{1 - e^2}\right)^2 + \dfrac{y^2}{1 - e^2} = \dfrac{e^2 d^2}{(1 - e^2)^2}$ **(1)**. If $e < 1$, we recognize Equation 1 as the equation of an

ellipse. In fact, it is of the form $\dfrac{(x - h)^2}{a^2} + \dfrac{y^2}{b^2} = 1$, where $h = -\dfrac{e^2 d}{1 - e^2}$, $a^2 = \dfrac{e^2 d^2}{(1 - e^2)^2}$ **(⋆)**, and

$b^2 = \dfrac{e^2 d^2}{1 - e^2}$.

3. If $e > 1$, then $1 - e^2 < 0$ and we see that Equation 1 represents a hyperbola. Just as we did in Problem 2, we could

rewrite Equation 1 in the form $\dfrac{(x - h)^2}{a^2} - \dfrac{y^2}{b^2} = 1$ and see that $e = \dfrac{c}{a}$, where $c^2 = a^2 + b^2$.

4. By solving $r = e(d - r\cos\theta)$ for r, we see that the polar equation of the conic shown in Figure 1 can be written as

$r = \dfrac{ed}{1 + e\cos\theta}$.

5. (a) $r = \dfrac{4}{1 + 3\cos\theta} \;\Rightarrow\; e = 3 > 1 \;\Rightarrow\;$ hyperbola;

$ed = 4 \;\Rightarrow\; d = \frac{4}{3} \;\Rightarrow\;$ directrix $x = \frac{4}{3}$; vertices $(1, 0)$ and

$(-2, \pi) = (2, 0)$; center $\left(\frac{3}{2}, 0\right)$; asymptotes parallel to

$\theta = \pm\cos^{-1}\left(-\frac{1}{3}\right)$

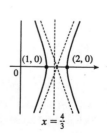

(b) $r = \dfrac{8}{3 + 3\cos\theta} = \dfrac{\frac{8}{3}}{1 + \cos\theta}$ $\Rightarrow$ $e = 1$

$\Rightarrow$ parabola; $ed = \frac{8}{3}$ $\Rightarrow$ $d = \frac{8}{3}$ $\Rightarrow$

directrix $x = \frac{8}{3}$; vertex $\left(\frac{4}{3}, 0\right)$

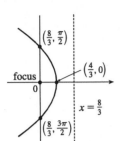

(c) $r = \dfrac{2}{2 + \cos\theta} = \dfrac{1}{1 + \frac{1}{2}\cos\theta}$ $\Rightarrow$

$e = \frac{1}{2} < 1$ $\Rightarrow$ ellipse;

$ed = 1$ $\Rightarrow$ $d = 2$ $\Rightarrow$ directrix $x = 2$;

vertices $\left(\frac{2}{3}, 0\right)$ and $(2, \pi) = (-2, 0)$.

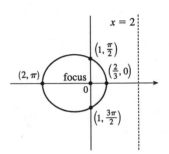

6. For $e < 1$ the curve is an ellipse. It is nearly circular when e is close to 0. As e increases, the graph is stretched out to the right, and grows larger (that is, its right-hand focus moves to the right while its left-hand focus remains at the origin.) At $e = 1$, the curve becomes a parabola with focus at the origin.

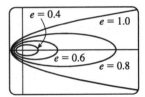

7. (a) If the directrix is $x = d$, then $r = \dfrac{ed}{1 + e\cos\theta}$ and, from ($\star$) in Problem 2,

$a^2 = \dfrac{e^2 d^2}{(1 - e^2)^2}$ $\Rightarrow$ $ed = a(1 - e^2)$. Therefore, $r = \dfrac{a(1 - e^2)}{1 + e\cos\theta}$.

(b) $e = 0.017$ and the length of the major axis $= 2a = 2.99 \times 10^8$ $\Rightarrow$ $a = 1.495 \times 10^8$. Therefore,

$r = \dfrac{1.495 \times 10^8 \left[1 - (0.017)^2\right]}{1 + 0.017\cos\theta} \approx \dfrac{1.495 \times 10^8}{1 + 0.017\cos\theta}$.

8. (a) The Sun is at point F in Figure 1 so that perihelion is in the positive x-direction and aphelion is in the negative x-direction. At perihelion, $\theta = 0$, so $r = \dfrac{a(1 - e^2)}{1 + e\cos 0} = \dfrac{a(1 - e)(1 + e)}{1 + e} = a(1 - e)$.

At aphelion, $\theta = \pi$, so $r = \dfrac{a(1 - e^2)}{1 + e\cos\pi} = \dfrac{a(1 - e)(1 + e)}{1 - e} = a(1 + e)$.

(b) At perihelion, $r = a(1 - e) \approx (1.495 \times 10^8)(1 - 0.017) \approx 1.47 \times 10^8$ km.

At aphelion, $r = a(1 + e) \approx (1.495 \times 10^8)(1 + 0.017) \approx 1.52 \times 10^8$ km.

9. (a) The minimum distance is at perihelion, where

$4.6 \times 10^7 = r = a(1 - e) = a(1 - 0.206) = a(0.794)$ $\Rightarrow$ $a = 4.6 \times 10^7 / 0.794$. So the maximum distance, which is at aphelion, is $r = a(1 + e) = (4.6 \times 10^7 / 0.794)(1.206) \approx 7.0 \times 10^7$ km.

(b) From part (a), we have $e = 0.206$ and $a(1 - e) = 4.6 \times 10^7$ km. Thus, $a = 4.6 \times 10^7/0.794$. From Problem 7,

we can write the equation of Mercury's orbit as $r = a\dfrac{1 - e^2}{1 + e \cos \theta}$. So since $\dfrac{dr}{d\theta} = \dfrac{a(1 - e^2)\, e \sin \theta}{(1 - e \cos \theta)^2}$ $\Rightarrow$

$r^2 + \left(\dfrac{dr}{d\theta}\right)^2 = \dfrac{a^2(1 - e^2)^2}{(1 + e \cos \theta)^2} + \dfrac{a^2(1 - e^2)^2\, e^2 \sin^2 \theta}{(1 + e \cos \theta)^4} = \dfrac{a^2(1 - e^2)^2}{(1 + e \cos \theta)^4}(1 + 2e \cos \theta + e^2)$, the length of

the orbit is $L = \displaystyle\int_0^{2\pi} \sqrt{r^2 + (dr/d\theta)^2}\, d\theta = a(1 - e^2) \int_0^{2\pi} \dfrac{\sqrt{1 + e^2 + 2e \cos \theta}}{(1 + e \cos \theta)^2}\, d\theta \approx 3.6 \times 10^8$ km.

This seems reasonable, since Mercury's orbit is nearly circular, and the circumference of a circle of radius a is $2\pi a \approx 3.6 \times 10^8$ km.

Complex Numbers • • • • • • • • • • • • •

1. $(3 + 2i) + (7 - 3i) = (3 + 7) + (2 - 3)i = 10 - i$

2. $(1 + i) - (2 - 3i) = (1 - 2) + (1 + 3)i = -1 + 4i$

3. $(3 - i)(4 + i) = 12 + 3i - 4i - (-1)\ [i^2 = -1] = 13 - i$

4. $(4 - 7i)(1 + 3i) = 4 + 12i - 7i - 21(-1) = 25 + 5i$

5. $\overline{12 + 7i} = 12 - 7i$

6. $2i\left(\frac{1}{2} - i\right) = i - 2(-1) = 2 + i$ $\Rightarrow$ $\overline{2i\left(\frac{1}{2} - i\right)} = \overline{2 + i} = 2 - i$

7. $\dfrac{2 + 3i}{1 - 5i} = \dfrac{2 + 3i}{1 - 5i} \cdot \dfrac{1 + 5i}{1 + 5i} = \dfrac{2 + 10i + 3i + 15(-1)}{1 - 25(-1)} = \dfrac{-13 + 13i}{26} = -\dfrac{1}{2} + \dfrac{1}{2}i$

8. $\dfrac{5 - i}{3 + 4i} = \dfrac{5 - i}{3 + 4i} \cdot \dfrac{3 - 4i}{3 - 4i} = \dfrac{15 - 20i - 3i + 4(-1)}{9 - 16(-1)} = \dfrac{11 - 23i}{25} = \dfrac{11}{25} - \dfrac{23}{25}i$

9. $\dfrac{1}{1 + i} = \dfrac{1}{1 + i} \cdot \dfrac{1 - i}{1 - i} = \dfrac{1 - i}{1 - (-1)} = \dfrac{1 - i}{2} = \dfrac{1}{2} - \dfrac{1}{2}i$

10. $\dfrac{3}{4 - 3i} = \dfrac{3}{4 - 3i} \cdot \dfrac{4 + 3i}{4 + 3i} = \dfrac{12 + 9i}{16 - 9(-1)} = \dfrac{12}{25} + \dfrac{9}{25}i$

11. $i^3 = i^2 \cdot i = (-1)i = -i$

12. $i^{100} = \left(i^2\right)^{50} = (-1)^{50} = 1$

13. $\sqrt{-25} = \sqrt{25}\, i = 5i$

14. $\sqrt{-3}\sqrt{-12} = \sqrt{3}\, i \sqrt{12}\, i = \sqrt{3 \cdot 12}\, i^2 = \sqrt{36}\,(-1) = -6$

15. $\overline{3 + 4i} = 3 - 4i$, $|3 + 4i| = \sqrt{3^2 + 4^2} = \sqrt{25} = 5$

16. $\overline{\sqrt{3} - i} = \sqrt{3} + i$, $\left|\sqrt{3} - i\right| = \sqrt{\left(\sqrt{3}\right)^2 + (-1)^2} = \sqrt{4} = 2$

17. $\overline{-4i} = \overline{0 - 4i} = 0 + 4i = 4i$, $|-4i| = \sqrt{0^2 + (-4)^2} = \sqrt{16} = 4$

18. Let $z = a + bi$, $w = c + di$.

   (a) $\overline{z + w} = \overline{(a + bi) + (c + di)} = \overline{(a + c) + (b + d)i}$
       $= (a + c) - (b + d)i = (a - bi) + (c - di) = \overline{z} + \overline{w}$

   (b) $\overline{zw} = \overline{(a + bi)(c + di)} = \overline{(ac - bd) + (ad + bc)i} = (ac - bd) - (ad + bc)i$.
       On the other hand, $\overline{z}\,\overline{w} = (a - bi)(c - di) = (ac - bd) - (ad + bc)i = \overline{zw}$.

(c) Use mathematical induction and part (b): Let S_n be the statement that $\overline{z^n} = \overline{z}^n$.

S_1 is true because $\overline{z^1} = \overline{z} = \overline{z}^1$. Assume S_k is true, that is $\overline{z^k} = \overline{z}^k$. Then

$\overline{z^{k+1}} = \overline{z^{1+k}} = \overline{z z^k} = \overline{z}\,\overline{z^k}$ [part (b) with $w = z^k$] $= \overline{z}^1 \overline{z}^k = \overline{z}^{1+k} = \overline{z}^{k+1}$, which shows that S_{k+1} is true.

Therefore, by mathematical induction, $\overline{z^n} = \overline{z}^n$ for every positive integer n.

Another proof: Use part (b) with $w = z$, and mathematical induction.

19. $4x^2 + 9 = 0 \iff 4x^2 = -9 \iff x^2 = -\frac{9}{4} \iff x = \pm\sqrt{-\frac{9}{4}} = \pm\sqrt{\frac{9}{4}}\,i = \pm\frac{3}{2}i.$

20. $x^4 = 1 \iff x^4 - 1 = 0 \iff (x^2 - 1)(x^2 + 1) = 0 \iff x^2 - 1 = 0$ or $x^2 + 1 = 0 \iff$

$x = \pm 1$ or $x = \pm i.$

21. By the quadratic formula, $x^2 - 8x + 17 = 0 \iff x = \frac{-(-8) \pm \sqrt{(-8)^2 - 4(1)(17)}}{2(1)} = \frac{8 \pm \sqrt{-4}}{2} = \frac{8 \pm 2i}{2} = 4 \pm i.$

22. $x^2 - 4x + 5 = 0 \iff x = \frac{-(-4) \pm \sqrt{(-4)^2 - 4(1)(5)}}{2(1)} = \frac{4 \pm \sqrt{-4}}{2} = \frac{4 \pm 2i}{2} = 2 \pm i$

23. By the quadratic formula, $z^2 + z + 2 = 0 \iff z = \frac{-1 \pm \sqrt{1^2 - 4(1)(2)}}{2(1)} = \frac{-1 \pm \sqrt{-7}}{2} = -\frac{1}{2} \pm \frac{\sqrt{7}}{2}i.$

24. $z^2 + \frac{1}{2}z + \frac{1}{4} = 0 \iff 4z^2 + 2z + 1 = 0 \iff$

$z = \frac{-2 \pm \sqrt{2^2 - 4(4)(1)}}{2(4)} = \frac{-2 \pm \sqrt{-12}}{8} = \frac{-2 \pm 2\sqrt{3}i}{8} = -\frac{1}{4} \pm \frac{\sqrt{3}}{4}i$

25. For $z = -3 + 3i$, $r = \sqrt{(-3)^2 + 3^2} = 3\sqrt{2}$ and $\tan\theta = \frac{3}{-3} = -1 \implies \theta = \frac{3\pi}{4}$ (since z lies in the second quadrant). Therefore, $-3 + 3i = 3\sqrt{2}\left(\cos\frac{3\pi}{4} + i\sin\frac{3\pi}{4}\right).$

26. For $z = 1 - \sqrt{3}\,i$, $r = \sqrt{1^2 + \left(-\sqrt{3}\right)^2} = 2$ and $\tan\theta = \frac{-\sqrt{3}}{1} = -\sqrt{3} \implies \theta = \frac{5\pi}{3}$ (since z lies in the fourth quadrant). Therefore, $1 - \sqrt{3}\,i = 2\left(\cos\frac{5\pi}{3} + i\sin\frac{5\pi}{3}\right).$

27. For $z = 3 + 4i$, $r = \sqrt{3^2 + 4^2} = 5$ and $\tan\theta = \frac{4}{3} \implies \theta = \tan^{-1}\left(\frac{4}{3}\right)$ (since z lies in the first quadrant). Therefore, $3 + 4i = 5\left[\cos\left(\tan^{-1}\frac{4}{3}\right) + i\sin\left(\tan^{-1}\frac{4}{3}\right)\right].$

28. For $z = 8i$, $r = \sqrt{0^2 + 8^2} = 8$ and $\tan\theta = \frac{8}{0}$ is undefined, so $\theta = \frac{\pi}{2}$ (since z lies on the positive imaginary axis). Therefore, $8i = 8\left(\cos\frac{\pi}{2} + i\sin\frac{\pi}{2}\right).$

29. For $z = \sqrt{3} + i$, $r = \sqrt{\left(\sqrt{3}\right)^2 + 1^2} = 2$ and $\tan\theta = \frac{1}{\sqrt{3}} \implies \theta = \frac{\pi}{6} \implies z = 2\left(\cos\frac{\pi}{6} + i\sin\frac{\pi}{6}\right).$

For $w = 1 + \sqrt{3}\,i$, $r = 2$ and $\tan\theta = \sqrt{3} \implies \theta = \frac{\pi}{3} \implies w = 2\left(\cos\frac{\pi}{3} + i\sin\frac{\pi}{3}\right).$

Therefore, $zw = 2 \cdot 2\left[\cos\left(\frac{\pi}{6} + \frac{\pi}{3}\right) + i\sin\left(\frac{\pi}{6} + \frac{\pi}{3}\right)\right] = 4\left(\cos\frac{\pi}{2} + i\sin\frac{\pi}{2}\right),$

$z/w = \frac{2}{2}\left[\cos\left(\frac{\pi}{6} - \frac{\pi}{3}\right) + i\sin\left(\frac{\pi}{6} - \frac{\pi}{3}\right)\right] = \cos\left(-\frac{\pi}{6}\right) + i\sin\left(-\frac{\pi}{6}\right)$, and $1 = 1 + 0i = 1(\cos 0 + i\sin 0) \implies$

$1/z = \frac{1}{2}\left[\cos\left(0 - \frac{\pi}{6}\right) + i\sin\left(0 - \frac{\pi}{6}\right)\right] = \frac{1}{2}\left[\cos\left(-\frac{\pi}{6}\right) + i\sin\left(-\frac{\pi}{6}\right)\right].$ For $1/z$, we could also use the formula that precedes Example 5 to obtain $1/z = \frac{1}{8}\left(\cos\frac{\pi}{6} - i\sin\frac{\pi}{6}\right).$

30. For $z = 4\sqrt{3} - 4i$, $r = \sqrt{\left(4\sqrt{3}\right)^2 + (-4)^2} = \sqrt{64} = 8$ and $\tan\theta = \frac{-4}{4\sqrt{3}} = -\frac{1}{\sqrt{3}} \implies \theta = \frac{11\pi}{6} \implies$

$z = 8\left(\cos\frac{11\pi}{6} + i\sin\frac{11\pi}{6}\right).$ For $w = 8i$, $r = \sqrt{0^2 + 8^2} = 8$ and $\tan\theta = \frac{8}{0}$ is undefined, so $\theta = \frac{\pi}{2} \implies$

$w = 8\left(\cos\frac{\pi}{2} + i\sin\frac{\pi}{2}\right).$ Therefore, $zw = 8 \cdot 8\left[\cos\left(\frac{11\pi}{6} + \frac{\pi}{2}\right) + i\sin\left(\frac{11\pi}{6} + \frac{\pi}{2}\right)\right] = 64\left(\cos\frac{\pi}{3} + i\sin\frac{\pi}{3}\right),$

$z/w = \frac{8}{8}\left[\cos\left(\frac{11\pi}{6} - \frac{\pi}{2}\right) + i\sin\left(\frac{11\pi}{6} - \frac{\pi}{2}\right)\right] = \cos\frac{4\pi}{3} + i\sin\frac{4\pi}{3}$, and

$1 = 1 + 0i = 1(\cos 0 + i\sin 0) \implies 1/z = \frac{1}{8}\left[\cos\left(0 - \frac{11\pi}{6}\right) + i\sin\left(0 - \frac{11\pi}{6}\right)\right] = \frac{1}{8}\left[\cos\left(\frac{\pi}{6}\right) + i\sin\left(\frac{\pi}{6}\right)\right].$

For $1/z$, we could also use the formula that precedes Example 5 to obtain $1/z = \frac{1}{8}\left(\cos\frac{11\pi}{6} - i\sin\frac{11\pi}{6}\right).$

31. For $z = 2\sqrt{3} - 2i$, $r = \sqrt{\left(2\sqrt{3}\right)^2 + (-2)^2} = 4$ and $\tan\theta = \frac{-2}{2\sqrt{3}} = -\frac{1}{\sqrt{3}}$

$\Rightarrow \quad \theta = -\frac{\pi}{6} \quad \Rightarrow \quad z = 4\left[\cos\left(-\frac{\pi}{6}\right) + i\sin\left(-\frac{\pi}{6}\right)\right]$. For $w = -1 + i$, $r = \sqrt{2}$,

$\tan\theta = \frac{1}{-1} = -1 \quad \Rightarrow \quad \theta = \frac{3\pi}{4} \quad \Rightarrow \quad z = \sqrt{2}\left(\cos\frac{3\pi}{4} + i\sin\frac{3\pi}{4}\right)$. Therefore,

$zw = 4\sqrt{2}\left[\cos\left(-\frac{\pi}{6} + \frac{3\pi}{4}\right) + i\sin\left(-\frac{\pi}{6} + \frac{3\pi}{4}\right)\right] = 4\sqrt{2}\left(\cos\frac{7\pi}{12} + i\sin\frac{7\pi}{12}\right)$,

$z/w = \frac{4}{\sqrt{2}}\left[\cos\left(-\frac{\pi}{6} - \frac{3\pi}{4}\right) + i\sin\left(-\frac{\pi}{6} - \frac{3\pi}{4}\right)\right] = \frac{4}{\sqrt{2}}\left[\cos\left(-\frac{11\pi}{12}\right) + i\sin\left(-\frac{11\pi}{12}\right)\right]$

$\quad = 2\sqrt{2}\left(\cos\frac{13\pi}{12} + i\sin\frac{13\pi}{12}\right)$, and

$1/z = \frac{1}{4}\left[\cos\left(-\frac{\pi}{6}\right) - i\sin\left(-\frac{\pi}{6}\right)\right] = \frac{1}{4}\left(\cos\frac{\pi}{6} + i\sin\frac{\pi}{6}\right)$.

32. For $z = 4\left(\sqrt{3} + i\right) = 4\sqrt{3} + 4i$, $r = \sqrt{\left(4\sqrt{3}\right)^2 + 4^2} = \sqrt{64} = 8$ and $\tan\theta = \frac{4}{4\sqrt{3}} = \frac{1}{\sqrt{3}} \quad \Rightarrow \quad \theta = \frac{\pi}{6} \quad \Rightarrow$

$z = 8\left(\cos\frac{\pi}{6} + i\sin\frac{\pi}{6}\right)$. For $w = -3 - 3i$, $r = \sqrt{(-3)^2 + (-3)^2} = \sqrt{18} = 3\sqrt{2}$ and

$\tan\theta = \frac{-3}{-3} = 1 \quad \Rightarrow \quad \theta = \frac{5\pi}{4} \quad \Rightarrow \quad w = 3\sqrt{2}\left(\cos\frac{5\pi}{4} + i\sin\frac{5\pi}{4}\right)$. Therefore,

$zw = 8 \cdot 3\sqrt{2}\left[\cos\left(\frac{\pi}{6} + \frac{5\pi}{4}\right) + i\sin\left(\frac{\pi}{6} + \frac{5\pi}{4}\right)\right] = 24\sqrt{2}\left(\cos\frac{17\pi}{12} + i\sin\frac{17\pi}{12}\right)$,

$z/w = \frac{8}{3\sqrt{2}}\left[\cos\left(\frac{\pi}{6} - \frac{5\pi}{4}\right) + i\sin\left(\frac{\pi}{6} - \frac{5\pi}{4}\right)\right] = \frac{4\sqrt{2}}{3}\left[\cos\left(-\frac{13\pi}{12}\right) + i\sin\left(-\frac{13\pi}{12}\right)\right]$, and

$1/z = \frac{1}{8}\left(\cos\frac{\pi}{6} - i\sin\frac{\pi}{6}\right)$.

33. For $z = 1 + i$, $r = \sqrt{2}$ and $\tan\theta = \frac{1}{1} = 1 \quad \Rightarrow \quad \theta = \frac{\pi}{4} \quad \Rightarrow \quad z = \sqrt{2}\left(\cos\frac{\pi}{4} + i\sin\frac{\pi}{4}\right)$. So by De Moivre's Theorem,

$$(1 + i)^{20} = \left[\sqrt{2}\left(\cos\frac{\pi}{4} + i\sin\frac{\pi}{4}\right)\right]^{20} = \left(2^{1/2}\right)^{20}\left(\cos\frac{20\cdot\pi}{4} + i\sin\frac{20\cdot\pi}{4}\right)$$

$$= 2^{10}(\cos 5\pi + i\sin 5\pi) = 2^{10}[-1 + i(0)] = -2^{10} = -1024$$

34. For $z = 1 - \sqrt{3}\,i$, $r = \sqrt{1^2 + \left(-\sqrt{3}\right)^2} = 2$ and $\tan\theta = \frac{-\sqrt{3}}{1} = -\sqrt{3} \quad \Rightarrow \quad \theta = \frac{5\pi}{3} \quad \Rightarrow$

$z = 2\left(\cos\frac{5\pi}{3} + i\sin\frac{5\pi}{3}\right)$. So by De Moivre's Theorem,

$$\left(1 - \sqrt{3}\,i\right)^5 = \left[2\left(\cos\frac{5\pi}{3} + i\sin\frac{5\pi}{3}\right)\right]^5 = 2^5\left(\cos\frac{5\cdot5\pi}{3} + i\sin\frac{5\cdot5\pi}{3}\right)$$

$$= 2^5\left(\cos\frac{\pi}{3} + i\sin\frac{\pi}{3}\right) = 32\left(\frac{1}{2} + \frac{\sqrt{3}}{2}\,i\right) = 16 + 16\sqrt{3}\,i$$

35. For $z = 2\sqrt{3} + 2i$, $r = \sqrt{\left(2\sqrt{3}\right)^2 + 2^2} = \sqrt{16} = 4$ and $\tan\theta = \frac{2}{2\sqrt{3}} = \frac{1}{\sqrt{3}} \quad \Rightarrow \quad \theta = \frac{\pi}{6} \quad \Rightarrow$

$z = 4\left(\cos\frac{\pi}{6} + i\sin\frac{\pi}{6}\right)$. So by De Moivre's Theorem,

$$\left(2\sqrt{3} + 2i\right)^5 = \left[4\left(\cos\frac{\pi}{6} + i\sin\frac{\pi}{6}\right)\right]^5 = 4^5\left(\cos\frac{5\pi}{6} + i\sin\frac{5\pi}{6}\right) = 1024\left[-\frac{\sqrt{3}}{2} + \frac{1}{2}i\right] = -512\sqrt{3} + 512i$$

36. For $z = 1 - i$, $r = \sqrt{2}$ and $\tan\theta = \frac{-1}{1} = -1 \quad \Rightarrow \quad \theta = \frac{7\pi}{4} \quad \Rightarrow \quad z = \sqrt{2}\left(\cos\frac{7\pi}{4} + i\sin\frac{7\pi}{4}\right) \quad \Rightarrow$

$$(1 - i)^8 = \left[\sqrt{2}\left(\cos\frac{7\pi}{4} + i\sin\frac{7\pi}{4}\right)\right]^8 = 2^4\left(\cos\frac{8\cdot7\pi}{4} + i\sin\frac{8\cdot7\pi}{4}\right)$$

$$= 16(\cos 14\pi + i\sin 14\pi) = 16(1 + 0i) = 16$$

37. $1 = 1 + 0i = 1\,(\cos 0 + i\sin 0)$. Using Equation 3 with $r = 1$, $n = 8$, and $\theta = 0$, we have

$$w_k = 1^{1/8}\left[\cos\left(\frac{0 + 2k\pi}{8}\right) + i\sin\left(\frac{0 + 2k\pi}{8}\right)\right] = \cos\frac{k\pi}{4} + i\sin\frac{k\pi}{4}, \text{ where } k = 0, 1, 2, \ldots, 7.$$

$w_0 = 1(\cos 0 + i \sin 0) = 1, \; w_1 = 1\left(\cos \frac{\pi}{4} + i \sin \frac{\pi}{4}\right) = \frac{1}{\sqrt{2}} + \frac{1}{\sqrt{2}}i,$

$w_2 = 1\left(\cos \frac{\pi}{2} + i \sin \frac{\pi}{2}\right) = i, \; w_3 = 1\left(\cos \frac{3\pi}{4} + i \sin \frac{3\pi}{4}\right) = -\frac{1}{\sqrt{2}} + \frac{1}{\sqrt{2}}i,$

$w_4 = 1(\cos \pi + i \sin \pi) = -1, \; w_5 = 1\left(\cos \frac{5\pi}{4} + i \sin \frac{5\pi}{4}\right) = -\frac{1}{\sqrt{2}} - \frac{1}{\sqrt{2}}i,$

$w_6 = 1\left(\cos \frac{3\pi}{2} + i \sin \frac{3\pi}{2}\right) = -i, \; w_7 = 1\left(\cos \frac{7\pi}{4} + i \sin \frac{7\pi}{4}\right) = \frac{1}{\sqrt{2}} - \frac{1}{\sqrt{2}}i$

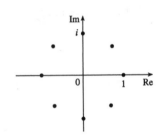

38. $32 = 32 + 0i = 32\,(\cos 0 + i \sin 0)$. Using Equation 3 with $r = 32$, $n = 5$, and $\theta = 0$, we have

$w_k = 32^{1/5}\left[\cos\left(\frac{0 + 2k\pi}{5}\right) + i\sin\left(\frac{0 + 2k\pi}{5}\right)\right] = 2\left(\cos \frac{2}{5}\pi k + i \sin \frac{2}{5}\pi k\right)$, where $k = 0, 1, 2, 3, 4$.

$w_0 = 2(\cos 0 + i \sin 0) = 2$

$w_1 = 2\left(\cos \frac{2\pi}{5} + i \sin \frac{2\pi}{5}\right)$

$w_2 = 2\left(\cos \frac{4\pi}{5} + i \sin \frac{4\pi}{5}\right)$

$w_3 = 2\left(\cos \frac{6\pi}{5} + i \sin \frac{6\pi}{5}\right)$

$w_4 = 2\left(\cos \frac{8\pi}{5} + i \sin \frac{8\pi}{5}\right)$

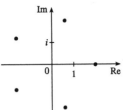

39. $i = 0 + i = 1\left(\cos \frac{\pi}{2} + i \sin \frac{\pi}{2}\right)$. Using Equation 3 with $r = 1$, $n = 3$, and $\theta = \frac{\pi}{2}$, we have

$w_k = 1^{1/3}\left[\cos\left(\frac{\frac{\pi}{2} + 2k\pi}{3}\right) + i\sin\left(\frac{\frac{\pi}{2} + 2k\pi}{3}\right)\right]$, where $k = 0, 1, 2$.

$w_0 = \left(\cos \frac{\pi}{6} + i \sin \frac{\pi}{6}\right) = \frac{\sqrt{3}}{2} + \frac{1}{2}i$

$w_1 = \left(\cos \frac{5\pi}{6} + i \sin \frac{5\pi}{6}\right) = -\frac{\sqrt{3}}{2} + \frac{1}{2}i$

$w_2 = \left(\cos \frac{9\pi}{6} + i \sin \frac{9\pi}{6}\right) = -i$

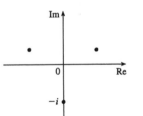

40. $1 + i = \sqrt{2}\left(\cos \frac{\pi}{4} + i \sin \frac{\pi}{4}\right)$. Using Equation 3 with $r = \sqrt{2}$, $n = 3$, and $\theta = \frac{\pi}{4}$, we have

$w_k = \left(\sqrt{2}\right)^{1/3}\left[\cos\left(\frac{\frac{\pi}{4} + 2k\pi}{3}\right) + i\sin\left(\frac{\frac{\pi}{4} + 2k\pi}{3}\right)\right]$, where $k = 0, 1, 2$.

$w_0 = 2^{1/6}\left(\cos \frac{\pi}{12} + i \sin \frac{\pi}{12}\right)$

$w_1 = 2^{1/6}\left(\cos \frac{3\pi}{4} + i \sin \frac{3\pi}{4}\right) = 2^{1/6}\left(-\frac{1}{\sqrt{2}} + \frac{1}{\sqrt{2}}i\right) = -2^{-1/3} + 2^{-1/3}i$

$w_2 = 2^{1/6}\left(\cos \frac{17\pi}{12} + i \sin \frac{17\pi}{12}\right)$

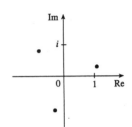

41. Using Euler's formula (6) with $y = \frac{\pi}{2}$, we have $e^{i\pi/2} = \cos \frac{\pi}{2} + i \sin \frac{\pi}{2} = 0 + 1i = i$.

42. Using Euler's formula (6) with $y = 2\pi$, we have $e^{2\pi i} = \cos 2\pi + i \sin 2\pi = 1$.

43. Using Euler's formula (6) with $y = \frac{3\pi}{4}$, we have $e^{i3\pi/4} = \cos \frac{3\pi}{4} + i \sin \frac{3\pi}{4} = -\frac{1}{\sqrt{2}} + \frac{1}{\sqrt{2}}i$.

44. Using Euler's formula (6) with $y = -\pi$, we have $e^{-i\pi} = \cos(-\pi) + i \sin(-\pi) = -1$.

45. Using Equation 7 with $x = 2$ and $y = \pi$, we have $e^{2+i\pi} = e^2 e^{i\pi} = e^2(\cos \pi + i \sin \pi) = e^2(-1 + 0) = -e^2$.

46. Using Equation 7 with $x = 1$ and $y = 2$, we have $e^{1+2i} = e^1 e^{2i} = e(\cos 2 + i \sin 2) = e \cos 2 + (e \sin 2)i$.

47. Take $r = 1$ and $n = 3$ in De Moivre's Theorem to get

$$[1(\cos\theta + i\sin\theta)]^3 = 1^3(\cos 3\theta + i\sin 3\theta)$$

$$(\cos\theta + i\sin\theta)^3 = \cos 3\theta + i\sin 3\theta$$

$$\cos^3\theta + 3(\cos^2\theta)(i\sin\theta) + 3(\cos\theta)(i\sin\theta)^2 + (i\sin\theta)^3 = \cos 3\theta + i\sin 3\theta$$

$$\cos^3\theta + (3\cos^2\theta\,\sin\theta)i - 3\cos\theta\,\sin^2\theta - (\sin^3\theta)i = \cos 3\theta + i\sin 3\theta$$

$$(\cos^3\theta - 3\sin^2\theta\,\cos\theta) + (3\sin\theta\,\cos^2\theta - \sin^3\theta)i = \cos 3\theta + i\sin 3\theta$$

Equating real and imaginary parts gives

$$\cos 3\theta = \cos^3\theta - 3\sin^2\theta\,\cos\theta \quad\text{and}\quad \sin 3\theta = 3\sin\theta\,\cos^2\theta - \sin^3\theta$$

48. Using Formula 6,

$$e^{ix} + e^{-ix} = (\cos x + i\sin x) + [\cos(-x) + i\sin(-x)]$$

$$= \cos x + i\sin x + \cos x - i\sin x = 2\cos x$$

Thus, $\cos x = \dfrac{e^{ix} + e^{-ix}}{2}$.

Similarly,

$$e^{ix} - e^{-ix} = (\cos x + i\sin x) - [\cos(-x) + i\sin(-x)]$$

$$= \cos x + i\sin x - \cos x - (-i\sin x) = 2i\sin x$$

Therefore, $\sin x = \dfrac{e^{ix} - e^{-ix}}{2i}$.

49. $F(x) = e^{rx} = e^{(a+bi)x} = e^{ax+bxi} = e^{ax}(\cos bx + i\sin bx) = e^{ax}\cos bx + i(e^{ax}\sin bx) \Rightarrow$
$F'(x) = (e^{ax}\cos bx)' + i(e^{ax}\sin bx)' = (ae^{ax}\cos bx - be^{ax}\sin bx) + i(ae^{ax}\sin bx + be^{ax}\cos bx)$

$= a\left[e^{ax}(\cos bx + i\sin bx)\right] + b\left[e^{ax}(-\sin bx + i\cos bx)\right] = ae^{rx} + b\left[e^{ax}(i^2\sin bx + i\cos bx)\right]$

$= ae^{rx} + bi\left[e^{ax}(\cos bx + i\sin bx)\right] = ae^{rx} + bie^{rx} = (a + bi)e^{rx} = re^{rx}$

50. (a) From Exercise 49, $F(x) = e^{(1+i)x} \Rightarrow F'(x) = (1+i)e^{(1+i)x}$. So

$$\int e^{(1+i)x}\,dx = \frac{1}{1+i}\int F'(x)\,dx = \frac{1}{1+i}F(x) + C = \frac{1-i}{2}F(x) + C = \frac{1-i}{2}e^{(1+i)x} + C$$

(b) $\int e^{(1+i)x}\,dx = \int e^x e^{ix}\,dx = \int e^x(\cos x + i\sin x)\,dx = \int e^x\cos x\,dx + i\int e^x\sin x\,dx$ **(1)**.
Using the above result for $e^{(1+i)x}$ (without the $\int dx$), we have

$$\frac{1-i}{2}e^{(1+i)x} = \tfrac{1}{2}e^{(1+i)x} - \tfrac{1}{2}ie^{(1+i)x} = \tfrac{1}{2}e^{x+ix} - \tfrac{1}{2}ie^{x+ix}$$

$$= \tfrac{1}{2}e^x(\cos x + i\sin x) - \tfrac{1}{2}ie^x(\cos x + i\sin x)$$

$$= \tfrac{1}{2}e^x\cos x + \tfrac{1}{2}e^x\sin x + \tfrac{1}{2}ie^x\sin x - \tfrac{1}{2}ie^x\cos x$$

$$= \tfrac{1}{2}e^x(\cos x + \sin x) + i\left[\tfrac{1}{2}e^x(\sin x - \cos x)\right] \quad\textbf{(2)}$$

Equating the real and imaginary parts in **(1)** and **(2)**, we see that $\int e^x\cos x\,dx = \tfrac{1}{2}e^x(\cos x + \sin x) + C$ and $\int e^x\sin x\,dx = \tfrac{1}{2}e^x(\sin x - \cos x) + C$.